THE WORLD OF THE ATOM

°°°°°°°°°°°°°°°

The WORLD
of the ATOM

°°°°°°°°°°°°°°°°

VOLUME

I

EDITED WITH COMMENTARIES BY

Henry A. Boorse and Lloyd Motz

Foreword by I. I. Rabi

BASIC BOOKS, INC., PUBLISHERS

NEW YORK · LONDON

FOREWORD

Anthologies may not be the scholar's dish; for the student or lay-man, however, they can be not only instructive in subject matter but also charming and even fascinating. A proper selection of important works in a historical and biographical setting can be an illuminating guide to the student and to the amateur scholar. Palgrave's *Golden Treasury* was one of the important elements in forming my own taste for both poetry and language. The book has continued to be a source of pleasure, although the English course in which I first had to use it is long since forgotten.

There is no reason why anthologies in other fields of creative thought should not meet with similar success. Clearly, an anthology cannot be a first introduction to a field of study. One does not go all at once from Mother Goose to T. S. Eliot, but, for those who are properly prepared, an anthology allows one to dip into a varied buffet. Properly selected, the constituents will all be good, but some items will go down easily, whereas others, like caviar, are not for the general. There, the notes both bio-graphical and expository of the editor should prepare one to acquire the taste leading to appreciation and understanding.

The World of the Atom takes one through the profound and exciting theme of atomism. Our period is so much the age of atomism that it is difficult to believe that, in the latter part of the nineteenth century and even the early part of this century, atomism was very much under a cloud.

The great Austrian physicist and philosopher Ernst Mach, who died in 1916, never believed in the real existence of atoms. Whether to take this as a reflection on Mach's understanding or as a cautionary tale to the contemporary physicist is a matter of philosophical taste. Mach was far from conventional in his views; he had deep physical insight, but was skep-tical of the unseen. Since then, atoms have really been "seen." The question as to whether atoms do really exist—or, rather, whether the ideas

v

of atomism that the variety of the world comes about from the interactions of basic units, as with Democritus, or whether, as in field theory, that the atoms are only some particular convolution of space—is not settled to this day. At present, the atoms or particles are in the ascendancy.

Today we speak not only of atoms which meant "indivisible" in the first place, but of the structure of the atom. The atom's constituents are electrons, neutrons, and protons. This was gospel for a few years in the early 1930's. Now there are also positrons or antielectrons, antineutrons, antiprotons, and in addition neutrinos and their antiparticles, mesons, baryons and their antiparticles, and light quanta. All these are perfectly good particles discovered in the past thirty years and almost as well demonstrated as our humdrum hydrogen, oxygen, nitrogen, and carbon atoms that are so basic to the existence of physicists. The very richness of this display makes one begin to feel twinges of doubt whether atomism is here to stay after all. Perhaps this variety has something behind it that is not atomic or particulate after all.

This book, which takes selections from the atomists through the ages, is a timely volume on a timeless subject. Too often, the student or layman takes the current ideas either as gospel or, worse still, as obvious. In *The World of the Atom*, we meet many of the great masters of physics. One learns something of their lives and of some of their great works. Because their thoughts and methods are presented in juxtaposition, one has the opportunity to gain an insight into their variety.

In many ways, the world has dealt unfairly with the physicist. Far too little attention has been paid to the biography of scientists, to their personal lives as living, breathing human beings with their doubts, their struggles, and their moments of insight. Their scientific contributions are known only in snatches, even to professionals. They are unread and unsung, and even the very great, like Newton and Einstein, are remembered for a few phrases, a few equations. It is as though Shakespeare were known only as a man from Stratford, a successful playwright who wrote "To be or not to be. . . ."

Perhaps, through anthologies such as this as well as proper biographies of scientists and histories of science, the intellectual climate may change and the intellectual will again look outward at the world and not only inward on himself. In the world of "educated" men, too little is known about science which is the glory of our great age. The subtle, always elusive mystery of nature, our hope and our despair, challenge us to further discovery and broader understanding. This challenge is not only intellectual, but also moral.

I. I. RABI
Professor of Physics
Columbia University

PREFACE

The World of the Atom presents the actual texts of the landmark documents in the history of atomic physics. Because of the arrangement of these original papers in chronological order, it is possible for the inquiring reader to follow at first hand the growth of atomic science from ancient times to the present day. Each chapter is introduced by a description of its contents and a biography of its author. Through these commentaries and personal accounts, the evolving scientific subject will be more clearly appreciated as a continuous human endeavor whose story cannot be separated from the personalities of the innovators any more than from the varied social and intellectual conditions out of which it arises.

Readers are often prone to suppose that the great figures of science were a breed of supermen whose emotions, attitudes, and lofty outlooks were far removed from those of their ordinary contemporaries. The life stories presented here will show how little truth there is in that supposition. Indeed, the great investigators—coming from diverse social and cultural backgrounds—display as much of the enormous range of human traits and behavior common to "ordinary men" as they show differences among themselves as a "breed." The stories of their lives are given in differing degrees of detail. Where the greatest figures are concerned, the biographies are extensive by virtue of their consequential importance; but some of the lesser known figures have so caught our fancy that we took intrinsic pleasure in presenting their stories at length. For contemporary scientists, the biographies necessarily had to be shorter than we would have wished.

Each paper included here has made its contribution to the development of atomic science, even where the relevance is not immediately evident. The determination of the mechanical equivalent of heat by Joule, for example, was of the greatest importance in establishing the principle of the conservation of energy, which is basic to atomic theory. Similarly, experiments with gases and gas theory were indispensable to the evolution of atomic science. Still, it must be emphasized that this volume should not be mistaken for a *history* of atomic theory. Such a work would require a much more extensive and more elaborate analysis of the complete works of the scientists whose papers are presented here; this anthology represents documents that are absolutely *necessary* for the history of atomic science, but it is not *sufficient* for such a history.

The volume opens with a selection from *De Rerum Natura,* by Lucretius—the only work taken from ancient science—not only because it preserves the atomistic speculations of Leucippus, Democritus, and Epicurus, but because these speculations deeply influenced the views of such founders of contemporary physics as Boyle, Newton, and Hooke. There are excerpts from Descartes, whose model of the universe rested on corpuscular ideas despite his disbelief in Democritus' atomism. In turn, it is fascinating to note that Newton's physical ideas are almost devoid of Cartesian notions, even though Newton had studied Descartes carefully.

The principle of pursuing pure science because its applications could improve the condition of mankind was an idea developed by Francis Bacon at the beginning of the seventeenth century. One of the effects of his writings on Newton's elder contemporaries, Wilkins and Boyle, was their becoming instrumental in founding the Royal Society. The vigor of that group was so great and its accomplishments so impressive that it encouraged the formation of comparable societies throughout Europe. Perhaps foremost among these achievements is that, by its establishment and social functioning, the Royal Society marked the inception of a lasting scientific "organization," that is, *organized science* in the modern sense— the conscious attempt to coordinate research and foster cooperation among independent investigators. The influence of the Royal Society on the development of atomic physics (and sometimes its hindrance to that development) will be seen in many of the original papers and in our commentaries.

As the theory of atomism evolved from Newton to Bernoulli, it is obvious that "atoms" were a purely *speculative* entity. Only with Dalton's discoveries in atomic chemistry, a century after Newton, was the experimental basis of atomism established. Once this breakthrough occurred, the use of atomic ideas in developing a theory of matter became increasingly powerful; theory and experiment proceeded at an ever-increasing rate. The level of insight to which both theory and experiment were thus raised and the understanding they provide today are documented in the papers presented in the latter part of the work.

The desire to reduce the apparently infinite complexity of the observable world to an intellectually comprehensible and aesthetically satisfying order has been part of man's history since ancient times. Both in classical philosophy and in contemporary science, the principal direction of inquiry has been toward grasping the comparatively few basic constituents out of which arise the infinite combinations that make up that "complexity" and to formulate laws to explain those combinations. The quest for these constituents and the desire to make manifest such laws remain the essential orientations of physics in the present decade. With the investigation of the structure of nucleons—protons and neutrons—atomism has entered a new and deeper level in its investigation of the physical universe. The nucleons are but two examples of still lesser entities in the hierarchical order of elementary particles.

We have ended this volume with an essay on the subject of such elementary particles and the new vistas of atomism. Our study appears to have come full circle. Atoms, which were once conceived of as the ultimately indivisible entities composing gross material reality, are now the gross phenomena for which modern physics is seeking a more subtle elementary understanding.

The editors wish to acknowledge their indebtedness to Mrs. Janet Halebsky, Mrs. Hannah Simon, Mrs. Diane James, Mrs. Joy Robertson, and Mrs. Barbara Murry for their assistance in typing the manuscript; to Miss Sarah K. Thomson, Reference Librarian, Barnard College, for her assistance in locating textual and biographical material, and to Professor Renée Geen of the French Department, Barnard College, for translating the more difficult passages from Descartes's *Principia Philosophiae*. Each of us wishes to express a debt of gratitude to his wife for her helpfulness and forbearance during the preparation of this work.

HENRY A. BOORSE
LLOYD MOTZ

New York City
December 1965

ooooooooooo

CONTENTS

ooooooooooo

Volume I

PART I THE FOUNDATIONS OF ATOMIC THEORY

PART III **THE FOUNDATIONS OF THE KINETIC THEORY OF MATTER**

Volume II

○○○○○○○○○○○

THE FOUNDATIONS
OF ATOMIC THEORY

○○○○○○○○○○

1

ooooooooooo

ATOMISM IN ANTIQUITY

ooooooooooo

Lucretius

(TITUS LUCRETIUS CARUS *ca.* 99-55 B.C.)

In order to understand the ancient origin of the concept of atoms, we must recognize that science as we now understand it was not pursued in the classical world. The Greek intellectual was preoccupied with questions of philosophy. It was in his attempts to solve philosophical problems that the idea of the smallest particle of matter, namely an atom, came into being.

We shall follow Van Melsen [1] in outlining the nature of this metaphysical endeavor and see how Democritus, who had inherited the concept of the atomic theory from Leucippus, utilized it to solve a specific philosophical problem. Democritus' ideas were in turn adopted by Epicurus as a basis for a materialistic philosophy. This philosophy was preserved and widely disseminated through the Western world by the celebrated work *De Rerum Natura* of the Roman poet Titus Lucretius Carus, better known as Lucretius.

De Rerum Natura had the most profound effect on the thought of Western scholars some seventeen centuries later, when experimental science was reborn. In England the atomic idea taught by *De Rerum Natura* was especially fruitful; it greatly influenced Boyle, the founder of modern chemistry, and Newton, the father of mathematical physics. Their influence, in turn, was immensely powerful in affecting the views of the able empiricists whose experiments grounded and then extended atomic theory. It is for this reason that a literary work which may seem to have little relevance to modern physics appears in this volume.

---

[1] Andrew G. Van Melsen, *From Atomos to Atom,* trans. Henry J. Koren (Pittsburgh: Duquesne University Press, 1952).

3

But to understand the work and its setting, its background needs a brief explanation. In antiquity, philosophy first concerned itself with efforts to explain the natural world. The oldest bits of systematic thought of this kind are attributed to Thales of Miletus, who lived about 600 B.C. He was concerned with reducing the "manifold of phenomena" to some kind of unity. To do so, he assumed that there was a "primary matter" which, modified in various ways, produced all the matter that we recognize about us. This idea of primary matter has survived with extraordinary persistence, and we shall see it reappear from time to time in the following pages. "Prout's hypothesis" (1815) is perhaps its most famous reincarnation. But Thales did not stop with a "philosophical" solution. Although his supporting arguments are lost to us, we know that he identified primary matter as water.

Heraclitus (*ca.* 480 B.C.), who followed Thales, was concerned with a very different problem, namely that of change. As a result of experience, he was convinced of the thesis that *to be* was to change. Therefore, he reasoned, the primary matter from which all things are made must exhibit this principle. Fire fulfills it well, for as it exists it is continually composed of different burning matter. Because it is not the same from one instant to the next, fire was to be identified with primary matter.

Parmenides, whose influence prevailed about the same time as that of Heraclitus, was also concerned with the problem of permanency and change, but his conclusion, interestingly enough, was in direct contrast: permanency is real and change is only an illusion. Parmenides' argument was a metaphysical one, which, to quote Van Melsen, runs as follows:

> All that *is,* together forms being . . . that which is must be *one,* i.e., it must possess unity, for if it were manifold, there would have to be something which divides it. But outside being, nothing is. Therefore there is nothing that can divide being, and therefore, being is *one.* This one being is also unchangeable. For what could be the meaning of change? It could mean either the transition from one kind of being to another . . . or the transition from non-being to being. . . . The transition from one kind of being to another kind of being . . . really amounts to being remaining what it is. . . . Because non-being is not, . . . it cannot become anything.[2]

Probably the reader will have serious reservations about these arguments, which may seem tautological; but however we view them today, Parmenides made a profound impression on his contemporaries and on Democritus, whose opinions flourished some seventy years later. Democritus saw that, if change was impossible, then a science of nature was not possible. To solve the problem he contradicted Parmenides with the asser-

---

[2] *Ibid.,* p. 15.

tion that being is not *one,* but is divided into many "beings," each permanent and indivisible. These "beings" he called atoms. Democritus also asserted that *nothing* does exist—*nothing* implying what we would call a *void.* Thus, *to be,* for him, meant to be *atom* or to be *void.* According to this view, change consists only in the rearrangement of eternal and unchanging atoms. This part of his argument agreed with Parmenides—the permanence of atoms is real and the change one sees is an illusion—for the permanent atoms always remain. To make change intelligible, he postulated that atoms are infinite in number and ceaselessly in motion in infinite space. All atoms consist of the same primary material. The only differences in atoms is their size, shape, and weight. These characteristics manifest themselves in differences visible in the different objects around us.

These ideas of Democritus, as noted above, were adopted by Epicurus as the basis for a materialistic philosophy. It was the purpose of this philosophy to abolish superstitious fears of intervention of the gods in the world of men and of the punishment of the soul in life after death. Epicurus attempted to do this by showing that the world is rational, i.e., governed by laws of nature. All that exists is corporeal. The intangible is nonexistent or empty space. It is in this way that Democritus' ideas were incorporated in Epicurus' philosophical system. As for punishment in afterlife, he asserted that the soul perishes with the body. All of this is faithfully expounded by Lucretius. It is not, however, embodied in the excerpt below, inasmuch as our attempt is to distill from the work the atomic ideas of Democritus.

A careful reading of Lucretius' work offers some surprises. In the third paragraph following the opening of Book II—Movements and Shapes of Atoms—he discusses the motion of dust motes visible in a beam of light. We have all seen such motions and perhaps dismissed them as arising from convection currents in the air (which in fact they are on this large a scale). Lucretius however suggests something different—"their dancing is an actual indication of underlying movements of matter that are hidden from our sight . . . you . . . see many particles under the impact of invisible blows changing their course . . . this way and that, in all directions. You must understand that they all derive this restlessness from the atoms. *It originates with the atoms, which move of themselves. . . . So the movement mounts up from the atoms and gradually emerges to the level of our senses . . .*" (Editors' italics).

These words are indeed arresting because they assert not only a kinetic theory of matter but they also tell us that the observed motion of very small (actually microscopic) particles in a gas is a consequence of atomic agitation. Just this kind of motion was found for microscopic particles in a liquid by the British botanist Brown in 1827 and ever since it has been known as "Brownian motion." At the time of its discovery its origin was a complete mystery despite the fact that a kinetic hypothesis of matter had already been suggested by Boyle, Hooke, Bernoulli and others. In fact it was not until after Clausius and Maxwell had firmly established the kinetic theory of gases (1860) that even suggestions were made as to the origin of the Brownian motion. It is interesting to speculate how much faster the progress of science might have been if the Victorian scientists had been as aware of Lucretius as their illustrious precursors, Boyle, Newton and Hooke had been.

Another interesting statement which Lucretius makes a few paragraphs later in Book II relates to falling bodies: ". . . through undisturbed vacuum all bodies must travel at equal speed though impelled by unequal weights." This statement is, of course, completely at variance with Aristotelian ideas and the establishment of its validity had to await the experimental methods in mechanics introduced by Galileo.

Of Lucretius, the author of *De Rerum Natura,* relatively little is known. He seems to have been of Roman origin and to have been born sometime between the years 98 to 95 B.C., dying in 55 B.C. Greek teachers of the Epicurean sect settled in Rome during Lucretius' youth and soon formed close ties with the governing class, who had developed a new taste for philosophy. The inference that Lucretius belonged to this class is found in the manner in which he addresses Memmius, a Roman aristocrat and friend of the author. According to one account Lucretius became mad as a result of taking a love philter, composed *De Rerum Natura* in lucid intervals, and finally died by suicide in his forty-fourth year. This story appears of doubtful credibility. A work characterized by such imagery and continuity of thought seems hardly the effort of an unsound mind. The internal evidence is that the poem (it is not reproduced here in poetic form) was left in an unfinished state by the death of the author.

ᴏᴏᴏᴏᴏᴏᴏ

LUCRETIUS

De Rerum Natura [3]
("The Nature of the Universe")

BOOK I. MATTER AND SPACE

FOR WHAT IS TO FOLLOW, my Memmius, lay aside your cares and lend undistracted ears and an attentive mind to true reason. Do not scornfully reject, before you have understood them, the gifts I have marshalled for you with zealous devotion. I will set out to discourse to you on the ultimate realities of heaven and the gods. I will reveal those *atoms* from which nature creates all things and increases and feeds them and into which, when they perish, nature again resolves them. To these in my discourse I commonly give such names as the "raw material," or "generative bodies" or "seeds" of things. Or I may call them "primary particles," because they come first and everything else is composed of them.

. . . In tackling this theme, our starting point will be this principle: *Nothing can ever be created by divine power out of nothing.* The reason why all mortals are so gripped by fear is that they see all sorts of things happening on the earth and in the sky with no discernible cause, and these they attribute to the will of a god. Accordingly, when we have seen that nothing can be created out of nothing, we shall then have a clearer picture of the path ahead, the problem of how things are created and occasioned without the aid of the gods.

First then, if things were made out of nothing, any species could spring from any source and nothing would require seed. Men could arise from the sea and scaly fish from the earth, and birds could be hatched out of the sky. Cattle and other domestic animals and every kind of wild beast, multiplying indiscriminately, would occupy cultivated and waste lands alike. The same fruits would not grow constantly on the same trees, but they would keep changing: any tree might bear any fruit. If each species were not composed of its own generative bodies, why should each be born always of the same kind of mother? Actually, since each is formed out of specific seeds, it is born and emerges into the sunlit world only from a place where there exists the right material, the right kind of atoms. This is why everything cannot be born of everything, but a specific power of generation inheres in specific objects.

Again, why do we see roses appear in spring, grain in summer's heat, grapes under the spell of autumn? Surely, because it is only after specific seeds have drifted together at their own proper time that every created thing stands revealed, when the season is favourable and the life-giving earth can safely deliver delicate growths into the sunlit world. If they were made out of nothing, they would spring up suddenly after varying lapses of time and at abnormal seasons, since there would of course be no primary bodies which could be prevented by the harshness of the season from entering into generative unions. Similarly, in order that things might grow, there would be no need of any lapse of time for the accumulation of seed. Tiny tots would turn suddenly into grown men, and trees would shoot up spontaneously out of the earth. But it is obvious that none of these

---

[3] From Lucretius, *The Nature of the Universe,* trans. R. E. Latham (Penguin Books, 1951), pp. 27–45, 55–59, 90–95.

things happens, since everything grows gradually, as is natural, from a specific seed and retains its specific character. It is a fair inference that each is increased and nourished by its own raw material.

Here is a further point. Without seasonable showers the earth cannot send up gladdening growths. Lacking food, animals cannot reproduce their kind or sustain life. This points to the conclusion that many elements are common to many things, as letters are to words, rather than to the theory that anything can come into existence without atoms.

Or again, why has not nature been able to produce men on such a scale that they could ford the ocean on foot or demolish high mountains with their hands or prolong their lives over many generations? Surely, because each thing requires for its birth a particular material which determines what can be produced. It must therefore be admitted that nothing can be made out of nothing, because everything must be generated from a seed before it can emerge into the unresisting air.

Lastly, we see that tilled plots are superior to untilled, and their fruits are improved by cultivation. This is because the earth contains certain atoms which we rouse to productivity by turning the fruitful clods with the ploughshare and stirring up the soil. But for these, you would see great improvements arising spontaneously without any aid from our labours.

The second great principle is this: *nature resolves everything into its component atoms and never reduces anything to nothing.* If anything were perishable in all its parts, anything might perish all of a sudden and vanish from sight. There would be no need of any force to separate its parts and loosen their links. In actual fact, since everything is composed of indestructible seeds, nature obviously does not allow anything to perish till it has encountered a force that shatters it with a blow or creeps into chinks and unknits it.

If the things that are banished from the scene by age are annihilated through the exhaustion of their material, from what source does Venus bring back the several races of animals into the light of life? And, when they are brought back, where does the inventive earth find for each the special food required for its sustenance and growth? From what fount is the sea replenished by its native springs and the streams that flow into it from afar? Whence does the ether draw nutriment for the stars? For everything consisting of a mortal body must have been exhausted by the long day of time, the illimitable past. If throughout this bygone eternity there have persisted bodies from which the universe has been perpetually renewed, they must certainly be possessed of immortality. Therefore things cannot be reduced to nothing.

Again, all objects would regularly be destroyed by the same force and the same cause, were it not that they are sustained by imperishable matter more or less tightly fastened together. Why, a mere touch would be enough to bring about destruction supposing there were no imperishable bodies whose union could be dissolved only by the appropriate force. Actually, because the fastenings of the atoms are of various kinds while their matter is imperishable, compound objects remain intact until one of them encounters a force that proves strong enough to break up its particular constitution. Therefore nothing returns to nothing, but everything is resolved into its constituent bodies. . . .

Well, Memmius, I have taught you that things cannot be created out of nothing nor, once born, be summoned back to nothing. Perhaps, however, you are becoming mistrustful of my words, because these atoms of mine are not visible to the eye. Consider, therefore, this further evidence of *bodies whose existence you must acknowledge though they cannot be seen.* First, wind, when its force is roused, whips up waves, founders tall ships and scatters cloud rack. Sometimes scouring plains with hurricane force it strews them with huge trees and batters mountain peaks with blasts that hew down forests. Such is wind in its fury, when it whoops aloud with a mad menace in its shouting. Without question, therefore, there must be invisible particles of wind which sweep sea and land and the clouds in the sky, swooping upon them and whirling them along in a headlong hurricane. In the way they flow and the havoc they spread they are no different from a torrential flood of water when it rushes down in a sudden spate from the mountain heights, swollen by heavy rains, and heaps together wreckage from the forest and entire trees. Soft though it is by nature, the sudden shock of oncoming water is more than even stout bridges can withstand, so furious is the force with which the turbid, storm-flushed torrent surges against their piers. With a mighty roar it lays them low, rolling huge rocks under its waves and brushing aside every obstacle from its course. Such, therefore, must be the movement of blasts of wind also. When they have come surging along some course like a rushing river, they push obstacles before them and buffet them with repeated blows; and sometimes, eddying round and round, they snatch them up and carry them along in a swiftly circling vortex. Here then is proof upon proof that winds have invisible bodies, since in their actions and behaviour they are found to rival great rivers, whose bodies are plain to see.

Then again, we smell the various scents of things though we never see them approaching our nostrils. Similarly, heat and cold cannot be detected by our eyes, and we do not see sounds. Yet all these must be composed of bodies, since they are able to impinge upon our senses. For nothing can touch or be touched except body.

Again, clothes hung out on a surf-beaten shore grow moist. Spread in the sun they grow dry. But we do not see how the moisture has soaked into them, nor again how it has been dispelled by the heat. It follows that the moisture is split up into minute parts which the eye cannot possibly see.

Again, in the course of many annual revolutions of the sun a ring is worn thin next to the finger with continual rubbing. Dripping water hollows a stone. A curved ploughshare, iron though it is, dwindles imperceptibly in the furrow. We see the cobblestones of the highway worn by the feet of many wayfarers. The bronze statues by the city gates show their right hands worn thin by the touch of travellers who have greeted them in passing. We see that all these are being diminished, since they are worn away. But to perceive what particles drop off at any particular time is a power grudged to us by our ungenerous sense of sight.

To sum up, whatever is added to things gradually by nature and the passage of days, causing a cumulative increase, eludes the most attentive scrutiny of our eyes. Conversely, you cannot see what objects lose by the wastage of age—sheer sea cliffs, for instance, exposed to prolonged erosion by the mordant brine—or at what time the loss occurs. It follows that nature works through the agency of invisible bodies.

On the other hand, things are not hemmed in by the pressure of solid bodies in a tight mass. This is because *there is vacuity in things*. A grasp of this fact will be helpful to you in many respects and will save you from much bewildered doubting and questioning about the universe and from mistrust of my teaching. Well then, by vacuity I mean intangible and empty space. If it did not exist, things could not move at all. For the distinctive action of matter, which is counteraction and obstruction, would be in force always and everywhere. Nothing could proceed, because nothing would give it a starting point by receding. As it is, we see with our own eyes at sea and on land and high up in the sky that all sorts of things in all sorts of ways are on the move. If there were no empty space, these things would be denied the power of restless movement—or rather, they could not possibly have come into existence, embedded as they would have been in motionless matter.

Besides, there are clear indications that things that pass for solid are in fact porous. Even in rocks a trickle of water seeps through into caves, and copious drops ooze from every surface. Food percolates to every part of an animal's body. Trees grow and bring forth their fruit in season, because their food is distributed throughout their length from the tips of the roots through the trunk and along every branch. Noises pass through walls and fly into closed buildings. Freezing cold penetrates to the bones. If there were no vacancies through which the various bodies could make their way, none of these phenomena would be possible.

Again, why do we find some things outweigh others of equal volume? If there is as much matter in a ball of wool as in one of lead, it is natural that it should weigh as heavily, since it is the function of matter to press everything downwards, while it is the function of space on the other hand to remain weightless. Accordingly, when one thing is not less bulky than another but obviously lighter, it plainly declares that there is more vacuum in it, while the heavier object proclaims that there is more matter in it and much less empty space. We have therefore reached the goal of our diligent enquiry: there is in things an admixture of what we call vacuity.

In case you should be misled on this question by the idle imagining of certain theorists, I must anticipate their argument. They maintain that water yields and opens a penetrable path to the scaly bodies of fish that push against it, because they leave spaces behind them into which the yielding water can flow together. In the same way, they suppose, other things can move by mutually changing places, although every place remains filled. This theory has been adopted utterly without warrant. For how can the fish advance till the water has given way? And how can the water retire when the fish cannot move? There are thus only two alternatives: either all bodies are devoid of movement, or you must admit that things contain an admixture of vacuity whereby each is enabled to make the first move.

Lastly, if two bodies suddenly spring apart from contact on a broad surface, all the intervening space must be void until it is occupied by air. However quickly the air rushes in all round, the entire space cannot be filled instantaneously. The air must occupy one spot after another until it has taken possession of the whole space. If anyone supposes that this consequence of such springing apart is made possible by the condensation of air, he is mistaken. For condensation implies that something that was full becomes empty, or vice versa. And I contend that air could not condense so as to produce this effect; or at any rate, if there were no vacuum, it could not thus shrink into itself and draw its parts together.

. . . All nature as it is in itself consists of two things—bodies and the vacant space in which the bodies are situated and through which they move in different directions. The existence of bodies is vouched for by the agreement of the senses. If a belief resting directly on this foundation is not valid, there will be no standard to which we can refer any doubt on obscure questions for rational confirmation. If there were no place and space, which we call vacuity, these bodies could not be situated anywhere or move in any direction whatever. This I have just demonstrated. It remains to show that *nothing exists that is distinct both from body and from vacuity* and could be ranked with the others as a third substance. For whatever *is* must also be something. If it offers resistance to touch, however light and slight, it will increase the mass of body by such amount, great or small, as it may amount to, and will rank with it. If, on the other hand, it is intangible, so that it offers no resistance whatever to anything passing through it, then it will be that empty space which we call vacuity. Besides, whatever it may be in itself, either it will act in some way, or react to other things acting upon it, or else it will be such that things can be and happen in it. But without body nothing can act or react; and nothing can afford a place except emptiness and vacancy. Therefore, besides matter and vacuity, we cannot include in the number of things any third substance that can either affect our senses at any time or be grasped by the reasoning of our minds.

You will find that anything that can be named is either a property or an accident of these two. A *property* is something that cannot be detached or separated from a thing without destroying it, as weight is a property of rocks, heat of fire, fluidity of water, tangibility of all bodies, intangibility of vacuum. On the other hand, servitude and liberty, poverty and riches, war and peace, and all other things whose advent or departure leaves the essence of a thing intact, all these it is our practice to call by their appropriate name, *accidents*.

Similarly, time by itself does not exist; but from things themselves there results a sense of what has already taken place, what is now going on and what is to ensue. It must not be claimed that anyone can sense time by itself apart from the movement of things or their restful immobility. . . .

Material objects are of two kinds, atoms and compounds of atoms. The atoms themselves cannot be swamped by any force, for they are preserved indefinitely by their absolute solidity. Admittedly, it is hard to believe that anything can exist that is absolutely solid. The lightning stroke from the sky penetrates closed buildings, as do shouts and other noises. Iron glows molten in the fire, and hot rocks are cracked by untempered scorching. Hard gold is softened and melted by heat; and bronze, icelike, is liquefied by flame. Both heat and piercing cold seep through silver, since we feel both alike when a cooling shower of water is poured into a goblet that we hold ceremonially in our hands. All these facts point to the conclusion that nothing is really solid. But sound reasoning and nature itself drive us to the opposite conclusion. Pay attention, therefore, while I demonstrate in a few lines that there exist certain bodies that are absolutely solid and indestructible, namely, those atoms which according to our teaching are the seeds or prime units of things from which the whole universe is built up.

In the first place, we have found that nature is twofold, consisting of two totally different things, matter and the space in which things happen. Hence each of these must exist by itself without admixture of the other. For, where there is empty space (what we call vacuity), there matter is not; where matter exists, there cannot be a vacuum. Therefore the prime units of matter are solid and free from vacuity.

Again, since composite things contain some vacuum, the surrounding matter must be solid. For you cannot reasonably maintain that anything can hide vacuity and hold it within its body unless you allow that the container itself is solid. And what contains the vacuum in things can only be an accumulation of matter. Hence matter, which possesses absolute solidity, can be everlasting when other things are decomposed.

Again, if there were no empty space, everything would be one solid mass; if there were no material objects with the property of filling the space they occupy, all existing space would be utterly void. It is clear, then, that there is an alternation of matter and vacuity, mutually distinct, since the whole is neither completely full nor completely empty. There are therefore solid bodies, causing the distinction between empty space and full. And these, as I have just shown, can be neither decomposed by blows from without nor invaded and unknit from within nor destroyed by any other form of assault. For it seems that a thing without vacuum can be neither knocked to bits nor snapped nor chopped in two by cutting; nor can it let in moisture or seeping cold or piercing fire, the universal agents of destruction. The more vacuum a thing contains within it, the more readily it yields to these assailants. Hence, if the units of matter are solid and without vacuity, as I have shown, they must be everlasting.

Yet again, if the matter in things had not been everlasting, everything by now would have gone back to nothing, and the things we see would be the product of rebirth out of nothing. But, since I have already shown that nothing can be created out of nothing nor any existing thing be summoned back to nothing, the atoms must be made of imperishable stuff into which everything can be resolved in the end, so that there may be a stock of matter for building the world anew. The atoms, therefore, are absolutely solid and unalloyed. In no other way could they have survived throughout infinite time to keep the world in being.

Furthermore, if nature had set no limit to the breaking of things, the particles of matter in the course of ages would have been ground so small that nothing could be generated from them so as to attain in the fullness of time to the summit of its growth. For we see that anything can be more speedily disintegrated than put together again. Hence, what the long day of time, the bygone eternity, has already shaken and loosened to fragments could never in the residue of time be reconstructed. As it is, there is evidently a limit set to breaking, since we see that everything is renewed and each according to its kind has a fixed period in which to grow to its prime.

Here is a further argument. Granted that the particles of matter are absolutely solid, we can still explain the composition and behaviour of soft things—air, water, earth, fire—by their intermixture with empty space. On the other hand, supposing the atoms to be soft, we cannot account for the origin of hard flint and iron. For there would be no foundation for nature to build on. Therefore there must be bodies strong in their unalloyed solidity by whose closer clustering things can be knit together and display unyielding toughness.

If we suppose that there is no limit set to the breaking of matter, we must still admit that material objects consist of particles which throughout eternity have resisted the forces of destruction. To say that these are breakable does not square with the fact that they have survived throughout eternity under a perpetual bombardment of innumerable blows.

Again, there is laid down for each thing a specific limit to its growth and its tenure of life, and the laws of nature ordain what each can do and what it cannot. No species is ever changed, but each remains so much itself that every kind of bird displays on its body its own specific markings. This is a further proof that their bodies are composed of changeless matter. For, if the atoms could yield in any way to change, there would be no certainty as to what could arise and what could not, at what point the power of everything was limited by an immovable frontier post; nor could successive generations so regularly repeat the nature, behaviour, habits and movements of their parents.

To proceed with our argument, there is an ultimate point in visible objects which represents the smallest thing that can be seen. So also there must be an ultimate point in objects that lie below the limit of perception by our senses. This point is without parts and is the smallest thing that can exist. It never has been and never will be able to exist by itself, but only as one primary part of something else. It is with a mass of such parts, solidly jammed together in order, that matter is filled up. Since they cannot exist by themselves, they must needs stick together in a mass from which they cannot by any means be prized loose. The atoms therefore are absolutely solid and unalloyed, consisting of a mass of least parts tightly packed together. They are not compounds formed by the coalescence of their parts, but bodies of absolute and everlasting solidity. To these nature allows no loss or diminution, but guards them as seeds for things. If there are no such least parts, even the smallest bodies will consist of an infinite number of parts, since they can always be halved and their halves halved again without limit. On this showing, what difference will there be between the whole universe and the very least of things? None at all. For, however endlessly infinite the universe may be, yet the smallest things will equally consist of an infinite number of parts. Since true reason cries out against this and denies that the mind can believe it, you must needs give in and admit that there are least parts which themselves are partless. Granted that these parts exist, you must needs admit that the atoms they compose are also solid and everlasting. But, if all things were compelled by all-creating nature to be broken up into these least parts, nature would lack the power to rebuild anything out of them. For partless objects cannot have the essential properties of generative matter—those varieties of attachment, weight, impetus, impact and movement on which everything depends. . . .

Well then, since I have shown that there are completely solid indestructible particles of matter flying about through all eternity, let us elucidate whether or not there is any limit to their number. Similarly, as we have found that there is a vacuum, the place or space in which things happen, let us see whether its whole extent is limited or whether it stretches far and wide into immeasurable depths.

Learn, therefore, that *the universe is not bounded in any direction.* If it were, it would necessarily have a limit somewhere. But clearly a thing cannot have a limit unless there is something outside to limit it, so that the eye can follow it up to a certain point but not beyond. Since you must admit that there is nothing outside the universe, it can have no limit and is accordingly without end or measure. It makes no odds in which part of it you may take your stand: whatever spot anyone may occupy, the universe stretches away from him just the same in all directions without limit. Suppose for a moment that the whole of space were bounded and that someone made his way to its uttermost boundary and threw a flying dart. Do you choose to suppose that the missile, hurled with might and main, would speed along the course on which it was aimed? Or do you think something would block the way and stop it? You must assume one alternative or the other. But neither of them leaves you a loophole. Both force you to admit that the universe continues without end. Whether there is some obstacle lying on the boundary line that prevents the dart from going farther on its course or whether it flies on beyond, it cannot in fact have started from the boundary. With this argument I will pursue you. Wherever you may place the ultimate limit of things, I will ask you: "Well then, what does happen to the dart?" The upshot is that the boundary cannot stand firm anywhere, and final escape from this conclusion is precluded by the limitless possibility of running away from it.

It is a matter of observation that one thing is limited by another. The hills are demarcated by air, and air by the hills. Land sets bounds to sea, and sea to every land. But the universe has nothing outside to limit it.

Further, if all the space in the universe were shut in and confined on every side by definite boundaries, the supply of matter would already have accumulated by its own weight at the bottom, and nothing could happen under the dome of the sky—indeed, there would be no sky and no sunlight, since all the available matter would have settled down and would be lying in a heap throughout eternity. As it is, no rest is given to the atoms, because there is no bottom where they can accumulate and take up their abode. Things go on happening all the time through ceaseless movement in every direction; and atoms of matter bouncing up from below are supplied out of the infinite. There is therefore a limitless abyss of space, such that even the dazzling flashes of the lightning cannot traverse it in their course, racing through an interminable tract of time, nor can they even shorten the distance still to be covered. So vast is the scope that lies open to things far and wide without limit in any dimension.

The universe is restrained from setting any limit to itself by nature, which compels body to be bounded by vacuum and vacuum by body.

Thus nature either makes them both infinite in alternation, or else one of them, if it is not bounded by the other, must extend in a pure state without limit. Space, however, being infinite, so must matter be. Otherwise, neither sea nor land nor the bright zones of the sky nor mortal beings nor the holy bodies of the gods could endure for one brief hour of time. The supply of matter would be shaken loose from combination and swept through the vastness of the void in isolated particles; or rather, it would never have coalesced to form anything, since its scattered particles could never have been driven into union.

Certainly the atoms did not post themselves purposefully in due order by an act of intelligence, nor did they stipulate what movements each should perform. As they have been rushing everlastingly throughout all space in their myriads, undergoing myriad changes under the disturbing impact of collisions, they have experienced every variety of movement and conjunction till they have fallen into the particular pattern by which this world of ours is constituted. This world has persisted many a long year, having once been set going in the appropriate motions. From these everything else follows. The rivers replenish the thirsty sea with profuse streams of water. Incubated by the sun's heat, the earth renews its fruits, and the brood of animals that springs from it grows lustily. The gliding fires of ether sustain their life. None of these results would be possible if there were not an ample supply of matter to bounce up out of infinite space in replacement of all that is lost. Just as animals deprived of food waste away through loss of body, so everything must decay as soon as its supply of matter goes astray and is cut off.

Whatever world the atoms have combined to form, impacts from without cannot preserve it at every point. By continual battering they can hold back part of it till others come along to make good the deficiency. But they are compelled now and then to bounce back and in so doing to leave space and time for the atoms to break loose from combination. It is thus essential that there should be great numbers of atoms coming up. Indeed, the impacts themselves could not be maintained without an unlimited supply of matter from all quarters.

BOOK II. MOVEMENT AND SHAPES OF ATOMS

As a further indication that all particles of matter are on the move, remember that the universe is bottomless: there is no place where the atoms could come to rest. As I have already shown by various arguments and proved conclusively, space is without end or limit and spreads out immeasurably in all directions alike.

It clearly follows that no rest is given to the atoms in their course through the depths of space. Driven along in an incessant but variable movement, some of them bounce far apart after a collision while others recoil only a short distance from the impact. From those that do not recoil far, being driven into a closer union and held there by the entanglement of their own interlocking shapes, are composed firmly rooted rock, the stubborn strength of steel and the like. Those others that move freely through larger tracts of space, springing far apart and carried far by the rebound—these provide for us thin air and blazing sunlight. Besides these, there are many other atoms at large in empty space which have been thrown out of compound bodies and have nowhere even been granted admittance so as to bring their motions into harmony.

This process, as I might point out, is illustrated by an image of it that is continually taking place before our very eyes. Observe what happens when sunbeams are admitted into a building and shed light on its shadowy places. You will see a multitude of tiny particles mingling in a multitude of ways in the empty space within the light of the beam, as though contending in everlasting conflict, rushing into battle rank upon rank with never a moment's pause in a rapid sequence of unions and disunions. From this you may picture what it is for the atoms to be perpetually tossed about in the illimitable void. To some extent a small thing may afford an illustration and an imperfect image of great things. Besides, there is a further reason why you should give your mind to these particles that are seen dancing in a sunbeam: their dancing is an actual indication of underlying movements of matter that are hidden from our sight. There you will see many particles under the impact of invisible blows changing their course and driven back upon their tracks, this way and that, in all directions. You must understand that they all derive this restlessness from the atoms. It originates with the atoms, which move of themselves. Then those small compound bodies that are least removed from the impetus of the atoms are set in motion by the impact of their invisible blows and in turn cannon against slightly larger bodies. So the movement mounts up from the atoms and gradually emerges to the level of our senses, so that those bodies are in motion that we see in sunbeams, moved by blows that remain invisible. In this connexion there is another fact that I want you to grasp. *When the atoms are travelling straight down through empty space by their own weight, at quite indeterminate times and places they swerve ever so little from their course,* just so much that you can call it a change of direction. If it were not for this swerve, everything would fall downwards like raindrops through the abyss of space. No collision would take place and no impact of atom on atom would be created. Thus nature would never have created anything.

If anyone supposes that heavier atoms on a straight course through empty space could outstrip lighter ones and fall on them from above, thus causing impacts that might give rise to generative motions, he is going far astray from the path of truth. The reason why objects falling through water or thin air vary in speed according to their weight is simply that the matter composing water or air cannot obstruct all objects equally, but is forced to give way more speedily to heavier ones. But empty space can offer no resistance to any object in any quarter at any time, so as not to yield free passage as its own nature demands. Therefore, through undisturbed vacuum all bodies must travel at equal speed though impelled by unequal weights. The heavier will never be able to fall on the lighter from above or generate of themselves impacts leading to that variety of motions out of which nature can produce things. We are thus forced back to the conclusion that the atoms swerve a little—but only a very little, or we shall be caught imagining slantwise movements, and the facts will prove us wrong. For we see plainly and palpably that weights, when they come tumbling down, have no power of their own to move aslant, so far as meets the eye. But who can possibly perceive that they do not diverge in the very least from a vertical course? In this connexion there is one fact that need occasion no surprise. *Although all the atoms are in motion, their totality appears to stand totally motionless,* except for such movements as particular objects may make with their own bodies. This is because the atoms all lie far below the range of our senses. Since they are themselves invisible, their movements also must elude observation. Indeed, even visible objects, when set at a distance, often disguise their movements. Often on a hillside fleecy sheep, as they crop their lush pasture, creep slowly onward, lured this way or that by grass that sparkles with fresh dew, while the full-fed lambs gaily frisk and butt. And yet, when we gaze from a distance, we see only a blur—a white patch stationary on the green hillside. Take another example. Mighty legions, waging mimic war, are thronging the plain with their manoeuvres. The dazzling sheen flashes to the sky and all around the earth is ablaze with bronze. Down below there sounds the tramp of a myriad marching feet. A noise of shouting strikes upon the hills and reverberates to the celestial vault. Wheeling horsemen gallop hot-foot across the midst of the plain, till it quakes under the fury of their charge. And yet there is a vantage-ground high among the hills from which all these appear immobile—a blaze of light stationary upon the plain.

And now let us turn to a new theme—*the characteristics of the atoms of all substances, the extent to which they differ in shape and the rich multiplicity of their forms.* Not that there are not many of the same shape, but they are by no means all identical with one another. And no wonder. When the multitude of them, as I have shown, is such that it is without limit or count, it is not to be expected that they should all be identical in build and configuration.

Consider the race of men, the scaly fish that swim in silence, the lusty herds, the creatures of the wild and the various feathered breeds, those that throng the vivifying watery places, by river banks and springs and lakes, and those that flock and flutter through pathless woodlands. Take a representative of any of these diverse species and you will still find that it differs in form from others of its kind. Otherwise the young could not recognize their mother, nor the mother her young. But we see that this can happen, and that individuals of these species are mutually recognizable no less than human beings.

Among ears of corn, whatever the kind, you will not find one just like another; but each will be marked by some distinctive feature. The same holds good of the various shells we see adorning the bosom of the land where the sea with pliant ripples laps on the thirsty sands of its winding shore. Here, then, is proof upon proof that in the stream of atoms likewise, since they exist by nature and are not handmade to a fixed pattern, there are certain individual differences of shape.

On this principle it is quite easy to explain why the fire of lightning is far more penetrative than our fire which springs from earthly torches. You can say that the heavenly fire of the lightning is of finer texture, being composed of smaller atoms, and can therefore pass through apertures impervious to this fire of ours, which springs from wood and is generated by a torch. Again, light passes through horn, but rain is dashed back. Why, if not because the particles of light are smaller than those that form the life-giving drops of water? We see that wine flows through a strainer as fast as it is poured in; but sluggish oil loiters. This, no doubt, is either because oil consists of larger atoms, or because these are more hooked and intertangled and, therefore, cannot separate as rapidly, so as to trickle through the holes one by one. . . .

To the foregoing demonstration I will link on another fact which will gain credence from this context: *the number of different forms of atoms is finite*. If it were not so, some of the atoms would have to be of infinite magnitude. Within the narrow limits of any single particle, there can be only a limited range of forms. Suppose that atoms consist of three minimum parts, or enlarge them by a few more. When by fitting on parts at top or bottom and transposing left and right you have exhausted every shape that can be given to the whole body by all possible arrangements of the parts, you are obviously left with no means of varying its form further except by adding other parts. Thence it will follow, if you wish to vary its form still further, that the arrangement will demand still other parts in exactly the same way. Variation in shape goes with increase in size. You cannot believe, therefore, that the atoms are distinguished by an infinity of forms; or you will compel some of them to be of enormous magnitude, which I have already proved to be demonstrably impossible.

To the foregoing demonstration I will link on another fact, which will gain credence from this context: *the number of atoms of any one form is infinite*. Since the varieties of form are limited, the number of uniform atoms must be unlimited. Otherwise the totality of matter would be finite, which I have proved in my verses is not so. I have shown that the universe is kept going by an infinite succession of atoms, so that the chain of impacts from all directions remains unbroken.

You may object that certain species of animals appear to be relatively rare, so that nature seems less well stocked with their seeds. But some other zone or environment in lands remote may abound in these, so as to make good the deficiency. As the outstanding instance among quadrupeds, we may note the snaky-handed elephants. Countless thousands of these must have gone to the making of that impenetrable ivory wall with which India is barricaded. Such is the abundance of these beasts, of which we see only very few samples. Give your mind now to the true reasoning I have to unfold. A new fact is battling strenuously for access to your ears. A new aspect of the universe is striving to reveal itself. But no fact is so simple that it is not harder to believe than to doubt at the first presentation. Equally, there is nothing so mighty or so marvellous that the wonder it evokes does not tend to diminish in time. Take first the pure and undimmed lustre of the sky and all that it enshrines: the stars that roam across its surface, the moon and the surpassing splendour of the sunlight. If all these sights were now displayed to mortal view for the first time by a swift unforeseen revelation, what miracle could be recounted greater than this? What would men before the revelation have been less prone to conceive as possible? Nothing, surely. So marvellous would have been that sight—a sight which no one now, you will admit, thinks worthy of an upward glance into the luminous regions of the sky. So has satiety blunted the appetite of our eyes. Desist, therefore, from thrusting out reasoning from your mind because of its disconcerting novelty. Weigh it, rather, with discerning judgment. Then, if it seems to you true, give in. If it is false, gird yourself to oppose it. For the mind wants to discover by reasoning what exists in the infinity of space that lies out there, beyond the ramparts of this world—that region into which the intellect longs to peer and into which the free projection of the mind does actually extend its flight.

Here, then, is my first point. In all dimensions alike, on this side or that, upward or downward through the universe, there is no end. This I have shown, and indeed the fact proclaims itself aloud and the nature of space makes it crystal clear. Granted, then, that empty space extends without limit in every direction and that seeds innumerable in number are rushing on countless courses through an unfathomable universe under the impulse of perpetual motion, *it is in the highest degree unlikely that this earth and sky is the only one to have been created* and that all those particles of matter outside are accomplishing nothing. This follows from the fact that our world has been made by nature through the spontaneous and casual collision and the multifarious, accidental, random and purposeless congregation and coalescence of atoms whose suddenly formed combinations could serve on each occasion as the starting-point of substantial fabrics—earth and sea and sky and the races of living creatures. On every ground, therefore, you must admit that there exist elsewhere other congeries of matter similar to this one which the ether clasps in ardent embrace. . . .

2

ооооооооооо

VORTICES AND PARTICLES

ооооооооооо

René Descartes (1596-1650)

We have seen how the concept of the atomic theory had its origin in the philosophies of Democritus, and Epicurus, and how their ideas were preserved by Lucretius, as exemplified in the preceding excerpt from *De Rerum Natura*. But seventeen centuries were to elapse before men of learning again concerned themselves seriously with these ideas. With the rebirth of experimental science at the height of the Renaissance, the scholars of western Europe were caught in the grip of a germinating scientific revolution.

While Kepler was immersed in the researches that gave validity and new meaning to the Copernican hypothesis and Galileo was laying the foundation for Newtonian mechanics, there occurred at La Haye in the province of Touraine, France, an event of the greatest consequence to the subsequent development of mathematics and to the scientific outlook for more than a century. This was the birth of René Descartes on March 31, 1596.

His father, Joachim, was a successful lawyer and counselor to the local parliament of Brittany. His mother, Jeanne Brochard, was unfortunately destined to live less than a year after his birth. Like many another who had achieved intellectual fame, Descartes was a delicate child; throughout his early years it was feared that he would not survive to attain maturity. But delicate health may not always be a detriment to intellectual development, and in Descartes's case his afflictions led to a novel way of life. Entered at the newly founded Jesuit College at La Flèche in Anjou at the age of eight, his health was such that the rector accorded him the unusual privilege of pursuing his studies abed until mid-day. This practice, conducive to reflection in his active mind, was continued by Descartes throughout life. The eight years he spent at La

Flèche he remembered not only with affection but with gratitude for the superior instruction. In later years he spoke of the school as one of the best in Europe.

But an increasing dissatisfaction with formal study led Descartes at sixteen to leave La Flèche and to settle for a time in Paris. Instead of leading a social life in the capital, he spent a year in almost solitary study before turning again to formal instruction, this time at the University of Poitiers. His desire to understand man and society and to observe life firsthand led him to a new, and for a scholar, unusual act. In May 1617, at the age of twenty-one, he enlisted as a volunteer in the military school at Breda, Holland. His two years at Breda are noteworthy in only one respect; he met there, quite by chance, the rector of the College at Dorchecht, Isaac Beekman, an accomplished mathematician, who became his good friend. This friendship continued throughout Descartes's later life.

After two years at Breda, Descartes enlisted in the army of the Duke of Bavaria. In November 1619 he was stationed at Neuberg on the Danube. Because of the severe weather, he shut himself in a warm room (not in a stove as is sometimes fancifully stated), and gave himself completely to deep meditation. It was here that he conceived the basis for his own system of philosophy—the idea that what is seen clearly and distinctly must be true. In order to amass further experience, he continued his wanderings all over Europe for the next eight years, sometimes in military service and sometimes out.

In 1628, at the age of thirty-two, he had had his fill of wandering and decided to find a haven in which he could at last devote himself to philosophical reform and contemplation. Holland had won her independence from Spain and was enjoying a peaceful period of prosperity. It was a country in which new academies and universities were being founded in an atmosphere of religious toleration. It was to Holland therefore, that Descartes chose to go to carry out the work to which he had dedicated his life. Here he lived for the next twenty years, as he described it, "in thirteen different places and in twenty-four different abodes." Despite his desire for domestic privacy, it must not be imagined that Descartes always led a solitary life. He had many friends, including Isaac Beekman, the mathematician, and Constantin Huygens, secretary to the Prince of Orange and father of the celebrated Christian Huygens, founder of the wave theory of light. Descartes was not hesitant in engaging in learned disputes. "Indeed," writes one of his biographers, "he had a special talent for dividing scholars among themselves, and for prolonging the disputes he had aroused."

Despite the absence of scholarly publication during his years of wandering, Descartes now began developing those ideas that had been maturing since his youth. His first work was a great treatise on the physical system of the world, entitled *Le Monde, un Traité de la Lumière,* which he finished in 1633. On the eve of its publication the news reached Descartes of Galileo's censure by the Inquisition. Always sensitive to Catholic authority and opinion, and realizing that his views, like Galileo's, agreed with a Copernican system of the world, he immediately withdrew the work. Although parts of *Le Monde* appeared subsequently, in the *Discours de la méthode* (1637) and the accompanying essays *La Dioptrique, Les Météores,* and *La Géométrie,* together with further developments in the *Principia philosophiae* (1644), it was never published in its entirety. His *Meditationes de prima philosophia* was published in 1641, and finally the *Traité des passions de l'âme* in 1649.

In this same year, 1649, M. Channut, French Ambassador to the Swedish Court and an admirer of Descartes, suggested to Queen Christina that as a patroness of learning she would do well to have this learned philosopher as an ornament in the regal circle. In due time Descartes received the royal command and with reluctance departed for Stockholm in October. But the northern climate and the necessity of interviews with the Queen at five in the morning were too much for his frail constitution. On February 1, 1650, he contracted an illness that developed into pneumonia. Ten days later he was dead. Not yet fifty-four years old, he had exerted a profound influence that continued to dominate European learning for more than another half century.

It is because of Descartes's wide influence that he is included among those who have shaped atomistic thought, even though his views were contrary to the atomic hypothesis. His system of the world as a group of vortices was widely accepted and was in fashion at Cambridge years after Newton had propounded the theory of universal gravitation. Descartes was the first to attempt a mechanical explanation of the solar system. His explanation did not endorse the notion of action at a distance, but instead proposed a material method for the transmission of motion to heavenly bodies. Descartes proposed that celestial matter was everywhere in motion in the form of vortices, a single mechanical principle that explained the movements of the planetary system. To many contemporary scientists Newton's idea of planets suspended in empty space and retained in orbit by an invisible force seemed the essence of occult doctrine. Nevertheless, Descartes's vortex theory, on closer inspection, proved to be mechanically unsound; it was not susceptible to calculation and precise prediction, characteristics that won for Newtonian ideas the adherence of eighteenth-century astronomers, and brought science from the medieval world into the modern.

The selections that follow are chosen to show Descartes's ideas about the constitution of matter. His disbelief in the theory of "atoms and the void" of Democritus is expressed in his "Principles," reprinted at the end of these comments. To a large extent, Descartes's system followed from his basic tenet expressed in Principle XVI: ". . . it is absolutely inconceivable that nothing [i.e., emptiness] should possess extension." To exist, a void must have extension; but, says Descartes, emptiness cannot have extension. Thus space, which is all around us, having extension, can have no void and must consequently be a continuum of matter.

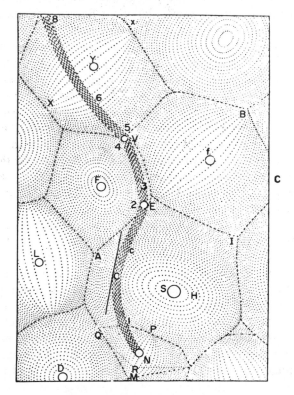

Fig. 2–1. Descartes's vortices.

The way in which Descartes worked out a world picture on this basis has interest because it produced ideas that affected the shape of physics in later years. Newton and Boyle both were strongly influenced by Descartes: Newton by his mathematical and inertial ideas and Boyle by his system of smallest particles. For strange as it may appear, Descartes was forced to develop a theory of particles in constructing his scheme of the universe. The way in which a particulate scheme can exist in a material continuum was developed in his vortex theory.

Fig. 2–1 illustrates a group of such vortices, with *AEI* representing the vortex of the solar system. In the beginning, vortex *AEI,* like the others, consisted of a number of small parts, each rotating around its own center as well as around *S,* the central start of the vortex. According to Descartes, this kind of motion ground the corners of the celestial matter so that the parts became rounded. The resulting globules were supposed, as the result of inertia, to move to the outside of the vortex; the parings of the original particles, ground to fine dust, tended to collect at the center of the vortex. This "finer matter" is the so-called *first* matter of Descartes, and constitutes the sun and stars. The spherical particles are the *second* matter; they envelop the central accumulation of first matter and constitute the heavens.

There is also a *third* matter produced from the original particles. Some of the filings, produced by rubbing, pass through the revolving spherical particles, are caught, twisted, and channeled. This coarsest material was assigned the property of *mass,* depending on the amount of this material in a body, it possessed more or less of the property known as mass. This material could also form a dense crust around a central nucleus. Such a "degraded" star could be caught up by another vortex and settle into the latter where its velocity was the same as the velocity of that part of the vortex. Such phenomena accounted for the presence of the planets. One may compare these ideas of Descartes with the mode in turbulent theories of the origin of the solar system.

While these considerations sound very speculative and contrived to the present analytical mind, the whole system in its day was highly regarded by contemporary philosophers. It must not be overlooked that Descartes's ideas contained several very notable advances over previous systems, and so paved the way for the modern astronomical ideas instituted by Newton. Thus we recognize that according to Descartes, matter in the solar system is not different than that on earth. By contrast, the Aristotelian system had taught that the sphere encompassed by the radius to the moon contained "corruptible" material; i.e., it was a space in which change was possible, but the sphere beyond the moon was "incorruptible" and in it no change occurred.

Descartes's system also banished spirits and genii, which even Kepler had considered as guardians of the planetary motions. Finally, it presented a view of the cosmos in which events occurred on a rational, physical basis as they would on earth. It was this rational view, despite its many shortcomings, that marks Descartes's scheme as a substantial advance toward modern ideas.

ᴏᴏᴏᴏᴏᴏᴏ

DESCARTES

Principia Philosophiae [1]

PRINCIPLE XVI.

That it is contrary to reason to say that there is a vacuum or space in which there is absolutely nothing.

AS REGARDS A VACUUM IN the philosophic sense of the word, i.e., a space in which there is no substance, it is evident that such cannot exist, because the extension of space or internal place, is not different from that of body. For, from the mere fact that a body is extended in length, breadth, or depth, we have reason to conclude that it is a substance, because it is absolutely inconceivable that nothing should possess extension, we ought to conclude also that the same is true of the space which is supposed to be void, i.e. that since there is in it extension, there is necessarily also substance.

PRINCIPLE XVII.

That a vacuum, in the ordinary sense, does not exclude all body.

And when we take this word vacuum in its ordinary sense, we do not mean a place or space in which there is absolutely nothing, but only a place in which there are none of those things which we expected to find there. Thus because a pitcher is made to hold water, we say that it is empty when it contains nothing but air; or if there are no fish in a fishpond, we say that there is nothing in it, even though it be full of water; similarly we say a vessel is empty, when, in place of the merchandise which it was designed to carry, it is loaded only with sand, so that it may resist the impetuous violence of the wind; and finally we say in the same way that a space is empty when it contains nothing sensible, even though it contain created matter and self-existent substance; for we are not wont to consider things excepting those with which our senses succeed in presenting us. And if, in

---

[1] From René Descartes, *Principles of Philosophy,* in *The Philosophical Works of Descartes,* trans. E. S. Haldane and G. R. T. Ross (New York: Dover, 1955), pp. 262–264, 297–299, 302.

place of keeping in mind what we should comprehend by these words—vacuum and nothing—we afterwards suppose that in the space which is termed vacuum there is not only nothing sensible, but nothing at all, we shall fall into the same error as if, because a pitcher is usually termed empty since it contains nothing but air, we were therefore to judge that the air contained in it is not a substantive thing.

PRINCIPLE XVIII.

How the prejudice concerning the absolute vacuum is to be corrected.

We have almost all lapsed into this error from the beginning of our lives, for, seeing that there is no necessary connection between the vessel and the body it contains, we thought that God at least could remove all the body contained in the vessel without its being necessary that any other body should take its place. But in order that we may be able to correct this error, it is necessary to remark that while there is no connection between the vessel and that particular body which it contains, there is an absolutely necessary one between the concave figure of the vessel and the extension considered generally which must be comprised in this cavity; so that there is not more contradiction in conceiving a mountain without a valley, than such a cavity without the extension which it contains, or this extension without the substance which is extended, because nothing, as has already been frequently remarked, cannot have extension. And therefore, if it is asked what would happen if God removed all the body contained in a vessel without permitting its place being occupied by another body, we shall answer that the sides of the vessel will thereby come into immediate contiguity with one another. For two bodies must touch when there is nothing between them, because it is manifestly contradictory for these two bodies to be apart from one another, or that there should be a distance between them, and yet that this distance should be nothing; for distance is a mode of extension, and without extended substance it cannot therefore exist.

PRINCIPLE XIX.

That this confirms what was said of rarefaction.

After we have thus remarked that the nature of material substance consists only in its being an extended thing, or that its extension is not different from what has been attributed to space however empty, it is easy to discover that it is impossible that any one of these parts should in any way occupy more space at one time than another, and thus that it may be rarefied otherwise than in the manner explained above; or again it is easy to perceive that there cannot be more matter or corporeal substance in a vessel when it is filled with gold or lead, or any other body that is heavy and hard, than when it only contains air and appears to be empty; for the quantity of the parts of matter does not depend on their weight or hardness, but only on the extension which is always equal in the same vessel.

PRINCIPLE XX.

That from this may be demonstrated the non-existence of atoms.

We also know that there cannot be any atoms or parts of matter which are indivisible of their own nature (as certain philosophers have imagined). For however small the parts are supposed to be, yet because they are necessarily extended we are always able in thought to divide any one of them into two or more parts; and thus we know that they are divisible. For there is nothing which we can divide in thought, which we do not thereby recognise to be divisible; and therefore if we judged it to be indivisible, our judgment would be contrary to the knowledge we have of the matter. And even should we suppose that God had reduced some portion of matter to a smallness so extreme that it could not be divided into smaller, it would not for all that be properly termed indivisible. For though God had rendered the particle so small that it was beyond the power of any creature to divide it, He could not deprive Himself of His power of division, because it is absolutely impossible that He should lessen His own omnipotence as was said before. And therefore, absolutely speaking, its divisibility remains (to the smallest extended particle) because from its nature it is such.

PRINCIPLE CCI.

That certain sensible bodies are composed of insensible particles.

I consider that there are many particles in each body which cannot be perceived by our senses, and this will perhaps not be approved by those who take their senses as a measure of the things they can know. (But it seems to me to be doing great wrong to human reason if we do not consider that knowledge goes beyond the seen; for no one can doubt that there are bodies so small that they cannot be perceived by any of our senses, if only we consider what is being added each moment to those bodies which increase little by little, and what is removed from those which diminish in the same fashion.) We day by day see a tree grow, and it is impossible to comprehend how it becomes larger than it was before, unless by conceiving that some body is added to it. But who has ever observed by means of the senses what are the small bodies which are each day added to the plant that grows? Those at least who hold quantity to be finitely divisible should acknowledge that the particles may become so small as to be absolutely imperceptible. And indeed it should not be wondered at that we are unable to perceive very minute bodies, for the nerves, which must be moved by objects in order to cause us to perceive, are not very minute, but are like small cords which consist of a quantity of yet smaller fibres, and thus they cannot be moved by the minutest of bodies. Nor do I think that anyone who uses his reason will deny that we do much better to judge of what takes place in small bodies which their minuteness alone prevents us from perceiving, by what we see occurring in those that we do perceive (and thus explain all that is in nature, as I have tried to do in this treatise), than, in order to explain certain given things, to invent all sorts of novelties, that have no relation to those that we perceive (such as are first matter, substantial forms, and all the great array of qualities which many are in the habit of assuming, any of which it is more difficult to understand than all the things which we profess to explain by their means).

PRINCIPLE CCII.

That the philosophy of Democritus is not less different from ours than from the vulgar.

But Democritus also imagined that there were certain corpuscles that had various figures, sizes and motions, from the heaping together and mutual concourse of which all sensible bodies took their origin; and nevertheless his philosophy is by common consent universally rejected. To this I reply that it never was rejected by anyone because in it he considered bodies smaller than those that can be perceived by the senses, and attributed to them various sizes, figures and motions, for no one can doubt that there are in reality many such, as has been already shown. But this philosophy was rejected in the first place, because it presupposed certain indivisible corpuscles, which hypothesis I also completely reject; in the second place it was rejected because Democritus imagined a void about them, which I demonstrate to be an impossibility; in the third place because he attributed to them gravity, the existence of which I deny in any body in so far as it is considered by itself, because this is a quality depending on the relationship in respect of situation and motion which bodies bear to one another; and finally because he had not explained in detail how all things arose from the concourse of the corpuscles alone, or, if he explained it in regard to certain cases, his reasoning was not in all cases by any means coherent (or such as was capable of proving to us that all nature can be explained in the same way). If we are to judge of his opinions from what has been preserved regarding his opinions, this at least is the verdict we must give on his philosophy. I leave it to others to judge as to whether what I have written in philosophy possesses sufficient coherence in itself and whether it is fertile enough in yielding us conclusions. (And inasmuch as because the consideration of figure, magnitude and motion has been admitted by Aristotle and all others, as well as by Democritus, and as I reject all that the latter has supposed with this one exception, while I reject practically all that has been supposed by the others, it is clear that this method of philosophising has no more affinity with that of Democritus than with any of the other particular sects.)

PRINCIPLE CCVII.

Nevertheless all my opinions are submitted to the authority of the church.

At the same time, recalling my insignificance, I affirm nothing, but submit all these opinions to the authority of the Catholic Church, and to the judgment of the more sage; and I wish no one to believe anything I have written, unless he is personally persuaded by the force and evidence of reason.

PART III. THE VISIBLE WORLD[2]

48. *How all the parts of heaven have become round.*

We consider that all the matter which composes the universe, having in the beginning been divided into several equal parts, these parts could not at first have been round since several spheres joined together do not constitute an entirely solid and continuous body, as is this universe, in which I have previously shown that there can be no vacuum. But whatever shape these parts may have had originally, they gradually must have become round since they had various circular motions; and because the force that moved them in the beginning was great enough to separate them, this same force which they retained must have been great enough to smooth out all their angles as they collided, since less force is necessary for this latter effect than for the former; and, all the angles of a body being thus smoothed out, it is easy to conceive that this body is round since all that protrudes from its spherical shape is taken care of in this way.

52. *That there are three principal elements in the visible world.*

We can state that we have already found two different forms within matter which can be considered the forms of the two first elements of the visible world. First, the shavings which must have come off the other parts of matter as they became round and which are propelled by such speed that the mere force of their agitation causes them, when meeting other bodies, to be crumbled and divided into infinitely small parts shaped in such a way as to always fill exactly all the corners and small intervals they find

[2] Trans. Prof. Renée Geen, Dept. of French, Barnard College, New York, *Oeuvres of Descartes* (Paris, 1824).

around these bodies. Second, remaining matter, made up of round particles, very small in comparison to earthly bodies but having nonetheless
some determinate quantity so that they can be further divided [into much
smaller ones]. And we shall see a third form in some parts of matter,
namely those which because of their size and shape cannot be moved as
easily as the preceding ones: and I shall attempt to show that all bodies
in this visible world are made up of these three forms found in matter as
well as of three different elements; namely that the sun and fixed stars
partake of the first element, the heavens of the second, the earth, planets
and comets of the third. We can see that the sun and fixed stars emit light,
that the heavens let it through, that the earth, planets and comets reject
and reflect it; therefore it seems to me that I have some justification, when
I distinguish the three elements of this visible world. . . .

88. . . . There must be some particles in the matter of the first element that are smaller and less agitated than others: and since we suppose
that they resulted from the shavings of the particles of the second element
as these became round, their figure must have been very angular and extremely impeding: this is why they attach easily to one another and transfer a great amount of their agitation to those particles which are smaller
and less agitated. . . .

89. . . . The particles thus attached . . . make up certain small
bodies, the figure of which I shall now attempt to explain in greater detail
since it deserves attention.

76. *The manner in which the matter of the first element moves among
the particles of the second element in the heavens.*

Concerning the matter of the first element, it should also be noticed that
when among the small spheres that constitute heaven, . . . besides its
two motions—a linear one which carries it from [the] poles [of the solar
vortex] to the sun, then from the sun to the ecliptic, and a circular one
around these poles which it has in common with the rest of this heaven—it
uses most of its agitation to move in all ways required to change continually the shape of its small parts so as to fill exactly all the corners around
the small spheres through which it passes; as a result its force, being divided, is weakened and the small amount of matter in each of the little
corners where it passes is always ready to leave and yield to the motion of
these spheres in order to continue its own linear motion in any direction.

90. *What is the shape of these particles which we shall call fluted.*

First in width and depth they must be triangular since they go through
the small triangular spaces which are to be found among any three touch-

ing parts of the second element; their length is hard to determine since it depends only on the abundance of matter present in the areas where these small bodies are formed; but it will suffice to conceive of them as small fluted columns with three grooves or canals and turned like a snail shell in such a way that they can twist through the small intervals shaped like the curvinilear triangle FIG [see Fig. 2–2], invariably found whenever

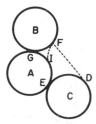

Fig. 2–2. The curvilinear triangle FIG.

three spheres touch one another. For since these fluted parts can be much longer than wide and since they move very rapidly through the particles of the second element as the latter follow the movement of the vortex which carries them around its axis, we can easily conceive that the three canals on the surface of each one must be turned like a screw or a shell and that these three canals are more or less turned depending on their distance from this axis, since they move faster when further away from this axis.

54. *How the sun and stars have been formed.*

The parts of the second element having since the beginning rubbed against each other, the matter of the first element, composed of the shavings of their angles, gradually increased; and when there was more than necessary to fill the gaps which the round particles of the second element must of necessity leave among themselves, the remainder flowed toward the center *SFf* [see Fig. 2–1] and formed extremely subtile and fluid bodies, namely the sun at center *S* and stars at other centers; for, after all the angles of the parts that made up the second element were smoothed out, and after these parts were rounded off, they occupied less space than they previously had and no longer extended to the center; moving away from the center at equal distances all around, they left circular spaces immediately filled by the matter of the first element which flowed abundantly from all around, because the laws of nature are such that all bodies moving in a circle must continuously make an effort to move away from the centers around which they revolve.

30. *That all planets are carried around the sun by the heavens which contain them.*

. . . We believe that the heavenly matter where the planets are found is in constant circular motion, like a vortex with the sun at its center, and that those parts which are near to the sun move faster than those located up to a certain distance from it, and that all planets (among which we shall henceforth include the earth) remain constantly suspended among the same parts of this heavenly matter; for by this hypothesis alone, and without any other mechanics, [machinamentis] we can easily explain all that can be observed about them. Just as in the windings of a river where the water turns and in its swirling motion describes circles, if there are floating bits of straw or other light bodies, we can see that the water carries them and makes them move in a circle; among these bits of straw some can often be observed turning at the same time around their own axis; those nearer to the center of the whirlpool complete their revolution sooner than those further away from it; and finally, although these whirlpools always move in a circle, they hardly ever describe perfect circles but stretch sometimes in length, sometimes in width in such a way that all the parts of the circumference they describe are not equally distant from the center; thus we can easily imagine the same to be true of planets; and by this alone all their phenomena may be explained.

3

ooooooooooo

PARTICLES IN THE ATMOSPHERE

ooooooooooo

Robert Boyle (1627-1691)

From the millions that constitute humanity, there occasionally emerges a man of exceptional character and ability who consciously devotes himself to the larger interests of mankind. Such a man was Robert Boyle.

Most of our information about his life comes from an abbreviated autobiography *Philaretus,* written in his twenties, and a supplementary life by Thomas Birch. Both are fascinating documents included in the *Collected Works of the Honourable Robert Boyle* published by Birch in 1744. No one can read these histories without being deeply impressed by Boyle's Anglican conviction, his incorruptible integrity, and his high-minded view of the worth and dignity of man. He conceived of himself as an instrument of the Divine plan for the betterment of mankind, a result to be achieved through charity and the application of Baconian philosophy—the improvement of the human condition through science.

In a day when science hardly existed and had little prestige, Boyle's social position and attractive, courteous personality exerted a powerful influence in raising the social status of this occupation. He was one of the founding Fellows of the Royal Society and a member of its first council. Throughout his residence in London he regularly attended the society's meetings and remained one of its most influential members. His peers elected him president in 1680, but he refused the honor on the ground that the society's charter required the taking of an oath, an act which his conscience would not allow.

Boyle was deeply religious and it was said of him that he never men-

35

tioned God without a preliminary pause for veneration, a custom which his friends vouchsafed was unfailing over a period of forty years. He spent much time in meditation, wrote many tracts on religion and theology, and was able to quote passages of Scripture as freely in Greek as in English.

Boyle was a director for sixteen years (1661–1677) of the famed East India Company. He took the post because of his interest in Christianizing native populations throughout the world, and he was influential in persuading his fellow directors to do more for the improvement of the social condition of the natives and less toward their exploitation. To the same end he personally supported translations of the Bible into Turkish, Arabic, and Malayan languages, and into American-Indian dialects for the Massachusetts Colony; he saw to the distribution of these translations to the natives. About a third of his large income was spent for charitable purposes and for science.

Boyle never married, perhaps because of religious conviction, but probably because of his poor health. During the latter twenty-three years of his life, when he lived in London, he made his home with his elder sister Katherine, Viscountess Ranelagh.

Despite his station and his wealth, Boyle lived very simply. He was sincere and exceptionally courteous, considerate of the feelings of others; as a part of his self-discipline he schooled himself to listen carefully to the opinions of others. His interest in people made him much sought after in London, and he received a constant stream of visitors from abroad, although he complained privately that many of them wasted his time. He freely published the details of his experiments and his scientific ideas, never attempting to make use of them for gain or for self-aggrandizement.

The details of Boyle's life are useful for an understanding of his outlook, his milieu, and his influence on science. His ancestors were a landed Herefordshire family who could trace their lineage to pre-Conquest times. His father, after a Cambridge education, and training in law at the Middle Temple, London, saw little future for himself in England and emigrated to Ireland in 1588, where he eventually accumulated a huge fortune. He built a great country estate, Lismore, in the province of Munster, and in 1620 was created Earl of Cork. His fourteenth child and seventh son, Robert, was born at Lismore on January 25, 1627.

The boy's schooling was begun at home by tutors, but at the age of eight he was sent to Eton. There he showed a great interest in learning and apparently found reading more stimulating than play. He had been at Eton almost four years when his father settled him briefly at Stalbridge, a new estate acquired in Dorsetshire. In October of that year (1638) at the age of twelve, he was sent with his brother and a Swiss tutor to Geneva to complete his education.

Unlikely as it may seem, during his stay in Geneva the event that was most determinative for his later life was a violent electrical storm. It made a profound and lasting impression on young Boyle. He viewed the storm as a demonstration of Divine power and the awe he felt made him resolve to devote his life to those activities that promote God's work on earth. But the channel through which to perform his self-imposed task was revealed to him only as the result of a chance acquaintance which he made after his return to England. Because of pecuniary difficulties resulting from the rebellion in Ireland in 1642, and the temporary loss of the family estates, his return had been delayed until 1644, when he was seventeen. During a brief sojourn in London with his sister, Lady Ranelagh, he met a Polish Protestant refugee, Samuel Hartlib, who supplied the direction he was seeking.

Hartlib was a utopian, interested in founding a "philosophical" college in which experiment would be the method of exploring nature, and useful knowledge the aim of inquiry. Boyle was immensely impressed with these ideas; in a few months, when he retired to Stalbridge, which he had inherited on his father's death, he began to study science in earnest: anatomy, medicine, natural philosophy, astronomy, chemistry, and physics, together with theology. Except for two years in Ireland, which were required for the supervision of his property, Boyle spent most of the next nine years at his Dorset manor. All the while he maintained his contacts with science in London through Hartlib, and became especially interested in chemistry.

On his return from Ireland in 1654, Boyle was persuaded by John Wilkins, warden of Wadham College, to take up residence in Oxford. Wilkins was a devoted advocate of the new experimental philosophy; before going to Oxford he had been the moving spirit of a small but distinguished scientific group in London. He had a remarkable gift for inspiring friendship and respect, and an unusual talent for bringing people together for the exchange of ideas and for serious discussion of experimental natural science. The group that met regularly in his rooms at Wadham included John Wallis and Seth Ward, respectively the Savilian professors of geometry and astronomy; Johnathan Goddard, warden of Merton College; Ralph Bathurst, fellow and subsequently president of Trinity College; Dr. Thomas Willis, physician, later Sedleian professor of natural philosophy; and Christopher Wren, fellow of All Souls College, destined to be the celebrated architect who would rebuild London after the great fire of 1666. Some of these men had been part of Wilkins' group in London; later all would become founding members of the Royal Society.

Wilkins' invitation must have been very attractive to Boyle, because it offered a congenial and stimulating atmosphere to carry on his theological studies as well as his experimental science. But Boyle always felt that he was not a "Professor of Philosophy nor a gown-man." This conviction, coupled with the state of his health and the desire for sufficient space to experiment, caused him to reside in lodgings in the High Street next to University College. His stay in Oxford began in June of 1654, when he was twenty-seven years old, and continued for fourteen years.

As far as physical science was concerned these were the great productive years of his life. During this time he conducted his famous experiments on the properties of the air and published the observations on which he had reflected since he began taking a serious interest in science.

Boyle's research on the properties of the atmosphere was inspired by von Guericke's sensational experiments at Magdeburg, Germany, described in a book entitled *Mechanica hydraulica-pneumatica,* published in 1657 by a Jesuit, Gaspar Schott, at Frankfort. Boyle obtained a copy and was fascinated with all he read. Von Guericke had shown that if two hollow metal hemispheres were placed base to base and the spherical interior thus formed was exhausted of air, the pressure of the atmosphere was sufficient to hold the halves together against the force exerted by two teams of six horses pulling in opposite directions. But the air pump used to evacuate the hemispheres seemed to Boyle capable of improvement and the experiments susceptible to wider inquiry. Boyle needed an assistant who knew what the pump was meant to do and who was inventive enough to make a better one. Willis, a member of the Wilkins group, recommended a Christ Church student named Hooke, who had been his assistant in chemistry. Hooke, then in his early twenties, accepted Boyle's offer, went to live in his lodgings, and very quickly produced a successful pump for the pneumatic experiments. This effort began a fruitful association between the two men that lasted throughout Boyle's lifetime and gave Hooke his entree into the Royal Society and the opportunity to achieve the fame he later enjoyed. Without Boyle's friendship, it is doubtful if his genius would have been realized. Hooke was not prepossessing either in appearance or manner. He lacked tact and had little skill in personal relations; moreover, in seventeenth-century England, he suffered the even greater handicap of not being a "gentleman."

In 1660, the first results of the pneumatic experiments were published in *New Experiments, Physico-Mechanical, Touching the Spring of the Air and Its Effects.* Two basic results were recorded: (1) That air, like other material substances has weight, and (2) that it contains a "vital Quintessence" essential to animal life, although most of it serves no such purpose.

Boyle thus recognized the nonhomogeneity of air, a fact not proved until the discovery of oxygen by Priestley. From the discovery that air has weight Boyle concluded, after further experiments, that the atmosphere near the earth is compressed and that its pressure is sufficient to support a mercury column about 29 inches high. *New Experiments . . .* was followed by *Certain Physiological Essays* (1661), *Sceptical Chymist* (1661),

New Experiments Touching the Spring and Weight of the Air (1662), *Usefulness of Experimental Natural Philosophy* (1663), *Experimental History of Colours* (1664), *Experimental History of Cold* (1665), *Hydrostatical Paradoxes* (1666), and *Origins of Forms and Qualities According to the Corpuscular Philosophy* (1666). Many of these works had been written or partially written during the preceding fifteen years. In the *Essays* and the *Origin of Forms,* as well as in the *Sceptical Chymist,* Boyle sets forth his unqualified adherence to the corpuscular (atomic) hypothesis. It is difficult, however, to find succinct statements of his views in these papers because his style is prolix and he talks around his subject, often without coming directly to grips with it.

The Wilkins group, which had been so stimulating to Boyle when he first moved to Oxford, gradually broke up as a result of the changes accompanying the end of the Commonwealth and the advent of the Restoration. Wilkins himself left Oxford in 1659 to become, very briefly, the master of Trinity College, Cambridge. Goddard had left the year before to take up an appointment as professor of physics in Gresham College, London. It was there that the Royal Society was founded in November of 1660. Thus, the center of science in England was transferred to London. In 1662 Boyle recommended his assistant Hooke as the Society's curator, ending for a period their close association. Boyle's experiments, however, continued with other assistants; despite periodic trips to London, he did not move there permanently until 1668 when he was forty-one years old. From then until his death twenty-three years later, he made his home with his sister Lady Ranelagh in Pall Mall.

In 1672 he published an "Essay about the Origin and Virtue of Gems" in which he notes the regular structure of crystals as evidence for an atomic theory of matter. This was followed in 1675 by the publication of an account of experiments (made more than twenty years earlier) on "Quicksilver Growing Hot with Gold." Boyle believed that he had evidence for transmutation. Newton, then immersed in his own secret alchemical experiments, wrote to Oldenberg, the secretary of the Royal Society, that Boyle's result "may possibly be an inlet to something more noble, not to be communicated without immense damage to the world. . . ." Newton, in his Cambridge years, despite his great and penetrating insight into the mechanism of nature, nevertheless had a strange streak of magic in his make-up, a quality that has been luminously discussed by Lord Keynes (see Chapter 5).

In reflecting on Boyle's research, it is interesting to observe that his methods were rather different from those of his contemporaries and very much like those of the present day. Instead of attempting much of the work with his own hands (although he did not abstain by any means from actual experimentation himself), he employed assistants to construct equipment and carry out manipulations while he supplied the ideas and supervision. His voluminous publications were also produced in much the same way; he did not write his tracts but dictated his thoughts to amanuenses.

These deviations from the usual procedures of his day are quite understandable in view of his special circumstances. Because of his social position and affluence it would have been considered improper for him to do much of the laboratory work himself. In fact, it was considered socially disgraceful for a man of title to be familiar with workmen and processing arts. But such familiarity was necessary if science was to progress. This is one of the reasons why, throughout his life, Boyle resisted all attempts on the part of others to obtain a title or high public office for him. He comments in his autobiography on his fortunate situation, remarking that a lower birth would have exposed him to the inconveniences of a "lower descent." On the other hand, had he been the eldest of a great family, he would have been forced into entanglements in public affairs to further family interests.

Another reason for his research and writing methods was his health. Shortly after he took up residence at Stalbridge, and before he was twenty, Boyle began to suffer from severe attacks of kidney stones. Throughout his adult years he was almost excessively anxious about his health and became so addicted to dosing himself with all kinds of nostrum that his physician warned him that his cures were sometimes worse than his disease. His regimen also consisted in observing a rigid diet so that he never ate for pleasure but only to keep himself alive. In physique he was tall and thin, and in later years his strict diet made him look pale and emaciated. Gilbert Burnet, Bishop of Salisbury and his long-time friend, said in Boyle's funeral sermon that "he escaped the smallpox, but for forty years laboured under such a feebleness of body and such a lowness of strength and spirits that it was astonishing how he could read, meditate, try experiments and write as he did."

Boyle did write all his life. In his later years, during the 1680's, his papers were mostly of a religious nature. In the latter part of the decade he began to fail, but he continued industriously to the end. Death overtook him on December 30, 1691, as he lay quietly in bed correcting proofs of his *Essay on the General History of the Air,* a subject on which he had spent a lifetime of reflection. As Birch, his biographer, remarks: "His life was spent in the pursuit of nature . . . and in the most rational as well as devout adoration of its divine Author."

Both in his *New Experiments* and in his *General History of the Air,* excerpts from which follow, Boyle hypothesizes that air is composed of several kinds of particles that have different functions. In the former paper he considers that the elasticity (compressibility) of the air arises from static elastic atoms in contact, or alternatively from atoms being caught up in a whirling motion, an idea evidently borrowed from Descartes's vortex theory. In his "General History of the Air," which reflects a maturer period, Boyle is more explicit and talks of three kinds of particles composing the atmosphere: first, vapors from various sources; second, smaller or "subtile" particles that carry magnetic effects and light; and, third, particles responsible for the elastic behavior of the air. (The idea that elementary particles are of different sizes is also in accord with Cartesian notions.) But the elastic particles, which may be of the nature of coiled springs, he seems to imply, may be *mixed* with others that beat off their neighbors solely because of their whirling motion.

Boyle's outlook was strongly conditioned by Descartes. His experiments and the questions they raised went straight to the heart of the Cartesian physics, i.e., that ex*tension* is synonymous with matter, and that a true vacuum is impossible because it could have no dimensions. If it could be shown that a true vacuum existed, then Descartes's position would have to be abandoned. Such a proof was impossible for Boyle to demonstrate, for removing the air from a receiver was insufficient to produce a vacuum. What about the more "subtile" material, the ether that the Cartesian theory envisioned? Boyle tried to demonstrate the existence of this subtle material in several experiments that he described in a later publication, but his attempts yielded no positive results. What he has to say about the problem, reproduced in the third article below, is basic not only to atomic theory but to any physical theory as well.

ooooooo

B O Y L E

New Experiments, Physico-Mechanical, Touching the Spring of the Air [1]

THE AIR NEAR THE EARTH — may be conceived of as a heap of little bodies, lying one upon another, as may be resembled to a fleece of wool. For this . . . consists of many slender and flexible hairs, each of which may indeed, like a little spring, be easily bent or rolled up, but will also like a spring be still endeavouring to stretch

---

[1] From Robert Boyle, *Collected Works* (London: Thomas Birch, 1772), vol. 1, pp. 11–12.

itself out again. For though both these hairs, and the aërial corpuscles to which we liken them, do easily yield to external pressures, yet each of them (by virtue of its structure) is endowed with a power or principle of self-dilatation; . . .

There is another way to explicate the spring of air, namely by supposing with that most ingenious gentleman Monsieur DesCartes, that the air is nothing but . . . a heap of small and . . . flexible particles, of several sizes and of all kinds of figures, which are rarefied by heat . . . into that subtile and aetherial fluid that surrounds the earth, and by the restless agitation of that celestial matter . . . are so whirled around, that each corpuscle endeavours to beat off all the others from coming within the little sphere requisite to its motion about its own centre; and in case any, by intruding into that sphere, shall oppose its free rotation, to expel or drive it away: so that, according to this doctrine it imports very little, whether the particles of the air have the structure requisite to springs, or be of any other form, . . . since their elastical power is not made to depend upon their shape or structure, but upon the vehement agitation and . . . brandishing motion, which they receive from the fluid aether, that swiftly flows between them and whirling about each of them (independently from the rest) not only keeps those slender aërial bodies separated and stretched out . . . but also makes them hit against and knock away at each other and consequently require more room than that, which, if they were compressed, they would take up.

But though the former one be . . . somewhat more easy, [and] I shall for the most part make use of it in the following discourse, yet I am not willing to declare peremptorily for either of them against the other . . . .

General History of the Air [2]

Of the Constant and Permanent Ingredients of the Air

A short answer to a question about the nature of the air given by Mr. Boyle to Mr. H. Oldenberg.

I T   S E E M S   T H E N   N O T   I M P R O B A B L E   to me that our atmospherical air may consist of three differing kinds of corpuscles. The first is made of that numberless multitude and great variety of particles which under the form of vapours or dry exhalations ascend from the earth, water, minerals, vegetables, and animals, etc., and, in a word, of whatever substances are elevated by the celestial or subterraneal heats,

[2] Boyle, *General History of the Air, ibid.,* V, 613.

and make to diffuse themselves into the atmosphere. The second sort of particles, that make the air, may be yet more subtile than the former, and consist of such exceeding minute parts as to make up the magnetical steams of our terrestrial globe, that the sun and other stars, that seem to shine of themselves, do either emit out of their own bodies, or by their pressure thrust against our eyes and thereby produce what we call light; which whether we explicate it by the Epicurean or Cartesian hypothesis, argues a great plenty of a celestial (or some other very subtile) matter to be dispersed through, or harboured in, the intervals of the stabler or grosser corpuscles of the atmosphere.

But because you expect from me a distinguishing and as it were, characteristic quality . . . to which most of the phenomena of our engine and many other pneumatical experiments seem to be due, I shall add a third sort of atmospherical particles. . . . And this sort of particles are those, which are not only for a while, by manifest outward agents made elastical, but are permanently so, and on that account may be stiled perennial air.

Of the structure of the elastical particles of the air, divers conceptions may be framed, according to the several contrivances men may devise to answer the phenomena, for we may think them to be like the springs of watches, coiled up and still endeavouring to fly abroad. One may also fancy a portion of air to be like a lock or parcel of curled hairs of wood, which being compressed by an external force, or their own weight, may have a continual endeavour to stretch themselves out, and thrust away the neighbouring particles, and whatever other bodies would hinder them to recover their former state, or attain their full liberty. One may also fancy them like extremely slender wires such as those of gold and silver, that tradesmen rewind from some cylindrical bodies of differing sizes, on which they were rolled, which pieces of spiralled or curled wire may be, as of differing substances and consistencies, so of very differing lengths and thicknesses, and have their curls greater or lesser, nearer each other or more distant, and be otherwise diversified, and yet all have springiness in theory and (notwithstanding) be by reason of their shape, readily expansible on the score of their native structure as also by heat, gyrations, and other motions, and compressible by an external force into a very little room. I remember too, that I have among other comparisons of this kind, represented the spring of particles of the air, like the very thin shavings of wood . . . and I will allow you to suspect that there may be sometimes mingled with the particles that are springy, . . . some others that owe their elasticity not so much to their structure, as their motion, which variously brandishing them and whirling them about, may make them beat off the neighbouring particles and thereby promote an expansive endeavour in the air, whereof they are parts . . . .

[In the following excerpt, from the same work as the preceding passage, Boyle challenges one of the basic tenets of Descartes's physical philosophy —Editors.]

To me it yet seems, that as to those spaces which the Vacuists would have to be empty, because they are manifestly devoid of air and all grosser bodies; the Plenists (if I may so call them) do not prove that such spaces are replenished with such a subtile matter as they speak of, by any sensible effects, or operations of it (of which divers new trials purposely made, have not yet shewn me any) but only conclude that there must be such a body, because there cannot be a void. And the reason why there cannot be a void, being by them taken, not from any experiments, or phenomena of nature, that clearly and particularly prove their hypothesis, but from their notion of a body, whose nature, according to them, consisting only in extension (which indeed seems the property most essential to, because inseparable from a body) to say a space devoid of body, is, to speak in the schoolmen's phrase, a contradiction *in adjecto*. This reason, I say, being thus desumed, seems to make the controversy about a vacuum rather a metaphysical, than a physiological [3] question; which therefore we shall here no longer debate, finding it very difficult either to satisfy Naturalists with this Cartesian notion of a body, or to manifest wherein it is erroneous, and substitute a better in its stead.

○○○○○○○

Boyle's chemical ideas, as elaborated in the "Sceptical Chymist," constitute a rejection of classical and medieval concepts of chemical elements. To the modern mind, the chemistry—or alchemy—of the mid-seventeenth century is almost unintelligible. Chemistry as a science did not exist and "philosophers" or alchemists were concerned chiefly with transmutations of material substances. Every material was presumed to be composed of one or more of the Aristotelian four elements—earth, air, fire, and water— or, according to the belief of the experimenter, of the three "principles" of Paracelsus—salt, sulfur, and mercury. But very often it was not the actual substance that was meant in the chemical writings, but the "soul" or etherial substratum of the substance. It was not a rational, but a magical scheme of nature in which the experimenter forced his results into the form demanded by an intellectually constructed theory.

Against this magical view, Boyle pleaded for the elimination of ambiguity and a science founded on unbiased experimental observation. Part of this enterprise had to be an empirical determination of the chemical elements. It required genius to see that the old systems needed to be swept

---

[3] This use of "physiological" is now obsolete; in Boyle's time the word "physiology" sometimes meant natural science.

away, but it also required genius to find what the chemical elements actually were. Good manipulator that he was, Boyle had no method to realize his own receipe; it took two hundred more years of patient work before most of the elements were revealed and their combinations placed on a sound atomic footing. In the meantime transmutation, the great chimera of the alchemists, died a lingering death, but not before Boyle and his great contemporary Newton had each dabbled in the art.

ഠഠഠഠഠഠഠ

Sceptical Chymist [4]

Definition of Element

I . . . MUST NOT LOOK UPON any body as a true principle or element, but as yet compounded which is not perfectly homogenous, but is further resoluble into any number of distinct substances, how small soever . . . I now mean by elements, as those chymists that speak plainest do by their principles, certain primitive and simple, or perfectly unmingled bodies; which not being made of any other bodies, or of one another, are the ingredients of which all those called perfectly mixt bodies are immediately compounded, and into which they are ultimately resolved: now whether there be any one such body to be constantly met with in all, and each, of those that are said to be elemented bodies, is the thing I now question.

ഠഠഠഠഠഠഠ

The investigation for which Boyle is most remembered, the pressure-volume relation of gases (known as Boyle's law), was carried out to answer criticisms of his earlier work advanced by Thomas Hobbes, the famous political philosopher, and by an obscure Aristotelian, Franciscus Linus. Hobbes' objections to the idea that air was made up of "flexible particles" arose from his position as a Plenist (a follower of the Cartesian doctrine that all space had to be occupied). Linus maintained that the mercury column in a Torricellian tube was held up by an invisible membrane or cord (funiculus) contained in the space above.

Since the maximum height of the mercury column in a Toricellian vacuum is approximately 30 inches, it could be concluded that the funiculus would hold it no higher. Boyle showed in the experiment described below that the mercury can indeed rise in the long arm of his "J-tube"

---

[4] From Boyle, "Sceptical Chymist," *ibid.*, vol. 1, p. 502.

apparatus (see Fig. 3–1) following a reduction in pressure at the top, even when the mercury was approximately 100 inches high. He says ". . . we took care when the mercurial cylinder in the longer leg of the pipe was about an hundred inches high, to cause one to suck at the open orifice whereupon (as we expected) the mercury in the tube did notably ascend. Which considerable phenomenon cannot be ascribed to our examiner's Funiculus, since by his own confession that cannot pull up the mercury if the mercurial cylinder be above 29 or 30 inches of mercury."[5] Boyle then goes on to give the proper explanation: ". . . the pressure of the incumbent air being in part taken off by its expanding itself into the sucker's dilated chest; the imprisoned air was thereby enabled to dilate itself manifestly and repel the mercury that comprest it, till there was an

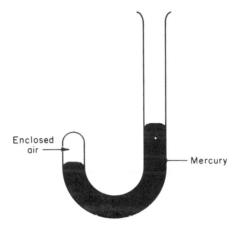

Fig. 3–1. Boyle's J-tube.

equality of force betwixt the strong spring of that comprest air on the one part, and the tall mercurial cylinder, together with the contiguous dilated air, on the other part."

Table 3–1 gives the results of experiments when the pressure of the gas in the enclosed space of the J-tube is greater than atmospheric pressure; Table 3–2, when it is less than atmospheric. Column A in the tables gives a number proportional to the enclosed volume of the gas, assuming the bore of the tube to be uniform, while column D gives the absolute pressure of the gas measured in inches of mercury. The product of these is PV and is approximately constant in all of the trials.

It is interesting that stress is not placed on the pressure-volume relationship in the discussion of the experiment. The law is "hidden," in a sense, in column E of both tables. This column compares the pressure

---

[5] *Collected Works*, vol. 1, p. 159.

which should have been observed with that actually found, column D, on the basis that $PV = $ constant. This constancy of PV was apparently discovered by others and called to Boyle's attention, as explained in the following passage [6] by Boyle:

> . . . I shall readily acknowledge, that I had not reduced the trials I had made about measuring the expansion of the air to any certain hypothesis, when that ingenious gentleman Mr. Richard Townley was pleased to inform me, that having by the perusal of my physico-mechanical experiments been satisfied that the spring of the air was the cause of it, he endeavoured (and I wish in such attempts other ingenious men would follow his example) to supply what I had omitted concerning the reducing to a precise estimate, how much air dilated of itself loses of its elastical force, according to the measures of its dilatation. He added, that he had begun to set down what occurred to him to this purpose in a short discourse, whereof he afterwards did me the favour to shew me the beginning, which gives me a just curiosity to see it perfected. But, because I neither know, nor (by reason of the great distance betwixt our places of residence) have at present the opportunity to inquire, whether he will think fit to annex his discourse to our appendix, or to publish it by itself, or at all; and because he hath not yet, for aught I know, met with fit glasses to make an any-thing-accurate table of the decrement of the force of the dilated air; our present design invites us to present the reader with that which follows, wherein I had the assistance of the same person [the reference appears to be to Hooke], that I took notice of in the former chapter, as having written something about rarefaction: whom I the rather make mention of on this occasion, because when he first heard me speak of Mr. Townley's suppositions about the proportion, wherein air loses of its spring by dilatation, he told me he had the year before (and not long after the publication of my pneumatical treatise) made observations to the same purpose, which he acknowledged to agree well enough with Mr. Townley's theory: and so did (as their author was pleased to tell me) some trials made about the same time by that noble virtuoso and eminent mathematician the Lord Brouncker, from whose further enquiries into this matter, if his occasions will allow him to make them, the curious may well hope for something very accurate.

 oooooooo

Boyle's Law [7]

WE TOOK THEN A LONG glass-tube, which, by a dexterous hand and the help of a lamp, was in such a manner crooked at the bottom, that the part turned up was almost parallel to the rest of the tube,

---

[6] *Collected Works,* vol. 1, p. 160.
[7] *Collected Works,* vol. 1, pp. 156–160.

and the orifice of this shorter leg of the siphon (if I may so call the whole instrument) being hermetically sealed, the length of it was divided into inches (each of which was subdivided into eight parts) by a straight list of paper, which containing those divisions, was carefully pasted all along it. Then putting in as much quicksilver as served to fill the arch or bended part of the siphon, that the mercury standing in a level might reach in the one leg to the bottom of the divided paper, and just to the same height or horizontal line in the other; we took care, by frequently inclining the tube, so that the air might freely pass from one leg into the other by the sides of the mercury (we took, I say, care) that the air at last included in the shorter cylinder should be of the same laxity with the rest of the air about it. This done, we began to pour quicksilver into the longer leg of the siphon, which by its weight pressing up that in the shorter leg, did by degrees streighten the included air: and continuing this pouring in of quicksilver till the air in the shorter leg was by condensation reduced to take up but half of the space it possessed (I say, possessed, not filled) before; we cast our eyes upon the longer leg of the glass, on which was likewise pasted a list of paper carefully divided into inches and parts, and we observed, not without delight and satisfaction, that the quicksilver in that longer part of the tube was 29 inches higher than the other. Now that this observation does both very well agree with and confirm our hypothesis, will be easily discerned by him, that take notice what we teach; and Monsieur *Paschal* and our English friend's experiments prove, that the greater the weight is that leans upon the air, the more forcible is its endeavour of dilation, and consequently its power of resistance (as other springs are stronger when bent by greater weights). For this being considered, it will appear to agree rarely-well with the hypothesis, that as according to it the air in that degree of density and correspondent measure of resistance, to which the weight of the encumbent atmosphere had brought it, was able to counterbalance and resist the pressure of a mercurial cylinder of about 29 inches, as we are taught by the Torricellian experiment; so here the same air being brought to a degree of density about twice as great as that it had before, obtains a spring twice as strong as formerly. As may appear by its being able to sustain or resist a cylinder of 29 inches in the longer tube, together with the weight of the atmospherical cylinder that leaned upon those 29 inches of mercury; and, as we just now inferred from the Torricellian experiment, was equivalent to them.

We were hindered from prosecuting the trial at that time by the casual breaking of the tube. But because an accurate experiment of this nature would be of great importance to the doctrine of the spring of air, and has not yet been made (that I know) by any man; and because also it is more uneasy to be made than one would think, in regard of the difficulty as well of procuring crooked tubes fit for the purpose, as of making a just estimate of the true place of the protruberant mercury's surface; we at last procured a tube which tube, though of a pretty bigness, was so long, that the cylinder, whereof the shorter leg of it consisted, admitted a list of paper, which had before been divided into twelve inches and their quarters and the longer leg admitted another list of paper of divers feet in length, and divided after the same manner. Then quicksilver being poured in to fill up the bended part of the glass, that the surface of it in either leg might rest in the same horizontal line, as we lately taught, there was more and more quicksilver poured into the longer tube; and notice being watchfully taken how far the mercury was risen in that longer tube, when it appeared to have ascended to any of the divisions in the shorter tube, the several observations, that were thus effectively made, and as they were set down, afforded us [Table 3–1].

TABLE 3–1 *A Table of Condensation of the Air*

A′	A	B	C	D	E
48	12	00	Added to 29 1/8 inches	29 2/16	29 2/16
46	11 1/2	01 7/16		30 9/16	30 6/16 *
44	11	02 13/16		31 15/16	31 12/16
42	10 1/2	04 6/16		33 8/16	33 1/7
40	10	06 3/16		35 5/16	35
38	9 1/2	07 14/16		37	36 15/19
36	9	10 2/16		39 5/16	38 7/8
34	8 1/2	12 8/16		41 10/16	41 2/17
32	8	15 1/16		44 3/16	43 11/16
30	7 1/2	17 15/16		47 1/16	46 3/5
28	7	21 3/16		50 5/16	50
26	6 1/2	25 3/16		54 5/16	53 10/13
24	6	29 11/16		58 13/16	58 3/8
23	5 3/4	32 3/16		61 5/16	60 18/23
22	5 1/2	34 15/16		64 1/16	63 6/11
21	5 1/4	37 15/16		67 1/16	66 4/7
20	5	41 9/16		70 11/16	70
19	4 3/4	45		74 3/16	73 11/19
18	4 1/2	48 12/16		77 14/16	77 2/3
17	4 1/4	53 11/16		82 12/16	82 4/17
16	4	58 2/16		87 14/16	87 3/8
15	3 3/4	63 15/16		93 1/16	93 1/5
14	3 1/2	71 5/16		100 7/16	99 6/7
13	3 1/4	78 11/16		107 13/16	107 7/13
12	3	88 7/16		117 9/16	116 4/8

A′A. The number of equal spaces in the shorter leg, that contained the same parcel of air diversly extended.

B. The height of the mercurial cylinder in the longer leg that compressed the air into those dimensions.

C. The height of the mercurial cylinder, that counterbalanced the pressure of the atmosphere.

D. The aggregate of the two last columns B and C, exhibiting the pressure sustained by the included air.

E. What the pressure should be according to the hypothesis, that supposes the pressures and expansions to be in reciprocal proportion.

* Corrected value—Editors.

TABLE 3-2 *A Table of Rarefaction of the Air*

A	B	C	D	E	
1	00%		$29\frac{3}{4}$	$29\frac{3}{4}$	A. The number of equal spaces at the top of the tube, that contained the same parcel of air.
$1\frac{1}{2}$	$10\frac{5}{8}$		$19\frac{1}{8}$	$19\frac{5}{8}$	
2	$15\frac{3}{8}$		$14\frac{3}{8}$	$14\frac{7}{8}$	
3	$20\frac{2}{3}$		$9\frac{1}{8}$	$9\frac{15}{12}$	B. The height of the mercurial cylinder, that together with the spring of the included air counterbalanced the pressure of the atmosphere.
4	$22\frac{5}{8}$		$7\frac{1}{8}$	$7\frac{7}{16}$	
5	$24\frac{1}{8}$	*Subtracted from $29\frac{3}{4}$ leaves*	$5\frac{5}{8}$	$5\frac{19}{20}$	
6	$24\frac{7}{8}$		$4\frac{7}{8}$	$4\frac{27}{26}$	
7	$25\frac{1}{8}$		$4\frac{2}{3}$	$4\frac{1}{4}$	
8	26%		$3\frac{3}{8}$	$3\frac{23}{32}$	C. The pressure of the atmosphere.
9	$26\frac{3}{8}$		$3\frac{3}{8}$	$3\frac{11}{36}$	
10	$26\frac{6}{8}$		3%	$2\frac{39}{40}$	
12	$27\frac{1}{8}$		$2\frac{5}{8}$	$2\frac{23}{48}$	D. The complement of B to C, exhibiting the pressure sustained by the included air.
14	$27\frac{1}{4}$		$2\frac{2}{8}$	$2\frac{1}{8}$	
16	$27\frac{7}{8}$		2%	$1\frac{55}{64}$	
18	$27\frac{7}{8}$		$1\frac{7}{8}$	$1\frac{47}{72}$	
20	28%		$1\frac{6}{8}$	$1\frac{9}{80}$	E. What that pressure should be according to the hypothesis.
24	$28\frac{2}{8}$		$1\frac{4}{8}$	$1\frac{23}{96}$	
28	$28\frac{3}{8}$		$1\frac{3}{8}$	$1\frac{1}{16}$	
32	$28\frac{1}{8}$		$1\frac{2}{8}$	$0\frac{119}{128}$	

For the better understanding of this experiment, it may not be amiss to take notice of the following particulars:

1. That the tube being so tall, that we could not conveniently make use of it in a chamber, we were fain to use it on a pair of stairs, which yet were very lightsome, the tube being for preservation's sake by strings so suspended, that it did not scarce touch the box presently to be mentioned.

2. The lower and crooked part of the pipe was placed in a square, wooden box, of a good largeness and depth, to prevent the loss of the quicksilver that might fall aside in the transfusion from the vessel into the pipe, and to receive the whole quicksilver in case the tube should break.

3. That we were two to make the observation together, the one to take notice at the bottom, how the quicksilver rose in the shorter cylinder, and the other to pour in the top of the longer; it being very hard and troublesome for one man alone to do both accurately.

4. That the quicksilver was poured in but by little and little, according to the direction of him that observed below; it being far easier to pour in more, than to take out any, in case too much at once had been poured in.

5. That at the beginning of the operation, that we might the more truely discern where the quicksilver rested from time to time, we made use of a

small looking glass, held in a convenient posture to reflect to the eye what we desired to discern.

6. That when the air was so compressed, as to be crowded into less than a quarter of the space it possessed before, we tried whether the cold of a linen cloth dipped into water would then condense it. And it sometimes seemed a little to shrink, but not so manifestly as that we dare build any thing upon it. We then tried likewise, whether heat would, notwithstanding so forcible a compressure, dilate it; and approaching the flame of a candle to that part where the air was pent up, the heat had a more sensible operation than the cold had before; so that we scarce doubted, but that the expansion of the air would, notwithstanding the weight that opprest it, have been made conspicuous, if the fear of unseasonably breaking the glass had not kept us from increasing the heat. . . .

Now if to what we have thus delivered concerning the compression of the air, we add some observations concerning its spontaneous expansion, it will the better appear how much the phenomena of these mercurial experiments depend upon the differing measures of strength to be met with in the air's spring, according to its various degrees of compression and laxity.

4

○○○○○○○○○○

MATTER AND MOTION

○○○○○○○○○○

Robert Hooke (1635-1703)

If by some miraculous machine we could be transported back through three centuries of time to the city of London, then being rebuilt after the Great Fire of 1666, it is quite likely that we would soon notice an unusual-looking figure as he scurried along on his business through the city streets. This figure would be none other than Robert Hooke; for if we are to believe Richard Waller, secretary of the Royal Society, "he went stooping and very fast . . . having but a light body to carry, and a great deal of spirits and activity. . . ."

Waller published Hooke's *Posthumous Works* in 1705 with a dedication to Newton, who was then president of the Society. Such a dedication is very difficult to understand, unless it was made as a gesture to Newton's eminence. Hooke had had the misfortune to cross Newton's path with respect to priorities for discoveries in optics and celestial mechanics. Newton, as the excerpts to follow will show, had a pathological aversion to engagement in any kind of controversy; as time passed his involvement with Hooke filled him with such a loathing that he would neither publish his book on *Opticks* nor accept the presidency of the Royal Society while Hooke was alive. It must be apparent, therefore, that a posthumous publication with a dedication approved by Newton must make Hooke appear as unfavorably as possible, for Newton could be both petty and mean and seldom forgot or forgave any slight or argument. With this background it is interesting to see what Waller has to say about Hooke:

> As to his person he was but despicable, being very crooked, though I have heard from himself and others that he was straight till about sixteen years of age when he first grew awry, by frequent practicing turning with a turn-lathe and the like incurvating exercises being but of a thin weak habit of

body, which increased as he grew older so as to be very remarkable at last: this made him but low of stature though by his limbs he should have been moderately tall. He was always very pale and lean, and latterly, nothing but skin and bone . . . his eyes grey and full with a sharp, ingenious look while young . . . his chin sharp and forehead large, his head of a middle size. He wore his own hair of a dark brown color very long and hanging neglected over his face, uncut and lank, which about three years before his death, he cut off, and wore a periwig. He went stooping and very fast (till his weakness a few years before his death hindered him), having but a light body to carry, and a great deal of spirits and activity, especially in his youth.

He was of an active, restless, indefatigable genius even almost to the last, and always slept little to his death, seldom going to sleep till two, three or four o'clock in the morning and seldomer to bed, often continuing his studies all night, and taking a short nap in the day. His temper was melancholy, mistrustful and jealous, which increased upon him with his years.[1]

Most of this description is probably correct but Waller goes on to say that in his younger years Hooke freely communicated his scientific ideas "till some accidents made him to a crime close and reserved," and that he always led a "monastic life . . . so like a hermit or cynic too penuriously."

That this estimate is wrong in important respects has become clear as the result of the publication of Hooke's diaries in 1935, the tercentenary of his birth. Hooke never meant the diaries for publication, and their contents were of such a candid nature that for more than two centuries it was considered unsuitable to put them in print. It seems clear, therefore, that the impression we get from reading the diaries is entirely trustworthy: that he led a very active, full life; that he possessed warm, human feelings; and that, unlike Newton, whom he had the great misfortune to cross, he harbored no lasting grudges or ill will. A brief review of his life will help to give some perspective of his place in science, his effect on his contemporaries, and the achievements that he bequeathed to those who came after him.

Robert Hooke was born the son of a curate in a small parish at Freshwater in the Isle of Wight on July 18, 1635. He was a sickly infant afflicted with a weak stomach, and as a young boy was troubled almost continuously with headaches. Despite these painful handicaps he was lively and quick to learn, but as regular lessons under his father made his headaches worse (perhaps with reason!) the arrangement was given up. For several years thereafter he had no regular schooling but spent his time making mechanical contrivances and sketching. He showed such

---

[1] *Posthumous Works of Robert Hooke* (London: Richard Waller, 1705), pp. xxvi–xxvii.

unusual aptitude in the latter of these endeavors, that on his father's death, in 1648, he was sent to London at the age of thirteen with the idea that he would be an apprentice to the great portrait painter, Sir Peter Lely.

But Robert soon tired of art and instead entered the Westminster School where he made excellent progress in mathematics, especially geometry, and in mechanics, Latin, and Greek. In 1653, at eighteen, he entered Christ Church, Oxford, as a chorister; but because church music had been suspended during the Commonwealth, he was in effect on a small scholarship. After two years at Oxford, he was engaged as an assistant in chemistry by Dr. Thomas Willis, one of the illustrious group dedicated to science whose focus was John Wilkins, then master of Wadham College. Wilkins was the moving spirit behind the new experimental philosophy that was growing up in England, and perhaps more than any one man he was later responsible for the founding of the Royal Society. Through active support of science Boyle had just been lured to Oxford, and because of similar interests Wren, then a fellow of All Souls, became a member of the club. When Boyle was casting about for an intelligent assistant to improve his air pump, Willis suggested Hooke. The resulting engagement determined the whole of Hooke's life, for he was ever afterward associated with Boyle and Wren, and through them with the Royal Society and the work that it sponsored.

There is little need to comment on the great success of his pump. The results established Boyle's reputation as a scientist and Hooke's as an able experimenter and mechanician. He continued with Boyle until 1662 when the Royal Society, founded two years earlier at Gresham College in London, felt that it needed a curator. The curator was required to take charge of the Society's apparatus and to "furnish three or four considerable experiments" every day they met. Since they met once a week, this was a formidable assignment, but Hooke accepted it, after having been recommended by Boyle. It is a monument to Hooke's fertile imagination that he carried out his duties with outstanding skill for many years. Certainly his demonstrations and discussions contributed in no small measure to the success of the society in its early years.

The Society's meetings at Gresham soon led to an academic appointment for Hooke. The distinguished mathematician, Isaac Barrow, who came to Gresham at the same time as Hooke, resigned as professor of geometry in 1664 to become the first Lucasian professor of mathematics (and the predecessor of Newton) at Cambridge. Hooke was chosen to succeed him, but owing to an irregularity in the election he was not confirmed in the post until the next year. At about the same time, he also accepted the obligation of delivering the Cutlerian lectures on industrial processes at Gresham. Despite ill health and his later duties as surveyor for the city of London and secretary of the Royal Society, he carried on the curator's duties and the two lectureships for over thirty years. It is not difficult to believe Waller's assertion that he seldom went to sleep "till two, three or four o'clock in the morning."

Shortly after becoming a Gresham professor in 1665, Hooke published his *Micrographia* under the auspices of the Royal Society. The work represents not only the results of his original research and observations using the microscope he had constructed, but it contains a number of beautifully drawn illustrations that further emphasize his unusual gifts as a draftsman. Unlike most of the scientific work of that time, Hooke's work was written in English and thus was readily accessible to a wide audience. It was immediately popular and earned the praise of the learned world. Pepys, the indefatigable busybody, said of it: "Before I went to bed, I sat up till two o'clock in my chamber reading Mr. Hooke's *Microscopical Observations,* the most ingenious book that I ever read in my life." We know also that Newton read it with care and made copious notes on it.

In September 1666, the Great Fire of London destroyed something like 13,000 dwelling houses, more than 80 parish churches, St. Paul's Cathedral, 44 city companies' halls, and most of the other public and semi-public buildings, including the Guildhall and the Royal Exchange. The fire was hardly cold before Wren, Evelyn, and Hooke presented plans for rebuilding. Hooke's plan, submitted through the Royal Society, does not survive, but it appears to have been one with streets at right angles to one another, as in modern American cities. In the end none of the plans was adopted, but Wren and Hooke became the dominant members of a rebuilding committee for the city.

The reconstruction was at its height between 1668 and 1674; these were years of furious activity for Hooke. He spent countless hours in conferences, committee work, inspections on site, conferring and transacting business with Wren. From these he would rush away to give his Cutlerian or Gresham lectures, to conduct an experiment at the Royal Society, to a book auction, or to his favorite diversion—discussing some aspect of science with a friend in the coffee houses, the taverns, or at a private home. His closest friend and associate was Wren, but his relationship with Boyle also remained close and he often dined with him and his sister, Lady Ranelagh. He had many friends in the Royal Society and his diary abounds with their names.

In 1677, Oldenberg, who had been the active secretary of the Royal Society (two were originally appointed, the famous and able John Wilkins being the other), died and Hooke was elected in his place. Oldenberg's passing must have been a great relief to Hooke for there was cordial dislike between the two from the start. Hooke had serious disputes both with Oldenberg, about credit for the invention of spring-driven timepieces, and with Newton about discoveries in optics. It seems clear that Oldenberg did his best to keep Newton's dislike of Hooke active. Oldenberg, despite his important service to the Royal Society, including his founding and editorship of the *Philosophical Transactions,* the earliest periodical in the world devoted exclusively to natural science, appears to have been something of a rascal. It is possible that he passed the details of Hooke's spring-driven clock (which Hooke tried to patent about 1660) to Huygens and then, in turn, tried to patent Huygens' watch inventions for which Hooke claimed precedence. Whatever the merits of this dispute, it is clear that Hooke, with his fertile mind and hundreds of inventions, was too busy thinking up new ones to perfect any more than a few of the old ones. Oldenberg, as secretary, corresponded widely with academies and persons on the Continent, and made a trade of intelligence. Whether any of this was treasonable is also questionable, but in June 1667, at the height of the Dutch War, Oldenberg was arrested and locked in the Tower. He was released two months later without any formal charge ever having been placed against him.

Hooke's term as secretary was not notable and ended in 1682 when he was forty-seven. He continued to be active as curator, in his lectureships, and to report on a variety of subjects to the Royal Society. Much of this activity is described in his *Posthumous Works.* In 1687 his niece, Grace Hooke, to whom he was deeply attached, died at the age of twenty-eight. He never seemed to recover fully from this blow, and the death in 1691 of Boyle, with whom he had always been intimate, must have increased his unhappiness.

Despite his prodigious energy, Hooke suffered from poor health throughout his life, being continually affected with dizziness, noises in the head, an uneasy digestion, and insomnia. He continually experimented on himself with all kinds of medicines and purges, and endured periodic bouts of melancholy. Hooke also suffered emotionally all his adult life because, by seventeenth-century standards, he was not born a gentleman; his life, however, was spent largely in the company of men who were so regarded. In this anomalous status, his directness was considered by many as uncouth and his lack of social graces must have prejudiced many who otherwise might have admired his genius. It is hardly any wonder that in a life so afflicted by ill health and a sensitivity to his social standing, he should have been accounted by many as ill-tempered and morose.

In 1696 his health, always precarious, became seriously impaired and his condition became steadily worse in the few years that remained to him. He gradually lost his sight and his strength, and in the last year of his life he was bedridden. He died on March 3, 1703, at the age of sixty-seven.

In this abbreviated biography much of the detail of Hooke's scientific contribution has been passed over. His best-known contribution is the law of the elastic behavior of solids, known as Hooke's law, and which in its simplest form may be stated that "within the elastic limit in a solid, extension is proportional to the applied stress." This law is of the most fundamental importance in the design of structures, instruments, and mechanical devices. He had an acute physical insight and was the first to state clearly that the motions of bodies in the solar system must be regarded as a mechanical problem. His astronomical views and his presentment of universal gravitation were sufficiently profound to bring him into sharp conflict with Newton, but he was unable to develop his ideas for lack of mathematical skill. He demonstrated the rotation of Jupiter, and reasoned that the orientation of comets' tails must be due to a repelling action originating in the sun. His efforts to discover motion of the "fixed" stars later led to Bradley's discovery of the aberration of light.

In the field of optics he developed an imperfect wave theory of light with the vibrations transverse to the direction of propagation; he anticipated the idea of interference and he independently observed the diffraction of light. As a result he was able to discover and explain the property of "resolving power," the limitation on the magnification of an optical system. His interest in the improvement of microscopes and their use resulted in his *Micrographia.* He showed how to improve the illumination of objects under examination and pointed out the advantages of liquid immersion of the object and the objective lens of the microscope.

Coupled with his gifted insight into the structure of nature Hooke displayed great mechanical gifts. His development of the air pump for Boyle only began a long train of inventions which greatly improved scientific devices. In the field of astronomical instruments he invented telescopic sights, increased the accuracy of measurement by the addition of fine screw adjustments, and designed a clock-driven telescope mount so that a given area of the sky could be kept under constant observation without the necessity for human adjustment. In the field of timekeeping, he developed spring-driven clocks and invented the first machine for cutting clock wheels. He invented what we now call the "universal" joint (used in automobiles to transmit power from the engine to the rear driving wheels), the spirit level with the moving bubble, which is essential in all building construction and in many scientific instruments; again, returning to optics, Hooke invented the iris diaphragm, so necessary for controlling the sharpness of images and now used in all cameras.

This is by no means all that came from his fertile brain, but it will serve to show the great range of his mind, his genius for invention, and his outstanding ability to construct the visions of his imagination.

One of the principal reasons for including Hooke in this collection lies in his insistence on the kinetic view of matter. In this he seems to have been more penetrating than Newton, for if we are to infer anything from Proposition 23, Theorem 18, of Book II of the *Principia,* then we must conclude that in addition to being an atomist, Newton had specific views about the nature of a gas. He assumed that gas atoms were static but mutually repulsive with a force that varied as the distance (see Chapter 6 on Newton). In this respect, however, there appears to be a curious dichotomy in Newton's views, for he says in Query 5 in his *Opticks,* "Does not . . . light . . ." act upon bodies "heating them, and putting their parts into a vibrating motion wherein heat consists?" The same idea that there is internal motion in bodies occurs in Query 31, when he speaks about the heat produced in chemical mixing; but further on in the same query he observes: this "vast contraction and expansion seems unintelligible, by feigning the particles of air to be springy and ramous, or rolled up like hoops [a model suggested by Boyle], or by any other means than a repulsive power." Whatever he precisely intended, Dalton understood him to hypothesize static atoms and adopted his hypothesis without question.

While Hooke's kinetic hypothesis differs from the current view, nevertheless his advocacy of such ideas was much in advance of his time. He considers the particles of all bodies to be in incessant motion, those of differing mass having different speeds. A heavy particle has a low vibration frequency, and a light one, a high frequency. Energy exchanges take place only between particles having the same frequency. He also considers that all particles everywhere are immersed in a subtile fluid (we meet again the idea of an all-pervading ether) that communicates motion. Hooke's explanation of the manner in which the earth holds its atmosphere is surprisingly modern, although his explanation of gas expansion is not. Excerpts taken from his paper "De Potentia Restitutiva" or "Of Spring" published in London in 1678 follow.

๐๐๐๐๐๐๐๐

HOOKE

De Potentia Restitutiva [2]

THIS VIBRATIVE MOTION I DO not suppose inherent or inseparable from the particles of body, but communicated by impulses given from other bodies in the universe. This only I suppose,

---

[2] From Robert Hooke, "Lectiones Cutlerianae" (London: 1679), pp. 9–12, 15–16.

that the magnitude or bulk of the body doth make it receptive of this or that peculiar motion that is communicated, and not of any other. That is, every particle of matter according to its determinate or present magnitude is receptive of this or that peculiar motion and no other, so that magnitude and receptivity of motion seems the same thing. To explain this by a similitude or example: suppose a number of musical strings, as A B C D E, etc., tuned to certain tones, and a like number of other strings, as a b c d e, etc., tuned to the same sounds respectively, A shall be receptive of the motion of a, but not of that of b, c, nor d; in like manner B shall be receptive of the motion of b, but not of the motion of a, c or d. And so of the rest. This is that which I call *Congruity* and *Incongruity*.

Now as we find that musical strings will be moved by unisons and eighths, and other harmonious chords, though not in the same degree; so do I suppose that *the particles of matter* will be moved principally by such motions as are unisons, as I may call them, or of equal velocity with their motions, and by other harmonious motions in a less degree.

I do further suppose, a subtile matter that incompasseth and pervades all other bodies, which is the menstruum in which they swim which maintains and continues all such bodies in their motion, and which is the medium that conveys all homogeneous or harmonical motions from body to body.

Further I suppose, that all such particles of matter as are of a like nature, when not separated by others of a differing nature will remain together, and strengthen the common vibration of them all against the differing vibrations of the ambient bodies.

According to this notion I suppose the whole universe and all the particles thereof to be in a continued motion, and every one to take its share of space or room in the same, according to the bulk of its body, or according to the particular power it hath to receive, and continue this or that peculiar motion.

Two or more of these particles joined immediately together, and coalescing into one become of another nature, and receptive of another degree of motion and vibration, and make a compounded particle differing in nature from each of the other particles.

All bulky and sensible bodies whatsoever I suppose to be made up or composed of such particles which have their peculiar and appropriate motions which are kept together by the differing or dissonant vibrations of the ambient bodies or fluid.

The particles of all solid bodies do immediately touch each other; that is, the vibrative motions of the bodies do every one touch each other at every vibration. For explication, let A B C represent three bodies, each of these bodies I suppose to have a vibrative motion on either side of it,

A between D and E, B between E and F, and C between F and G [see
Figure 4–1]. I suppose then that B in every one of its vibrations doth meet
A at E, and C at F, and so the motions are continually interchanged: that
is, B communicates its motion to A at E, and A at the same time and place
communicates its motion to B, which returning to F meets there with C, and
communicates its received motion to C, which at the same instant and
place communicates its own motion to B, which returns it back to E: so
that the velocity of these bodies is always the same, and each body
impresseth on the contiguous bodies such a determinate number of pulses
within a certain space of time. Suppose for instance, in every second of
time B communicates to A and to C one million of pulses, and hath
received as many from each of them, by which means each of them doth
preserve its own space of vibration, according to the power of its vibration, that neither of the contiguous bodies can enter into it. The extreme
particles A and C are repercussed by the motion of the ambient hetero-

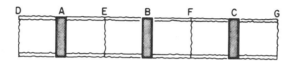

Fig. 4–1. Communication of vibratory motion among bodies.

geneous fluid, whereof though the bodies are of differing magnitudes, yet
the body and motion of the one are equivalent to the body and motion of
the other, so that whatever the body be less, the motion is quicker; and
where the body is bigger, the motion is less. But the particles of fluid
bodies do not immediately touch each other, but permit the mixture of
the other heterogeneous fluid near the earth, which serves to communicate the motion from particle to particle without the immediate contact
of the vibrations of the particles. . . .

The air then is a body consisting of particles so small as to be almost
equal to the particles of the heterogeneous fluid medium incompassing
the earth. It is bounded but on one side, namely, towards the earth, and
is indefinitely extended upward being only hindered from flying away that
way by its own gravity (the cause of which I shall some other time explain). It consists of the same particles single and separated, of which
water and other fluids do, conjoined and compounded, and being made of
particles exceeding small, its motion (to make its balance with the rest
of the earthy bodies) is exceeding swift, and its vibrative spaces exceeding large, comparative to the vibrative spaces of other terrestrial bodies.
I suppose that of the air next the earth in its natural state may be eight
thousand times greater than that of steel, and above a thousand times

greater than that of common water, and proportionably I suppose that its motion must be eight thousand times swifter than the former, and above a thousand times swifter than the latter. If therefore a quantity of this body be inclosed by a solid body, and that be so contrived as to compress it into less room, the motion thereof (supposing the heat the same) will continue the same, and consequently the vibrations and occursions will be increased in reciprocal proportion, that is, if it be condensed into half the space the vibrations and occursions will be double in number: if into a quarter the vibrations and occursions will be quadruple, etc.

Again, if the containing vessel be so contrived as to leave it more space, the length of the vibrations will be proportionably inlarged, and the number of vibrations and occursions will be reciprocally diminished, that is, if it be suffered to extend to twice its former dimensions, its vibrations will be twice as long, and the number of its vibrations and occursions will be fewer by half, and consequently its indeavours outward will be also weaker by half.

5

○○○○○○○○○○○

A WAVE THEORY OF LIGHT

○○○○○○○○○○○

Christian Huygens (1629-1695)

In the physical sciences one finds few investigators born into families of power and influence, who were also able to write their names in large letters on the history of their chosen subject. Despite their general rarity, we find two such men not only in the same century but as contemporaries with close birth dates and almost identical life spans. Robert Boyle, son of the first Earl of Cork, the man who founded modern chemistry and who for years was one of the mainstays of the Royal Society, was born on January 26, 1627, and died December 30, 1692. Christian Huygens, son of the outstanding intellectual, poet, and diplomat Constantin Huygens, grandson of the widely influential secretary of William the Silent, Christian Huygens, was born April 14, 1629 and died June 8, 1695.

Constantin Huygens, Christian's father, has been considered by some critics as the most brilliant figure in Dutch literary history. He not only displayed extraordinary gifts in music, art, and poetry, but he also possessed unusual physical beauty and vigor and was one of the most accomplished athletes of his time. As a young man he went to England several times in various diplomatic capacities, studied at Oxford, and, in 1622, when only twenty-six, was given an English knighthood by King James I. This paragon, for no other adjective seems to fit him, married his cousin Susanna van Baerle in 1627 and settled in The Hague. Four sons and a daughter were born to this marriage, Christian being the second son. Both Christian and his elder brother Constantin early showed signs of intellectual brilliance and they were carefully educated at home under their father's watchful supervision. When Christian was eight years old his mother died, and after a short time the family moved to a large new house at Voorburg, not far from The Hague. Here the elder Huygens, a member of the Council of State, entertained many visitors from France, including René Descartes, who was then composing the philosophical and mathematical works that were to have such a profound influence on the thought of Europe for many decades to come. It can easily be imagined how strong Descartes's influence was on the Huygens family and how much it affected the outlook of Christian, who was already beginning to show signs of unusual ability in mathematics. In 1645, at sixteen, both Christian and Constantin were enrolled at Leiden University. Descartes's *Principia* had just been published the year before; as a consequence, during the next few years the university became a battleground between the ideas of Aristotle and Descartes. In this atmosphere of intellectual ferment Christian continued his studies in mathematics and commenced others in mechanics. After two years he left Leiden and continued for two more at the College of Breda where he also studied law. But mathematics soon commanded his complete attention and in 1651, at the age of twenty-one, his first published work, *Cyclometriae,* a treatise written to expose the mathematical fallacies of Gregory de St. Vincent, appeared. This was followed in 1654 by a larger mathematical work in which many geometrical problems were solved by means of algebraic analysis, an accomplishment that established him among the leading mathematicians of the time. In the same period he began working on the improvement of the telescope, especially the reduction of chromatic and spherical aberration errors. An improved objective lens, made with the help of his brother Constantin, led to the discovery in 1655 of Titan, the sixth satellite of Saturn, although another year was to elapse before Huygens was able to announce the discovery of Saturn's rings. Previous telescopes had not afforded sufficient resolution to determine the exact nature of the puzzling image of this planet.

In July 1655, Huygens, then twenty-six, made his first trip to Paris to meet the leading astronomers and mathematicians of France. This visit not only encouraged his work in astronomy but impressed on him the need for more accurate timekeeping in such measurements. It was in the solution of this problem that he was led to investigate the pendulum as an isochronous element and to apply it to the movement of a practicable clock. It must be remembered that clocks of that period were notoriously inexact timekeepers; although Galileo had noted the approximately isochronous nature of pendulum swings as early as 1581, only a few crude applications to clocks had been made of this observation. Huygens' first pendulum clock was completed in 1657, and his *Horologium* describing his work on the clock appeared the following year.

The necessity for accurate timekeeping was not only a scientific astronomical problem, but a practical one as well. The problem of the determination of longitude at sea still remained to be solved and an accurate clock was needed for this purpose. The States-General of the Netherlands had offered a prize of 10,000 florins for a method of longitude determination and in 1641 Galileo had submitted a method based on occultations of the moons of Jupiter together with an impractically crude pendulum clock, but this was not accepted. In order to develop a suitable marine clock Huygens examined the amplitude-time dependence of pendulum motion and found that isochronous vibrations required a cycloidal motion of the pendulum bob. To achieve such a motion in an actual model he hung the lower rigid part of the pendulum from a thin flexible metal strip that could fit itself, as the pendulum was drawn aside, to the contour of a cycloidal-shaped metal guide. One of these was located on each side of the pendulum support. Huygens patented this device and made some profit from it, but its usefulness was short-lived.

The pendulum clock never proved practicable at sea owing to the ship's motion; moreover, in this particular model the friction of the flexible metal strip on its cycloidal guide introduced errors more than sufficient to compensate for the introduction of the guide itself. For small oscillations Huygens showed that the simple pendulum was also highly isochronous. The use of such oscillations by Clement in London in 1680 combined with his anchor escapement made the cycloidal pendulum obsolete. Attempts to improve the pendulum clock as a timekeeping instrument at sea nevertheless occupied Huygens throughout his life.

In November 1660 Huygens was again in Paris discussing Saturn and lens-grinding with astronomers, pendulums with mathematicians, and timekeepers with the clockmakers. He went to meetings of leading scientists called the "Montmor" group (after their host) where he met many of the savants who would later constitute the French Academy of Sciences. In March 1661 he departed for London to meet the men who had organized the Royal Society and who were meeting regularly at Gresham College—in particular Brounker, Wallis, Goddard, Boyle, and Oldenberg. The latter, as first secretary of the Society, remained a faithful correspondent of Huygens and kept him informed of the Society's activities. Even after assuming leadership in the French Academy, Huygens always regarded the Royal Society with the greatest admiration and considered it the pre-eminent scientific society in existence. Boyle's work on the properties of the air impressed him especially. On his return to Holland he had a copy of Boyle's pump made so that he could repeat the experiments himself.

In 1663 Huygens was again briefly in London to study the organization of the Royal Society. Subsequently, he went on to Paris to receive an award from Louis XIV for his development of the pendulum clock. He returned to Holland after wintering in the French capital but it was clear that he would soon be recalled to a position in the new Academy of Sciences that Colbert, the King's minister, was arranging. Two years later, in 1666, the Academy came into being, and Huygens was installed in the Bibliothèque du Roi to guide its activities.

His own work entered a new phase as he turned from astronomy and clockmaking to pursue wider problems in mechanics. Most elementary textbooks of physics dealing with what we now call Newton's three laws of motion seem to imply that these concepts emerged full-blown from Newton's mind without any previous understanding of them by his predecessors or contemporaries. Despite Newton's genius, it is clear that what we call the first law was known to Galileo, Descartes, and Huygens; with respect to the second law, Newton himself says that "what Mr. Huygens has published since about centrifugal force I suppose he had before me." In fact, Huygens must have used the concepts behind the second law in 1659 to arrive at his theorems on centrifugal force. The proper appreciation of the second law, which relates force, mass, and acceleration, also requires a distinction to be made between mass and weight. But this too was made by Huygens in his treatment of 1659.

The results of Huygens' study appeared in 1673 in his great work, *Horologium oscillatorium*. It contained, in addition to his studies relating to the pendulum and its period of oscillation, the solution of the general problem of the center of oscillation, the theory of evolutes, the cycloid as its own evolute, theorems on the composition of forces in circular motion, and the general idea of the conservation of energy. We know that Newton read the work and admired it and that he considered Huygens the "most elegant writer of modern times." At about this time Leibnitz, the great mathematician, and Huygens were intimately associated, Leibnitz having come to Paris in 1672. In 1674 Huygens presented to the French Academy Leibnitz' first paper on differential calculus, a study in which Huygens never became proficient.

It is appropriate at this time to say something about Huygens' health, which was never robust. Ever since his youth he had been subject to a kind of debility accompanied with violent headaches and insomnia. In 1670, little more than three years after his Paris appointment, he had an attack of such severity that he made preparations for his own death, including arrangements for the transfer of his papers to the Royal Society. However, he recovered sufficiently in a few months to travel to his home in Holland where he spent the winter, returning in the spring of 1671. In March 1676 he again became ill but before being completely incapacitated he returned to The Hague. This time with Colbert's permission he stayed for two years, not returning until June 1678. It was during this period that Roemer discovered the velocity of light by measurements of the eclipses of Jupiter's moons. This undoubtedly must have drawn Huygens' thoughts to his earlier studies in optics, for during the two years in the quiet of his country home he thought out the wave theory of light for which his name is particularly remembered in physics. All of this work is set forth in his *Traité de la lumière,* which was not published until 1690, although he reported it in detail to the Academy on his return from Holland in 1678. His explanations of wave propagation, and of reflection and refraction as taken from his treatise are set forth at the end of this article.

It may seem somewhat far-fetched that in a development of atomic theory one should include material on the nature of light; nevertheless, any detailed picture of modern physics is impossible without an understanding of the interaction of light both visible and invisible with atoms themselves. From the standpoint of the development and acceptance of physical theories it is interesting to realize that Huygens' wave theory of light was developed almost coincidentally with Newton's corpuscular theory. Both published the results of their researches years after the concepts were formed: Huygens in 1690 and Newton in his *Opticks,* which first appeared in 1704. Both theories were incomplete and acceptance of either one involved uncertainties which varied with the phenomena that were chosen for explanation. Thus, Newton's corpuscular theory easily explained the straight-line propagation of light, whereas a wave theory required a propagation like that of sound—a spreading of the wave around corners. But the wavelength of light is so short that this effect is obscured, and even though Grimaldi had observed the effect before 1665, it was not established for approximately another century. By applying the laws of mechanics to his corpuscles of light, Newton accounted for the manner in which light bends when passing from one medium to a more dense one, such as from air to water. His explanation required, however, that light travel faster in water than in air. On the wave theory, as will appear in the following excerpt, just the opposite is true. Thus an *experimentum crucis* was presented to determine which of the two theories was correct but the means to effect the experiment were not present at that time.

Largely because of Newton's overwhelming scientific prestige, the corpuscular theory gained almost universal acceptance and retained it until the opening of the nineteenth century. At that time Thomas Young was able to demonstrate clearly interference effects required by the wave theory; shortly after, Fresnel used the theory to explain a wide range of diffraction effects. If this was not enough to discredit the corpuscular theory, the *coup de grâce* was given by Fizeau in 1849 when he performed the crucial experiment of measuring the velocity of light in water and found it to be less than in air. Nevertheless, the ensuing half century disclosed experiments whose explanation demanded a corpuscular hypothesis. These will be discussed in Chapter 33.

But we must return to Huygens to follow the later events of his life. After his report on the wave theory in 1678, only another year elapsed before he again fell ill; fortunately, this attack was not severe enough to force him to give up work for any extended period. However, early in 1681 he suffered a violent relapse and, when able to travel, departed once more for Holland. Although the French Academy was now thriving, Huygens' position was by no means secure. There were internal rivalries in the society of pro- and anti-Cartesian factions. Huygens was not completely in one or the other. He accepted Descartes's vortices as the scheme of the world and even after the appearance of the *Principia* in 1687 never could be persuaded that Newton's universal gravitation was anything more than a fiction. He could not accept the fact that matter could act on distant matter without some understandable mechanism intervening.

Huygens was not ready to return to Paris until early in 1683. At this time the Dutch East India Company again became interested in marine clocks and Huygens spent the summer working on this project. Colbert, his patron, died in September 1683, and the opposition to Huygens' return was sufficient to prevent it. In the meantime France became increasingly anti-Protestant and the feeling of the Academy against foreigners became stronger than ever. Despite all attempts in the next few years he was never able to resume his position.

During the period 1685–1690 Huygens was busy attempting to perfect a marine pendulum clock, but these efforts continued to be unsuccessful. After this time he returned to spring-driven movements but his efforts reached no conclusive outcome. In 1687 his father died at the advanced age of ninety-one and in the following year his brother went to England with William III, who, with Mary, succeeded to the English throne following the deposed James II. Huygens now began to hope for a position in England and in 1689 spent the summer months there. He attended a meeting of the Royal Society at Gresham College, met Boyle on several occasions, and Newton for the first time. Later he went to Cambridge and it is recorded that early on a bright July morning he and Newton rode together in the coach from Cambridge to London. Huygens was then sixty years old and Newton forty-seven. The *Principia* had been published two years before and although Newton's fame was everywhere growing, he was then in one of his moods in which he was weary of science. Indeed this journey was prompted by his application for the post of provost of King's College, a post which incidentally he did not receive. There is unfortunately no record of what the two men talked about on this journey, however interesting it would be to know it. It is possible that they said very little, for Huygens' English was never fluent and Newton was often remote and taciturn. Huygens must have felt that his fortunes were ebbing and Newton in turn must have been concerned with efforts to change his own.

After returning from England, Huygens spent his remaining years in Holland. He never married, and the decline of his scientific work and his health, coupled with the fact that he was now cut off from close contact with others who were active in science, led to an increasing sense of loneliness. In March of 1695 he again fell ill and his condition became progressively worse. He died on June 8, 1695.

Some idea of his powerful scientific imagination as well as the basis of the wave theory of light can be gained from the following excerpt from his *Treatise on Light*. After a charming preface in which he explains why he is publishing his discoveries and why he waited so long to "bring this work to the light," he presents a systematic, almost axiomatic development of the principles which guided him in his analysis of optical phenomena. In the first few pages of his treatise Huygens boldly outlines the principal lines along which he proposes to conduct his investigations and states the essential problem that must be solved to account for the propagation of light in straight lines and to explain why rays of light emitted by different bodies do not interfere when they cross. Huygens stated the problem as follows:

> For I do not find that any one has yet given a probable explanation of the first and most notable phenomena of light, namely why it is not propagated except in straight lines, and how visible rays, coming from an infinitude of diverse places, cross one another without hindering one another in any way.[1]

To account for some of the observed properties of light Huygens immediately introduces the idea that light "consists in the motion of some sort of matter," for it is clear to him that only motion can account for such things as "fire and flame" from which light stems. He goes on to introduce the idea that light is transmitted from a source to the observer by the "movement of matter which exists between us and the luminous body." Here we have again the Cartesian concept of an ether filling all space which was later to prove so fruitful in the hands of Faraday and Maxwell even though it had finally to be discarded with the introduction of the theory of relativity.

With the introduction of these ideas of motion as the cause of light, Huygens implicitly accepted a kinetic (that is, a molecular) theory of matter, for he remarks that ". . . in the true Philosophy, . . . one conceives the causes of all natural effects in terms of mechanical motions." He further emphasizes the kinetic bases of his theory of light by stating that

> . . . all of those bodies that are liquid, such as flames, and apparently the sun and the stars, are composed of particles which float in a much more subtle medium which agitates them with great rapidity and makes them strike against the particles of the ether which surrounds them and which are much smaller than they.[2]

---

[1] From Christian Huygens, *Treatise on Light,* trans. S. P. Thompson (New York: Dover, 1912), p. 2.

[2] *Ibid.,* p. 10.

He compares the emission of light with the emission of sound and points out that the cause in both cases is motion but that the motion responsible for light must be exceedingly more rapid than that causing sound.

Having introduced an ether with kinetic properties, Huygens first develops the idea that light is propagated through the ether by the continual collision of the particles of the ether, and from this he goes on to the concept of spherical waves. These, he argues, are emitted when the particles in a source of light, such as the flame of a candle, are set vibrating. Each point in the source then emits concentric spherical waves, with the waves from separate points moving independently of each other.

To account for the propagation of light in a straight line and to explain the various observed optical phenomena, Huygens now introduces his famous concept of partial waves, which are shown in his figure on page 79. Here he explains how the successive wave fronts emanating from a point source of light can be constructed from previous wave fronts by picturing each point on a previous wave front as generating partial wavelets. The new wave front is then the surface that simultaneously touches one point of each of the partial wavelets that originate from all the points on a previous wave front. This leads to an extremely powerful technique for following the propagation of light through various media and for explaining such phenomena as reflection, refraction, and diffraction.

Although Huygens could have had no idea of the modern conception of the nature of light, the electromagnetic theory originated by Maxwell, still his wave theory for the propagation of light is as correct and useful today as it was when he first introduced it. Indeed, Huygens' concept of partial waves as contributing to the final wave front has been carried over by R. Feynman into the modern wave concept of matter to explain more clearly the quantum behavior of such elementary particles as electrons.

ᴏᴏᴏᴏᴏᴏᴏ

HUYGENS

Treatise on Light [3]

PREFACE

I WROTE THIS TREATISE DURING my sojourn in France twelve years ago, and I communicated it in the year 1678 to the learned persons who then composed the Royal Academy of Science, to

[3] *Ibid.*, pp. v–vii, 1–4, 10–24, 28, 34–37.

the membership of which the King had done me the honour of calling me. Several of that body who are still alive will remember being present when I read it, and above the rest those amongst them who applied themselves particularly to the study of Mathematics; of whom I cannot cite more than the celebrated gentlemen Cassini, Römer, and De la Hire. And although I have since corrected and changed some parts, the copies which I had made of it at that time may serve for proof that I have yet added nothing to it save some conjectures touching the formation of Iceland Crystal, and a novel observation on the refraction of Rock Crystal. I have desired to relate these particles to make known how long I have meditated the things which now I publish, and not for the purpose of detracting from the merit of those who, without having seen anything that I have written, may be found to have treated of like matters: as has in fact occurred to two eminent Geometricians, Messieurs Newton and Leibnitz, with respect to the Problem of the figure of glasses for collecting rays when one of the surfaces is given.

One may ask why I have so long delayed to bring this work to the light. The reason is that I wrote it rather carelessly in the Language in which it appears, with the intention of translating it into Latin, so doing in order to obtain greater attention to the thing. After which I proposed to myself to give it out along with another Treatise on Dioptrics, in which I explain the effects of Telescopes and those things which belong more to that Science. But the pleasure of novelty being past, I have put off from time to time the execution of this design, and I know not when I shall ever come to an end of it, being often turned aside either by business or by some new study.

. . . I would believe then that those who love to know the Causes of things and who are able to admire the marvels of Light, will find some satisfaction in these various speculations regarding it, and in the new explanation of its famous property which is the main foundation of the construction of our eyes and of those great inventions which extend so vastly the use of them. I hope also that there will be some who by following these beginnings will penetrate much further into this question than I have been able to do, since the subject must be far from being exhausted. This appears from the passages which I have indicated where I leave certain difficulties without having resolved them, and still more from matters which I have not touched at all, such as Luminous Bodies of several sorts, and all that concerns Colours; in which no one until now can boast of having succeeded. Finally, there remains much more to be investigated touching the nature of Light which I do not pretend to have disclosed, and I shall owe much in return to him who shall be able to supplement that which is here lacking to me in knowledge.

CHAPTER I

On Rays Propagated in Straight Lines

As happens in all the sciences in which Geometry is applied to matter, the demonstrations concerning Optics are founded on truths drawn from experience. Such are that the rays of light are propagated in straight lines; that the angles of reflexion and of incidence are equal; and that in refraction the ray is bent according to the law of sines, now so well known, and which is no less certain than the preceding laws.

The majority of those who have written touching the various parts of Optics have contented themselves with presuming these truths. But some, more inquiring, have desired to investigate the origin and the causes, considering these to be in themselves wonderful effects of Nature. In which they advanced some ingenious things, but not however such that the most intelligent folk do not wish for better and more satisfactory explanations. Wherefore I here desire to propound what I have meditated on the subject, so as to contribute as much as I can to the explanation of this department of Natural Science, which, not without reason, is reputed to be one of its most difficult parts. I recognize myself to be much indebted to those who were the first to begin to dissipate the strange obscurity in which these things were enveloped, and to give us hope that they might be explained by intelligible reasoning. But, on the other hand I am astonished also that even here these have often been willing to offer, as assured and demonstrative, reasonings which were far from conclusive. For I do not find that any one has yet given a probable explanation of the first and most notable phenomena of light, namely why it is not propagated except in straight lines, and how visible rays, coming from an infinitude of diverse places, cross one another without hindering one another in any way.

I shall therefore essay in this book, to give, in accordance with the principles accepted in the Philosophy of the present day, some clearer and more probable reasons, firstly of these properties of light propagated rectilinearly; secondly of light which is reflected on meeting other bodies. Then I shall explain the phenomena of those rays which are said to suffer refraction on passing through transparent bodies of different sorts; and in this part I shall also explain the effects of the refraction of the air by the different densities of the Atmosphere.

. . . Finally I shall treat of the various shapes of transparent and reflecting bodies by which rays are collected at a point or are turned aside in various ways. From this it will be seen with what facility, following our new Theory, we find not only the Ellipses, Hyperbolas, and other curves which Mr. Des Cartes has ingeniously invented for this purpose; but also those which the surface of a glass lens ought to possess when its other surface is given as spherical or plane, or of any other figure that may be.

It is inconceivable to doubt that light consists in the motion of some sort of matter. For whether one considers its production, one sees that here upon the Earth it is chiefly engendered by fire and flame which contain without doubt bodies that are in rapid motion, since they dissolve and melt many other bodies, even the most solid; or whether one considers its effects, one sees that when light is collected, as by concave mirrors, it has the property of burning as a fire does, that is to say it disunites the particles of bodies. This is assuredly the mark of motion, at least in the true Philosophy, in which one conceives the causes of all natural effects in terms of mechanical motions. This, in my opinion, we must necessarily do, or else renounce all hopes of ever comprehending anything in Physics.

And as, according to this Philosophy, one holds as certain that the sensation of sight is excited only by the impression of some movement of a kind of matter which acts on the nerves at the back of our eyes, there is here yet one reason more for believing that light consists in a movement of the matter which exists between us and the luminous body.

Further, when one considers the extreme speed with which light spreads on every side, and how, when it comes from different regions, even from those directly opposite, the rays traverse one another without hindrance, one may well understand that when we see a luminous object, it cannot be by any transport of matter coming to us from this object, in the way in which a shot or an arrow traverses the air; for assuredly that would too greatly impugn these two properties of light, especially the second of them. It is then in some other way that light spreads; and that which can lead us to comprehend it is the knowledge which we have of the spreading of Sound in the air.

We know that by means of the air, which is an invisible and impalpable body, Sound spreads around the spot where it has been produced, by a movement which is passed on successively from one part of the air to another; and that the spreading of this movement, taking place equally rapidly on all sides, ought to form spherical surfaces ever enlarging and which strike our ears. Now there is no doubt at all that light also comes from the luminous body to our eyes by some movement impressed on the matter which is between the two; since, as we have already seen, it cannot be by the transport of a body which passes from one to the other. If, in addition, light takes time for its passage—which we are now going to examine—it will follow that this movement, impressed on the intervening matter, is successive; and consequently it spreads, as Sound does, by spherical surfaces and waves: for I call them waves from their resemblance to those which are seen to be formed in water when a stone is thrown into it, and which present a successive spreading of circles, though these arise from another cause, and are only in a flat surface. . . .

Now the successive movement of Light being confirmed in this way, it follows, as I have said, that it spreads by spherical waves, like the movement of Sound.

But if the one resembles the other in this respect, they differ in many other things; to wit, in the first production of the movement which causes them; in the matter in which the movement spreads; and in the manner in which it is propagated. As to that which occurs in the production of Sound, one knows that it is occasioned by the agitation undergone by an entire body, or by a considerable part of one, which shakes all the contiguous air. But the movement of the Light must originate as from each point of the luminous object, else we should not be able to perceive all the different parts of that object, as will be more evident in that which follows. And I do not believe that this movement can be better explained than by supposing that all those of the luminous bodies which are liquid, such as flames, and apparently the sun and the stars, are composed of particles which float in a much more subtle medium which agitates them with great rapidity, and makes them strike against the particles of the ether which surrounds them, and which are much smaller than they. But I hold also that in luminous solids such as charcoal or metal made red hot in the fire, this same movement is caused by the violent agitation of the particles of the metal or of the wood; those of them which are on the surface striking similarly against the ethereal matter. The agitation, moreover, of the particles which engender the light ought to be much more prompt and more rapid than is that of the bodies which cause sound, since we do not see that the tremors of a body which is giving out a sound are capable of giving rise to Light, even as the movement of the hand in the air is not capable of producing Sound.

Now if one examines what this matter may be in which the movement coming from the luminous body is propagated, which I call Ethereal matter, one will see that it is not the same that serves for the propagation of Sound. For one finds that the latter is really that which we feel and which we breathe, and which being removed from any place still leaves there the other kind of matter that serves to convey Light. This may be proved by shutting up a sounding body in a glass vessel from which the air is withdrawn by the machine which Mr. Boyle has given us, and with which he has performed so many beautiful experiments. But in doing this of which I speak, care must be taken to place the sounding body on cotton or on feathers, in such a way that it cannot communicate its tremors either to the glass vessel which encloses it, or to the machine; a precaution which has hitherto been neglected. For then after having exhausted all the air one hears no Sound from the metal, though it is struck.

One sees here not only that our air, which does not penetrate through glass, is the matter by which Sound spreads; but also that it is not the same air but another kind of matter in which Light spreads; since if the air is removed from the vessel the Light does not cease to traverse it as before.

And this last point is demonstrated even more clearly by the celebrated experiment of Torricelli, in which the tube of glass from which the quicksilver has withdrawn itself, remaining void of air, transmits Light just the same as when air is in it. For this proves that a matter different from air exists in this tube, and that this matter must have penetrated the glass or the quicksilver, either one or the other, though they are both impenetrable to the air. And when, in the same experiment, one makes the vacuum after putting a little water above the quicksilver, one concludes equally that the said matter passes through glass or water, or through both.

As regards the different modes in which I have said the movements of Sound and of Light are communicated, one may sufficiently comprehend how this occurs in the case of Sound if one considers that the air is of such a nature that it can be compressed and reduced to a much smaller space than that which it ordinarily occupies. And in proportion as it is compressed the more does it exert an effort to regain its volume; for this property along with its penetrability, which remains notwithstanding its compression, seems to prove that it is made up of small bodies which float about and which are agitated very rapidly in the ethereal matter composed of much smaller parts. So that the cause of the spreading of Sound is the effort which these little bodies make in collisions with one another, to regain freedom when they are a little more squeezed together in the circuit of these waves than elsewhere.

But the extreme velocity of Light, and other properties which it has, cannot admit of such a propagation of motion, and I am about to show here the way in which I conceive it must occur. For this, it is needful to explain the property which hard bodies must possess to transmit movement from one to another.

When one takes a number of spheres of equal size, made of some very hard substance, and arranges them in a straight line, so that they touch one another, one finds, on striking with a similar sphere against the first of these spheres, that the motion passes as in an instant to the last of them, which separates itself from the row, without one's being able to perceive that the others have been stirred. And even that one which was used to strike remains motionless with them. Whence one sees that the movement passes with an extreme velocity which is the greater, the greater the hardness of the substance of the spheres.

But it is still certain that this progression of motion is not instantaneous, but successive, and therefore must take time. For if the movement, or the disposition to movement, if you will have it so, did not pass successively through all these spheres, they would all acquire the movement at the same time, and hence would all advance together; which does not happen. For the last one leaves the whole row and acquires the speed of the one which was pushed. Moreover there are experiments which demonstrate that all the bodies which we reckon of the hardest kind, such as quenched steel, glass, and agate, act as springs and bend somehow, not only when extended as rods but also when they are in the form of spheres or of other shapes. That is to say they yield a little in themselves at the place where they are struck, and immediately regain their former figure. For I have found that on striking with a ball of glass or of agate against a large and quite thick piece of the same substance which had a flat surface, slightly soiled with breath or in some other way, there remained round marks, of smaller or larger size according as the blow had been weak or strong. This makes it evident that these substances yield where they meet, and spring back: and for this time must be required.

Now in applying this kind of movement to that which produces Light there is nothing to hinder us from estimating the particles of the ether to be of a substance as nearly approaching to perfect hardness and possessing a springiness as prompt as we choose. It is not necessary to examine here the causes of this hardness, or of that springiness, the consideration of which would lead us too far from our subject. I will say, however, in passing that we may conceive that the particles of the ether, notwithstanding their smallness, are in turn composed of other parts and that their springiness consists in the very rapid movement of a subtle matter which penetrates them from every side and constrains their structure to assume such a disposition as to give to this fluid matter the most overt and easy passage possible. This accords with the explanation which Mr. Des Cartes gives for the spring, though I do not, like him, suppose the pores to be in the form of round hollow canals. And it must not be thought that in this there is anything absurd or impossible, it being on the contrary quite credible that it is this infinite series of different sizes of corpuscles, having different degrees of velocity, of which Nature makes use to produce so many marvellous effects.

But though we shall ignore the true cause of springiness we still see that there are many bodies which possess this property; and thus there is nothing strange in supposing that it exists also in little invisible bodies like the particles of the Ether. Also if one wishes to seek for any other way in which the movement of Light is successively communicated, one will find none which agrees better, with uniform progression, as seems to be necessary, than the property of springiness; because if this movement should grow slower in proportion as it is shared over a greater quantity of matter, in moving away from the source of the light, it could not conserve this great velocity over great distances. But by supposing springiness in the ethereal matter, its particles will have the property of equally rapid restitution whether they are pushed strongly or feebly; and thus the propagation of Light will always go on with an equal velocity.

And it must be known that although the particles of the ether are not ranged thus in straight lines, as in our row of spheres, but confusedly, so that one of them touches several others, this does not hinder them from transmitting their movement and from spreading it always forward. As to this it is to be remarked that there is a law of motion serving for this propagation, and verifiable by experiment. It is that when a sphere, such as A [in Figure 5–1], touches several other similar spheres CCC, if it is struck by another sphere B in such a way as to exert an impulse against all the spheres CCC which touch it, it transmits to them the whole of its movement, and remains after that motionless like the sphere B. And with-

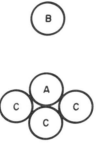

Fig. 5–1. The propagation of movement.

out supposing that the ethereal particles are of spherical form (for I see indeed no need to suppose them so) one may well understand that this property of communicating an impulse does not fail to contribute to the aforesaid propagation of movement.

Equality of size seems to be more necessary, because otherwise there ought to be some reflexion of movement backwards when it passes from a smaller particle to a larger one, according to the Laws of Percussion which I published some years ago.

However, one will see hereafter that we have to suppose such an equality not so much as a necessity for the propagation of light as for rendering that propagation easier and more powerful; for it is not beyond the limits of probability that the particles of the ether have been made equal for a purpose so important as that of light, at least in that vast space which is beyond the region of atmosphere and which seems to serve only to transmit the light of the Sun and the Stars.

I have then shown in what manner one may conceive Light to spread successively, by spherical waves, and how it is possible that this spreading is accomplished with as great a velocity as that which experiments and celestial observations demand. Whence it may be further remarked that although the particles are supposed to be in continual movement (for there are many reasons for this) the successive propagation of the waves cannot be hindered by this; because the propagation consists nowise in the transport of those particles but merely in a small agitation which they cannot help communicating to those surrounding, notwithstanding any movement which may act on them causing them to be changing positions amongst themselves.

But we must consider still more particularly the origin of these waves, and the manner in which they spread. And, first, it follows from what

Fig. 5–2. The propagation of light by spherical waves.

has been said on the production of Light, that each little region of a luminous body, such as the Sun, a candle, or a burning coal, generates its own waves of which that region is the centre. Thus in the flame of a candle [see Figure 5–2], having distinguished the points A, B, C, concentric circles described about each of these points represent the waves which come from them. And one must imagine the same about every point of the surface and of the part within the flame.

But as the percussions at the centres of these waves possess no regular succession, it must not be supposed that the waves themselves follow one another at equal distances: and if the distances marked in the figure appear to be such, it is rather to mark the progression of one and the same wave at equal intervals of time than to represent several of them issuing from one and the same centre.

After all, this prodigious quantity of waves which traverse one another without confusion and without effacing one another must not be deemed inconceivable; it being certain that one and the same particle of matter can serve for many waves coming from different sides or even from contrary directions, not only if it is struck by blows which follow one another closely but even for those which act on it at the same instant. It can do so because the spreading of the movement is successive. This may be proved by the row of equal spheres of hard matter, spoken of above. If against this row there are pushed from two opposite sides at the same time two similar spheres A and D [see Figure 5–3], one will see each of them rebound with the same velocity which it had in striking, yet the whole row will remain in its place, although the movement has passed along its whole length twice over. And if these contrary movements happen to meet one another at the middle sphere, B, or at some other such as C, that sphere will yield and act as a spring at both sides, and so will serve at the same instant to transmit these two movements.

Fig. 5–3. The propagation of two impulses moving in opposite directions along a row of spheres in contact.

But what may at first appear full strange and even incredible is that the undulations produced by such small movements and corpuscles, should spread to such immense distances; as for example from the Sun or from the Stars to us. For the force of these waves must grow feeble in proportion as they move away from their origin, so that the action of each one in particular will without doubt become incapable of making itself felt to our sight. But one will cease to be astonished by considering how at a great distance from the luminous body an infinitude of waves, though they have issued from different points of this body, unite together in such a way that they sensibly compose one single wave only, which, consequently, ought to have enough force to make itself felt. Thus this infinite number of waves which originate at the same instant from all points of a fixed star, big it may be as the Sun, make practically only one single wave which may well have force enough to produce an impression on our eyes. Moreover from each luminous point there may come many thousands of waves in the smallest imaginable time, by the frequent percussion of the corpuscles which strike the Ether at these points: which further contributes to rendering their action more sensible.

There is the further consideration in the emanation of these waves, that each particle of matter in which a wave spreads, ought not to communicate its motion only to the next particle which is in the straight line drawn from the luminous point, but that it also imparts some of it necessarily to all the others which touch it and which oppose themselves to its movement. So it arises that around each particle there is made a wave of which that particle is the centre. Thus if DCF [see Figure 5–4] is a wave emanating from the luminous point A, which is its centre, the particle B, one of those comprised within the sphere DCF, will have made its particular or partial wave KCL, which will touch the wave DCF at C at the same moment that the principal wave emanating from the point A has arrived at DCF; and it is clear that it will be only the region C of the wave KCL which will touch the wave DCF, to wit, that which is in the straight line drawn through AB. Similarly the other particles of the sphere DCF, such as *bb, dd,* etc., will each make its own wave. But each of

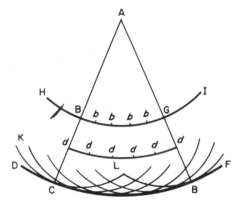

Fig. 5–4. Every point on a primary wave is a source of secondary spherical waves.

these waves can be infinitely feeble only as compared with the wave DCF, to the composition of which all the others contribute by the part of their surface which is most distant from the centre A.

One sees, in addition, that the wave DCF is determined by the distance attained in a certain space of time by the movement which started from the point A; there being no movement beyond this wave, though there will be in the space which it encloses, namely in parts of the particular waves, those parts which do not touch the sphere DCF. And all this ought not to seem fraught with too much minuteness or subtlety, since we shall see in the sequel that all the properties of Light, and everything pertaining to its reflexion and its refraction, can be explained in principle by this means. This is a matter which has been quite unknown to those who hitherto have begun to consider the waves of light, amongst whom are Mr. Hooke in his *Micrographia,* and Father Pardies, who, in a treatise of which he let me see a portion, and which he was unable to complete as he died shortly afterward, had undertaken to prove by these waves the effects of reflexion and refraction. But the chief foundation, which consists in the remark I have just made, was lacking in his demonstrations; and for the rest he had opinions very different from mine, as may be will appear some day if his writing has been preserved.

To come to the properties of Light. We remark first that each portion of a wave ought to spread in such a way that its extremities lie always between the same straight lines drawn from the luminous point. Thus the portion BG of the wave, having the luminous point A as its centre, will spread into the arc CE bounded by the straight lines ABC, AGE. For although the particular waves produced by the particles comprised within the space CAE spread also outside this space, they yet do not concur at the same instant to compose a wave which terminates the movement, as they do precisely at the circumference CE, which is their common tangent.

And hence one sees the reason why light, at least if its rays are not reflected or broken, spreads only by straight lines, so that it illuminates no object except when the path from its source to that object is open along such lines. For if, for example, there were an opening BG, limited by opaque bodies BH, GI, the wave of light which issues from the point A will always be terminated by the straight lines AC, AE, as has just been shown; the parts of the partial waves which spread outside the space ACE being too feeble to produce light there.

Now, however small we make the opening BG, there is always the same reason causing the light there to pass between straight lines; since this opening is always large enough to contain a great number of particles of the ethereal matter, which are of an inconceivable smallness; so that it appears that each little portion of the wave necessarily advances following the straight line which comes from the luminous point. Thus then we may take the rays of light as if they were straight lines.

It appears, moreover, by what has been remarked touching the feebleness of the particular waves, that it is not needful that all the particles of the Ether should be equal amongst themselves, though equality is more apt for the propagation of the movement. For it is true that inequality will cause a particle by pushing against another larger one to strive to recoil with a part of its movement; but it will thereby merely generate backwards towards the luminous point some partial waves incapable of causing light, and not a wave compounded of many as CE was.

Another property of waves of light, and one of the most marvellous, is that when some of them come from different or even from opposing sides, they produce their effect across one another without any hindrance. Whence also it comes about that a number of spectators may view different objects at the same time through the same opening, and that two persons can at the same time see one another's eyes. Now according to the explanation which has been given of the action of light, how the waves do not destroy nor interrupt one another when they cross one another, these effects which I have just mentioned are easily conceived. But in my judgement they are not at all easy to explain according to the views of Mr. Des Cartes, who makes Light to consist in a continuous pressure merely tending to movement. For this pressure not being able to act from two opposite sides at the same time, against bodies which have no inclination to approach one another, it is impossible so to understand what I have been saying about two persons mutually seeing one another's eyes, or how two torches can illuminate one another.

CHAPTER II

On Reflexion

Having explained the effects of waves of light which spread in a homogeneous matter, we will examine next that which happens to them on encountering other bodies. We will first make evident how the Reflexion of light is explained by these same waves, and why it preserves equality of angles.

Let there be a surface AB, plane and polished, of some metal, glass, or other body, which at first I will consider as perfectly uniform (reserving to myself to deal at the end of this demonstration with the inequalities from which it cannot be exempt), and let a line AC, inclined to AB, represent a portion of a wave of light, the centre of which is so distant that this portion AC may be considered as a straight line; for I consider all this as in one plane, imagining to myself that the plane in which this figure is cuts the sphere of the wave through its centre and intersects the plane AB at right angles. This explanation will suffice once for all [see Figure 5–5].

The piece C of the wave AC, will in a certain space of time advance as far as the plane AB at B, following the straight line CB, which may be supposed to come from the luminous centre, and which in consequence is perpendicular to AC. Now in this same space of time the portion A of the same wave, which has been hindered from communicating its movement beyond the plane AB, or at least partly so, ought to have continued its movement in the matter which is above this plane, and this along a distance equal to CB, making its own partial spherical wave, according to what has been said above. Which wave is here represented by the circumference SNR, the centre of which is A, and its semi-diameter AN equal to CB.

If one considers further the other pieces H of the wave AC, it appears that they will not only have reached the surface AB by straight lines HK parallel to CB, but that in addition they will have generated in the transparent air, from the centres K, K, K, particular spherical waves, repre-

sented here by circumferences the semi-diameters of which are equal to
KM, that is to say to the continuations of HK as far as the line BG
parallel to AC. But all these circumferences have as a common tangent
the straight line BN, namely the same which is drawn from B as a
tangent to the first of the circles, of which A is the centre, and AN the
semi-diameter equal to BC, as is easy to see.

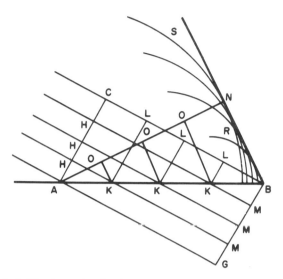

Fig. 5–5. The law of reflection derived from Huygen's principle.

It is then the line BN (comprised between B and the point N where the
perpendicular from the point A falls) which is as it were formed by all
these circumferences, and which terminates the movement which is made
by the reflexion of the wave AC; and it is also the place where the movement occurs in much greater quantity than anywhere else. Wherefore,
according to that which has been explained, BN is the propagation of the
wave AC at the moment when the piece C of it has arrived at B. For there
is no other line which like BN is a common tangent to all the aforesaid
circles, except BG below the plane AB; which line BG would be the
propagation of the wave if the movement could have spread in a medium
homogeneous with that which is above the plane. . . .

CHAPTER III

On Refraction

In the same way as the effects of Reflexion have been explained by
waves of light reflected at the surface of polished bodies, we will ex-

plain . . . phenomena of refraction by waves which spread within and across diaphanous bodies, both solids, such as glass, and liquids, such as water, oils, etc. . . . .

Let us pass now to the explanation of the effects of Refraction, assuming, as we have done, the passage of waves of light through transparent bodies, and the diminution of velocity which these same waves suffer in them.

The chief property of Refraction is that a ray of light, such as AB [see Figure 5–6], being in the air, and falling obliquely upon the polished surface of a transparent body, such as FG, is broken at the point of incidence B, in such a way that with the straight line DBE which cuts the surface perpendicularly it makes an angle CBE less than ABD which it made

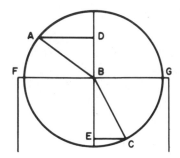

Fig. 5–6. The law of refraction derived from Huygen's principle.

with the same perpendicular when in the air. And the measure of these angles is found by describing, about the point B, a circle which cuts the radii AB, BC. For the perpendiculars AB, CE, let fall from the points of intersection upon the straight line DE, which are called the Sines of the angles ABD, CBE, have a certain ratio between themselves; which ratio is always the same for all inclinations of the incident ray, at least for a given transparent body. This ratio is, in glass, very nearly as 3 to 2; and in water very nearly as 4 to 3; and is likewise different in other diaphanous bodies.

Another property, similar to this, is that the refractions are reciprocal between the rays entering into a transparent body and those which are leaving it. That is to say that if the ray AB in entering the transparent body is refracted into BC [see Figure 5–7], then likewise CB being taken as a ray in the interior of this body will be refracted, on passing out, into BA.

To explain then the reasons of these phenomena according to our principles, let AB be the straight line which represents a plane surface bounding the transparent substances which lie towards C and towards N.

When I say plane, that does not signify a perfect evenness, but such as has been understood in treating of reflexion, and for the same reason. Let the line AC represent a portion of a wave of light, the centre of which is supposed so distant that this portion may be considered as a straight line. The piece C, then, of the wave AC, will in a certain space of time have advanced as far as the plane AB following the straight line CB, which may be imagined as coming from the luminous centre, and which consequently will cut AC at right angles. Now in the same time the piece A would have come to G along the straight line AG, equal and parallel to CB; and all the portion of wave AC would be at GB if the matter of the transparent body transmitted the movement of the wave as quickly as

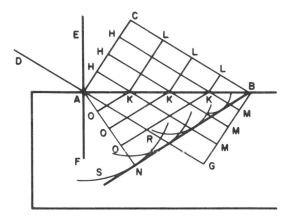

Fig. 5–7. The law of refraction derived from Huygen's principle.

the matter of the Ether. But let us suppose that it transmits this movement less quickly, by one-third, for instance. Movement will then be spread from the point A, in the matter of the transparent body through a distance equal to two-thirds of CB, making its own particular spherical wave according to what has been said before. This wave is then represented by the circumference SNR, the centre of which is A, and its semi-diameter equal to two-thirds of CB. Then if one considers in order the other pieces H of the wave AC, it appears that in the same time that the piece C reaches B they will not only have arrived at the surface AB along the straight lines HK parallel to CB, but that, in addition, they will have generated in the diaphanous substance from the centres K, partial waves, represented here by circumferences the semi-diameters of which are equal to two-thirds of the lines KM, that is to say, to two-thirds of the prolongations of HK down to the straight line BG; for these semi-diameters would have been equal to entire lengths of KM if the two transparent substances had been of the same penetrability.

Now all these circumferences have for a common tangent the straight line BN; namely the same line which is drawn as a tangent from the point B to the circumference SNR which we considered first. For it is easy to see that all the other circumferences will touch the same BN, from B up to the point of contact N, which is the same point where AN falls perpendicularly on BN.

It is then BN, which is formed by small arcs of these circumferences, which terminates the movement that the wave AC has communicated within the transparent body, and where this movement occurs in much greater amount than anywhere else. And for that reason this line, in accordance with what has been said more than once, is the propagation of the wave AC at the moment when its piece C has reached B. For there is no other line below the plane AB which is, like BN, a common tangent to all these partial waves. And if one would know how the wave AC has come progressively to BN, it is necessary only to draw in the same figure the straight lines KO parallel to BN, and all the lines KL parallel to AC. Thus one will see that the wave CA, from being a straight line, has become broken in all the positions LKO successively, and that it has again become a straight line at BN. This being evident by what has already been demonstrated, there is no need to explain it further. . . .

6

ooooooooooo

NEWTON ON PARTICLES
AND KINETICS

ooooooooooo

Isaac Newton (1642-1727)

In this section on Newton are reproduced passages from his writings that document his position with respect to atomic theory. Whatever Newton proposed had enormous influence on his contemporaries and those who followed, especially, as we shall see, on Dalton, the founder of experimental atomic chemistry. Newton's station in the history of atomism is secured primarily through this indirect influence, the effect of his vision on the ideas of others.

The celebrated French mathematician the Marquis de l'Hôpital, writing of Newton, said, "I picture him to myself as a celestial genius." These words state, perhaps most aptly, the common reverence that Newton's name has inspired in the generations since his death. More than a century later, the great English poet Wordsworth, contemplating the heroic marble statue in the antechapel at Trinity College, Cambridge, was moved to write

> . . . Newton, with his prism and silent face
> The marble index of a mind
> Voyaging through strange seas of thought alone.

The Victorians especially built his image to almost godlike proportions. Certainly Sir David Brewster's biography published in 1832 did much to launch this attitude. But Brewster knew more than he wished to write, for despite Newton's greatness—and indeed no one has ever questioned how sublimely gifted he was—there were facets to his character that were distinctly strange, human, and unpleasant.

In 1946, the Royal Society's tercentenary celebration of Newton's birth, which should have been commemorated in 1942 but had to be postponed because of World War II, brought to public notice new evaluations of Newton as a man. One of these, by the late Lord Keynes, is reproduced from the tercentenary celebration volume. His sketch reveals a strange and hitherto unknown side of this formidable man. But however strange Newton actually may have been, Keynes also reinforces the reverence Newton has received as that owed, as l'Hôpital says, to a "celestial genius."

Before presenting Keynes's essay it may be useful to review the salient facts of Newton's life. He was born on Christmas Day, 1642, at the manor of Woolsthorpe, a small farm close to the village of Colsterworth in Lincolnshire, England. The nearest town of any size to appear on an ordinary map is Grantham, which lies about eight miles to the north. Newton's birthplace still stands today in an excellent state of preservation; the visitor may see the room in which he was born and the room that he used as a study during the years when Cambridge University was closed, when he laid the foundation of his future greatness. Several apple trees grow on the lawn, perhaps to serve as a reminder of the popular tale regarding the origin of the theory of universal gravitation.

The Newton family were inconspicuous country farmers and Newton's father, Isaac, was apparently a quite ordinary man; his mother, Hannah Ayscough, seems to have been a capable but average country woman. Nowhere in his forebears can one find evidence of outstanding ability; his emergence as one of the greatest minds of all time seems therefore all the more remarkable. Newton's father died at the early age of thirty-six, a few months after his marriage. As if to compound the misfortune, Newton was so small at birth that it was said he could have been put in a quart mug, and it was not expected that he would live. But in this instance, as in many other aspects of his life, Newton confounded the expectations of those about him.

When Newton was only two years old his mother remarried, this time the Rev. Barnabas Smith, rector of the small parish of nearby North Witham. The boy was spared the trials of a stepfather, being left throughout his youth at Woolsthorpe with his maternal grandmother. In 1656 the Rev. Smith died and Newton's mother, with her three children by this marriage, a son and two daughters, returned to the Newton farm. At this time young Isaac was fourteen years old and had been for several years a student in the grammar school at Grantham.

It might be expected that he would have shown evidence of the peerless mind that was destined to revolutionize the thinking of mankind, but we find instead a rather solitary boy, interested in constructing mechanical devices and in books, and indifferent to formal study. But a schoolboy fight picked by a student who did better at his lessons than Newton awakened a desire to surpass his rival and gradually his schoolwork became outstanding.

On his mother's return to Woolsthorpe, Newton was taken out of school and it was expected that he would devote himself to working the family lands. But farm work was alien to his awakened and active mind, and on trips to the Grantham market with the family servant he would speed off to seek out the books in the apothecary's home where he had boarded when at school. His continuing absorption in intellectual pursuits and his dislike of farm life led his maternal uncle, rector of a neighboring parish and graduate of Trinity College, Cambridge, to persuade the boy's mother to prepare him for the same training.

Fortunately, reason prevailed and young Newton was reentered in the Grantham school. And thus it was that in June of 1661 there appeared in Cambridge a withdrawn and intense eighteen-year-old of country background and manners who, following the star of his destiny, had arrived at the gates of that ancient university. In the early years at Trinity, as at Grantham, Newton attracted little attention. Having little money he had to earn his way as a "subsizar," a student assigned to odd jobs and to assisting his tutor. Because of the combination of slender financial resources, a sober background, solitary habits, and the gift of intense concentration, it appears likely that he mixed little with his fellow students. In fact, Newton was so inconspicuous that we know practically nothing of his undergraduate life except what he was willing to write in later years. It is known that he applied himself assiduously to mathematics and that he read Euclid (which he considered at first a "trifling book") and then Descartes's geometry. Also, references in his *Opticks,* published many years later, show that he had begun to make careful observations of natural phenomena, for he describes in particular the measurements he made on halos about the moon seen on the night of February 19, 1664.

Newton completed his B.A. degree in January 1665. Because the seniority list for the students of that year is missing, there is no official report of his standing, but from his own account it is clear that he had made phenomenal progress in mathematics and in "natural philosophy," as physics was then called. He had made a strong impression on Isaac Barrow, Lucasian professor of mathematics in the university, but, as far as we know, on no one else.

Barrow recognized the potentialities in his intense young student and encouraged Newton to remain at Trinity and continue his studies. Sometime during the summer of 1665 the plague, which had broken out earlier in London, assumed epidemic proportions and began to spread through England. Trinity College was officially closed early in August, but from the records we gather that Newton had already returned to Woolsthorpe. It was between this date and the spring of 1667, when the university reopened, that he laid the foundation of all the great discoveries that have immortalized his name. As Andrade remarks, "In those two great years he had to the full two priceless gifts which no one enjoys today, full leisure and quiet." [1] What he did with it we can hear from Newton himself:

> In the beginning of the year 1665, I found the method for approximating series and the rule for reducing any [power] of any binomial to such a series [i.e., binomial theorem]. The same year in May [probably while still at Cambridge] I found the method of tangents of Gregory and Slusius, and in November had the direct method of fluxions [differential calculus] and the next year in January had the theory of colours and in the May following I had the entrance into the inverse method of fluxions [integral calculus] and in the same year I began to think of gravity extending to the orb of the moon . . . and having thereby compared the force requisite to keep the moon in her orb with the force of gravity at the surface of the earth, and found them to answer pretty nearly. All this was in the two years 1665 to 1666 for in those years I was in the prime of my age for invention and minded mathematics and philosophy more than anytime since." [2]

The magnitude of this accomplishment is difficult to comprehend, and it is the more astonishing when we think that it was all done when Newton was in his twenty-third and twenty-fourth years. Although Newton tells us specifically just when he developed the concept of differential and integral calculus, the theory of colors, and when he had the idea of "gravity extending to the moon," it is curious that he does not mention one of his most fundamental and celebrated achievements—an understanding of the laws of motion. To a large extent this must have been accomplished before he could say that he had found the comparison of the force requisite "to keep the moon in her orb" with "the force of gravity at the surface of the earth" . . . "to answer pretty nearly." It meant that he had not only generalized the idea of inertial mass of Descartes and Galileo and had taken the step to equate it to gravitational mass but had gone a great step further and incorporated the notions of force, mass, and acceleration, including centripetal acceleration, into a universal relationship—his second law, namely that force equals mass times acceleration, which lies at the heart of dynamics.

It seems worthwhile to point out here that Newton's world scheme, based on the idea of gravitation, presented an entirely different approach to the understanding of the solar system and the cosmos as compared with the Cartesian views, which were widely held at that time. Instead of mechanical vortices that kept the planets in their paths about the sun, Newton substituted the mysterious and unseen inertial and gravitational forces that together guided these orbs in their revolution through the depths of

---

[1] E. N. daC. Andrade, *Sir Isaac Newton* (New York: Doubleday and Co., 1958).
[2] *Portsmouth Collection,* Sec. I, div. X, number 41.

an empty space. It is hardly any wonder that even in Cambridge, Cartesian ideas were accepted long after the publication of Newton's great work the *Principia,* in which all these topics were explained.

Newton returned to Cambridge in the spring of 1667. The following October he was elected a fellow of Trinity and early the next year, in March, he took his M.A. In these years he was extending his study of optics and the development of calculus, but we also learn that he had bought chemicals and a furnace, apparently for chemical experiments. The nature of these experiments has long been obscure, but, as Lord Keynes's article "Newton the Man" points out, Newton had a streak of magic in his make-up. He had a passionate and driving interest in alchemy and spent years in its study and experimentation. Because Newton was excessively secretive this mystical side of his nature did not come to light until the "Portsmouth Papers" disclosed his preoccupation with occult ideas and with certain esoteric aspects of Biblical and theological inquiry. On the latter subject he left a huge collection of manuscripts many of which have not been investigated to this day. It is this aspect of Newton that we shall leave for Keynes's description.

Despite Newton's reluctance to reveal his activities and his discoveries, he presented to Barrow in June of 1669 a paper summarizing his work on the binomial theorem and calculus. This work and perhaps Barrow's knowledge of Newton's optical researches, which included the construction of a small reflecting telescope (quite an achievement at that time), produced an unexpected change in Newton's fortunes. Barrow resigned his chair in the latter part of the summer; on October 29, 1669, Newton, who had published nothing and was not yet twenty-seven, became Lucasian Professor of Mathematics.

Newton's optical researches had convinced him that lenses free from chromatic aberrations could not be constructed; accordingly, he had turned to a reflecting mirror to produce a telescope in which sharp images could be obtained. The choice of metal for the mirror, its casting, and the subsequent polishing were all done by Newton's own hand. After his death, the composition of the alloy that he used was found to be very close to what is now known as speculum metal and the polishing was done with techniques that with slight changes would be acceptable in modern practice.

This uncanny knack of devising correct procedures and finding correct solutions makes it seem almost as though he were at times endowed with the kind of superhuman vision and with the magic he so earnestly sought. His telescope was of sufficient power to show the moons of Jupiter and to observe the phases of Venus. He then made a second and somewhat improved instrument; an account of it was read to the Royal Society in January 1672, when he was elected a fellow. A month later he forwarded his first paper describing some of his optical studies on refraction and reflection, and his proof that white light consists of colors of different refrangibility. A second paper, delivered the following year, contained a corpuscular theory of light and the supposition of an all-pervading ether. The vibrations of a denser ether in a substance of higher index of refraction produced "fits" of easy reflection and easy refraction depending on the phase of the vibration with respect to the incident corpuscle. In this way he was also able to account for interference and diffraction and color effects in thin films. All of this inevitably drew disagreement and controversy, some with Hooke and some with scientists on the Continent. Newton was so painfully sensitive to this intrusion on his thoughts and his time that he said his "affection to philosophy" was worn out and he was as little concerned with it "as a countryman about learning."

Unfortunately for Hooke and for Newton this was not to be their only clash. Another occurred in 1679 regarding the path of a falling body, taking into account the earth's rotation. Still another occurred in 1684 as a result of a discussion which took place among Hooke, the astronomer Edmund Halley, and Sir Christopher Wren. These three, members of the Royal Society, were in agreement that the gravitational force decreased inversely as the square of the distance, despite the lack of a general proof. For Halley an even more interesting question was a solution to the astronomical problem of the path taken by a body moving around a center of force which exerted an attraction that varied as the inverse square of the distance. Hooke professed to have solved this problem but did not produce his result. After waiting for several months Halley decided in August 1684 to go to Cambridge and ask Newton. He was astonished to get the immediate reply "an ellipse." Newton thereupon offered to show Halley the solution but was unable to locate it among his papers. Halley returned to London with Newton's assurance that he would reproduce the calculation. It was forwarded in November and after reading it Halley again went to Cambridge for further discussion with Newton. The result of these conversations was a report in February 1685 to the Royal Society of Newton's work and the appearance of a paper "De Motu Corporum," which was the beginning of the *Principia*. It is entirely characteristic that Newton should have completed the solution of the problem of universal gravitation, which he had started in 1666, as well as the motion of satellites in a central field of force without revealing it to anyone.

It was clear to Halley that the great body of Newton's work must be made available to the scientific world, and he set about coaxing Newton to prepare it for publication. In order to expedite it, Halley himself assumed the cost of its publication, placated Newton in the controversies stirred up in its preparation, saw the book through the press, and arranged for its sale. The whole work, which opened a new world to science and philosophy, was completed in about eighteen months and appeared for sale in the summer of 1687. Newton was then forty-four years old.

The task of preparing the *Principia* seems to have exhausted Newton and put him again in the frame of mind in which science no longer held his interest. During the spring of 1687, when he was completing the *Principia,* he took part in the legal proceedings in which Cambridge University defied King James II in his efforts to change the religious basis for the conferring of the M.A. degree. The following year James II was deposed and Newton was elected to represent Cambridge University in the so-called Convention Parliament. Newton's residence in London and the formation of new friendships called attention to his modest way of life and it was suggested that a man of his eminence should be placed in a government position as a tangible mark of national gratitude. Newton seems to have acquiesced to this idea, but it was not fulfilled for another five years.

In 1689 his mother died. Despite his residence at Cambridge, the record shows that Newton over the years returned to Woolsthorpe very frequently, sometimes spending long periods there. His relationship with his mother seems to have been close and a strong bond of affection existed between them. In her last illness it is said that he sat up all night with her. Whether it was his mother's death, his changing interests, or the delay of his friends in finding him a high salaried administrative post, Newton became dissatisfied and depressed. By 1693 he had fallen into periods of deep melancholy in which he imagined that his friends had deserted him or were attempting to involve him in unpleasant situations. He suffered long periods of sleeplessness, and his usually suspicious nature became greatly exaggerated. For instance, he wrote Pepys, whom he did not know well, saying that they must never see each other again. He also wrote his friends that Charles Montague, longtime fellow of Trinity and later Earl of Halifax, who was working in his behalf, "bore him a grudge and was false to him." This strange behavior was certainly symptomatic of a nervous breakdown but Newton did not, as some accounts claim, become insane. Toward the close of 1693 he seems to have recovered and it is interesting that Montague, whose friendship he had questioned, should have been the person to whom he eventually owed his appointment in London. As Chancellor of the Exchequer, Montague was able to arrange matters so that Newton became Warden of the Mint. This appointment proved useful to both men; Montague was effecting the recoinage of the currency, and Newton gave the problem his complete attention. In 1699 Newton was advanced to Master of the Mint.

In the years that followed, long-deferred honors began to accrue. In 1703 he was elected president of the Royal Society, a post to which he was reelected annually for the rest of his life. The first edition of his *Opticks* appeared in the next year. In 1705 Queen Anne and a royal retinue journeyed to Cambridge to confer knighthood on Newton at the scene of his great achievements. In 1713, with the assistance of Roger Cotes, Plumian professor of astronomy at Cambridge, a second edition of the *Principia* was published. A third edition was prepared in his lifetime by Henry Pemberton. His health remained good until 1725, when he suffered an attack of inflammation of the lungs and he was advised to move to the purer air of Kensington. In February 1727 he felt unusually well and took the opportunity to drive in his coach to London to preside at a meeting of the Royal Society. But the rigors of the journey proved too much for him and he suffered a relapse. Returning to Kensington, he gradually grew weaker and died on March 20 at the age of eighty-four.

Newton was buried in Westminster Abbey with the greatest honors England could bestow. On his monument is written: "Let mortals rejoice that such and so great an ornament of the human race has existed." As great a man as Einstein said of him more than two centuries later, "Nature to him was an open book whose letters he could read without effort." Perhaps the most thought-provoking comment was made by Andrade, speaking at the Newton Tercentenary, when he said: "I feel that Newton derived his knowledge by something more like a direct contact with the unknown sources that surrounded us, with the world of mystery, than has been vouchsafed to any other man of science."

ᴑᴑᴑᴑᴑᴑᴑᴑ

LORD KEYNES

Newton, the Man [3]

The MS. of this lecture was actually prepared by the late Lord Keynes some years ago for delivery to an audience at Trinity College. It was also read to a small private audience at the Royal Society Club in 1942.

Although he had intended to use this MS. as the basis of his lecture on this occasion, he would no doubt have made certain alterations. His draft as read by Mr Geoffrey Keynes must be regarded as unfinished.

IT IS WITH SOME DIFFIDENCE that I try to speak to you in his own home of Newton as he was himself. I have long

----

[3] Lord Keynes, in *Newton Tercentenary Celebration* (London: Royal Society, 1947), pp. 27–34.

been a student of the records and had the intention to put my impressions into writing to be ready for Christmas Day, 1942, the tercentenary of his birth. The war has deprived me both of leisure to treat adequately so great a theme and of opportunity to consult my library and my papers and to verify my impressions. So if the brief study which I shall lay before you to-day is more perfunctory than it should be, I hope you will excuse me.

One other preliminary matter. I believe that Newton was different from the conventional picture of him. But I do not believe he was less great. He was less ordinary, more extraordinary, than the nineteenth century cared to make him out. Geniuses *are* very peculiar. Let no one here suppose that my object to-day is to lessen, by describing, Cambridge's greatest son. I am trying rather to see him as his own friends and contemporaries saw him. And they without exception regarded him as one of the greatest of men.

In the eighteenth century and since, Newton came to be thought of as the first and greatest of the modern age of scientists, a rationalist, one who taught us to think on the lines of cold and untinctured reason.

I do not see him in this light. I do not think that any one who has pored over the contents of that box which he packed up when he finally left Cambridge in 1696 and which, though partly dispersed, have come down to us, can see him like that. Newton was not the first of the age of reason. He was the last of the magicians, the last of the Babylonians and Sumerians, the last great mind which looked out on the visible and intellectual world with the same eyes as those who began to build our intellectual inheritance rather less than 10,000 years ago. Isaac Newton, a posthumous child born with no father on Christmas Day, 1642, was the last wonder-child to whom the Magi could do sincere and appropriate homage.

Had there been time, I should have liked to read to you the contemporary record of the child Newton. For, though it is well known to his biographers, it has never been published *in extenso,* without comment, just as it stands. Here, indeed, is the making of a legend of the young magician, a most joyous picture of the opening mind of genius free from the uneasiness, the melancholy and nervous agitation of the young man and student.

For in vulgar modern terms Newton was profoundly neurotic of a not unfamiliar type, but—I should say from the records—a most extreme example. His deepest instincts were occult, esoteric, semantic—with profound shrinking from the world, a paralyzing fear of exposing his thoughts, his beliefs, his discoveries in all nakedness to the inspection and criticism of the world. 'Of the most fearful, cautious and suspicious temper that I ever knew', said Whiston, his successor in the Lucasian Chair. The too well-known conflicts and ignoble quarrels with Hooke, Flamsteed, Leibnitz are only too clear an evidence of this. Like all his type he was wholly aloof from women. He parted with and published nothing except under the extreme pressure of friends. Until the second phase of his life, he was a wrapt, consecrated solitary, pursuing his studies by intense introspection with a mental endurance perhaps never equalled.

I believe that the clue to his mind is to be found in his unusual powers of continuous concentrated introspection. A case can be made out, as it also can with Descartes, for regarding him as an accomplished experimentalist. Nothing can be more charming than the tales of his mechanical contrivances when he was a boy. There are his telescopes and his optical experiments. These were essential accomplishments, part of his unequalled all-round technique, but not, I am sure, his *peculiar* gift, especially amongst his contemporaries. His peculiar gift was the power of holding continuously in his mind a purely mental problem until he had seen straight through it. I fancy his pre-eminence is due to his muscles of intuition being the strongest and most enduring with which a man has ever been gifted. Anyone who has ever attempted pure scientific or philosophical thought knows how one can hold a problem momentarily in one's mind and apply all one's powers of concentration to piercing through it, and how it will dissolve and escape and you find that what you are surveying is a blank. I believe that Newton could hold a problem in his mind for hours and days and weeks until it surrendered to him its secret. Then being a supreme mathematical technician he could dress it up, how you will, for purposes of exposition, but it was his intuition which was pre-eminently extraordinary—'so happy in his conjectures', said de Morgan, 'as to seem to know more than he could possibly have any means of proving'. The proofs, for what they are worth, were, as I have said, dressed up afterwards—they were not the instrument of discovery.

There is the story of how he informed Halley of one of his most fundamental discoveries of planetary motion. 'Yes,' replied Halley, 'but how do you know that? Have you proved it?' Newton was taken aback—'Why, I've known it for years', he replied. 'If you'll give me a few days, I'll certainly find you a proof of it'—as in due course he did.

Again, there is some evidence that Newton in preparing the *Principia* was held up almost to the last moment by lack of proof that you could treat a solid sphere as though all its mass was concentrated at the centre, and only hit on the proof a year before publication. But this was a truth which he had known for certain and had always assumed for many years.

Certainly there can be no doubt that the peculiar geometrical form in which the exposition of the *Principia* is dressed up bears no resemblance at all to the mental processes by which Newton actually arrived at his conclusions.

His experiments were always, I suspect, a means, not of discovery, but always of verifying what he knew already.

Why do I call him a magician? Because he looked on the whole universe and all that is in it *as a riddle,* as a secret which could be read by applying pure thought to certain evidence, certain mystic clues which God had laid about the world to allow a sort of philosopher's treasure hunt to the esoteric brotherhood. He believed that these clues were to be found partly in the evidence of the heavens and in the constitution of elements (and that is what gives the false suggestion of his being an experimental natural philosopher), but also partly in certain papers and traditions handed down by the brethren in an unbroken chain back to the original cryptic revelation in Babylonia. He regarded the universe as a cryptogram set by the Almighty—just as he himself wrapt the discovery of the calculus in a cryptogram when he communicated with Leibnitz. By pure thought, by concentration of mind, the riddle, he believed, would be revealed to the initiate.

He *did* read the riddle of the heavens. And he believed that by the same powers of his introspective imagination he would read the riddle of the Godhead, the riddle of past and future events divinely fore-ordained, the riddle of the elements and their constitution from an original undifferentiated first matter, the riddle of health and of immortality. All would be revealed to him if only he could persevere to the end, uninterrupted, by himself, no one coming into the room, reading, copying, testing—all by himself, no interruption for God's sake, no disclosure, no discordant breakings in or criticism, with fear and shrinking as he assailed these half-ordained, half-forbidden things, creeping back into the bosom of the Godhead as into his mother's womb. 'Voyaging through strange seas of thought *alone*', notes Charles Lamb 'a fellow who believed nothing unless it was as clear as the three sides of a triangle'.

And so he continued for some twenty-five years. . . .

Here in Trinity it is right that I should give you an account of how he lived amongst you during these years of his greatest achievement. The east end of the Chapel projects farther eastwards than the Great Gate. In the second half of the seventeenth century there was a walled garden in the free space between Trinity Street and the building which joins the Great Gate to the Chapel. The south wall ran out from the turret of the Gate to a distance overlapping the Chapel by at least the width of the present pavement. Thus the garden was of modest but reasonable size. . . . This was Newton's garden. He had the Fellow's set of rooms between the Porter's Lodge and the Chapel—that, I suppose, now occupied by Professor Broad. The garden was reached by a stairway which was attached to a veranda raised on wooden pillars projecting into the garden from the range of buildings. At the top of this stairway stood his telescope—not to be confused with the observatory erected on the top of the Great Gate during Newton's lifetime (but after he had left Cambridge) for the use of Roger Cotes and Newton's successor, Whiston. This wooden erection was, I think, demolished by Whewell in 1856 and replaced by the stone bay of Professor Broad's bedroom. At the Chapel end of the garden was a small two-storied building, also of wood, which was his laboratory. When he decided to prepare the *Principia* for publication he engaged a young kinsman, Humphrey Newton, to act as his amanuensis (the MS. of the *Principia,* as it went to the press, is clearly in the hand of Humphrey). Humphrey remained with him for five years—from 1684 to 1689. When Newton died Humphrey's son-in-law Conduitt wrote to him for his reminiscences, and among the papers I have is Humphrey's reply.

During these twenty-five years of intense study mathematics and astronomy were only a part, and perhaps not the most absorbing, of his occupations. Our record of these is almost wholly confined to the papers which he kept and put in his box when he left Trinity for London.

Let me give some brief indications of their subject. They are enormously voluminous—I should say that upwards of 1,000,000 words in his handwriting still survive. They have, beyond doubt, no substantial value whatever except as a fascinating sidelight on the mind of our greatest genius.

Let me not exaggerate through reaction against the other Newton myth which has been so sedulously created for the last two hundred years. There was extreme method in his madness. All his unpublished works on esoteric and theological matters are marked by careful learning, accurate method and extreme sobriety of statement. They are just as *sane* as the *Principia,* if their whole matter and purpose were not magical. They were nearly all composed during the same twenty-five years of his mathematical studies. They fall into several groups.

Very early in life Newton abandoned orthodox belief in the Trinity. At this time the Socinians were an important Arian sect amongst intellectual circles. It may be that Newton fell under Socinian influences, but I think not. He was rather a Judaic monotheist of the school of Maimonides. He arrived at this conclusion, not on so-to-speak rational or sceptical grounds, but entirely on the interpretation of ancient authority. He was persuaded that the revealed documents give no support to the Trinitarian doctrines which were due to late falsifications. The revealed God was one God.

But this was a dreadful secret which Newton was at desperate pains to conceal all his life. It was the reason why he refused Holy Orders, and therefore had to obtain a special dispensation to hold his Fellowship and Lucasian Chair and could not be Master of Trinity. Even the Toleration Act of 1689 excepted anti-Trinitarians. Some rumours there were, but not at the dangerous dates when he was a young Fellow of Trinity. In the main the secret died with him. But it was revealed in many writings in his big box. After his death Bishop Horsley was asked to inspect the box with a view to publication. He saw the contents with horror and slammed the lid. A hundred years later Sir David Brewster looked into the box. He covered up the traces with carefully selected extracts and some straight fibbing. His latest biographer, Mr More, has been more candid. Newton's extensive anti-Trinitarian pamphlets are, in my judgement, the most interesting of his unpublished papers. Apart from his more serious affirmation of belief I have a completed pamphlet showing up what Newton thought of the extreme dishonesty and falsification of records for which St Athanasius was responsible, in particular for his putting about the false calumny that Arius died in a privy. The victory of the Trinitarians in England in the latter half of the seventeenth century was not only as complete, but also as extraordinary, as St Athanasius's original triumph. There is good reason for thinking that Locke was a Unitarian. I have seen it argued that Milton was. It is a blot on Newton's record that he did not murmur a word when Whiston, his successor in the Lucasian Chair, was thrown out of his professorship and out of the University for publicly avowing opinions which Newton himself had secretly held for upwards of fifty years past.

That he held this heresy was a further aggravation of his silence and secrecy and inwardness of disposition.

Another large section is concerned with all branches of apocalyptic writings from which he sought to deduce the secret truths of the Universe— the measurements of Solomon's Temple, the Book of David, the Book of Revelations, an enormous volume of work of which some part was published in his later days. Along with this are hundreds of pages of Church History and the like, designed to discover the truth of tradition.

A large section, judging by the handwriting amongst the earliest, relates to alchemy—transmutation, the philosopher's stone, the elixir of life. The scope and character of these papers have been hushed up, or at least minimized, by nearly all those who have inspected them. About 1650 there was a considerable group in London, round the publisher Cooper, who during the next twenty years revived interest not only in the English alchemists of the fifteenth century, but also in translations of the medieval and post-medieval alchemists.

There is an unusual number of manuscripts of the early English alchemists in the libraries of Cambridge. It may be that there was some continuous esoteric tradition within the University which sprang into activity again in the twenty years from 1650 to 1670. At any rate, Newton was clearly an unbridled addict. It is this with which he was occupied 'about 6 weeks at spring and 6 at the fall when the fire in the elaboratory scarcely went out' at the very years when he was composing the *Principia*—and about this he told Humphrey Newton not a word. Moreover, he was almost entirely concerned, not in serious experiment but in trying to read the riddle of tradition, to find meaning in cryptic verses, to imitate the alleged but largely imaginary experiments of the initiates of past centuries. Newton has left behind him a vast mass of records of these studies. I believe that the greater part are translations and copies made by him of existing books and manuscripts. But there are also extensive records of experiments. I have glanced through a great quantity of this—at least 100,000 words, I should say. It is utterly impossible to deny that it is wholly magical and wholly devoid of scientific value; and also impossible not to admit that Newton devoted years of work to it. Some time it might be interesting, but not useful, for some student better equipped and more idle than I to work out Newton's exact relationship to the tradition and MSS. of his time.

In these mixed and extraordinary studies, with one foot in the Middle Ages and one foot treading a path for modern science, Newton spent the first phase of his life, the period of life in Trinity when he did all his real work. Now let me pass to the second phase.

After the publication of the *Principia* there is a complete change in his habit and way of life. I believe that his friends, above all Halifax, came to the conclusion that he must be rooted out of the life he was leading at Trinity which must soon lead to decay of mind and health. Broadly speaking, of his own motion or under persuasion, he abandons his studies. He takes up University business, represents the University in Parliament; his friends are busy trying to get a dignified and remunerative job for him— the Provostship of King's, the Mastership of Charterhouse, the Controllership of the Mint.

Newton could not be Master of Trinity because he was a Unitarian and so not in Holy Orders. He was rejected as Provost of King's for the more prosaic reason that he was not an Etonian. Newton took this rejection very ill and prepared a long legalistic brief, which I possess, giving reasons why it was not unlawful for him to be accepted as Provost. But, as ill-luck had it, Newton's nomination for the Provostship came at the moment when King's had decided to fight against the right of Crown nomination, a struggle in which the College was successful.

Newton was well qualified for any of these offices. It must not be inferred from his introspection, his absent-mindedness, his secrecy and his solitude that he lacked aptitude for affairs when he chose to exercise it. There are many records to prove his very great capacity. Read, for example, his correspondence with Dr. Covell, the Vice-Chancellor when, as the University's representative in Parliament, he had to deal with the delicate question of the oaths after the revolution of 1688. With Pepys and Lowndes he became one of the greatest and most efficient of our civil servants. He was a very successful investor of funds, surmounting the crisis of the South Sea Bubble, and died a rich man. He possessed in exceptional degree almost every kind of intellectual aptitude—lawyer, historian, theologian, not less than mathematician, physicist, astronomer.

And when the turn of his life came and he put his books of magic back into the box, it was easy for him to drop the seventeenth century behind him and to evolve into the eighteenth-century figure which is the traditional Newton.

Nevertheless, the move on the part of his friends to change his life came almost too late. In 1689 his mother, to whom he was deeply attached, died. Somewhere about his fiftieth birthday on Christmas Day, 1692, he suffered what we should now term a severe nervous breakdown. Melancholia, sleeplessness, fears of persecution—he writes to Pepys and to Locke and no doubt to others letters which lead them to think that his mind is deranged. He lost, in his own words, the 'former consistency of his mind'. He never again concentrated after the old fashion or did any fresh work. The breakdown probably lasted nearly two years, and from it emerged, slightly 'gaga', but still, no doubt, with one of the most powerful minds of England, the Sir Isaac Newton of tradition.

In 1696 his friends were finally successful in digging him out of Cambridge, and for more than another twenty years he reigned in London as the most famous man of his age, of Europe, and—as his powers gradually waned and his affability increased—perhaps of all time, so it seemed to his contemporaries.

He set up house with his niece Catharine Barton, who was beyond reasonable doubt the mistress of his old and loyal friend Charles Montague, Earl of Halifax and Chancellor of the Exchequer, who had been one of Newton's intimate friends when he was an undergraduate at Trinity. Catharine was reputed to be one of the most brilliant and charming women in the London of Congreve, Swift and Pope. She is celebrated, not least for the broadness of her stories, in Swift's *Journal to Stella*. Newton puts on rather too much weight for his moderate height. When he rode in his coach one arm would be out of his coach on one side and the other on the other. His pink face, beneath a mass of snow-white hair, which 'when his peruke was off was a venerable sight', is increasingly both benevolent and majestic. One night in Trinity after Hall he is knighted by Queen Anne. For nearly twenty-four years he reigns as President of the Royal Society. He becomes one of the principal sights of London for all visiting intellectual foreigners, whom he entertains handsomely. He liked to have clever young men about him to edit new editions of the *Principia*—and sometimes merely plausible ones as in the case of Facio de Duillier.

Magic was quite forgotten. He has become the Sage and Monarch of the Age of Reason. The Sir Isaac Newton of orthodox tradition—the eighteenth-century Sir Isaac, so remote from the child magician born in the first half of the seventeenth century—was being built up. Voltaire returning from his trip to London was able to report of Sir Isaac—' 'twas his peculiar felicity, not only to be born in a country of liberty, but in an Age when all scholastic impertinences were banished from the World. Reason alone was cultivated and Mankind could only be his Pupil, not his Enemy.'

Newton, whose secret heresies and scholastic superstitions it had been the study of a lifetime to conceal!

But he never concentrated, never recovered 'the former consistency of his mind.' 'He spoke very little in company.' 'He had something rather languid in his look and manner.'

And he looked very seldom, I expect, into the chest where, when he left Cambridge, he had packed all the evidences of what had occupied and so absorbed his intense and flaming spirit in his rooms and his garden and his elaboratory between the Great Gate and Chapel.

But he did not destroy them. They remained in the box to shock profoundly any eighteenth- or nineteenth-century prying eyes. They became the possession of Catharine Barton and then of her daughter, the Countess of Portsmouth. So Newton's chest, with many hundreds of thousands of words of his unpublished writings, came to contain the 'Portsmouth Papers.'

In 1888 the mathematical portion was given to the University Library at Cambridge. They have been indexed, but they have never been edited. The rest, a very large collection, were dispersed in the auction room in 1936 by Catharine Barton's descendant, the present Lord Lymington. Disturbed by this impiety, I managed gradually to reassemble about half of them, including nearly the whole of the biographical portion, that is, the 'Conduitt Papers', in order to bring them to Cambridge which I hope they will never leave. The greater part of the rest were snatched out of my reach by a syndicate which hoped to sell them at a high price, probably in America, on the occasion of the recent tercentenary.

As one broods over these queer collections, it seems easier to understand—with an understanding which is not, I hope, distorted in the other direction—this strange spirit, who was tempted by the Devil to believe at the time when within these walls he was solving so much, that he could reach *all* the secrets of God and Nature by the pure power of mind—Copernicus and Faustus in one.

oooooooo

Newton's motto in the *Principia* is "*Hypotheses non fingo* (I frame no hypotheses)." It is this absence of preconceived notions that accounts in a large measure for his success as a physicist. An example of this attitude occurs in a letter to Bentley, written about six years after the first publication of the *Principia*. In 1692, as the first Boyle Lecturer, Bentley had delivered a series of sermons, under the general title "A Confutation of Atheism." A part of his argument was the assertion that the design evident in the physical world, as revealed by Newton's discoveries, was a demonstration of divine Providence. Although a person of the most presumptious confidence, Bentley seems to have experienced momentary feelings of caution, for in preparing the lectures for publication, he wrote Newton asking for confirmation of the ideas he had expressed. An interesting part of Newton's answer follows:

> You sometimes speak of gravity as essential and inherent to matter. Pray do not ascribe that notion to me, for the cause of gravity is what I do not pretend to know.

This caution, which is so characteristic, disappears in the queries at the end of Book III of the *Opticks,* and Newton "takes down his hair" for his readers and allows himself, contrary to his motto, to indulge in hypothetical speculations. Query 31 contains interesting ideas on atomic theory and is partly reproduced below.

ͻͻͻͻͻͻͻͻ

NEWTON

Opticks [4]

IT SEEMS PROBABLE TO ME, that God in the Beginning form'd Matter in solid, massy, hard, impenetrable, moveable Particles, of such Sizes and Figures, and with such other Properties, and in such Proportion to Space, as most conduced to the End for which he form'd them; and that these primitive Particles being Solids, are incomparably harder than any porous Bodies compounded of them; even so very hard, as never to wear or break in pieces; no ordinary Power being able to divide what God himself made one in the first Creation. While the Particles continue entire, they may compose Bodies of one and the same Nature and Texture in all Ages: But should they wear away, or break in pieces, the Nature of Things depending on them, would be changed. Water and Earth, composed of old worn Particles and Fragments of Particles, would not be of the same Nature and Texture now, with Water and Earth composed of entire Particles in the Beginning. And

---

[4] From Sir Isaac Newton, *Opticks* (New York: Dover, 1952), pp. 400–405.

therefore, that Nature may be lasting, the Changes of corporeal Things are to be placed only in the various Separations and new Associations and Motions of these permanent Particles; compound Bodies being apt to break, not in the midst of solid Particles, but where those Particles are laid together, and only touch in a few Points.

It seems to me farther, that these Particles have not only a *Vis inertiæ*, accompanied with such passive Laws of Motion as naturally result from that Force, but also that they are moved by certain active Principles, such as is that of Gravity, and that which causes Fermentation, and the Cohesion of Bodies. These Principles I consider, not as occult Qualities, supposed to result from the specifick Forms of Things, but as general Laws of Nature, by which the Things themselves are form'd; their Truth appearing to us by Phænomena, though their Causes be not yet discover'd. For these are manifest Qualities, and their Causes only are occult. And the *Aristotelians* gave the Name of occult Qualities, not to manifest Qualities, but to such Qualities only as they supposed to lie hid in Bodies, and to be the unknown Causes of manifest Effects: Such as would be the Causes of Gravity, and of magnetick and electrick Attractions, and of Fermentations, if we should suppose that these Forces or Actions arose from Qualities unknown to us, and uncapable of being discovered and made manifest. Such occult Qualities put a stop to the Improvement of natural Philosophy, and therefore of late Years have been rejected. To tell us that every Species of Things is endow'd with an occult specifick Quality by which it acts and produces manifest Effects, is to tell us nothing: But to derive two or three general Principles of Motion from Phænomena, and afterwards to tell us how the Properties and Actions of all corporeal Things follow from those manifest Principles, would be a very great step in Philosophy, though the Causes of those Principles were not yet discover'd: And therefore I scruple not to propose the Principles of Motion above-mention'd, they being of very general Extent, and leave their Causes to be found out.

Now by the help of these Principles, all material Things seem to have been composed of the hard and solid Particles above-mentioned, variously associated in the first Creation by the Counsel of an intelligent Agent. For it became him who created them to set them in order. And if he did so, it's unphilosophical to seek for any other Origin of the World, or to pretend that it might arise out of a Chaos by the mere Laws of Nature; though being once form'd, it may continue by those Laws for many Ages. For while Comets move in very excentrick Orbs in all manner of Positions, blind Fate could never make all the Planets move one and the same way in Orbs concentrick, some inconsiderable Irregularities excepted, which may have risen from the mutual Actions of Comets and Planets upon one another, and which will be apt to increase, till this System wants a Reformation. Such a wonderful Uniformity in the Planetary System must be allowed the Effect of Choice. . . .

And since Space is divisible *in infinitum,* and Matter is not necessarily in all places, it may be also allow'd that God is able to create Particles of Matter of several Sizes and Figures, and in several Proportions to Space, and perhaps of different Densities and Forces, and thereby to vary the Laws of Nature, and make Worlds of several sorts in several Parts of the Universe. At least, I see nothing of Contradiction in all this.

As in Mathematicks, so in Natural Philosophy, the Investigation of difficult Things by the Method of Analysis, ought ever to precede the Method of Composition. This Analysis consists in making Experiments and Observations, and in drawing general Conclusions from them by Induction, and admitting of no Objections against the Conclusions, but such as are taken from Experiments, or other certain Truths. For Hypotheses are not to be regarded in experimental Philosophy. And although the arguing from Experiments and Observations by Induction be no Demonstration of general Conclusions; yet it is the best way of arguing which the Nature of Things admits of, and may be looked upon as so much the stronger, by how much the Induction is more general. And if no Exception occur from Phænomena, the Conclusion may be pronounced generally. But if at any time afterwards any Exception shall occur from Experiments, it may then begin to be pronounced with such Exceptions as occur. By this way of Analysis we may proceed from Compounds to Ingredients, and from Motions to the Forces producing them; and in general, from Effects to their Causes, and from particular Causes to more general ones, till the argument end in the most general. This is the Method of Analysis: And the Synthesis consists in assuming the Causes discover'd, and establish'd as Principles, and by them explaining the Phænomena proceeding from them, and proving the Explanations.

○○○○○○○

From various statements that occur in the queries at the end of Book III of the *Opticks,* the reader infers that Newton pictured the ultimate particles of liquid and solid bodies in motion. In Query 28 he says:

A dense fluid . . . in the pores of bodies . . . serves only to stop the vibrating motions of their parts, wherein their heat and activity consists.

And in "An Hypothesis Explaining the Properties of Light":

So in fluids . . . their parts . . . are in perpetual motion.

When he discusses gases per se, however, Newton is by no means so explicit. For instance, in Query 31 of the *Opticks* he writes:

> [This] . . . vast contraction and expansion seems unintelligible by feigning the particles of air to be springy or ramous, or rolled up like hoops [proposed by Boyle] or by any other means than a repulsive force.

Finally we may turn to the *Principia* itself, Book II, Proposition 23, Theorem 18, which is often cited as Newton's mathematical derivation of Boyle's law. Here again we see nothing explicit in regard to a kinetic assumption; the theorem seems to be based on a picture of static gas particles that are mutually repulsive. Certainly this is the view that many in reading the theorem afterward understood, and took to be Newton's view of gases. Dalton, in particular, may be cited as accepting this picture. But is it really Newton's? We may let the great man speak for himself.

> But whether elastic fluids do really consist of particles so repelling each other, is a physical question. We have here demonstrated mathematically the property of fluids consisting of particles of this kind, that hence philosophers may take occasion to discuss that question.

. . . Newton's Theorem XVIII may be restated in modern terms: . . . If a fluid be composed of mutually repelling particles and the density be proportional to the pressure, the repelling forces of the particles will be inversely proportional to the distance between their centers. Conversely, particles repelling each other with forces inversely proportional to the distance separating their centers compose an elastic fluid whose density is proportional to the pressure.

The phrase "density proportional to the pressure" is another way of stating Boyle's law, provided, of course, that the temperature is assumed to remain constant. If attention is directed to the converse statement of the theorem, Newton gives a particle model of a gas, i.e., static particles that experience a force of repulsion inversely proportional to the distance between their centers, which leads to Boyle's law.

The modern student reading this proof should note that where Newton speaks of "the pressure with which the square DP urges the enclosed fluid" he means, according to present usage, not pressure, but force. If the steps of the argument are then written out, the proof follows with little difficulty, as may be seen in [the] Appendix. . . .

oooooooo

Philosophiae Naturalis Principia Mathematica [5]

BOOK II: THE MOTION OF BODIES

Proposition XXIII. Theorem XVIII

If a fluid be composed of particles fleeing from each other, and the density be as the compression, the centrifugal forces of the particles will be inversely proportional to the distances of their centres. And, conversely, particles fleeing from each other, with forces that are inversely proportional to the distances of their centres, compose an elastic fluid, whose density is as the compression.

LET THE FLUID BE SUPPOSED to be included in a cubic space ACE, and then to be reduced by compression into a lesser cubic space *ace*; and the distances of the particles retaining a like situation with respect to each other in both the spaces, will be as the sides AB, *ab* of the cubes; and the densities of the mediums will be inversely as the containing spaces AB^3, ab^3. [See Figure 6–1.] In the plane side of the greater cube

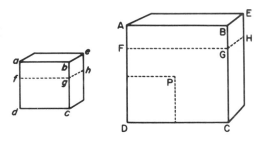

Fig. 6–1.

ABCD take the square DP equal to the plane side *db* of the lesser cube; and, by the supposition the pressure with which the square DP urges the inclosed fluid will be to the pressure with which that square *db* urges the inclosed fluid as the densities of the mediums are to each other, that is, as ab^3 to AB^3. But the pressure with which the square DB urges the included fluid is to the pressure with which the square DP urges the same fluid as the square DB to the square DP, that is, as AB^2 to ab^2. Therefore, multiplying together corresponding terms of the proportions, the pressure

[5] From Sir Isaac Newton, *Mathematical Principles of Natural Philosophy*, trans. A. Mott (1729) and revised by F. Cajori (Berkeley: University of California Press, 1947), p. 300.

with which the square DB urges the fluid is to the pressure with which the square *db* urges the fluid as *ab* to AB. Let the planes FGH, *fgh* be drawn through the interior of the two cubes, and divide the fluid into two parts. These parts will press each other with the same forces with which they are themselves pressed by the planes AC, *ac,* that is, in the proportion of *ab* to AB: and therefore the centrifugal forces by which these pressures are sustained are in the same ratio. The number of particles being equal, and the situation alike, in both cubes, the forces which all the particles exert, according to the planes FGH, *fgh,* upon all, are as the forces which each exerts on each. Therefore the forces which each exerts on each, according to the plane FGH in the greater cube, are to the forces which each exerts on each, according to the plane *fgh* in the lesser cube, as *ab* to AB, that is, inversely as the distances of the particles from each other. Q.E.D.

And, conversely, if the forces of the single particles are inversely as the distances, that is, inversely as the sides of the cubes AB, *ab;* the sums of the forces will be in the same ratio, and the pressures of the sides DB, *db* as the sums of the forces; and the pressure of the square DP to the pressure of the side DB as ab^2 to AB^2. And, multiplying together corresponding terms of the proportions, one obtains the pressure of the square DP to the pressure of the side *db* as ab^3 to AB^3; that is, the force of compression in the one is to the force of compression in the other as the density in the former to the density of the latter. Q.E.D.

APPENDIX

Proof of Newton's Theorem XVIII

To rephrase the argument, let us suppose that

d_o = the original distance between particles of the gas
d_c = the distance between particles after compression

Then *if* the particles retain a configuration after compression, similar to that before, then their distance of separation may be written

$$d_o:d_c = AB:ab$$

and from the definition of the density of the gas, ρ we have

$$\rho_o:\rho_c = \frac{m}{(AB)^3} : \frac{m}{(ab)^3} = \frac{1}{(AB)^3} : \frac{1}{(ab)^3}$$

where m is the mass of the particles in the container. Now *assuming* Boyle's law (pressure is proportional to the density at constant temperature):

$$p_o:p_c = \rho_o:\rho_c = (ab)^3:(AB)^3$$

or $\quad p_o:p_c = (ab)^3:(AB)^3$

Next realizing that the force which a side of the box exerts on the gas is proportional to the area, $F = p.A$ or $p = F/A$ and that Newton means the *force* of a side, rather than the *pressure:*

$$\frac{F_o}{F_c} = \frac{p_o \cdot (AB)^2}{p_c \cdot (ab)^2} = \frac{(ab)^3 \cdot (AB)^2}{(AB)^3 \cdot (ab)^2} = \frac{ab}{AB}$$

But the forces in each instance arise from the action of the same number of particles pressing (statically) against a face. Hence dividing the total force F, by the number of particles n, i.e., $\frac{F}{n} = f$; we get the force per particle:

$$\frac{f_o}{f_c} = \frac{ab}{AB}$$

But from the first proportion, $ab/AB = d_c/d_o$, hence,

$$\frac{f_o}{f_c} = \frac{d_c}{d_o}$$

Q.E.D.

7

ooooooooooo

A KINETIC THEORY
OF GASES

ooooooooooo

Daniel Bernoulli (1700-1782)

In politics, in music, in finance, and other fields of human endeavor, history occasionally furnishes us with the story of an illustrious family whose members over a series of generations continue the contributions that have founded their fame. The Churchills, the Bachs, the Rothschilds are among them. But in science we find fewer outstanding examples—the Bernoulli family being perhaps the foremost. Bell [1] in his *Men of Mathematics* enlarges on their fame by telling us that: "No fewer than 120 of the descendants of the Mathematical Bernoullis have been traced genealogically and of this considerable posterity the majority achieved distinction—sometimes amounting to eminence—in the law, scholarship, science, literature, the learned professions, administration and the arts. None were failures."

In the earliest records, the family resided in Antwerp, but because of their adherence to Protestantism, they moved briefly to Frankfurt in 1583 and later to Basle, Switzerland. There the brothers Jacques (Jacob) (1654–1705) and Jean (John) (1667–1748) the father of Daniel, first demonstrated the mathematical genius for which the family is noted. In 1676, although only twenty-four, Jacques traveled to England where it is said he was "admitted to the meetings of Robert Boyle, Hooke, and other learned and scientific men," [2] evidently the Royal Society. After six years of travel in Europe he returned to Basle in 1682, where he opened a

---

[1] E. T. Bell, *Men of Mathematics* (New York: Simon and Schuster, 1937).
[2] Encyclopaedia Brittanica (11th ed.; London: 1910).

public seminary for experimental physics. Five years later he was appointed to the chair of mathematics in the University of Basle, a position he held until his death.

Daniel's father, Jean, though an able mathematician, would be characterized today as a disturbed person. As Newman [3] remarks, "He was violent, abusive, jealous, and when necessary, dishonest." His first academic post was the chair of mathematics at Groningen, Holland. His difficulties there were many; nevertheless, he continued in this position for ten years. It was during his sojourn at Groningen that Daniel was born. In 1705 the family returned to Basle where Jean accepted the chair of mathematics left vacant by his brother's death. He had already been accused of dishonesty at Groningen, and he was then suspected of cheating in a prize competition for the solution to the isoperimetrical problem (the shortest perimeter enclosing a given area), first proposed by his brother Jacques nine years earlier. His relations with Daniel were even more reprehensible. He not only disliked his son and discouraged his efforts to study mathematics but he also adopted a repressive severity toward the boy calculated to undermine his self-confidence. Despite this hostility, Daniel began his mathematics at eleven under the tutelage of his older brother Nicholas, and later continued his studies in Italy. Before surrendering to the family passion, Daniel thought he preferred medicine; after completing this study, he was for a time a physician.

But medicine proved only a passing fancy and when Daniel was twenty-five, both he and Nicholas accepted appointments as professors of mathematics at St. Petersburg, Russia. The collaboration was short-lived; eight months later, in July 1726, Nicholas lay dead of a fever. Daniel stayed on another seven years, enduring as well as he could the Russian manners and climate. He returned to Basle in 1733 as professor of anatomy and botany, an appointment that was changed later to professor of experimental and speculative philosophy. He spent almost fifty years in these posts, during which he won or shared no fewer than ten prizes awarded by the Paris Academy of Sciences, a record equaled only by his friend, the great mathematician, Leonhard Euler. He was elected to almost every learned society in Europe, and he succeeded his father as Foreign Associate of the Academy of Paris. His work in his later years was concerned mostly with the development of the theory of probability. Although he suffered from asthma, he remained vigorous and active until almost eighty. He lived only a few years after retirement, passing away in Basle on March 17, 1782.

Bernoulli's discussion of gas dynamics, taken from the tenth section of

[3] James R. Newman, *The World of Mathematics* (New York: Simon and Schuster, 1956).

his *Hydrodynamica* (1738), was the first mathematical treatment of that branch of physics now known as the kinetic theory of gases. It is remarkable on many counts. First, it presents his picture of a gas as composed of an enormous number of particles in very rapid chaotic motion. This description came at a time when the physical nature of gases was quite unknown, the atomic nature of matter highly speculative, and the kinetic hypothesis equally so. Second, his theory showed mathematically that gas pressure could be accounted for as a result of direct particle impacts on the walls of the container. Third, he clearly recognized the distinction between heat and temperature, which was understood only after the work of Joseph Black years later. Fourth, he assumed that the addition of heat increases the speed of the gas particles—a statement of the conversion of heat to mechanical energy that was established by James P. Joule's work over a century later. Fifth, he recognized that the pressure-volume relation may not hold at higher densities than those of normal air. Sixth, he realized that the validity of the pressure-volume relation holds only if the temperature is kept constant. Finally, he inferred that the particle velocity is not dependent on the pressure. It is amazing that all these ideas without exception are valid.

The language used in certain parts of the paper needs some explanation for the modern reader, as do some of the mathematical deductions which do not follow readily from the text. Thus, in Section 3, first paragraph, there is some confusion according to present usage between the terms "weight" and "pressure." The meaning will be clearer if "weight" is substituted for "pressure" in the two instances where this word occurs. The last paragraph dealing with the "fourth proportional" may be easily understood if the proportion is written:

$$\frac{\text{Surface area of the earth}}{\text{Surface area of the piston}} = \frac{\text{Weight of all the atmosphere}}{\text{Weight of air in the frustum of the cone whose smaller base is the area of the piston}}$$

A further explanation of the mathematics of this paper will be found in the Appendix.

०००००००

BERNOULLI

Hydrodynamica [1]

1. In the consideration of elastic fluids we may assign to them such a constitution as will be consistent with all their known properties, that so we may approach the study of their other properties, which have not yet been sufficiently investigated. The particular properties of elastic fluids are as follows: 1. They are heavy; 2. they expand in all directions unless they are restrained; and 3. they are continually more and more compressed when the force of compression increases. Air is a body of this sort, to which especially the present investigation pertains.

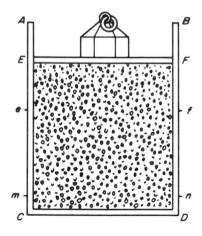

Fig. 7–1.

2. Consider a cylindrical vessel *ACDB* [Fig. 7–1] set vertically, and a movable piston *EF* in it, on which is placed a weight *P:* let the cavity *ECDF* contain very minute corpuscles, which are driven hither and thither

---

[1] From Daniel Bernoulli, *Hydrodynamica* (Basle: 1738) in *A Source Book of Physics,* trans. W. F. Magie (New York: McGraw-Hill, 1935), pp. 247–251.

with a very rapid motion; so that these corpuscles, when they strike against the piston *EF* and sustain it by their repeated impacts, form an elastic fluid which will expand of itself if the weight *P* is removed or diminished, which will be condensed if the weight is increased, and which gravitates toward the horizontal bottom *CD* just as if it were endowed with no elastic powers: for whether the corpuscles are at rest or are agitated they do not lose their weight, so that the bottom sustains not only the weight but the elasticity of the fluid. Such therefore is the fluid which we shall substitute for air. Its properties agree with those which we have already assumed for elastic fluids, and by them we shall explain other properties which have been found for air and shall point out others which have not yet been sufficiently considered.

3. We consider the corpuscles which are contained in the cylindrical cavity as practically infinite in number, and when they occupy the space *ECDF* we assume that they constitute ordinary air, to which as a standard all our measurements are to be referred: and so the weight *P* holding the piston in the position *EF* does not differ from the pressure [weight] of the superincumbent atmosphere, which therefore we shall designate by *P* in what follows.

It should be noticed that this pressure [weight] is not exactly equal to the absolute weight of a vertical cylinder of air resting on the piston *EF*, as hitherto most authors have asserted without sufficient consideration; rather it is equal to the fourth proportional to the surface of the earth, to the size of the piston *EF*, and to the weight of all the atmosphere on the surface of the earth.

4. We shall now investigate the weight π, which is sufficient to condense the air *ECDF* into the space *eCDf*, on the assumption that the velocity of the particles is the same in both conditions of the air, the natural condition as well as the condensed. Let $EC = 1$ and $eC = s$. When the piston *EF* is moved to *ef*, it appears that a greater effort is made by the fluid for two reasons: first, because the number of particles is now greater in the ratio of the space in which they are contained, and secondly, because each particle repeats its impacts more often. That we may properly calculate the increment which depends on the first cause we may consider the particles as if they were at rest. We shall set the number of them which are contiguous to the piston in the position $EF = n$; then the like number when the piston is in the position *ef* will be $= n : \left(\dfrac{eC}{EC}\right)^{\frac{2}{3}}$ or $= n : s^{\frac{2}{3}}$.

It should be noticed that the fluid is no more condensed in the lower part than in the upper part, because the weight *P* is infinitely greater than the weight of the fluid itself: hence it is plain that for this reason the force of the fluid is in the ratio of the numbers n and $n : s^{\frac{2}{3}}$ that is, as $s^{\frac{2}{3}}$ is to 1. Now in reference to the other increment arising from the second cause, this is found by considering the motion of the particles, and it appears that their impacts are made more often by as much as the particles are closer together: therefore the numbers of the impacts will be reciprocally as the mean distances between the surfaces of the particles, and these mean distances will be thus determined.

We assume that the particles are spheres. We represent by D the mean distance between the centers of the spheres when the piston is in the position EF, and by d the diameter of a sphere. Then the mean distance between the surfaces of the spheres will be $D - d$. But it is evident that when the piston is in the position ef, the mean distance between the centers of the spheres $= D\sqrt[3]{s}$ and therefore the mean distance between the surfaces of the spheres $= D\sqrt[3]{s} - d$. Therefore, with respect to the second cause, the force of the natural air in $ECDF$ will be to the force of the compressed air in $eCDf$ as $\dfrac{1}{D - d}$ to $\dfrac{1}{D\sqrt[3]{s} - d}$, or as $D\sqrt[3]{s} - d$ to $D - d$. When both causes are joined the predicted forces will be $s^{2/3} \times (D\sqrt[3]{s} - d)$ to $D - d$.

For the ratio of D to d we may substitute one which is easier to understand: for if we think of the piston EF as depressed by an infinite weight, so that it descends to the position mn, in which all the particles are in contact, and if we represent the line mC by m, we shall have D is to d as 1 is to $\sqrt[3]{m}$. If we substitute this in the ratio above, we shall find that the force of the natural air in $ECDF$ is to the force of the compressed air in $eCDf$ as $s^{2/3} \times (\sqrt[3]{s} - \sqrt[3]{m})$ is to $1 - \sqrt[3]{m}$, or as $s - \sqrt[3]{mss}$ is to $1 - \sqrt[3]{m}$. Therefore $\pi = \dfrac{1 - \sqrt[3]{m}}{s - \sqrt[3]{mss}} \times P$.

5. From all the facts known we may conclude that natural air can be very much condensed and compressed into a practically infinitely small space; so that we may set $m = 0$, and hence $\pi = P/s$; so that the compressing weights are almost in the inverse ratio of the spaces which air occupies when compressed by different amounts. This law has been proved by many experiments. It certainly may be safely adopted for air that is less dense than natural air; whether it holds for considerably denser air I have not sufficiently investigated: nor have there yet been experiments instituted with the accuracy which is necessary in this case. There is special need of an experiment to find the value of m, but this experiment must be most accurately carried out and with air under very high pressure; and the temperature of the air while it is being compressed must be carefully kept constant.

6. The elasticity of air is not only increased by condensation but by heat supplied to it, and since it is admitted that heat may be considered as an increasing internal motion of the particles, it follows that if the elasticity of air of which the volume does not change is increased, this indicates a more intense motion in the particles of air; which fits in well with our

hypothesis; for it is plain that so much the greater weight P is needed to keep the air in the condition *ECDF*, as the aerial particles are agitated by the greater velocity. It is not difficult to see that the weight P should be in the duplicate ratio of this velocity because, when the velocity increases, not only the number of impacts but also the intensity of each of them increases equally, and each of them is proportional to the weight P.

Therefore, if the velocity of the particles is called v, the weight which is able to sustain the piston in the position $EF = vvp$ and in the position

$$ef = \frac{1 - \sqrt[3]{m}}{s - \sqrt[3]{mss}} \times vvP,\ \text{or approximately} = \frac{vvP}{s},\ \text{because as we have seen}$$

the number m is very small in comparison with unity or with the number s.

7. This theorem, as I have presented it in the preceding paragraph, in which it is shown that in air of any density but at a fixed temperature, the elasticities are proportional to the densities, and further that the increments of elasticity which are produced by equal changes of temperature are proportional to the densities, this theorem, I say, D. Amontons discovered by experiment and presented it in the Memoirs of the Royal Academy of Sciences in Paris in 1702. . . .

APPENDIX

Explanation of Bernoulli's Mathematics

In Section 4, the ratio $n : s^{\frac{2}{3}}$ is given without deduction. Its validity may be shown as [illustrated by Figure 7–2].

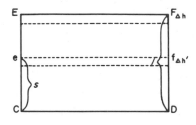

Fig. 7–2.

Let n be the number of particles in Δh all of which strike the under surface of the piston in time Δt. Then this number will be given by

$$n = \text{volume for impacts} \times \frac{\text{no. of particles}}{\text{unit volume}} = (A \cdot \Delta h) \cdot \rho$$

The number of particles n' that strike the piston in the same time interval Δt will be increased when the gas is compressed into the volume *efcd* because to obtain the increased pressure more particles strike it, the particle speed remaining the same. Thus

$$n' = A \cdot \Delta h' \cdot \rho'$$

But $\rho = \dfrac{\text{number of particles}}{A \cdot (EC)}$ and $\rho' = \dfrac{\text{number of particles}}{A \cdot s}$

Thus, $\rho'/\rho = \dfrac{EC}{s}$ or $\rho' = \rho \cdot \dfrac{EC}{s}$.

Substituting this result in the expression for n', we get

$$n' = A \cdot \Delta h' \cdot \rho \left(\frac{EC}{s}\right)$$

and dividing this expression by the previous one for n:

$$\frac{n'}{n} = \frac{A \cdot \Delta h' \cdot \rho}{A \cdot \Delta h \cdot \rho} \cdot \left(\frac{EC}{s}\right) = \frac{\Delta h'}{\Delta h} \cdot \left(\frac{EC}{s}\right)$$

$$n' = n \cdot \frac{(EC/s)}{\left(\dfrac{\Delta h}{\Delta h'}\right)} = n \cdot \frac{(EC/s)}{(EC/s)^{\frac{1}{3}}} = n \left(\frac{EC}{s}\right)^{\frac{2}{3}} = n/s^{\frac{2}{3}}$$

In this last result it was assumed that $\dfrac{\Delta h}{\Delta h'} = \left(\dfrac{EC}{s}\right)^{\frac{1}{3}}$. To obtain this result, one can at the same time demonstrate the contention in the second paragraph of this section that the mean distance between the center of the spheres in the compressed condition is $D\sqrt[3]{s}$. If r is the radius of the cylinder:

The original volume $= \pi r^2 \cdot 1 \sim D^3$

The compressed volume $= \pi r^2 \cdot s \sim D'^3$

$$\therefore s/1 = D'^3/D^3$$

Hence $\qquad D'^3 = D^3 \cdot s$

or $\qquad D' = D \cdot \sqrt[3]{s}$

accordingly $\qquad \Delta h' = \Delta h \cdot s^{\frac{1}{3}}$

8

ooooooooooo

THE ATOM AS A CENTER
OF FORCE

ooooooooooo

Roger Joseph Boscovich (1711-1787)

The early atomists seem, with few exceptions, to have pictured the atom as a very small, massive, and hard particle. Newton in his *Opticks* is explicit when he observed that ". . . it seems probable to me that God in the beginning formed matter in solid, massy, hard, impenetrable, moveable particles. . . ." Certainly many of the atomists who lived after him adopted this picture, and the "little billiard ball atom," as one might call it, seemed prevalent in the minds of the early chemists as well as those who developed the kinetic theory of gases. But this idea clearly was not universally held, for the picture originated by Roger Joseph Boscovich and presented in his *Theory of Natural Philosophy,* first published in 1758, is entirely different.

Boscovich was one of the early supporters of Newtonian ideas in Italy. His interest in atomic ideas seems to have followed from his study of Newton's mechanics, specifically those of collision. If one imagines that atoms are hard spheres, which are homogenous (being without parts) and incompressible, then a dilemma is raised if one imagines collisions between them. Since they cannot deform, they must in general suffer an instantaneous change of velocity in collision. But, says Boscovich, this violates the law of continuity which must be observed. Accordingly, atoms cannot be hard, rigid, massive spheres and some other model must be sought.

On the basis that atoms cannot come into contact Boscovich builds up a picture consisting of point centers having position and mass but no extension. In order to account for the physical behavior of bodies com-

117

posed of atoms he assumed that at large distances atoms attract according to the gravitational forces postulated by Newton. As one atom approaches another at distances smaller than those appropriate to Newtonian attraction, the attractive force at first increases then decreases to zero, becomes a repulsion which increases and then decreases to zero, then an attraction, and so on. These alternating attractions and repulsions exist as spheres of force around an atom, and it is only when very close approach is involved that the force becomes asymptotically repulsive. A schematic plot of the magnitude of the force at various distances from the "point atom" is included in the following excerpt from Boscovich's theory.

The number of these spheres of attraction and repulsion is not specified but the necessity for this alternation of force arose from the need to explain certain physical actions, such as cohesion and vaporization, as well as chemical actions. In the instance of the vaporization of liquids, let us imagine that the atoms in the liquid are very close together. Then an attempt to compress the liquid brings into play the asymptotic repulsion of the atoms and the volume cannot be much reduced even with very large forces of compression. On the other hand, if actions (such as heating) occur to increase the distance between the atoms, cohesion or attraction comes into play and acts until the distance becomes too great, when it falls to zero. To account for atoms of vapor, a repulsion is assumed that takes place when the distance between atoms is sufficiently great. Thus, the atoms can exist as vapor, and in the vapor phase we recognize that they exert a pressure. This pressure, according to Boscovich, is a consequence of the mutual repulsion of the vapor particles. Finally, if the distance grows larger, the force of universal gravitation exerts an attraction.

Using the alternating attraction and repulsion forces, it was possible to account in a qualitative way for the melting and boiling points in a given substance, as well as for the differences in these temperatures for various materials. The explanation of crystalline forms also followed; whereas, with the hypothesis of a spherical, hard atom, in an atmosphere of repelling caloric, how could a given substance be assumed to display a given crystalline form rather than an amorphous one? Or if such structures were possible, why did a substance always show the same crystalline form? Indeed, how did chemical reactions take place at all in this picture of hard, spherical atoms? Evidently other *ad hoc* assumptions were needed. But with the Boscovichian atom, reactions occurred when the atoms' force fields meshed so as to produce a resultant attraction. That some compounds were more stable than others depended on the strength of the force fields involved. These few examples illustrate the qualitative attractiveness of Boscovich's theory—a theory that is now hardly known but one that in the nineteenth century enjoyed a considerable vogue. Both

Davy and Faraday, especially the latter, were more sympathetic to the atomic theory in this form—the atom as a seat of forces—than to the Daltonian picture.

Boscovich himself had an interesting history. He was born in Dubrovnik, Yugoslavia (then Ragusa), on May 18, 1711. His father and grandfather were merchants; his mother Pava Bettera, who came from a cultivated Italian merchant family, had the hardihood to live to the astonishing (in that day at least) age of one hundred and three years. The family were serious and pious Roman Catholics. Roger was the eighth of nine children and the youngest of six sons. At about the age of eight, he was enrolled in Ragusa's Jesuit College. Then, in September 1725, when just over fourteen, he was sent to Rome to begin studies for the priesthood. After two years as a novitiate, he entered the Collegium Romanum. He distinguished himself in mathematics, physics, and astronomy, and was one of the first to advocate Newtonian ideas in Italy. He began teaching in 1732 while carrying forward research in astronomy. He published his first paper in 1736 on the determination of the sun's equator and the period of the sun's rotation. Other papers followed on various subjects, including the shape of the earth, and the aberration of the fixed stars. In 1740, at the age of twenty-nine, he was appointed to the chair of mathematics at the Collegium Romanum. It was not until 1744, however, that he took his vows as a priest and was made a full member of the Society of Jesus. Following his ordination at thirty-three, he spent fourteen years as a teacher and scholar. His scientific papers, the mapping of the Papal States, the figure of the earth, the confirmation of Bradley's theory of the aberration of light, and his own reputation as a brilliant intellect earned him admission to scientific societies all over Europe. But Boscovich had other than scholarly sides to his character; his ability as a poet as well as a scientist gave him entrée to an active social life in the highest ecclesiastical, academic, and diplomatic circles. He became, it appears, something of a social climber and a snob. It was in the capacity of a scholar-diplomat that he was sent to Vienna in 1757. There between April and the following February of 1758 Boscovich wrote his *Theoria Philosophiæ Naturalis,* a work that had been maturing during the previous twelve years. It developed atomic theory, as described above, from a completely new point of view, placing attention on the fields of force around the atom rather than on the atom itself. Some sections from the *Theoria* describing this point of view are given following this biography.

After returning to Rome, Boscovich was again sent on a long tour of Europe beginning in 1759. The reason for this journey is not clear but he was away from Rome for over four years. The first part of this tour was spent in Paris and London, where he arrived in May 1760. Here he was introduced to many of the outstanding personages of the era, attended several meetings of the Royal Society, met Benjamin Franklin, and saw him demonstrate electrical experiments. He also visited Oxford and Cambridge. His impression on the members of the Royal Society was such that he was elected a foreign fellow, but not until after his departure in December 1760. After leaving England he traveled on the Continent and journeyed as far as Constantinople, returning to Rome in 1763. He was then fifty-two years old, and he was soon to realize that the star of his success had passed its zenith. Whether in the meantime his *Theoria* had caused his superiors to view him with suspicion or whether his absence had been so long as to demand a replacement is not clear; at any rate his professorship was no longer open to him. However, in the Seminarium Romanum he was free to continue his studies and his research. In 1764 he accepted the chair of mathematics in the University of Pavia, which under the Austrian government was then in a very backward state. He remained at Pavia until 1769 when he was transferred to the Scuola Palatina in Milan. Also situated in this city was the Jesuit College of Santa Maria de Brera for which Boscovich had designed an observatory during his stay at Pavia and at which he became, in addition to his duties at the Scuola Palatina, a lecturer in astronomy. Boscovich's prominence as an emissary of the Vatican, coupled with his sense of importance derived from his academic honors all over Europe, his social connections with the nobility, and his proprietary feeling concerning the Brera Observatory soon brought him into impossible relations with his colleagues. In August 1772, during an absence on vacation, he was dismissed from his post at the observatory. He then went to Venice from which he sent his resignation the following year. Much of his own money had been spent for instruments at the observatory, and his financial situation was now precarious. Added to this misfortune, pressure against the whole Jesuit order had been growing for years all over Europe and was then coming to a head. On June 8, 1773, Pope Clement XIV signed an order suppressing the society. Boscovich was then sixty-two years old, and his future must have appeared exceedingly dark. Fortunately, powerful friends in France were able to persuade King Louis XV to create a special post for him in the French Navy as Director of Naval Optics. Despite Louis's death the following year, the post was confirmed by his successor, Louis XVI. Protected by the great and powerful whom he so successfully cultivated, Boscovich remained in Paris for nine years until July 1782. Then, for reasons of health and his desire to prepare his collected works for publication, he took leave of his post and returned to Italy. There in various places in northern Italy he was able to complete his editing in the next three years. In the fall of 1786, he began to show signs of mental disturbance which developed into pathological melancholia. Saved from an attempted suicide he lived on in mental confusion until February 13, 1787, when a series of complications ended his life.

০০০০০০০

BOSCOVICH

A Theory of Natural Philosophy . . .[1]

PART I

IN THE FIRST SIX ARTICLES, I state the time at which I evolved my Theory, what led me to it, & where I have discussed it hitherto in essays already published: also what it has in common with the theories of Leibniz and Newton; in what it differs from either of these, & in what it is really superior to them both. In addition I state what I have published elsewhere about equilibrium & the centre of oscillation; & how, having found out that these matters followed quite easily from a single theorem of the most simple & elegant kind, I proposed to write a short essay thereon; but when I set to work to deduce the matter from this principle, the discussion, quite unexpectedly to me, developed into a whole work of considerable magnitude.

From this until Art. 11, I explain the Theory itself: that matter is unchangeable, and consists of points that are perfectly simple, indivisible, of no extent, & separated from one another; that each of these points has a property of inertia, & in addition a mutual active force depending on the distance in such a way that, if the distance is given, both the magnitude & the direction of this force are given; but if the distance is altered, so also is the force altered; & if the distance is diminished indefinitely, the force is repulsive, & in fact also increases indefinitely; whilst if the distance is increased, the force will be diminished, vanish, be changed to an attractive force that first of all increases, then decreases, vanishes, is again turned into a repulsive force, & so on many times over; until at greater distances it finally becomes an attractive force that decreases approximately in the inverse ratio of the squares of the distances. This connection between the forces & distances, & their passing

---

[1] Roger Joseph Boscovich, *A Theory of Natural Philosophy* (Venice: 1763), trans. J. M. Child (Chicago and London: Open Court Publishing Co., 1922), p. 36.

from positive to negative, or from repulsive to attractive, & conversely, I illustrate by the force with which the two ends of a spring strive to approach towards, or recede from, one another, according as they are pulled apart, or drawn together, by more than the natural amount.

From here on to Art. 16 I show that it is not merely an aggregate of forces combined haphazard, but that it is represented by a single continuous curve, by means of abscissæ representing the distances & ordinates representing the forces. I expound the construction & nature of this curve; & I show how it differs from the hyperbola of the third degree which represents Newtonian gravitation. Finally, here too I set forth the scope of the whole work & the nature of the parts into which it is divided.

These statements having been made, I start to expound the whole of the analysis, by which I came upon a Theory of this kind, & from which I believe I have deduced the whole of it by a straightforward & perfectly rigorous chain of reasoning. I contend indeed, from here on until Art. 19, that, in the collision of solid bodies, either there must be compenetration, or the Law of Continuity must be violated by a sudden change of velocity, if the bodies come into immediate contact with unequal velocities. Now since the Law of Continuity must (as I prove that it must) be observed in every case, I infer that, before the bodies reach the point of actual contact, their velocities must be altered by some force which is capable of destroying the velocity, or the difference of the velocities, no matter how great that may be.

From Art. 19 to Art. 28 I consider the artifice, adopted for the purpose of evading the strength of my argument by those who deny the existence of hard bodies; as a matter of fact this cannot be used as an argument against me by the Newtonians, or the Corpuscularians in general, for they assume that the elementary particles of solids are perfectly hard. Moreover, those who admit that all the particles of solids, however small they may be, are soft or elastic, yet do not escape the difficulty, but transfer it to prime surfaces, or points; & here a sudden change would be made & the Law of Continuity violated. . . .

7. The primary elements of matter are in my opinion perfectly indivisible & non-extended points; they are so scattered in an immense vacuum that every two of them are separated from one another by a definite interval; this interval can be indefinitely increased or diminished, but can never vanish altogether without compenetration of the points themselves; for I do not admit as possible any immediate contact between them. On the contrary I consider that it is a certainty that, if the distance between two points of matter should become absolutely nothing, then the very same indivisible point of space, according to the usual idea of it, must be occupied by both together, & we have true compenetration in every way. Therefore indeed I do not admit the idea of vacuum inter-

spersed amongst matter, but I consider that matter is interspersed in a vacuum & floats in it.

8. As an attribute of these points I admit an inherent propensity to remain in the same state of rest, or of uniform motion in a straight line, (*a*) in which they are initially set, if each exists by itself in Nature. . . .

9. I therefore consider that any two points of matter are subject to a determination to approach one another at some distances, & in an equal degree recede from one another at other distances. This determination I call 'force'; in the first case 'attractive', in the second case 'repulsive'; this term does not denote the mode of action, but the propensity itself, whatever its origin, of which the magnitude changes as the distances change; this is in accordance with a certain definite law, which can be represented by a geometrical curve or by an algebraical formula, & visualized in the manner customary with Mechanicians. We have an example of a force dependent on distance, & varying with varying distance, & pertaining to all distances either great or small, throughout the vastness of space, in the Newtonian idea of general gravitation that changes according to the inverse squares of the distances: this, on account of the law governing it, can never pass from positive to negative; & thus on no occasion does it pass from being attractive to being repulsive, i.e., from a propensity to approach to a propensity to recession. Further, in bent springs we have an illustration of that kind of mutual force that varies according as the distance varies, & passes from a propensity to recession to a propensity to approach, and vice versa. For here, if the two ends of the spring approach one another on compressing the spring, they acquire a propensity for recession that is the greater, the more the distance diminishes between them as the spring is compressed. But, if the distance between the ends is increased, the force of recession is diminished, until at a certain distance it vanishes and becomes absolutely nothing. Then, if the distance is still further increased, there begins a propensity to approach, which increases more & more as the ends recede further & further away from one another. If now, on the contrary, the distance between the ends is continually diminished, the propensity to approach also diminishes, vanishes, & becomes changed into a propensity to recession. . . .

10. Now the law of forces is of this kind; the forces are repulsive at very small distances, & become indefinitely greater & greater, as the distances are diminished indefinitely, in such a manner that they are capable of destroying any velocity, no matter how large it may be, with which one point may approach another, before ever the distance between them vanishes. When the distance between them is increased, they are

diminished in such a way that at a certain distance, which is extremely small, the force becomes nothing. Then as the distance is still further increased, the forces are changed to attractive forces; these at first increase, then diminish, vanish, & become repulsive forces, which in the same way first increase, then diminish, vanish, & become once more attractive; & so on, in turn, for a very great number of distances, which are all still very minute: until, finally, when we get to comparatively great distances, they begin to be continually attractive & approximately inversely proportional to the squares of the distances. This holds good as the distances are increased indefinitely to any extent, or at any rate until we get to distances that are far greater than all the distances of the planets and comets [see Fig. 8–1].

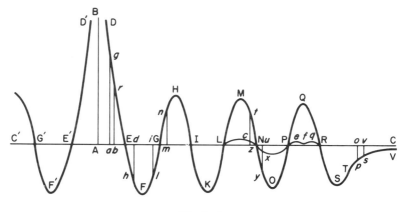

Fig. 8–1.

78. First of all, the gravitation of all bodies towards the Earth, which is an everyday experience, proves sufficiently that the repulsion that we found for very small distances does not extend to all distances; but that at distances that are now great there is a propensity for approach, which we have called an attractive force. Moreover the Keplerian Laws in astronomy, so skilfully employed by Newton to deduce the law of universal gravitation, & applied even to the comets, show perfectly well that gravitation extends, either to infinity or at least to the limits of the system including all the planets & comets, in the inverse ratio of the squares of the distances. Hence the curve will have an arc lying on the opposite side of the axis, which, as far as can be perceived by our senses, approximates to that hyperbola of the third degree, of which the ordinates are in the inverse ratio of the squares of the distances; & this indeed is the arc STV in Fig. 8–1. Now from this it is evident that there is some point E, in which a curve of this kind cuts the axis; and this is a limit-point for at-

tractions and repulsions, at which the passage from one to the other of these forces is made.

79. The phenomenon of vapour arising from water, & that of gas produced from fixed bodies lead us to admit two more of these limit-points, i.e., two other intersections, say, at G & I. Since in these there would be initially no repulsion, nay rather there would be an attraction due to cohesion, by which, when one part is retracted, another generally followed it: & since in the former, repulsion is clearly evidenced by the greatness of the expansion, & by the force of its elasticity; it therefore follows that there is, somewhere or other, a passage from repulsion at very small distances to attraction, then back again to repulsion, & from that back once more to the attractions of universal gravitation. Effervescences & fermentations of many different kinds, in which the particles go & return with as many different velocities, & now approach towards & now recede from one another, certainly indicate many more of these limit-points & transitions. But the existence of these limit-points is perfectly proved by the case of soft substances like wax; for in these substances a large number of compressions are acquired with very different distances, yet in all of these there must be limit-points. For, if the front part is drawn out, the part behind will follow; or if the former is pushed inwards, the latter will recede from it, the distances remaining approximately unchanged. This, on account of the repulsions existing at very small distances, which prevent contiguity, cannot take place in any way, unless there are limit-points there in all those distances between attractions & repulsions; namely, those that are requisite to account for the fact that one part will follow the other when the latter is drawn out, & will recede in front of the latter when that is pushed in.

80. Therefore there are a large number of limit-points, & a large number of flexures on the curve, first on one side & then on the other side of the axis, in addition to two arcs, one of which, ED, is continued to infinity & is asymptotic, & the other, STV, is asymptotic also, provided that universal gravitation extends to infinity. It approximates to the form of the hyperbola of the third degree mentioned above so closely that the difference from it is imperceptible; but it cannot altogether coincide with it, because, in that case it would never depart from it. For, of two curves of different nature, there cannot be any continuous arcs, no matter how short, that absolutely coincide; they can only cut, or touch, or osculate one another in an indefinitely great number of points, & approximate to one another indefinitely closely. Thus we now have the whole form of the curve of forces, of the nature that I gave at the commencement, derived by a straightforward chain of reasoning from natural phenomena,

& sound principles. It only remains for us now to determine the constitution of the primary elements of matter, derived from these forces; & in this manner the whole of the Theory that I enunciated at the start will become quite clear, & it will not appear to be a mere arbitrary hypothesis. We can proceed to remove certain apparent difficulties, & to apply it with great profit to the whole of Physics in general, explaining some things fully &, to prevent the work from growing to an unreasonable size, merely mentioning others.

81. Now, because the repulsive force is indefinitely increased when the distances are indefinitely diminished, it is quite easy to see clearly that no part of matter can be contiguous to any other part; for the repulsive force would at once separate one from the other. Therefore it necessarily follows that the primary elements of matter are perfectly simple, & that they are not composed of any parts contiguous to one another. This is an immediate & necessary deduction from the constitution of the forces, which are repulsive at very small distances & increase indefinitely.

102. There are indeed certain things that relate to the law of forces of which we are altogether ignorant, such as the number & distances of the intersections of the curve with the axis, the shape of the intervening arcs, & other things of that sort; these indeed far surpass human understanding, & He alone, Who founded the universe, had the whole before His eyes. But truly there is no reason on that account, why a thing, whose existence we fully recognize, & many of the properties & results of which are readily understood, should not be accepted; although certainly there do remain many other things pertaining to it that are unknown to us. For instance, nobody would call gold an unknown & mysterious substance, & still less would deny its existence, simply because it is quite probable that many of its properties are unknown to us, to be discovered perhaps in the future, as so many others have been already discovered from time to time, or because it is not visually apparent what is the texture of the particles composing it, or why & in what way Nature adopts that particular composition. Again, as regards action at a distance, we amply guard against this by the same means; for, if this is admitted, then it would be possible for any point to act upon itself, & to be determined as to its direction of action & energy apart from another point, or that God should produce in either point a motion according to some arbitrary law fixed by Him when founding the universe. To my mind indeed it is clear that motions produced by these forces depending on the distances are not a whit more mysterious, involved or difficult of understanding than the production of motion by immediate impulse as it is usually accepted; in which impenetrability determines the motion, & the latter has to be derived just

the same either from the nature of solid bodies, or from an arbitrary law of the founder of the universe.

450. Now those things, which are commonly called the Elements, Earth, Water, Air & Fire, are nothing else in my Theory but different solids & fluids, formed of the same homogeneous points differently arranged; & from the admixture of these with others, other still more compound bodies are produced. Indeed Earth consists of particles that are not connected together by any force; & these particles acquire solidity when mixed with other particles, as ashes when mixed with oils; or even by some change in their internal arrangement, such as comes about in vitrification; we will leave the discussion of the manner in which these transformations take place till the end. Water is a liquid fluid devoid of elasticity such as comes within the scope of the senses through a sensible compression; although there is a strong repulsive force exerted between its particles, which is sufficient to sustain the pressure of an external force or of its own weight without sensible diminution of the distances. Air is an elastic fluid, which in all probability consists of particles of very many different sorts; for it is generated from very many totally different fixed bodies, as we shall see when we discuss transformations. For that reason, it contains a very large number of vapours & exhalations, & heterogeneous corpuscles that float in it. Its particles, however, repel one another with a fairly large force; & this repulsive force of the particles lasts for a long while as the distances are diminished, & pertains to a space that bears a very large ratio to the so much smaller distance, to which it can be reduced by compression; & at this distance too the force still increases, the arc of the curve corresponding to it still receding from the axis. But after that, the curve must return very steeply, so that in the neighbourhood of the next limit-point there may yet be had in the space that remains great variations in the arcs & the limit-points. Further such great extension of the repulsive arc is indicated by the great compression induced by the pressure due to a large force; & this, in order that the compression may be proportional to the impressed force, shows, as we pointed out in Art. 352, that there must be repulsive forces inversely proportional to the distances of the particles from one another. Moreover it can pass into & through a fixed & solid body; & the reason of this also I will state when I deal with transformations towards the end. Fire is also a highly elastic fluid, which is agitated by the most vigorous internal motions; it excites fermentations, or even consists of this very fermentation; it emits light. . . .

451. The principles of chemical operations are derived from the same source, namely, from the distinctions between particles; some of these being inert with regard to themselves & in combination with certain others,

some attract others to themselves, some repel others continuously through a fairly great interval; & the attraction itself with some is greater, & with others is less, until when the distance is sufficiently increased it becomes practically nothing. Further, some of them with respect to others have a very great alternation of forces; & this can vary if the structure is changed slightly, or if the particles are grouped & intermingled with others; in this case there follows another law of forces for the compound particles, which is different to that which we saw obeyed by the simple particles. If all these things are kept carefully in view, I really think that there can be found in this Theory the general theory for all chemical operations.

9

ooooooooooo

ATOMIC CHEMISTRY
BEFORE DALTON

ooooooooooo

Bryan Higgins (1737-1820)
William Higgins (1769-1825)

Not everyone familiar with atomic science knows that the chemical atomic theory, i.e., that elementary substances in a chemical reaction combine atom with atom, was proposed by others before Dalton. The first proponent of such a theory appears to have been an Irish chemist and teacher of chemistry working in London, Bryan Higgins. The second was his nephew William Higgins. Because it is sometimes claimed that Dalton has received credit that rightfully should go to the Higginses, it is necessary to summarize their contributions so that the reader may be able to make a judgment for himself.

Bryan Higgins' ideas were formulated in four publications: "Syllabus of Chemical and Philosophical Inquiries" (1775), "A Philosophical Essay Concerning Light" (1776), "Experiments and Observations Relating to Acetous Acid, etc." (1786), and "Minutes of a Society for Philosophical Experiments and Conversations" (1795). The atomic theory developed in these works has been summed up by Professor J. R. Partington, as follows:

1. There are seven elements—earth, air, water [the elements of the ancients to which Higgins added] acid, alkali, phlogiston and light. Fire [the fourth element of the ancients] Higgins assumed to be a compound of phlogiston and light.

129

2. Atoms of the elements are all hard, and completely spherical or nearly so.

3. Atoms attract one another by forces depending on distance and polarity. The forces between atoms are dependent on the inverse nth power of the distance between them, i.e., force $= f \left(\dfrac{1}{r^n} \right)$.

4. Fire pervades all bodies and gives effects opposed to attraction.

5. Gases are produced by the addition of fire to solids and liquids.

6. Combination in definite proportions ("saturation") is an effect of attractive and repulsive forces.

7. Molecules of binary compounds always contain one atom of each constituent.

8. Particles in gases are surrounded by repelling atmospheres of fire. In chemical combination these atmospheres must be broken or blended.[1]

A comparison with Dalton's atomic ideas shows some points of similarity, i.e., spherical atoms, gaseous particles separated by a repelling atmosphere of fire (heat), and combination in definite proportions. The first two—spherical atoms and gaseous particles separated by a repelling atmosphere of fire—represent more or less general thinking of atomists of the time. The third is a consequence of the assumption of atomic combination. As Dalton read very little of the work of others, there seems to be little reason to suppose that he knew about these ideas.

The details of chemical reaction imagined by Higgins will not be elaborated upon, his theory shows considerable ingenuity and his work reflects the influence of Newton's ideas. According to Partington, "the explanation of combination in definitive proportions ('saturation') in terms of attractive and especially repulsive forces between the atoms is the first example of the application of the Newtonian theory to chemical changes."[2]

---

[1] J. R. Partington, *Annals of Science*, 4 (1939), 269 [not a direct quote—Editors].

[2] *Ibid.*, p. 272.

○○○○○○○

PARTINGTON

William Higgins [3]

ALTHOUGH LITTLE NOTICE WAS TAKEN of Bryan Higgins, the same cannot be said of his nephew William Higgins, who has repeatedly been proclaimed as an anticipator of Dalton since his work was brought into notice by Davy in 1810–12.

William Higgins, born in Sligo in 1768 (?), died in Dublin in 1825, was educated at Pembroke College, Oxford, where he was an "operator" to Beddoes. In 1791 he became chemist to the Apothecaries' Company in Dublin and in 1795 Librarian to the Royal Dublin Society, where he held a kind of professorship. His views are set out in an interesting book, *A Comparative View of the Phlogistic [4] and Antiphlogistic Theories,* published in 1789 and again in 1791, bearing on the title-page the very appropriate quotation from Horace: *Est quodam podire tenus, si non datur ultra,* which curiously enough also embellishes the title-page of Dalton's first book, *Meteorological Observations and Essays,* published in 1793. Higgins's book is essentially a detailed refutation of the *Essay of Phlogiston* of his patron Richard Kirwan, published in 1787 with refutations by Lavoisier and his colleagues, this being the edition referred to by Higgins. Higgins's book is thus probably the first English work in which the Antiphlogistic doctrine is openly defended, and as such is of great historical interest. The atomic speculations in it are introduced only as an additional weapon to attack phlogiston and for this reason probably attracted less notice than they would have done in an essay devoted to atomic theory alone. Higgins himself does not seem then to have recognized that they were of wider interest. Of the several references to the theory it will be possible to refer only to one or two, which exhibit all the essential points of his arguments and do full justice to Higgins.

He assumes that the "ultimate particles " (his usual name for atoms) of sulphur and oxygen are equal in weight from the composition of sulphur

---

[3] *Ibid.,* pp. 272–274.

[4] "Phlogiston" was the name given to the so-called "burning principle." When a substance burned, phlogiston was assumed to be given off into the air—Editors.

dioxide, and that the ultimate particles of nitrogen and oxygen are also equal in weight, from the densities of the two gases. In cases where the densities of gases at the same temperature and pressure are very different, he still assumes that the ultimate particles are equal in weight, because the particles are at different distances in the gases, owing to the atmospheres of fire which he assumes (with Bryan Higgins) to surround the particles. Thus,

> the gravitating particles of nitrous air [NO] are thrice the distance from each other that the ultimate particles of dephlogisticated air are in the same temperature, and of course their atmospheres of fire must be in size proportionable.

This idea he owed to Austin, with whom Higgins collaborated in his experiments. This assumption of equal weights of atoms is maintained by Higgins even in 1814, when he is trying to establish his priority of Dalton, and it is especially to be noted that Higgins assumes equality in weight of the atoms in the only three cases where he makes specific reference to this matter, viz. for oxygen, sulphur and nitrogen, and there is thus more than a little justification for the statement of Roscoe and Schorlemmer that

> all previous upholders of an atomic theory, including even Higgins, had assumed that the relative weights of the atoms of the various elements are the same.

Meldrum has criticized his statement, and refers to the only passage to be found in Higgins's book which might suggest that he considered atoms to have different weights, viz. when he says that 100 grains of tin may combine with 7½ or 15 grains of oxygen (the correct figures are 13½ and 27), but although this shows that Higgins had a clear idea of multiple proportions, it seems that he never had any clear idea of suggesting that each element has an atom of definite weight different from those of atoms of other elements. This conclusion is in agreement with the impression received by older readers of Higgins.

William Higgins in his explanation of "saturation" (*i.e.* combination in definite proportions) extended the theory of Bryan Higgins to cover cases of combination of two elements in more than one proportion, which was clearly proved in the compounds of sulphur and of nitrogen with oxygen. In doing this, he hardly mentions the repulsive force, which was the most important for Bryan Higgins, and emphasizes only the attractions. Davy had already pointed out that many ideas of William Higgins had been anticipated by Bryan Higgins in 1786 (actually in 1775) and, as these were known to William Higgins, it is very difficult not to allow the merits of prior conception, as well as of very ingenious illustration, to the elder writer.

ooooooo

Several cases of atomic combination are schematically diagramed in the excerpt below taken from Higgins' book. The simplest case consists of the union of two atoms labeled *P* and *a*. Suppose *P* to be an "ultimate particle (atom) of phlogisticated air which attracts dephlogisticated air with a force of 3." And, says Higgins, assume that *a* is a particle of dephlogisticated air which attracts *P* with a force of 3 *more*. In order to understand this situation it is necessary to ask initially what the 3-unit force exerted by *P* acts on. If it acts on *a*, then by the principle of action and reaction *a must* pull on *P* with a force of 3 units. Thus, the statement that *a* acts on *P* with a force of 3 *more* seems meaningless, as does the conclusion that they will "unite with a force of 6."

The origin or nature of the forces is also unspecified. If they were seen as central forces, i.e., gravitational forces as hinted in the last example, they would vary inversely as the square of the distance between atomic centers, but there is no indication of this. If the atoms are hard spheres (in conformity with the expressed ideas of Bryan Higgins) then we might assume that chemical combination would put the atomic spheres in contact. Assuming contact and atoms of equal size, the distance between the centers of all the atoms would be alike, at least until combinations were considered involving more than six atoms with the one under consideration. But the idea of central forces is ruled out by Higgins' discussion of all cases in which *P*, the atom under consideration, unites with two or more others. The force of attraction exerted by *P*, 3 units, Higgins imagines split equally between *a* and *b*. The atoms *a* and *b* in turn each exert a unilateral force on *P*, making the force between *P* and *a* and *P* and *b* each 4½ units. The division of the force *P* is impossible on the basis of a central force model; the force would be of magnitude 3 on *all* the atoms at the same distance. Regardless of the model, the requirement of action and reaction would not allow the force between particles to be 4½. The same erroneous method is used in all the examples. None of these ideas occurs in Dalton's atomic theory, so that it seems improbable that Dalton knew of Higgins' theory.

The parallels between Higgins' and Dalton's atomic theories were first brought to the attention of the scientific world in November of 1810, when Davy discussed them in his Bakerian lecture of that year. Davy's standing was such that it at once publicized Higgins throughout Europe and set off a long controversy between the two rival theorists; the inevitable suggestion arose that Dalton was guilty of plagiarism. Dalton's prior claims were strongly supported by Dr. Thomas Thomson, chemist and editor of the *Annals of Philosophy,* by Dr. W. C. Henry, and by a succession of Manchester chemists, including Angus Smith, Roscoe and Schorlemmer.

Considering that Dalton read very little, that he had a limited acquaintance with chemists, and that his theory began as a *physical* theory connected with the diffusion of gases and the mutual interaction of mixed gases in the atmosphere, it seems unlikely that he knew of Higgins' work before Davy's announcement in 1810. This was affirmed later by many of Dalton's friends.

While it must be admitted that Higgins' idea of atomic combination in chemical reactions predated Dalton's, the credit for a scientific discovery goes to the investigator who gives it a solid foundation and brings it to the scientific world on this basis. In the opinion of his contemporaries, William Higgins failed to do this. Consequently, Davy, who called him to the attention of scientists in 1810, passed this severe judgment on Higgins at his death in 1825:

> It is impossible not to regret that he did not establish principles which belong to the highest department of chemistry, and that he suffered so fertile and promising a field to be entirely cultivated by others; for though possessed of great means of improving chemistry, he did little or nothing during the last thirty years of his life.[5]

 o o o o o o o o

WILLIAM HIGGINS

A Comparative View of Phlogistic and Antiphlogistic Theories [6]

IN MY OPINION, THE PUREST nitrous [nitric] acid contains 5 of dephlogisticated to 1 of phlogisticated air. Nitrous air [NO], according to Kirwan, contains 2 of dephlogisticated to 1 of phlogisticated air. According to Lavoisier, 100 gr. of nitrous air contains 32 gr. of

---

[5] Sir Humphry Davy, "Annual Address to the Royal Society" (*Ca.* 1825).
[6] William Higgins, *A Comparative View of Phlogistic and Antiphlogistic Theories* (London: 1789).

phlogisticated air, and 68 of dephlogisticated air. I am myself of the former philosopher's opinion. I am likewise of the opinion, that every primary particle of phlogisticated air is united to two of dephlogisticated air, and that these molecules are surrounded with one common atmosphere of fire.

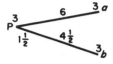

Fig. 9–1.

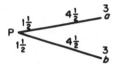

Fig. 9–2.

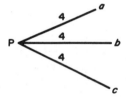

Fig. 9–3.

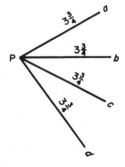

Fig. 9–4.

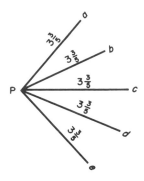

Fig. 9–5.

To render this more explicable, let us suppose P to be an ultimate particle of phlogisticated air, which attracts dephlogisticated air with the force of 3; let *a* be a particle of dephlogisticated air, whose attraction to P we will suppose to be 3 more, by which they unite with the force of 6; the nature of this compound will be hereinafter explained. [See Figure 9–1.]

Let us consider this to be the utmost force that can subsist between dephlogisticated and phlogisticated air. Let us suppose another particle of dephlogisticated air *b* [see Figure 9–2] to unite to P, they will not unite with the force of 6, but with the force of $4\frac{1}{2}$; that is, the whole power of P, which is but 3, will be equally divided and directed in two points towards *a* and *b;* so that P and *a b* will unite with the forces annexed to them; for the attraction of *a* and *b* to P meeting with no interruption, will suffer no diminution. This I consider to be the true state of nitrous air. Let us now suppose another particle of dephlogisticated air *c* [see Figure 9–3] to unite to P, it will combine only with the force of 4, whereby *a b c* and P will gravitate toward one another. Such is the state of the red nitrous vapour, or the red nitrous acid.

Let us again suppose a fourth particle of dephlogisticated air *d* [see Figure 9–4] to combine with P, it will unite only with a force of $3\frac{3}{4}$. This I think is the state of the pale or straw coloured nitrous acid.

Lastly, let us suppose a fifth particle of dephlogisticated air *e* [see Figure 9–5] to unite to P, it will combine with the force of $3\frac{3}{5}$, so that *a b c d* and *e* will each gravitate towards P as their common centre of gravity. This is the most perfect state of colourless nitrous [nitric] acid; and in my opinion no more dephlogisticated air can unite to the phlogisticated air, as having its whole force of attraction expended on the particles of dephlogisticated air, *a b c d e*. This illustrates the nature of saturation.

THE FOUNDATIONS
OF ATOMIC CHEMISTRY

ooooooooooo

10

○○○○○○○○○○○

THE BIRTH
OF ATOMIC THEORY

○○○○○○○○○○○

John Dalton (1766-1844)

It is a sobering thought that two thousand years of atomic speculation produced no mind able to formulate atomic theory in questions simple enough for direct experimental answers. Even Newton's derivation of Boyle's law on the assumption of gas particles that repelled each other with a force decreasing inversely as the distance and, some half century later, Daniel Bernoulli's brilliant deduction of the same law on a kinetic particle hypothesis opened no doors to the world of the atom. It would be logical to expect that if the greatest minds of two millennia had found no way to question nature in atomic terms, only a demigod might be expected to see where mortals were blind. But no demigod appeared. Instead, the fates sent an unprepossessing country schoolmaster of silent mien and uncouth manners, who, in a chance flash of revelation, caught a glimpse of an open door and passed through.

John Dalton came into this world on September 5, 1766, the son of a poverty-stricken weaver in Eaglesfield, Cumberland County, a shire in the north of England. When it came time, the boy was sent to what was known as the Pardshaw Hall School, near his village, where his formal education continued through his eleventh year. At that time the master, a Mr. John Fletcher, resigned, and Dalton himself reopened the school first in his own home and then in the local Friends' Meeting House. How anyone could entrust a boy twelve years old with the regular teaching of his contemporaries boggles the imagination. Had he been thrust into this position because of outstanding brilliance, we could wonder somewhat less, but Dalton was never characterized in these terms. We can only surmise that

139

the dogged perseverance, insensitive self-reliance, and patient concentration that marked his adult years had already attracted his elders' attention.

After two years as a schoolmaster and one of farming, Dalton, then only fifteen, left home to join his brother Jonathan and a cousin in Kendal, about 40 miles to the south, where they conducted a school for the children of the Friends. During the next twelve years (1781–1793) he taught and studied. In the latter eight years of this period he laid the foundation for his future discoveries through a fortunate friendship with John Gough, an impressive and remarkable young man, some ten years Dalton's senior. Although handicapped by blindness from infancy, Gough possessed those qualities that Dalton lacked: brilliance of mind, comfortable means, grace of person, and a broad intellectual training. Together with these assets, he harbored a taste for science and mathematics, and it was these subjects that the two studied most often, with Gough as tutor and Dalton as student. Meteorology was one of their mutual pursuits, and in March 1787, Gough persuaded Dalton to start a journal of weather observations. So devoted did he become, that, with but a few lapses, he continued it to the day preceding his death. Unlikely as this avenue might appear, it was through meteorology that Dalton was eventually led to his explanation of chemical reactions and to the undying renown that he acquired as the founder of modern atomic theory.

The formative years at Kendal came to an end in 1793. In the spring of that year, largely through Gough's recommendation, Dalton received the offer of an appointment as tutor in mathematics and natural philosophy at the New College in Manchester. He accepted the offer and took up his abode in the college buildings. He was ready for a larger sphere of activity, and his acceptance of this post at the age of twenty-six marks the beginning of his intellectually mature years.

Shortly after his arrival, Dalton published his first scientific treatise, "Meteorological Observations and Essays," the data for which had been accumulated at Kendal. In it we find most of the ideas with which he was concerned during the next ten years, ideas on problems associated with "mixed gases" found in the atmosphere. Less than a year later, he joined the Manchester Literary and Philosophical Society. It is interesting that his first communication to the Society was not on the properties of gases but on the subject of color vision. In this paper he discusses his red-green color blindness, a defect that has since become known as "Daltonism." Since in the next five years he presented but one more scientific communication, it seems reasonable to conclude that his duties at New College absorbed all his effort except for his meteorological observations. Had his connection with the college continued, he probably would not have had the leisure for original investigation. But in 1799, the college closed and moved to York. Deprived of his comfortable though demanding position, Dalton reverted to private teaching, supporting himself in this capacity for most of the remainder of his life.

Fortunately for science, the Philosophical Society permitted him to occupy one of the lower rooms of its house on George Street, which he used as a schoolroom, study, and laboratory through the succeeding years. He had never before carried on systematic experimental research, but once this was begun, he brought to fruition in a few years all the ideas for which he is remembered: the diffusion of gases, the law of partial pressures, the phenomena of water vapor in the atmosphere, including the dew point, and the chemical atomic theory. From this impressive list of contributions it is natural to assume that Dalton must have brought to his studies a high order of experimental skill. The judgment of his contemporaries is, curiously enough, quite the opposite.

At the close of the eighteenth century, the characteristics of gases were still poorly understood. The kinetic hypothesis, the fundamental basis for understanding the behavior of gases, although already proposed by Hooke and treated mathematically by Bernoulli, was hardly known despite the stature of these champions. The scientific world, dazzled by Lavoisier's genius, made chemistry the vogue of contemporary investigation. Mysterious phenomena were made plausible by "chemical" assumptions. The puzzling fact that oxygen and nitrogen in the air remained thoroughly mixed, and did not separate into distinct strata despite their different specific gravities, was accounted for by saying that the two gases had entered into a "loose" chemical union. Just what this was, in comparison with examples of regular chemical union, could only be characterized as "loose" thinking. Another example of this same kind of "chemical" action was exemplified by the movement of water molecules into the air and their continued presence as water vapor.

Dalton, being innocent of chemical notions when he formed his ideas on these subjects, approached them from a physical point of view. Being influenced by Newton and his particle conception of gases, he advanced a physical theory of diffusion, of partial pressures, and of the behavior of water vapor in air. All these were developed in a long paper entitled, "Experimental essays on the constitution of mixed gases; on the force of steam or vapour from water and other liquids in different temperatures, both in a Torricellian vacuum and in air; on evaporation; and on the expansion of gases by heat," and read before the Literary and Philosophical Society in October 1801. The physical theory of diffusion depended upon Dalton's assumption of Newton's mutually repelling particles. Attacking the problem experimentally, he showed that at any given temperature there was a maximum pressure of water vapor in the air, the saturation pressure, and this pressure had a constant value regardless of whether air or any other gas was present. In fact, the result was the same if no gas were present, and the water evaporated into a vacuum. This situation led naturally to the law of partial pressures—that each gas of a mixture exerted a partial pressure which was equal to the pressure it would exert if it filled the container alone.

Following up the saturation-pressure phenomenon, he showed that any attempt to increase the saturation pressure resulted only in condensation. Furthermore, if the partial pressure of water vapor in the air was less than the pressure at which saturation took place, a sufficient reduction in temperature would produce saturation, i.e., the dew point would be reached. Some of this material, his explanation of diffusion, and his law of partial pressures were included in his *New System of Chemical Philosophy,* Part I, published in 1808.

His theory of diffusion, which he assumed accounted for the inevitable and complete mixing of two dissimilar gases in a confined space, led to the prediction that in the atmosphere, if one were to go high enough, separation of the gases would result. In order to test his theory he began analyzing samples of air. His method of analysis consisted in reacting air with nitrous oxide (NO); he found that the proportions in which the two gases unite depended on the manner in which the reaction was effected. The investigation of this variability extended from the latter part of 1802 through the summer of 1803. From his notebooks it seems clear that not until August 4 did the reason for the variability of the reacting proportions become clear. The conclusion reached may be given in his own words:

> If 100 measures of common air be put to 36 of pure nitrous gas in a tube $\frac{3}{10}$ths of an inch wide and 5 inches long, after a few minutes the whole will be reduced to 79 or 80 measures, and exhibit no signs of either oxygenous or nitrous gas.
>
> If 100 measures of common air be admitted to 72 of nitrous gas in a wide vessel over water, such as to form a thin stratum of air, and an immediate momentary agitation be used, there will as before be found 79 or 80 measures of pure azotic gas for a residuum.
>
> If in the last experiment, *less* than 72 measures of nitrous gas be used, there will be a residuum containing oxygenous gas; if *more* then some residuary nitrous gas will be found.
>
> . . . *these facts clearly point out the theory of the process: the elements of oxygen may combine with a certain portion of nitrous gas, or with twice that portion but with no intermediate quantity.* In the former case nitric acid is the result; in the latter nitrous acid. . . . But as both of these may be formed at the same time, one part of the oxygen going to one of nitrous gas, and another to two, the quantity of nitrous gas absorbed should be variable.[1]

---

[1] H. E. Roscoe and A. Harden, *The New View of Dalton's Atomic Theory* (New York: Macmillan, 1896), pp. 32–33.

At this point it is worth emphasizing the way in which science actually develops as compared with the way popular accounts lead the reader to believe. No great deductive discovery ever springs suddenly with noonday clarity into an investigator's head. Usually experimental evidence hints at a generalization whose scope is hazy; a great deal of thought must be spent on the idea to link it with the known relevant facts. In this way the concept begins to take a definite shape whose validity and limits finally come into some sort of focus. The ultimate value and importance of a new discovery can rarely, if ever, be fully apprehended at the time of its enunciation; it is in what follows that its true value is established.

With the facts of definite proportion in a chemical reaction finally unmasked, what was its meaning? Imbued with the physical, particle picture of gases, Dalton was led to the assumption that the free particles of a given gas—atoms, as he soon called them—are all alike, and a chemical reaction is only the combination of an atom of one substance with that of another. Thus was the atomic theory at last placed on an experimental basis. But there was more to it. By the following month, he was led to see that from the masses of two simple substances that reacted completely and an assumption regarding the formula of the compound, it was possible to infer the relative weights of the constituent atoms. He immediately proceeded to make up a table of relative atomic weights together with a set of symbols for the elements, and at the October meeting of the Literary and Philosophical Society presented a resumé of this work. We have no information about the members' reaction to this communication; probably only a handful were present at the meeting, and it is questionable if any of those had a glimmering of its real importance.

At about this time or shortly after, Dalton accepted an invitation to deliver the 1803 Christmas lectures at the Royal Institution. The institution, destined to play a great role in British science, was then only newly founded under the direction of the vigorous and colorful Count Rumford, alias Benjamin Thompson, the Massachusetts Tory who on the eve of the Revolutionary War fled a wife considerably his senior, several children, and the mounting ire of his colonial neighbors. For the scientific direction of the institute, Rumford, with characteristic foresight, had already hired a brilliant and personable young Cornishman, then in his early twenties, one Humphry Davy. It was Davy who arranged Dalton's stay and the details connected with the presentation of his lectures. Certainly Dalton must have communicated his atomic theory to Davy, but all we know for certain is that the theory was presented to his audiences at that time. Although Davy came to acknowledge the power of the atomic theory, he never accepted its basic tenets or a belief in the reality of atoms.

Dalton's papers of 1802–1803 propounding the atomic hypothesis were not published until 1805, when they appeared in the latest volume of the society's memoirs. In the meantime, Dr. Thomas Thomson of Glasgow, a chemist of repute and author of a widely used treatise on chemistry, visited Dalton in August 1804 to discuss obscurities in his diffusion theory. Although this discussion was not too fruitful, Thomson listened eagerly to Dalton's chemical experiments and his atomic theory. When the next edition of Thomson's textbook appeared in 1807, it contained the first generally available description of the atomic theory. Dalton's own account was not published until the following year in his *New System of Chemical Philosophy*, Part I. This is reproduced in the second excerpt.

The diffusion hypothesis that had been responsible for his atomic theory was never straightened out. At first, Dalton assumed that the atoms of a gas were all the same size, but Thomson's objections led him to change his view and to assume that although all the atoms of a given substance were identical in all respects, the atoms of different substances were of different size. Still later he reverted to his original belief that all atoms were of the same size. The diffusion theory was also complicated by the assumption that, while atoms of gas A repelled each other and those of gas B did likewise, atoms of A and B had no mutual force between them. This fitted well enough with his law of partial pressures, but if the repulsion were due to "the atmosphere of heat," i.e., caloric (an idea borrowed from Lavoisier), which surrounded all atoms, it was hard to see why atoms of A and B did not act on each other. This point also was never resolved. Dalton spent the years after 1804 elaborating the ideas he had already expounded and in further chemical experiments. None of these produced any memorable results. After he had enunciated the atomic theory, it seemed that he became hopelessly confused in a maze of rapidly accumulating, but seemingly contradictory, chemical data.

The acceptance of the atomic theory was slow, and among Englishmen it found few champions. On the continent, and especially in France, it fared better. Gay-Lussac's experiments, published in 1809, demonstrated that gases combined in equal volumes or in small volume ratios. These experiments were explained in 1811 in terms of Dalton's theory by the Italian physicist Amedeo Avogadro. Explained, that is, if one were willing to believe in atoms and "half atoms." Dalton, in fact, had assumed that the free particles in any elemental gas were atoms and he never distinguished between what we now call atoms and molecules. The distinction between atoms and molecules of an element and the tangle that developed in determining atomic weights as the result of Dalton's arbitrary rules for chemical combination had to wait another half century for the analyzing genius of Cannizzaro. Even though many chemists, like Davy, did not accept the reality of atoms, nevertheless the atomic theory became widely accepted as a potent tool in understanding chemical reactions.

There is little more to say about Dalton the scientist, but there is much more to illuminate the character of Dalton the man.

In the year following his discovery of atomic combination Dalton became a boarder in the home of the Rev. William Johns in George Street close to the society's building, an arrangement that continued with complete amity for twenty-six years until the Johnses moved to the suburbs of Manchester. In these years, Dalton's life was much like that of the hero of Jules Verne's *Around the World in Eighty Days*—he was "un homme mathématiquement précis." His days in the laboratory never varied, and his neighbors knew the time to the minute from his observation of his outdoor thermometers. In the evenings, he finished his day at nine, had dinner, and then sat with the family quietly puffing his pipe. He took little part in the conversation, but remained interested and listening, occasionally interjecting a remark or a laconic witticism. Every Thursday afternoon, "shop" was closed for his weekly recreation. After his noonday meal, he would set out for the bowling green adjoining the Dog and Partridge Tavern, where he would enter into the game with a zest and enthusiasm that amused all the spectators. His usual staid and austere manner would be dropped, and he would pursue the ball and wave his arms as if to direct it in its course. A few modest bets, always carefully noted, were part of the game, which was always followed by tea and a smoke on his long pipe. Then he would walk home in time for a final reading of his barometer and thermometers. On Sundays, dressed in his Quaker knee breeches, gray stockings, and buckled shoes, he always attended public worship twice. He appeared to feel it his duty to express his religious observance in this way, although he adopted little of the Quaker phraseology and never discussed his views on religion. It was as though he felt an obligation to observe the outward form of his faith in order to maintain the morale of others or to escape their censure, whereas his own emotional life was not vitally concerned with it. In most company he was withdrawn, a condition that stemmed partly from his physical make-up and partly from his country background and lack of youthful social training. Apparently, many people were repelled by his physical awkwardness and lack of social grace. Dr. Davy, the brother of Sir Humphry Davy, says that "his aspect and manner were repulsive . . . his voice harsh and brawling; his gait stiff and awkward." The testimony of a fellow member of the Literary and Philosophical Society was much the same: "His voice was deep and gruff, and his articulation thick, indistinct and mumbling; so much so as to give a stranger almost the idea of uncouthness. . . ." From these descriptions, it is at once clear why Dalton was never very successful as a lecturer, although this alone does not seem to be responsible. As a demonstrator he was not skillful and many of his lecture experiments failed. This lack of experimental skill even extended to his researches, for his biographer, Dr. W. C. Henry, writes that: "His instruments of research, chiefly made by his own hands, were incapable of affording accurate results, and his manner of experimenting was loose, if not slovenly." He did not possess "the manual dexterity or the mental habits or temperament essential to rigorous experimental determinations." Nevertheless, those close to him, especially in his scientific work, recognized his ability and his devotion. The Manchester Literary and Philosophical Society voted him secretary in 1800, vice president in 1808, and president in 1817. He was continuously re-elected to the latter office throughout his life. But here again his lack of social understanding and the limitations of his outlook prevented his incumbency from being distinguished or inspiring. He was not a reader, often boasting that he "could carry his library on his back and yet had not read half the books." It was this point of view that characterized his extreme reluctance to increase the small store of scientific books of the society, despite the fact that it was then the only such library in Manchester. It must be remembered also that the society had professed literary as well as philosophical pursuits. As chairman, however, Dalton was inclined to discourage the reading of literary essays. It must have been amusing for those sufficiently detached, but very annoying to the authors, to hear him pass judgment that such readings "contributed no positive facts to the stock of knowledge and proved nothing."

As the value of Dalton's theory became recognized he began to receive appropriate recognition. The French Academy elected him a corresponding member in 1816 and the Royal Society, with Davy as president, elected him a regular member in 1822. In 1826 the Royal Society again honored him with the award of a Royal Medal and one of the two George IV prizes of fifty guineas. In 1830, the French Academy awarded him its highest honor by electing him one of its eight foreign associates, a place previously held by Davy, who had died the year before. When the British Association for the Advancement of Science held its meetings in Oxford two years later, the university conferred on him the degree of Doctor of Laws along with the illustrious Faraday, Robert Brown, and Sir David Brewster. The following year at the Cambridge meeting it was announced that the government had awarded him an annual pension of £150. Three years later this pension was doubled. In 1834 he received the LL.D. degree from Edinburgh University and in the same year he was presented to King William IV at a levee in St. James Palace. For this ceremony, it was necessary to wear a military sword, a requirement not only out of keeping with his character but also with his Quaker beliefs. The problem was solved by dressing him in his Oxford Doctor of Science gown. It is reported that the King's greeting was "Well, Mr. Dalton, how are you getting on in Manchester, all quiet I suppose?" This remark was not quite as vacuous as it sounds, since the King had reference to the riots that had occurred in Manchester some years before. Dalton in characteristic fashion answered: "Well, I don't know—just middlin', I think." When asked by a friend if he did not consider his manner of address a breach of court etiquette, he replied with a lapse into his native Cumberland dialect: "Mebbe sae, but what can yan say to sic like fowk?"

It is fortunate that his honors should have come in time, for in the spring of 1837 Dalton was afflicted with two paralytic strokes from which he never recovered. Though able to continue his work at a slower pace, his mental vigor began to diminish, so that by 1840 a paper contributed to the Royal Society was declined to save his reputation. In June 1842, the British Association met in Manchester, and it was hoped that he might be made president of the meeting. But by this time his articulation, never clear, was so bad as to be unintelligible and his health so infirm as to render the appointment impossible. Nevertheless he was made vice president—the last public recognition during his life of the eminence he had achieved in the scientific world. He lingered for two more years, conscientiously taking his meteorological observations until a stroke on July 27, 1844, freed him forever from his self-imposed obligation.

The excerpts given below are taken from Dalton's *New System of Chemical Philosophy,* 2nd Edition, London, Part I, published in 1842. The excerpts from "On the Constitution of Bodies" and "On Mixed Elastic Fluids" are reprinted to give the reader a general view of Dalton's concept of the atomic nature of matter. The section "On Chemical Synthesis" gives his version of chemical reactions. It was the chemical atomic theory that first provided a direct experimental basis for belief in the existence of atoms and thus opened the door to widespread chemical research and acceptance by the scientific community.

ooooooo

DALTON

New System of Chemical Philosophy [2]

ON THE CONSTITUTION OF BODIES

THERE ARE THREE DISTINCTIONS IN the kinds of bodies, or three states, which have more especially claimed the attention of philosophical chemists; namely, those which are marked by the terms *elastic fluids, liquids, and solids.* A very familiar instance is exhibited to us in water, of a body, which, in certain circumstances, is capable of as-

---

[2] John Dalton, *New System of Chemical Philosophy,* Part I, Chap. II (London: 1842).

suming all the three states. In steam we recognise a perfectly elastic fluid, in water, a perfect liquid, and in ice a complete solid. These observations have tacitly led to the conclusion which seems universally adopted, that all bodies of sensible magnitude, whether liquid or solid, are constituted of a vast number of extremely small particles, or atoms of matter, bound together by a force of attraction, which is more or less powerful according to circumstances, and which, as it endeavours to prevent their separation, is very properly called in that view, *attraction of cohesion;* but as it collects them from a dispersed state (as from steam into water) it is called, *attraction of aggregation,* or, more simply, *affinity.* Whatever names it may go by, they still signify one and the same power. It is not my design to call in question this conclusion, which appears completely satisfactory, but to shew that we have hitherto made no use of it, and that the consequence of the neglect has been a very obscure view of chemical agency, which is daily growing more so in proportion to the new lights attempted to be thrown upon it.

The opinions I more particularly allude to, are those of Berthollet on the Laws of Chemical Affinity; such as that chemical agency is proportional to the mass, and that in all chemical unions there exist insensible gradations in the proportions of the constituent principles. The inconsistence of these opinions, both with reason and observation, cannot, I think, fail to strike every one who takes a proper view of the phenomena.

Whether the ultimate particles of a body, such as water, are all alike, that is, of the same figure, weight, &c., is a question of some importance. From what is known, we have no reason to apprehend a diversity in these particulars: if it does exist in water, it must equally exist in the elements constituting water, namely, hydrogen and oxygen. Now, it is scarcely possible to conceive how the aggregates of dissimilar particles should be so uniformly the same. If some of the particles of water were heavier than others—if a parcel of the liquid on any occasion were constituted principally of these heavier particles, it must be supposed to affect the specific gravity of the mass, a circumstance not known. Similar observations may be made on other substances; therefore, we may conclude that *the ultimate particles of all homogeneous bodies are perfectly alike in weight, figure, &c.* In other words, every particle of water is like every other particle of water; every particle of hydrogen is like every other particle of hydrogen, &c.

Besides the force of attraction, which, in one character or another, belongs universally to ponderable bodies, we find another force that is likewise universal, or acts upon all matter which comes under our cognizance, namely, a force of repulsion. This is now generally, and I think properly, ascribed to the agency of heat. An atmosphere of this subtile fluid constantly surrounds the atoms of all bodies, and prevents them from being drawn into actual contact. This appears to be satisfactorily proved by the observation, that the bulk of a body may be diminished by abstracting some of its heat: but . . . it should seem that enlargement and diminution of bulk depend perhaps more on the arrangement, than on the size of the ultimate particles. Be this as it may, we cannot avoid inferring, from the preceding doctrine on heat, and particularly from the section on the natural zero of temperature, that solid bodies, such as ice, contain a large portion, perhaps ⅘ of the heat which the same are found to contain in an elastic state, as steam.

We are now to consider how these two great antagonist powers of attraction and repulsion are adjusted, so as to allow of the three different states of *elastic fluids, liquids, and solids.*—We shall divide the subject into four Sections; namely, first, *on the constitution of pure elastic fluids;* second, *on the constitution of mixed elastic fluids;* third, *on the constitution of liquids,* and fourth, *on the constitution of solids.*[3]

ON MIXED ELASTIC FLUIDS

. . . I shall now proceed to give my present views on the subject of mixed gases, which are somewhat different from what they were when the theory was announced, in consequence of the fresh lights which succeeding experience has diffused. In prosecuting my enquiries into the nature of elastic fluids, I soon perceived it was necessary, if possible, to ascertain whether the atoms or ultimate particles of the different gases are of the same size or volume in like circumstances of temperature and pressure. By the size or volume of an ultimate particle, I mean in this place, the space it occupies in the state of a pure elastic fluid: in this sense the bulk of the particle signifies the bulk of the supposed impenetrable nucleus, together with that of its surrounding repulsive atmosphere of heat. At the time I formed the theory of mixed gases, I had a confused idea, as many have, I suppose, at this time, that the particles of elastic fluids are all of the same size; that a given volume of oxygenous gas contains just as many particles as the same volume of hydrogenous; or if not, that we had no data from which the question could be solved. But from a train of reasoning, . . . I became convinced that different gases have *not* their particles of the same sizes and that the following may be adopted as a maxim, till some reason appears to the contrary: namely,—

That every species of pure elastic fluid has its particles globular and all of a size; but that no two species agree in the size of their particles, the pressure and temperature being the same.

---

[3] *Ibid.,* Chapter 2.

There was another thing concerning which I was dubious; whether heat was the cause of repulsion. I was rather inclined to ascribe repulsion to a force resembling magnetism, which acts on one kind of matter, and has no effect on another. For, if heat were the cause of repulsion, there seemed no reason why a particle of oxygen should not repel one of hydrogen with the same force as one of its own kind, especially if they were both of a size. Upon more mature consideration, I see no sufficient reason for discarding the common opinion, which ascribes repulsion to heat; and I think the phenomena of mixed gases may still be accounted for, by repulsion, without the postulatum, that their particles are mutually inelastic, and free from such of the preceding objections as I have left unanswered.

When we contemplate upon the disposition of the globular particles in a volume of pure elastic fluid, we perceive it must be analogous to that of a square pile of shot; the particles must be disposed into horizontal strata, each four particles forming a square: in a superior stratum, each particle rests upon four particles below, the points of its contact with all four being 45° above the horizontal plane, or that plane which passes through the centres of the four particles. On this account the pressure is steady and uniform throughout. But when a measure of one gas is presented to a measure of another in any vessel, we have then a surface of elastic globular particles of one size in contact with an equal surface of particles of another: in such case the points of contact of the heterogeneous particles must vary all the way from 40° to 90°; an intestine motion must arise from this inequality, and the particles of one kind be propelled amongst those of the other. The same cause which prevented the two elastic surfaces from maintaining an equilibrium, will always subsist, the particles of one kind being, from their size, unable to apply properly to the other, so that no equilibrium can ever take place amongst the heterogeneous particles. The intestine motion must therefore continue till the particles arrive at the opposite surface of the vessel against any point of which they can rest with stability, and the equilibrium at length is acquired when each gas is uniformly diffused through the other. In the open atmosphere no equilibrium can take place in such case till the particles have ascended so far as to be restrained by their own weight. . . .

It is remarkable that when two equal measures of different gases are thus diffused, and sustain an invaried pressure, as that of the atmosphere, the pressure upon each particle after the mixture is less than before. This points out the active principle of diffusion; for, particles of fluids are always disposed to move to that situation where the pressure is least. Thus, in a mixture of equal measures of oxygen and hydrogen, the common pressure on each particle before mixture being denoted by 1, that after the mixture when the gas becomes of half its density, will be denoted by $\sqrt[3]{1/2} = .794$.

This view of the constitution of mixed gases agrees with that which I have given before, in the two following particulars, which I consider as essential to every theory on the subject to give it plausibility.

1st. The diffusion of gases through each other is effected by means of the repulsion belonging to the homogenous particles; or to that principle which is always energetic to produce the dilatation of the gas.

2nd. When any two or more mixed gases acquire an equilibrium, the elastic energy [pressure] of each against the surface of the vessel or of any liquid, is precisely the same as if it were the only gas present occupying the whole space, and all the rest were withdrawn.[4]

In other respects I think the last view accords better with the phenomena, and obviates the objections which Dr. Thomson has brought against the former; particularly in regard to the query, why mixed gases that are known on certain occasions to combine, do not always combine; and why any gaseous particle in its nascent state is more disposed to combination than when it has already assumed the elastic form. It will also more clearly explain the reason of one gas making so powerful and durable a resistance to the entrance of another.

One difficulty still remains respecting vapour, which neither view of the subject altogether removes: though vapour may subsist in the atmosphere upon either supposition, as far as the temperature will admit, not being subject to any more pressure than would arise from its own particles, were the others removed, yet it may be enquired, how does it rise from the surface of water subject to the pressure of the atmosphere? how does vapour, which ascends with an elastic force of only half an inch of mercury, detach itself from water when it has the weight of 30 inches of mercury to oppose its ascent. This difficulty applies nearly the same to all theories of the solution of water in air, and it is therefore of consequence for every one, let him adopt what opinion he may, to remove it. Chemical solution but ill explains it; for, the affinity of air for vapour is always described as weak, and yet it is sufficient to overcome the pressure of a powerful force equal to the weight of the atmosphere. I have endeavoured to shew in another place . . . what my own ideas on the subject are. It appears to me, that it is not till the depth of 10 or 12 strata of particles of any liquid, that the pressure upon each perpendicular column becomes uniform; and that several of the particles in the uppermost stratum are in reality subject to but little pressure.[5]

---

[4] This is a statement of Dalton's law of partial pressure—Editors.

[5] *Ibid.*, Chapter 2, Section 2.

ON CHEMICAL SYNTHESIS

When any body exists in the elastic state, its ultimate particles are separated from each other to a much greater distance than in any other state; each particle occupies the centre of a comparatively large sphere, and supports its dignity by keeping all the rest, which by their gravity, or otherwise are disposed to encroach upon it, at a respectful distance. When we attempt to conceive the *number* of particles in an atmosphere, it is somewhat like attempting to conceive the number of stars in the universe; we are confounded with the thought. But if we limit the subject, by taking a given volume of any gas, we seem persuaded that, let the divisions be ever so minute, the number of particles must be finite; just as in a given space of the universe, the number of stars and planets cannot be infinite.

Chemical analysis and synthesis go no farther than to the separation of particles one from another, and to their reunion. No new creation or destruction of matter is within the reach of chemical agency. We might as well attempt to introduce a new planet into the solar system, or to annihilate one already in existence, as to create or destroy a particle of hydrogen. All the changes we can produce, consist in separating particles that are in a state of cohesion or combination, and joining those that were previously at a distance.

In all chemical investigations, it has justly been considered an important object to ascertain the relative *weights* of the simples which constitute a compound. But unfortunately the enquiry has terminated here; whereas, from the relative weights in the mass, the relative weights of the ultimate particles or atoms of the bodies might have been inferred, from which their number and weight in various other compounds would appear, in order to assist and to guide future investigations, and to correct their results. Now it is one great object of this work, to show the importance and advantage of ascertaining *the relative weights of the ultimate particles, both of simple and compound bodies, the number of simple elementary particles which constitute one compound particle, and the number of less compound particles which enter into the formation of one more compound particle.*

If there are two bodies, A and B, which are disposed to combine, the following is the order in which the combinations may take place, beginning with the most simple, viz.:

> 1 atom of A + 1 atom of B = 1 atom of C, binary.
> 1 atom of A + 2 atoms of B = 1 atom of D, ternary.
> 2 atoms of A + 1 atom of B = 1 atom of E, ternary.
> 1 atom of A + 3 atoms of B = 1 atom of F, quaternary.
> 3 atoms of A + 1 atom of B = 1 atom of G, quaternary.
> &c. &c.

The following general rules may be adopted as guides in all our investigations respecting chemical synthesis.

1st. When only one combination of two bodies can be obtained, it must be presumed to be a *binary* one, unless some cause appear to the contrary.

2nd. When two combinations are observed, they must be presumed to be a *binary* and a *ternary*.

3rd. When three combinations are obtained, we may expect one to be a *binary* and the other two *ternary*.

4th. When four combinations are observed, we should expect one *binary,* two *ternary,* and one *quaternary,* &c.

5th. A *binary* compound should always be specifically heavier than the mere mixture of its two ingredients.

6th. A *ternary* compound should be specifically heavier than the mixture of a binary and a simple, which would, if combined, constitute it; &c.

7th. The above rules and observations equally apply, when two bodies, such as C and D, D and E, &c. are combined.

From the application of these rules, to the chemical facts already well ascertained, we deduce the following conclusions;—1st. That water is a binary compound of hydrogen and oxygen, and the relative weights of the two elementary atoms are as 1:7, nearly;—2nd. That ammonia is a binary compound of hydrogen and azote, and the relative weights of the two atoms are as 1:5, nearly;—3rd. That nitrous gas is a binary compound of azote and oxygen, the atoms of which weigh 5 and 7 respectively; that nitric acid is a binary or ternary compound according as it is derived, and consists of one atom of azote and two of oxygen, together weighing 19; that nitrous oxide is a compound similar to nitric acid, and consists of one atom of oxygen and two of azote, weighing 17; that nitrous acid is a binary compound of nitric acid and nitrous gas, weighing 31; that oxynitric acid is a binary compound of nitric acid and oxygen, weighing 26;—4th. That carbonic oxide is a binary compound, consisting of one atom of charcoal, and one of oxygen, together weighing nearly 12; that carbonic acid is a ternary compound, (but sometimes binary) consisting of one atom of charcoal, and two of oxygen, weighing 19; &c. &c. In all these cases the weights are expressed in atoms of hydrogen, each of which is denoted by unity.

In the sequel, the facts and experiments from which these conclusions are derived, will be detailed; as well as a great variety of others from which are inferred the constitution and weight of the ultimate particles of the principal acids, the alkalis, the earths, the metals, the metallic oxides and sulphurets, the long train of neutral salts, and in short, all the chemical compounds which have hitherto obtained a tolerably good analysis. Several of the conclusions will be supported by original experiments.

From the novelty as well as importance of the ideas suggested in this chapter, it is deemed expedient to give plates, exhibiting the mode of combination in some of the more simple cases. A specimen of these accompanies this first part. The elements or atoms of such bodies as are conceived at present to be simple, are denoted by a small circle, with some distinctive mark; and the combinations consist in the juxtaposition of two or more of these: when three or more particles of elastic fluids are combined together in one, it is to be supposed that the particles of the same kind repel each other, and therefore take their stations accordingly.[6]

○○○○○○○

The next excerpt is Dalton's scheme of atomic weights:

Hydrogen, its relative weight	1	Strontites	46
Azote	5	Barytes	68
Carbone or charcoal	5	Iron	38
Oxygen	7	Zinc	56
Phosphorus	9	Copper	56
Sulphur	13	Lead	95
Magnesia	20	Silver	100
Lime	23	Platina	100
Soda	28	Gold	140
Potash	42	Mercury	167

An atom of water or steam, composed of 1 of oxygen and 1 of hydrogen, retained in physical contact by a strong affinity, and supposed to be surrounded by a common atmosphere of heat; its relative weight =	8
An atom of ammonia, composed of 1 of azote and 1 of hydrogen	6
An atom of nitrous gas, composed of 1 of azote and 1 of oxygen	12
An atom of olefiant gas, composed of 1 of carbone and 1 of hydrogen	6
An atom of carbonic oxide composed of 1 of carbone and 1 oxygen	12
An atom of nitrous oxide, 2 azote + 1 oxygen	17
An atom of nitric acid, 1 azote + 2 oxygen	19
An atom of carbonic acid, 1 carbone + 2 oxygen	19
An atom of carburretted hydrogen, 1 carbone + 2 hydrogen	7
An atom of oxynitric acid, 1 azote + 3 oxygen	26
An atom of sulphuric acid, 1 sulphur + 3 oxygen	34
An atom of sulphuretted hydrogen, 1 sulphur + 3 hydrogen	16
An atom of alcohol, 3 carbone, + 1 hydrogen	16
An atom of nitrous acid, 1 nitric acid + 1 nitrous gas	31
An atom of acetous acid, 2 carbone + 2 water	26
An atom of nitrate of ammonia, 1 nitric acid + 1 ammonia + 1 water	33
An atom of sugar, 1 alcohol + 1 carbonic acid	35

---

[6] *Ibid.,* Chapter 3.

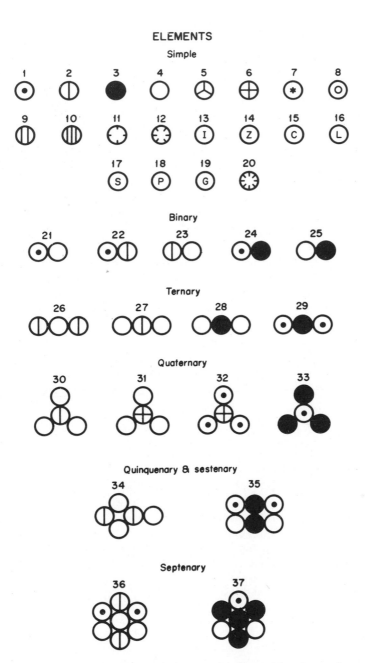

Fig. 10–1. Dalton's chemical symbols for the table of atomic weights.

Figure 10–1 above gives Dalton's chemical symbols for the 20 elements in the preceding table and his concept of the particulate structure of atomic combinations to form the binary, ternary, etc. compounds described in the table.

ຠຠຠຠຠຠຠ

Enough has been given to shew the method; it will be quite unnecessary to devise characters and combinations of them to exhibit to view in this way all the subjects that come under investigation nor is it necessary to insist upon the accuracy of all these compounds, both in number and weight; the principle will be entered into more particularly hereafter, as far as respects the individual results. It is not to be understood that all those articles marked as simple substances are necessarily such by the theory; they are only necessarily of such weights. Soda and potash, such as they are found in combination with acids, are 28 and 42 respectively in weight; but according to Mr. Davy's very important discoveries, they are metallic oxides; the former then must be considered as composed of an atom of metal, 21, and one of oxygen, 7; and the latter, of an atom of metal, 35, and one of oxygen, 7. Or, soda contains 75 per cent. metal and 25 oxygen; potash, 83.3 metal and 16.7 oxygen. It is particularly remarkable, that according to the above-mentioned gentleman's Essay on the Decomposition and Composition of the fixed alkalis, in the Philosophical Transactions (a copy of which Essay he has just favoured me with) it appears that "the largest quantity of oxygen indicated by these experiments was, for potash 17, and for soda, 26 parts in 100, and the smallest 13 and 19."

11

ooooooooooo

THE VOLUME

COMBINATION OF GASES

ooooooooooo

Joseph Louis Gay-Lussac (1778-1850)

Dalton's atomic theory, which envisioned chemical combination as an atom to atom union, was most immediately useful in settling the question of combination in definite proportions. But like most newly born theories, it included basic assumptions that needed experimental confirmation. The one that, from the standpoint of the subsequent development of chemistry, produced a morass of confusion, was the supposition that the ultimate naturally occurring unit of any element was the single atom itself. This "monatomic" hypothesis created difficulties in understanding chemical reactions that required almost half a century to dissipate.

What is most remarkable is that this confusion need hardly have arisen. A set of experimental results published by Joseph Louis Gay-Lussac in 1809, the year after the appearance of Dalton's first volume of a *New System of Chemical Philosophy,* contained the data that might have avoided this confusion, although Gay-Lussac's data alone would not have been sufficient. Even more remarkable is that the proper interpretation of Gay-Lussac's experiments (demanding a deep understanding of the possibilities of the atomic hypothesis—deeper certainly than Dalton himself possessed) was supplied just two years later by an obscure Italian scholar, Amedeo Avogadro.

Gay-Lussac showed that if gases enter into chemical reaction, they do so in numerically simple volume ratios, and the volume of the products, if gaseous, may be expressed by simple integral numerical ratios to the volume of the original reactants. For example, if one unit volume of nitrogen is reacted with one of oxygen, two volumes of nitrous oxide are pro-

157

duced. If one volume of nitrogen is reacted with three of hydrogen, two volumes of ammonia result. These simple relationships indicated some very fundamental aspect of chemical combination, but what was it?

At that time, the explanation was obscured by several factors. First, there was no general agreement as to whether or not chemical combination occurred in definite proportion; second, no distinction between the atom and the molecule of a given substance had yet been made. Once Dalton's hypothesis was accepted the first difficulty was settled. But the second distinction had to be made along with a far-reaching supposition as to the number of molecules in equal volumes of gases. This was Avogadro's contribution. However, before we examine Avogadro's work we shall review what Gay-Lussac accomplished.

In his personal and professional life Joseph Louis Gay-Lussac may be described as the always-successful man. He was born on December 6, 1778, in St. Léonard in the department of Haute-Vienne. His father, Antoine Gay, was a judge, who after establishing his residence at St. Léonard acquired nearby property named Lussac. He then added this to his surname to distinguish himself from others having the same family name. Young Joseph Louis grew up in the troubled times preceding and during the French Revolution; as a consequence, he received his early education at home. His father was imprisoned briefly as a suspected "aristocrat" after the outbreak of the Revolution in 1789 and did not consider it safe to send his son to Paris for schooling until 1795. After two years of preparatory study in Paris Joseph Louis was admitted at the age of nineteen to the École Polytechnique after passing a brilliant examination.

In 1800, he transferred to the École des Ponts et Chaussées and became research assistant to the great chemist Berthollet, who had just returned from service on Napoleon's personal staff with the French army in Egypt. Berthollet recognized young Gay-Lussac's outstanding abilities, adopted him as a "son-in-science," and gave him a place in his private laboratory at Arcueil. This fortunate association greatly assisted Gay-Lussac's rapid professional advancement. In 1802, he was appointed demonstrator for Professor Antoine F. Fourcroy at the École Polytechnique while continuing his work with Berthollet. As the latter's pupil he began work in the same year on the expansion of gases by heat and discovered the very important result that we now know as Charles's law, namely, that the ratio of volume to absolute temperature of an enclosed gas is constant if the pressure is held constant. Before publishing his results he was chagrined to find that the same conclusion had been reached fifteen years earlier by Charles, who had not considered it sufficiently important to publish.

In 1804, as a result of balloon flights in Germany and Russia, it was reported that the strength of the earth's magnetic field decreased with altitude. The French Academy, wishing to verify the result, selected Gay-

Lussac and Jean B. Biot to make the test. On August 24 they ascended from the garden of the Conservatoire des Arts et Métier in a hydrogen-filled balloon and reached an altitude of 13,120 feet, but found, despite some difficulties, no change in the magnetic field. Dissatisfied with the results, but well aware of the danger involved, Gay-Lussac volunteered to make a second ascent alone to improve the accuracy of the measurements and to obtain meteorological data not then available. He accomplished this on September 16, rising to a record height of 23,040 feet. Despite an extreme temperature of $-9.5°$ C., he carried out a series of magnetic measurements over a period of several hours, measured the temperature and humidity of the air, and obtained air samples to find out if the composition of the atmosphere changed with altitude. The results showed no diminution of the magnetic field and no change in the composition of the atmosphere within the height attained. Despite the negative results, the whole undertaking cannot help but excite admiration for so daring an investigation, as well as respect for the high competence evident in managing such a flight alone and in securing all the scientific information for which the venture was organized. It is worth noting that the possibility of aerial navigation had been demonstrated by the Montgolfier brothers only twenty years previously and that the hazards of using hydrogen as a lifting gas had been shown by fatal accidents in the intervening years.

Two weeks after this flight Gay-Lussac, in conjunction with Alexander von Humboldt (later to win fame as a naturalist), read a paper that publicized the first results on the volume combination of gases. Further research on this subject was delayed by a long trip through Europe which Gay-Lussac took with Von Humboldt for the purpose of making magnetic measurements. While this work was still in progress, he was elected in 1806, at the age of twenty-eight, to the French Academy. His investigation on the volume combination of gases was finished in 1808 and the results read before the Societé Philomathic on the last day of that year; this is the paper that is given at the end of this chapter.

Gay-Lussac married in 1808 in a manner that offers an interesting sidelight on his character. While in a "linen draper's shop" in Paris he saw a young woman clerk reading a book on chemistry. He promptly paid court to the lady and married her after which he proceeded to have her educated as he thought proper, in English and Italian. Probably as a consequence of assuming family obligations, Gay-Lussac's attention, following the completion of his study of the combination of gases, turned increasingly to applied chemistry. His reputation was such that his services as a technical consultant were in wide demand. He was already active as a member of the Consultative Committee on the Arts and Manufactures, and this interest increased in the years ahead.

In 1808 he was also appointed professor of physics in the Sorbonne, a post he held until 1832; on January 1, 1810, he succeeded Fourcroy as professor of chemistry at the École Polytechnique. His last outstanding piece of pure research was on prussic acid in the period 1811–1815. In the succeeding years, he became superintendent of the government gunpowder factory (1818) and, in 1829, assayer to the mint. However, he continued to maintain his laboratory work in chemistry and to lecture at the École. A report quoted by Partington on his lectures in 1820 states that "he had a slender and handsome figure, his voice was gentle but firm and clear, his diction terse and choice and the lecture was a superlative specimen of continuous unassailable experimental reasoning." In 1831, when fifty-two, he was elected to the Chamber of Deputies to represent his native Department of Haute-Vienne and in 1839 he entered the House of Peers, having been created a peer by King Louis Philippe. He was editor with Arago of the *Annales de Chemie et Physique,* a task which he continued almost to the end of his days.

In summing up his personal life it is clear that he was, to quote Sir Humphry Davy, "quick, lively, ingenious and profound with great activity of mind and great facility of manipulation." But his early outstanding success in both academic and public life made him increasingly aware of his own merit, a feeling manifested by an aloofness and chilly reserve that increased as he grew older. He became, in fact, somewhat of a prig, but this should not blind us to the fact that he was a bold, energetic, and courageous man whose work, characterized by high competence, perseverance, and a consuming passion for accuracy, greatly enriched science and mankind. He died in Paris on May 9, 1850, at the age of seventy-one.

೦೦೦೦೦೦೦೦

GAY-LUSSAC

Memoir on the Combination of Gaseous Substances with Each Other [1]

SUBSTANCES, WHETHER IN THE SOLID, liquid, or gaseous state, possess properties which are independent of the force of cohesion; but they also possess others which appear to be modified by this

---

[1] Joseph Louis Gay-Lussac, in *Alembic Club Reprint #4* (London: Simpkin, Marshall, Hamilton, Kent & Company, 1890).

force (so variable in its density), and which no longer follow any regular law. The same pressure applied to all solid or liquid substances would produce a diminution of volume differing in each case, while it would be equal for all elastic fluids. Similarly, heat expands all substances; but the dilations of liquids and solids have hitherto presented no regularity, and it is only those of elastic fluids which are equal and independent of the nature of each gas. The attraction of the molecules in solids and liquids is, therefore, the cause which modifies their special properties; and it appears that it is only when the attraction is entirely destroyed, as in gases, that bodies under similar conditions obey simple and regular laws. I hope by this means to give a proof of an idea advanced by several very distinguished chemists—that we are perhaps not far removed from the time when we shall be able to submit the bulk of chemical phenomena to calculation.

It is a very important question in itself, and one much discussed amongst chemists, to ascertain if compounds are formed in all sorts of proportions. M. Proust, who appears first to have fixed his attention on this subject, is of opinion that the metals are susceptible of only two degrees of oxidation; *a minimum* and *a maximum;* but led away by this seductive theory, he has seen himself forced to entertain principles contrary to physics in order to reduce to two oxides all those which the same metal sometimes presents. M. Berthollet thinks, on the other hand—reasoning from general considerations and his own experiments—that compounds are always formed in very variable proportions, unless they are determined by special causes, such as crystallisation, insolubility, or elasticity. Lastly, Dalton has advanced the idea that compounds of two bodies are formed in such a way that one atom of the one unites with one, two, three, or more atoms of the other. It would follow from this mode of looking at compounds that they are formed in constant proportions, the existence of intermediate bodies being excluded, and in this respect Dalton's theory would resemble that of M. Proust; but M. Berthollet has already strongly opposed it in the Introduction he has written to Thomas's Chemistry, and we shall see that in reality it is not entirely exact. Such is the state of the question now under discussion; it is still very far from receiving its solution, but I hope that the facts which I now proceed to set forth, facts which had entirely escaped the notice of chemists, will contribute to its elucidation.

Suspecting, from the exact ratio of 100 of oxygen to 200 of hydrogen, which E. Humboldt and I had determined for the proportions of water, that other gases might also combine in simple ratios, I have made the following experiments. I prepared fluoboric, muriatic, and carbonic gases, and made them combine successively with ammonia gas, and the salt which is formed from them is perfectly neutral, whether one or other of the gases is in excess. Fluoboric gas, on the contrary, unites in two proportions with ammonia gas. When the acid gas is put first into the graduated tube, and the other gas is then passed in, it is found that equal volumes of the two condense, and that the salt formed is neutral. But if we begin by first putting the ammonia gas into the tube, and then admitting the fluoboric gas in single bubbles, there will result a salt with excess of base, composed of 100 of fluoboric gas and 200 of ammonia gas. If carbonic gas is brought into contact with ammonia gas, by passing it sometimes first, sometimes second into the tube, there is always formed a sub-carbonate composed of 100 parts of carbonic gas and 200 of ammonia gas. It may, however, be proved that neutral carbonate of ammonia would be composed of equal volumes of each of these components. M. Berthollet, who analyzed this salt, obtained by passing carbonic gas into the sub-carbonate, found that it was composed of 73.34 parts by weight of carbonic gas and 26.66 of ammonia gas. Now, if we suppose it to be composed of equal volumes of its components, we find from their known specific gravity, that it contains by weight

> 71.81 of carbonic acid,
> 28.19 of ammonia,
> ―――――
> 100.0

a proportion differing only slightly from the preceding.

If the neutral carbonate of ammonia could be formed by the mixture of carbonic gas and ammonia gas, as much of one gas as of the other would be absorbed; and since we can only obtain it through the intervention of water, we must conclude that it is the affinity of this liquid which competes with that of the ammonia to overcome the elasticity of the carbonic acid, and that the neutral carbonate of ammonia can only exist through the medium of water.

Thus we may conclude that muriatic, fluoboric, and carbonic acids take exactly their own volume of ammonia gas to form neutral salts, and that the last two take twice as much to form sub-salts. It is very remarkable to see acids so different from one another neutralize a volume of ammonia gas equal to their own; and from this we may suspect that if all acids and all alkalis could be obtained in the gaseous state, neutrality would result from the combination of equal volumes of acid and alkali.

It is not less remarkable that, whether we obtain a neutral salt or a sub-salt, their elements combine in simple ratios which may be considered as limits to their proportions. Accordingly, if we accept the specific gravity of muriatic acid determined by M. Biot and myself, and those of carbonic gas and ammonia given by MM. Biot and Arago, we find that dry muriate of ammonia is composed of

> Ammonia,   100.0   or   38.35
> Muriatic acid, 160.7   61.65
> ―――――
> 100.00

a proportion very far from that of M. Berthollet—

    100 of ammonia,
    213 of acid.

In the same way, we find that sub-carbonate of ammonia contains

    Ammonia,   100.0   or   43.98
    Carbonic acid, 127.3   56.02
                               ———————
                               100.00

and the neutral carbonate

    Ammonia,   100.0   or   28.19
    Carbonic acid, 254.6   71.81
                               ———————
                               100.00

It is easy from the preceding results to ascertain the ratios of the capacity of fluoboric, muriatic, and carbonic acids; for since these three gases saturate the same volume of ammonia gas, their relative capacities will be inversely as their densities, allowance having been made for the water contained in muriatic acid.

We might even now conclude that gases combine with each other in very simple ratios; but I shall still give some fresh proofs.

According to the experiments of M. Berthollet, ammonia is composed of

    100 of nitrogen
    300 of hydrogen,

by volume.

I have found that sulphuric acid is composed of

    100 of sulphurous gas,
    50 of oxygen gas.

When a mixture of 50 parts of oxygen and 100 of carbonic oxide (formed by the distillation of oxide of zinc with strongly calcined charcoal) is inflamed, these two gases are destroyed and their place taken by 100 parts of carbonic acid gas. Consequently carbonic acid may be considered as being composed of

    100 of carbonic oxide gas
    50 of oxygen gas.

Davy, from the analysis of various compounds of nitrogen with oxygen, has found the following proportions by weight:

	NITROGEN	OXYGEN
Nitrous oxide	63.30	36.70
Nitrous gas	44.05	55.95
Nitric acid	29.50	70.50

Reducing these proportions by volumes we find:

	NITROGEN	OXYGEN
Nitrous oxide	100	49.5
Nitrous gas	100	108.9
Nitric acid	100	204.7

The first and the last of these proportions differ only slightly from 100 to 50, and 100 to 200; it is only the second which diverges somewhat from 100 to 100. The difference, however, is not very great, and is such as we might expect in experiments of this sort; and I have assured myself that it is actually nil. On burning the new combustible substance from potash in 100 parts by volume of nitrous gas, there remained over exactly 50 parts of nitrogen, the weight of which, deducted from that of the nitrous gas (determined with great care by M. Berard at Arcueil), yields as a result that this gas is composed of equal parts by volume of nitrogen and oxygen.

We may then admit the following numbers for the proportions by volume of the compounds of nitrogen with oxygen:

	NITROGEN	OXYGEN
Nitrous oxide	100	50
Nitrous gas	100	100
Nitric acid	100	200

From my experiments, which differ very little from those of M. Chenevix, oxygenated muriatic acid is composed by weight of

Oxygen	22.92
Muriatic acid	77.08

Converting these quantities into volumes, we find that oxygenated muriatic acid is formed of

Muriatic gas	300.0
Oxygen gas	103.2

a proportion very nearly

Muriatic gas	300
Oxygen gas	100 *

---

* In the proportion of weight of oxygenated muriatic acid, the muriatic acid is supposed to be free from water, whilst in the proportion by volume it is supposed to be combined with a fourth of its weight of water, which, since the reading of this paper, M. Thénard and I have proved to be absolutely necessary for its existence in the gaseous state. But since the simple ratio of 300 of acid to 100 of oxygen cannot be due to chance, we must conclude that water by combining with dry muriatic acid to form ordinary muriatic acid does not sensibly change its specific gravity. We should be led to the same conclusion from

Thus it appears evident to me that gases always combine in the simplest proportions when they act on one another; and we have seen in reality in all the preceding examples that the ratio of combination is 1 to 1, 1 to 2, or 1 to 3. It is very important to observe that in considering weights there is no simple and finite relation between the elements of any one compound; it is only when there is a second compound between the same elements that the new proportion of the element that has been added is a multiple of the first quantity. Gases, on the contrary, in whatever proportions they may combine, always give rise to compounds whose elements by volume are multiples of each other.

Not only, however, do gases combine in very simple proportions, as we have just seen, but the apparent contraction of volume which they experience on combination has also a simple relation to the volume of the gases, or at least to that of one of them.

I have said, following M. Berthollet, that 100 parts of carbonic oxide gas, prepared by distilling oxide of zinc and strongly calcined charcoal, produce 100 parts of carbonic gas on combining with 50 of oxygen. It follows from this that the apparent contraction of the two gases is precisely equal to the volume of oxygen gas added. The density of carbonic gas is thus equal to that of carbonic oxide gas plus half the density of oxygen gas; or, conversely, the density of carbonic oxide gas is equal to that of carbonic gas, minus half that of oxygen gas. Accordingly, taking the density of air as unity, we find the density of carbonic oxide gas to be 0.9678, instead of 0.9569 experimentally determined by Cruickshanks. We know, besides, that a given volume of oxygen produces an equal volume of carbonic acid; consequently oxygen gas doubles its volume on forming carbonic oxide gas with carbon, and so does carbonic gas on being passed over red-hot charcoal. Since oxygen produces an equal volume of carbonic gas, and the density of the latter is well known, it is easy to calculate the proportion of its elements. In this way we find that carbonic gas is composed of

27.38 of carbon,
72.62 of oxygen,

and carbonic oxide of

42.99 of carbon,
57.01 of oxygen.

---

the consideration that the specific gravity of oxygenated muriatic acid, which from our experiments contains no water, is exactly the same as that obtained by adding the density of oxygen gas to three times that of muriatic gas, and taking half of this sum. M. Thénard and I have also found that oxygenated muriatic gas contains precisely half its volume of oxygen, and that it can destroy in consequence its own volume of hydrogen.

Pursuing a similar course, we find that if sulphur takes 100 parts of oxygen to produce sulphurous acid, it takes 150 parts to produce sulphuric acid. As a matter of fact, we find that sulphuric acid, according to the experiments of MM. Klaproth, Bucholz, and Richter, is composed of 100 parts by weight of sulphur and 138 of oxygen.

On the other hand sulphuric acid is composed of 2 parts by volume of sulphurous gas, and 1 of oxygen gas. Consequently the weight of a certain quantity of sulphuric acid should be the same as that of 2 parts of sulphurous acid and 1 of oxygen gas, i.e., 2×2.265, plus $1.10359 - 5.63359$; seeing that, according to Kirwan, sulphurous gas weighs 2.265, the density of air being taken as unity. But from the proportion of 100 of sulphur to 138 of oxygen, this quantity contains 3.26653 of oxygen, and if we subtract from it 1.10359 there will remain 2.16294 for the weight of oxygen contained in 1 part.

Now as this last quantity only differs by 2 per cent. from 1.10359, which represents the weight of oxygen gas, it must be concluded that oxygen gas, in combining with sulphur to form sulphurous gas, only experiences a diminution of a fiftieth of its volume, and this would probably be nil if the data I have employed were more exact. On this last supposition, using Kirwan's value for the specific gravity of sulphurous gas, we should find that this acid is composed of

    100.00 of sulphur,
    95.02 of oxygen.

But, if, adopting the preceding proportions for sulphuric acid, we allow, as appears probable, that 100 of sulphurous gas contain 100 of oxygen gas, and that 50 have still to be added to convert it into sulphuric acid, we shall obtain for the proportions in sulphurous acid

    100.00 of sulphur,
    92.0 of oxygen.

Its specific gravity calculated on the same suppositions, and referred to that of air, would be 2.30314, instead of 2.2650 as Kirwan found directly.*

---

* In order to remove these differences it would be necessary to make new experiments on the density of sulphurous gas, on the direct union of oxygen gas with sulphur to see if there is contraction, and on the union of sulphurous gas with ammonia gas. I have found, it is true, on heating cinnabar in oxygen gas, that 100 parts of this gas only produce 93 of sulphurous gas. It also appeared as if less sulphurous gas than ammonia gas was necessary to form a neutral salt. But these experiments were not made under suitable conditions—especially the last, which could only be made in presence of water, the sulphurous gas decomposing and precipitating sulphur immediately on being mixed with ammonia gas,—I intend to repeat them and determine exactly all the conditions

Phosphorus is very closely connected with sulphur, seeing that both have nearly the same specific gravity. Consequently phosphorus should take up twice as much oxygen to become phosphorous acid, as to pass from this state into phosphoric acid. Since the latter is composed, according to Rose, of

    100.0 of phosphorus,
     76.0 of oxygen,

it follows that phosphorous acid should contain 100.0 of phosphorus, 76.0 of oxygen.

We have seen that 100 parts of nitrogen gas take 50 parts of oxygen gas to form nitrous oxide, and 100 of oxygen gas to form nitrous gas. In the first case, the contraction is a little greater than the volume of oxygen added; for the specific gravity of nitrous oxide, calculated on this hypothesis, is 1.52092, while that given by Davy is 1.61414. But it is easy to show, from some of Davy's experiments, that the apparent contraction is precisely equal to the volume of oxygen gas added. On passing the electric spark through a mixture of 100 parts of hydrogen and 97.5 of nitrous oxide the hydrogen is destroyed, and 102 parts of nitrogen remain, including that quantity which is almost always mixed with the hydrogen, and a little of the latter gas which has escaped combustion. The residue, after making all corrections, would be nearly equal in volume to the nitrous oxide employed. Similarly, on passing the electric spark through a mixture of 100 parts of phosphoretted hydrogen and 250 of nitrous oxide, water and phosphoric acid are formed, and exactly 250 parts of nitrogen remain, —another evident proof that the apparent contraction of the elements of nitrous oxide is equal to the whole volume of oxygen added. From this circumstance, its specific gravity referred to that of air should be 1.52092.

The apparent contraction of the elements of nitrous gas appears, on the other hand, to be nil. If we admit, as I have shown, that it is composed of equal parts of oxygen and nitrogen, we find that its density, calculated on the assumption that there is no contraction, is 1.036, while that determined directly is 1.038.

Ammonia gas is composed of three parts by volume of hydrogen and one of nitrogen, and its density compared to air is 0.596. But if we suppose the apparent contraction to be half of the whole volume, we find 0.594 for the density. Thus it is proved, by this almost perfect concordance, that the apparent contraction of its elements is precisely half the total volume or rather double the volume of the nitrogen.

---

before drawing any conclusion from them. This is all the more necessary, as sulphurous gas can be used to analyze sulphuretted hydrogen gas, if its proportions are well known.

I have already proved that oxygenated muriatic gas is composed of 300 parts of muriatic gas and 100 of oxygen gas. Admitting that the apparent contraction of the two gases is half the whole volume, we find 2.468 for its density, and by experiment 2.470. I have also assured myself by several experiments that the proportions of its elements are such that it forms neutral salts with the metals. For example, if we pass oxygenated muriatic gas over copper, there is formed a slightly acid green muriate, and a little oxide of copper is precipitated, because the salt cannot be obtained perfectly neutral. It follows from this that in all the muriates, as in oxygenated muriatic acid, the acid reduced to volume is thrice the oxygen. It would be the same for carbonates and fluorides, the acids of which have for equal volumes the same saturation capacity as muriatic acid.

We see, then, from these various examples, that the contraction experienced by two gases on combination is in almost exact relation with their volume, or rather with the volume of one of them. Only very slight differences exist between the densities of compounds obtained by calculation and those given by experiment, and it is probable that, on undertaking new researches, we shall see them vanish entirely.

Recalling the great law of chemical affinity, that every combination involves an approximation of the elementary molecules, it is difficult to conceive why carbonic oxide gas should be lighter than oxygen. Indeed, that is the principal reason which has led M. Berthollet to assume the existence of hydrogen in this gas, and thus explain its low density. But it seems to me that the difficulty arises from supposing that the approximation of the elementary molecules is represented in gases by the diminution of volume which they suffer on combination. This supposition is not always true, and we might cite several gaseous combinations, the constituent molecules of which would be brought very close together, although there is not only no diminution of volume, but even a dilatation. Such, for example, is nitrous gas, whether we consider it as being formed directly from nitrogen and oxygen, or from nitrous oxide and oxygen. In the first case, there is no diminution of volume; and in the second, there would be dilatation, for 100 parts of nitrous oxide and 50 of oxygen would produce 200 of nitrous gas. We know too that carbonic gas represents an exactly equal volume of oxygen, and that the affinity which unites its elements is very powerful. Nevertheless, if we admitted an immediate relation between the condensation of the elements and the condensation of volume, we should conclude, contrary to experiment, that there is no condensation. Otherwise it would be necessary to suppose that if carbon were in the gaseous state it would combine in equal volumes (or in any other proportion) with oxygen, and that the apparent condensation would then be equal to the whole volume of the gaseous carbon. But if we make this supposition for carbonic acid, we may also make it for carbonic oxide, by assuming, for instance, that

100 parts of gaseous carbon would produce 100 parts of the gas on combining with 50 parts of oxygen. However it may stand with these suppositions, which only serve to make it conceivable that oxygen can produce a compound lighter than itself by combining with a solid substance, we must admit, as a truth founded on a great number of observations, that the condensation of the molecules of two combining substances, in particular of two gases, has no immediate relation to the condensation of volume, since we often see that whilst one is very great the other is very small or even nil.

According to Dalton's ingenious idea, that combinations are formed from atom to atom, the various compounds which two substances can form would be produced by the union of one molecule of the one with one molecule of the other, or with two, or with a greater number, but always without intermediate compounds. Thomson and Wollaston have indeed described experiments which appear to confirm this theory. Thomson has found that super-oxalate of potash contains twice as much acid as is necessary to saturate the alkali; and Wollaston, that the sub-carbonate of potash contains, on the other hand, twice as much alkali as is necessary to saturate the acid.

The numerous results I have brought forward in this Memoir are also very favorable to the theory. But M. Berthollet, who thinks that combinations are made continuously, cites in proof of his opinion the acid sulphates, glass alloys, mixtures of various liquids,—all of which are compounds with very variable proportions, and he insists principally on the identity of the force which produces chemical compounds and solutions.

Each of these two opinions has, therefore, a large number of facts in its favour; although they are apparently utterly opposed, it is easy to reconcile them.

We must first of all admit, with M. Berthollet, that chemical action is exercised indefinitely in a continuous manner between the molecules of substances, whatever their number and ratio may be, and that in general we can obtain compounds with very variable proportions. But then we must admit at the same time that,—apart from insolubility, cohesion, and elasticity, which tend to produce compounds in fixed proportions,—chemical action is exerted more powerfully when the elements are in simple ratios or in multiple proportions among themselves, and that compounds are thus produced which separate out more easily. In this way we reconcile the two opinions, and maintain the great chemical law, that whenever two substances are in presence of each other they act in their sphere of activity according to their masses, and give rise in general to compounds with very variable proportions, unless these proportions are determined by special circumstances.

CONCLUSION

I have shown in this Memoir that the compounds of gaseous substances with each other are always formed in very simple ratios, so that representing one of the terms by unity, the other is 1, or 2, or at most 3. These ratios by volume are not observed with solid or liquid substances, nor when we consider weights, and they form a new proof that it is only in the gaseous state that substances are in the same circumstances and obey regular laws. It is remarkable to see that ammonia gas neutralizes exactly its own volume of gaseous acids; and it is probable that if all acids and alkalies were in the elastic state, they would all combine in equal volumes to produce neutral salts. The capacity of saturation of acids and alkalies measured by volume would then be the same, and this might perhaps be the true manner of determining it. The apparent contraction of volume suffered by gases on combination is also very simple related to the volume of one of them, and this property likewise is peculiar to gaseous substances.

12

○○○○○○○○○○○

ATOMS AND MOLECULES—
AVOGADRO'S LAW

○○○○○○○○○○○

Amedeo Avogadro (1776-1856)

The clarification of atomic weights, the formulas of chemical compounds, the development of the periodic table of the elements, and indeed a rational science of chemistry, all have their roots in the application of Avogadro's principle that equal volumes of different gases at the same temperature and pressure contain the same number of molecules.

The deduction of this law, set forth in Avogadro's paper, and its application to various chemical combinations on the basis of Gay-Lussac's measurements, is a model of presentation and clear-headed logic based on experimental evidence. By his principle Avogadro correctly deduced the chemical formula for water, ammonia, nitrous oxide, nitric oxide, and nitrogen dioxide. However, for the principle to be valid it was necessary to introduce a new hypothesis, namely, that the ultimate particles of many of the elementary gases such as hydrogen and nitrogen were molecules, i.e., combinations of two, or sometimes more, atoms. Ideas on combination then current made this suggestion too implausible for the chemists of that day to accept and the science of chemistry fell into a morass of "systems" that greatly impeded progress. Recovery finally came through the genius of Stanislao Cannizzaro who dispelled the confusion by the thoroughgoing application of Avogadro's principle. Some idea of the confusion in which chemistry found itself and the nature of Cannizzaro's contribution will be found in Chapter 19.

Amedeo Avogadro—or Lorenzo Romano Amedeo Carlo Avogadro di Quaregna e di Cerreto, to use his full name—was born in Turin, August 9, 1776, the son of Count Filippo and Anna Vercellone Avogadro. Of

171

his early life and interests, and his ability as a student, scant information appears to exist. All that is known is that his family had been prominent since the eleventh century in the political life of the nearby province of Vercelli. His forebears for generations had been lawyers for the Roman church; "Avogadro," denoting this occupation came to be the family name as a consequence, and the original family name was lost.

Amedeo, as might be expected, was destined for the legal profession and his education was directed to that end. In 1792, at the age of sixteen, he received his bachelor of laws degree and three years later, that of doctor of jurisprudence. At twenty, he earned his doctorate in ecclesiastical law. During the next four years, he served as a lawyer in several government offices, but at the end of this time he had apparently made up his mind about his life's work, for he abandoned his legal career and devoted his full energies to the study of physics and mathematics for the next five years. It was in this period, at the age of twenty-seven, that he published with his brother Felice his first original paper entitled "Analytical Essay on Electricity." This was followed shortly by other papers on the same subject; as a result of these publications he was elected to membership in the Turin Royal Academy of Sciences in 1804. Shortly after he was appointed tutor in the Royal College of Vercelli and, in 1809, professor—a post he held until 1820. His famous principle, published in 1811, when he was thirty-five, was composed there.

The fourteen years at Vercelli were followed by an appointment as professor of mathematics and physics at Turin; however, owing to political unrest and the attendant reactionary policies imposed on the university, his professorship was canceled in 1822. As a sop, he was made professor emeritus and given a small pension. It was not until 1832 that a change of government restored the canceled professorship.

Avogadro's former chair was not immediately offered to him, but was given instead to the celebrated mathematician Cauchy. After only a year at Turin, Cauchy accepted an appointment in Prague; a year later Avogadro was reinstated in his former professorship. He held this post until his retirement at the age of seventy-four in 1850. He lived six more years, passing away in Turin, in 1856, at the age of eighty.

Factual details of his life give very little insight into the kind of man Avogadro was. His portrait suggests a physically small, gentle person of slight build, and his features show a prominent hooked nose that gave him a rather birdlike appearance. Except for his initial collaboration with his brother Felice, all of his mature work was done alone. He attended no meetings and sought no colleagues with whom to discuss scientific ideas. He was modest to the point of self-effacement, apparently because of a complete indifference to the world rather than any fear of it. Although he did not live to see the recognition of the true value of his principle, nevertheless he attained a measure of scientific acclaim in his lifetime. To this he seemed completely oblivious, and never utilized his recognition to push himself or to attain scientific or political position. He cultivated no influential friendships and seemed completely devoid of personal ambition. All of this might lead to the conclusion that he was a recluse, but that would be quite wrong. He married and reared a family of six children, two sons and four daughters. He formed warm personal relationships and he not only took his duties as a teacher seriously, but was successful also in imparting his knowledge to students. He was thoughtful of others: it was even stated that he resigned his professorship so that his protégé, Felice Chio, might be advanced. Although he published little, he was a prodigious writer, leaving at his death seventy-five volumes of manuscript, each containing approximately seven hundred pages of hand-written notes consisting of résumés on astronomy, organic and inorganic chemistry, and physics. He was, in short, a perpetual student, happy with his family and a small circle of friends, oblivious to most of the external world, and devoted to the quiet life of contemplation and scholarship.

It is important to recognize that Avogadro's principle is a twofold one. It states first that equal volumes of gases (at the same temperature and pressure) contain the same number of molecules. Second, that the elemental particles of a gas may consist of more than one atom, e.g., a nitrogen molecule is diatomic, N_2. The latter fact is so well recognized today that it is scarcely noted, but in Avogadro's time and later, this supposition was not accepted. Its rejection was based on a widely held theory of chemical combination, advanced by Berzelius, that assumed an electric charge on individual atoms. Like atoms were assumed to hold like charges and hence to repel each other. Berzelius was one of the most influential chemists of his era. Avogadro on the other hand was unknown and his ideas appear to have been equally so until Cannizzaro's time. The result was that chemistry fell into confusion, a situation that points up the necessity in science of the reiteration of opposing ideas until a secure solution is reached. The simple diagrams in figures 12–1 and 12–2 show how useful Avogadro's ideas were and how easily they could have explained to the chemists of the day the integral relationships that appeared in Gay-Lussac's experiments.

Let us consider a gaseous reaction, such as hydrogen with chlorine to produce hydrochloric acid. Here we find that one volume of hydrogen combining with one of chlorine produces two volumes of hydrochloric acid gas. We shall make the assumption that the gases are polyatomic; specifically, in this instance, diatomic. Then, representing diatomic atoms by the symbol •—•, i.e., two atoms joined together by a force of attraction, we may picture the reaction as in Figure 12–1. It is clear that as a result of the production of HCl, *two volumes* should result. Let us apply the same ideas to the formation of water vapor from a reaction of gaseous hydrogen and oxygen. Experiment shows that if the reaction is to be complete, i.e., with none of the original constituents remaining, two volumes of hydrogen must be reacted with one of oxygen. (See Figure 12–2.) We see that assuming oxygen to be diatomic, the appearance of two volumes of water vapor indicates the formula for water is H_2O.

Next we need to see whether this simple view is consistent with other facts obtained by weighing. Suppose we adopt a standard volume such that when it is filled with hydrogen at some standard temperature and one atmosphere pressure, the weight of the enclosed hydrogen is 2 grams. On

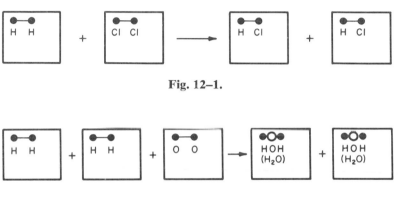

Fig. 12–1.

Fig. 12–2.

the same basis, the weight of chlorine in the initial experiment above is found to be 71 grams. Experiment shows that each container of product, HCl, weighs 36.5 grams. If a table of atomic weights referred to hydrogen is started on this basis, H = 1, Cl = 35.5, and HCl weighs 36.5 grams. Now let us consider the second experiment. As a consequence of the "standard" volume chosen for hydrogen, the same volume of oxygen would be found to weigh 32 grams; accordingly H_2O should thus have a molecular weight 18, as experiment corroborates. If further experiments of this kind were made on the synthesis of the oxides of nitrogen, all of the results would be found to be consistent with the starting hypotheses. Further, the atomic weight of nitrogen from the volumes involved would be found to be approximately 14.

୦୦୦୦୦୦୦୦

AVOGADRO

A Manner of Determining the Relative Masses of the Elementary Molecules of Bodies and the Proportions in Which They Enter into These Compounds [1]

M . G A Y - L U S S A C   H A S   S H O W N in an interesting Memoir (Memoires de la Societe d'Arcueil, Tome II) that gases always unite in a very simple proportion by volume, and that when the result of the union is a gas, its volume also is very simply related to those of its components. But the quantitative proportions of substances in compounds seem only to depend on the relative number of molecules which combine, and on the number of composite molecules which result. It must then be admitted that very simple relations also exist between the volumes of gaseous substances and the numbers of simple or compound molecules which form them. *The first hypothesis to present itself in this connection, and apparently even the only admissible one, is the supposition that the number of integral molecules in [all] gases is always the same for equal volumes,* [2] or always proportional to the volumes. Indeed, if we were to suppose that the number of molecules contained in a given volume were different for different gases, it would scarcely be possible to conceive that the law regulating the distance of molecules could give in all cases relations so simple as those which the facts just detailed compel us to acknowledge between the volume and the number of molecules. On the other hand, it is very well conceivable that the molecules of gases being at such a distance that their mutual attraction cannot be exercised, their varying attraction for caloric may be limited to condensing a greater or smaller quantity around them, without the atmosphere formed by this fluid having any greater extent in the one case than in the other, and, conse-

---

[1] Amedeo Avogadro, in *Alembic Club Reprint No. 4* (London: Simpkin, Marshall, Hamilton, Kent & Company, 1890).

[2] Editors' italics.

quently, without the distance between the molecules varying; or, in other words, without the number of molecules contained in a given volume being different. Dalton, it is true, has proposed a hypothesis directly opposed to this, namely, that the quantity of caloric is always the same for the molecules of all bodies whatsoever in the gaseous state, and that the greater or less attraction for caloric only results in producing a greater or less condensation of this quantity around the molecules, and thus varying the distance between the molecules themselves. But in our present ignorance of the manner in which this attraction of the molecules for caloric is exerted, there is nothing to decide us *a priori* in favour of the one of these hypotheses rather than the other; and we should rather be inclined to adopt a neutral hypothesis, which would make the distance between the molecules and the quantities of caloric vary according to unknown laws, were it not that the hypothesis we have just proposed is based on that simplicity of relation between the volumes of gases on combination, which would appear to be otherwise inexplicable.

Setting out from this hypothesis, it is apparent that we have the means of determining very easily the relative masses of the molecules of substances obtainable in the gaseous state, and the relative number of these molecules in compounds; for the ratios of the masses of the molecules are then the same as those of the densities of the different gases at equal temperature and pressure, and the relative number of molecules in a compound is given at once by the ratio of the volumes of the gases that form it. For example, since the numbers 1.10359 and 0.07321 express the densities of the two gases oxygen and hydrogen compared to that of atmospheric air as unity, and the ratio of the two numbers consequently represents the ratio between the masses of equal volumes of these two gases, it will also represent in our hypothesis the ratio of the masses of their molecules. Thus the mass of the molecule of oxygen will be about 15 times that of the molecule of hydrogen, or, more exactly, as 15.074 to 1. In the same way the mass of the molecule of nitrogen will be to that of hydrogen as 0.96913 to 0.07321, that is, as 13, or more exactly 13.238, to 1. On the other hand, since we know that the ratio of the volumes of hydrogen and oxygen in the formation of water is 2 to 1, it follows that water results from the union of each molecule of oxygen with two molecules of hydrogen. Similarly, according to the proportions by volume established by M. Gay-Lussac for the elements of ammonia, nitrous oxide, nitrous gas, and nitric acid, ammonia will result from the union of one molecule of nitrogen with three of hydrogen, nitrous oxide from one molecule of oxygen with three of hydrogen, nitrous oxide from one molecule of oxygen with two of nitrogen, nitrous gas from one molecule of nitrogen with one of oxygen, and nitric acid from one of nitrogen with two of oxygen.

There is a consideration which appears at first sight to be opposed to the admission of our hypothesis with respect to compound substances. It seems that a molecule composed of two or more elementary molecules should have its mass equal to the sum of the masses of these molecules; and that in particular; if in a compound one molecule of one substance unites with two or more molecules of another substance, the number of compound molecules should remain the same as the number of molecules of the first substance. Accordingly, on our hypothesis when a gas combines with two or more times its volume of another gas, the resulting compound, if gaseous, must have a volume equal to that of the first of these gases. Now, in general, this is not actually the case. For instance, the volume of water in the gaseous state is, as M. Gay-Lussac has shown, twice as great as the volume of oxygen which enters into it, or, what comes to the same thing, equal to that of the hydrogen instead of being equal to that of the oxygen. But a means of explaining facts of this type in conformity with our hypothesis presents itself naturally enough: *we suppose, namely, that the constituent molecules of any simple gas whatever* (i.e., *the molecules which are at such a distance from each other that they cannot exercise their mutual action*) *are not formed of a solitary elementary molecule, but are made up of a certain number of these molecules united by attraction to form a single one,*[3] and further, that when molecules of another substance unite with the former to form a compound molecule, the integral molecule which should result splits up into two or more parts (or integral molecules) composed of half, quarter, etc., the number of elementary molecules going to form the constituent molecule of the first substance, combined with half, quarter, etc., the number of constituent molecules of the second substance that ought to enter into combination with one constituent molecule of the first substance (or, what comes to the same thing, combined with a number equal to this last of half-molecules, quarter molecules, etc., of the second substance); so that the number of integral molecules of the compound becomes double, quadruple, etc., what it would have been if there had been no splitting-up, and exactly what is necessary to satisfy the volume of the resulting gas.*

On reviewing the various compound gases most generally known, I only find examples of duplication of the volume relatively to the volume of that one of the constituents which combines with one or more volumes of the other. We have already seen this for water. In the same way, we know that the volume of ammonia gas is twice that of the nitrogen which enters into it. M. Gay-Lussac has also shown that the volume of nitrous

---

[3] Editors' italics.

* Thus, for example, the integral molecule of water will be composed of a half-molecule of oxygen with one molecule, or, what is the same thing, two half-molecules of hydrogen.

oxide is equal to that of the oxygen. Finally, nitrous gas, which contains equal volumes of nitrogen and oxygen, has a volume equal to the sum of the two constituent gases, that is to say, double that of each of them. Thus, in all these cases there must be a division of the molecule into two; but it is possible that in other cases the division might be into four, eight, etc. The possibility of this division of compound molecules might have been conjectured *a priori;* for otherwise the integral molecules of bodies composed of several substances with a relatively large number of molecules, would come to have a mass excessive in comparison with the molecules of simple substance. We might therefore imagine that nature has some means of bringing them back to the order of the latter, and the facts have pointed out to us the existence of such means. Besides, there is another consideration which would seem to make us admit in some cases the division in question; for how could one otherwise conceive a real combination between two gaseous substances uniting in equal volumes without condensation, such as takes place in the formation of nitrous gas? Supposing the molecules to remain at such a distance that the mutual attraction of those of each gas could not be exercised, we cannot imagine that a new attraction could take place between the molecules of one gas and those of the other. But on the hypothesis of division of the molecule, it is easy to see that the combination really reduces two different molecules to one, and that there would be contraction by the whole volume of one of the gases if each compound molecule did not split up into two molecules of the same nature. M. Gay-Lussac clearly saw that, according to the facts, the diminution of volume on the combination of gases cannot represent the approximation of their elementary *molecules*. The divisions of molecules on combination explains to us how these two things may be made independent of each other.

Dalton, on arbitrary suppositions as to the most likely relative number of molecules in compounds, has endeavoured to fix ratios between the masses of the molecules of simple substances. Our hypothesis, supposing it well-founded, puts us in a position to confirm or rectify his results from precise data, and, above all, to assign the magnitude of compound molecules according to the volumes of the gaseous compounds, which depend partly on the division of molecules entirely unsuspected by this physicist.

Thus Dalton supposes * that water is formed by the union of hydrogen and oxygen, molecule to molecule. From this, and from the ratio by weight of the two components, it would follow that the mass of the molecule of oxygen would be to that of hydrogen as $7\frac{1}{2}$ to 1 nearly, or according to Dalton's evaluation, as 6 to 1. This ratio on our hypothesis is, as we saw, twice as great, namely, as 15 to 1. As for the molecule of water, its mass

---

* In what follows I shall make use of the exposition of Dalton's ideas given in Thomson's System of Chemistry.

ought to be roughly expressed by $15 + 2 = 17$ (taking for unity that of hydrogen), if there were no division of the molecule into two; but on account of this division it is reduced to half, $8\frac{1}{2}$, or more exactly 8.537, as may also be found directly by dividing the density of aqueous vapour 0.625 (Gay-Lussac) by the density of hydrogen 0.0732. This mass only differs from 7, that assigned to it by Dalton, by the difference in the values for the composition of water; so that in this respect Dalton's result is approximately correct from the combination of two compensating errors,—the error in the mass of the molecule of oxygen, and his neglect of the division of the molecule.

Dalton supposes that in nitrous gas the combination of nitrogen and oxygen is molecule to molecule; we have seen on our hypothesis that this is actually the case. Thus Dalton would have found the same molecular mass for nitrogen as we have, always supposing that of hydrogen to be unity, if he had not set out from a different value for that of oxygen, and if he had taken precisely the same value for the quantities of the elements in nitrous gas by weight. But by supposing the molecule of oxygen to be less than half what we find, he has been obliged to make that of nitrogen also equal to less than half the value we have assigned to it, viz., 5 instead of 13. As regards the molecule of nitrous gas itself, his neglect of the division of the molecule again makes his result approach ours; he has made it $6 + 5 = 11$, whilst according to us it is about $\dfrac{15 + 13}{2} = 14$, or more exactly $\dfrac{15.074 + 13.238}{2} = 14.156$, as we also find by dividing 1.03636, the density of nitrous gas according to Gay-Lussac, by 0.07321. Dalton has likewise fixed in the same manner as the facts given us, the relative number of molecules in nitrous oxide and in nitric acid, and in the first case the same circumstance has rectified his result for the magnitude of the molecule. He makes it $6 + [2 \times 5] = 16$, whilst according to our method it should be $\dfrac{15.074 + [2 \times 13.238]}{2} = 20.775$, a number which is also obtained by dividing 1.52092, Gay-Lussac's value for the density of nitrous oxide, by the density of hydrogen.

In the case of ammonia, Dalton's supposition as to the relative number of molecules in its composition is on our hypothesis entirely at fault. He supposes nitrogen and hydrogen to be united in it molecule to molecule, whereas we have seen that one molecule of nitrogen unites with three molecules of hydrogen. According to him the molecule of ammonia would be $5 + 1 = 6$: according to us it should be $\dfrac{13 + 3}{2} = 8$, or more exactly 8.119, as may also be deduced directly from the density of ammonia gas. The division of the moleclule, which does not enter into Dalton's calculations, partly corrects in this case also the error which would result from his other suppositions.

All the compounds we have just discussed are produced by the union of one molecule of one of the components with one or more molecules of the other. In nitrous acid we have another compound of two of the substances already spoken of, in which the terms of the ratio between the number of molecules both differ from unity. From Gay-Lussac's experiments (Societe d'Arcueil, same volume), it appears that this acid is formed from 1 part by volume of oxygen and 3 of nitrous gas, or, what comes to the same thing, of 3 parts of nitrogen and 5 of oxygen; whence it would follow, on our hypothesis, that its molecule should be composed of 3 molecules of nitrogen and 5 of oxygen, leaving the possibility of division out of account. But this mode of combination can be referred to the preceding simpler forms by considering it as the result of the union of 1 molecule of oxygen with 3 of nitrous gas, *i.e.,* with 3 molecules, each composed of a half-molecule of oxygen and a half-molecule of nitrogen, which thus already includes the division of some of the molecules of oxygen which enter into that of nitrous acid. Supposing there to be no other division, the mass of this last molecule would be 57.542, that of hydrogen being taken as unity, and the density of nitrous acid gas would be 4.21267, the density of air being taken as unity. But it is probable that there is at least another division into two, and consequently a reduction of the density to half: we must wait until this density has been determined by experiment. . . .

It will have been in general remarked on reading this Memoir that there are many points of agreement between our special results and those of Dalton, although we set out from a general principle, and Dalton has only been guided by considerations of detail. This agreement is an argument in favour of our hypothesis, which is at bottom merely Dalton's system furnished with a new means of precision from the connection we have found between it and the general fact established by M. Gay-Lussac. Dalton's system supposes that compounds are made in general in fixed proportions, and this is what experiment shows with regard to the more stable compounds and those more interesting to the chemist. It would appear that it is only combinations of this sort that can take place amongst gases, on account of the enormous size of the molecules which would result from ratios expressed by larger numbers, in spite of the division of the molecules, which is in all probability confined within narrow limits. We perceive that the close packing of the molecules in solids and liquids, which only leaves between the integral molecules distances of the same order as those between the elementary molecules, can give rise to more complicated ratios, and even to combinations in all proportions; but these compounds will be so to speak of a different type from those with which we have been concerned, and this distinction may serve to reconcile M. Berthollet's ideas as to compounds with the theory of fixed proportions.

13

○○○○○○○○○○

THE SEARCH FOR A

PRIMORDIAL MATERIAL

○○○○○○○○○○

William Prout (1785-1850)

The notion that all matter is composed of the same primary substance and that when organized in different ways produces the various elements, occurs far back in antiquity. Empedocles, about 440 B.C., suggested that there were only four elements: earth, air, fire, and water. But Aristotle, the giant intellect of the ancient world, could not accept immutable elements; instead he proposed a world in which visible matter was the result of the incorporation of "qualities," such as hot, dry, cold, and wet, with the great substratum of formless primary material. This material, when incorporated with the qualities hot and dry, resulted in fire; with hot and wet, air; with cold and dry, earth; and finally with cold and wet, water. This doctrine of the four elements led easily to the idea of transmutation, for were not all the elements composed of the same material and only modified in their qualities? Thus, the mere substitution of wet for dry should be sufficient to change fire into air. However naïve these ideas seem to us now, we should not forget that they held the belief of scientific men to the time of Boyle and Newton, a mere three hundred years ago.

An idea long established in the minds of men dies very hard. Although the revolution introduced into chemistry by Boyle swept away the four elements, it pronounced no such fate for the concept of a "first material." How then did this idea fare in the newer world of Daltonian theory, where atoms were distinguished by their different masses? As the first halting experiments in the new chemistry measured these masses, many turned out to be closely integral, assuming the value for the atomic weight of hydrogen as the basic unit and common denominator. How natural, there-

181

fore, for anyone steeped in the ancient lore to perpetuate the idea of the "first material" by identifying it as hydrogen.

The suggestion that the atoms of all elements are simply combinations of hydrogen first appeared in two anonymous papers published successively in the *Annals of Philosophy* for the years 1815 and 1816. Later, in 1816, Thomas Thomson, the editor of *Annals of Philosophy,* disclosed that the author was a London physician named William Prout, a man, it turned out, of unusual interest and ability in chemistry. Prout's suggestion soon became known as *Prout's hypothesis* and for more than a century it stood as a guidepost in the geography of atomic research. In the end, the direction it pointed proved erroneous but not until many explorers had thoroughly mapped the wilderness of atomic weights. This was its importance: it pointed the way to regions that had to be explored before atomic theory could safely widen its horizons.

It is worthwhile to review briefly the vicissitudes that Prout's hypothesis endured in order to see how pervasive its influence has been. Thomas Thomson, himself a chemist of note and the first to publicize Dalton's atomic theory, had been making atomic weight determinations for several years when Prout's papers appeared. Thomson became a strong supporter of the hypothesis, but his chemistry was criticized by Berzelius, who opposed Prout's ideas. In 1833, Edward Turner, at the invitation of the British Association for the Advancement of Science, undertook a series of analyses and concluded that the hypothesis was not exact (although it may be noted that his results did not justify the assertion). The same conclusion was reached by Frederick Penny in Glasgow in 1839. A determination of the atomic weight of carbon by Dumas and Stas in 1839–1840 and the synthesis of water by Dumas in 1843 both supported the hypothesis. A series of researches by de Marignac of Geneva at the same time led to the conclusion that the principle might be exact if the unit were half as large. A further investigation by Stas in 1860 led him to "consider Prout's law as a pure illusion."

Although the general result of these studies showed that there was not always close agreement with the hypothesis, some experiments demonstrated an approximation so close that it seemed necessary to postulate the existence of an underlying regularity that further research must explain.

Even as late as 1886, Sir William Crookes (see Chapter 23) gave strong support to the theory in his presidential address to the chemistry section of the British Association. In it he proposed a primary substance *protyle* out of which the atoms were formed; hydrogen he considered the first and simplest. He recognized the integral value of the atomic mass of a great number of the elements but questioned the "absolute uniformity in the mass of every ultimate atom of the same chemical element. Probably our atomic weights merely represent a mean value around which the actual [integral] atomic weights of the atoms vary within certain narrow limits." In this way he accounted for those atoms of nonintegral atomic weights such as chlorine. This suggestion proved indeed prophetic, as will be seen when we consider the discovery of isotopes by Frederick Soddy (see Chapter 47). In the meantime let us look briefly at the life of the man whose suggestion so strongly stimulated the progress of atomic investigation.

William Prout was born at Horton, Gloucestershire, England on January 15, 1785. He showed a marked interest in chemistry in his early schooling but eventually chose the practice of medicine as a profession. He obtained his M.D. degree at Edinburgh University at the age of twenty-six, in June 1811. The following year he began his practice in London, where he resided for the rest of his life. His interest in chemistry was shown not only by the papers that formed the basis of his hypothesis (reproduced in part in the following pages) but also by his contributions in physiological chemistry. Of these, the most important was his demonstration that free hydrochloric acid is present in the stomach, where it is an important factor in digestion.

Prout was elected a fellow of the Royal Society in 1819, and ten years later became a fellow of the Royal College of Physicians. After receiving the latter honor, he turned his attention almost completely to medical questions and to his practice. Toward the end of his life he became deaf and withdrew from active social life. He died at his home on Sackville Street, Piccadilly, on April 9, 1850, at the age of sixty-five.

In reading Prout's paper it is interesting to observe that he incorrectly believed atmospheric air to be a chemical compound, in fact, N_2O. This seems strange since the oxides of nitrogen were then well known and the chemical properties of the compound quite distinct from air. The relative weights of oxygen and nitrogen, taken as 10 and 17.5, are also unusually erroneous; however, accepting these values together with N_2O as the formula for air, the relative weight of an air molecule would then be $2N + O = 2 \times (17.5 + 10) = 45$ and the parts by weight of oxygen in the air would be $10/45 = 22.22\%$ and of nitrogen $35/45 = 77.77\%$.

To find the specific gravities of oxygen and nitrogen relative to air we may ignore Prout's indicated calculation and verbalize it as follows. One fifth of a unit volume of air is composed of oxygen with relative weight 10, and four fifths of nitrogen, with relative weight 35. The total weight is 45. One fifth of the air volume thus has weight 9, and accordingly the specific gravity of oxygen relative to air is $10/9 = 1.1111$. The nitrogen has relative weight 35 but an equal volume of air has weight $4/5 \times 45 = 36$. The specific gravity of nitrogen relative to air is thus $35/36 = 0.9722$.

To determine the specific gravity of hydrogen Prout employed the known specific gravity of one of its compounds, ammonia (NH_3) given relative to air by Davy as approximately 0.5902. Recognizing that three volumes of hydrogen when reacted with one of nitrogen condense into two volumes of ammonia, it follows at once that three times the specific gravity of hydrogen plus the specific gravity of nitrogen (found above) equals twice the specific gravity of ammonia. Inserting the numbers, the specific gravity of hydrogen relative to air is found to be 0.0694. The specific gravity of oxygen relative to hydrogen is thus $1.1111/0.0694 = 16$ and that of nitrogen, $0.9722/0.0694 = 14$. Other calculations in the paper may be readily followed with this introduction.

The reader should note that Avogadro's hypothesis is not mentioned, although it had been published before Prout's paper was written. It is probable that Prout was unaware of it. In assuming that the relative specific gravities of the gaseous elements, hydrogen being unity, gave the relative weights of the atoms, he tacitly assumed that equal volumes of gases have an equal number of particles, but he did not consider, as Avogadro had, that the "particles" might be polyatomic. Nevertheless, the fact that one volume of hydrogen combined with a half volume of oxygen to produce one volume of water vapor suggested that oxygen, on the basis that hydrogen equals unity, should have an atomic weight of eight, rather than sixteen, the weight ratio of equal volumes.

ᴏᴏᴏᴏᴏᴏᴏᴏ

PROUT

Article I

ON THE RELATION BETWEEN THE SPECIFIC GRAVITIES OF BODIES IN THEIR GASEOUS STATE AND THE WEIGHTS OF THEIR ATOMS[1]

THE AUTHOR OF THE FOLLOWING essay submits it to the public with the greatest diffidence; for though he has taken the utmost pains to arrive at the truth, yet he has not that confidence in his

---

[1] William Prout, *Annals of Philosophy*, 6 (1815), 321–327.

abilities as an experimentalist as to induce him to dictate to others far superior to himself in chemical acquirements and fame. He trusts, however, that its importance will be seen, and that some one will undertake to examine it, and thus verify or refute its conclusions. If these should be proved erroneous, still new facts may be brought to light, or old ones better established, by the investigation; but if they should be verified, a new and interesting light will be thrown upon the whole science of chemistry.

It will perhaps be necessary to premise that the observations about to be offered are chiefly founded on the doctrine of volumes at first generalized by M. Gay-Lussac; and which, as far as the author is aware at least, is now universally admitted by chemists.

ON THE SPECIFIC GRAVITIES OF THE ELEMENTARY GASES

OXYGEN AND AZOTE Chemists do not appear to have considered atmospheric air in the light of a compound formed upon chemical principles, or at least little stress has been laid upon this circumstance. It has, however, been long known to be constituted by bulk of four volumes of azote and one volume of oxygen; and if we consider the atom of oxygen as 10, and the atom of azote as 17·5, it will be found by weight to consist of one atom of oxygen and two atoms of azote, or per cent. of

Oxygen   22·22
Azote   77·77

Hence, then, it must be considered in the light of a pure chemical compound; and indeed nothing but this supposition will account for its uniformity all over the world, as demonstrated by numerous experiments. From these data the specific gravities of oxygen and azote (atmospheric air being 1·000) will be found to be,*

Oxygen   1·1111
Azote   ·9722

---

* Let x = sp. gr. of oxygen. 22·22 = a
  y = sp. gr. of azote.   77·77 = b

Then $\dfrac{x + 4y}{5} = 1$.

And $x : 4y :: a : b$.

Hence $5 - 4y = \dfrac{4ay}{b}$

And $y = \dfrac{5b}{4a + 4b} = $ ·9722. And $x = 5 - 4y = 1\cdot11111$.

HYDROGEN   The specific gravity of hydrogen, on account of its great levity, and the obstinacy with which it retains water, has always been considered as the most difficult to take of any other gas. These obstacles made me (to speak in the first person) despair of arriving at a more just conclusion than had been before obtained by the usual process of weighing; and it occurred to me that its specific gravity might be much more accurately obtained by calculation from the specific gravity of a denser compound into which it entered in a known proportion. Ammoniacal gas appeared to be the best suited to my purpose, as its specific gravity had been taken with great care by Sir H. Davy, and the chance of error had been much diminished from the slight difference between its sp. gr. and that of steam. Moreover, Biot and Arrago had obtained almost precisely the same result as Sir H. Davy. The sp. gr. of ammonia, according to Sir H. Davy, is ·590164, atmospheric air being 1·000. We shall consider it as ·5902; and this we are authorized in doing, as Biot and Arrago state it somewhat higher than Sir H. Davy. Now ammonia consists of three volumes of hydrogen and one volume of azote condensed into two volumes. Hence the sp. gr. of hydrogen will be found to be · 0694,* atmospheric air being 1·0000. It will be also observed that the sp. gr. of oxygen as obtained above is just 16 times that of hydrogen as now ascertained, and the sp. gr. of azote just 14 times.†

CHLORINE   The specific gravity of muriatic acid, according to Sir H. Davy's experiments, which coincide exactly with those of Biot and Arrago, is 1·278. Now if we suppose this sp. gr. to be erroneous in the same proportion that we found in the sp. gr. of oxygen and azote to be above (which, though not rigidly accurate, may yet be fairly done, since the experiments were conducted in a similar manner), the sp. gr. of this gas will come out about 1·2845; ‡ and since it is a compound of one volume chlorine and one volume hydrogen, the specific gravity of chlorine will be found by calculation to be 2·5.§ Dr. Thomson states, that he has found 2·483 to be near the truth,|| and Gay-Lussac almost coincides with

---

* Let x = sp. gr, of hydrogen.

Then $\dfrac{3x + ·9722}{2} = ·5902.$

Hence $x = \dfrac{1·1804 - ·9722}{3} = ·0694.$

† $1·11111 \div ·0694 = 16.$ And $·9722 \div ·0694 = 14.$

‡ As $1·104 : 1·11111 :: 1·278 : 1·286.$
And as $·969 : ·9722 :: 1·278 : 1·283.$ The mean of these is $1·2845.$

§ Let x = sp. gr. of chlorine.

Then $\dfrac{x + ·0694}{2} = 1·2845.$

And $x = 2·569 - ·0694 = 2·5$ very nearly.

|| *Annals of Philosophy*, vol. iv. p. 13.

him.* Hence there is every reason for concluding that the sp. gr. of chlorine does not differ much from 2·5. On this supposition, the sp. gr. of chlorine will be found exactly 36 times that of hydrogen.

ON THE SPECIFIC GRAVITIES OF ELEMENTARY SUBSTANCES IN A GASEOUS STATE THAT DO NOT AT ORDINARY TEMPERATURES EXIST IN THAT STATE

IODINE   I had some reason to suspect that M. Gay-Lussac had in his excellent memoir rated the weight of an atom of this substance somewhat too high; and in order to prove this 50 grains of iodine, which had been distilled from lime, were digested with 30 grs. of very pure lamellated zinc. The solution formed was transparent and colourless; and it was found that 12·9 grains of zinc had been dissolved. 100 parts of iodine, therefore, according to this experment, will combine with 25.8 parts of zinc, and the weight of an atom of iodine will be 155,† zinc being supposed to be 40. From these data, the sp. gr. of iodine in a state of gas will be found by calculation to be 8·611111, or exactly 124 times that of hydrogen.‡

CARBON   I assume the weight of an atom of carbon at 7·5. Hence the sp. gr. of a volume of it in a state of gas will be found by calculation to be ·4166, or exactly 12 times that of hydrogen.

SULPHUR   The weight of an atom of sulphur is 20. Hence the specific gravity of its gas is the same as that of oxygen, or 1·1111, and consequently just 16 times that of hydrogen.

PHOSPHORUS   I have made many experiments in order to ascertain the weight of an atom of this substance; but, after all, have not been able to satisfy myself, and want of leisure will not permit me to pursue the

---

* Ditto, vol. vi. p. 126.

† As 25·8 : 100 :: 40 : 55. According to experiment 8th, stated below, the weight of an atom of zinc is 40. Dr. Thomson makes it 40·9, which differs very little. See *Annals of Philosophy,* vol. iv. p. 94.

‡ One volume of hydrogen combines with only half a volume of oxygen, but with a whole volume of gaseous iodine, according to M. Gay-Lussac. The ratio in volume, therefore, between oxygen and iodine is as ½ to 1, and the ratio in weight is as 1 to 15·5. Now ·5555, the density of half a volume of oxygen, multiplied by 15·5, gives 8·61111, and 8·61111 ÷ ·06944 = 124. Or generally, to find the sp. gr. of any substance in a state of gas, we have only to multiply half the sp. gr. of oxygen by the weight of the atom of the substances with respect to oxygen. See *Annals of Philosophy,* vol. v. p. 105.

subject further at present. The results I have obtained approached nearly to those given by Dr. Wollaston, which I am therefore satisfied are correct, or nearly so, and which fix phosphorus at about 17·5, and phosphoric acid at 37·5,* and these numbers at present I adopt.

C A L C I U M   Dr. Marcet found carbonate of lime composed of 43·9 carbonic acid and 56·1 lime.† Hence as 43·9 : 56·1 :: 27·5 : 35·1, or 35 very nearly; and 35 − 10 = 25, for the atom of calcium. The sp. gr. of a volume of its gas will therefore be 1·3888, or exactly 20 times that of hydrogen.

S O D I U M   100 grains of dilute muriatic acid dissolved 18·6 grs. of carbonate of lime, and the same quantity of the same dilute acid dissolved only 8·2 grs. of carbonate of lime, after there had been previously added 30 grs. of a very pure crystallized subcarbonate of soda. Hence 30 grs. of crystallized subcarbonate of soda are equivalent to 10·4 grs. of carbonate of lime, and as 10·4 : 30 :: 62·5 : 180. Now 100 grs. of crystallized subcarbonate of soda were found by application of heat to lose 62·5 of water. Hence 180 grs. of the same salt contain 112·5 water, equal to 10 atoms, and 67·5 dry subcarbonate of soda, and 67·5 − 27·5 = 40 for the atom of soda, and 40 − 10 = 30 for the atom of sodium. Hence a volume of it in a gaseous state will weigh 1·6666, or exactly 24 times that of hydrogen.

I R O N   100 grs. of dilute muriatic acid dissolved as before 18·6 grs. of carbonate of lime, and the same quantity of the same acid dissolved 10·45 of iron. Hence as 18·6 : 10·45 :: 62·5 : 35·1, or for the sake of analogy, 35, the weight of an atom of iron. The sp. gr. of a volume of this metal in a gaseous state will be 1·9444, or exactly 28 times that of hydrogen.

Z I N C   100 grs. of the same dilute acid dissolved, as before, 18·6 of carbonate of lime and 11·85 of zinc. Hence as 18·6 : 11·85 :: 62·5 : 39·82, the weight of the atom of zinc, considered from analogy to be 40. Hence the sp. gr. of a volume of it in a gaseous state will be 2·222, or exactly 32 times that of hydrogen.

---

* Some of my experiments approached nearer to 20 phosphorus and 40 phosphoric acid.

† I quote on the authority of Dr. Thomson, *Annals of Philosophy*, vol. iii. p. 376. Dr. Wollaston makes it somewhat different, or that carbonate of lime consists of 43·7 acid and 56·3 lime. Phil. Trans. vol. civ. p. 8.

P O T A S S I U M   100 grs. of the same dilute acid dissolved, as before, 18·6 carbonate of lime; but after the addition of 20 grs. of super-carbonate of potash, only 8·7 carbonate of lime. Hence 20 grs. of super-carbonate of potash are equivalent to 9·9 carbonate of lime; and as 9·9 : 20 :: 62·5 : 126·26, the weight of the atom of super-carbonate of potash. Now $126·26 - \overline{55 + 11·25} = 60$, the weight of the atom of potash, and $60 - 10 = 50$, the weight of the atom of potassium. Hence a volume of it in a state of gas will weigh 2·7777, or exactly 40 times as much as hydrogen.

B A R Y T I U M   100 grs. of the same dilute acid dissolved exactly as much again of carbonate of barytes as of carbonate of lime. Hence the weight of the atom of carbonate of barytes is 125; and $125 - 27·5 = 97·5$, the weight of the atom of barytes, and $97·5 - 10 = 87·5$, the weight of the atom of barytium. The sp. gr. therefore, of a volume of its gas will be 4·8611, or exactly 70 times that of hydrogen.

With respect to the above experiments, I may add, that they were made with the greatest possible attention to accuracy, and most of them were many times repeated with almost precisely the same results.

[Table 13–1] exhibits a general view of the above results, and at the same time the proportions, both in volume and weight, in which they unite with oxygen and hydrogen: also the weights of other substances, which have not been rigidly examined, are here stated from analogy.

On a general review . . . , we may notice,

1. That all the elementary numbers, hydrogen being considered as 1, are divisible by 4, except carbon, azote, and barytium, and these are divisible by 2, appearing therefore to indicate that they are modified by a higher number than that of unity or hydrogen. Is the other number 16, or oxygen? And are all substances compounded of these two elements?

2. That oxygen does not appear to enter into a compound in the ratio of two volumes or four atoms.

3. That all the gases, after having been dried as much as possible, still contain water, the quantity of which, supposing the present views are correct, may be ascertained with the greatest accuracy.

Others might doubtless be mentioned; but I submit the matter for the present to the consideration of the chemical world.

TABLE 13–1 *Elementary Substances*

Name	Sp. gr. hydr. being 1.	Wt. of atom, hydr. being 1.	Wt. of atom, oxygen being 10.	Wt. of atom, oxygen being 10, from experiment.	Sp. gr. atmospheric air being 1.	Sp. gr. atmospheric air being 1, from experiment.	Wt. in grs. of 100 cub. inches. Barom. 30, Therm. 60.	Wt. in grs. of 100 cub. in. from exper.
Hydrogen	1	1	1·25	1·32	·06944	·073[1]	2·118	2·23
Carbon	6	6	7·5	7·54[2]	·4166	—	12·708	—
Azote	14	14	17·5	17·54	·9722	·969[3]	29·652	29·56
Phosphorus	14	14	17·5	17·4[4]	·9722	—	29·652	—
Oxygen	16	8	10	10	1·1111	1·104[5]	33·888	33·672
Sulphur	16	16	20	20[6]	1·1111	—	33·888	—
Calcium	20	20	25	25·46[7]	1·3888	—	42·36	—
Sodium	24	24	30	29·1[8]	1·6666	—	50·832	—
Iron	28	28	35	34·5[9]	1·9444	—	59·302	—
Zinc	32	32	40	41[10]	2·222	—	67·777	—
Chlorine	36	36	45	44·1[11]	2·5	2·483[12]	76·248	—
Potassium	40	40	50	49·1[13]	2·7777	—	84·72	—
Barytium	70	70	87·5	87[14]	4·8611	—	148·26	—
Iodine	124	124	155	156·21[15]	8·6111	—	262·632	—

Observations.

[1] Dr. Thomson. See *Annals of Philosophy*, i. 177.
[2] Dr. Wollaston, from Biot and Arrago. Phil. Trans. civ. 20. Dr. Thomson makes it 7·51. *Annals of Philosophy*, ii. 42.
[3] Dr. W. from Biot and Arrago.
[4] Dr. W. from Berzelius and Rose.
[5] Dr. Thomson, from a mean of several experiments.
[6] Dr. W. from Berzelius.
[7] Dr. W. from experiment.
[8] Dr. W. from Davy.
[9] Dr. W. from Thenard and Berzelius.
[10] Dr. W. from Gay-Lussac.
[11] Dr. W. from Berzelius.
[12] Quoted from Dr. Thomson, *Annals of Philosophy*, iv. 13.
[13] Dr. W. from Berzelius.
[14] Dr. W. from Berzelius and Klaproth.
[15] Gay-Lussac. Ann. de Chim. xci. 5.

Gaseous Bodies and the Weight of Their Atoms [2]

. . . THERE IS AN ADVANTAGE IN considering the volume of hydrogen equal to the atom, as in this case the specific gravities of most, or perhaps all, elementary substances (hydrogen being 1) will either exactly coincide with, or be some multiple of, the weights of their atoms; whereas if we make the volume of oxygen unity, the weights of the atoms of most elementary substances, except oxygen, will be double that of their specific gravities with respect to hydrogen. The assumption of the volume of hydrogen being equal to the atom will also enable us to find more readily the specific gravities of bodies in their gaseous state (either with respect to hydrogen or atmospheric air), by means of Dr. Wollaston's logometric scale.

If the views we have ventured to advance be correct, we may almost consider the πρώτη ὕλη of the ancients to be realised in hydrogen; an opinion, by the by, not altogether new. If we actually consider this to be the case, and further consider the specific gravities of bodies in their gaseous state to represent the number of volumes condensed into one; or, in other words, the number of the absolute weight of a single volume of the first matter (πρώτη ὕλη) which they contain, which is extremely probable, multiples in weight must always indicate multiples in volume, and *vice versâ;* and the specific gravities, or absolute weights of all bodies in a gaseous state, must be multiples of the specific gravity or absolute weight of the first matter (πρώτη ὕλη), because all bodies in a gaseous state which unite with one another unite with reference to their volume.

---

[2] *Ibid.,* 7 (1816), 111.

THE FOUNDATIONS
OF THE KINETIC THEORY
OF MATTER

14

ooooooooooo

ATOMS IN MOTION

ooooooooooo

John Herapath (1790-1868)

While chemistry was yielding results leading to belief in the atomic composition of matter, another avenue supporting this same point of view was developing in the kinetic theory of gases. Only Bernoulli had tried to fix such ideas quantitatively, but his brilliant efforts had attracted no serious attention because the concept of atoms was then highly speculative. But by 1820 the outlook of science had been changed by Dalton's atomism and although some first-rank scientists, such as Sir Humphry Davy, still questioned the actual existence of atoms, nevertheless many were disposed to concede their reality. It is not surprising therefore that a new advocate of the kinetic atomic hypothesis concerning gases should have appeared: one John Herapath, a contentious, argumentative, quick-tempered schoolmaster and amateur scientist. We consider him now because he had a direct influence on others, specifically James P. Joule, who in time extended Herapath's ideas and calculated molecular velocities.

Herapath was born in Bristol, England, May 30, 1790. As the son of a maltster he was put to work in his father's business. But mathematics and physics had captured his imagination and at the age of twenty-one he was already amusing himself by calculating lunar orbits as a result of reading Newton's *Principia.* The differences between his observations of the moon's position and the predictions of his calculations, even after using the methods of Laplace in the *Mechanique Celeste,* caused him to examine the nature of gravitation. Newton in his *Opticks* had suggested that gravitation might arise from the variation in density of an elastic medium filling all space. Herapath supposed that the density and hence the pressure of this medium on the sun side of a planet was less than on the dark side. Hence the planet would be "attracted" to the sun. This idea

195

led him to consider the relationship between temperature, pressure, and density of the supposed ethereal medium. He rejected the idea of heat being an elastic fluid and of static, gaseous particles repelling each other. Instead, he adopted the kinetic view stated in his papers and began developing a kinetic theory of gases. The background for this development accounts for the strange title of his paper, "A Mathematical Inquiry into the Causes, Laws, and Principal Phenomena of Heat, Gases, Gravitation, etc.," which is reproduced later in this chapter. Whether it was the implausible title or the contents of the paper that repelled its referees, we do not know, but at any rate it was denied publication in the *Philosophical Transactions* of the Royal Society. Never one to shrink from a controversy, Herapath aired the rejection in the *Annals of Philosophy,* where the paper appeared in 1821.

During the development of his theory, which took place in the period 1814 to 1820, he abandoned his father's business, married in 1815, and set up a mathematical academy at Knole Hill, Bristol. Apparently it did not prosper, for he moved to a London suburb in the latter part of 1820, settling there as a tutor of mathematics. This period of his life, extending from thirty through forty-two, was spent principally as a teacher; he had sought an appointment as professor of mathematics in the University of London and had attempted to write a treatise on differential and integral calculus, but neither of these attempts came to any fruitful conclusion.

In 1832, Herapath gave up teaching and entered the employment of the Eastern Counties Railway Company. Four years later, at the age of forty-six, he became part proprietor and manager of the railway magazine which he continued, as editor, under the title *Railway Magazine and Annals of Science.* In 1839, he turned over the management of the magazine to his son, Edwin, and returned again to mathematics and physics, publishing two volumes of *Mathematical Principles of Natural Philosophy* in 1847. He was then fifty-seven years old. He began a third volume, but little progress was made on it. He died at the age of seventy-seven at Lewisham, a London suburb.

Dr. Eric Mendoza of Manchester University, who has made a study of Herapath's life and work, comments on his theory as follows:

> It is not difficult to see that, from the point of view of physicists of the time [1820] . . . an insuperable difficulty [was] in the way of such a theory. It was that the collisions between atoms must be perfectly elastic. . . . No such substances were known in nature, even steel balls colliding with one another would certainly run down after a short time. An even more serious difficulty was that for a particle to be perfectly elastic it must be able to deform and this meant that it must have a structure . . . but this was impossible if the particle were an atom, for by definition it could not be further divided. . . .

The most important content of his work was a verbose but correct proof relating the pressure and volume of a gas to the velocities and masses of the rapidly moving atoms. [The formula states that *pv,* the product of pressure and volume, is proportional to the product of gas density and the mean squared molecular velocity.] John Herapath's achievement in deriving it was considerable.[1]

Herapath's procedures in "proving" these relationships are set forth in his Propositions VII and VIII, reproduced in the following pages. The earlier propositions deal mostly with the mechanics of impact, discussions that can be found today in any good general physics textbook. Attention should be directed to the last few lines of the selection in which the temperature resulting from a mixture of gases, initially at temperatures F and F_1, is calculated. Here absolute zero on the Fahrenheit scale enters into the calculation. There is no discussion of this calculation or explanation of it anywhere in the article. Evidently, the volume contraction for gases had been determined experimentally as $\frac{1}{480}$ of the volume at 32°F.

The gravest theoretical error in the paper was the attempt to identify temperature with the momentum of the gas particles, instead of their kinetic energy. Although this prevented any further development of his theory, the later elaboration of his ideas in his two-volume *Mathematical Principles of Natural Philosophy,* published in 1847, drew serious considerations from Joule, who acknowledged the value of Herapath's work to his own investigations. The eventual discovery of Bernoulli's prior treatment of gas kinetics made Herapath's pioneer work seem less important, and, gradually, reference to his name disappeared from the scientific literature. Kelvin, however, in reviewing the history of kinetic theory wrote that "it was developed by Herapath and made a reality by Joule."

---

[1] Eric Mendoza, *Memoirs and Proceedings of the Manchester Literary and Philosophical Society,* Session 1962–63, p. 5.

ooooooo

HERAPATH

A Mathematical Inquiry into the Causes, Laws, and Principal Phænomena of Heat, Gases, Gravitation, &c. [2]

POSTULATA

1. LET IT BE GRANTED THAT matter is composed of inert, massy, perfectly hard, indestructible atoms, incapable of receiving any change or impression in their original figure and nature.

2. Let it be granted that all solid and fluid bodies have their smaller parts composed of these atoms, which may be of different sizes and figures, and variously associated, according to the manner which the constitution and nature of the bodies require.

3. Let it be granted that gaseous or aeriform bodies consist of atoms, or particles, moving about, and among one another, with perfect freedom.

4. Let it be granted that what we call heat arises from an intestine motion of the atoms, or particles, and is proportional to their individual momentum.[3]

5. Let it be granted that a gaseous body of very great tenuity in its parts fills all space, and extends to its utmost limits.

I have purposely put these hypotheses (if indeed we can call those things hypotheses which have been deduced from the analysis of phænomena) into the form of postulata, to avoid being obliged to establish them by direct demonstration. It is not my intention, for the reasons I have already given in the beginning of this memoir, to make any comparative remarks on their relative simplicity and probability. I shall only say a few words for the purpose of explaining the difference between my views on certain points and those which have been taken by others.

One of the sublimest ideas of the ancients was, that there is but one kind of matter,[4] from the different sizes, figures, and arrangements of whose

---

[2] John Herapath, *Annals of Philosophy,* 2 (1821), pp. 343–346; 401–403.

[3] This is the principal error of the paper—Editors.

[4] See the preceding article by Prout which expresses an identical point of view—Editors.

primitive particles, arises all that beautiful variety of colour, hardness and softness, solidity and fluidity, opacity and transparency, &c. which is observed in the productions of nature. Our first two postulata do not necessarily require that there should be but one kind of matter; there may be several kinds. But since it seems possible to account for all the phænomena on the supposition of one kind only, and since nature is always disposed to employ the simplest machinery, probability is strongly in favour of the ancient idea. In fact it does not seem to be impossible, from some of the phænomena of light and other circumstances, to show that nature has embraced the simplest means, and has likewise, if not in the size, at least in the figure of the atoms, confined herself within certain limits. But these things are too recondite to be pursued in this memoir; and experiments have not yet furnished us with sufficient data to be able to exhibit the exact line and rule with which nature has laid out her work.

Philosophers, since the time of Newton, have taught us that the elasticity of gases is owing to a mutual repulsion between their particles, by which they endeavour to fly from one another; but by our third postulatum we have divested matter of this repulsive property, and . . . if gases, instead of having their particles endued with repulsive forces, subject to so curious a limitation as Newton proposed, were made up of particles, or atoms, mutually impinging on one another, and the sides of the vessel containing them, such a constitution of aeriform bodies would not only be more simple than repulsive powers, but, as far as I could perceive, would be consistent with phænomena in other respects, and would admit of an easy application of the theory of heat by intestine motion. Such bodies I easily saw possessed several of the properties of gases; for instance, they would expand, and, if the particles be vastly small, contract almost indefinitely; their elastic force would increase by an increase of motion or temperature, and diminish by a diminution; they would conceive heat rapidly, and conduct it slowly; would generate heat by sudden compression, and destroy it by sudden rarefaction; and any two, having ever so small a communication, would quickly and equally intermix.

The advocates for the theory of heat by intestine motion have usually considered the temperature as measured by the velocity of vibration; and I am not aware that any of them have defined it otherwise. This will do very well for different temperatures of the same body; but it seems to require the theory I have given in the fourth postulatum to enable us, under all circumstances, to compare the temperatures of different bodies.

. . . If a number of small bodies be inclosed in any hollow body, and be continually impinging on one another, and on the sides of the enclosing body; and if the motions of the bodies be conserved by an equivalent action in the sides of the containing body, then will these small bodies compose a medium, whose elastic force will be like that of our air and other gaseous bodies; for if the bodies be exceedingly small, the medium might, like any aeriform body, be compressed into a very small space; and yet, if it had no other tendency than what would arise from the internal collision of its atoms, it would, if left to itself, extend to the occupation of a space of almost indefinite greatness. And its temperature remaining the same, its elasticity [pressure] would also be greater when occupying a less, and less when occupying a greater space; for in a condensed state the number of atoms striking against a given portion of the containing vessel must be augmented; and the space in which the atoms have to move being less, their returns, or periods, must be shorter; and the number of them, in a given time, consequently greater, on both of which accounts the elasticity [pressure] is greater, the greater the condensation. Besides, when other things are the same, the elastic force [pressure] augments with an augmentation of temperature, and diminishes with a diminution; for an increase of temperature, according to our theory, must necessarily be attended with an increase of velocity; and, therefore, with an increase in the number of collisions. . . .

PROP. VII

If a given portion of a fluid gas, composed of particles mutually impinging on one another and the sides of the containing body, in the manner that has been described, has its temperature the same; and if the particles be indefinitely small, its elastic force, under different compressions, is reciprocally proportional to the space it occupies.[5]

Let us suppose that equal portions of the same gas be enclosed in two vessels of unequal capacity. Then, by the last Prop. it is immaterial whether these vessels be of the same or of different figures; the difference of figures would have no influence upon the ratio of the elasticities; but, for the sake of simplicity, we will suppose the two figures similar. Now because the only change that is supposed to take place is in the space which the gas occupies, the motions and collisions of a particle in the one will be similar to those of a corresponding particle in the other; and the temperature, that is, in this case, the velocity being the same in each, the numbers of revolutions [back and forth motions, i.e., excursions] that two corresponding particles in the two media make in a given time must be inversely proportional to the paths the particles describe; that is these paths being alike and described with equal velocities in the inverse sub-triplicate [cube root] ratio of the spaces occupied by the equal portion of gases. But because the elasticity of a gas is proportional to the action of

---

[5] This Prop. is essentially Boyle's law—Editors.

its particles against a given portion of the surface of the containing body, the ratio of the elastic forces, arising from the repeated actions of equal numbers of corresponding particles in the two media, will likewise, their velocities being the same in both media, be inversely as the subtriplicate of the spaces occupied. And if we conceive the two gases to be divided into strata, parallel to the sides of the bodies on which the elastic forces are measured, and of one, two, or any number of particles thick, it is manifest, since the motions of the particles are alike in each medium, that if the elasticity in one medium arises from the action of the particles of the first stratum alone, so it does also in the other medium; and if it arises from the action of the particles of the two first, three first, or n first strata in one medium, the same holds true with the elasticity in the other medium. But the number of particles of any one stratum that strike against a given portion of the containing surface of one medium, is to the number of particles of the corresponding stratum that strike against an equal and similar portion of the other medium, in the duplisubtriplicate ratio [two-thirds power] of the numeratoms [number of atoms per unit volume] directly; that is, in the duplisubtriplicate ratio of the spaces occupied by equal portions of the gases inversely. Therefore as the whole elastic forces of these corresponding strata are in a ratio compounded of the ratios of the numbers of particles that strike against equal portions of the sides of the containing bodies, and of the numbers of returns which they make to the sides in a given time, that ratio must be equal to one compounded of the inverse duplisubtriplicate and of the inverse subtriplicate ratios of the spaces occupied by the two gases; it must, therefore, be equal to the simple inverse ratio of the spaces occupied.[6] And since the same number of strata affects the elasticity of the one gas as of the other; and since the inverse ratio of the spaces is the ratio of the elastic force of any two corresponding strata, it is consequently the ratio of the united elastic forces of all the strata that affect the elasticity; and is, therefore, the ratio of the elastic forces of the two gases.

Cor.—Because the numeratoms are reciprocally proportional to the spaces occupied, it follows that the elasticities are, under equal temperatures, directly as the numeratoms.

Scholium

We have in the two preceding theorems and their corollaries supposed the atoms, or particles, to be perfectly hard; but the same consequences would follow if they were either perfectly or imperfectly elastic, and the containing vessel either elastic or hard. For the temperature being in-

---

[6] $\frac{1}{V^{2/3}} \times \frac{1}{V^{1/3}} = \frac{1}{V}.$

variable, the intensity of the collisions, and consequently of the reflections, would remain the same in a rare as in a denser medium. The law, therefore, that the elasticities and compressions are proportional, under equal temperatures, is true not only in permanent airs or gases, but in all kinds of vapours, which is conformable to experience.

P R O P. V I I I

The same things remaining, the elasticity [pressure] of a gas under a variable temperature and compression, is proportional to its numeratom and the square of its temperature conjointly; or the elasticity varies as the square of the temperature directly, and the simple of the space inversely.[7]

If we first suppose in two portions of the same gas the numeratoms to be equal, the elasticities of those portions will have the same ratio as the elasticities arising from the actions of corresponding particles in the two media; for the change of temperature does not alter the manner in which the corresponding particles act in the media, but only the intensity of action. This being the case, the elasticities due to the actions of corresponding particles are to one another as their momenta [actually as their kinetic energies] and the number of their revolutions or returns in a given time; that is, as their temperatures and velocities. But the masses of the corresponding particles being the same, the velocities are as the temperatures; therefore, the elasticities due to corresponding particles, and consequently the elasticities of the media, are as the squares of the temperatures. And by the cor. to the preceding prop. the temperatures being the same, the elasticities are as the numeratoms. Whence, if neither the temperatures, nor the numeratoms are the same, the elasticities are in a ratio compounded of the ratio of the numeratoms, and that of the squares of the temperatures, or, which is the same, in a ratio compounded of the inverse ratio of the volumes and the duplicate direct of the temperatures.

The advocates for the theory of heat by intestine motion have usually considered the temperature as measured by the velocity of vibration; and I am not aware that any of them have defined it otherwise. This will do very well for different temperatures of the same body; but it seems to require the theory I have given in the fourth postulatum to enable us, under all circumstances, to compare the temperatures of different bodies.[8]

---

[7] $p \sim nT^2$. This is incorrect but since he sets $v = T$, then $p \sim nv^2$, a correct relation if v^2 is the mean squared speed.

[8] Herapath, *op. cit.*, pp. 343–346.

GENERAL SCHOLIUM

Sudden condensation in all gaseous or aeriform bodies produces heat, and sudden rarefaction cold; but if the condensation or rarefaction be made slowly, no perceptible change in the temperature takes place. These are natural consequences of our theory of the constitution of gases. For if it be a condensation, by the motion inward, for instance, of one of the sides of the containing body, it is evident that the particles which strike against this side and are reflected back among the rest, will no longer be reflected by the same force only, with which they were previous to the commencement of the condensation, but by a force, which will augment their velocity individually by a quantity equal to the velocity of the moving side. And this excess of velocity being distributed to the rest of the particles, or communicated to them by the continuance of the stroke, will generate an excess of temperature throughout the medium proportional chiefly to the velocity of condensation. On the contrary, in the case of rarefaction, those particles, instead of returning among the rest with the celerity with which they did before the side began to move, will now return with a diminution of their velocity, equal to the velocity of the moving side. This diminution must, therefore, cause a decrease of temperature in the medium, in the same manner as the excess of velocity would cause an increase. In both these cases, the excess of defect of temperature will be proportional to the celerity of condensation or rarefaction, supposing the time occupied by the change of volume to be of sufficient length for the stroke to be propagated to all parts of the medium. Therefore, if the celerity of the stroke be great, a great change in the temperature will ensue; and if it be small, there will be little or none.

Our theory of gases likewise explains another phænomenon, which has usually been attributed to a different cause. It is well known that if two gases be placed in any position with respect to each other, and have ever so small a communication, they will intermix, and become equally diffused the one throughout the other. This has been accounted for on the principle that all gases have a slight affinity for one another, or in other words, that though the parts of all gaseous bodies individually considered mutually repel each other, yet the parts of different gases, however great or however small that difference may be, mutually attract each other. It is repugnant to my intention to attempt any refutation of this idea, or to make any observations on the confusion that would result from thus burthening nature with hypotheses; I shall, therefore, merely show that the phænomenon in question is an easy consequence of our theory. Suppose that portions of the surfaces of two media are exposed to each other, and that parallel to these portions the media are divided into strata. Then because a difference in the numeratoms, a difference in the motions of the particles of the two strata, or a cornered irregular figure in the particles, would render it impossible for the particles of one stratum to be so reflected by the particles of the other, that each stratum would retain its particles entire and unmixed with those of the other, the two strata would intermix; and would not arrive to a state of equilibrious action, until the particles were uniformly and equally disposed in each stratum. For the same reasons, these newly compounded strata would mix with their next; and thus it would go on stratum intermixing with stratum, until an equilibrious action throughout was restored, by the equal and uniform intermixture of the two gases.

By the same principles it is easily perceived, why gases so readily acquire the temperature of the surrounding bodies; why they transmit temperature so rapidly and so feebly in right lines; and why, according to the manner in which Mr. Leslie, Sir H. Davy, and MM. Dulong and Petit, have made their experiments, it is owing to the gravitation of the gases alone, that the lighter gases cool bodies immersed in them quicker than the heavier. When I first turned my attention to the cooling power of gases, I was surprised to find from my theory, that all gases, under the same circumstances, ought to cool equally fast. This inference for some time perplexed me very much. As soon, however, as I had read the ingenious treatise of Prof. Leslie on Heat and Moisture, and had considered anew the manner in which Sir H. Davy had conducted his experiments, which were about that time published, I saw that the theory and phænomena still agreed; and that the circumstances of my investigation precisely coincided with Mr. Leslie's cooling by gaseous pulsation; while the error that I had committed, with respect to Sir H. Davy's experiments, rested wholly on my not having taken into account the earth's attraction.

Their temperatures and elasticities being the same, the ratio of the numeratoms of two homogeneous gases appears by our theory to be equal to the subduplicate [square root] ratio of the weights or specific gravities of equal volumes. Supposing, therefore, that oxygen and hydrogen are homogeneous (the truth of which in oxygen I much doubt), the numeratom of the former will be quadruple that of the latter. So that if two in volume of hydrogen unite with one in volume of oxygen to form water, the atoms of oxygen will be double in number those of hydrogen; and the numeratom of the compound gas before being condensed will be the geometrical mean between the numeratoms of the two simples. It has commonly been conceived that two atoms of hydrogen and one of oxygen form a particle of water; but whether this, or whether the result of our theory, or whether neither of them be true, it is out of our power to determine. Such kind of speculations transcends the corroboration of any experiment yet devised. I simply mention this theorem, which is one among several that I have investigated, relative to the mixture of gases, to give some small idea of the powers of our theory of the universe for unravelling the secret operations of nature.

By the same theory I have found that if equal portions of the same gas be mixed together at different temperatures F, F_1, accounting in degrees of Fahrenheit, according to the indications of the air thermometer, the mean resulting temperature F_1, of the mixture, measured on the same scale, and no extraneous force interfering, will be equal to

$$(448 + F) \times \left(\frac{\sqrt{\dfrac{448 + F_1}{448 + F}} + 1}{2} \right)^2 - 448,[9]$$

supposing F to represent the degrees at the lower, and F_1 those at the higher temperature. . . .[10]

---

[9] 448 represents the degree of absolute cold below the zero of Fahrenheit employing the air thermometer, and estimating in Fahrenheit's scale of degrees.

[10] Herapath, *op. cit.*, pp. 401–403.

15

ооооооооооо

"ACTIVE MOLECULES"— BROWNIAN MOTION

ооооооооооо

Robert Brown (1773-1858)

It is a truism that among the many investigators working in a given discipline few ever make an outstanding discovery. It is therefore even more rare that a scientist should make a contribution of fundamental importance in a field quite apart from his own. But it is this distinction that must be accorded to Robert Brown for his discovery of what is now known as "Brownian motion," an effect arising from the imbalance of molecular impacts on a free microscopic particle. Brown, a botanist, made his discovery of "active molecules" in 1827 while attempting to determine the behavior of pollen grains suspended in water on a microscopic slide. He found the grains to be in active, chaotic motion, and at first associated the motion with the vitality of the pollen, as his article shows. But in pursuing the investigation he soon found that all small particles under the same conditions behaved the same way. The reason for the motion was not then suspected since the kinetic theory of gases was only a nebulous suggestion; indeed, Dalton's atomic theory was still in its infancy. Herapath had just attempted to develop a kinetic theory of gases, as shown in the preceding article; but, where it had not been ignored, it had drawn only opposition and ridicule. A further attempt, which suffered much the same fate, was made about twenty years later by Waterston, but the real impetus for its acceptance came from a calculation of molecular speeds (1851) by Joule and from the work of other recognized scientists —Kronig and Clausius, and especially Maxwell in 1859. Although these developments put kinetic theory on a firm basis, Brownian motion was not linked to these ideas. The first suggested connection between the two is probably owed to Wiener in Germany, in 1863, to Fathers Delsaulx

206

and Carbonelle, 1877 to 1880, and to Guoy, 1888, all of whom are noted in Perrin's article on the determination of Avogadro's number, which appears later in this work.

Robert Brown was born on December 21, 1773, the son of a minister of the Scottish Episcopal Church, in Montrose, Scotland. His mother, Helen Taylor, was the daughter of an Episcopal clergyman. His early education was in the grammar school at Montrose; in 1787, when not quite fourteen, he entered Marischal College, Aberdeen. He remained there for two years, withdrawing when the family moved to Edinburgh. Although he spent several years at Edinburgh University studying medicine, he did not attain a degree. Both in Aberdeen and Edinburgh, he devoted much of his leisure time to the study of plants in which he showed unusual aptitude. His first botanical work appeared when he was eighteen and consisted of a list of all the Scottish plants not previously described in Lightfoot's *Flora Scotica.* Many of the plants were his own discovery.

In 1795, when twenty-one, he obtained a commission in the Fifeshire Regiment, which was detailed to duty in northern Ireland where he spent most of the next five years. During this time he employed much of his leisure in botanical explorations and further established his standing in the field of botany. There was, however, one eventful break in his duty that changed the course of his life. In the latter months of 1798 and the early ones of 1799, Brown was transferred to London on recruiting duty. While there, he was allowed to use the library and collections of Sir Joseph Banks, longtime president of the Royal Society, upon whom he made a very favorable impression.

In 1800, when Sir Joseph sought a naturalist for an expedition that was to sail the following year to explore the coasts of Australia, his choice immediately fell upon Brown. It is said that two days after Brown received Banks's letter, he had resigned from the military service, left his regiment, and was on the way to England. The expedition departed from Portsmouth in the summer of 1801, and for four years Brown studied and classified the plants of the coastal regions of Australia and the island of Tasmania. When he returned to England in October of 1805 at the age of thirty-one, he brought with him dried plants of almost 4,000 species, most of which were new to science. He was immediately elected librarian of the Linnaean Society, and this enabled him to continue his work on these new species. His first volume of results, *Prodomus Florae Nova Hollandiae et Isulae Van Diemen,* appeared in 1810 and brought further wide acclaim. At the close of that year, he became librarian to Sir Joseph Banks, who on his death in 1820 bequeathed his protégé the use of his library and collections for life. Seven years later, they were transferred with Brown's permission to the British Museum, where he was made keeper of the botanical department. He continued in the position for thirty-two years until his death in his eighty-fifth year on June 10, 1858. His botanical writings were characterized by the minutest accuracy of detail together with the most comprehensive generalizations, a combination that gave his investigations an unusual stamp of completeness. These masterly publications brought him a reputation in his day as the greatest botanist England had produced.

Among his many honors were election to the Royal Society in 1811, several elections to its council, an honorary Doctor of Common Law degree from Oxford in 1832, along with Dalton, Faraday, and Sir David Brewster, election in 1833 as one of the eight foreign associates of the Academy of Sciences of the Institut de France, award of the Copley Medal of the Royal Society in 1839, president of the Linnaean Society 1849–1853, and membership in almost all the scientific societies of Europe. In private life, he was considered by friends to be warm, outgoing, and kind-hearted, but to those outside his circle it is said that he was cold, distant, and reserved.

୦୦୦୦୦୦୦୦

BROWN

A Brief Account of Microscopical Observations Made in the Months of June, July, and August 1827 on the Particles Contained in the Pollen of Plants; and on the General Existence of Active Molecules in Organic and Inorganic Bodies [1]

THE OBSERVATIONS, OF WHICH IT is my intention to give a summary in the following pages, have all been made with a simple microscope, and indeed with one and the same lens, the focal length of which is about $\frac{1}{32}$nd of an inch. . . .

My inquiry . . . was commenced in June 1827, and the first plant examined proved in some respects remarkably well adapted to the object in view.

This plant was *Clarckia pulchella,* of which the grains of pollen, taken

---

[1] Robert Brown, *Philosophical Magazine,* 4 (1828), 161–169.

from antherae full grown, but before bursting, were filled with particles or granules of unusually large size, varying from nearly $\frac{1}{4000}$th to about $\frac{1}{5000}$th of an inch in length, and of a figure between cylindrical and oblong, perhaps slightly flattened, and having rounded and equal extremities. While examining the form of these particles immersed in water, I observed many of them very evidently in motion; their motion consisting not only of a change of place in the fluid, manifested by alterations in their relative positions, but also not unfrequently of a change of form in the particle itself; a contraction or curvature taking place repeatedly about the middle of one side, accompanied by a corresponding swelling or convexity on the opposite side of the particle. In a few instances the particle was seen to turn on its longer axis. These motions were such as to satisfy me, after frequently repeated observation, that they arose neither from currents in the fluid, nor from its gradual evaporation, but belonged to the particle itself.

Grains of pollen of the same plant taken from antherae immediately after bursting, contained similar subcylindrical particles, in reduced numbers, however, and mixed with other particles, at least as numerous, of much smaller size, apparently spherical, and in rapid oscillatory motion.

These smaller particles, or Molecules as I shall term them, when first seen, I considered to be some of the cylindrical particles swimming vertically in the fluid. But frequent and careful examination lessened my confidence in this supposition; and on continuing to observe them until the water had entirely evaporated, both the cylindrical particles and spherical molecules were found on the stage of the microscope.

In extending my observations to many other plants of the same natural family, namely Onagrariae, the same general form and similar motions of particles were ascertained to exist. . . .

Having found motion in the particles of the pollen of all the living plants which I had examined, I was led next to inquire whether this property continued after the death of the plant, and for what length of time it was retained.

In plants, either dried or immersed in spirit for a few days only, the particles of pollen of both kinds were found in motion equally evident with that observed in the living plant; specimens of several plants, some of which had been dried and preserved in an herbarium for upwards of twenty years, and others not less than a century, still exhibited the molecules or smaller spherical particles in considerable numbers, and in evident motion, along with a few of the larger particles, whose motions were much less manifest, and in some cases not observable.

In this stage of the investigation having found, as I believed, a peculiar character in the motions of the particles of pollen in water, it occurred to me to appeal to this peculiarity as a test in certain families of Cryptogamous plants, namely, Mosses, and the genus Equisetum, in which the existence of sexual organs had not been universally admitted.

In the supposed stamina of both these families, namely, in the cylindrical antherae or pollen of Mosses, and on the surface of the four spathulate bodies surrounding the naked ovulum, as it may be considered, of Equisetum, I found minute spherical particles, apparently of the same size with the molecule described in Onagrariae, and having equally vivid motion on immersion in water; and this motion was still observable in specimens both of Mosses and of Equiseta, which had been dried upwards of one hundred years.

The very unexpected fact of seeming vitality retained by these minute particles so long after the death of the plant would not perhaps have materially lessened my confidence in the supposed peculiarity. But I at the same time observed, that on bruising the ovula or seeds of Equisetum, which at first happened accidentally, I so greatly increased the number of moving particles, that the source of the added quantity could not be doubted. I found also that on bruising first the floral leaves of Mosses, and then all other parts of those plants, that I readily obtained similar particles, not in equal quantity indeed, but equally in motion. My supposed test of the male organ was therefore necessarily abandoned.

Reflecting on all the facts with which I had now become acquainted, I was disposed to believe that the minute spherical particles or molecules of apparently uniform size, first seen in the advanced state of the pollen of Onagrariae, and most other Phaenogamous plants,—then in the antherae of Mosses and on the surface of the bodies regarded as the stamina of Equisetum,—and lastly in bruised portions of other parts of the same plants, were in reality the supposed constituent or elementary Molecules of organic bodies, first so considered by Buffon and Needham, then by Wrisberg with greater precision, soon after and still more particularly by Müller, and, very recently, by Dr. Milne Edwards, who has revived the doctrine and supported it with much interesting detail. I now therefore expected to find these molecules in all organic bodies: and accordingly on examining the various animal and vegetable tissues, whether living or dead, they were always found to exist; and merely by bruising these substances in water, I never failed to disengage the molecules in sufficient numbers to ascertain their apparent identity in size, form, and motion, with the smaller particles of the grains of pollen.

I examined also various products of organic bodies, particularly the gum resins, and substances of vegetable origin, extending my inquiry even to pit-coal; and in all these bodies Molecules were found in abundance. I remark here also, partly as a caution to those who may hereafter engage in the same inquiry, that the dust or soot deposited on all bodies in such quantity, especially in London, is entirely composed of these molecules.

One of the substances examined was a specimen of fossil wood, found in Wiltshire oolite, in a state to burn with flame; and as I found these molecules abundantly, and in motion in this specimen, I supposed that their existence, though in smaller quantity, might be ascertained in mineralized vegetable remains. With this view a minute portion of silicified wood, which exhibited the structure of Coniferae, was bruised, and spherical particles, or molecules in all respects like those so frequently mentioned, were readily obtained from it; in such quantity, however, that the whole substance of the petrifaction seemed to be formed of them. But hence I inferred that these molecules were not limited to organic bodies, nor even to their products.

To establish the correctness of the inference, and to ascertain to what extent the molecules existed in mineral bodies, became the next object of inquiry. The first substance examined was a minute fragment of window-glass, from which, when merely bruised on the stage of the microscope, I readily and copiously obtained molecules agreeing in size, form, and motion with those which I had already seen.

I then proceeded to examine, and with similar results, such minerals as I either had at hand or could readily obtain, including several of the simple earths and metals, with many of their combinations.

Rocks of all ages, including those in which organic remains have never been found, yielded the molecules in abundance. Their existence was ascertained in each of the constituent minerals of granite, a fragment of the Sphinx being one of the specimens examined.

To mention all the mineral substances in which I have found these molecules would be tedious; and I shall confine myself in this summary to an enumeration of a few of the most remarkable. These were both of aqueous and igneous origin, as travertine, stalactites, lava, obsidian, pumice, volcanic ashes, and meteorites from various localities. Of metals I may mention manganese, nickel, plumbago, bismuth, antimony, and arsenic. In a word, in every mineral which I could reduce to a powder, sufficiently fine to be temporarily suspended in water, I found these molecules more or less copiously; and in some cases, more particularly in siliceous crystals, the whole body submitted to examination appeared to be composed of them.

My manner of estimating the absolute magnitude and uniformity in the size of the molecules, found in the various bodies submitted to examination, was by placing them on a micrometer divided to five thousandths of an inch, the lines of which were very distinct; or more rarely on one divided to ten thousandths, with fainter lines, not readily visible without the application of plumbago, as employed by Dr. Wollaston, but which in my subject was inadmissible.

The results so obtained can only be regarded as approximations on which perhaps, for an obvious reason, much reliance will not be placed.

From the number and degree of accordance of my observations, however, I am upon the whole disposed to believe the simple molecule to be of uniform size, though as existing in various substances and examined in circumstances more or less favourable, it is necessary to state that its diameter appeared to vary from $\frac{1}{15,000}$th to $\frac{1}{20,000}$th of an inch.

NOTE: An independent appraisal by Mr. Dolland of the supposed pollen of *Equisetum virgatum* with a compound microscope having in its focus a glass divided in 10,000ths of an inch, most particles seen were about $\frac{1}{20,000}$th but the smallest did not exceed $\frac{1}{30,000}$th of an inch.

16

ooooooooooo

THE TRAGEDY

OF A GENIUS

ooooooooooo

John James Waterston[1] *(1811-1883)*

In the history of the men and women who have devoted themselves to discovery in atomic science it would be hard to find any whose rejection presents so great a tragedy as that of John James Waterston. His paper on kinetic theory, submitted to the Royal Society in 1845 and partly reproduced at the end of this biography, gave a new and greatly extended mathematical development of that theory. It not only corrected the fundamental error of Herapath in assuming that temperature was proportional to the average velocity of the molecules, but it went much further, giving, for example, the first statement of the law of equipartition of energy among the different kinds of gas molecules in a mixture at thermal equilibrium. He derived, in fact, practically all the consequences that follow from the now well-known equation which relates the pressure p exerted by a gas to the number of molecules per cubic centimeter z, their mass m, and their mean squared velocity $\overline{v^2}$, i.e., $p \sim zm\overline{v^2}$.

The judgments of the two referees to whom the paper was sent for an opinion on publication are illuminating and give some insight into the "professional's" view of the atomic theory of matter in 1845. One referee remarked that "the paper is nonsense, unfit even for reading before the

---

[1] For additional information on Waterston, see *The Collected Scientific Papers of John James Waterston*, J. S. Haldane, ed. (Edinburgh: Oliver & Boyd, 1928), and Stephen G. Brush, "John James Waterston and the Kinetic Theory of Gases," *American Scientist*, **49** (1961), 202–214.

Society." The other, more open-minded, noted that the paper "exhibits much skill and many remarkable accordances with the general facts . . . but the original principle [is] . . . by no means a satisfactory basis for a mathematical theory." The paper was not rejected outright but was relegated unpublished to the society's archives; only an abstract appeared in the *Proceedings of the Royal Society* for 1846. Had it been rejected it could have been published elsewhere, but having been retained it was consigned to practical oblivion.

In 1851 Waterston again attempted to draw attention to it in an abstract in the *Report of the British Association*. Both of these abstracts are reprinted with the excerpt from his paper. Waterston next made reference to his gas theory in a paper "On a general Law of density in Saturated Vapors" published in the *Philosophical Transactions* of 1852, and then discussed his theory and that of Herapath at length in an article on the theory of sound published in the *Philosophical Magazine* in 1858. As will be seen in Lord Rayleigh's introduction, it was the reference in the paper on the theory of sound that led Rayleigh to read the paper in the society's archives in 1891 and to discover the tragic error the reviewers had made. By then, the accomplishments of others had far outdistanced the developments that Waterston had been able to achieve. As J. S. Haldane, his biographer, remarks: "It is probable that in the long and honorable history of the Royal Society no mistake, more disastrous in its actual consequences for the progress of science and the reputation of British science . . . was ever made." In an effort to atone in some measure for the wrong that had been done, Rayleigh reprinted Waterston's paper in the *Philosophical Transactions* of the Royal Society in 1892.

We return to Haldane to glimpse something of the life of this unfortunate man. John James Waterston was born in Edinburgh, Scotland, in 1811, the son of George Waterston, a sealing wax and stationery manufacturer, and the grandson of William Waterston. The latter married Catherine Sandeman, niece of Robert Sandeman, the founder of the religious sect known as the Sandemanians. Michael Faraday's father and Faraday himself were members of this church in London. Catherine's brother, George Sandeman, founded the London firm of wine merchants of that name, which is not only still in business but is familiar to many in the English-speaking world.

Young Waterston grew up in comfortable circumstances and in an atmosphere of culture. He was educated at the Edinburgh High School and Edinburgh University, where he studied mathematics and physics under Sir John Leslie and was medalist for his year in Leslie's class. While studying at the university, he was also employed in a firm of civil engineers. At twenty-one, he went to London to work at drafting and surveying for the expanding railway system in England. But he found this work too demanding for his scientific interests and for this reason he accepted for a time an appointment in the hydrographer's office in the Admiralty. Captain Beaufort, head of the office, recognized Waterston's ability and, sympathizing with his desire for a scientific career, suggested a teaching position as naval instructor to the East India Company's cadets at Bombay. Waterston obtained the appointment and went to India in 1839, being then twenty-eight years old. Here he found the leisure he had been seeking together with access to a scientific library at Grant College, Bombay. His first book, *Thoughts on the Mental Functions,* was, strangely enough, a work on the physiology of the central nervous system with application of molecular theory to biology. It was published anonymously in Edinburgh in 1843 and contained the elements of his later paper on kinetic theory. With a misleading title and speculative contents, it is doubtful if anyone read the book. Two years later, in December of 1845, Captain Beaufort forwarded to the Royal Society Waterston's developed kinetic theory, which is the object of this review. None of Waterston's efforts to get this paper published ever succeeded.

Waterston remained in Bombay until 1857 when he resigned and returned to Edinburgh. Although he was then only forty-six, his health had been permanently impaired as a consequence of a severe heat stroke suffered in India. This left him subject to attacks of dizziness in crowded rooms or in confined quarters while traveling. It is this infirmity that best explains his singular reluctance to attend any scientific gatherings or to meet any of the scientists such as Maxwell, a fellow Scot vitally interested in the same ideas, who might have assisted him in gaining the recognition that his past work deserved. During the eleven years following his return from India, Waterston published twenty papers in the *Philosophical Magazine,* his last being dated 1868, which was the year that Sir David Brewster, one of the editors of the magazine, died. This coincidence has led Haldane to suggest that it was Brewster's influence that was responsible for the acceptance of Waterston's contributions. This seems a very harsh judgment because the papers were not ill-founded or of uncertain value. In 1878 Waterston sent two papers to the Royal Astronomical Society. Both were rejected. In the only retaliation open to him Waterston then resigned from the Astronomical Society after having been a member for twenty-six years. If it did not seem incredible, it would almost appear that a conspiracy existed to shut him from all avenues of scientific expression. It is therefore to be expected that Waterston grew increasingly bitter as the years passed by. His nephew, George Waterston, wrote Lord Rayleigh after his uncle's death that he "seemed to me strangely contemptuous of scientific men with but few exceptions. He had not a word of complaint, nor did he speak of being neglected or ill-used. . . . He would not attend the meetings of the Royal Society of Edinburgh . . .

and rather avoided the society of scientific men. He was of a most social, kind disposition, enjoying the society of young people." He never married and Haldane suggests that apart from the deep disappointments of his scientific life, which he took pains to conceal, his life in Scotland was happy. He lived the life of a popular bachelor, enjoying the best music, billiards, cigars, and chess. In his last days he lived in rooms on Gayfield Square off Leith Walk in Edinburgh. It was from here that on June 18, 1883, he set out for a walk in the morning air. By nightfall he had not returned; he was never again seen by anybody. It was as though he had vanished in thin air. His passing was but another episode in the same tragedy that had haunted his life.

Perhaps the best explanation of his disappearance is given by his nephew, in the letter to Lord Rayleigh referred to above:

> My uncle . . . was fond of walking out by a new breakwater recently built at Leith, very well exposed to a fine sea breeze, but from its construction very dangerous to foot passengers. At this place the tide runs out very fast, and if he had fallen in he would have been carried out to sea. We know of no place near Edinburgh where he could so easily have disappeared, and no one who knew him thought of suicide as likely in his case.

For the modern reader there is more that can be said about Waterston's paper than either he or Lord Rayleigh allowed in their introductions, both of which follow below. Most elementary physics courses now give a brief treatment under equilibrium conditions of the kinetic theory of gases. In this treatment, one of the principal results obtained is a relation between the pressure p exerted by the gas, the number density z of the gas molecules (number per unit volume), the mass of an individual molecule, m, and $\overline{v^2}$, the square of the molecular speed v averaged over all the molecules, or as it is usually denoted, the mean squared speed. Specifically this relation is found to be $p = zmv^2/3$. All of the relations that Waterston obtains can be described in terms of this formula.

Initially let us examine his results, labeled I and II. Result I states that the elastic force (pressure) of the medium is proportional to the number of impacts per second per unit area of confining surface, v being constant. Result II goes on to show that the number of impacts is proportional to the number density z of the molecules of the gas. The net result of I and II is to assert that p, the pressure, is proportional to z, or symbolically stated, $p \sim z$, a result that follows from our general formula above. Later, in paragraph 6, Waterston points out that this result is equivalent to Mariotte's (Boyle's) law. To see how the pV relation follows from $p \sim z$, let z be considered as the number of particle N/Volume, then $p \sim N/V$ or $pV \sim N$ or $pV =$ constant, which is Boyle's law.

Result III states that z being constant, $p \sim \overline{v^2}$, as is evident from the formula also. To obtain result IV rewrite the general formula $m\overline{v^2} = 3p/z$. It then follows that the *vis viva* (twice the kinetic energy) contained in a unit volume of the gas is inversely proportional to z, the number density, provided the pressure p is kept constant. The relation $m\overline{v^2} = 3p/z$ may be written using previous substitutions, $m\overline{v^2} = (3/N)pV$. Holding p constant we have $V \sim (m/p)\overline{v^2}$, or since m also is constant, $V \sim \overline{v^2}$. This is the law of Dalton and Gay-Lussac that Waterston refers to in paragraph 6. As we saw in the article on Gay-Lussac, the relation between volume V and temperature T, namely $V/T =$ constant for p constant, was found by him and by Charles before him. It is now usually called Charles's law. Comparing $V \sim T$ by Charles's law with the relation $V \sim \overline{v^2}$ we see that $\overline{v^2} \sim T$, as Waterston indicates. Relation V which also follows immediately from our general formula is a very important result. It says in effect that if media have equal pressure and density, then $\overline{v^2} \sim 1/m$, or $\sqrt{\overline{v^2}} \sim 1/\sqrt{m}$. This follows at once from the fact that if $3p/z$ is the same for two gases, $m\overline{v^2} = m_1\overline{v_1^2}$. Hence, for each gas $\sqrt{\overline{v^2}} \sim 1/\sqrt{m}$. Result VII is already contained in this argument. Finally, attention should be called again to paragraph 15 in which Waterston comes to conclusions that support Avogadro's hypothesis and anticipate the work of Cannizzaro. Had views such as these been generally known, chemistry, and atomic theory with it, would not have had to wait another fifteen years before reaching the firm footing provided by Cannizzaro and the brilliant theorist James Clerk Maxwell.

०००००००

WATERSTON

On the Physics of Media That Are Composed of Free and Perfectly Elastic Molecules in a State of Motion [2]

INTRODUCTION BY LORD RAYLEIGH, SEC.R.S.

THE PUBLICATION OF THIS PAPER after nearly half a century demands a word of explanation; and the opportunity may be taken to point out in what respects the received theory of gases had

[2] John James Waterston, *Philosophical Transactions*, 183 (1892), 1–79.

been anticipated by Waterston, and to offer some suggestions as to the origin of certain errors and deficiencies in his views.

So far as I am aware, the paper, though always accessible in the Archives of the Royal Society, has remained absolutely unnoticed. Most unfortunately the abstract printed at the time (*Roy. Soc. Proc.,* 1846, vol. 5, p. 604; here reprinted as Appendix I) gave no adequate idea of the scope of the memoir, and still less of the nature of the results arrived at. The deficiency was in some degree supplied by a short account in the *Report of the British Association* for 1851 (here reprinted as Appendix II), where is distinctly stated the law, which was afterwards to become so famous, of the equality of the kinetic energies of different molecules at the same temperature.

My own attention was attracted in the first instance to Waterston's work upon the connection between molecular forces and the latent heat of evaporation, and thence to a paper in the *Philosophical Magazine* for 1858, "On the Theory of Sound." He there alludes to the theory of gases under consideration as having been started by Herapath in 1821, and he proceeds:

"Mr. Herapath unfortunately assumed heat or temperature to be represented by the simple ratio of the velocity instead of the square of the velocity—being in this apparently led astray by the definition of motion generally received—and thus was baffled in his attempts to reconcile his theory with observation. If we make this change in Mr. Herapath's definition of heat or temperature, viz., that it is proportional to the *vis viva,* or square velocity of the moving particle, not to the momentum, or simple ratio of the velocity, we can without much difficulty deduce, not only the primary laws of elastic fluids, but also the other physical properties of gases enumerated above in the third objection to Newton's hypothesis. In the Archives of the Royal Society for 1845–1846, there is a paper "On the Physics of Media that consists of perfectly Elastic Molecules in a State of Motion," which contains the synthetical reasoning upon which the demonstration of these matters rests. The velocity of sound is therein deduced to be equal to the velocity acquired in falling through three-fourths of a uniform atmosphere. This theory does not take account of the size of the molecules. It assumes that no time is lost at the impact, and that if the impacts produce rotatory motion, the *vis viva* thus invested bears a constant ratio to the rectilineal *vis viva,* so as not to require separate consideration. It also does not take account of the probable internal motion of composite molecules; yet the results so closely accord with observation in every part of the subject as to leave no doubt that Mr. Herapath's idea of the physical constitution of gases approximates closely to the truth. M. Krönig appears to have entered upon the subject in an independent manner, and arrives at the same result; M. Clausius, too, as we learn from his paper "On the Nature of the Motion We Call Heat" (*Phil. Mag.,* vol. 14, 1857, p. 108).

Impressed with the above passage and with the general ingenuity and soundness of Waterston's views, I took the first opportunity of consulting the Archives, and saw at once that the memoir justified the large claims made for it, and that it marks an immense advance in the direction of the now generally received theory. The omission to publish it at the time was a misfortune, which probably retarded the development of the subject by ten or fifteen years. It is singular that Waterston appears to have advanced no claim for subsequent publication, whether in the Transactions of the Society, or through some other channel. At any time since 1860 reference would naturally have been made to Maxwell, and it cannot be doubted that he would have at once recommended that everything possible should be done to atone for the original failure of appreciation.

It is difficult to put oneself in imagination into the position of the reader of 1845, and one can understand that the substance of the memoir should have appeared speculative and that its mathematical style should have failed to attract. But it is startling to find a referee expressing the opinion that "the paper is nothing but nonsense, unfit even for reading before the Society." Another remarks "that the whole investigation is confessedly founded on a principle entirely hypothetical, from which it is the object to deduce a mathematical representation of the phenomena of elastic media. It exhibits much skill and many remarkable accordances with the general facts, as well as numerical values furnished by observation. . . . The original principle itself involves an assumption which seems to me very difficult to admit, and by no means a satisfactory basis for a mathematical theory, viz., that the elasticity of a medium is to be measured by supposing its molecules in vertical motion, and making a succession of impacts against an elastic gravitating plane." These remarks are not here quoted with the idea of reflecting upon the judgment of the referee, who was one of the best qualified authorities of the day, and evidently devoted to a most difficult task his careful attention; but rather with the view of throwing light upon the attitude then assumed by men of science in regard to this question, and in order to point a moral. *The history of this paper suggests that highly speculative investigations, especially by an unknown author, are best brought before the world through some other channel than a scientific society, which naturally hesitates to admit into its printed records matter of uncertain value. Perhaps one may go further and say that a young author who believes himself capable of great things would usually do well to secure the favourable recognition of the scientific world by work whose scope is limited, and whose value is easily judged, before embarking upon higher flights.*[3]

One circumstance which may have told unfavourably upon the recep-

---

[3] Editors' italics.

tion of Waterston's paper is that he mentions no predecessors. Had he put forward his investigation as a development of the theory of D. Bernoulli, a referee might have hesitated to call it nonsense. It is probable, however, that Waterston was unacquainted with Bernoulli's work, and doubtful whether at that time he knew that Herapath had to some extent fore-shadowed similar views.

At the present time the interest of Waterston's paper can, of course, be little more than historical. What strikes one most is the marvellous courage with which he attacked questions, some of which even now present serious difficulties. *To say that he was not always successful is only to deny his claim to rank among the foremost theorists of all ages.*[4] The character of the advance to be dated from this paper will be at once understood when it is realised that Waterston was the first to introduce into the theory the conception that heat and temperature are to be measured by *vis viva*. This enabled him at a stroke to complete Bernoulli's explanation of pressure by showing the accordance of the hypothetical medium with the law of Dalton and Gay-Lussac. In the second section the great feature is the statement (VII), that "in mixed media the mean square molecular velocity is inversely proportional to the specific weight of the molecules." The proof which Waterston gave is doubtless not satisfactory; but the same may be said of that advanced by Maxwell fifteen years later. The law of Avogadro follows at once, as well as that of Graham relative to diffusion. Since the law of equal energies was actually published in 1851, there can be no hesitation, I think, in attaching Waterston's name to it. The attainment of correct results in the third section, dealing with adiabatic expansion, was only prevented by a slip of calculation.

In a few important respects Waterston stopped short. There is no indication, so far as I can see, that he recognised any other form of motion, or energy, than the translatory motion, though this is sometimes spoken of as vibratory. In this matter the priority in a wider view rests with Clausius. According to Waterston the ratio of specific heats should be (as for mercury vapour) $1 \cdot 67$ in all cases. Again, although he was well aware that the molecular velocity cannot be constant, there is no anticipation of the law of distribution of velocities established by Maxwell.

A large part of the paper deals with chemistry, and shows that his views upon that subject also were much in advance of those generally held at the time.

The following extract from a letter by Professor McLeod will put the reader into possession of the main facts of the case:

> It seems a misfortune that the paper was not printed when it was written, for it shadows forth many of the ideas of modern chemistry which

---

[4] *Loc. cit.*

have been adopted since 1845, and it might have been the means of hastening their reception by chemists.

The author compares the masses of equal volumes of gaseous and volatile elements and compounds, and taking the mass of a unit volume of hydrogen as unity, he regards the masses of the same volume of other volatile bodies as representing their molecular weight, and in the case of the elements he employs their symbols to indicate the molecules.

In water he considers that the molecule of hydrogen is combined with half a molecule of oxygen, forming one of steam, and he therefore represents the compound as $HO_{1/2}$. He does not make use of the term "atom" (although he speaks of atomic weight on p. 18, but thinks it divisible), and if he had called the smallest proportion of an element which enters into combination an atom, he would probably have been led to believe that the molecules of some of the simple bodies contain two atoms, and he might have adopted two volumes to represent the molecule, as is done at the present time. The author calls one volume or molecule of chlorine Cl, one volume or molecule of hydrogen H, and one volume or molecule of hydrochloric acid $H_{1/2}Cl_{1/2}$. If he had regarded the molecules as containing two indivisible atoms, these bodies would have been represented, as now, by the formulæ Cl_2, H_2, and HCl respectively, all occupying two volumes. § 15 shows how near he was to his conception. Gerhardt in the Fourth Part of his *Traité de Chimie Organique,* published in 1856, points out the uniformity introduced into chemical theory by the adoption of this system.

For carbon he makes $C = 12$, as now accepted, although I do not find how he arrives at this number. He seems to have anticipated one of Ramsay's recent discoveries, that nitrous anhydride (hyponitrous acid, $ON_{2/3}$, No. 26 in the table) dissociates on evaporation into nitric oxide (binoxide of nitrogen, No. 23) and nitric peroxide (nitrous acid, No. 25).

The values for the symbols for sulphur, phosphorus, and arsenic taken from the vapour densities (and which are multiples of what are believed to be the true atomic weights), cause some complexity in the formulæ of their compounds.

There seem to be errors in the formulæ of alcohol and ether on p. 49, for they do not agree with those in the table. They ought probably to be written

$$2(HC_{1/2}) + O_{1/2}2H_{1/2} \text{ and } 4(HC_{1/2}) + O_{1/2}2H_{1/2}.$$

Considering how nearly Waterston approached what is now believed to be the true theory, it is disappointing to read his controversy with Odling in 1863 and 1864 (*Phil. Mag.,* vols. 26 and 27), where he seems to oppose the new formulæ then being introduced. He is very dogmatic about the constitution of hydrate of potash: he very properly insists that we can only obtain a knowledge of the molecular weight of bodies that can be volatilized, and of which the vapour densities can be determined, but he does not see the analogy between the hydrate and oxide of potassium with alcohol and ether, probably because he regards these latter bodies as combinations of water with different quantities of olefiant gas. He writes water $HO_{1/2} = 9$, alcohol $CH_2HO_{1/2} = 23$, and ether $C_2H_4 \cdot HO_{1/2} = 37$, whilst he considers potassic hydrate $KO_{1/2} \cdot HO_{1/2} = 56$, and oxide of potassium $KO_{1/2} = 47$, the hydrate having a higher molecular weight than the oxide. If we regard these compounds as derived from water by the replacement of hydrogen by ethyl and potassium respectively, the analogy between the two series is complete (ethyl was discovered in 1849 and is mentioned by Waterston).

$$H_2O = 18 \qquad\qquad H_2O = 18.$$
$$(C_2H_5)HO = 46 \qquad KHO = 56.$$
$$(C_2H_5)_2O = 74 \qquad K_2O = 94.$$

From a remark in the *Phil. Mag.* (vol. 26, p. 520), I imagined that Waterston had arrived at the double atomic weights of many of the metals now adopted, for he gives that of iron as 56 and that of aluminum as 27 calculated from their specific beats, but there is an error in his arithmetic, for $3 \cdot 3$ divided by the specific heat of iron $\cdot 1138$ gives $28 \cdot 998$, and $3 \cdot 3$ divided by the specific heat of aluminum $\cdot 2143$ gives $15 \cdot 399$.

With the exception of some corrections relating merely to stops and spelling the paper is here reproduced exactly as it stands in the author's manuscript—Dec. 1891.

AUTHOR'S INTRODUCTION

Of the physical theories of heat that have claimed attention since the time of Bacon, that which ascribes its cause to the intense vibrations of the elementary parts of bodies has received a considerable accession of probability from the recent experiments of Forbes and Melloni. It is admitted that these have been the means of demonstrating that the mode of its radiation is identical with that of light in the quantities of refraction and polarization. The evidence that has been accumulated in favour of the undulatory theory of light has thus been made to support with a great portion of its weight a like theory of the phenomena of heat; and we are, perhaps, justified in expecting that the complete development of this theory will have a much more important influence on the progress of science, because of its more obvious connection and intimate blending with almost every appearance of Nature. Heat is not only the subject of direct sensation and the vivifier of organic life, but it is manifested as the accompaniment of mechanical force. It is related to it both as cause and effect, and submits itself readily to measurement by means of the mechanical changes that are among the most prominent indications of its change of intensity. The undulatory theory at once leads us to the conclusion that, inasmuch as the temperature of a body is a persistent quality due to the motion of its molecules, its internal constitution must admit of it retaining a vast amount of living force [kinetic energy]. Indeed, it seems to be almost impossible now to escape from the inference that heat is essentially molecular *vis viva*. In solids, the molecular oscillations may be viewed as being restrained by the intense forces of aggregation. In vapours and gases these seem to be overcome; vibrations can no longer be produced by the inherent *vis insita* of the molecules struggling with attractive and repellant forces; the struggle is over and the molecules are free; but they, nevertheless, continue to maintain a certain temperature; they are capable of heating and being heated; they are endowed with the quality heat, which, being of itself motion, compels us to infer that a molecule in motion without any force to restrain or qualify it, is in every respect to be considered as a free projectile. Allow such free projectiles to be endowed with perfect elasticity, and likewise extend the same property to the elementary parts of all bodies that they strike against, and we immediately introduce the principle of the conservation of *vis viva* to regulate the general effects of their fortuitous encounters. Whether gases do consist of such minute elastic projectiles or not, it seems worth while to enquire into the physical attributes of media so constituted, and to see what analogy they bear to the elegant and symmetrical laws of aeriform bodies.

Some years ago I made an attempt to do so, proceeding synthetically from this fundamental hypothesis, and have lately obtained demonstration of one or two points where the proof was then deficient. The results have appeared so encouraging, although derived from very humble applications of mathematics, that I have been led to hope a popular account of the train of reasoning may not prove unacceptable to the Royal Society —Sept. 1, 1845.

OF A HOMOGENEOUS MEDIUM AND THE LAWS OF ITS ELASTICITY

§ 1. The term medium is, perhaps, not quite appropriate to what is here intended to be signified. We speak of a resisting medium, of the medium of light, and in each expression something is referred to as intervening between bodies, and it is the quality of interposition that entitles it to the name. Here, for want of better, it is employed to denote a certain hypothetical condition of matter which it is the object of this Paper to show has physical properties that resemble those that have been found to belong to aeriform bodies. Inasmuch, therefore, as the word may be applied to a simple unmixed gas so as to speak of it as an oxygen medium or a hydrogen medium, &c., so far we may be allowed the use of it in treating of a hypothetical medium, which we have carefully to refrain from assimilating to any known form of matter until, by synthetical reasoning, circumstantial evidence has been accumulated sufficient to prove or render probable its identity.

To have a proper conception of what the medium is that forms the subject of speculation, we must imagine a vast multitude of small particles of matter, perfectly alike in every respect, perfectly elastic as glass or ivory—but of size, form and texture that requires not to be specified further than that they are not liable to change by mutual action—to be enclosed by elastic walls or surfaces in a space so much greater than their aggregate bulk as to allow them freely to move amongst each other in every direction. As all consideration of attractive forces is left out at present, it is obvious that each particle must proceed on a straight line until it strikes against another, or against the sides of the enclosure; that it must then be reflected and driven into another line of motion, traversing backwards and forwards in every direction, so that the intestine condition of the multitude of these that form the medium may be likened to the familiar appearance of a swarm of gnats in a sunbeam.

The quality of perfect elasticity being common to all the particles, the original amount of *vis viva,* or living, acting force [kinetic energy] of the whole multitude must for ever remain the same. If undisturbed by external action it cannot, of itself, diminish or increase, but must for ever remain as unchanged as the matter that is associated with it and that it endows with activity. Such is the case if we view the whole mass of moving particles as one object, but each individual of the multitude must at every encounter give or receive, according to the ever-changing angle and plane of impact, some portion of its force, so that, considered separately, they are for ever continually changing the velocity and direction of their individual motions; striking against and rebounding from each other, they run rapidly in their zig-zag conflict through every possible mode of concurrence, and *at each point of the medium we may thus conceive that particles are moving in every possible direction and encountering each other in every possible manner during so small an elapsed interval of time that it may be viewed as infinitesimal in respect to any sensible period.* The medium must in this way become endowed with a permanent state of elastic energy or disposition to expand, uniformly sustained in every part and communicating it to the physical character of an elastic fluid.

The simplicity of this hypothesis facilitates the application of mathematics in ascertaining the nature and properties of such media, and the study acquires much interest from the analogies that it unfolds. For if the reasoning is correct, the physical laws common to all gases and vapours —those laws, namely, that concern heat and pressure—do actually belong to such media, and may be synthetically deduced from the constitution which has now been assigned to them.

The characteristic which renders a medium susceptible of mathematical treatment is that of its being composed of particles perfectly alike in every respect, but it is chiefly their identity in weight or mass that is the important point of distinction. A particle thus conforms to the definition that the eminent physicist Ampère has given to the term molecule, which we may therefore adopt as a more significant name for the element of a medium.

The first department of the subject must naturally be devoted to the consideration of the circumstances that determine the equilibrium of such a homogeneous medium considered by itself. Its density, by which is to be understood not its specific gravity but the number of molecules in a constant volume,* may be supposed to vary without disturbing its homogeneity. The mean square velocity of the molecules (which in any infinitesimal portion of the medium may be assumed as uniform) we also have to consider as a variable quantity, and the physical qualities of a medium being dependent on these two elements of its constitution, it is necessary to determine clearly their mathematical relations.

§ 2. It is evident from the definition of the hypothesis, that the medium must exert some expansive force on the surface that encloses it; but the nature of the force is not strictly continuous, it is composed of a multitude of successive strokes. Nevertheless, their succession is certainly continuous, and it is not difficult to conceive how they may be sufficient to counterbalance and support a superincumbent weight. To obtain an exact idea of this, let us suppose that a small elastic plane whose weight is n times that of a molecule, is supported by a regular succession of such molecules striking its centre of gravity with a velocity v. We seek to know the condition of their mutual action when an equilibrium is maintained.

The following are the well-known equations that express the law of elastic collision. They are necessarily the foundation of all reasoning on the effects of the mutual action of elastic bodies by impact.

The Meeting Impact

Two molecules, B and D, meet directly in an intermediate point and strike each other with the respective velocities β and δ. The velocities after impact are respectively:

$$\beta_0 = -\beta + \frac{2(\delta + \beta)D}{(B + D)} \text{ and } \delta_0 = \delta - \frac{2(\delta + \beta)B}{(B + D)}$$

the direction of D's motion being reckoned positive.

---

* Attention should be directed to this use of the word "density"—R.

The Overtaking Impact

The two molecules, B and D, with the same velocities, β and δ, move in the same direction and D overtakes B; the velocities after impact are respectively:

$$\beta_1 = \beta + \frac{2(\delta - \beta)D}{(B + D)} \text{ and } \delta_1 = \delta - \frac{2(\delta - \beta)B}{(B + D)};$$

the direction of D's motion being reckoned positive.

In the first of these let $\beta_0 = \beta$, $\delta = v$, $B = nD$; then shall

$$\beta = -\beta + \frac{2(v + \beta)}{n + 1}, \text{ or } \beta = \frac{v}{n},*$$

which evidently expresses the upward velocity given to the plane by the impulse of one molecule when the velocity of incidence and reflexion is the same. The plane ascends and descends the height due to this velocity, and then encounters the next in the succession of molecular impacts without any transference of force taking place between them; and n being taken an indefinitely great number, β is infinitesimal in respect to v, and the height through which the plane traverses is also infinitesimal, so that it is supported as if by a continuous force of upward pressure. The time between each impact is, according to the law of falling bodies, equal to the time taken by the force of gravity to destroy and reproduce the infinitesimal velocity v/n. This is $2v/gn$: the velocity which a free body gains or loses in a unit of time by the force of gravity being represented by g. The number of impacts in a unit of time is therefore $gn/2v = A$. This, then, is the relation between the weight of the plane, in terms of that of the molecule unity, and the rapidity of the succession of impacts necessary to support it in a condition of statical equilibrium. Now, if the plane forms part of the surface that encloses the medium and that counterbalances by its weight the effect of the impacts of the confined molecules, such effect must correspond with the succession represented by A; and we deduce that *the elastic force of a medium, as represented by the weight or pressure required to confine it, is directly proportional to the number of molecular impacts that take place against a unit surface in a unit time with a constant velocity* (or $e \doteqdot A$, if v is constant) . . . I.

§ 3. Such being the nature of the elastic force, it will not be difficult

---

* The case is that where the particle (mass 1) and the plane (mass n) both reverse their velocities at impact. The conservation of *vis viva* is thereby secured, and the condition of momentum gives at once $n\beta = v$ —R.

to prove that it increases exactly as the density of the medium. The proposition stands thus: if the number of molecules in a volume of the medium be doubled, the number of impacts that take place on a constant surface in a constant time will also be doubled, the velocity being unchanged.

Suppose the number octupled, the mean distance is reduced to one-half. If they were equidistant and moving in one direction with the constant velocity, it is evident that eight times the previous number would pass the same imaginary plane in the same time, and if the plane were solid that eight times the previous number would impinge against it. Now, although all do not move in one direction, yet in both cases the same proportion of the whole must in each case do so. Whatever may be the density no preference can be assigned to one direction more than to another in the molecular movements; they must in every case be equally distributed in every direction, and if the number is increased eight times in any one direction it must be so in every other.

This may be viewed in another light. Suppose in both cases, the density being 1 and 8 respectively, that the molecules are arrested in their motion. It is evident that opposite a unit of surface in density 8 there will, in the first row, be four times as many molecules as in density 1, and that the average distance between the rows is only one-half. Suppose the molecules to resume their motion, and compare density 8 with density 1, it is obvious that in half the time four times the number will impinge on the unit of surface, and in the same time eight times the number. Now it has been shown (§ 2) that the elastic force is proportional to the number of molecular impacts made with a constant velocity against a unit of surface in a unit of time, hence we deduce that *the elastic force* (e) *of a medium with a constant mean molecular velocity* (v) *is proportional to its density* (Δ^3) (or $e \doteq \Delta^3$, if v or v^2 is constant) . . . . II.

§ 4. Hitherto the molecular velocity has been supposed constant. We have now to inquire how the elasticity of the medium is affected by a change in the velocity from v to mv. The intestine action of the medium may be viewed as the traversing of a certain mean distance, L, by the molecules in a given time, t; and in this time a certain mean number, A, of impacts take place against a unit of surface. If the velocity is increased m times, the distance L is traversed in $1/m$th the time t, or t/m, and in this reduced time the same number of impacts must take place as before took place in the time t; for there is nothing in the change of velocity simply that can alter the ratio that subsists between the mean distance traversed and the mean number of impacts, unless that ratio were subject to change without any change whatever in the medium, which is absurd; hence, in the original time, t, there is m times the original number of impacts, A.

It was shown in § 2 that if the weight of each of the molecules were represented by 1, their mean velocity by v, and weight of plane supported by their impinging action n, the number of impacts in a second or unit of time required to support the plane is $gn/2v = A$, or $n = 2/g\ Av$, and this equation must evidently be maintained in altering the value of the terms. Now, it has been shown that in changing v to mv in a medium that does not alter its density we cause A to become mA, and $2/g\ Av$ becomes $2/g\ Amvm = 2/g\ Avm^2 = nm^2$. Hence n, the weight of the plane, or measure of tension, must be increased m^2 times so that it may continue to equilibrate the impinging action. Thus, we deduce that while the molecular velocity increases from v to mv, the elasticity increases from n to m^2n or *the elasticity of a medium having a constant density is proportional to the mean square molecular velocity or* vis viva *of the medium* (or $e \doteqdot v^2$, when Δ^3 is constant) . . . . III.

§ 5. Combining II. with III. it appears that when both the density and the *vis viva* are subject to change that the elasticity is equal to their product, or $e \doteqdot \Delta^3 v^2$, and this is the law that includes all the conditions of equilibrium of an enclosed homonogenous medium. One other condition only remains to be specified. *Under a constant pressure the density is inversely as the* vis viva *or mean square molecular velocity* ($\Delta^3 \doteqdot 1/v^2$, if e is constant) . . . . IV.

§ 6. In concluding this part of the subject, we cannot fail of being sensible of the analogies that subsist between these synthetical deductions and the chief properties that distinguish aeriform fluids.

The first point that was inductively established is Mariotte's law, viz.: *at the same temperature the density of air is as its compression.* This is analogous to the second deduction:—The square of the velocity being constant, the elastic force of a medium is proportional to its density. The accordance appears as complete as could be desired, and there is a residual evidence in favour of v^2 being identical with temperature, or being a quality that varies simultaneously with it.

The second point is Dalton and Gay-Lussac's law of expansion. By experimenting upon the same weight of air at different temperatures under a constant pressure, these philosophers found that an increment of one degree caused always the same augmentation of bulk, and that this amounted to $\frac{1}{480}$th part of the space that it occupied at 32°. Thus, if the same law hold good at all temperatures, 480 cubic inches of air at this temperature should diminish one inch in bulk for every degree it was lowered in temperature, and would become zero in bulk at 480° below the freezing point of water, or $-448°$ on Fahrenheit scale.

Now in IV. we had $\Delta^3 \doteqdot 1/v^2$, or $v^2 \doteqdot 1/\Delta^3$, when e is constant; but $1/\Delta^3$ is the volume occupied by a constant number of molecules; hence with the same constant number of molecules the volume is as the mean square molecular velocity, and a constant increment of *vis viva* is followed by the same increment of volume under a constant pressure, and as the constant increment of volume (1 cubic inch) is to the constant increment of *vis viva* (1°) so is the volume (480 cubic inches) corresponding to a certain *vis viva* (32° Fahr.) to that *vis viva* (480°).

The analogy therefore still holds good, and the evidence continues in favour of the absolute temperature being represented by v^2. . . .

Thus, the laws of Mariotte and of Dalton and Gay-Lussac are represented by the formula $(448 + t) \, \Delta^3 = e$; in which t = temperature, Fahrenheit scale; Δ^3 = density, and e = elasticity. . . .

ON THE PHYSICAL RELATIONS OF MEDIA THAT DIFFER FROM EACH OTHER IN THE SPECIFIC WEIGHT OF THEIR MOLECULES

§ 7. The synthetical deductions of [the] last section apply to a homogeneous medium without respect to the absolute weight of its molecules, if the weight of each molecule is the same. This weight, common to all, may be viewed as the specific molecular weight of the medium, and distinguishes it from any other medium with a different specific molecular weight. We have now to enquire into the relations that subsist between the density and molecular velocity of two such media that have the same elasticity, or that are in equilibrium of pressure and also of *vis viva*.

We deduced from the law of impinging elastic bodies that if v represents the mean molecular velocity in feet per second, A the number of molecular impacts in a second upon a small elastic plane which is equal in weight to n molecules, then $n = 2/g \, Av$. Let ω represent the specific weight of the molecules, we have $\omega n = 2\omega/g \, Av = e$ = the elastic force exerted by the medium on a unit of surface; * and as this must in the present enquiry be assumed constant, we may easily remark how a change in ω affects v and A.

It is evident that since $2\omega/g \, Av$ is a constant quantity and ω, A, and v variable, we have $Av \doteqdot 1/\omega$; but $e = \omega\Delta^3 v^2 (\S 5) = 2\omega/g \, Av$, and therefore, $\Delta^3 v = 2/g \, A$, or $A = g/2 \, \Delta^3 v$, and $Av \doteqdot \Delta^3 v^2$. Hence it is obvious that if Δ^3, the density or number of molecules in a constant volume, as well as e, the tension, are constant, while the molecular velocity and specific weight are variable, these variables are bound by the relation expressed by $v^2 \doteqdot 1/\omega$, which signifies that if two media are in equilibrium of pressure and have in the same volume of each the same number of molecules,

---

* e is the absolute weight of the small elastic plane that is supported by the succession of A number of molecular impacts per second, the weight of each of which is ω, and their common impinging velocity v feet per second.

the squares of their molecular velocities must be inversely as their specific molecular weights. Hence, we deduce that *if any number of separate media have equal density and tension, the molecular velocity of each must be proportional to the inverse square root of their specific molecular weight, or to the inverse square root of the specific gravity of the media respectively* *   .   .   .   .   V.

.   .   .   § 8. We have supposed hitherto that the media are separate while their respective elasticities are compared. Let us now enquire into the effects of allowing them to have access to each other. The united media immediately obtain a heterogeneous character, for it requires no demonstration to convince us that the molecules of each will permeate through the volume occupied by the other, the vacuities in the space occupied by each presenting no more obstacle to the motion of one set of molecules than it does to the other; and as collision must take place amongst them in every possible manner and direction, the common space of the united media are free alike to each individual molecule of both to range through in its zig-zag course. Consequently, *media in contact with each other become gradually equally diffused through their common volume* .   .   . VI.

The internal condition of the mixture must after a time become settled so that in any infinitesimal portion the same mean velocity will be found proper to the molecules of each medium respectively.

But as each of the two sets of molecules, although completely mixed together, preserve their specific weights, so must they have corresponding specific velocities that remain intact, notwithstanding that they as often impinge on molecules of the other set as on the molecules of their own kind. It is of consequence to settle what the ratio of these specific velocities is, for upon this point depends the nature of the *vis viva* equilibrium of different media, and we have to determine the relative condition of two media when they are in equilibrium both of pressure and of *vis viva*.

§ 9. We must now refer back to the equations of impact (§ 2). It is apparent that the sum of the impinging *vis viva* of both molecules does not alter in either the meeting or overtaking impact; what is gained by one is lost by the other, or $\beta^2 B + \delta^2 D = \beta_0^2 B + \delta_0^2 D = \beta_1^2 B + \delta_1^2 D$. But in every case except one a transference of *vis viva* must take place from the one to the other.

The exception is found in the meeting impact when $\beta \doteqdot 1/B$ and $\delta \doteqdot 1/D$; then shall $\beta_0 = \beta$ and $\delta_0 = \delta$, but at the same time β_1 is not

---

* The deduction of V. appears to be correct, though much embarrassed by the irrelevant *g*. In his first memoir on the theory of gases (*Pogg. Ann.*, vol. 100, 1857), Clausius arrives at the same conclusion. His assumption that the density (in Waterston's sense) of various gases is the same, appears to have been made upon chemical grounds—R.

equal to β, or δ_1 to δ; in every other case β_0 is not equal to β nor to β_1, nor is δ_0 equal to δ or to δ_1.

It can seldom happen that the molecules strike each other directly. In taking account of the collective result of their fortuitous concourse we must view the position of the plane of concurrence and the respective inclinations of the line of motion of each molecule to it as three independent variables. The incident velocity of each is the absolute velocity resolved perpendicular to the plane, and the equations apply to this portion only of the *vis viva* of the molecules.

Although the variety in the mode of impact is infinite, it is certain that one direction of motion is as likely as any other, and hence, that the opposite of any direction is equally probable to the direction itself.

Let us confine our attention to any single case of impact and suppose that the directions of the motions of the two impinging molecules lie on one side of the plane of concurrence, then it appears that the nature of the impact must be *overtaking*. Again, let us suppose that they lie similarly disposed on the other side of the plane; the nature of the impact is again *overtaking*. Now, instead of having the opposite of both the original lines of motion, suppose the opposite of one only is taken; it is clear that the nature of the impact is in this case of the *meeting* kind; and the opposite of the other line of motion being taken while the first is in its original position, the impact is again of the meeting kind.

Each of these four cases are equally probable, and the resolved velocities, or the values of β and δ, are the same in all, but two are meeting impacts and two are overtaking, each couple having perfectly distinct numerical equations to define the relation between the incident and reflected *vis viva*.

We are thus obliged to infer that the intestine action of the medium must be viewed in this manner as divided into two kinds of impacts specifically distinct in the numerical relation that subsists between the velocity before and after concurrence, and when employing the equations for summing up the results of the whole indefinitely great multitude that take place in mixed media, the effect of any one *meeting* impact must be considered along with its counterpart overtaking impact with the same velocities.

§ 10. We have remarked that it is only the resolved portion of the whole *vis viva* of a molecule that is dealt with by the equations—that forms the force of impact—and it may be questioned whether the mean of these forces in each kind of molecules bears the same proportion to each other as the whole *vis viva* of each. That the ratio is the same is best seen by the *reductio ad absurdum* method of reasoning. If the ratio is different, the motions of the heavier molecules must be resolved in a different way from those of the lighter, or the plane of concurrence must incline to one set of molecules in a different manner to that of the other set. Now any such effect is quite inconsistent with the fundamental hypothesis, and would require us to admit the influence of a modifying power whose nature and mode of bringing about the effect in question is unknown.

The ratio ρ of the resolved to the absolute *vis viva* is actually one-third, and will become obvious in the next section, but it seems needless to require the demonstration in this place as all that we have to be assured of is the constancy of the ratio, whatever its actual value may be.

In seeking to demonstrate the nature of the *vis viva* equilibrium, the solitary condition that we have to reason from is that the mean value of $(\beta_0{}^2 + \beta_1{}^2)$ is equal to $2\beta^2$ (§ 2) and the mean value of $(\delta_0{}^2 + \delta_1{}^2) = 2\delta^2$. That this is a necessary condition is obvious, because if either were less there would be a continual transfer from the molecules B to the molecules D, or from D to B and *vice versâ*.

By squaring the equations in § 2 and adding, we have the following:

$$\beta_0{}^2 + \beta_1{}^2 = 2\{\beta^2 - \frac{4D}{B+D} \cdot \beta^2 + \frac{4D^2}{(B+D)^2} \cdot (\delta^2 + \beta^2)\}$$

$$\beta_0{}^2 + \beta_1{}^3 = 2\{\beta^2 - \frac{4D}{B+D} \cdot \delta^2 + \frac{4B^2}{(B+D)^2} \cdot (\delta^2 + \beta^2)\}.$$

If in any case it happens that $\beta_0{}^2 + \beta_1{}^2 = \beta^2$, we shall have

$$\beta^2 \left(\frac{4D}{B+D}\right) = \frac{4D^2}{(B+D)^2} \cdot (\delta^2 + \beta^2),$$

or $\beta^2 B = \delta^2 D$, and $\delta_0{}^2 + \delta_1{}^2 = 2\delta^2$. Hence, if the squares of the impinging velocities happen to be in the inverse ratio of the molecular weights, then in either molecule the sum of the *vis viva* of the twofold encounter (one *meeting*, the other *overtaking* with the same impinging velocities) before impact, or $2\beta^2$, is equal to the sum after impact, or to $\beta_0{}^2 + \beta_1{}^2$.

But this is only one case out of an infinite number where the ratio is different. Generally, we may express the equation thus:

$$\beta_0{}^2 + \beta_1{}^2 = 2\beta^2 + p, \text{ and } \delta_0{}^2 + \delta_1{}^2 = 2\delta^2 + q.$$

Now, suppose that in an indefinitely great multitude of impacts the sum of all the individual values of $\beta_0{}^2 + \beta_1{}^2$ and $\delta_0{}^2 + \delta_1{}^2$ are taken, we shall have the mean of the values of the first equal to $\beta_m{}^2\rho$, in accordance with the necessary condition of permanence noticed above (by $\beta_m{}^2$ we mean to denote the mean molecular *vis viva* or mean square velocity of the B molecules, &c.). The mean value of $\beta^2 + p$ is, therefore, $\beta_m{}^2\rho$, but the mean value of β^2 is also evidently equal to $\beta_m{}^2\rho$, as above; hence, the mean value of p is 0, or the positive values of p balance the negative values. In the same way, it may be shown that the mean of the values of q is also 0. Hence, we deduce that $\beta_m{}^2B = \delta_m{}^2D$, or that *in mixed media the mean square molecular velocity is inversely proportional to the specific weight of the molecules* . . . . **VII.**

This is the law of the equilibrium of *vis viva*.

§ 11. Thus, it appears that the inverse ratio of the specific molecular weight is that which is naturally assumed by the mean square molecular velocity of media in contact, and according to the foregoing reasoning (§ 10), this is also the ratio that ensures an equilibrium of pressure between media of the same density, or which have the same number of molecules contained in the same volume. Thus, by combining V. with VII. we deduce that *media in equilibrium of pressure and* vis viva *are of equal density, or have specific gravities respectively proportional to their specific molecular weights* . . . . **VIII.**

§ 12. We may likewise remark that as the mean value of the product β^2B is equal to the mean δ^2D, or $B_m{}^2 = \delta_m{}^2D$, *there is the same amount of* vis viva *or mechanical force contained in equal volumes of all media that are in equilibrium of pressure and* vis viva . . . . **IX.**

§ 13. If different media are placed in contact they must diffuse themselves through their common volume with velocities proportional to their mean molecular velocity; but this velocity being in each inversely as the square root of its specific molecular weight, which is equal to the square root of its specific gravity, we may deduce, by combining VI. with VII., that *media in equilibrium of pressure and* vis viva *diffuse themselves through their common volume with velocities inversely proportional to the square root of their specific gravity* . . . . **X.**

§ 14. Such are the principal points by which different media are related to each other. Their analogies to the properties of gases may be stated as follows:

(1.) The specific gravities of gases of the same *temperature* and pressure are respectively proportional to their atomic weight. (The combining equivalents or proportions may be viewed as simple multiples or divisors of the atomic weight or specific gravity.)

This is analogous to the VIII. deduction. Media in equilibrium of *vis viva* and pressure have specific gravities proportional to their molecular weight. It will be remarked that here again we have temperature represented by *vis viva*. . . .

§ 15. In the first point of analogy it was stated the atomic weight of a gas corresponded with its specific gravity, *but with the reservation that the combining proporctions are simple multiples or quotients of the same.*[5] This appears to me to be the fair statement of the remarkable connec-

---

[5] Editors' italics.

tion that is always found between the combining volume and combining weight. *It seems impossible that the fact of a volume of every gas containing the same number of molecules can ever be inductively established, but all analogy leads us to this conclusion.*[6] One volume of oxygen combines with two volumes of hydrogen to form two volumes of aqueous vapour. If we inferred from this that one molecule of oxygen combined with two molecules of hydrogen to form one of steam, we must admit that the molecule of steam occupies double the volume of a molecule of hydrogen or oxygen. If it is admitted, on the other hand, that the oxygen molecule is capable of disintegration, and that half a molecule combines with one of hydrogen to form one of steam, the bulk of the three molecules are equal. This last is the view that is responded to by the hypothetical media. *The objection to it is plausible from the natural repugnance to the idea of dividing what has been considered as an ultimate element into parts, and of supposing it possible that an element should have a strong affinity to itself—for this point is also involved. Half molecules of oxygen must have a powerful attraction to each other as they never appear separate. It is the same with all the other simple gases and vapours that combine in half or other fractional volumes.*[7] . . .

APPENDIX I. EXTRACT FROM THE PROCEEDINGS OF THE ROYAL SOCIETY

This memoir contains the enunciation of a new theory of heat, capable of explaining the phenomena of its radiation and polarization, and the elasticity of various bodies, founded on the hypothesis of a medium consisting of a vast multitude of particles of matter endowed with perfect elasticity, and enclosed in elastic walls, but moving in all directions within that space, with perfect freedom, and in every possible direction. In the course of these motions, the particles must be supposed to encounter one another in every possible manner, during an interval of time so small as to allow of their being considered infinitesimal in respect to any sensible period; still, however, preserving the molecular *vis viva* constant and undiminished.

The author then enters into extensive analytical investigations; first, of the conditions that determine the equilibrium of such a homogeneous medium as is implied by the hypothesis, and of the laws of its elasticity; secondly, of the physical relations of media that differ from each other in

---

[6] Editors' italics. This is a remarkable paragraph, for Waterston, apparently independently, proposed Avogadro's Principle and offers interesting views on molecules that are correct and ahead of his time—Editors.

[7] Editors' italics.

the specific weight of their molecules; thirdly, of the phenomena that attend the condensing and dilating of media, and of the mechanical value of their molecular *vis viva;* fourthly, of the resistance of media to a moving surface; fifthly, of the vertical equilibrium of a medium surrounding a planet and constituting its atmosphere; and lastly, of the velocity with which impulses are transmitted through a medium so constituted. . . .

APPENDIX II. EXTRACT FROM THE REPORT OF THE MEETING OF THE BRITISH ASSOCIATION

The author deduces the properties of gases, with respect to heat and elasticity, from a peculiar form of the theory which regards heat as consisting in small but rapid motions of the particles of matter. He conceives that the atoms of a gas, being perfectly elastic, are in continual motion in all directions, being restrained within a limited space by their collisions with each other, and with the particles of surrounding bodies. The *vis viva* of those motions in a given portion of gas constitutes the quantity of heat contained in it.

He shows that the result of this state of motion must be to give the gas an elasticity proportional to the mean square of the velocity of the molecular motions, and to the total mass of the atoms contained in unity of bulk; that is to say, to the density of the medium. This elasticity, in a given gas, is the measure of temperature. Equilibrium of pressure and heat between two gases takes place when the number of atoms in unity of volume is equal, and the *vis viva* of each atom equal. Temperature, therefore, in all gases, is proportional to the mass of one atom multiplied by the mean square of the velocity of the molecular motions, being measured from an *absolute zero* 491° below the zero of Fahrenheit's thermometer.

If a gas be compressed, the mechanical power expended in the compression is transferred to the molecules of the gas, increasing their *vis viva;* and conversely, when the gas expands, the mechanical power given out during the expansion is obtained at the expense of the *vis viva* of the atoms. This principle explains the variations of temperature produced by the expansion and condensation of gases—the laws of their specific heat under different circumstances, and of the velocity of sound in them. The fall of temperature found on ascending in the atmosphere, if not disturbed by radiation and other causes, would correspond with the *vis viva* necessary to raise the atoms through the given height.

The author shows that the velocity with which gases diffuse themselves is proportional to that possessed by their atoms according to his hypothesis.

17

ooooooooooo

THE CONSERVATION
OF ENERGY,
THE MECHANICAL
EQUIVALENT OF HEAT

ooooooooooo

James Prescott Joule (1818-1889)

The principle of the conservation of energy is one of the greatest and most far-reaching in the whole structure of physics; nowhere has it been of more value than in the development of atomic and nuclear science. Like other great generalizations in science, it required a long period of gestation for its birth. If any one person can be credited with providing its scientific basis, that person is James Prescott Joule, for to him we owe the experimental determination of the mechanical equivalent of heat.

For the eighteenth-century scientist, heat was a subtle substance called "caloric" that permeated all bodies. When increased, it made the body hotter. It was one of the many fluids that afflicted the infancy of physics, and its existence was almost universally accepted. A few lone thinkers had ventured the thought that heat, instead of being a substance, was the effect of motion. But not until the middle of the eighteenth century was a clear distinction made between heat and temperature. The difference between these fundamental ideas was first pointed out by Joseph Black (1728–1799) in his lectures to students at Glasgow and Edinburgh universities.

To understand the development of the conservation of energy, it is necessary that the meaning of thermal terms be made clear. One of the

236

classical erroneous statements, often repeated, is that "heat is the sum total of all the energy of the molecules of a body." This is precisely what heat is not. The sum total of all the energy of the molecules is patently nothing but the "internal energy" of the body. The temperature of any body is related to the energy of the *translational* motion of its molecules. To increase this motion, it is necessary to add energy to the body. If the transfer of energy occurs solely as a result of a temperature difference between the body and its surroundings, then, by definition, *heat* has been transferred to it. On this basis, heat is properly defined as energy in transit due solely to a temperature difference.

In the light of these clear distinctions, it is interesting to see how some of the celebrated minds who did not accept the caloric doctrine regarded the idea of heat. Newton, in the queries in Book III of his *Opticks,* asks in part in query 5:

> Does not . . . light act . . . upon bodies . . . heating them, and putting their parts into a vibrating motion wherein heat consists?

John Locke, who was undoubtedly influenced by Newton, writes thus in 1706:

> Heat is a very brisk agitation of the insensible parts of the object, which produces in us the sensation from which we denote the object hot; so what in our sensation is heat, in the object is nothing but motion.

Daniel Bernoulli, as we have already read in his deduction of Boyle's law, states that

> it is admitted that heat may be considered as an increasing internal motion of the particles.

Lavoisier and Laplace in 1780 were even more explicit in their *Mémoire sur la Chaleur:*

> Heat is the *vis viva* resulting from the insensible movements of the molecules of a body. It is the sum of the products of the mass of each molecule by the square of its velocity. [A definition of *vis viva* of the body—Editors.]

All of these definitions are correct in identifying heat with energy, and Lavoisier and Laplace are amazingly specific and modern in their ideas. However, none of these assertions could be backed up by any experimental evidence, and what is more unfortunate these views seem to have made no deep impression on the development of physical science.

The first experiments that pointed strongly to the inadequacy of the caloric theory and equally strongly to the energetic theory were performed by Count Rumford at Munich during his service as Minister of War to the Elector of Bavaria. Another was performed by Humphry Davy (1799), whom Rumford had hired to assist him while founding the Royal Institution in London. Davy's experiment consisted in rubbing together two pieces of ice to produce melting at reduced pressure in a container surrounded by ice. The ingress of caloric was thus minimized. Nevertheless the ice melted. Rumford's experiment was more convincing, although it too was not conclusive. Here is the story in Rumford's own words:

> Being engaged, lately, in superintending the boring of cannon, in the workshops of the military arsenal at Munich, I was struck with the very considerable degree of heat which a brass gun acquires, in a short time, in being bored; and with the still more intense heat (much greater than that of boiling water, as I found by experiment) of the metallic chips separated from it by the borer.
>
> The more I meditated on these phenomena, the more they appeared to me to be curious and interesting. A thorough investigation of them seemed even to bid fair to give a farther insight into the hidden nature of heat; and to enable us to form some reasonable conjectures respecting the existence, or nonexistence, of an *igneous fluid:* a subject on which the opinions of philosophers have, in all ages, been much divided.
>
> In order that the Society may have clear and distinct ideas of the speculations and reasonings to which these appearances gave rise in my mind, and also of the specific objects of philosophical investigation they suggested to me, I must beg leave to state them at some length, and in such manner as I shall think best suited to answer this purpose.
>
> From *whence comes* the heat actually produced in the mechanical operation above mentioned?
>
> Is it furnished by the metallic chips which are separated by the borer from the solid mass of metal?
>
> If this were the case, then, according to the modern doctrines of latent heat, and of caloric, the *capacity for heat* of the parts of the metal, so reduced to chips, ought not only to be changed, but the change undergone by them should be sufficiently great to account for all the heat produced.
>
> But no such change had taken place; for I found, upon taking equal quantities, by weight, of these chips, and of thin slips of the same block of metal separated by means of a fine saw, and putting them, at the same temperature (that of boiling water) into equal quantities of cold water (that is to say, at the temperature of 59½ °F) the portion of water into which the chips were put was not, to all appearance, heated either less or more than the other portion, in which the slips of metal were put.
>
> This experiment being repeated several times, the results were always so nearly the same, that I could not determine whether any, or what change, had been produced in the metal, *in regard to its capacity for heat,* by being reduced to chips by the borer.

From hence it is evident, that the heat produced could not possibly have been furnished at the expense of the latent heat in the metallic chips.[1]

The experiments of Rumford and Davy were concerned with the transformation of work into heat; the much more difficult problem of the transformation of heat into work was studied by Sadi Carnot (1824). Carnot's researches display the work of a thoroughly original mind, and his great contributions consisted in pointing out that the efficiency of thermal engines is not dependent on the substance that powers the engine but only on the difference in temperature through which this substance is taken in cyclical operation. The cyclical operation to achieve the maximum efficiency was also defined, and it is known to every scientist today as the Carnot cycle. The great flaw in Carnot's work was the assumption that heat was a substance, caloric, which was conserved when mechanical work was produced. This assumption was generally accepted by the leading scientists of the time, including Michael Faraday, and accounts for the indifference that met the ideas of Julius Robert Mayer and Joule in the 1840's. From posthumous papers published in 1872, it appears that Carnot changed his ideas very radically before his death in 1832. But these ideas were unknown, and did not influence the development of the theories of heat and energy.

The conservation of energy in a limited form was already understood through the formulation of mechanics by Newton and Huygens. Thus, a pendulum moving without friction maintains a constant energy, but not always of the same kind. At the end of its swing its energy is all potential, while at the middle it is all kinetic. The idea that mechanical energy could be transformed into internal energy and thus produce the same effect as "heating" a body and that a fixed ratio existed between mechanical work and thermal units (calories or Btu's) originated with an obscure German physician, Julius Robert Mayer, in 1842. Mayer was not trained in the physical sciences and he carried on no experimental investigations. Using data then available he was able to deduce a value (corrected) of 725 ft-lb per Btu. The details were published in a paper that appeared in *Liebig's Annalen* in 1842, and were accompanied by the first clear statement of the conservation of energy:

. . . force [term then also connoting energy] once in existence cannot be annihilated; it can only change its form.

---

[1] Count Rumford, *Collected Works,* Vol. II, Essay IX. Read before the Royal Society on January 25, 1798. Later published in *Philosophical Transactions,* 88 (1798), p. 80, and reprinted in *The Complete Works of Count Rumford* (Boston: American Academy of Arts and Sciences, 1870), I, 471 ff.

From this it would appear that the credit for the conception both of the mechanical equivalent of heat and of the conservation of energy should go to Mayer, whereas these great advances are usually credited to Joule and Helmholtz. The reason is that Mayer's work was inadequate and in some respects erroneous, as was pointed out in the early 1860's by Lord Kelvin and P. G. Tait, and by Sir G. G. Stokes. However, a subsequent paper of Mayer's in 1845 expanded his ideas with great power and insight. He discussed, among other phenomena, the idea that heat and energy output in man must be equated to his intake, and that the process of the combustion of plants and coal was a process of recapturing the heat previously obtained from the sun. In the latter connection he proposed the contraction theory for the origin of the sun's heat; this was later elaborated by Kelvin. As a belated recognition for his services to physics, Mayer was awarded the Copley medal of the Royal Society in 1871. The main credit, however, for firmly establishing the existence of a mechanical equivalent of heat, and indirectly the conservation of energy, justly belongs to Joule for his long series of experiments on the mechanical equivalent.

James Prescott Joule was born on Christmas Eve, 1818, at Salford near Manchester, England. His father and grandfather were both brewers, and the family lived in comfortable financial circumstances. As a boy, Joule was not robust, and he was educated by tutors at home until he was sixteen. In 1835, he was sent with his brother Benjamin to study under Dalton, who by then had been plied with honors, including the presidency of the Manchester Literary and Philosophical Society. Dalton taught them algebra and geometry and had started on chemistry when he suffered his first paralytic stroke in the spring of 1837. Although Dalton's illness terminated the arrangement, his influence encouraged Joule to begin scientific investigations of his own. Using a room in his home as a laboratory, he began electrical and magnetic experiments, and at the age of twenty he published his first paper "On an Electromagnetic Engine" in Sturgeon's *Annals of Electricity*. Two years later in a paper published in 1840, he described the first known attempt to determine a unit of electric current. For this measurement he used a voltameter, a device subsequently employed in the definition of the international ampere.

Joule presented his first paper before the Manchester Literary and Philosophical Society in November 1841, with Dalton as chairman of the meeting. It is reported that, on the conclusion of the paper, Dalton moved a vote of thanks to the author, the first such courtesy he extended in all his years as president of the society. Joule was elected a member two months later and was successively librarian, in 1844, honorary secretary, in 1846, a vice president, in 1851, and finally president, in 1860.

In 1841 Joule sent to the Royal Society a paper in which he announced, as a definite law, that the heat evolved by an electric current in a given time is proportional to the resistance of the conductor multi-plied by the square of the current. To this day, this phenomenon is still referred to as "Joule heat." From his experiments with batteries and currents, Joule was led to see clearly that chemical energy in the battery is converted to electrical energy in the circuit and that this in turn is converted into heat. To follow up these ideas he set up an experiment to measure the heat produced by currents induced in coils rotated under water, together with the mechanical effort needed to turn the coils. By hindsight, it is evident that this arrangement was overly complex. But with it, he was able to deduce his first value for the mechanical equivalent—838 ft-lb of work per Btu of heat. He reported this finding together with another result obtained from an independent method—the viscous flow of water through fine tubes (770 ft-lb per Btu), at the British Associa-tion meeting held at Cork, Ireland, in August 1843. To quote his own words, "the subject did not excite much general attention."

The lack of precision in his findings led Joule to modify his apparatus; as a consequence he adopted the well-known arrangement of a paddle wheel churning water in a closed, insulated container. The first result, 890 ft-lb per Btu, was communicated to the British Association Meet-ing in Cambridge in 1845. Joule must have felt that his experiments should be made known to a wider audience, for he sent to the editor of the Philosophical Magazine the letter that is reprinted at the end of this commentary.

Two years later, Joule, then twenty-eight, had new results obtained with the paddle-wheel apparatus, and he forwarded a paper for the British Association Meeting at Oxford, in August 1847. But the chairman sug-gested that, owing to the press of business, Joule should not read the paper but instead give a verbal description of his experiments. "This I endeavored to do," Joule wrote later, "and, discussion not being invited, the communication would have passed without comment if a young man had not arisen in the Section, and by his intelligent observations created a lively interest in the new theory." The young man was William Thom-son, later Lord Kelvin, then only twenty-three years old. Thomson's com-ments made Joule's paper the sensation of the meeting, but few of those present, including Faraday, were persuaded of the correctness of the new views, which contradicted Carnot and the long entrenched caloric theory.

There is another anecdote about Joule and Thomson that is worthy of inclusion at this point. Three days after the Oxford meeting, Joule married Amelia Grimes, the daughter of the collector of customs at the port of Liverpool. In his discussion with Thomson, there had been no reason to mention his impending marriage; nor had Thomson mentioned that he would depart shortly for a holiday in Switzerland. This occasioned an amusing incident, for a fortnight later Thomson, while walking in the valley of the Chamonix, saw a young man coming toward him carrying what looked like a stick. On closer approach the man turned out to be Joule, with a long thermometer! His wife had preceded him in the *char-à-banc* (to which he would not entrust the thermometer), and he was walking to the top of a neighboring waterfall. If his ideas were right, there must be a difference in temperature of the water between the bottom and the top, due to the dissipation of kinetic energy at the bottom of the fall. Evidently a wedding trip did not separate Joule completely from his science. This chance meeting encouraged the friendship which had begun at Oxford and led to a collaboration that lasted throughout Joule's life.

If, despite Joule's presentation at the Oxford meeting, scientists were reluctant to re-examine their views on caloric, or on heat and work, Hermann von Helmholtz's classic paper "Über die Erhaltung der Kraft" soon thundered an ultimatum that could not be ignored.

As to Joule, he continued improving the precision of his measurements, obtaining the new value of 772 ft-lb per Btu. On June 21, 1849, he presented this result to the Royal Society. His paper, as published in the *Philosophical Transactions,* Part I, 1850, is reproduced in the following pages.

As a reward for his epoch-making studies, Joule was elected a fellow of the Royal Society in 1850 and awarded the Royal medal in 1852. It was during this period that he performed his other famous experiment on the free expansion of a gas and followed it by systematic studies with Thomson on the change in temperature when a gas expands through a porous plug (Joule-Thomson effect). These studies clarified ideas regarding real gases and led to the notion that the internal energy of an ideal gas is a function of the temperature only. In 1860 he was honored with the Copley medal for the same work with the citation that "The award of two medals for the same researches is an exceedingly rare proceeding in our Society—and rightly so."

Osborne Reynolds in a memoir on Joule, prepared for the Manchester Literary and Philosophical Society in 1892, leaves behind these personal impressions:

At fifty-one, he was rather under medium height, somewhat stout and rounded in figure, and his dress, though neat, was commonplace in the extreme. His attitude and movements were possessed of no natural grace, and his manner was somewhat nervous. He possessed no great facility of speech and conveyed an impression of the simplicity and utter absence of all affectation which characterized his life. It was not merely veneration arising from his fame that inspired members of the Society, but the inherent loveability of his character—kindly, noble, and chivalrous in the extreme, though modest and devoid of mere personal ambition. He was jealous for the interests of his friends and the Society in general, and in particular, jealous in the interest of everything truly scientific. Anything that looked like ostentation or quackery excited Joule's indignation, particularly when exhibited by those possessing the popular ear. On the other hand, he always noticed with encouragement the efforts of those who were yet unknown, and resented any attempt at the disparagement of their work—as though his own early experience had left him with a fellow-feeling for those who were struggling to get their views taken up.

All of the ideas for which Joule is remembered he had explored and published before he was thirty-four years old. His work during the remaining years of his life was devoted to the improvement of its accuracy, its place in the structure of physics, and in furthering the progress of science. His health began to fail in his middle fifties, and he was compelled to live quietly until his death at the age of seventy-one in 1889.

"I believe," he told his brother in 1887, "I have done two or three little things but nothing to make a fuss about." The judgment of his peers was by no means so modest. A tablet in Westminster Abbey honoring his "establishing the Law of the Conservation of Energy and determining the Mechanical Equivalent of Heat" is placed amid the memorials to the greatest names in British science.

০০০০০০০০

J O U L E

A Letter to the Editors of the *Philosophical Magazine* [2]

THE PRINCIPAL PART OF THIS letter was brought under the notice of the British Association at its last meeting at Cambridge. I have hitherto hesitated to give it further publication, not because I was in any degree doubtful of the conclusions at which I had arrived, but because I intended to make slight alteration in the apparatus calculated to give still greater precision to the experiments. Being unable, however, just at present to spare the time necessary to fulfill this design, and being at the same time most anxious to convince the scientific world

---

[2] James Prescott Joule, *Philosophical Magazine,* 27 (1845), 205.

of the truth of the positions I have maintained, I hope you will do me the favor of publishing this letter in your excellent magazine.

The apparatus exhibited before the Association consisted of a brass paddle wheel working *horizontally* in a can of water. Motion could be communicated to this paddle by means of weights, pulleys, &c., exactly in the manner described in a previous paper.

The paddle moved with great resistance in the can of water, so that the weights (each of four pounds) descended at the slow rate of about one foot per second. The height of the pulleys from the ground was twelve yards, and consequently, when the weights had descended through that distance, they had to be wound up again in order to renew the motion of the paddle. After this operation had been repeated sixteen times, the increase of the temperature of the water was ascertained by means of a very sensible [sensitive] and accurate thermometer.

A series of nine experiments was performed in the above manner, and nine experiments were made in order to eliminate the cooling or heating effects of the atmosphere. After reducing the result to the capacity for heat of a pound of water,[3] it appeared that for each degree of heat evolved by the friction of water, a mechanical power equal to that which can raise a weight of 890 lbs to the height of one foot, had been expended.

The equivalents I have already obtained are,—first, 823 lbs, derived from magneto-electrical experiments, second, 795 lbs, deduced from the cold produced by the rarefaction of air; and third, 774 lbs from experiments (hitherto unpublished) on the motion of water through narrow tubes. This last class of experiments being similar to that with the paddle wheel, we may take the mean of 774 and 890, or 832 lbs, as the equivalent derived from the friction of water. In such delicate experiments, where one hardly ever collects more than half a degree of heat, greater accordance of the results with one another than that above exhibited could hardly have been expected. I may therefore conclude that the existence of an equivalent relation between heat and the ordinary forms of mechanical power is proved; and assume 817 lbs, the mean of the results of three distinct classes of experiments, as the equivalent, until still more accurate experiments shall have been made.[4]

Any of your readers who are so fortunate as to reside amid the romantic scenery of Wales or Scotland, could, I doubt not, confirm my experiments by trying the temperature of the water at the top and at the bottom of a cascade. If my views be correct, a fall of 817 feet will of course generate one degree of heat; and the temperature of the river Niagara will be raised about one fifth of a degree by its fall of 160 feet.

---

[3] That is, the specific heat, or amount of heat required to raise the temperature of one pound of substance by one degree Fahrenheit.

[4] The present value is 778 foot-pounds.

Admitting the correctness of the equivalent I have named, it is obvious that the *vis viva* [5] of the particles of a pound of water at (say) 51° is equal to the *vis viva* possessed by a pound of water at 50° plus the *vis viva* which would be acquired by a weight of 817 lbs after falling through the perpendicular height of one foot.

Assuming that the expansion of elastic fluids on the removal of pressure is owing to the centrifugal force of revolving atmospheres of electricity,[6] we can easily estimate the absolute quantity of heat in matter. For in an elastic fluid the pressure will be proportional to the square of the velocity of the revolving atmospheres; and the *vis viva* of the atmospheres will also be proportional to the square of their velocity; consequently the pressure will be proportional to the *vis viva*. Now the ratio of the pressures of elastic fluids at the temperatures 32° and 33° is 480 : 481, consequently the zero of temperature must be 480° below the freezing point of water.[7]

We see then what an enormous quantity of *vis viva* exists in matter. A single pound of water at 60° must possess 480° + 28° = 508° of heat, in other words, it must possess a *vis viva* equal to that acquired by a weight of 415036 lbs after falling through the perpendicular height of one foot. The velocity with which the atmospheres of electricity must revolve in order to present this enormous amount of *vis viva*, must of course be prodigious, and equal probably to the velocity of light in the planetary space, or to that of an electric discharge as determined by the experiments of Wheatstone.

On the Mechanical Equivalent of Heat [8]

IN ACCORDANCE WITH THE PLEDGE I gave the Royal Society some years ago, I have now the honor to present it with the results of the experiments I have made in order to determine the mechanical equivalent of heat with exactness. I will commence with a slight sketch of the progress of the mechanical doctrine, endeavoring to confine myself, for the sake of conciseness, to the notice of such researches as are immediately connected with the subject. I shall not therefore be able to review the valuable labors of Mr. Forbes [9] and other illustrious men,

---

[5] Twice the kinetic energy.

[6] A strange idea, quite at variance with Joule's later ideas on kinetic theory.

[7] Actually 492°R below the freezing point, or −460°F.

[8] Joule, *Philosophical Transactions of the Royal Society*, 140 (1850), 61–82.

[9] James D. Forbes (1809–1868), professor of physics at Edinburgh. See Chap. 18 on Maxwell.

whose researches on radiant heat and other subjects do not come exactly within the scope of the present memoir.

For a long time it had been a favorite hypothesis that heat consists of "a force or power belonging to bodies," but it was reserved for Count Rumford to make the first experiments decidedly in favor of that view. That justly celebrated natural philosopher demonstrated by his ingenious experiments that the very great quantity of heat excited by the boring of cannon could not be ascribed to a change taking place in the calorific capacity of the metal; and he therefore concluded that the motion of the borer was communicated to the particles of metal, thus producing the phenomena of heat: "It appears to me," he remarks, "extremely difficult, if not quite impossible, to form any distinct idea of anything, capable of being excited and communicated, in the manner the heat was excited and communicated in these experiments, except it be motion."

One of the most important parts of Count Rumford's paper, though one to which little attention has hitherto been paid, is that in which he makes an estimate of the quantity of mechanical force required to produce a certain amount of heat. Referring to his third experiment, he remarks that the "total quantity of ice-cold water which, with the heat actually generated by friction, and accumulated in 2^h 30^m, might have been heated 180°, or made to boil, $= 26.58$ lbs." In the next page he states that "the machinery used in the experiment could easily be carried round by the force of one horse (though, to render the work lighter, two horses were actually employed in doing it)." Now the power of a horse is estimated by Watt at 33,000 foot-pounds per minute,[10] and therefore if continued for two hours and a half will amount to 4,950,000 foot-pounds, which, according to Count Rumford's experiment, will be equivalent to 26.58 lbs of water raised 180°. Hence the heat required to raise a lb of water 1° will be equivalent to the force [energy] represented by 1034 foot-pounds. This result is not very widely different from that which I have deduced from my own experiments related in this paper, viz., 772 foot-pounds; and it must be observed that the excess of Count Rumford's equivalent is just such as might have been anticipated from the circumstance, which he himself mentions, that "no estimate was made of the heat accumulated in the wooden box, nor of that dispersed during the experiment."

About the end of the last century Sir Humphry Davy communicated a paper to Dr. Beddoes' West Country Contributions, entitled, "Researches on Heat, Light, and Respiration," in which he gave ample confirmation to the views of Count Rumford. By rubbing two pieces of ice against one another in the vacuum of an air pump, part of them was melted, although the temperature of the receiver was kept below the freez-

---

[10] Present definition of the horsepower.

ing point. This experiment was the more decisively in favor of the doctrine of the immateriality of heat, inasmuch as the capacity of ice for heat is much less than that of water.[11] It was therefore with good reason that Davy drew the inference that "the immediate cause of the phenomena of heat is motion, and the laws of its communication are precisely the same as the laws of the communication of motion."

The researches of Dulong [12] on the specific heat of elastic fluids were rewarded by the discovery of the remarkable fact that "equal volumes of all the elastic fluids, taken at the same temperature, and under the same pressure, being compressed or dilated suddenly to the same fraction of their volume, disengage or absorb the same *absolute quantity of heat.*" [13] This law is of the utmost importance in the development of the theory of heat, inasmuch as it proves that the calorific effect is, under certain conditions, proportional to the force expended.

In 1834 Dr. Faraday demonstrated the "Identity of the Chemical and Electrical Forces." This law, along with others subsequently discovered by that great man, showing the relations which subsist between magnetism, electricity, and light, have enabled him to advance the idea that the so-called imponderable bodies are merely the exponents of different forms of force. Mr. Grove and M. Mayer have also given their powerful advocacy to similar views.

My own experiments in reference to the subject were commenced in 1840, in which year I communicated to the Royal Society my discovery of the law of the heat evolved by voltaic electricity, a law from which the immediate deductions were drawn,—first, that the heat evolved by any voltaic pair is proportional, *caeteris paribus,* to its intensity or electromotive force; and second, that the heat evolved by the combustion of a body is proportional to the intensity of its affinity for oxygen. I thus succeeded in establishing relations between heat and chemical affinity. In 1843 I showed that the heat evolved by magneto-electricity is proportional to the force [energy] absorbed; and that the force of the electromagnetic engine is derived from the force of chemical affinity in the battery, a force which otherwise would be evolved in the form of heat: from these facts I considered myself justified in announcing "that the quantity of heat capable of increasing the temperature of a lb of water by one degree of Fahrenheit's scale, is equal to, and may be converted into, a mechanical force capable of raising 838 lbs to the perpendicular height of one foot."

In a subsequent paper, read before the Royal Society in 1844, I en-

---

[11] The specific heat of ice is approximately half that of water.

[12] Pierre Dulong (1785–1838), professor of physics at the École Polytechnique, Paris.

[13] The work done in compression *or* expansion in a given fraction volume change is identical.

deavored to show that the heat absorbed and evolved by the rarefaction and condensation of air is proportional to the force [energy] evolved and absorbed in those operations. The quantitative relation between force [work] and heat deduced from these experiments, is almost identical with that derived from the electromagnetic experiments just referred to, and is confirmed by the experiments of M. Séguin on the dilatation of steam.

From the explanation given by Count Rumford of the heat arising from the friction of solids, one might have anticipated, as a matter of course, that the evolution of heat would also be detected in the friction of liquid and gaseous bodies. Moreover there were many facts, such as, for instance, the warmth of the sea after a few days of stormy weather, which had long been commonly attributed to fluid friction. Nevertheless the scientific world, preoccupied with the hypothesis that heat is a substance, and following the deductions drawn by Pictet from experiments not sufficiently delicate, have almost unanimously denied the possibility of generating heat in that way. The first mention, so far as I am aware, of experiments in which the evolution of heat from fluid friction is asserted, was in 1842 by M. Mayer, who states that he has raised the temperature of water from 12°C to 13°C, by agitating it, without however indicating the quantity of force [energy] employed, or the precautions taken to secure a correct result. In 1843 I announced the fact that "heat is evolved by the passage of water through narrow tubes," and that each degree of heat per lb of water required for its evolution in this way a mechanical force represented by 770 foot-pounds. Subsequently in 1845, and 1847, I employed a paddle wheel to produce the fluid friction, and obtained the equivalents $781 \cdot 5$, $782 \cdot 1$ and $787 \cdot 6$, respectively, from the agitation of water, sperm oil, and mercury. Results so closely coinciding with one another, and with those previously derived from experiments with elastic fluids and the electromagnetic machine, left no doubt on my mind as to the existence of an equivalent relation between force [energy] and heat; but still it appeared of the highest importance to obtain that relation with still greater accuracy. This I have attempted in the present paper.

DESCRIPTION OF APPARATUS

The thermometers employed had their tubes calibrated and graduated according to the method first indicated by M. Regnault.[14] Two of them, which I shall designate by A and B, were constructed by Mr. Dancer of

---

[14] Henri Victor Regnault (1810–1878). Reference is to a constant-volume gas thermometer.

Manchester; the third, designated by *C*, was made by M. Fastré of Paris. The graduation of these instruments was so correct, that when compared together their indications coincided to about $\frac{1}{100}$ of a degree Fahr. I also possessed another exact instrument made by Mr. Dancer, the scale of which embraced both the freezing and boiling points. The latter point in this standard thermometer was obtained, in the usual manner, by immersing the bulb and stem in the steam arising from a considerable quantity of pure water in rapid ebullition. During the trial the barometer stood at 29.94 inches, and the temperature of the air was 50°; so that the observed point required very little correction to reduce it to 0.760 metre and 0°C, the pressure used in France, and I believe the Continent generally, for determining the boiling point, and which has been employed by me on account of the number of accurate thermometrical researches which have been constructed on that basis.* The values of the scales of thermometers *A* and *B* were ascertained by plunging them along with the standard in large volumes of water kept constantly at various temperatures. The value of the scale of thermometer *C* was determined by comparison with *A*. It was thus found that the number of divisions corresponding to 1° Fahr in the thermometers *A, B,* and *C* were 12.951, 9.829 and 11.647, respectively. And since constant practice had enabled me to read off with the naked eye to $\frac{1}{20}$th of a division, it followed that $\frac{1}{200}$th of a degree Fahr was an appreciable temperature.

[Fig. 17–1] represents a vertical, and [Fig. 17–2] a horizontal plan for the apparatus employed for producing the friction of water, consisting of a brass paddle wheel furnished with eight sets of revolving arms, *a, a,* working between four sets of stationary vanes, *b, b,* affixed to a framework also in sheet brass. The brass axis of the paddle wheel worked freely, but without shaking, on its bearings at *c, c,* and at *d* was divided into two parts by a piece of boxwood intervening, so as to prevent the conduction of heat in that direction.

[Fig. 17–3] represents the copper vessel into which the revolving apparatus was firmly fitted: it had a copper lid, the flange of which, furnished with a very thin washer of leather saturated with white lead, could be screwed perfectly watertight to the flange of the copper vessel. In the lid there were two necks, *a, b,* the former for the axis to revolve in without touching, the latter for the insertion of the thermometer. . . .

---

* A barometrical pressure of 30 inches of mercury at 60° is very generally employed in this country, and fortunately agrees almost exactly with the Continental standard. In the "Report of the Committee appointed by the Royal Society to consider the best method of adjusting the Fixed Points of Thermometers," *Phil. Trans.,* abridged, vol. xiv, p. 258, the barometrical pressure 29.8 is recommended, but the temperature is not named—a remarkable omission in a work so exact in other respects.

[Fig. 17–4] is a perspective view of the machinery employed to set the frictional apparatus just described in motion; *a a* are wooden pulleys, 1 foot in diameter and 2 inches thick, having wooden rollers, *bb, bb,* 2 inches in diameter, and steel axles, *cc, cc,* one quarter of an inch in diameter. The pulleys were turned perfectly true and equal to one another.

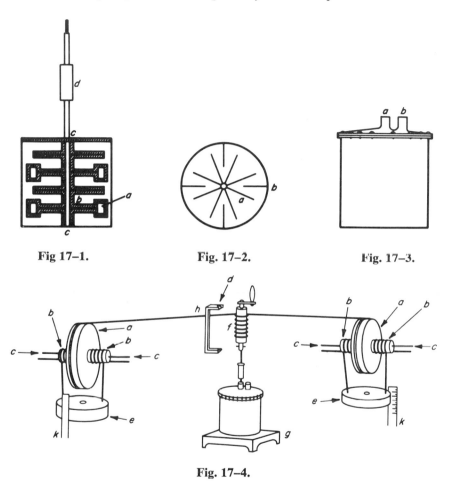

Fig 17–1.   **Fig. 17–2.**   Fig. 17–3.

Fig. 17–4.

Their axles were supported by brass friction wheels *dddd, dddd,* the steel axles of which worked in holes drilled into brass plates attached to a very strong wooden framework firmly fixed into the walls of the apartment.*

The leaden weights *e, e,* which in some of the ensuing experiments weighed about 29 lbs and in others about 10 lbs a piece, were suspended

---

* This was a spacious cellar, which had the advantage of possessing a uniformity of temperature far superior to that of any other laboratory I could have used.

by string from the rollers *bb, bb;* and fine twine attached to the pulleys *aa* connected them with the central roller *f,* which, by means of a pin, could with facility be attached to, or removed from, the axis of the frictional apparatus.

The wooden stool *g,* upon which the frictional apparatus stood, was perforated by a number of transverse slits, so cut out that only a very few points of wood came in contact with the metal, whilst the air had free access to almost every part of it. In this way the conduction of heat to the substance of the stool was avoided.

A large wooden screen (not represented in the figure) completely obviated the effects of radiant heat from the person of the experimenter.

The method of experimenting was simply as follows: The temperature of the frictional apparatus having been ascertained and the weights wound up with the assistance of the stand *h,* the roller was refixed to the axis. The precise height of the weights above the ground having then been determined by means of the graduated slips of wood, *k, k,* the roller was set at liberty and allowed to revolve until the weights reached the flagged floor of the laboratory, after accomplishing a fall of about 63 inches. The roller was then removed to the stand, the weights wound up again, and the friction renewed. After this had been repeated twenty times, the experiment was concluded with another observation of the temperature of the apparatus. The mean temperature of the laboratory was determined by observations made at the commencement, middle and termination of each experiment.

Previously to, or immediately after each of the experiments, I made trial of the effect of radiation and conduction of heat to or from the atmosphere, in depressing or raising the temperature of the frictional apparatus. In these trials, the position of the apparatus, the quantity of water contained by it, the time occupied, the method of observing the thermometers, the position of the experimenter, in short everything, with the exception of the apparatus being at rest, was the same as in the experiments in which the effect of friction was observed.

FIRST SERIES OF EXPERIMENTS

Friction of Water

Weight of the leaden weights along with as much of the string in connexion with them as served to increase the pressure, 203066 grs. and 203086 grs. Velocity of the weights in descending, 2.42 inches per second. Time occupied by each experiment, 35 minutes. Thermometer employed for ascertaining the temperature of the water, *A.* Thermometer for registering the temperature of the air, *B.*

TABLE 17-1

1	2	3	Difference between mean of Columns 5 and 6 and Column 3	5	6	7
No. of experiment and cause of change of temperature	Total fall of weights in inches	Mean temperature of air		Temperature of apparatus		Gain or loss of heat during experiment
				Commencement of experiment	Termination of experiment	
1 Friction	1256·96	57·698	2·252 −	55·118	55·774	0·656 gain
1 Radiation	0	57·868	2·040 −	55·774	55·882	0·108 gain
2 Friction	1255·16	58·085	1·875 −	55·882	56·539	0·657 gain
2 Radiation	0	58·370	1·789 −	56·539	56·624	0·085 gain
3 Friction	1253·66	60·788	1·596 −	58·870	59·515	0·645 gain
3 Radiation	0	60·926	1·373 −	59·715	59·592	0·077 gain
4 Friction	1252·74	61·001	1·110 −	59·592	60·191	0·599 gain
4 Radiation	0	60·890	0·684 −	60·191	60·222	0·031 gain
5 Friction	1251·81	60·940	0·431 −	60·222	60·797	0·575 gain
5 Radiation	0	61·035	0·237 −	60·797	60·799	0·002 gain
6 Radiation	0	59·675	0·125 +	59·805	59·795	0·010 loss
6 Friction	1254·71	59·919	0·157 +	59·795	60·357	0·562 gain
7 Radiation	0	59·888	0·209 −	59·677	59·681	0·004 gain
7 Friction	1254·02	60·076	0·111 −	59·681	60·249	0·568 gain
8 Radiation	0	59·240	0·609 +	58·871	58·828	0·043 loss
8 Friction	1251·22	58·237	0·842 +	58·828	59·330	0·502 gain
9 Friction	1253·92	55·328	0·070 +	55·118	55·678	0·560 gain
9 Radiation	0	55·528	0·148 +	55·678	55·674	0·004 loss
10 Radiation	0	54·941	0·324 −	54·614	54·620	0·006 gain
10 Friction	1257·96	54·985	0·085 −	54·620	55·180	0·560 gain

[This table in Joule's paper lists 40 sets of readings of which only the first 10 are reproduced here. The averages of the data appear in Table 17–2—Editors.]

TABLE 17-2

1	2	3	4	5	6	7
Mean Friction	1260.248		0.305075 −			0.575250 gain
Mean Radiation	0		0.322950 −			0.012975 gain

From the various experiments in [Table 17–1] in which the effect of radiation was observed, it may be readily gathered that the effect of the temperature of the surrounding air upon the apparatus was, for each degree of difference between the mean temperature of the air and that of the apparatus, 0.04654°. Therefore, since the excess of the temperature of the atmosphere over that of the apparatus was 0.32295° in the mean of the radiation experiments, but only 0.305075° in the mean of the friction experiments, it follows that 0.000832° must be added to the difference between 0.57525° and 0.012975°, and the result, 0.563107°, will be the proximate heating effect of the friction. But to this quantity a small correction must be applied on account of the mean of the temperatures of the apparatus at the commencement and termination of each friction experiment having been taken for the true mean temperature, which was not strictly the case, owing to the somewhat less rapid increase of temperature towards the termination of the experiment when the water had become warmer. The mean temperature of the apparatus in the friction experiments ought therefore to be estimated 0.002184° higher, which will diminish the heating effect of the atmosphere by 0.000102°. This, added to 0.563107°, gives 0.563209° as the true mean increase of temperature due to the friction of water.*

In order to ascertain the absolute quantity of heat evolved, it was necessary to find the capacity for heat of the copper vessel and brass paddle wheel. That of the former was easily deduced from the specific heat of copper according to M. Regnault. Thus, capacity of 25541 grs.† of copper × 0.09515 = capacity of 2430.2 grs. of water. A series of seven very careful experiments with the brass paddle wheel gave me 1783 grs. of water as its capacity, after making all the requisite corrections for the heat occasioned by the contact of the water with the surface of the metal, &c. But on account of the magnitude of these corrections, amounting to one thirtieth of the whole capacity, I prefer to avail myself to M. Regnault's law, viz., *that the capacity in metallic alloys is equal to the sum of the capacities of their constituent metals.* Analysis of a part of the wheel proved it to consist of a very pure brass containing 3933 grs. of zinc to 14968 grs. of copper. Hence

Cap. 14968 grs. copper × 0.09515 = cap. 1424.2 grs. water.
Cap. 3933 grs. zinc × 0.09555 = cap. 375.8 grs. water.
——
    Total cap brass wheel   = cap. 1800 grs. water.

---

* This increase of temperature was, it is necessary to observe, a mixed quantity, depending partly upon the friction of the water, and partly upon the friction of the vertical axis of the apparatus upon its pivot and bearing, *cc*, Fig. 17–1. The latter source of heat was however only equal to about $\frac{1}{80}$th of the former. Similarly also, in the experiments on the friction of solids hereafter detailed, the cast-iron discs revolving in mercury rendered it impossible to avoid a very small degree of friction among the particles of that fluid. But since it was found that the quantity of heat evolved was the same, for the same quantity of force [energy] expended, in both cases, i.e., whether a minute quantity of heat arising from friction of solids was mixed with the heat arising from the friction of a fluid, or whether, on the other hand, a minute quantity of heat arising from the friction of a fluid was mingled with the heat developed by the friction of solids, I thought there could be no impropriety in considering the heat as if developed from a simple source—in the one case entirely from the friction of a fluid, and in the other entirely from the friction of a solid body.

† The washer, weighing only 38 grs., was reckoned as copper in this estimate.

The capacity of a brass stopper which was placed in the neck *b* (Fig. 17–3) for the purpose of preventing the contact of air with the water as much as possible, was equal to that of 10.3 grs. of water: the capacity of the thermometer had not to be estimated, because it was always brought to the expected temperature before immersion. The entire capacity of the apparatus was therefore as follows:

Water	93229.7
Copper as water	2430.2
Brass as water	1810.3
Total	97470.2

So that the total quantity of heat evolved was 0.563209° in 97470.2 grs. of water, or, in other words, 1° Fahr in 7.842299 lbs of water.

The estimate of the force applied in generating this heat may be made as follows:

The weights amounted to 406152 grs., from which must be subtracted the friction arising from the pulleys and the rigidity of the string; which was found by connecting the two pulleys with twine passing round a roller of equal diameter to that employed in the experiments. Under these circumstances, the weight required to be added to one of the leaden weights in order to maintain them in equable [uniform] motion was found to be 2955 grs. The same result, in the opposite direction, was obtained by adding 3055 grs. to the other leaden weight. Deducting 168 grs., the friction of the roller on its pivots, from 3005, the mean of the above numbers, we have 2837 grs. as the amount of friction in the experiments, which, subtracted from the leaden weights, leaves 403315 grs. as the actual pressure applied.

The velocity with which the leaden weights came to the ground, viz., 2.42 inches per second, is equivalent to an altitude of 0.0076 inch. This, multiplied by 20, the number of times the weights were wound up in each experiment, produces 0.152 inch, which, subtracted from 1260.248, leaves 1260.096 as the corrected mean height from which the weights fell.

This fall, accompanied by the above-mentioned pressure, represents a force equivalent to 6050.186 lbs through one foot; and 0.8464 × 20 = 16.928 lbs added to it, for the force developed by the elasticity of the string after the weights had touched the ground,[15] gives 6067.114 foot-pounds as the mean corrected force.

Hence $\dfrac{6067.114}{7.842299} = 773.64$ foot-pounds, will be the force [energy]

---

[15] Joule estimated that the weights stretched the string enough to add an additional 0.8464 ft-lb of work each time the weights dropped.

which, according to the above experiments on the friction of water, is equivalent to 1° Fahr in a lb of water.

[The data for two series of experiments on mercury and two series on cast iron are omitted—Editors.]

[Table 17–3] contains a summary of the equivalents derived from the experiments above detailed. In its fourth column I have supplied the results with the correction necessary to reduce them to vacuum.

TABLE 17–3

No. of series	Material employed	Equivalent in air	Equivalent in vacuo	Mean
1	Water	773.640	772.692	772.692
2	Mercury	773.762	772.814 ⎫	774.083
3	Mercury	776.303	775.352 ⎭	
4	Cast iron	776.997	776.045 ⎫	774.987
5	Cast iron	774.880	773.930 ⎭	

It is highly probable that the equivalent from cast iron was somewhat increased by the abrasion of particles of the metal during friction, which could not occur without the absorption of a certain quantity of force in overcoming the attraction of cohesion. But since the quantity abraded was not considerable enough to be weighed after the experiments were completed, the error from this source cannot be of much moment. I consider that 772.692, the equivalent derived from the friction of water, is the most correct, both on account of the number of experiments tried, and the great capacity of the apparatus for heat. And since, even in the friction of fluids, it was impossible entirely to avoid vibration and the production of a slight sound, it is probable that the above number is slightly in excess. I will therefore conclude by considering it as demonstrated by the experiments contained in this paper,

1st. *That the quantity of heat produced by the friction of bodies, whether solid or liquid, is always proportional to the quantity of force [energy] expended.* And,

2nd. *That the quantity of heat capable of increasing the temperature of a pound of water (weighed in vacuo, and taken at between 55° and 60°) by 1° Fahr, requires for its evolution the expenditure of a mechanical force [energy] represented by the fall of 772 lbs through the space of one foot.*

ΟΟΟΟΟΟΟ

Joule's establishment of the mechanical equivalent of heat was not his only contribution to the development of physical science. Among others, but one of the least known, was his calculation of the speed of gas molecules. This calculation in itself was not of great significance. What it did accomplish in the end was to draw the attention of scientists to a neglected area of physics that opened up new avenues to the world of atoms and molecules. Bernoulli had introduced kinetic theory in his remarkable paper of 1738, but at that time molecules and atoms had only the vaguest speculative pretensions to reality and his paper could hardly have been taken as more than an interesting exercise. Herapath independently "rediscovered" gas kinetics in the period 1816 to 1821, a time sufficiently after Dalton's chemical atomic theory for such ideas to be given more serious consideration. But his thinking was too new and his standing in science too uncertain to command the ear of established contemporary investigators. Waterston in 1846, also unknown, but of sounder ideas, fared worse, for his paper was consigned to oblivion. To be respectable, to be accepted, and to fulfill the possibility of yielding a much broader basis for belief in atomistics, kinetic theory needed the backing of a scientist of secure standing. This was the service that Joule rendered. It is interesting to see that Joule, who must have been convinced of the reality of the kinetic hypothesis from his own work, was deeply influenced by Herapath and by the kinetic ideas of Sir Humphry Davy. By joining Herapath's hypothesis with those of so prominent a scientist as Davy, and by using the mixture as a basis for his own contribution, Joule conferred on this kind of speculation the stamp of respectability that kinetic theory so badly needed.

Joule's calculation of the velocity of hydrogen molecules was first published in the *Memoirs of the Manchester Literary and Philosophical Society* in 1851. Owing to the limited circulation of this journal, the paper remained generally unknown. Nevertheless, it found its mark in Germany, catching the eye and the serious interest of Rudolph Clausius. In his hands kinetic theory was developed with sufficient accuracy and completeness (1857) to command the attention of the scientific world and to immediately encourage another master mind, James Clerk Maxwell, to deepen its foundations and extend its scope. It would be inaccurate to leave the impression that Joule's paper was solely or even mainly responsible for the general growth of interest in gas kinetics. Much more was engendered by August Karl Kronig, in 1856, by a paper that had an influence entirely out of proportion to its substance. Nevertheless, it must be clear that the backing of Joule and Kronig was instrumental in drawing serious interest to gas theory. Joule's paper can be considered as hardly more than a suggestive and interesting calculation, but as such it served a valuable and useful function.

ooooooo

The Velocity of Gas Molecules [16]

THE EXPERIMENTS ON THE CHANGES of temperature produced by the rarefaction and condensation of air give likewise an insight into the constitution of elastic fluids, for they show that the heat of elastic fluids is the mechanical force possessed by them; and since it is known that the temperature of a gas determines its elastic force, it follows that the elastic force, or pressure, must be the effect of the motion of the constituent particles in any gas. This motion may exist in several ways, and still account for the phænomena presented by elastic fluids. Davy, to whom belongs the signal merit of having made the first experiment absolutely demonstrative of the immateriality of heat, enunciated the beautiful hypothesis of a rotatory motion. He says, "It seems possible to account for all the phænomena of heat, if it be supposed that in solids the particles are in a constant state of vibratory motion, the particles of the hottest bodies moving with the greatest velocity and through the greatest space: that in fluids and elastic fluids, besides the vibratory motion, which must be considered greatest in the last, the particles have a motion round their own axes with different velocities, the particles of elastic fluids moving with the greatest quickness; and that in ætheral substances the particles move round their own axes and separate from each other, penetrating in right lines through space. Temperature may be conceived to depend upon the velocity of the vibrations, increase of capacity on the motion being performed in greater space; and the diminution of temperature during the conversion of solids into fluids or gases may be explained on the idea of the loss of vibratory motion, in consequence of the revolution of particles round their axes at the moment when the body becomes fluid or aëriform, or from the loss of rapidity of vibration in consequence of the motion of the particles through greater space." I have myself endeavoured to prove that a rotary motion, such as that described by Sir H. Davy, will account for the law of Boyle and Mariotte, and other phænomena presented by elastic fluids; nevertheless, since the hypothesis of Herapath, in which it is assumed that the particles

---

[16] Joule, *Philosophical Magazine,* 14 (1857), 211.

of a gas are constantly flying about in every direction with great velocity, the pressure of the gas being owing to the impact of the particles against any surface presented to them, is somewhat simpler, I shall employ it in the following remarks on the constitution of elastic fluids; premising, however, that the hypothesis of a rotatory motion accords equally well with the phænomena.

Let us suppose an envelope of the size and shape of a cubic foot to be filled with hydrogen gas, which, at 60° temperature and 30 inches barometrical pressure, will weigh 36.927 grs. Further, let us suppose the above quantity to be divided into three equal and indefinitely small elastic particles, each weighing 12.309 grs.; and, further, that each of these particles vibrates between opposite sides of the cube, and maintains a uniform velocity except at the instant of impact; it is required to find the velocity at which each particle must move so as to produce the atmospherical pressure of 14,831,712 grs. on each of the sides of the cube. In the first place, it is known that if a body moving with the velocity of $32\frac{1}{6}$ feet per second be opposed, during one second, by a pressure equal to its weight its motion will be stopped, and that, if the pressure be continued one second longer, the particle will acquire the velocity of $32\frac{1}{6}$ feet per second in the contrary direction. At this velocity there will be $32\frac{1}{6}$ collisions of a particle of 12.309 grs. against each side of the cubical vessel in every two seconds of time; and the pressure occasioned thereby will be $12.309 \times 32\frac{1}{6} = 395.938$ grs. Therefore, since it is manifest that the pressure will be proportional to the square of the velocity of the particles, we shall have for the velocity of the particles requisite to produce the pressure of 14,831,712 grs. on each side of the cubical vessel,

$$v = \sqrt{\left(\frac{14,831,712}{395.938}\right)}\ 32\frac{1}{6} = 6225 \text{ feet per second}$$

The above velocity will be found equal to produce the atmospheric pressure, whether the particles strike each other before they arrive at the sides of the cubical vessel, whether they strike the sides obliquely, and, thirdly, into whatever number of particles the 36.927 grs. of hydrogen are divided.

If only one half the weight of hydrogen, or 18.4635 grs., be enclosed in the cubical vessel, and the velocity of the particles be, as before, 6225 feet per second, the pressure will manifestly be only one half of what it was previously; which shows that the law of Boyle and Mariotte flows naturally from the hypothesis.

The velocity above named is that of hydrogen at the temperature of 60°; but we know that the pressure of an elastic fluid at 60° is to that at 32° as 519 is to 491. Therefore the velocity of the particles at 60° will be to that at 32° as $\sqrt{519} : \sqrt{491}$; which shows that the velocity at the freezing temperature of water is 6055 feet per second.

In the above calculations it is supposed that the particles of hydrogen have no sensible magnitude, otherwise the velocity corresponding to the same pressure would be lessened.

Since the pressure of a gas increases with its temperature in arithmetical progression, and since the pressure is proportional to the squares of the velocity of the particles, in other words to their *vis viva*, it follows that the absolute temperature, pressure, and *vis viva* are proportional to one another, and that the zero of temperature is 491° below the freezing-point of water. Further, the absolute heat of the gas, or, in other words, its capacity, will be represented by the whole amount of *vis viva* at a given temperature. . . .

18

ooooooooooo

THE RANGE OF MOLECULAR
SPEEDS IN A GAS

ooooooooooo

James Clerk Maxwell (1831-1879)

In previous commentaries on Bernoulli, Herapath, Waterston, and Joule, the contributions that each of these men made to the development of atomic physics through the kinetic theory of gases have been reviewed and excerpts from their significant work presented. For reasons discussed in those articles, none of these contributions except Joule's proved effective in directing the serious attention of capable scientific investigators into this fruitful area of research. Joule's calculation of the mean molecular velocity in hydrogen at normal temperatures was originally published in the *Memoirs of the Manchester Literary and Philosophical Society,* a journal that was not widely read; the effect of Joule's contribution, therefore, was correspondingly small, although important. The reception given to kinetic theory changed markedly in 1856 as the result of a paper by Kronig; in the following year the first of several papers by Clausius placed the subject on an entirely different footing. Clausius' work caught the eye of James Clerk Maxwell and in Maxwell's hands the treatment took on significant new dimensions.

In 1860 Maxwell published in the *Philosophical Magazine,* Vol. 19, a long mathematical paper entitled "Illustrations of the Dynamical Theory of Gases." Among other new results, there appeared a calculation for the distribution of molecular speeds—a signal advance in the knowledge of molecular motion—and a formula for the coefficient of viscosity of a gas which showed this quantity to be independent of pressure, a most unexpected and surprising result.

This paper did much to establish Maxwell's contemporary scientific reputation. But his greatest contribution, and one that places him among

260

the great physicists of all time, was his electromagnetic theory, including his deduction that light is propagated as an electromagnetic vibration. This work was first presented in 1864. Unfortunately, experimental electricity had not caught up with theory, and many years were to elapse before the full significance of this paper came to be appreciated. The demonstration of electromagnetic waves, for instance, was not made until 1888, when Heinrich Hertz showed their reality. This was a lapse of almost a quarter of a century. The importance of Maxwell's theory to the development of atomic physics was very real, for it showed how to treat the emission and absorption of radiation. Hence later in this volume some aspects of his electromagnetic theory are also presented. Before these achievements are examined, a brief account of Maxwell's life should serve to give us some appreciation of how he appeared to his contemporaries and the way in which he prepared and carried out his life's work.

When we read the story of genius, it is always interesting to recognize the influences that channel and mold its character. In Maxwell's case, it is clear that his outlook and bent were deeply conditioned by his father, with whom he had an unusually close and happy relationship. No man is an island unto himself, and to appreciate Maxwell both as a person and a scientist it is necessary to know something of his family, particularly his father, John Clerk.

The Clerks of Penicuik had for years been a distinguished Scots family. A forebear, Sir John Clerk, was Baron of the Exchequer in Scotland from 1707 to 1755. According to R. T. Glazebrook, George Clerk, one of Sir John's sons, married a first cousin, Dorothea Maxwell, the heiress of Middlebie in Dumfriesshire, and took the name Maxwell. Succeeding Clerks who accepted any of the inheritance of Middlebie also were obliged to assume the Maxwell name; among these was James Clerk Maxwell's father, John Clerk.

By 1826, John Clerk had inherited a new family home in Edinburgh at 14 India Street, had been admitted to the practice of law, and had married Miss Frances Cay of North Charlton, Northumberland. Being of an easygoing disposition, his practice was not particularly arduous, and he had time to follow a bent for practical mechanics, invention, and a curiosity about manufacturing processes. For several years the couple maintained their residence at 14 India Street, but a desire to establish a country estate led them to improve what remained of the Middlebie property and to add to it by purchasing an adjacent estate called Glenlair. No house existed on these properties, and during the construction of a suitable dwelling the couple lived intermittently in Edinburgh. There James Clerk Maxwell was born on June 13, 1831. Jamsie, as he came to be called, was soon taken to Glenlair, where he spent an active, inquiring childhood full of country fun and freedom. From the first, his inquisitiveness was very marked and his precocious, "Show me how it goes," or, "What is the go of that?" must, at times, have been trying, though amusing. When the explanation was not completely satisfying, he would press the question with, "But what is the *particular* go of that?"

This active, happy, country childhood was rudely shaken at the age of eight by his mother's death from cancer. For two more years, father and son continued at Glenlair, but the growing necessity for appropriate schooling made it clear that young James should be educated in Edinburgh. The strong family ties of the Clerks provided a happy solution. His father's sister, Isabella, now the widowed Mrs. Wedderburn with a large house at 31 Heriot Row, opened her doors to this unusual boy and his perplexed parent. For the next nine years, James would spend his winters there or with a maternal aunt, Miss Cay, deeply and happily absorbed in exploring the world of books, ideas, and physical science. When he had free time, his father was always at hand to encourage his interests, show him the "useful arts" or immerse him in church activities. In the summer, there were long, carefree months at Glenlair.

James's introduction to school life at the Edinburgh Academy was not without its trials, some of them amusing. Youth is seldom kindly disposed to differences in appearance and manners; being different in both, young James was soon a target for some of his rougher schoolmates. He arrived the first day dressed in a country jacket with a lace collar and square-toed shoes made to his father's design by a country bootmaker. On being asked who made his shoes, we are told that he made the following answer:

> Div ye ken 'twas a man
> And he lived in a house
> In whilk was a mouse.

Doubtless this reply baffled his schoolboy inquisitors, but it was one of the sides of the puzzling personality which characterized Maxwell throughout his life. As Niven remarks, his speech was often "obscure in substance and the manner of expressing himself." Jamsie not only looked different from the other boys, but he *was* different, a fact that prompted his school mates to give him the nickname "Dafty."

Initially his school record was undistinguished, but gradually he began to excel in his studies. Around the time of his thirteenth birthday, before he had begun geometry, he became interested in solid figures and wrote to his father that he had made a "tetrahedron, a dodecahedron and two other hedrons whose names I don't know." At the end of the following school year, his talent in geometry and mathematics became clearly evident and he was awarded the annual mathematical medal. When he was fourteen, his father began taking him to meetings of the Edinburgh Royal Society, rather rigorous mental fare for one so young. Yet the meetings must have acted as an additional spur to his interest in mathematics for he began investigating the properties of ovals. His father took the drawings to Professor James D. Forbes at Edinburgh University, who realized that their construction presented novel features not in the mathematical literature. As a result, Forbes submitted the work to the Edinburgh Royal Society under the title "On the Description of Oval Curves and Those Having a Plurality of Foci." It was read at the March meeting, 1846.

During the next school year, Maxwell became interested in optics and began experimenting with Newton's rings and polarized light. As a result, he was taken to see William Nicol, the inventor of the polarizing prism. Stimulated by this visit, he made an examination of the colors of unannealed glass in polarized light, using a glass plate as polarizer. His drawings, in color, were sent to Nicol, who rewarded the young man with a pair of his prisms.

In the spring of 1847, young Maxwell completed his studies at the academy, being first in mathematics, first in English, and "nearly first" in Latin. The following autumn, at the age of sixteen, he began his studies at Edinburgh University. But his studies were by no means limited to his university instruction, and during vacations at Glenlair, he improvised a laboratory to carry out his own experiments. He remained at the university for three years, increasing his intellectual debt to Forbes, and developing his skills in mathematics and physics. His expanding powers were further demonstrated by the contribution of two more papers to the Edinburgh Royal Society. The first, on the theory of "Rolling Curves," was presented in the spring of 1849, and a second, on "The Equilibrium of Elastic Solids," a year later.

In October of 1850, then nineteen, Maxwell was entered by his father at Peterhouse College, Cambridge. Peterhouse was traditionally the college chosen by outstanding Scottish scholars, but after a few months Maxwell felt that his chances for an eventual fellowship were better at Trinity and transferred there at the end of his first term. Despite his years at the Edinburgh Academy and the university, there was still much of the eccentric in him, and the mother of a school friend noted that "his manners are very peculiar . . . but I doubt not of his becoming a distinguished man." At Trinity, he was no recluse but was completely taken up with college life. His brilliance was quickly recognized, and no less a man than the great Cambridge tutor Hopkins characterized him as "the most extraordinary man I have ever met. It appears impossible for him to think incorrectly on physical subjects." At first, he lodged away from the college, but at the end of his second year he was elected a scholar and obtained rooms in Trinity.

Always an individualist, Maxwell experimented even with hours of sleeping and studying. For a while, he slept from 5:00 to 9:30 P.M., studied from 10:00 to 2:00, exercised from 2:00 to 2:30 A.M., and slept until 7:00. The exercise consisted in running along the upper corridor, downstairs, along the lower corridor, then up to repeat the procedure all over again. This went on until the inhabitants of the rooms along his path took shots at him with hairbrushes, boots, or any other loose objects as he passed.

For the students the period from December 1852 to June 1853 was one of intense concentration for the coming tripos examinations. It was characteristic of Maxwell that he should have chosen to spend a few days of the Easter recess in Birmingham with a friend, using most of the time to inspect manufacturing processes in the local industries. In June he suffered a nervous breakdown. The effects lasted for some months, and he had not completely recovered when he took the tripos examinations in January 1854. These examinations, the culmination of his undergraduate study at Cambridge, were held in the Senate House where the temperature was so low that, at his father's suggestion, he wrote his examinations with his feet and legs wrapped in a rug to ward off the chilling cold. When the results of the examinations were announced, Edward Routh, an accomplished mathematician and later a noted Cambridge tutor, received the designation senior wrangler. Maxwell had finished second. In the more advanced competition for the Smith prize, the two were given equal standing.

After receiving his degree, Maxwell continued at Cambridge and, the following October, at twenty-four, was elected a fellow of Trinity. He assumed the duties of university lecturer and began serious work on the mathematical theory of electricity and magnetism. A few months later, in February, he was advised by his old mentor, Professor Forbes, that the chair of natural philosophy at Marischal College, Aberdeen, was vacant and that he should apply for it. His father was now in poor health, and the prospect of their being closer was certainly one of the factors influencing Maxwell's application. However, in April, while father and son were together at Glenlair, his father unexpectedly died. Although his situation had thus become completely altered, Maxwell nevertheless accepted Marischal's subsequent offer and began teaching when the autumn session commenced in November. His success as a teacher, both initially and in later years, appears to have been rather indifferent. This was not for want of concern. Some of his difficulty must be attributed to shyness and to his habit, in the momentary excitement of problems and explanations, of breaking off into a quirk of ironical humor. It has been said that in scientific discussions his colleagues often were not sure whether he was serious or slyly joking.

The Adams prize, awarded by St. Johns College, Cambridge, was offered in 1857 for the best paper on "The Motions of Saturn's Rings."

The problem was "to demonstrate what type of structure adequately explained the motion and permanence of the rings." Maxwell entered the competition and submitted a paper that demonstrated that the only stable structure would be one composed of disconnected particles. It not only won the prize but earned the praise of Airy, the Astronomer Royal, who characterized it as "one of the most remarkable applications of mathematics" he had ever seen. This paper established Maxwell in the forefront of mathematical physicists. He was then twenty-six years old. But, in a sense, it did much more because it awakened his interest in the motions of groups of particles—the fundamental problem of the kinetic theory of gases. This interest soon led to his brilliant deduction of the distribution of molecular speeds in a gas at equilibrium at any temperature. This great step forward in the understanding of the behavior of the elementary particles of gases represents one of the major advances in the progress of the atomic theory of matter. The paper, entitled "Illustrations of the Dynamical Theory of Gases," was published in the *Philosophical Magazine,* Vol. 19, 1860, and is reproduced in part following this biography and commentary.

About this time, Maxwell became engaged to the daughter of the principal of Marischal College, Katherine Mary Dewar, and after a short engagement, they were married in June of 1858.

Two years later, Marischal College was absorbed into the University of Aberdeen, with the result that Maxwell's post was eliminated. However, then twenty-nine, he was appointed immediately to the professorship in natural philosophy at Kings College, London. He held this post for five years, a period in which he was at the height of his powers. These years were spent in developing the electromagnetic theory, ideas on the dynamic theory of gases, and on the electromagnetic theory of light, which probably began to germinate in his thoughts about 1861. His greatest electrical paper, "A Dynamical Theory of the Electromagnetic Field," was read to the Royal Society of London on December 8, 1864. His experiments on the viscosity of gases demonstrating the unexpected result that within wide limits the viscosity was independent of pressure, formed the basis for his Bakerian lecture to the Royal Society on February 8, 1866. The experiments on which this paper was based were carried out, as usual, in his own home, this time in a large garret running the length of his residence at 8 Palace Gardens, Kensington. The description of part of his procedure is interesting: "To maintain the proper temperature a large fire was for some days kept up in the room in the midst of very hot weather. Kettles were kept on the fire and large quantities of steam allowed to flow into the room. Mrs. Maxwell acted as stoker. . . . After this the room was kept cool for subsequent experiments by the employment of a considerable amount of ice."

Apart from his theoretical work, the years in London were notable for his part in the experimental determination of the standard ohm and in the measurement of the ratio of the electromagnetic to the electrostatic unit of electricity. He gave public lectures and found time to develop an acquaintance with Faraday. But perhaps such concentrated activity was too much for his liking, for Maxwell resigned his post in the spring of 1865. Much of the remaining year was spent in London. But, except for a trip to Italy, he devoted most of the period 1866–1870 to working at Glenlair, on his "Electricity and Magnetism," and his book on *Heat*.

Maxwell's absence from a university post did not sever his academic connections. During this period he acted as examiner in the mathematical tripos at Cambridge and introduced new life into the examinations by posing challenging questions on heat and electricity and magnetism. His innovations emphasized that there was then no instruction in these subjects at Cambridge. As a consequence, a university committee that included Stokes and Routh was appointed to recommend revisions of the curriculum. The committee recommended that instruction be given in heat, electricity, and magnetism, and that a professor be appointed and a laboratory provided for experimental physics. In order to obtain the funds, the committee canvassed the separate colleges of the university regarding their willingness to be taxed for this purpose. It is not surprising that the usual narrow collegiate interests prevailed and that they answered with the greatest disinterest to an undertaking for which they felt no responsibility. But by good fortune, the Chancellor of the University, the seventh Duke of Devonshire, was a man not only of great wealth but of unusual brilliance, having been second wrangler in the mathematical tripos of 1829 and first Smith prizeman. Moved by his understanding of the needs of the university and his connection with science, he offered the necessary funds in October of 1870 for the construction of a laboratory and the purchase of appropriate apparatus. This was the origin of the Cavendish Laboratory. In later years, under J. J. Thomson and Rutherford, it was to become the scene of those great experiments that have furnished much of the foundation of modern atomic physics.

But even with the money available, a man was needed to fill the new professorship and guide the building of the laboratory. The position was offered first to Lord Kelvin, who promptly declined. It was then offered to Maxwell, who accepted. He began his teaching in the autumn of 1871, at the age of forty.

In connection with his return to Cambridge, an interesting anecdote is owed to Sir Horace Lamb, and recounted by Sir J. J. Thomson in his *Recollections and Reflections*. As Thomson notes, it was the custom then for newly appointed professors to deliver an inaugural lecture and for the senior professors to attend as a compliment to the appointee. For reasons not clear, the announcement of Maxwell's inaugural was made in such a way that it did not come to the attention of the senior members of the university. Also, his address was given in an obscure lecture room and not in the Senate House, the usual place for such events. The result was that only about twenty persons were present, principally young mathematicians who had taken or were about to take the mathematical tripos examination. A few days later, however, an announcement was made in the usual way, stating that Maxwell would commence his lectures on heat. Unaware that the inaugural lecture had been given, the great mathematicians and philosophers appeared at the appointed time and place with Adams, Cayley, and Stokes seated in the front row. Maxwell, with a twinkle in his eye, spent the time explaining to his distinguished audience the difference between the Fahrenheit and Centigrade scales of temperature!

The rumor circulated afterward that Maxwell might not be entirely innocent in this confusion, and that a combination of personal modesty and his mischievous sense of humor may have prompted him to avoid the usual formal introduction to his Cambridge colleagues. If we can believe Maxwell's involvement in this episode, it offers another interesting sidelight on his character. His standing at that time was principally a consequence of his paper on the distribution of molecular speeds. None of the scientists of that day could know how great his contribution to electricity and magnetism was to become. His present-day reputation, which eventually came as a result of the confirmation of his electromagnetic theory, was then still many years in the future.

Aside from the reasons previously cited for the Duke of Devonshire's gift, there may have been another consideration in the Duke's mind, which was not evident until after the completion of the laboratory in June 1874. This was nothing less than the editing and publication of Henry Cavendish's studies in electricity. Cavendish, a relative of the Duke's forebears, had published during his lifetime only two electrical papers, but had left in his effects some twenty packets of manuscript on mathematical and experimental electricity. In retrospect, it seems unfortunate that Maxwell acceded to the Duke's wish; the preparation of the manuscript proved a long and arduous task that extended over five years and was not finished until 1879. His absorption in this task was so complete that it practically precluded all professional work except his university duties. Although there is no doubt that the result did much to place Cavendish in his rightful place in the history of experimental physics, there is also no doubt that it occupied most of Maxwell's available time and energy in the short time he had yet to live. It was also during this period that his wife entered a long illness, and Maxwell, with his characteristic sense of devotion to those who were close to him, insisted on assuming her care. On one occasion he did not sleep in a bed for three weeks, but nevertheless conducted his lectures and experiments as usual.

About Easter of 1879, Maxwell consulted his doctor about a stomach ailment that had troubled him during the preceding two years. The problem was not immediately diagnosed and the Maxwells, both ill, left in June for their customary stay at Glenlair. During the summer, he suffered great pain and became progressively weaker. In October, he was told that he had no more than a month to live. Rather than stay in isolation at Glenlair, he and Mrs. Maxwell returned to Cambridge, where medical aid was more readily available. His condition rapidly grew worse, and he died at the age of forty-eight on November 5, 1879, a victim of cancer, the disease that had carried off his mother at the same age.

Maxwell's deduction of the distribution of molecular speeds in a gas is only a part of a long paper in which he presented a systematic development of the fundamentals of kinetic theory. His deduction of the distribution of the velocities of gas molecules was based on the accepted microscopic picture already developed, i.e., independent elastic spheres of negligible size each of the same mass and endowed with completely random rectilinear motion. Collisions of the molecules with each other and with the walls of the container were assumed to be perfectly elastic (that is, with no net loss of energy) and to be governed by the usual laws of mechanics. The mean squared velocity under these conditions is proportional to the absolute temperature. (See, for instance, the commentary in Chapter 16.)

In the earlier treatments of gas kinetics no one had attempted to examine the distribution of molecular speeds—probably because no promising avenue had appeared along which the problem might be attacked. It is here, of course, that Maxwell's genius lay, for he saw that by the application of the laws of probability a solution could be obtained. The mathematics is not difficult and it may be helpful to review his method before reading his paper.

Maxwell first considers the three mutually perpendicular components of the velocity of a molecule. He assigns to each of these components its own distribution function and then considers the distribution of all three components together as the *product* of these three separate distributions. This is another way of stating that the probability that a molecule has a velocity in a certain range is proportional to the probability that the x component of the velocity have the desired value, times the probability that the y component have the proper value, times the probability that the z component of the velocity have its proper value. If all the velocity components lie in the correct range, the velocity itself will lie in the desired range. As Maxwell points out, it is permissible to treat the three components of the velocity independently because the three components are mutually perpendicular and therefore do not affect each other.

Having expressed the probability for the molecular velocity to lie in a certain range as a product of the probabilities that the components of the velocity lie in the proper range, Maxwell then introduces the crucial step in his reasoning. He points out that no direction in space for the velocity is to be preferred over any other direction; all directions are equally probable. This means that the probability function cannot depend on the direction of the velocity and hence depends only on the magnitude of the velocity. Now the magnitude of the velocity depends on (indeed, it is equal to) the sum of the squares of the components of the velocity. In other words, if v_x, v_y, v_z are the components of the velocity v in the three mutually perpendicular directions x, y, and z, then the probability for these components to have a certain range of values depends only on $v_x^2 + v_y^2 + v_z^2$. But the probability is also given by a product of three terms, the first of which depends only on v_x, the second only on v_y, and the third only on v_z. If we equate these two expressions for the probability, as Maxwell does, we see that the probability must be an expression that can be written either as a product of three terms, each involving one and only one component of the velocity, or as a single expression that contains the sum of the squares of the three components of the velocity. It is easy to show that the exponential function is the only mathematical quantity that has this property.

The exponential function is defined as follows: Consider the following infinite sum: $1 + 1 + (1/2) + 1/(2 \times 3) + 1/(2 \times 3 \times 4) + \ldots$ where each new term in the sum is obtained from the preceding term by multiplying its denominator by the next integer. This is called the exponential infinite series and is designated by the letter e. The numerical value of this sum is very nearly equal to 2.718. Let us now raise e to some power x. We write this as e^x, and this is called the exponential function; it is also written as $\exp(x)$.

Maxwell's discovery is equivalent to saying that the probability that a molecule in the gas will be moving with a velocity whose x component lies in a small range around v_x is proportional to $\exp(-v_x^2/\beta)$, where β is some constant that depends on the mass of the molecule and the temperature of the gas. A similar expression holds for the y component of the velocity and for the z component. Maxwell evaluated the constant β in this expression by first using the expression for the probability to obtain the average value of the velocity of a molecule. This expression must, of course, contain β. But according to the work of Clausius, it is also related to the gas law, which in turn is related to the temperature of the gas. Hence β can be expressed in terms of the temperature of the gas. One then finds that β is equal to $2kT/m$, where m is the mass of the molecule, T is the absolute temperature of the gas, and k is the Boltzmann constant.

If we take all of these things into account, we see that the probability that a molecule of mass m in a gas of absolute temperature T has a velocity that lies in a small neighborhood around the value v is $\exp(-mv^2/2kT)$. This is one of the most important formulas in physics and is the basis of statistical mechanics. To see the significance of this formula in its application to all physical systems and not only to gases, we note that $mv^2/2$ is just the average kinetic energy of a molecule in the gas. We may therefore say that the probability that, on the average, a molecule in the gas will be moving in such a way that its kinetic energy will have a value lying in a small neighborhood around E is just $\exp(-E/kT)$. This is a basic formula that was also derived by Boltzmann and can be applied to systems in equilibrium at the absolute temperature T. The probability for finding any one of these systems with a given amount of energy (or in some particular state of energy) decreases as the energy increases. In other words, states of high energy are much less probable than states of low energy but the probability for states of high energy increases as the temperature of the system increases.

The great theoretical physicist Ludwig Boltzmann obtained the same expression for the probability of finding a particle in a given energy state, if it is a component of a system that is in statistical equilibrium at the absolute temperature T, by defining the observed macroscopic state of the system in terms of groups of microscopic states. Specifically, if there are N molecules (where N is very large) in a system and these are free to move without affecting each other, and if the entire system is in equilibrium at the temperature T (that is, the temperature of the system remains constant for a sufficiently long time), then this total number of molecules may be divided into groups in each of which the molecules will be moving in very nearly the same way (of course, molecules belonging to different groups will be moving differently). Each such sum of the molecular groups defines a macroscopic state of the system, but the groups themselves are called microscopic states.

Now it is clear that the same macroscopic state can be obtained by different microscopic groupings. Thus, if two molecules belonging to two different microscopic groups are interchanged, the number of molecules in each group remains the same, so that the macroscopic state is the same as before. Consequently, each macroscopic state of a system corresponds to many different microscopic states, and we see that the most probable macroscopic state is the one that can be realized by the largest number of microscopic states. If one then counts the number of microscopic states that correspond to a given macroscopic state and then chooses the macroscopic state with the largest number of microscopic states as the most probable state of the system, one obtains Maxwell's formula. This is the way Boltzmann solved the problem, and in doing so founded classical statistical mechanics.

০০০০০০০

MAXWELL

Illustrations of the Dynamical Theory of Gases [1]

ON THE MOTION AND COLLISIONS OF PERFECTLY ELASTIC SPHERES

So MANY OF THE PROPERTIES of matter, especially when in the gaseous form, can be deduced from the hypothesis that their minute parts are in rapid motion, the velocity increasing with the temperature, that the precise nature of this motion becomes a subject of rational curiosity. Daniel Bernoulli, Herapath, Joule, Krönig, Clausius, &c. have shown that the relations between pressure, temperature, and density in a perfect gas can be explained by supposing the particles to move with uniform velocity in straight lines, striking against the sides of the containing vessel and thus producing pressure. It is not necessary to suppose each particle to travel to any great distance in the same straight line; for the effect in producing pressure will be the same if the particles strike against each other; so that the straight line described may be very short. M. Clausius has determined the mean length of path in terms of the average distance of the particles, and the distance between the centres of two particles when collision takes place. We have at present no means of ascertaining either of these distances; but certain phaenomena, such as the internal friction of gases, the conduction of heat through a gas, and the diffusion of one gas through another, seem to indicate the possibility of determining accurately the mean length of path which a particle describes between two successive collisions. In order to lay the foundation of such investigations on strict mechanical principles, I shall demonstrate the laws of motion of an indefinite number of small, hard, and perfectly elastic spheres acting on one another only during impact.

If the properties of such a system of bodies are found to correspond to those of gases, an important physical analogy will be established, which may lead to more accurate knowledge of the properties of matter. If experiments on gases are inconsistent with the hypothesis of these propositions, then our theory, though consistent with itself, is proved to be in-

---

[1] James Clerk Maxwell, *Philosophical Magazine,* 19 (1860), 19–32.

capable of explaining the phaenomena of gases. In either case it is necessary to follow out the consequences of the hypothesis.

Instead of saying that the particles are hard, spherical, and elastic, we may if we please say that the particles are centres of force, of which the action is insensible except at a certain small distance, when it suddenly appears as a repulsive force of very great intensity. It is evident that either assumption will lead to the same results. For the sake of avoiding the repetition of a long phrase about these repulsive forces, I shall proceed upon the assumption of perfectly elastic spherical bodies. If we suppose those aggregate molecules which move together to have a bounding surface which is not spherical, then the rotatory motion of the system will store up a certain proportion of the whole *vis viva,* as has been shown by Clausius, and in this way we may account for the value of the specific heat being greater than on the more simple hypothesis. . . .

Prop. IV

To find the average number of particles whose velocities lie between given limits, after a great number of collisions among a great number of equal particles.

Let N be the whole number of particles. Let x, y, z, be the components of the velocity of each particle in three rectangular directions, and let the number of particles for which x lies between x and $x + dx$ be $Nf(x)dx$, where $f(x)$ is a function of x to be determined.

The number of particles for which y lies between y and $y + dy$ will be $Nf(y)dy$; and the number for which z lies between z and $z + dz$ will be $Nf(z)dz$, where f always stands for the same function.

Now the existence of the velocity x does not in any way affect that of the velocities y or z, since these are all at right angles to each other and independent, so that the number of particles whose velocity lies between x and $x + dx$, and also between y and $y + dy$, and also between z and $z + dz$, is

$$Nf(x)f(y)f(z)\,dx\,dy\,dz.$$

If we suppose the N particles to start from the origin at the same instant, then this will be the number in the element of volume ($dx\,dy\,dz$) after unit of time, and the number referred to unit of volume will be

$$Nf(x)f(y)f(z).$$

But the directions of the coordinates are perfectly arbitrary, and therefore this number must depend on the distance from the origin alone, that is

$$f(x)f(y)f(z) = \phi(x^2 + y^2 + z^2).$$

Solving this functional equation, we find

$$f(x) = Ce^{Ax^2}, \, \phi(r^2) = C^3 e^{Ar^2}$$

If we make A positive, the number of particles will increase with the velocity, and we should find the whole number of particles infinite. We therefore make A negative and equal to $-1/\alpha^2$, so that the number between x and $x + dx$ is

$$NCe^{-\frac{x^2}{\alpha^2}} dx.$$

Integrating from $x = -\infty$ to $x = +\infty$, we find the whole number of particles,

$$NC\sqrt{\pi\alpha} = N, \quad \therefore C = \frac{1}{\alpha\sqrt{\pi}},$$

$f(x)$ is therefore

$$\frac{1}{\alpha\sqrt{\pi}} e^{-\frac{x^2}{\alpha^2}}.$$

Whence we may draw the following conclusions:—

1st. The number of particles whose velocity, resolved in a certain direction, lies between x and $x + dx$ is

$$N \frac{1}{\alpha\sqrt{\pi}} e^{-\frac{x^2}{\alpha^2}} dx \quad . \quad . \quad . \quad . \quad . \quad . \quad . \quad . \quad . \quad . \quad (1)$$

2nd. The number whose actual velocity lies between v and $v + dv$ is

$$N \frac{4}{\alpha^3\sqrt{\pi}} v^2 e^{-\frac{v^2}{\alpha^2}} dv \quad . \quad . \quad . \quad . \quad . \quad . \quad . \quad . \quad (2)$$

3rd. To find the mean value of v, add the velocities of all the particles together and divide by the number of particles; the result is

$$\text{Mean velocity} = \frac{2\alpha}{\sqrt{\pi}}. \quad . \quad . \quad . \quad . \quad . \quad . \quad . \quad . \quad (3)$$

4th. To find the mean value of v^2, add all the values together and divide by N,

$$\text{Mean value of } v^2 = 3/2\alpha^2 \quad . \quad . \quad . \quad . \quad . \quad . \quad . \quad . \quad (4)$$

This is greater than the square of the mean velocity, as it ought to be.

It appears from this proposition that the velocities are distributed among the particles according to the same law as the errors are distributed among the observations in the theory of the "method of least squares." The velocities range from 0 to ∞, but the number of those having great velocities is comparatively small. In addition to these velocities, which are in all directions equally, there may be a general motion of translation of the entire system of particles which must be compounded with the motion of the particles relatively to one another. We may call the one the motion of translation, and the other the motion of agitation.

NEW CONFIRMATION
OF CHEMICAL ATOMIC
THEORY

ooooooooooo

19

ooooooooooo

POLYATOMIC MOLECULES

ooooooooooo

Stanislao Cannizzaro (1826-1910)

Stanislao Cannizzaro was born in Palermo, Sicily, on July 13, 1826. His father was a government official and was for some years a magistrate and minister of police in that city. His mother, Anna di Benedetto, was a member of a noble Sicilian house. Young Stanislao showed early an aptitude for study and was a prize pupil with special aptitude in mathematics. At fifteen he entered the University of Palermo, intending to prepare for the practice of medicine, but after attending for four years he left without taking a degree. Following a short period in the laboratory of the physicist Melloni in Naples he secured a position as assistant to Rafaelle Piria, professor of chemistry at Pisa. Piria was an able scientist and his influence on Cannizzaro was so profound that he won over his young assistant wholeheartedly to the study of chemistry.

It must be remembered that Europe at that time was in a state of political unrest that culminated in the 1848 revolutions. Conditions in Sicily, ruled from Naples by the Bourbon King Ferdinand II, were so oppressive that organized rebellion broke out in January 1848. This was the signal for uprisings all over Italy and Europe. Cannizzaro, then only twenty-one and full of patriotic fervor, had already thrown over his work at Pisa and returned to Sicily to join the insurgent cause as an artillery officer. By March of the following year, the government was able to put down the rebellion and Cannizzaro, one of the last to capitulate, escaped by sea to Marseilles. Making his way to Paris, he was able to devote himself to research in the laboratory of Chevreul. His exile was relatively brief for, two years later at the age of twenty-five, he returned to northern Italy to accept an appointment as professor of physical chemistry at the National School at Alessandria. There he was so occupied with teaching that he had little time to devote to laboratory investigations. This may

277

have been fortunate because his teaching required him to examine more closely the chaotic state in which chemistry was struggling and to ponder the basis of these problems.

In 1855, after four years at Alessandria, he was offered the chair of chemistry at Genoa, which he accepted despite the fact that there was no chemistry laboratory in the university. It took almost another year before he could obtain space to carry on his researches. Shortly after this move, Cannizzaro courted and married, in Florence, Henrietta Withers, the daughter of an English clergyman. The couple had two children, a daughter and a son who later became an architect in Rome.

During these years at Genoa he was also digging deeply into the competing ideas regarding chemical combination and the foundations of atomic theory. At this distance in time it is hard to realize that the greatest impediment to a rational system of chemistry was the almost universal idea that the ultimate particles of the elements had to be monatomic. Cannizzaro's great contribution was to adopt a molecular, i.e., polyatomic, view of the elements, and to show that the *atomic* weights of elements, prepared in volatile compounds, could be deduced by the application of Avogadro's hypothesis together with accurate combining weight data and vapor densities. This is the burden of his famous "Sketch of a Course of Chemical Philosophy," which appeared in 1858. He was then thirty-two years old.

The effect of the paper was not really felt throughout the chemical world until the Congress of Karlsruhe, which was held in September of 1860. Here the paper was distributed and Cannizzaro was able to expound his views to the assembled chemists. If many were not convinced at least one distinguished German was, for Professor Lothar Meyer wrote later that "It was as though scales fell from my eyes, doubt vanished, and was replaced by a feeling of peaceful certainty." The soundness of the new views was gradually appreciated, aided doubtless by Meyer's well-known treatise on *Modern Theories of Chemistry,* which appeared a few years later.

At this time political events in Sicily brought about a second short-lived rebellion but the subsequent resistance under Garibaldi and his famous Thousand began the movement that resulted in the unification of Italy. Always the patriot, Cannizzaro returned to Sicily to join the new regime, although he did not serve in the army. In 1861 he was made professor of chemistry at Palermo, and in the following ten years he served not only chemistry but education, becoming active in the establishment of municipal schools and for a time in administration as rector of the university. In 1871, at forty-five, he left Palermo to accept the chair of chemistry at the University of Rome. Here again there was no laboratory and space and equipment had to be found. At the same time he was made a Senator of the Kingdom in recognition of his patriotic services.

His position as a senator and as a member of the government led to his active participation in many official committees. One of the most important was the Council of Public Instruction of which he ultimately served as president. He was active in the organization of the Customs Laboratory, provision for public instruction in agriculture, and in the advancement of science generally in Italy. Although these activities precluded much of his former investigation in chemistry, his interest in students and his zeal for teaching were always paramount. It has been said that "for him to teach was to live." This was literally true, for when his strength began to fail in his eighty-third year and it no longer became possible for him to lecture, all of his ills increased and he passed away on May 10, 1910.

In order to understand what Cannizzaro accomplished it is necessary to form some conception of the state of chemistry in 1858. It should be made clear at the outset that the valence of many of the elements was uncertain and that this led to much confusion regarding the constitution of compounds. Thus J. J. Berzelius assigned the general formula RO to the chief metallic oxides, a designation agreed to by C. G. Gmelin. Gerhardt and Laurent, on the other hand, assigned a formula R_2O. Regnault, however, agreed with neither of these schools, assigning the formula RO to some metallic oxides and R_2O to others. He did this on the basis of specific heat measurements of the oxides together with the acceptance of the law of Dulong and Petit (1819). This law stated that the atomic heat (heat required to raise a weight of the element in grams equal to its atomic weight through a temperature change of one degree Centigrade) is approximately the same for all the elements, being about 6.2 calories. Exceptions to the law soon became known; by 1850, on the basis of Berzelius' system, they were silver, sodium, potassium, bismuth, carbon, and bromine. In Gmelin's system there were additional exceptions, viz., gold, iodine, phosphorus, arsenic, and antimony. These exceptions in nearly all cases had an atomic heat of 12.4, although for most of the elements it was 6.2. In Gerhardt and Laurent's system the exceptions were the same as in Gmelin's except for the addition of sulfur. Regnault's proposal to make the exceptions fewer by regarding the oxides of silver, potassium, and sodium as R_2O did not meet with general acceptance.

These different systems resulted, of course, in a diversity of formulas for the chemical substances. Thus water was variously HO, H_2O, H_2O_2, and so on. Worse still, the same formula might designate two different substances. Depending on the school to which a chemist belonged, H_2O_2 might mean water or hydrogen peroxide; C_2H_4, marsh gas or ethylene, and CuCl, cuprous or cupric chloride.

These difficulties which pervaded the whole field of chemistry were resolved by Cannizzaro by taking the point of view that the molecule of an element must, in general, be regarded as polyatomic and that *the atom must be defined in terms of the molecule.* Thus, he says: "*The different quantities of the same element contained in different molecules are all whole multiples of one and the same quantity, which, always being entire, has the right to be called an atom.*" This point of view, combined with Avogadro's hypothesis, accurate combining weight data (largely that of Berzelius) and precise vapor density data obtained by the method of J. B. Dumas, constituted the basic method by which a rational system was obtained.

Suppose we consider three gaseous elements: hydrogen, oxygen, chlorine, and several of their compounds. These are listed in the left-hand column of Table 19–1. In column 1, the density in grams/liter of each of the gases is given; in column 2, the weight percentage of the element of interest in the compound. The product of these gives the weight of the element in the compound. If now the smallest of these values is divided into the numbers in column 3, the results, a series of integers, appear in column 4. Since according to Avogadro's hypothesis the same number of molecules is present in each of the amounts of the five compounds say, of hydrogen, we shall *assume* that the compound having the least hydrogen is the one in which hydrogen occurs as a single atom in the molecule. This, of course, could be incorrect, but there are cross checks on the assumption, as we shall see. On this basis, elemental hydrogen, which has twice the least weight, would be composed of molecules having two atoms. In the ammonia molecule there would be three hydrogen atoms, etc.

Examining next the compounds of oxygen, one sees that water and carbon monoxide each contains the smallest amount of this element and hence the conclusion is that these compounds contain only one atom of oxygen. Since elemental oxygen has twice the least weight present in the oxygen compounds we conclude that it, like elemental hydrogen, is diatomic. Making use of the hydrogen and oxygen data we see that water consists of two atoms of hydrogen and one of oxygen, and hence its formula is H_2O. Dividing the weight of elemental oxygen by that of hydrogen, we find a ratio of 16. The ratio of the weights of the oxygen and hydrogen molecules is 16, and since each molecule contains two atoms, the relative *atomic* weights are $O:H = 16:1$. The chemical formula for various other compounds may be deduced by the same method as above, and atomic weights also.

As Cannizzaro pointed out, atomic weight determinations cannot always be made by the vapor density method. In the nonvolatile compounds an alternative method is to make use of specific heat data. If one considers cupric chloride, $CuCl$, and cuprous chloride, $CuCl_2$, a combining

TABLE 19–1 *Cannizzaro's Method of Atomic Weight Determination* [1]

	1.	2.	3.	4.
Substance	Density, grams per liter *	Percentage of element of interest, by weight	Products of values in 1 and 2	Values in 3 divided by least value
A. HYDROGEN AND ITS GASEOUS COMPOUNDS				
Hydrogen	0.0659	100	0.0659	2
Hydrogen chloride	1.19	2.76	0.0329	1
Water	0.589	11.2	0.0659	2
Ammonia	0.557	17.7	0.0986	3
Methane	0.524	25.1	0.132	4
B. OXYGEN AND ITS GASEOUS COMPOUNDS				
Oxygen	1.05	100	1.05	2
Water	0.589	88.8	0.523	1
Sulfur dioxide	2.09	50.0	1.05	2
Carbon monoxide	0.916	57.1	0.523	1
Carbon dioxide	1.44	72.7	1.05	2
C. CHLORINE AND ITS GASEOUS COMPOUNDS				
Chlorine	2.32	100	2.32	2
Hydrogen chloride	1.19	97.2	1.16	1
Chloroform	3.90	89.1	3.48	3
Methylene chloride	2.78	83.5	2.32	2
Carbon tetrachloride	5.03	92.2	4.64	4

weight percentage of the former was found to be 63.96/36.04 and of the latter 47.02/52.98. Assuming in the former case 35.5, the value already found as the atomic weight of chlorine, simple ratios give that of copper as 63.0. In the latter instance comparing the ratios $47.02/52.98 = x/2 \times 35.5$ we find that the atomic weight of copper is 63. If now the specific heat of copper 0.09515 (cal./gm.deg.) is multiplied by the value 63, we obtain 6.0 as the atomic heat. This, in comparison with similar data where it is known that the element is monatomic, indicates that the monatomic assumption for copper is not contradicted.

* All gas densities in this table are reported for the conditions 100°C and one atmosphere pressure.
[1] From F. T. Bonner and M. Phillips, *Principles of Physical Science* (Cambridge: Addison-Wesley, 1957), p. 152.

The consistent results of these methods inspired the confidence of chemists. The procedures were shown to be equally valid in organic as well as inorganic chemistry, and where these branches had been considered almost separate sciences, reunification was now apparent. The periodic system of the elements as originally proposed by Newlands was based on Cannizzaro's atomic weights. Indeed, until these weights had been settled, the over-all relationship of the elements to each other must have remained obscure.

 o0o0o0oo

CANNIZZARO

Sketch of a Course of Chemical Philosophy [2]

I BELIEVE THAT THE PROGRESS of science made in these last years has confirmed the hypothesis of Avogadro, of Ampère, and of Dumas on the similar constitution of substances in the gaseous state; that is, that equal volumes of these substances, whether simple or compound, contain an equal number of molecules: not however an equal number of atoms, since the molecules of the different substances, or those of the same substance in its different states, may contain a different number of atoms, whether of the same or of diverse nature.

In order to lead my students to the conviction which I have reached myself, I wish to place them on the same path as that by which I have arrived at it—the path, that is, of the historical examination of chemical theories.

I commence, then, in the first lecture by showing how, from the examination of the physical properties of gaseous bodies, and from the law of Gay-Lussac on the volume relations between components and compounds, there arose almost spontaneously the hypothesis alluded to above, which was first of all enunciated by Avogadro, and shortly afterwards by Ampère. Analysing the conception of these two physicists, I show that it contains nothing contradictory to known facts, provided that we distinguish, as they did, molecules from atoms; provided that we do not

---

[2] "Letter of Professor Stanislao Cannizzaro to Professor S. De Luca," trans. J. W., *Alembic Club Reprint No. 18* (Chicago: University of Chicago Press, 1911).

confuse the criteria by which the number and the weight of the former are compared, with the criteria which serve to deduce the weight of the latter; provided that, finally, we have not fixed in our minds the prejudice that whilst the molecules of compound substances may consist of different numbers of atoms, the molecules of the various simple substances must all contain either one atom, or at least an equal number of atoms.

In the second lecture I set myself the task of investigating the reasons why this hypothesis of Avogadro and Ampère was not immediately accepted by the majority of chemists. I therefore expound rapidly the work and the ideas of those who examined the relationships of the reacting quantities of substances without concerning themselves with the volumes which these substances occupy in the gaseous state; and I pause to explain the ideas of Berzelius, by the influence of which the hypothesis above cited appeared to chemists out of harmony with the facts.

I examine the order of the ideas of Berzelius, and show how on the one hand he developed and completed the dualistic theory of Lavoisier by his own electro-chemical hypothesis, and how on the other hand, influenced by the atomic theory of Dalton (which had been confirmed by the experiments of Wollaston), he applied this theory and took it for his guide in his later researches, bringing it into agreement with the dualistic electro-chemical theory, whilst at the same time he extended the laws of Richter and tried to harmonise them with the results of Proust. I bring out clearly the reason why he was led to assume that the atoms, whilst separate in simple bodies, should unite to form the atoms of a compound of the first order, and these in turn, uniting in simple proportions, should form composite atoms of the second order, and why (since he could not admit that when two substances give a single compound, a molecule of the one and a molecule of the other, instead of uniting to form a single molecule, should change into two molecules of the same nature) he could not accept the hypothesis of Avogadro and of Ampère, which in many cases leads to the conclusion just indicated.

I then show how Berzelius, being unable to escape from his own dualistic ideas, and yet wishing to explain the simple relations discovered by Gay-Lussac between the volumes of gaseous compounds and their gaseous components, was led to formulate a hypothesis very different from that of Avogadro and of Ampère, namely, that equal volumes of simple substances in the gaseous state contain the same number of atoms, which in combination unite intact; how, later, the vapour densities of many simple substances having been determined, he had to restrict this hypothesis by saying that only simple substances which are permanent gases obey this law; how, not believing that composite atoms even of the same order could be equidistant in the gaseous state under the same conditions, he was led to suppose that in the molecules of hydrochloric, hydriodic, and hydrobromic acids, and in those of water and sulphuretted hydrogen, there was contained the same quantity of hydrogen, although the different behaviour of these compounds confirmed the deductions from the hypothesis of Avogadro and of Ampère.

I conclude this lecture by showing that we have only to distinguish atoms from molecules in order to reconcile all the experimental results known to Berzelius, and have no need to assume any difference in constitution between permanent and coercible, or between simple and compound gases, in contradiction to the physical properties of all elastic fluids.

In the third lecture I pass in review the various researches of physicists on gaseous bodies, and show that all the new researches from Gay-Lussac to Clausius confirm the hypothesis of Avogadro and of Ampère that the distances between the molecules, so long as they remain in the gaseous state, do not depend on their nature, nor on their mass, nor on the number of atoms they contain, but only on their temperature and on the pressure to which they are subjected.

In the fourth lecture I pass under review the chemical theories since Berzelius: I pause to examine how Dumas, inclining to the idea of Ampère, had habituated chemists who busied themselves with *organic substances* to apply this idea in determining the molecular weights of compounds; and what were the reasons which had stopped him half way in the application of this theory. I then expound, in continuation of this, two different methods—the one due to Berzelius, the other to Ampère and Dumas—which were used to determine formulæ in inorganic and in organic chemistry respectively until Laurent and Gerhardt sought to bring both parts of the science into harmony. I explain clearly how the discoveries made by Gerhardt, Williamson, Hofmann, Wurtz, Berthelot, Frankland, and others, on the constitution of organic compounds confirm the hypothesis of Avogadro and Ampère, and how that part of Gerhardt's theory which corresponds best with the facts and best explains their connection, is nothing but the extension of Ampère's theory, that is, its complete application, already begun by Dumas.

I draw attention, however, to the fact that Gerhardt did not always consistently follow the theory which had given him such fertile results; since he assumed that equal volumes of gaseous bodies contain the same number of molecules, only in the majority of cases, but not always.

I show how he was constrained by a prejudice, the reverse of that of Berzelius, frequently to distort the facts. Whilst Berzelius, on the one hand, did not admit that the molecules of simple substances could be divided in the act of combination, Gerhardt supposes that all the molecules of simple substances are divisible in chemical action. This prejudice forces him to suppose that the molecule of mercury and of all the metals consists of two atoms, like that of hydrogen, and therefore that the compounds of all the metals are of the same type as those of hydrogen. This error even yet persists in the minds of chemists, and has prevented them from discovering amongst the metals the existence of biatomic radicals perfectly analogous to those lately discovered by Wurtz in organic chemistry.

From the historical examination of chemical theories, as well as from physical researches, I draw the conclusion that to bring into harmony all the branches of chemistry we must have recourse to the complete application of the theory of Avogadro and Ampère in order to compare the weights and the numbers of the molecules; and I propose in the sequel to show that the conclusions drawn from it are invariably in accordance with all physical and chemical laws hitherto discovered.

I begin in the fifth lecture by applying the hypothesis of Avogadro and Ampère to determine the weights of molecules even before their composition is known.

On the basis of the hypothesis cited above, the weights of the molecules are proportional to the densities of the substances in the gaseous state. If we wish the densities of vapours to express the weights of the molecules, it is expedient to refer them all to the density of a simple gas taken as unity, rather than to the weight of a mixture of two gases such as air.

Hydrogen being the lightest gas, we may take it as the unit to which we refer the densities of other gaseous bodies, which in such a case express the weights of the molecules compared to the weight of the molecule of hydrogen $= 1$.

Since I prefer to take as common unit for the weights of the molecules and for their fractions, the weight of a half and not of a whole molecule of hydrogen, I therefore refer the densities of the various gaseous bodies to that of hydrogen $= 2$. If the densities are referred to air $= 1$, it is sufficient to multiply by 14.438 to change them to those referred to that of hydrogen $= 1$; and by $28 \cdot 87$ to refer them to the density of hydrogen $= 2$.

I write the two series of numbers, expressing these weights [as shown in Table 19–2].

Whoever wishes to refer the densities to hydrogen $= 1$ and the weights of the molecules to the weight of half a molecule of hydrogen, can say that the weights of the molecules are all represented by the weight of two volumes.

I myself, however, for simplicity of exposition, prefer to refer the densities to that of hydrogen $= 2$, and so the weights of the molecules are all represented by the weight of one volume.

From the few examples contained in [Table 19–2], I show that the same substance in its different allotropic states can have different molecular weights, without concealing the fact that the experimental data on which this conclusion is founded still require confirmation.

TABLE 19-2

Names of Substances	Densities or weights of one volume, the volume of Hydrogen being made = 1, *i.e.*, weights of the molecules referred to the weight of a whole molecule of Hydrogen taken as unity	Densities referred to that of Hydrogen = 2, *i.e.*, weights of the molecules referred to the weight of half a molecule of Hydrogen taken as unity
Hydrogen	1	2
Oxygen, ordinary	16	32
Oxygen, electrised	64	128
Sulphur below 1000°	96	192
Sulphur * above 1000°	32	64
Chlorine	35·5	71
Bromine	80	160
Arsenic	150	300
Mercury	100	200
Water	9	18
Hydrochloric Acid	18·25	36·50 †
Acetic Acid	30	60

I assume that the study of the various compounds has been begun by determining the weights of the molecules, *i.e.,* their densities in the gaseous state, without enquiring if they are simple or compound.

I then come to the examination of the composition of these molecules. If the substance is undecomposable, we are forced to admit that its molecule is entirely made up by the weight of one and the same kind of matter. If the body is composite, its elementary analysis is made, and thus we discover the constant relations between the weights of its components: then the weight of the molecule is divided into parts proportional to the numbers expressing the relative weights of the components, and thus we obtain the quantities of these components contained in the molecule of the compound, referred to the same unit as that to which we refer the weights of all the molecules. By this method I have constructed [Table 19–3].

Once my students have become familiar with the importance of the numbers as they are exhibited in [Table 19–3], it is easy to lead them to discover the law which results from their comparison. "Compare," I

---

* This determination was made by Bineau, but I believe it requires confirmation.
† The numbers expressing the densities are approximate: we arrive at a closer approximation by comparing them with those derived from chemical data, and bringing the two into harmony.

TABLE 19-3

Name of Substance	Weight of one volume, *i.e.,* weight of the molecule referred to the weight of half a molecule of Hydrogen = 1	Component weights of one volume, *i.e.,* component weights of the molecule, all referred to the weight of half a molecule of Hydrogen = 1		
Hydrogen	2	2 Hydrogen		
Oxygen, ordinary	32	32 Oxygen		
" electrised	128	128 "		
Sulphur below 1000°	192	192 Sulphur		
" above 1000° (?)	64	64 "		
Phosphorus	124	124 Phosphorus		
Chlorine	71	71 Chlorine		
Bromine	160	160 Bromine		
Iodine	254	254 Iodine		
Nitrogen	28	28 Nitrogen		
Arsenic	300	300 Arsenic		
Mercury	200	200 Mercury		
Hydrochloric Acid	36·5	35·5 Chlorine	1 Hydrogen	
Hydrobromic Acid	81	80 Bromine	1 "	
Hydriodic Acid	128	127 Iodine	1 "	
Water	18	16 Oxygen	2 "	
Ammonia	17	14 Nitrogen	3 "	
Arseniuretted Hyd.	78	75 Arsenic	3 "	
Phosphuretted Hyd.	35	32 Phosphorus	3 "	
Calomel	235·5	35·5 Chlorine	200 Mercury	
Corrosive Sublimate	271	71 "	200 "	
Arsenic Trichloride	181·5	106·5 "	75 Arsenic	
Protochloride of Phosphorus	138·5	106·5 "	32 Phosphorus	
Perchloride of Iron	325	213 "	112 Iron	
Protoxide of Nitrogen	44	16 Oxygen	28 Nitrogen	
Binoxide of Nitrogen	30	16 "	14 "	
Carbonic Oxide	28	16 "	12 Carbon	
" Acid	44	32 "	12 "	
Ethylene	28	4 Hydrogen	24 "	
Propylene	42	6 "	36 "	
Acetic Acid, hydrated	60	{ 4 " 32 Oxygen 24 Carbon		
" anhydrous	102	{ 6 Hydrogen 48 Oxygen 48 Carbon		
Alcohol	46	{ 6 Hydrogen 16 Oxygen 24 Carbon		
Ether	74	{ 10 Hydrogen 16 Oxygen 48 Carbon		

say to them, "the various quantities of the same element contained in the molecule of the free substance and in those of all its different compounds, and you will not be able to escape the following law: *The different quantities of the same element contained in different molecules are all whole multiples of one and the same quantity, which, always being entire, has the right to be called an atom.*"

Thus:

One molecule of free hydrogen	contains 2 of hydrogen	=	2 × 1
" of hydrochloric acid	" 1 "	=	1 × 1
" of hydrobromic acid	" 1 "	=	1 × 1
" of hydriodic acid	" 1 "	=	1 × 1
" of hydrocyanic acid	" 1 "	=	1 × 1
" of water	" 2 "	=	2 × 1
" of sulphuretted hydrogen	" 2 "	=	2 × 1
" of formic acid	" 2 "	=	2 × 1
" of ammonia	" 3 "	=	3 × 1
" of gaseous phosphuretted hydrogen	" 3 "	=	3 × 1
" of acetic acid	" 4 "	=	4 × 1
" of ethylene	" 4 "	=	4 × 1
" of alcohol	" 6 "	=	6 × 1
" of ether	" 10 "	=	10 × 1

Thus all the various weights of hydrogen contained in the different molecules are integral multiples of the weight contained in the molecule of hydrochloric acid, which justifies our having taken it as common unit of the weights of the atoms and of the molecules. The atom of hydrogen is contained twice in the molecule of free hydrogen.

In the same way it is shown that the various quantities of chlorine existing in different molecules are all whole multiples of the quantity contained in the molecule of hydrochloric acid, that is, of 35·5; and that the quantities of oxygen existing in the different molecules are all whole multiples of the quantity contained in the molecule of water, that is, of 16, which quantity is half of that contained in the molecule of free oxygen, and an eighth part of that contained in the molecule of electrised oxygen (ozone).

Thus:

One molecule of free oxygen	contains 32 of oxygen	= 2 × 16
" of ozone	" 128 "	= 8 × 16
" of water	" 16 "	= 1 × 16
" of ether	" 16 "	= 1 × 16
" of acetic acid	" 32 "	= 2 × 16
etc. etc.		

One molecule of free chlorine	contains 71 of chlorine	= 2 × 35·5
" of hydrochloric acid	" 35·5 "	= 1 × 35·5
" of corrosive sublimate	" 71 "	= 1 × 35·5
" of chloride of arsenic	" 106·5 "	= 3 × 35·5
" of chloride of tin	" 142 "	= 4 × 35·5
etc. etc.		

In a similar way may be found the smallest quantity of each element which enters as a whole into the molecules which contain it, and to which may be given with reason the name of atom. In order, then, to find the atomic weight of each element, it is necessary first of all to know the weights of all or of the greater part of the molecules in which it is contained and their composition.

If it should appear to any one that this method of finding the weights of the molecules is too hypothetical, then let him compare the composition of equal volumes of substances in the gaseous state under the same conditions. He will not be able to escape the following law: *The various quantities of the same element contained in equal volumes either of the free element or of its compounds are all whole multiples of one and the same quantity;* that is, each element has a special numerical value by means of which and of integral coefficients the composition by weight of equal volumes of the different substances in which it is contained may be expressed. Now, since all chemical reactions take place between equal volumes, or integral multiples of them, it is possible to express all chemical reactions by means of the same numerical values and integral coefficients. The law enunciated in the form just indicated is a direct deduction from the facts: but who is not led to assume from this same law that the weights of equal volumes represent the molecular weights, although other proofs are wanting? I thus prefer to substitute in the expression of the law the word molecule instead of volume. This is advantageous for teaching, because, when the vapour densities cannot be determined, recourse is had to other means for deducing the weights of the molecules of compounds. The whole substance of my course consists in this: to prove the exactness of these latter methods by showing that they lead to the same results as the vapour density when both kinds of method can be adopted at the same time for determining molecular weights.

The law above enunciated, called by me the law of atoms, contains in itself that of multiple proportions and that of simple relations between the volumes; which I demonstrate amply in my lecture. After this I easily succeed in explaining how, expressing by symbols the different atomic weights of the various elements, it is possible to express by means of formulæ the composition of their molecules and of those of their compounds, and I pause a little to make my pupils familiar with the passage from gaseous volume to molecule, the first directly expressing the fact and the second interpreting it. Above all, I study to implant in their minds thoroughly the difference between molecule and atom. It is possible indeed to know the atomic weight of an element without knowing its molecular weight; this is seen in the case of carbon. A great number of the compounds of this substance being volatile, the weights of the molecules and their composition may be compared, and it is seen that the quantities of carbon which they contain are all integral multiples of 12, which quantity is thus the atom of carbon and expressed by the symbol C; but since we cannot determine the vapour density of free carbon we have no means of knowing the weight of its molecule, and thus we cannot know how many times the atom is contained in it. Analogy does not in any way help us, because we observe that the molecules of the most closely analogous substances (such as sulphur and oxygen), and even the molecules of the same substance in its allotropic states, are composed of different numbers of atoms. We have no means of predicting the vapour density of carbon; the only thing that we can say is that it will be either 12 or an integral multiple of 12 (in my system of numbers). The number which is given in different treatises on chemistry as the theoretical density of carbon is quite arbitrary, and a useless datum in chemical calculations; it is useless for calculating and verifying the weights of the molecules of the various compounds of carbon, because the weight of the molecule of free carbon may be ignored if we know the weights of the molecules of all its compounds; it is useless for determining the weight of the atom of carbon, because this is deduced by comparing the composition of a certain number of molecules containing carbon, and the knowledge of the weight of the molecule of this last would scarcely add a datum more to those which are already sufficient for the solution of the problem. Any one will easily convince himself of this by placing in the . . . manner [shown in Table 19–4] the numbers expressing the molecular weights derived from the densities and the weights of the components contained in them.

In the list of molecules containing carbon there might be placed also that of free carbon if the weight of it were known; but this would not have any greater utility than what we would derive by writing in the list one more compound of carbon; that is, it would do nothing but verify once more that the quantity of carbon contained in any molecule, whether of the element itself or of its compounds, is 12 or $n \times 12 = C^n$, n being an integral number.

I then discuss whether it is better to express the composition of the molecules of compounds as a function of the molecules of the components, or if, on the other hand, it is better, as I commence by doing, to express the composition of both in terms of those constant quantities which always enter by whole numbers into both, that is, by means of the atoms.

. . . I begin in the following lecture—the sixth—to examine the constitution of the molecules of the chlorides, bromides, and iodides. Since the greater part of these are volatile, and since we know their densities in the gaseous state, there cannot remain any doubt as to the approximate weights of the molecules, and so of the quantities of chlorine, bromine, and iodine contained in them. These quantities being always integral multiples of the weights of chlorine, bromine, and iodine contained in hydrochloric, hydrobromic, and hydrodic acids, *i.e.*, of the weights of the half molecules, there can remain no doubt as to the atomic weights of these substances, and thus as to the number of atoms existing in the molecules of their compounds, whose weights and composition are known.

TABLE 19-4

Names of Compounds of Carbon	Weights of the molecules referred to the atom of Hydrogen	Weights of the components of the molecules referred to the weight of the atom of Hydrogen taken as unity		Formulæ, making H = 1 C = 12 O = 16 S = 32
Carbonic Oxide	28	12 Carbon	16 Oxygen	CO
" Acid	44	12 "	32 "	CO^2
Sulphide of Carbon	76	12 "	64 Sulphur	CS^2
Marsh Gas	16	12 "	4 Hydrogen	CH^4
Ethylene	28	24 "	4 "	C^2H^4
Propylene	42	36 "	6 "	C^3H^6
Ether	74	$\left\{\begin{array}{l} 48 \text{ "} \quad 10 \text{ "} \\ 16 \text{ Oxygen} \end{array}\right\}$		$C^4H^{10}O$
etc.	etc.	etc.		etc.

A difficulty sometimes appears in deciding whether the quantity of the other element combined with one atom of these halogens is 1, 2, 3, or n atoms in the molecule; to decide this, it is necessary to compare the composition of all the other molecules containing the same element and find out the weight of this element which constantly enters as a whole. When we cannot determine the vapour densities of the other compounds of the element whose atomic weight we wish to determine, it is necessary then to have recourse to other criteria to know the weights of their molecules and to deduce the weight of the atom of the element. What I am to expound in the sequel serves to teach my pupils the method of employing these other criteria to verify or to determine atomic weights and the composition of molecules. I begin by making them study the following table of some chlorides, bromides, and iodides whose vapour densities are known; I write their formulæ, certain of justifying later the value assigned to the atomic weights of some elements existing in the compounds indicated. I do not omit to draw their attention once more to the atomic weights of hydrogen, chlorine, bromine, and iodine being all equal to the weights of half a molecule, and represented by the weight of half a volume, which I indicate in [Table 19–5]. These data being given, there follows [in Table 19–6] some compounds of the halogens.

TABLE 19–5

	Symbol	Weight
Weight of the atom of Hydrogen or half a molecule represented by the weight of ½ volume	H	1
Weight of the atom of Chlorine or half a molecule represented by the weight of ½ volume	Cl	35·5
Weight of the atom of Bromine or half a molecule represented by the weight of ½ volume	Br	80
Weight of the atom of Iodine or half a molecule represented by the weight of ½ volume	I	127

I stop to examine the composition of the molecules of the two chlorides and the two iodides of mercury. There can remain no doubt that the protochloride contains in its molecule the same quantity of chlorine as hydrochloric acid, that the bichloride contains twice as much, and that the quantity of mercury contained in the molecules of both is the same. The supposition made by some chemists that the quantities of chlorine contained in the two molecules are equal, and on the other hand that the quantities of mercury are different, is supported by no valid reason. The vapour densities of the two chlorides having been determined, and it having been observed that equal volumes of them contain the same quantity of mercury, and that the quantity of chlorine contained in one volume of the vapour of calomel is equal to that contained in the same volume of hydrochloric acid gas under the same conditions, whilst the quantity of chlorine contained in one volume of corrosive sublimate is twice that contained in an equal volume of calomel or of hydrochloric acid gas, the relative molecular composition of the two chlorides cannot be doubtful. The same may be said of the two iodides. Does the constant quantity of mercury existing in the molecules of these compounds, and represented by the number 200, correspond to one or more atoms? The observation that in these compounds the same quantity of mercury is combined with one or two atoms of chlorine or of iodine, would itself incline us to believe that this quantity is that which enters always as a whole into all the molecules containing mercury, namely, the atom; whence Hg = 200.

To verify this, it would be necessary to compare the various quantities

TABLE 19–6

Names of the Chlorides	Weights of equal volumes in the gaseous state, under the same conditions, referred to the weight of ½ volume of Hydrogen = 1; i.e., weights of the molecules referred to the weight of the atom of Hydrogen = 1	Composition of equal volumes in the gaseous state, under the same conditions, i.e., composition of the molecules, the weights of the components being all referred to the weight of the atom of Hydrogen taken as unity, i.e., the common unit adopted for the weights of atoms and of molecules	Formulæ expressing the composition of the molecules or of equal volumes in the gaseous state under the same conditions
Free Chlorine	71	71 of Chlorine	Cl²
Hydrochloric Acid	36·5	35·5 " 1 of Hydrogen	HCl
Protochloride of Mercury or Calomel	235·5	35·5 " 200 of Mercury	HgCl
Bichloride of Mercury or Corrosive Sublimate	271	71 " 200 "	HgCl²
Chloride of Ethyl	64·5	35·5 " 5 of Hydrogen 24 of Carbon	C²H⁵Cl
" Acetyl	78·5	35·5 " 3 " 24 of Carbon 16 of Oxygen	C²H³OCl
" Ethylene	99	71 of Chlorine 4 of Hydrogen 24 of Carbon	C²H⁴Cl²
" Arsenic	181·5	106·5 " 75 of Arsenic	AsCl³
Protochloride of Phosphorus	138·5	106·5 " 32 of Phosphorus	PCl³
Chloride of Boron	117·5	106·5 " 11 of Boron	BCl³
Bichloride of Tin	259·6	142 " 117·6 of Tin	SnCl⁴
" Titanium	198	142 " 56 of Titanium	TiCl⁴
Chloride of Silicon	170	142 " 28 of Silicon	SiCl⁴
" Zirconium	231	142 " 89 of Zirconium	ZrCl⁴
" Aluminium	267	213 " 54 of Aluminium	Al²Cl⁶
Perchloride of Iron	325	213 " 112 of Iron	Fe²Cl⁶
Sesquichloride of Chromium	319	213 " 106 of Chromium	Cr²Cl⁶

of mercury contained in all the molecules of its compounds whose weights
and composition are known with certainty. Few other compounds of
mercury besides those indicated above lend themselves to this; still there
are some in organic chemistry the formulæ of which express well the
molecular composition; in these formulæ we always find $Hg^2 = 200$,
chemists having made $Hg = 100$ and $H = 1$. This is a confirmation that
the atom of mercury is 200 and not 100, no compound of mercury existing whose molecule contains less than this quantity of it. For verification
I refer to the law of the specific heats of elements and of compounds.

I call the quantity of heat consumed by the atoms or the molecules the
product of their weights into their specific heats. I compare the heat consumed by the atom of mercury with that consumed by the atoms of iodine
and of bromine in the same physical state, and find them almost equal,
which confirms the accuracy of the relation between the atomic weight of
mercury and that of each of the two halogens, and thus also, indirectly,
between the atomic weight of mercury and that of hydrogen, whose specific heats cannot be directly compared. [See Table 19–7.]

TABLE 19 – 7

Name of substance	Atomic weight	Specific heat, i.e., heat required to heat unit weight 1°	Products of specific heats by atomic weights, i.e., heat required to heat the atom 1°
Solid Bromine	80	0·08432	6·74560
Iodine	127	0·05412	6·87324
Solid Mercury	200	0·03241	6·48200

The same thing is shown by comparing the specific heats of the different compounds of mercury. Woestyn and Garnier have shown that the
state of combination does not notably change the calorific capacity of the
atoms; and since this is almost equal in the various elements, the molecules would require, to heat them 1°, quantities of heat proportional to
the number of atoms which they contain. If $Hg = 200$, that is, if the
formulæ of the two chlorides and iodides of mercury are $HgCl$, HgI,
$HgCl^2$, HgI^2, it will be necessary that the molecules of the first pair
should consume twice as much heat as each separate atom, and those of
the second pair three times as much; and this is so in fact, as may be
seen in [Table 19–8].

Thus the weight 200 of mercury, whether as an element or in its compounds, requires to heat it 1° the same quantity of heat as 127 of iodine,
80 of bromine, and almost certainly as 35·5 of chlorine and 1 of hydrogen, if it were possible to compare these two last substances in the same

physical state as that in which the specific heats of the above-named substances have been compared.

TABLE 19-8

Formulæ of the compounds of Mercury	Weights of their molecules $= p$	Specific heats of unit weight $= c$	Specific heats of the molecules $= p \times c$	Number of atoms in the molecules $= n$	Specific heats of each atom $= \dfrac{p \times c}{n}$
HgCl	235·5	0·05205	12·257745	2	6·128872
HgI	327	0·03949	12·91323	2	6·45661
HgCl²	271	0·06889	18·66919	3	6·22306
HgI²	454	0·04197	19·05438	3	6·35146

But the atoms of hydrogen, iodine, and bromine are half their respective molecules: thus it is natural to ask if the weight 200 of mercury also corresponds to half a molecule of free mercury. It is sufficient to look at the table of numbers expressing the molecular weights to perceive that if 2 is the molecular weight of hydrogen, the weight of the molecule of mercury is 200, *i.e.*, equal to the weight of the atom. In other words, one volume of vapour, whether of protochloride or protoiodide, whether of bichloride or of biniodide, contains an equal volume of mercury vapour; so that each molecule of these compounds contains an entire molecule of mercury, which, entering as a whole into all the molecules, is the atom of this substance. This is confirmed by observing that the complete molecule of mercury requires for heating it 1°, the same quantity of heat as half a molecule of iodine, or half a molecule of bromine. It appears to me, then, that I can sustain that what enters into chemical actions is the half molecule of hydrogen and the whole molecule of mercury: both of these quantities are indivisible, at least *in the sphere of chemical actions actually known.* You will perceive that with this last expression I avoid the question if it is possible to divide this quantity further. I do not fail to apprise you that all those who faithfully applied the theory of Avogadro and of Ampère, have arrived at this same result. First Dumas and afterwards Gaudin showed that the molecule of mercury, differing from that of hydrogen, always entered as a whole into compounds. On this account Gaudin called the molecule of mercury monatomic, and that of hydrogen biatomic. However, I wish to avoid the use of these adjectives in this special sense, because to-day they are employed as you know in a very different sense, that is, to indicate the different capacity for saturation of the radicals. . . .

I then come to the examination of the two chlorides of copper. The analogy with those of mercury forces us to admit that they have a similar atomic constitution, but we cannot verify this directly by determining and comparing the weights and the compositions of the molecules, as we do not know the vapour densities of these two compounds.

The specific heats of free copper and of its compounds confirm the atomic constitution of the two chlorides of copper deduced from the analogy with those of mercury. Indeed the composition of the two chlorides leads us to conclude that if they have the formulæ $CuCl$, $CuCl^2$, the atomic weight of copper indicated by Cu is equal to 63, which may be seen from [Table 19–9].

T A B L E   1 9 – 9

	Ratio between the components expressed by numbers whose sum = 100	Ratio between the components expressed by atomic weights
Protochloride of Copper	36·04 : 63·96 Chlorine Copper	35·5 : 63 Cl Cu
Bichloride of Copper	52·98 : 47·02 Chlorine Copper	71 : 63 Cl^2 Cu

Now 63 multiplied by the specific heat of copper gives a product practically equal to that given by the atomic weight of iodine or of mercury into their respective specific heats. Thus:

$$\underset{\substack{\text{Atomic weight}\\ \text{of copper}}}{63} \qquad \times \qquad \underset{\substack{\text{Specific heat}\\ \text{of copper}}}{0\cdot09515} \qquad = \qquad 6$$

The same quantity of heat is required to heat the weight of 63 of copper in its compounds through 1°. [See Table 19–10.]

T A B L E   1 9 – 1 0

Formulæ of the compounds of Copper	Weights of their molecules $= p$	Specific heats of Unit weights $= c$	Specific heats of the molecules $= p \times c$	Number of atoms in the molecules $= n$	Specific heat of each atom $= \dfrac{p \times c}{n}$
CuCl	98·5	0·13827	13·619595	2	6·809797
CuI	190	0·06869	14·0511	2	7·0255

After this comes the question, whether this quantity of copper which enters as a whole into the compounds, the calorific capacity of the atoms being maintained, is an entire molecule or a sub-multiple of it. The analogy of the compounds of copper with those of mercury would make us inclined to believe that the atom of copper is a complete molecule. But having no other proof to confirm this, I prefer to declare that there is no means of knowing the molecular weight of free copper until the vapour density of this substance can be determined.

I then go on to examine the constitution of the chlorides, bromides, and iodides of potassium, sodium, lithium, and silver. Each of these metals makes with each of the halogens only one well characterised and definite compound; of none of these compounds is the vapour density known; we are therefore in want of the direct means of discovering if in their molecules there are one, two, or more atoms of the halogens. But their analogies with the protochloride of mercury, HgCl, and with the protochloride of copper, CuCl, and the specific heats of the free metals and of their compounds make us assume that in the molecules of each of these compounds there is one atom of metal and one of halogen. According to this supposition, the atomic weight of potassium K = 39, that of sodium Na = 23, that of silver Ag = 108. These numbers multiplied by the respective specific heats give the same product as the atomic weights of the substances previously examined. [See Table 19–11.]

TABLE 19–11

Name of Substance	Atomic weight $= p$	Specific heats of unit weight $= c$	Specific heats of the atoms $= p \times c$
Solid Bromine	80	0·08432	6·74560
Iodine	127	0·05412	6·87324
Solid Mercury	200	0·03241	6·48200
Copper	63	0·09515	6
Potassium	39	0·169556	6·612684
Sodium	23	0·2934	6·7482
Silver	108	0·05701	6·15708

THE PERIODIC TABLE
OF THE ELEMENTS

○○○○○○○○○○○

Dmitri Ivanovich Mendeléev
(1834-1907)

The following obituary was published on Mendeléev's death by the Royal Society. It serves admirably as a commentary, both scientific and biographical, on Mendeléev's life. It is followed by extracts from Mendeléev's classic paper on the relationships between the elements and their atomic weights. Few other discussions were to have as far-reaching an effect upon the course of chemical atomism.

○○○○○○○○

ROYAL SOCIETY OF LONDON

Obituary Notice [1]

Dmitri Ivanovitch was the fourteenth child of his father, Ivan Pavlovitch Mendeléeff, Director of the Gymnasium at Tobolsk, in Siberia. His mother Marie Dimitrievna, belonged to the old Russian family of Korni-

---

[1] From "Obituary Notices of Fellows Deceased," *Proceedings of the Royal Society of London, Series A,* 84 (1910–11), xvii–xx.

leff, long settled as manufacturers of paper and glass in the neighbourhood of Tobolsk, the glass works being situated at the village of Arem-
ziansk. There can be no doubt that Dmitri Ivanovitch owed much of his
intellectual activity to his mother, who was evidently a woman of considerable mental power and self-instructed beyond the range of ordinary
female education of that period. This debt Mendeléeff acknowledges in
the introduction to his great work on Solutions, which he dedicated to the
memory of his mother in the following interesting lines: "This investigation is dedicated to the memory of a mother by her youngest offspring.
She could only educate him by her own work, conducting a factory. She
taught by example, corrected with love, and to devote him to science she
left Siberia, spending her last resources and strength. When dying she
said, 'Refrain from illusions, insist on work and not on words, search
patiently divine and scientific truth.' She knew how often dialectical methods deceive, how much there is still to be learned, but how with the aid
of science, without violence, with love but firmness, all superstition, un-
truth and error are removed, bringing in their stead the safety of discovered truth, freedom for further development, general welfare, and inward happiness. D. Mendeléeff regards as sacred a mother's dying words.
October, 1887." How full of energy she was is shown by the fact that at
her husband's death she continued to manage the glass works at Arem-
ziansk.

At the age of fifteen, Dmitri Ivanovitch came from his far-off birthplace
to Moscow in order to continue his education. A year later he entered the
chief Pedagogic Institute in St. Petersburg, where, being associated with
the University, he was able to devote himself chiefly to the physical sciences. At the end of this course he was appointed teacher in the Government school at Simferopol in the Crimea, and later at the gymnasium at
Odessa.

In 1856 he returned to St. Petersburg, and at the early age of twenty-
two he was appointed "privat-docent" at the University. At this time, like
most young chemists, to judge by the titles of his published papers, he
passed rapidly from one subject to another, but he soon found matter for
serious thought and experiment in the physical properties of liquids, especially in their expansibility by heat.

In 1859, by permission of the Minister of Public Instruction, Mendeléeff proceeded to Heidelberg, where, in a private laboratory, he devoted
himself to further study of the physical constants of chemical compounds,
communicating some of his results to *Liebig's Annalen* and to the French
Academy. Returning to St. Petersburg in 1861 he secured his doctorate,
and was appointed soon afterwards Professor of Chemistry in the Technological Institute. In 1866 he became Professor of General Chemistry in
the University, Boutleroff at the same time holding the Chair of Organic

Chemistry. He was frequently employed by the Government in connection with the investigation of questions of technical importance, and notably concerning the oil supplies of Baku and the Caspian; also in the department of weights and measures. The latter service brought him on several occasions to England, where his remarkable and distinguished figure was quite familiar in scientific circles. In 1904 he celebrated his seventieth birthday, on which occasion he received congratulatory addresses from the Chemical Society of London, and from many other scientific associations and academies with which he was connected.

Mendeléeff died on February 2 (N.S.), 1907. . . .

The name of Mendeléeff has long been honoured by the Royal Society. Though not the first to recognise a relation between the properties of the elements and their atomic weights, he was unquestionably the first to apply the principles embodied in the statement of the "Periodic Law" to the settlement of atomic weights, to the prevision of previously unknown elements, and to the recognition of the true relations of different groups of elements to one another. In recognition of the importance of these generalisations and of the great knowledge and enthusiasm with which he laboured at the subject, the Royal Society awarded to him, in 1882, the Davy Medal, jointly with Prof. Lothar Meyer; in 1892 the Fellowship of the Society, and in 1905 the Copley Medal . . .

The subject with which especially the name of Mendeléeff is indissolubly connected is the development of the Periodic Law. The several stages in the history of the recognition of relations between atomic weights and properties of elements extend over more than half a century. So soon as a sufficient number of atomic weights had been estimated with some approach to accuracy, by Berzelius and others, the hypothesis of Prout attracted attention, and down to the time of Stas was regarded with some favour. In 1829, Doebereiner pointed out the existence of triads of closely related elements, such as chlorine, bromine, iodine—lithium, sodium, potassium, in which the atomic weights are so related that the middle term of each series is nearly the arithmetical mean of the two extremes. Thirty years later Dumas drew attention to the close analogy observable in such series with homologous series of carbon compounds.

The first step toward the recognition of a periodic relation was taken in 1864–5 by John Newlands, and this was followed, soon afterwards, by a scheme of the known elements, arranged by Odling. But Newlands' attempt was very imperfect, as many of the elements were incorrectly placed, and no room was left for discovery of new elements. Odling, at the end of his article, refers to the probable existence of "some hitherto unrecognised general law."

The question being left in this condition, Mendeléeff communicated to the Russian Chemical Society, in March, 1869, a paper on "The Relations of the Properties to the Atomic Weights of the Elements." An abstract published in the *Zeitschrift für Chemie* contains several obvious misprints; but, correcting these, the following literal translation serves to show that Mendeléeff had discovered this unrecognised law and perceived most of its important consequences:—

"When the elements are arranged in vertical columns according to increasing atomic weight, so that the horizontal lines contain analogous elements again according to increasing atomic weight, an arrangement results from which several general conclusions may be drawn. (Here follows the table of elements.)

"1. The elements, arranged according to magnitude of atomic weight, show a periodic change of properties.

"2. Chemically analogous elements have atomic weights, either in close agreement (Pt, Ir, Os), or increasing by equal amounts (K, Rb, Cs).

"3. The arrangement according to atomic weights corresponds with the *valency* of the elements and, to a certain extent, to the difference in chemical behaviour, *e.g.,* Li, Be, B, C, N, O, F.

"4. The elements most widely distributed in nature have small atomic weights, and all such elements are distinguished by their characteristic behaviour. They are thus typical, and the lightest element, hydrogen, is therefore rightly chosen as the typical unit of mass.

"5. The magnitude of the atomic weight determines the properties of the element, whence, in the study of compounds, regard is to be paid not only to the number and properties of the elements and their mutual action, but to the atomic weights of the elements. Hence the compounds of S and Te, Cl and I, show, beside many analogies, striking differences.

"6. The discovery of many *new* elements may be foreseen; for example, analogues of Si and Al, with atomic weights between 65 and 75.

"7. Some atomic weights will presumably suffer correction; for example, Te cannot have the atomic weight 128, but 123 to 126.

"8. From the table, new analogies become apparent. Thus, U appears as an analogue of Bo and Al, which is in harmony with experience."

Many years later, Mendeléeff found a difficulty in placing the elements of the argon group and radium, these substances having been discovered long subsequently to the formulation of the "periodic" scheme.

In an article written for the "Russian Encyclopædia," and abstracted into English ("Nature," November, 1904), he later acknowledges the independent existence of these elements, and places the argon group in a column by themselves. The first place in the same column is assigned to the ether, which he assumed to be molecular in structure with a very small atomic weight.

How some of his earlier predictions have been verified by the discovery of gallium, of scandium, and of germanium, which correspond to Mendeléeff's theoretical elements, ekaluminium, ekaboron, and ekasilicon, is matter of common knowledge, and supplies a complete justification of the scheme. And though there are some outstanding difficulties about individual elements, the construction of this scheme and the enunciation of the periodic law as a principle applicable to the whole of the chemical elements constitute one of the most fertile conceptions in the whole range of modern chemistry.

ೲೲೲೲೲೲೲ

MENDELÉEV

The Relations between the Properties of Elements and Their Atomic Weights [2]

. . . THE INVESTIGATIONS REGARDING THE simple relations of atomic weights have caused many, in particular, Dumas, Pettenkofer, Sokelow and others, to point out the numerical relations between the atomic weights of those elements which form a group; but, so far as I know, they have not led to a systematic arrangement of all known elements. I know only of an attempt by Lensson to satisfy this requirement that seems so natural. However, this system of triads of single bodies suffers from a certain ambiguity, since it possesses no definite principle as a basis. Lensson endeavors to support his classification of elements into triads with the help of the relations between atomic weights (in every triad the atomic weight of the in-between element is equal to half the sum of the atomic weights of the two outside elements, as was done first by Kremers and others); further, he claims support in chemical similarity and the colour of compounds. However, the classification according to the latter principle becomes uncertain as a result of the differences noted in the colors of Co − Cr − Cu −, and many other compounds according to the external condition they have undergone or according to the form of combination in which they are found. Yet there are natural groups to be found in Lensson's system which agree quite frequently with our general concepts, such as, e.g., K, Na, and Li; Ba, Sr, and Ca; Mg, Zn, and Cd; Ag, Pb, and Hg; S, Se, and

---

[2] Dmitri Mendeléeff, in *Selected Readings in Natural Science* (Chicago: University of Chicago Press, 1947), pp. 824–836.

Te; P, As, and Sb; Os, Pt, and Ir; Pd, Ru, and Rh; W, V, and Mo; Ta, Sn, and Ti, and others. But to place into one group Si, B and F; O, N, and C; Cr, Ni, and Cu; Be, Zn, and U as Lennson does, is hardly possible, after all. Moreover in his system the tendency appears to be implicit to subjugate the natural grouping of elements to the triads, which scarcely correspond to nature, and this is also not consonant with the certainty that the known series of elements are incomplete. If space could be found in his system to accommodate elements which are still to be discovered, this would result in the destruction of groups considered to be complete up to this time.

When I undertook to write a handbook of chemistry entitled "Foundations of Chemistry," I had to make a decision in favour of some system of elements in order not to be guided in their classification by accidental, or instinctive reasons, but by some exact, definite principle. In what has been said above we have seen the nearly complete absence of numerical relations in the construction of systems of elements; every system, however, that is based upon exactly observed numbers is to be preferred of course to other systems not based upon numbers because then only little margin is left to arbitrariness. The numerical data available regarding elements are limited at this time. Even if the physical properties of some of them have been determined accurately, this is true only of a very small number of elements. Properties, such as the optical and even the electrical or magnetic ones, cannot serve as basis for the system naturally, since one and the same body, according to the state in which it happens to be at the moment, may show enormous differences in this regard. With respect to this fact, it is sufficient to remember graphite and diamond, ordinary and red phosphorus. The vapour density which enables us to know the molecular weight of bodies is not only unknown for most elements but it is subject also to changes which agree completely with the polymetric transformations as they have been observed for compound bodies. Oxygen and sulfur furnish unambiguous proof for this fact; the relations between nitrogen, phosphorus and arsenic provide another confirmation, in so far as these similar elements possess the molecular weights N_2, P_4, As_4 which are unequal to each other with respect to the number of atoms. But there is no doubt that the polymerization of an element must go hand in hand with the change of a number of its properties. One cannot be certain whether for any arbitrary chosen element, e.g., for platinum, another state would become known and that therefore, the place of a given element in the system would have to be changed according to its physical properties. However, everybody does understand that in all changes of properties of elements, something remains unchanged, and that when elements go into compounds this material something represents the [common] characteristics of compounds the given element can form. In this regard only a numerical value is known, and this is the atomic weight appropriate to the element. The magnitude of the atomic weight, according to the actual, essential nature of the concept, is a quantity which does not refer to the momentary state of an element but belongs to a material part of it, a part which it has in common with the free element and with all its compounds. The atomic weight does not belong to coal and to the diamond but to carbon. The procedure, according to which *Gerhardt* and *Cannizzaro* have determined the atomic weights of elements is based upon such unshakeable and indubitable methods that for the majority of bodies and, in particular, for those elements whose heat capacity in the free state was already determined, there exist no longer any doubts about the atomic weight of the element. These doubts still existed a few years earlier when the atomic weight was so often confused with the equivalent weight and when it was determined according to different, even contradictory, principles.

For this reason I have endeavored to found the system upon the quantity of the atomic weight.

The first attempt I undertook in this direction was the following: I selected the bodies with the smallest atomic weight and ordered them according to the magnitude of their atomic weights. Thereby it appeared that there exists, a periodicty of properties and that even according to valency, one element follows the other in the order of an arithmetical sequence. [See Table 20–1.]

TABLE 20-1

Li = 7	Be — 9.4	B = 11	C = 12	N = 14	O = 16	F = 19
Na = 23	Mg = 24	Al = 27.4	Si = 28	P = 31	S = 32	Cl = 35.3
K = 39	Ca = 40	....	Ti = 50	V = 51	......	....

In the division of elements with an atomic weight greater than 100 we encounter a completely analogous series:

Ag = 108 Cd = 112 U = 116 Sn = 118 Sb = 122 Te = 128 I = 127

It is seen that Li, Na, K, Ag show the same relationship to one another as do N, P, V, Sb, etc. Immediately the idea arose in me whether it was not possible to express the properties of elements by their atomic weights and whether one could not base a system upon this? In the following, the attempt as such a system is described.

In the proposed system, the atomic weight of an element serves to determine its place. Collecting the groups of elements known up to now, according to their atomic weight, leads to the conclusion that the method of ordering elements according to their atomic weight does not contradict the natural similarity existing among the elements but, on the contrary, points directly toward it. In this regard the collection of the . . . six groups [in Table 20–2] is sufficient.

TABLE 20–2

	Ca = 40	Sr = 87.6	Ba = 137
Na = 23	K = 39	Rb = 85.4	Cs = 133
F = 19	Cl = 35.5	Br = 80	I = 127
O = 16	S = 32	Se = 79.4	Te = 128
N = 14	P = 31	As = 75	Sb = 122
C = 12	Si = 28	. . . .	Sn = 118

These six groups show clearly that there exist certain, definite relations between the natural properties of elements and the magnitudes of their atomic weights. However, one should not imagine that such relations represent a picture of homology; this is not the case for the reason that, in those elements whose atomic weights are known with accuracy, no genuine homologous differences exist. Even though the difference in atomic weights of sodium and potassium, fluorine and chlorine, oxygen and sulfur, carbon and silicon amounts to 16, the difference between the atomic weights of nitrogen and phosphorus is 17, however, and— what is still more important—the differences between calcium and strontium, potassium and rubidium, chlorine and bromine, etc., are unequal; and the deviation in the first place, exhibits a certain regularity and, secondly it is much larger than the difference which could be ascribed to experimental error. In the collections indicated above the strict regularity is striking in the change of atomic weights within the horizontal rows and the vertical columns. Only the atomic weight of tellurium is out of place in the series; but this could easily be the case because it has not been determined accurately, and if we assume the atomic weight 126-124 instead of 128, then the system fits completely.

Thus the group of fluorine possesses elements which combine, preferentially, with a single atom of hydrogen, the group of oxygen with two, of nitrogen with three, of carbon with four atoms of hydrogen. Thus, in this respect, the naturalness of the group-classification, in an arrangement defined according to the numbers expressing the atomic weight, does not suffer any disturbance but, on the contrary, is suggested in advance.

In the first arrangement, we have 7 columns (perhaps the most natural ones also), of which Li and F are uni-valent and are most widely separated with respect to electrochemical behavior; Be and O which succeed them are bi-valent, then come B and N—tri-valent, and in the middle the quadri-valent carbon has its place. If we consider the distance of Na and Cl, Ag and I, and similar aspects, we notice that the arrangement of elements according to magnitude (of atomic weights) corresponds in a certain degree to thc valency and to the concept of similarity.

All comparisons carried out by me in this direction lead me to the conclusion that the magnitude of the atomic weight determines the properties and many reactions of a compound body. As soon as this assertion is verified in the further application of the proposed principle to the study of elements, then we shall approach the epoch where we understand conceptually the essential differences—and the reasons for the similarity, of the elements.

I state in advance that the law proposed by me does not contradict the general tendency in natural science and that, so far, it has not been proved, although suggestions of this kind did exist already. From now on, it appears to me, new interest will be awakened for the determination of atomic weights, for the discovery of new elements and for the finding of new analogies among the elements.

I shall now present one of the many systems of elements which are based upon the atomic weight. They form but one attempt to represent the results which can be achieved in this direction. I am quite conscious of the fact that this attempt is not final, but it appears to me to express quite clearly already the applicability of my proposed principle to all elements whose atomic weight is determined with some reliability. Above all I was interested to find out a general system of elements. The attempt is shown in Table 20–3. [This] table . . . has convinced me of the possibil-

TABLE 20-3

			Ti = 50	Zr = 90	? = 180
			V = 51	Nb = 94	Ta = 182
			Cr = 52	Mo = 96	W = 186
			Mn = 55	Rh = 104.4	Pt = 197.4
			Fe = 56	Ru = 104.4	Ir = 198
		Ni = Co = 59		Pd = 106.6	Os = 199
H = 1			Cu = 63.4	Ag = 108	Hg = 200
	Be = 9.4	Mg = 24	An = 66.2	Cd = 112	
	B = 11	Al = 27.4	? = 68	Ur = 116	Au = 197?
	C = 12	Si = 28	? = 70	Sn = 118	
	N = 14	P = 31	As = 75	Sb = 122	Bi = 210
	O = 16	S = 32	Se = 79.4	Te = 128?	
	F = 19	Cl = 35.5	Br = 80	I = 127	
Li = 7	Na = 23	K = 39	Rb = 85.4	Cs = 133	Ti = 204
		Ca = 4C	Sr = 87.6	Ba = 137	Pb = 207
		? = 45	Ce = 92		
		?Kr = 56	La = 94		
		?Yt = 60	Di = 95		
		?In = 75.6	Th = 118?		

ity that the atomic weight of elements may be used as the basis of the system.* Initially I had ordered the elements into an uninterrupted sequence according to the magnitude of their atomic weights; but I noticed immediately that in the series of elements thus obtained some discontinuities are present. If one starts, e.g., with H = 1, then until Na = 23 there are present at least eight elements, and nearly the same number is found between elements with atomic weights of 23 and 56, 63 and 90, 100 and 140, 180 and 210, and in these particular groups of elements alone, the analogy is apparent by arranging them according to their atomic weights. In many cases there exist strong doubts still regarding the place of such elements which are not yet sufficiently investigated and which are placed close to the edges of the system as, e.g., Vanadium; according to the investigation of *Roxoe* it should be ascribed a place in the nitrogen group, but on the grounds of its atomic weight (51) it should be placed between phosphorus and arsenic. The physical properties equally support this position of vanadium; thus vanadium oxychloride, $VOCl_3$, is a liquid, having at 14° the specific weight of 1.841 and boiling at 127°, by which proper-

---

* Perhaps it may be more rational to arrange the proposed table in the following way:

above	Li	Na	K	Rb	Cs	Tl
	—	—	—	Sr	Ba	Pb
then follows	—	—	Cr	Mo	—	—
	—	—	V	Cb	Ta	etc.
but below	O	S	Se	Te	—	—
	F	Cl	Br	I	—	—

This would possess the advantage that elements, which are sharply distinguished as are Cl and Na, form the most outside rows, between which the elements have to be placed having a chemical character with less pronounced distinction. However, in this case the centre of the table would be nearly empty, and, moreover, it would be of a rather doubtful kind; while in the present arrangement the centre is indubitable and possesses many representatives; and all less known elements are placed above and below at the edges.

The two following sketches may show how diverse the arrangement can be to the fundamental principle stated in this essay.

Li	Na	K	Cu	Rb	Ag	Cs	—	Tl
7	23	39	63.4	85.4	108	133		204
Be	Mg	Ca	Zn	Sr	Cd	Ba	—	Pb
B	Al	—	—	—	U	—	—	Bi?
C	Si	Ti	—	Zr	Sn	—	—	—
N	P	V	As	Cb	Sb	—	Ta	—
O	S	—	Se	—	Te	—	W	—
F	Cl	—	Br	—	I	—	—	—
19	35.5	58	80	100	127	160	190	220

Hereby the row Cr, Mn, Fe, Ni, Co must supply the transition (the atomic weights of 52-59) from the lower part of the 3rd column (where we have K, Ca, V) to the

ties it approaches the corresponding phosphorus compound and places itself somewhat higher than the latter. If one assigns vanadium its place between phosphorus and arsenic, then we have to include in our table above a special column for vanadium and for the elements corresponding to it. In this column then, in the row containing carbon, a place will be opened up also for titanium. Titanium is related, according to this system, to silicon and tin just as vanadium is to phosphorus and antimony. Among these, in the succeeding row, which contains oxygen and sulfur, chromium is to be placed, perhaps; for chromium exhibits the same behavior toward sulfur and tellurium, as titanium does toward carbon and tin. In this case, we would have to place manganese, Mn = 55, between chlorine and bromine.

Thus, this part of [Table 20–3] would be composed as [shown in Table 20–4]. Evidently thereby, the natural connection between members of a horizontal row is disrupted, although manganese does show some similarity to chlorine, as does chromium to sulfur.

TABLE   20–4

Si = 28	Ti = 50	? = 70
P = 31	V = 51	As = 75
S = 32	Cr = 52	Se = 79
Cl = 35.5	Mn = 55	Br = 80

upper part of the 4th column (i.e. up to Cu); and, similarly, Mo, Rh, Ru, Pd form the transition from the 5th to the 6th column (up to Ag), as well as Au, Pt, Os, Ir, Hg from the 8th to the 9th column. In this manner a system of spiral form is obtained, in which the similarity in the number of alternate rows is particularly noticeable, f.i. in the second row is Be, Ca, Sr, Ba, Pb, and also Mg, Zn, Cd. The difference in atomic weights, in this case, is nearly equal for each vertical and horizontal row. If one separates from this system the members which resemble each other most, one obtains a system of the following type:

Above there will be

Li	K	Rb	Cs
Be	Ca	Sr	Ba

in the middle there would stand

O	—	—	—
F	—	—	—
Na	Cu	Ag	—
Mg	Zn	Cd	—

but below

S	Se	Te	—
Cl	Br	I	—

Similar arrangements can be imagined in great numbers, but they do not change the essentials of the system.

On top of this, however, it would be necessary to introduce another column between arsenic and antimony in order to include in this group, columbium, Cb = 94, which represents the analogue of vanadium and antimony. Within the group magnesium, zinc and cadmium in this column, it appears that indium (In = 75.6) has to be placed provided it really belongs to this row (it is more volatile than Zn and Cd). Further, one would have to place zirconium in the row of carbon and tin, actually next to the latter, as the atomic weight of Zr is smaller than that of tin but larger than that of titanium. In this manner, there would be a vacant place in this horizontal row, for an element whose position would be between titanium and zirconium.

All the same, I decided not to construct the columns mentioned above, and this because analogies belonging indubitably to different rows would be left unconsidered. It suffices to point out that Mg, Zn, and Cd exhibit many analogies with Ca, Sr, and Ba, but to unite these bodies into one group: Mg = 24, Ca = 40, Zn = 65, Sr = 87.6, Cd = 112, Ba = 137, would, in my opinion, mean the destruction of the natural similarity of the elements.

For elements with small atomic weight, such as lithium and hydrogen, the first column is reserved, and in this way six columns would be obtained or eight, if we take special columns for Ti and Zr, over which all elements are distributed in horizontal rows whose numbers possess chemical similarity. Only the one row of lithium and sodium has representatives in all columns, the other rows have representatives only in a few columns, so that vacant places occur for elements which, perhaps, shall be discovered in the course of time.

It must be remarked here that all elements occurring more frequently in nature possess atomic weights between 1 and 60, and these elements are

H, C, N, O, Na, Al, Fe, Ca, K, Cl, S, P, Si, Mg;

the higher atomic weights belong to elements that are rarely encountered in nature, which do not form large deposits and which, therefore, have been studied relatively little.

With respect to the position of some elements, there exists, quite understandably, complete uncertainty. In particular, this holds for those elements that are little investigated and whose atomic weight has hardly been determined correctly. To these elements belong, for example, yttrium, thorium, and indium.

It must be remarked, moreover, that the upper members of the fourth column (Mn, Fe, Co, Ni, Zn) form the transition to the lower members of the (third) column in which Ca, K, Cl and similar elements are found; thus, cobalt and nickel, chromium, manganese, and iron represent, in their properties and with respect to atomic weight, the transition from copper and zinc to calcium and potassium. Perhaps their position may have to be changed for this reason; and if they were to be placed in the lower rows instead of the upper rows, then there would be three columns here which in many respects exhibit similarities; namely, one column comprising cobalt, nickel, chromium, manganese and iron, a second column with:— cerium, lanthanum and didymium, palladium, rhodium, ruthenium; finally a third column which contains platinum, iridium and osmium.

The system of elements proposed here is, of course, not to be considered as completely closed, but it appears to me to be based upon such data and such natural approximations, that its existence can hardly be regarded as doubtful; for the numbers confirm the similarities which result from the study of the compounds of the elements. A number of questions will arise when all elements are arranged into one whole, but the most interesting problem appears to me to be the arrangement of groups of similar elements, such as those of iron, cerium, palladium and platinum since, in this case, elements close to each other in their nature also exhibit approximately the same atomic weights, a circumstance not to be observed in other rows, for in the latter similar elements possess different atomic weights. It may be that the system of elements arranged in groups will, in consequence of the study of these groups, be changed in such a manner that in certain parts of the system, the similarity between members of horizontal rows has to be considered, but in other parts, the similarity between members of the vertical columns. In any event, it appears to be certain when we look at the proposed table, that in some rows the corresponding members are missing; this appears especially clearly, e.g., for the row of calcium; in which there are missing the members analogous to sodium and lithium; magnesium represents, to a certain degree, the analogue of sodium, but magnesium cannot be placed in the row of calcium, strontium and barium. This is proved not only by the properties of some compounds of these elements but also by those physical properties which are attributed to the metals themselves.

I cannot but direct attention to the fact that in the comparison of the lower members of the row with the upper there is noticeable a sharply distinct difference in properties and reactions. This is analogous to what we perceive in the series of organic homologues: in the upper members of the homologous series some of the characteristics belonging to the series are weakened; thus, for example, paraffin which was closed, at first, in the ethylene series, can be taken with the same (and naturally stronger) justification to belong to the series of marsh gas, since for such high homologues distinct characteristics cannot be expected in either this or that series. Similarly, characteristics of simple bodies, that show up strongly in the first column, become weakened in the last column formed by the heaviest elements. Lead, thallium, bismuth, gold, mercury, platinum, iridium, osmium and tungsten are not only less energetic elements, but at the same time they are heavy elements, from which in many respects one single group could even be constructed without thereby destroying the foremost requirements of analogy. Thallium and bismuth are more widely separated in this relation, however, than lead and thallium, or bismuth and gold, mercury and platinum. At the same time, the elements standing lower than the halogen row possess oxides which exhibit basic properties rather than acid ones and which are the best representatives of the metals; while those elements which stand higher than the row of halogens possess either complete acid character or show transitional characteristics which lie between acid and base. For the latter reason also I could not persuade myself to put the iron group with the erbium-group in the lower part of the table.

Hydrogen has not yet been assigned a definite position because of its small atomic weight; it appears to me to be the most natural to place it in the row of copper, silver, and mercury, although it is possible that it belongs in some unknown row lower than that of copper.

If it is permitted to express a wish when looking at the proposed [Table 20–3], then it is that the number of elements should be completed which stand closer to hydrogen. Those elements which form the transition from hydrogen to boron and carbon, would represent, naturally, the most important scientific achievement that may be expected upon acquaintance with bodies yet to be discovered.

With regard to the bodies of the second [vertical] row it would be most promising, in my view, to subject beryllium and boron to an exact study and I shall endeavor to carry this out as soon as possible. In general, the elements with low atomic weight deserve greater scientific interest, to judge from what has been said previously, than those elements whose atomic weight is high. Considering the characteristics of the system, the remark has still to be made that some analogies are clearly visible from the table. Thus, C, B, Si, Al stand together, as well as Ba, Pb, Tl or V, Cr, Cb, Mo, Ta, W; others can be guessed in advance so to speak. Thus, there is no doubt that, for uranium, (but not for gold which, perhaps, has to be placed in the row of iron) a place has to be made in the row of boron and of aluminum, and, indeed, between these elements no little similarity exists. Thus, e.g., Turmeric is turned brown by the action of uranium oxide as well as by boric acid; the composition of borax, $Na_2B_4O_7$, is analogous to that of the uranium compound $K_2U_4O_7$. The compounds which aluminum oxide forms with a base have been little studied so far, and this question which has interested me already for some time, is going to form the subject-matter of one of my next communications.

In conclusion I do not deem it superfluous to summarize the results of what has been said above:

1. The elements, if arranged according to their atomic weights, show a distinct periodicity of their properties.

2. Elements exhibiting similarities in their chemical behavior have atomic weights which are approximately equal (as in the case of Pt, Ir, Os) or they possess atomic weights which increase in a uniform manner (as in the case of K, Rb, Cs). The uniformity of such an increase in the various groups remained hidden to previous observers since in their calculations they did not make use of the conclusions drawn by Gerhardt, Regnault, Cannizzaro, and others, by which conclusions the true magnitude of the atomic weights of the elements was determined.

3. The arrangement of elements or of groups of elements according to their atomic weights corresponds to their valencies, as well as, to some extent, to their distinctive chemical properties, a fact which can be clearly seen from the row: Li, Be, B, C, N, O, F and which also occurs in the other rows.

4. The bodies most abundantly found in nature possess a small atomic weight; but all elements of small atomic weight are characterized by their distinct properties and are, therefore, typical elements. Hydrogen, being the lightest element, is reasonably to be chosen as the most typical element of all.

5. The magnitude of the atomic weight determines the character of the element, just as the magnitude of the molecule determines the properties of a compound body; it is therefore necessary in the study of compounds to direct attention not only towards the properties and number of the elements as well as to their mutual behavior, but also towards their atomic weight. Thus, the compounds, e.g., of S and Te, Cl and I and of others, present, in spite of all their resemblance, distinct differences.

6. The discovery of numerous unknown elements is still to be expected, for instance, of elements similar to Al and Si having atomic weights from 65–75.

7. The atomic weight of an element will have to be corrected, eventually, when its analogues become known. Thus, must not the atomic weight of tellurium be 123-126, and not 128?

BEYOND THE ATOM

ooooooooooo

21

ooooooooooo

ATOMS AND ELECTRICITY

ooooooooooo

Michael Faraday (1791-1867)

The development of physics has often been greatly accelerated by the simultaneous or at least coeval work of an outstanding experimentalist and a brilliant theoretician. This was particularly true of Michael Faraday, probably the greatest experimental physicist of all time, and James Clerk Maxwell, who incorporated Faraday's theory of electromagnetic induction into the magnificent electromagnetic theory of light. Without Faraday's discoveries Maxwell could not have constructed his own theory, which in part expresses in mathematical language Faraday's concept of "tubes of force" and his laws of electromagnetic induction.

That Faraday became the great physicist he was is all the more remarkable since he was almost entirely self-taught and approached his subject with scarcely any mathematical training. Nevertheless, his physical intuition and insight into nature more than compensated for this deficiency. That he even had a chance for a scientific career was in itself quite amazing since he came from a worker's family at a time when most children of the working class were lucky if they learned to read.

Born in London in 1791 to James Faraday, a blacksmith, Michael was apprenticed to a bookseller at the age of thirteen, since this was then a period of acute economic distress, and the Faraday family was at its lowest ebb. By that time he had learned reading, writing, and some arithmetic and was already probing into all kinds of areas. As he himself said, "I was a lively and imaginative person" and "facts were important to me. . . . I would trust a fact and always cross-examined an assertion." Although he read whatever he could lay his hands on, he preferred scientific books and was greatly influenced by Mrs. Marcet's *Conversations in Chemistry*. Even at that early age Faraday was not content to accept a statement but had to check it himself, for only in that way could he claim the fact as

315

his own. He says, "So when I questioned Mrs. Marcet's book by such little experiments as I could find means to perform and found it true to the facts as I could understand them, I felt I had got hold of an anchor in chemical knowledge and clung fast to it."

Michael might have remained a bookbinder all his life except for a chance occurrence and for his intense dislike of business and his equally intense love for science and philosophy. By the year 1810, Michael was doing so well in his apprenticeship that he had two boys working for him; but in spite of this he had money for little more than the bare necessities. Although he lived with his master, Mr. Ribeau, he was still very closely attached to his family; when a series of science lectures at the Royal Institution was announced, it was Michael's eldest brother Robert's savings that paid for Michael's attendance.

These lectures certainly had a great influence on him, for from then on he devoted all his spare time to science and philosophy and attended as many lectures as he could. Undoubtedly, this interest contributed greatly to his development as a devoted science lecturer later in his life. Fortunately, Mr. Ribeau and his wife were very sympathetic to Faraday's scientific interests and encouraged him as much as they could, but he never neglected his craft during this period, although he must certainly have had many doubts about continuing his career as a bookbinder.

When Faraday completed his apprenticeship in 1812 and went to work as a journeyman bookbinder for a Mr. De la Roche, he soon made up his mind to leave the world of commerce and to become a scientist. De la Roche was very fond of Faraday as a person and worker but he had no sympathy for Michael's interest in science and opposed it violently. This was the final factor that contributed to Faraday's decision to leave his profession, and in 1813 he described his change of career in the following charming passage:

> I was formerly a bookseller and binder, but am now turned philosopher, which happened thus: whilst an apprentice, I, for amusement, learnt a little chemistry and other parts of philosophy, and felt an eager desire to proceed in that way further. After being a journeyman for six months, under a disagreeable master, I gave up my business, and by the interest of Sir H. Davy, filled the situation of Chemical Assistant to the Royal Institution of Great Britain, in which office I now remain, and where I am constantly engaged in observing the works of Nature and tracing the manner in which she directs the arrangement and order of the world.

Faraday's association with Sir Humphry Davy was itself a matter of chance, for a customer of Ribeau's had given him tickets for a few of Davy's lectures at the Royal Institution and Michael took full advantage of this opportunity, as indicated in his own account of the affair (in a letter written in 1829):

> You asked me to give you an account of my first introduction to Sir H. Davy, which I am very happy to do, as I think the circumstances will bear testimony to the goodness of his heart. When I was a bookseller's apprentice I was very fond of experiment and very adverse to trade. It happened that a gentleman, a member of the Royal Institution, took me to hear some of Sir H. Davy's last lectures in Albemarle Street. I took notes, and afterwards wrote them out more fairly in a quarto volume. My desire to escape from trade, which I thought vicious and selfish, and to enter into the service of Science, which I imagined made its pursuers amiable and liberal, induced me at last to take the bold and simple step of writing to Sir H. Davy, expressing my wishes, and a hope that if an opportunity came in his way he would favour my views; at the same time I sent the notes I had taken of his lectures. . . .
>
> You will observe that this took place at the end of the year 1812, and early in 1813 he requested to see me and told me of the situation of assistant in the laboratory of the Royal Institution, then just vacant. At the same time he thus gratified my desires as to scientific employment, he still advised me not to give up the prospects I had before me, telling me that Science was a harsh mistress, and in a pecuniary point of view but poorly rewarding those who devoted themselves to her service. He smiled at my notion of the superior moral feelings of philosophic men, and said he would leave me to the experience of a few years to set me right in that matter.
>
> Finally, through his good efforts, I went to the Royal Institution, early in March of 1813, as assistant in the laboratory; and in October of the same year went with him abroad as his assistant in experiments and in writing. I returned with him in April 1815, resumed my station in the Royal Institution, and have, as you know, ever since remained there.

Davy's account of Faraday's request for work at the Royal Institution is quite amusing and clearly indicates the gentle quality of Davy's own character as shown in this brief exchange with an acquaintance of his, a Mr. Pepys:

"Pepys, what am I to do? Here is a letter from a young man named Faraday; he has been attending my lectures and wants me to give him employment at the Royal Institution—what can I do?" "Do?" replied Pepys, "put him to wash bottles; if he is good for anything he will do it directly; if not, he will refuse." "No, no," replied Davy, "we must try him with something better than that."

As suggested in this passage, Davy recognized Faraday's merit even before he had observed him in the laboratory, where he made him an assistant, and not a "bottle washer." This certainly was due to the skill and care with which Faraday had written up the lectures he had attended. He carried over this painstaking accuracy and attention to detail to everything he did, and Davy soon recognized that Michael Faraday was to become an outstanding scientist.

Faraday performed his duties as assistant to various professors at the Royal Institution in a most excellent manner, allowing no detail in the lecture room to escape his attention, and laying the foundation for his own career as a lecturer. But during this assistantship period the dominant idea in Faraday's mind was to perform his own experiments, and when, in 1816, the year after he had been reappointed to the institution, he published his first paper in the *Quarterly Journal of Science,* his dream was realized. After that, he rose very quickly and in 1823 became a fellow of the Royal Society.

This marked the beginning of his greatest experimental period which reached its peak in the discovery of electromagnetic induction, one of the most important scientific achievements of all time. Though he was extremely serious and devoted to his scientific work, Faraday's life, when he was not engaged in research, was filled with many gay and tender moments. His interests included poetry, the beauties of nature, all kinds of games, acrobatics, Punch and Judy shows, puzzles, and children, for whom he prepared very special and extremely instructive lectures.

The quality of his attitude toward all people and his humility, even toward his work, is indicated by an excerpt from a letter to Sara Barnard, shortly before he married her:

> You know me as well or better than I do myself. You know my former prejudices and my present thoughts—you know my weaknesses, my vanity, my whole mind. You have converted me from one erroneous way, let me hope that you will attempt to correct what others are wrong. . . . Again and again I attempt to say what I feel, but I cannot. Let me, however, claim not to be the selfish being that wishes to bind your affections for his own sake only. In whatever way I can best minister to your happiness either by assiduity or by absence it shall be done. Do not injure me by withdrawing your friendship, or punish me for aiming to be more than a friend by making me less; and if you cannot grant me more, leave me what I possess, but hear me.

This tenderness toward, and understanding of, others, regardless of his own interests, certainly had its roots, to some extent, in his religious convictions and his sense of the dignity of man. He belonged, in his own words, to a "very small and despised sect of Christians, known, if known at all, as Sandemanians," who believed that organized religion was bound to degenerate into the opposite of true Christianity and that the words of Christ were sufficient guides for living. They practiced brotherhood, humility, and charity.

Woven into the colorful fabric of his life and scientific work was a thread of tragedy, for quite early in his life Faraday began to suffer from attacks of giddiness, headache, and loss of memory, which finally were fatal. From 1831 to 1840 these symptoms became quite severe and he himself, believing no doctor understood his ailment, was convinced that he was suffering from a decay of his physicomental faculties and that there was no way to stop this deterioration. Nevertheless, in spite of this progressive disease, which at times left him momentarily paralyzed, his creative faculties remained as great as ever, and his productivity continued until he died on the afternoon of August 25, 1867, just one month short of seventy-six years after his birth.

Although Faraday's research ranged over all phases of electrical and magnetic phenomena, covering almost every aspect of this branch of physics, he is best known for his work on electromagnetic induction. After Oersted discovered in 1819 that an electric current deflects a magnetic needle, the whole scientific world began an intense study of the electric current and its effects, but only a few, among them Faraday, looked for the inverse of the Oersted effect, namely, the effect of magnetism on an electric current. These investigations ultimately led Faraday to try to obtain an electric current from magnetism, and in 1831 the following entry appeared as the first paragraph in his laboratory notebook: "Experiments on the Production of Electricity from Magnetism."

In his approach to this work, Faraday was greatly influenced by three things:

1. Newton's abhorrence of action at a distance. In a letter to Bentley, Newton wrote a remarkable passage to which Faraday constantly referred: "That gravity should be innate, inherent, and essential to matter so that one body may act upon another at a distance through a vacuum and without the mediation of anything else . . . is to me so great an absurdity that I believe that no man who has in philosophical matters a competent faculty of thinking can ever fall into it."

This led Faraday to introduce the concept of the field and the idea that the magnetic field between the magnet and the current affects the current in some way. He thus sought to explain interaction of magnet and current via a field, which was to prove so useful to Maxwell.

2. His own deficiency in mathematics. This forced him to represent physical phenomena in terms of physical models rather than by means of abstract mathematical formulas. Thus, his idea of "tubes of force" stemmed directly from the need for a model, and the model of the field with its "tubes of force" in turn led him to the explanation of induction as a cutting of the tubes of force. Whenever tubes of force are cut by a conductor, a current flows in the conductor; the faster the tubes are cut, the greater the electromotive force that is induced in the conductor.

3. His conviction that all forms of physical action are basically one, that is, the concept of the unified field.

In 1854, when he discovered a relationship between magnetism and light, he stated,

> I have long held an opinion, almost amounting to conviction . . . that the various forms under which the forms of matter are made manifest have one common origin: in other words, are so directly related and naturally dependent that they are convertible as it were into one another and possess equivalents of power in their action.

Following his discovery of electromagnetic induction—that the electromotive force induced in a loop of wire is proportional to the rate at which the magnetic flux through the loop is changing—Faraday began a series of experiments in electrochemistry which finally led him to the laws of electrolysis. These experiments, a description of which, as given by Faraday, is included in this volume, are of great importance in the development of atomic physics. Until this work was done, the concept of the atom and of the molecule was widely accepted and used, but nobody had any idea as to the nature of the forces that bound two or more atoms in a single molecule.

Faraday immediately suspected that electrical forces are at work in a molecule, for he reasoned that if one can obtain an electric current from a voltaic cell, which operates by the chemical reaction of the electrodes with a chemical solution, then the atoms in solution must have electrical charges in them.

To test this hypothesis, he sent various electric currents through different solutions and discovered that the same current flowing for the same length of time always decomposed the same quantity of material, or, to put it differently, the same number of ions of a given chemical compound. He then reasoned that each ion of the same kind has exactly the same charge. Later he discovered that all charges on ions are integral multiples of a single fundamental unit of charge and that one never finds fractions of this charge. He shows quite clearly that this accounts for the reversibility of electrochemical phenomena and

> that if the electrical power which holds the elements of a grain of water in combination, or which makes a grain of oxygen and hydrogen in the right proportions unite into water when they are made to combine could be thrown into the condition of a current, it would exactly equal the current required for the separation of that grain of water into its elements again.

Throughout these descriptions of his experiments we again detect Faraday's humility, his sense of wonder, and his trust in experimental data.

Thus he speaks of how "wonderful" it is "to observe how small a quantity of a compound body is decomposed by a certain portion of electricity," or, put differently, how large a quantity of electricity one can obtain from the combination of very small quantities of atoms. From this he concludes, correctly, that the electrical forces between ions are very large.

Finally, we cannot escape Faraday's sense of the beauty of nature and its laws, for he constantly speaks of "beautiful experiments," clearly indicating his belief that to him truth and beauty were one.

꘎꘎꘎꘎꘎꘎꘎

F A R A D A Y

Experimental Researches in Electricity [1]

852. THE THEORY OF DEFINITE ELECTROLYTI-cal or electro-chemical action appears to me to touch immediately upon the *absolute quantity* of electricity or electric power belonging to different bodies. It is impossible, perhaps, to speak on this point without committing oneself beyond what present facts will sustain; and yet it is equally impossible, and perhaps would be impolitic, not to reason upon the subject. Although we know nothing of what an atom is, yet we cannot resist forming some idea of a small particle, which represents it to the mind; and though we are in equal, if not greater, ignorance of electricity, so as to be unable to say whether it is a particular matter or matters, or mere motion of ordinary matter, or some third kind of power or agent, yet there is an immensity of facts which justify us in believing that the atoms of matter are in some way endowed or associated with electrical powers, to which they owe their most striking qualities, and amongst them their mutual chemical affinity. As soon as we perceive, through the teaching of Dalton, that chemical powers are, however varied the circumstances in which they are exerted, definite for each body, we learn to estimate the relative degree of force which resides in such bodies: and when upon that knowledge comes the fact, that the electricity, which we appear to be capable of loosening from its habita-

---

[1] Michael Faraday, "On the Absolute Quantity of Electricity Associated with the Particles or Atoms of Matter," in R. and J. E. Taylor, *Experimental Researches in Electricity* (London, 1939), Vol. 1, pp. 249–258.

tion for a while, and conveying from place to place, *whilst it retains its chemical force,* can be measured out, and being so measured is found to be *as definite in its action* as any of *those portions* which, remaining associated with the particles of matter, give them their *chemical relation;* we seem to have found the link which connects the proportion of that we have evolved to the proportion of that belonging to the particles in their natural state.

853. Now it is wonderful to observe how small a quantity of a compound body is decomposed by a certain portion of electricity. Let us, for instance, consider this and a few other points in relation to water. *One grain* of water, acidulated to facilitate conduction, will require an electric current to be continued for three minutes and three quarters of time to effect its decomposition, which current must be powerful enough to retain a platina wire $\frac{1}{104}$ of an inch in thickness,* red hot, in the air during the whole time; and if interrupted anywhere by charcoal points, will produce a very brilliant and constant star of light. If attention be paid to the instantaneous discharge of electricity of tension, as illustrated in the beautiful experiments of Mr. Wheatstone, and to what I have said elsewhere on the relation of common and voltaic electricity, it will not be too much to say that this necessary quantity of electricity is equal to a very powerful flash of lightning. Yet we have it under perfect command; can evolve, direct, and employ it at pleasure; and when it has performed its full work of electrolyzation, it has only separated the elements of *a single grain of water.*

855. Considering this close relation, namely, that without decomposition transmission of electricity does not occur; and, that for a given definite quantity of electricity passed, an equally definite and constant quantity of water or other matter is decomposed; considering also that the agent, which is electricity, is simply employed in overcoming electrical powers in the body subjected to its action; it seems a probable, and almost a natural consequence, that the quantity which passes is the *equivalent* of, and therefore equal to, that of the particles separated; *i. e.* that if the electrical power

---

* I have not stated the length of wire used, because I find by experiment, as would be expected in theory, that it is indifferent. The same quantity of electricity which, passed in a given time, can heat an inch of platina wire of a certain diameter red hot, can also heat a hundred, a thousand, or any length of the same wire to the same degree, provided the cooling circumstances are the same for every part in all cases. This I have proved by the volta-electrometer. I found that whether half an inch or eight inches were retained at one constant temperature of dull redness, equal quantities of water were decomposed in equal times. When the half-inch was used, only the centre portion of wire was ignited. A fine wire may even be used as a rough but ready regulator of a voltaic current; for if it be made part of the circuit, and the larger wires communicating with it be shifted nearer to or further apart, so as to keep the portion of wire in the circuit sensibly at the same temperature, the current passing through it will be nearly uniform.

which holds the elements of a grain of water in combination, or which makes a grain of oxygen and hydrogen in the right proportions unite into water when they are made to combine, could be thrown into the condition of *a current,* it would exactly equal the current required for the separation of that grain of water into its elements again.

856. This view of the subject gives an almost overwhelming idea of the extraordinary quantity or degree of electric power which naturally belongs to the particles of matter; but it is not inconsistent in the slightest degree with the facts which can be brought to bear on this point. To illustrate this I must say a few words on the voltaic pile.*

857. Intending hereafter to apply the results given in this and the preceding series of Researches to a close investigation of the source of electricity in the voltaic instrument, I have refrained from forming any decided opinion on the subject; and without at all meaning to dismiss metallic contact, or the contact of dissimilar substances, being conductors, but not metallic, as if they had nothing to do with the origin of the current, I still am fully of opinion with Davy, that it is at least continued by chemical action, and that the supply constituting the current is almost entirely from that source.

858. Those bodies which, being interposed between the metals of the voltaic pile, render it active, *are all of them electrolytes;* and it cannot but press upon the attention of every one engaged in considering this subject, that in those bodies (so essential to the pile) decomposition and the transmission of a current are so intimately connected, that one cannot happen without the other. This I have shown abundantly in water, and numerous other cases. If, then, a voltaic trough have its extremities connected by a body capable of being decomposed, as water, we shall have a continuous current through the apparatus; and whilst it remains in this state we may look at the part where the acid is acting upon the plates, and that where the current is acting upon the water, as the reciprocals of each other. In both parts we have the two conditions *inseparable in such bodies as these,* namely, the passing of the current, and decomposition; and this is as true of the cells in the battery as of the water cell; for no voltaic battery has as yet been constructed in which the chemical action is only that of combination: *decomposition is always included,* and is, I believe, an essential chemical part.

859. But the difference in the two parts of the connected battery, that is, the decomposition or experimental cell, and the acting cells, is simply

---

* By the term voltaic pile, I mean such apparatus or arrangement of metals as up to this time have been called so, and which contain water, brine, acids, or other aqueous solutions or decomposable substances, between their plates. Other kinds of electric apparatus may be hereafter invented, and I hope to construct some not belonging to the class of instruments discovered by Volta.

this. In the former we urge the current through, but it, apparently of necessity, is accompanied by decomposition: in the latter we cause decompositions by ordinary chemical actions (which are, however, themselves electrical), and, as a consequence, have the electrical current; and as the decomposition dependent upon the current is definite in the former case, so is the current associated with the decomposition also definite in the latter.

860. Let us apply this in support of what I have surmised respecting the enormous electric power of each particle or atom of matter. I showed in a former series of these Researches on the relation by measure of common and voltaic electricity, that two wires, one of platina and one of zinc, each one eighteenth of an inch in diameter, placed five sixteenths of an inch apart, and immersed to the depth of five eighths of an inch in acid, consisting of one drop of oil of vitriol and four ounces of distilled water at a temperature of about 60° Fahr., and connected at the other extremities by a copper wire eighteen feet long, and one eighteenth of an inch in thickness, yielded as much electricity in little more than three seconds of time as a Leyden battery charged by thirty turns of a very large and powerful plate electric machine in full action. This quantity, though sufficient if passed at once through the head of a rat or cat to have killed it, as by a flash of lightning, was evolved by the mutual action of so small a portion of the zinc wire and water in contact with it, that the loss of weight sustained by either would be inappreciable by our most delicate instruments; and as to the water which could be decomposed by that current, it must have been insensible in quantity, for no trace of hydrogen appeared upon the surface of the platina during those three seconds.

861. What an enormous quantity of electricity, therefore, is required for the decomposition of a single grain of water! We have already seen that it must be in quantity sufficient to sustain a platina wire $\frac{1}{104}$ of an inch in thickness, red hot, in contact with the air, for three minutes and three quarters, a quantity which is almost infinitely greater than that which could be evolved by the little standard voltaic arrangement to which I have just referred. I have endeavoured to make a comparison by the loss of weight of such a wire in a given time in such an acid, according to a principle and experiment to be almost immediately described; but the proportion is so high that I am almost afraid to mention it. It would appear that 800,000 such charges of the Leyden battery as I have referred to above, would be necessary to supply electricity sufficient to decompose a single grain of water; or, if I am right, to equal the quantity of electricity which is naturally associated with the elements of that grain of water, endowing them with their mutual chemical affinity.

862. In further proof of this high electric condition of the particles of matter, and the *identity as to quantity of that belonging to them with that*

necessary for their separation, I will describe an experiment of great simplicity but extreme beauty, when viewed in relation to the evolution of an
electric current and its decomposing powers.

863. A dilute sulphuric acid, made by adding about one part by measure of oil of vitriol to thirty parts of water, will act energetically upon a
piece of zinc plate in its ordinary and simple state: but, as Mr. Sturgeon
has shewn, not at all, or scarcely so, if the surface of the metal has in the
first instance been amalgamated; yet the amalgamated zinc will act powerfully with platina as an electrometer, hydrogen being evolved on the surface of the latter metal, as the zinc is oxidized and dissolved. The amalga-
mation is best effected by sprinkling a few drops of mercury upon the surface of the zinc, the latter being moistened with the dilute acid, and rubbing
with the fingers so as to extend the liquid metal over the whole of the
surface. Any mercury in excess, forming liquid drops upon the zinc,
should be wiped off.*

864. Two plates of zinc thus amalgamated were dried and accurately
weighed; one, which we will call A, weighed 163·1 grains; the other to be
called B, weighed 148·3 grains. They were about five inches long, and 0·4
of an inch wide. An earthenware pneumatic trough was filled with dilute
sulphuric acid, of the strength just described, and a gas jar, also filled with
the acid, inverted in it.† A plate of platina of nearly the same length, but
about three times as wide as the zinc plates, was put up into this jar. The
zinc plate A was also introduced into the jar, and brought in contact with
the platina, and at the same moment the plate B was put into the acid of
the trough, but out of contact with other metallic matter.

865. Strong action immediately occurred in the jar upon the contact of
the zinc and platina plates. Hydrogen gas rose from the platina, and was
collected in the jar, but no hydrogen or other gas rose from *either* zinc
plate. In about ten or twelve minutes, sufficient hydrogen having been collected, the experiment was stopped; during its progress a few small bubbles
had appeared upon plate B, but none upon plate A. The plates were
washed in distilled water, dried, and reweighed. Plate B weighed 148·3
grains, as before, having lost nothing by the direct chemical action of the
acid. Plate A weighed 154·65 grains, 8·45 grains of it having been oxidized and dissolved during the experiment.

866. The hydrogen gas was next transferred to a watertrough and
measured; it amounted to 12·5 cubic inches, the temperature being 52°,

* The experiment may be made with pure zinc which, as chemists well know, is
but slightly acted upon by dilute sulphruic acid in comparison with ordinary zinc,
which during the action is subject to an infinity of voltaic actions.

† The acid was left during a night with a small piece of unamalgamated zinc in it,
for the purpose of evolving such air as might be inclined to separate, and bringing
the whole into a constant state.

and the barometer 29·2 inches. This quantity, corrected for temperature, pressure, and moisture, becomes 12·15453 cubic inches of dry hydrogen at mean temperature and pressure; which, increased by one half for the oxygen that must have gone to the *anode, i.e.* to the zinc, gives 18·232 cubic inches as the quantity of oxygen and hydrogen evolved from the water decomposed by the electric current. According to the estimate of the weight of the mixed gas before adopted, this volume is equal to 2·3535544 grains, which therefore is the weight of water decomposed; and this quantity is to 8·45, the quantity of zinc oxidized, as 9 is to 32·31. Now taking 9 as the equivalent number of water, the number 32·5 is given as the equivalent number of zinc; a coincidence sufficiently near to show, what indeed could not but happen, that for an equivalent of zinc oxidized an equivalent of water must be decomposed.*

867. But let us observe *how* the water is decomposed. It is electrolyzed, *i.e* is decomposed voltaically, and not in the ordinary manner (as to appearance) of chemical decompositions; for the oxygen appears at the *anode* and the hydrogen at the *cathode* of the body under decomposition, and these were in many parts of the experiment above an inch asunder. Again, the ordinary chemical affinity was not enough under the circumstances to effect the decomposition of the water, as was abundantly proved by the inaction on plate B; the voltaic current was essential. And to prevent any idea that the chemical affinity was almost sufficient to decompose the water, and that a smaller current of electricity might under the circumstances, cause the hydrogen to pass to the *cathode,* I need only refer to the results which I have given to show that the chemical action at the electrodes has not the slightest influence over the *quantities* of water or other substances decomposed between them, but that they are entirely dependent upon the quantity of electricity which passes.

868. What, then, follows as a necessary consequence of the whole experiment? Why, this: that the chemical action upon 32·31 parts, or one equivalent of zinc, in this simple voltaic circle, was able to evolve such quantity of electricity in the form of a current, as passing through water, should decompose 9 parts, or one equivalent of that substance: and considering the definite relations of electricity as developed in the preceding parts of the present paper, the results prove that the quantity of electricity which, being naturally associated with the particles of matter, gives them their combining power, is able, when thrown into a current, to separate those particles from their state of combination; or, in other words, that *the electricity which decomposes, and that which is evolved by the decomposition of, a certain quantity of matter, are alike.*

869. The harmony which this theory of the definite evolution and the

---

* The experiment was repeated several times with the same results.

equivalent definite action of electricity introduces into the associated theories of definite proportions and electro-chemical affinity, is very great. According to it, the equivalent weights of bodies are simply those quantities of them which contain equal quantities of electricity, or have naturally equal electric powers; it being the ELECTRICITY which *determines* the equivalent number, *because* it determines the combining force. Or, if we adopt the atomic theory or phraseology, then the atoms of bodies which are equivalents to each other in their ordinary chemical action, have equal quantities of electricity naturally associated with them. But I must confess I am jealous of the term *atom;* for though it is very easy to talk of atoms, it is very difficult to form a clear idea of their nature, especially when compound bodies are under consideration.

870. I cannot refrain from recalling here the beautiful idea put forth, I believe, by Berzelius in his development of his views of the electro-chemical theory of affinity, that the heat and light evolved during cases of powerful combination are the consequence of the electric discharge which is at the moment taking place. The idea is in perfect accordance with the view I have taken of the *quantity* of electricity associated with the particles of matter.

871. In this exposition of the law of the definite action of electricity, and its corresponding definite proportion in the particles of bodies, I do not pretend to have brought, as yet, every case of chemical or electro-chemical action under its dominion. There are numerous considerations of a theoretical nature, especially respecting the compound particles of matter and the resulting electrical forces which they ought to possess, which I hope will gradually receive their development; and there are numerous experimental cases, as, for instance, those of compounds formed by weak affinities, the simultaneous decomposition of water and salts, &c., which still require investigation. But whatever the results on these and numerous other points may be, I do not believe that the facts which I have advanced, or even the general laws deduced from them, will suffer any serious change; and they are of sufficient importance to justify their publication, though much may yet remain imperfect or undone. Indeed, it is the great beauty of our science, Chemistry, that advancement in it, whether in a degree great or small, instead of exhausting the subjects of research, opens the doors to further and more abundant knowledge, overflowing with beauty and utility, to those who will be at the easy personal pains of undertaking its experimental investigation.

872. The definite production of electricity (868.) in association with its definite action proves, I think, that the current of electricity in the voltaic pile is sustained by chemical decomposition, or rather by chemical action, and not by contact only. But here, as elsewhere, I beg to reserve my opinion as to the real action of contact, not having yet been able to

make up my mind as to whether it is an exciting cause of the current, or merely necessary to allow of the conduction of electricity, otherwise generated, from one metal to the other.

873. But admitting that chemical action is the source of electricity, what an infinitely small fraction of that which is active do we obtain and employ in our voltaic batteries! Zinc and platina wires, one eighteenth of an inch in diameter and about half an inch long, dipped into dilute sulphuric acid, so weak that it is not sensibly sour to the tongue, or scarcely to our most delicate test papers, will evolve more electricity in one twentieth of a minute than any man would willingly allow to pass through his body at once. The chemical action of a grain of water upon four grains of zinc can evolve electricity equal in quantity to that of a powerful thunder-storm. Nor is it merely true that the quantity is active; it can be directed and made to perform its full equivalent duty. Is there not, then, great reason to hope and believe that, by a closer *experimental* investigation of the principles which govern the development and action of this subtile agent, we shall be able to increase the power of our batteries, or invent new instruments which shall a thousandfold surpass in energy those which we at present possess? . . .

22

ooooooooooo

ELECTROMAGNETIC
THEORY

ooooooooooo

James Clerk Maxwell (1831-1879)

As we noted in the commentary preceding the paper on molecular velocities, Maxwell's pioneering contribution to atomic theory is to be found also in his electromagnetic theory of light. Although Maxwell did not present his discovery as a contribution to the theory of atomic structure (the nature of the atom was hardly known at the time) we now know that without Maxwell's theory, we could hardly understand how the atom absorbs and emits radiation.

During the two hundred years or more from the time of Newton to the beginning of the twentieth century, the science of physics developed very unevenly, with most of the emphasis in the seventeenth, eighteenth, and nineteenth centuries on mechanics. Comparatively little was done in optics, and in electricity and magnetism—avenues that were to lead eventually to the inner world of the atom. This was quite natural, since Newton had already laid down the fundamental principles of mechanics, and it remained for the great mathematicians and theoretical physicists of those centuries to put these principles into the most elegant forms possible. Moreover, the rapid development of celestial mechanics, following Newton's discovery of the law of gravity, attracted the outstanding mathematicians of that period—Laplace, Euler, Lagrange, Gauss, and others. Classical mechanics was particularly appealing to mathematicians because it offered a closed, completely self-contained rational system that could be developed axiomatically. The historical culmination of this remarkable development is contained in the equations of Hamilton, and, finally, in the famous Hamilton-Jacobi differential equation. Optics, electricity, and

329

magnetism were laggards in this period because of the lack of a single fundamental principle, around which to develop a complete system.

Maxwell was to change this state of affairs. In his day, as now, the laws of mechanics could be checked by reference to the motions of ordinary bodies. But the behavior of light was difficult to analyze without very special equipment, and electricity and magnetism appeared to be mysterious phenomena that were unrelated to any other observable events.

Various optical theories had already been introduced, and, in time, as more and more optical data were collected, the wave theory, as first propounded by Huygens, became generally adopted. This was primarily due to the work of Young and Fresnel, who discovered the interference and diffraction of light, and explained these phenomena by using the wave theory. The acceptance of the theory that light travels as a wave was followed by a period of mathematical development; this, in turn, produced the equations that describe the propagation of a beam of light in practically the form in which they are still used today. Before Maxwell's discovery, these equations were used even though the nature of light itself was unknown; one simply assumed that some disturbance was propagated from point to point in a medium in the form of a wave; then one could apply all the mathematical techniques of wave motion. In this way most of the problems of refraction, diffraction, and interference were analyzed and explained. Although this was satisfactory from the point of view of the description of optical phenomena, physicists were not entirely satisfied with it because it had nothing to say about the nature of light itself. But this ultimate goal could not be reached until more was known about electricity and magnetism.

Although electricity and magnetism as separate phenomena were known to the ancient Greeks, Hans Christian Oersted, in 1820, first discovered that there is a relationship between them. As almost everyone now knows, he found that a wire carrying current is surrounded by a magnetic field and therefore deflects a compass needle placed near it. This discovery opened the door to the rapid experimental development that culminated in the discovery by Michael Faraday in England and by Joseph Henry in the United States that electricity and magnetism are reciprocal phenomena in the sense that, under appropriate conditions, each of them can induce the other. These two investigators found that if a conductor (a copper wire, for example) is moved through a magnetic field, an electric current is induced in the wire. As these induction phenomena were studied and their laws more clearly understood, a fairly complete mathematical formulation of fundamental electromagnetic principles was developed. But just as in the case of optics, the mathematics served only to describe the gross behavior of the electric and magnetic fields. The nature of electricity and magnetism was not yet understood.

Concurrent with studies of the relationship between magnetism and electricity, a great deal of research was done in electrostatics. With Charles Coulomb's discovery of the law of interaction between electric charges (mathematically similar to Newton's law), it was possible to develop the mathematical theory of static electricity. It became possible, also, to analyze the motion of conductors carrying currents and the mechanical interactions between such conductors. However, the relationship between electric charges and the behavior of an electromagnetic field was not clearly understood. In fact, all electric and magnetic phenomena were explained by the action, at a distance, of charges on each other. Since the concept of action at a distance dominated pre-Maxwellian physics, we shall consider its significance for a moment. Two electric charges (or two masses, or two magnets) do not have to be in direct contact to affect each other. Each charge induces an acceleration in the other even though the two charges may be quite far apart. This phenomenon, which has a certain mysterious quality about it if it is viewed merely as one charge exerting a force on the other without anything between them, is called "action at a distance."

At this point in the development of the theories of electricity, magnetism, and optics, James Clerk Maxwell, now viewed as the dominant figure of nineteenth-century physics, came upon the scene. During the course of his life, as described earlier, he provided the basis for modern electromagnetic theory. As Maxwell points out in the excerpt that follows this commentary, all the theories on electromagnetic phenomena that had been developed up to the time of his own work assumed "the existence of something either at rest or in motion in each body, constituting its electric or magnetic state, and capable of acting at a distance according to mathematical laws." On the basis of this assumption, theories about the electromagnetic interactions of these bodies were developed. Maxwell concludes his description of contemporary nineteenth-century thinking with the following observation:

> In these theories the force acting between the two bodies is treated with reference only to the condition of the bodies and their relative positions, and without any express consideration of the surrounding medium.

What is crucial in this sentence is the reference to the surrounding medium.

Maxwell did not reject the hypothesis that charged particles inside bodies are the carriers of electricity and magnetism. He denied only that a theory could be successful if it disregarded the interaction of the charged bodies with the surrounding medium. The most successful of such theories that had been developed up to that time, by Weber and Neumann, held that the force acting at a distance between two bodies must depend not only on their positions, but also on their relative velocity. Maxwell therefore rejected this theory because it led to mechanical difficulties which made it undesirable as an ultimate theory.

In the excerpt, Maxwell then outlines his plan of attack. His emphasis, he says, is to be on the surrounding medium:

> I have therefore preferred to seek an explanation of facts in another direction, by supposing them produced by actions which go in on the surrounding medium as well as in the excited bodies, and endeavoring to explain the action between distant bodies without assuming the existence of forces capable of acting directly at sensible distances.

He then goes on to say

> The theory I propose may therefore be called a theory of the *Electromagnetic Field* because it has to do with the space in the neighborhood of the electric or magnetic bodies, and it may be called a *Dynamical Theory*, because it assumes that in that space there is matter in motion, by which the observed electromagnetic phenomena are produced.
>
> The electromagnetic field is that part of space which contains and surrounds bodies in electric or magnetic conditions.

The great departure from previous developments taken by Maxwell lies in the manner in which he introduces the electromagnetic field. Previously, physicists had considered space as empty, and spoke of lines or tubes of force between charged particles as mere mathematical fictions. Maxwell, however, imparts a reality to the electromagnetic field that goes far beyond a mere mathematical convenience. This is one of those giant steps in science that herald a revolution in scientific thinking and mark the emergence of a great genius. Atomic theory could not have matured without Maxwell's contribution. The concept of the electromagnetic field has changed our entire way of looking at physical phenomena and has been of decisive importance in the development of the general theory of relativity, quantum electrodynamics, and the physics of elementary particles.

Interestingly enough, Maxwell thought it necessary to introduce a real ether or an ethereal substance as the carrier of his electromagnetic field. He believed that the "aethereal medium filling space and permeating bodies" was capable of motion and could transmit this motion to material bodies. He even believed that this ether had a small but finite density and that the energy of the electromagnetic field that was communicated to material bodies (in the form of the heat and motion of these bodies) was stored in the ether as potential energy or was present there in the form of the motion of the ethereal particles.

Although we know now that it is not necessary to introduce an ether in order to understand the propagation of light through empty space, Maxwell and the other physicists of his period thought that some kind of medium *was* necessary for the propagation of waves. According to Maxwell, the ether behaved like an elastic medium, which was capable of "receiving and storing up two kinds of energy, namely, the 'actual' energy, depending on the motion of its parts, and 'potential' energy, consisting of the work which the medium will do in recovering from its displacement in virtue of its elasticity." According to this picture the propagation of waves occurred because there was a continuous alternate transformation from one of these forms of energy to the other just as in a swinging pendulum or in a vibrating spring.

Starting from this idea of the ether as an elastic medium through which waves can be propagated according to the usual theories of wave motion, Maxwell set out to find the wave equation that governs the motion of electromagnetic waves. From his idea that there is a continual oscillation of energy in the ether, he was convinced that the electromagnetic field moves about as a kind of undulatory phenomenon. Maxwell then proceeded to derive the equations that describe this wave phenomenon in terms of the electromagnetic field quantities at a point such as the electric field strength and the magnetic field strength at that point. To do this, he analyzed the available experimental data related to the magnetic interaction of current-carrying conductors and to the induction of an electromotive force in a conductor, when the conductor cuts across the lines of force of a magnetic field.

The laws governing the interaction of the magnetic fields surrounding two conductors were well known at the time of Maxwell. They had been formulated mathematically by André Ampère. Moreover, the laws of electromagnetic induction, as discovered by Faraday, were also well known. These laws had also been expressed in mathematical form, although no one had yet been able to write down a single set of equations that could describe the behavior of the electromagnetic field as an entity consisting of an electric part and a magnetic part. There was no mathematical treatment that described the relationship in which each could be induced by the other and that could properly account for the oscillation of the energy in the electromagnetic field. In surveying what had been done previously, Maxwell was quick to see why previous attempts to obtain a unified theory of the electromagnetic field had been futile. The difficulty lay in the manner in which the electric current was treated.

Up to that time the current induced by an electromagnetic field had always been associated with a conductor. Maxwell's great contribution, and the one innovation that made possible his electromagnetic equations, was his idea of the displacement current, which he considered the natural extension of the current in a conductor. He arrived at his idea by considering what happens to a dielectric (or nonconductor) in the electromagnetic field.

In the ensuing paper, Maxwell notes that under the action of an electromotive force the dielectric undergoes a change of state because energy is stored in it. This is what is ordinarily called the polarization of the dielectric. It may be pictured as a kind of elastic strain, resulting from the stress imposed on it by the electromagnetic field. This strain, or polarization, is due to the displacement of the charged particles in the molecules of the dielectric. But, as Maxwell writes, this displacement in itself is not a current, but, as he states, "the commencement of a current." The next step in his analysis was to show that this idea of a displacement must be introduced even when no material dielectric is present, as in the region between two condenser plates carrying a time-varying charge.

To comprehend this more clearly, consider the empty space between two condenser plates that carry a charge. As long as the charge is constant, there is a constant electric field between the two plates with the lines of force of the field at right angles to the plates. Now suppose that the two plates are connected by a conductor, so that the negative charge on one of the plates can flow through the conductor to the other plate. While this is happening, a current flows through the conductor. The conductor is surrounded by a magnetic field in accordance with Oersted's discovery. What is happening in the space between the two plates while the current is flowing in the conductor? The answer is that the strength of the electric field is changing. It is, in fact, getting smaller. In analogy with what would happen to a dielectric if it were in the space between the two plates, Maxwell introduced the idea that there is a kind of current flowing between the two condenser plates while the current is flowing in the conductor. In other words, the space between the plates is to be treated as a kind of dielectric that is undergoing a change in its state of polarization, and hence, as a natural extension of the conductor. Maxwell calls this changing electric field between the condenser plates a displacement current and states that it is measured by the rate at which the electric field is changing.

It is true that this displacement current is not a current in the same sense as is a flow of charged particles inside a current-carrying conductor. But it exhibits all the mathematical properties of a current and behaves like the natural extension of the current in the conductor. With his innovation, Maxwell was able to write down a set of equations for the electromagnetic field in which the electric field and the magnetic field enter in a symmetrical way. From these equations he derived a single wave equation that describes the way any electromagnetic field is propagated.

From this equation he then derived two more very important results that led to the identification of his theory with the electromagnetic theory of light. First, his equations demonstrate that the speed of propagation of the electromagnetic field is exactly equal to the speed of light. He showed also that the propagated electromagnetic disturbance is at right angles (transverse) to the direction of propagation. In Maxwell's words "This velocity is so nearly that of light, that it seems we have strong reason to conclude that light itself [including radiant heat, and other radiations, if any] is an electromagnetic disturbance in the form of waves propagated through the electromagnetic field according to electromagnetic laws." Second, Maxwell's equations demonstrate that the square of the refractive index of a medium is "equal to the product of the specific dielectric capacity and the specific magnetic capacity." These two results together show clearly the relationship of light to the electromagnetic field. Later, Heinrich Hertz demonstrated that Maxwell's electromagnetic theory of light can be verified experimentally.

We close this discussion by noting briefly how the idea of the displacement current leads quite naturally to the propagation of the electromagnetic field. If we consider the varying field between the condenser plates as constituting a current, then this current must be surrounded by a magnetic field. But since this displacement current changes with time, the magnetic field surrounding it is also changing. It, in turn, is therefore linked to an electric field, and so on. In other words, as the condenser is discharged, a chain of electric and magnetic fields is set up extending out into space. But the current flowing from one condenser plate to the other does not stop even after the entire charge has flowed from one plate to the other, because of the inertia of the charge. Instead, the current oscillates back and forth and thus gives rise to an oscillating electromagnetic field that breaks away from the condenser and moves off into space.

Although we have described Maxwell's discovery in terms of the field between the plates of a condenser, his results are completely general and apply to electromagnetic fields everywhere: a varying electric field must be accompanied by a magnetic field, and such a combination of an oscillating electric and an oscillating magnetic field (called an "electromagnetic field") must move through space at the speed of light. In a vacuum, the direction of oscillation of the magnetic field and the direction of propagation of the two fields are mutually perpendicular to each other.

০০০০০০০

MAXWELL

A Dynamical Theory of the Electromagnetic Field [1]

. . . THE FIRST STEP, THEREFORE, IN reducing these phenomena into scientific form, is to ascertain the magnitude and direction of the force acting between the bodies, and when it is found that this force depends in a certain way upon the relative position of the bodies and on their electric or magnetic condition, it seems at first sight natural to explain the facts by assuming the existence of something either at rest or in motion in each body, constituting its electric or magnetic state, and capable of acting at a distance according to mathematical laws.

In this way mathematical theories of statical electricity, of magnetism, of the mechanical action between conductors carrying currents, and of the induction of currents have been formed. In these theories the force acting between the two bodies is treated with reference only to the condition of the bodies and their relative position, and without any express consideration of the surrounding medium.

These theories assume, more or less explicitly, the existence of substances the particles of which have the property of acting on one another at a distance by attraction or repulsion. The most complete development of a theory of this kind is that of M. W. Weber, who has made the same theory include electrostatic and electromagnetic phenomena.

In doing so, however, he has found it necessary to assume that the force between two electric particles depends on their relative velocity, as well as on their distance.

This theory, as developed by MM. W. Weber and C. Neumann, is exceedingly ingenious, and wonderfully comprehensive in its application to the phenomena of statical electricity, electromagnetic attractions, induction of currents and diamagnetic phenomena; and it comes to us with the more authority, as it has served to guide the speculations of one who has made so great an advance in the practical part of electric science, both by introducing a consistent system of units in electrical measurement, and by

---

[1] James Clerk Maxwell, *Philosophical Transactions,* 155 (1865), 459–512.

actually determining electrical quantities with an accuracy hitherto unknown.

(2) The mechanical difficulties, however, which are involved in the assumption of particles acting at a distance with forces which depend on their velocities are such as to prevent me from considering this theory as an ultimate one, though it may have been, and may yet be useful in leading to the coordination of phenomena.

I have therefore preferred to seek an explanation of the facts in another direction, by supposing them to be produced by actions which go on in the surrounding medium as well as in the excited bodies, and endeavouring to explain the action between distant bodies without assuming the existence of forces capable of acting directly at sensible distances.

(3) The theory I propose may therefore be called a theory of the *Electromagnetic Field,* because it has to do with the space in the neighbourhood of the electric or magnetic bodies, and it may be called a *Dynamical* Theory, because it assumes that in that space there is matter in motion, by which the observed electromagnetic phenomena are produced.

(4) The electromagnetic field is that part of space which contains and surrounds bodies in electric or magnetic conditions.

It may be filled with any kind of matter, or we may endeavour to render it empty of all gross matter, as in the case of Geissler's tubes and other so-called vacua.

There is always, however, enough of matter left to receive and transmit the undulations of light and heat, and it is because the transmission of these radiations is not greatly altered when transparent bodies of measurable density are substituted for the so-called vacuum, that we are obliged to admit that the undulations are those of an aethereal substance, and not of the gross matter, the presence of which merely modifies in some way the motion of the aether.

We have therefore some reason to believe, from the phenomena of light and heat, that there is an aethereal medium filling space and permeating bodies, capable of being set in motion and of transmitting that motion from one part to another, and of communicating that motion to gross matter so as to heat it and affect it in various ways.

(5) Now the energy communicated to the body in heating it must have formerly existed in the moving medium, for the undulations had left the source of heat some time before they reached the body, and during that time the energy must have been half in the form of motion of the medium and half in the form of elastic resilience. From these considerations Professor W. Thomson has argued, that the medium must have a density capable of comparison with that of gross matter, and has even assigned an inferior limit to that density.

(6) We may therefore receive, as a datum derived from a branch of

science independent of that with which we have to deal, the existence of a pervading medium, of small but real density, capable of being set in motion, and of transmitting motion from one part to another with great, but not infinite, velocity.

Hence the parts of this medium must be so connected that the motion of one part depends in some way on the motion of the rest; and at the same time these connexions must be capable of a certain kind of elastic yielding, since the communication of motion is not instantaneous, but occupies time.

The medium is therefore capable of receiving and storing up two kinds of energy, namely, the "actual" energy depending on the motion of its parts, and "potential" energy, consisting of the work which the medium will do in recovering from displacement in virtue of its elasticity.

The propagation of undulations consists in the continual transformation of one of these forms of energy into the other alternately, and at any instant the amount of energy in the whole medium is equally divided, so that half is energy of motion, and half is elastic resilience.

(7) A medium having such a constitution may be capable of other kinds of motion and displacement than those which produce the phenomena of light and heat, and some of these may be of such a kind that they may be evidenced to our senses by the phenomena they produce.

(8) Now we know that the luminiferous medium is in certain cases acted on by magnetism; for Faraday discovered that when a plane polarized ray traverses a transparent diamagnetic medium in the direction of the lines of magnetic force produced by magnets or currents in the neighbourhood, the plane of polarization is caused to rotate.

This rotation is always in the direction in which positive electricity must be carried round the diamagnetic body in order to produce the actual magnetization of the field.

M. Verdet has since discovered that if a paramagnetic body, such as solution of perchloride of iron in ether, be substituted for the diamagnetic body, the rotation is in the opposite direction.

Now Professor W. Thomson has pointed out that no distribution of forces acting between the parts of a medium whose only motion is that of the luminous vibrations, is sufficient to account for the phenomena, but that we must admit the existence of a motion in the medium depending on the magnetization, in addition to the vibratory motion which constitutes light.

It is true that the rotation by magnetism of the plane of polarization has been observed only in media of considerable density; but the properties of the magnetic field are not so much altered by the substitution of one medium for another, or for a vacuum, as to allow us to suppose that the dense medium does anything more than merely modify the motion of the ether.

We have therefore warrantable grounds for inquiring whether there may not be a motion of the aetheral medium going on whenever magnetic effects are observed, and we have some reason to suppose that this motion is one of rotation, having the direction of the magnetic force as its axis.

(9) We may now consider another phenomenon observed in the electromagnetic field. When a body is moved across the lines of magnetic force it experiences what is called an electromotive force; the two extremities of the body tend to become oppositely electrified, and an electric current tends to flow through the body. When the electromotive force is sufficiently powerful, and is made to act on certain compound bodies, it decomposes them, and causes one of their components to pass towards one extremity of the body, and the other in the opposite direction.

Here we have evidence of a force causing an electric current in spite of resistance; electrifying the extremities of a body in opposite ways, a condition which is sustained only by the action of the electromotive force, and which, as soon as that force is removed, tends, with an equal and opposite force, to produce a counter current through the body and to restore the original electrical state of the body; and finally, if strong enough, tearing to pieces chemical compounds and carrying their components in opposite directions, while their natural tendency is to combine, and to combine with a force which can generate an electromotive force in the reverse direction.

This, then, is a force acting on a body caused by its motion through the electromagnetic field, or by changes occurring in that field itself; and the effect of the force is either to produce a current and heat the body, or to decompose the body, or, when it can do neither, to put the body in a state of electric polarization,—a state of constraint in which opposite extremities are oppositely electrified, and from which the body tends to relieve itself as soon as the disturbing force is removed.

(10) According to the theory which I propose to explain, this "electromotive force" is the force called into play during the communication of motion from one part of the medium to another, and it is by means of this force that the motion of one part causes motion in another part. When electromotive force acts on a conducting circuit, it produces a current, which, as it meets with resistance, occasions a continual transformation of electrical energy into heat, which is incapable of being restored again to the form of electrical energy by any reversal of the process.

(11) But when electromotive force acts on a dielectric it produces a state of polarization of its parts similar in distribution to the polarity of the parts of a mass of iron under the influence of a magnet, and like the magnetic polarization, capable of being described as a state in which every particle has its opposite poles in opposite conditions.

In a dielectric under the action of electromotive force, we may conceive that the electricity in each molecule is so displaced that one side is rendered positively and the other negatively electrical, but that the electricity remains entirely connected with the molecule, and does not pass from one molecule to another. The effect of this action on the whole dielectric mass is to produce a general displacement of electricity in a certain direction. This displacement does not amount to a current, because when it has attained to a certain value it remains constant, but it is the commencement of a current, and its variations constitute currents in the positive or the negative direction according as the displacement is increasing or decreasing. In the interior of the dielectric there is no indication of electrification, because the electrification of the surface of any molecule is neutralized by the opposite electrification of the surface of the molecules in contact with it; but at the bounding surface of the dielectric, where the electrification is not neutralized, we find the phenomena which indicate positive or negative electrification.

The relation between the electromotive force and the amount of electric displacement it produces depends on the nature of the dielectric, the same electromotive force producing generally a greater electric displacement in solid dielectrics, such as glass or sulphur, than in air.

(12) Here, then, we perceive another effect of electromotive force, namely, electric displacement, which according to our theory is a kind of elastic yielding to the action of the force, similar to that which takes place in structures and machines owing to the want of perfect rigidity of the connexions.

(13) The practical investigation of the inductive capacity of dielectrics is rendered difficult on account of two disturbing phenomena. The first is the conductivity of the dielectric, which, though in many cases exceedingly small, is not altogether insensible. The second is the phenomenon called electric absorption, in virtue of which, when the dielectric is exposed to electromotive force, the electric displacement gradually increases, and when the electromotive force is removed, the dielectric does not instantly return to its primitive state, but only discharges a portion of its electrification, and when left to itself gradually acquires electrification on its surface, as the interior gradually becomes depolarized. Almost all solid dielectrics exhibit this phenomenon, which gives rise to the residual charge in the Leyden jar, and to several phenomena of electric cables described by Mr. F. Jenkin.

(14) We have here two other kinds of yielding besides the yielding of the perfect dielectric, which we have compared to a perfectly elastic body. The yielding due to conductivity may be compared to that of a viscous fluid (that is to say, a fluid having great internal friction), or a soft solid on which the smallest force produces a permanent alteration of figure increasing with the time during which the force acts. The yielding due to electric

absorption may be compared to that of a cellular elastic body containing a thick fluid in its cavities. Such a body, when subjected to pressure, is compressed by degrees on account of the gradual yielding of the thick fluid; and when the pressure is removed it does not at once recover its figure, because the elasticity of the substance of the body has gradually to overcome the tenacity of the fluid before it can regain complete equilibrium.

Several solid bodies in which no such structure as we have supposed can be found, seem to possess a mechanical property of this kind; and it seems probable that the same substances, if dielectrics, may possess the analogous electrical property, and if magnetic, may have corresponding properties relating to the acquisition, retention, and loss of magnetic polarity.

(15) It appears therefore that certain phenomena in electricity and magnetism lead to the same conclusion as those of optics, namely, that there is an aethereal medium pervading all bodies, and modified only in degree by their presence; that the parts of this medium are capable of being set in motion by electric currents and magnets; that this motion is communicated from one part of the medium to another by forces arising from the connexions of those parts; that under the action of these forces there is a certain yielding depending on the elasticity of these connexions; and that therefore energy in two different forms may exist in the medium, the one form being the actual energy of motion of its parts, and the other being the potential energy stored up in the connexions, in virtue of their elasticity.

(16) Thus, then, we are led to the conception of a complicated mechanism capable of a vast variety of motion, but at the same time so connected that the motion of one part depends, according to definite relations, on the motion of other parts, these motions being communicated by forces arising from the relative displacement of the connected parts, in virtue of their elasticity. Such a mechanism must be subject to the general laws of Dynamics, and we ought to be able to work out all the consequences of its motion, provided we know the form of the relation between the motions of the parts.

(17) We know that when an electric current is established in a conducting circuit, the neighbouring part of the field is characterized by certain magnetic properties, and that if two circuits are in the field, the magnetic properties of the field due to the two currents are combined. Thus each part of the field is in connexion with both currents, and the two currents are put in connexion with each other in virtue of their connexion with the magnetization of the field. The first result of this connexion that I propose to examine, is the induction of one current by another, and by the motion of conductors in the field.

The second result, which is deduced from this, is the mechanical action between conductors carrying currents. The phenomenon of the induction of currents has been deduced from their mechanical action by Helmholtz and Thomson. I have followed the reverse order, and deduced the mechanical action from the laws of induction. I have then described experimental methods of determining the quantities L, M, N, on which these phenomena depend.

(18) I then apply the phenomena of induction and attraction of currents to the exploration of the electromagnetic field, and the laying down systems of lines of magnetic force which indicate its magnetic properties. By exploring the same field with a magnet, I shew the distribution of its equipotential magnetic surfaces, cutting the lines of force at right angles.

In order to bring these results within the power of symbolical calculation, I then express them in the form of the General Equations of the Electromagnetic Field. These equations express—

(A) The relation between electric displacement, true conduction, and the total current, compounded of both.

(B) The relation between the lines of magnetic force and the inductive coefficients of a circuit, as already deduced from the laws of induction.

(C) The relation between the strength of a current and its magnetic effects, according to the electromagnetic system of measurement.

(D) The value of the electromotive force in a body, as arising from the motion of the body in the field, the alteration of the field itself, and the variation of electric potential from one part of the field to another.

(E) The relation between electric displacement, and the electromotive force which produces it.

(F) The relation between an electric current, and the electromotive force which produces it.

(G) The relation between the amount of free electricity at any point, and the electric displacements in the neighbourhood.

(H) The relation between the increase or diminution of free electricity and the electric currents in the neighbourhood.

There are twenty of these equations in all, involving twenty variable quantities.

(19) I then express in terms of these quantities the intrinsic energy of the Electromagnetic Field as depending partly on its magnetic and partly on its electric polarization at every point.

From this I determine the mechanical force acting, 1st, on a moveable conductor carrying an electric current; 2ndly, on a magnetic pole; 3rdly, on an electrified body.

The last result, namely, the mechanical force acting on an electrified body, gives rise to an independent method of electrical measurement founded on its electrostatic effects. The relation between the units employed in the two methods is shewn to depend on what I have called the "electric elasticity" of the medium, and to be a velocity, which has been experimentally determined by MM. Weber and Kohlrausch.

I then shew how to calculate the electrostatic capacity of a condenser, and the specific inductive capacity of a dielectric.

The case of a condenser composed of parallel layers of substances of different electric resistances and inductive capacities is next examined, and it is shewn that the phenomenon called electric absorption will generally occur, that is, the condenser, when suddenly discharged, will after a short time shew signs of a *residual* charge.

(20) The general equations are next applied to the case of a magnetic disturbance propagated through a non-conducting field, and it is shewn that the only disturbances which can be so propagated are those which are transverse to the direction of propagation, and that the velocity of propagation is the velocity v, found from experiments such as those of Weber, which expresses the number of electrostatic units of electricity which are contained in one electromagnetic unit.

This velocity is so nearly that of light, that it seems we have strong reason to conclude that light itself (including radiant heat, and other radiations if any) is an electromagnetic disturbance in the form of waves propagated through the electromagnetic field according to electromagnetic laws. If so, the agreement between the elasticity of the medium as calculated from the rapid alternations of luminous vibrations, and as found by the slow processes of electrical experiments, shews how perfect and regular the elastic properties of the medium must be when not encumbered with any matter denser than air. If the same character of the elasticity is retained in dense transparent bodies, it appears that the square of the index of refraction is equal to the product of the specific dielectric capacity and the specific magnetic capacity. Conducting media are shewn to absorb such radiations rapidly, and therefore to be generally opaque.

The conception of the propagation of transverse magnetic disturbances to the exclusion of normal ones is distinctly set forth by Professor Faraday in his "Thoughts on Ray Vibrations." The electromagnetic theory of light, as proposed by him, is the same in substance as that which I have begun to develope in this paper, except that in 1846 there were no data to calculate the velocity of propagation. . . .

23

○○○○○○○○○○

CATHODE RAYS—
A "FOURTH STATE
OF MATTER"

○○○○○○○○○○○

William Crookes (1832-1919)

The discovery of electromagnetic induction by Faraday in 1831 quickly led to successful attempts to use the phenomenon in technical applications. Thus, one outgrowth was the development of the spark coil, which consisted of a "primary" coil energized by a battery through an interrupter together with a separate secondary coil wound around the primary but insulated from it. The high voltage generated between the terminals of the secondary coil was often used for the production of a continuous spark discharge. At first these discharges were examined in air, but the first experiment on the discharge produced at low pressure in a glass envelope seems to have been made by a rather obscure French investigator named Masson in 1853. The spark discharge in air, which is an unsteady and noisy phenomenon, at reduced pressure becomes a quiet, soft glow that completely fills the discharge tube.

The study of the low-pressure discharge became popularized through the intricate tubes made by Heinrich Geissler, an accomplished glass blower and technical assistant of Prof. Julius Plücker at the University of Tübingen. Geissler's name soon became applied to all small discharge tubes used for spectroscopic or demonstration purposes and Geissler tubes were long used as an impressive scientific demonstration for beginners or in popular lectures bearing on electrical science.

Plücker, however, became interested in the phenomena that occur in the gas discharge as the pressure in the tube is progressively lowered. At

344

sufficiently low pressures, he found evidence for the appearance of a beam of radiation emanating from the cathode or negative pole of the tube, striking the glass walls and producing a greenish phosphorescence. Plücker is thus generally credited as the discoverer of what has come to be known as "cathode rays." The study of these rays was destined to produce results of the greatest importance to the development of physics, namely, the discovery of X-rays by Roentgen, and from the investigations of J. J. Thomson, the discovery of the electron. These future developments opened the doors to the wholly unsuspected world of particles smaller than atoms, of highly penetrating radiations, and to the quantum nature of radiation.

Such prospects were by no means apparent in the early days of the discovery. Cathode rays were difficult to observe because it was difficult to produce the low pressures necessary to study them. The nature of the radiation was obscure since no information on the fundamental (particle) nature of electricity existed. After Plücker's original paper, other researches were carried out by Hittorf and Goldstein. Perhaps the most important results achieved before 1878 were the demonstration that the unknown rays were emitted approximately at right angles to the cathode surface, that they traveled in straight lines away from the cathode after emission, and that they did not behave in the same manner as light, i.e., the rays emitted normal to the cathode surface did not cross. Thus a small object placed near an extended plane cathode was found to produce a shadow. Had the cathode surface been a light source, the rays from each point on the surface would have been emitted in all directions and the outer portions of the light-emitting surface would have produced rays crossing beyond the small object, thus eliminating any shadow on a more distant screen.

This was the situation when Sir William Crookes began his cathode-ray researches, which were reported in his famous paper "On the Illumination of Lines of Electrical Pressure and the Trajectory of Molecules" published in the *Philosophical Transactions* in 1879. This paper shows Crookes's genius for getting to the heart of a physical puzzle by very direct methods and his flair for clear-headed analysis of what was then a shadowy, amorphous, and ill-defined problem. His results were definitive, and they formed a solid base on which Thomson was able to proceed to one of the great discoveries of physics, the isolation of the electron.

But Crookes's reputation was not established by his paper on cathode rays. He had already established his position in science through his discovery by spectroscopic methods of the element thallium in 1861 at the age of twenty-nine. At that time he was already a free-lance scientist, inventor, and editor of a weekly journal, *Chemical News,* which he founded in 1859 and carried on until his death in 1919. He had the rare ability of organizing his work so that he could be effective in invention, editing, business affairs, and pure research at the same time. Personally, he was confident, optimistic, and even-tempered, devoted in his family life and considerate in his relations with others. In company he did not push himself, and he tended to be retiring, so that, as Sir Oliver Lodge remarked, his personality was not especially impressive. Photographs taken in his maturity suggest an unusually active and inquiring mind; the eye is particularly drawn to his long waxed mustache—a manifestation of an inner flamboyance uncommon among his fellow English scientists.

Like most scientists, Crookes did not come from a scientific background. His father, Joseph, was a London tailor whose Regent Street shop prospered enough to support, in turn, two wives and no less than twenty-one children. Five of these were by his first marriage and sixteen by his second to a Northamptonshire woman, Mary Scott. William, the first child of this second marriage, was born June 17, 1832. While the home life of this large family appears to have been happy, young Crookes's intellectual stimulation seems to have come from his uncle, who conducted a thriving bookshop next door. Of these formative years, Crookes tells us:

> From my earliest recollections I was always trying experiments and reading any book of science I could find. A little older, I fitted up a cupboard as a sort of laboratory and caused much annoyance and trouble in the house by generating smells and destroying furniture. I don't suppose any of my family even knew the meaning of the word "science."

In spite of unsettled economic conditions in England in the late 1830's and early 1840's, there was a growing feeling that technical education must be fostered to improve the industrial growth of the country. This conviction led to the founding in 1845 of the Royal College of Chemistry in London. Although Crookes's early schooling had been irregular, he entered the college in 1848 at the age of sixteen and did well enough to earn a scholarship for the following year. In 1850 he was appointed junior assistant to the youthful and inspiring August Wilhelm Hofmann, who had been brought from Germany as professor of chemistry. At the end of the year, Crookes published his first paper, "On the Selenocyanides," an investigation marked by an unusual maturity in method, content, and style. He continued at the college until 1854, interesting himself in photography and the infant science of spectroscopy. During this period he also took time to attend Faraday's lectures at the Royal Institution and to acquire from them an enthusiasm for physics.

It is interesting to see how his original research in selenium compounds, when he was only nineteen, started a long chain of connected investigations that occupied most of his efforts in pure research. Thus, while examining the optical spectrum of impure selenium in 1861, he was struck by the presence of a bright green line which, on investigation, proved to stem from an impurity in the metal. He very quickly showed that it originated in a previously unknown chemical element; wishing to indicate its "green" origin, he dubbed it thallium, from the Greek *thallus,* a budding twig.

This research secured his position in the scientific world and his election to the Royal Society in 1863. About ten years later, he returned to the thallium research in an attempt to carry out an accurate determination of the atomic weight of the element. In doing so, his attention was directed to some puzzling discrepancies that appeared in the weighings. With customary thoroughness, Crookes found that these discrepancies originated in conditions affecting the scale—the air pressure in the enclosed balance and the heat radiation in the case. The disturbance was maximal at air pressures intermediate between the highest and lowest at which the weighings were conducted. A separate investigation of the relation between air pressure and heat radiation on an experimental enclosed vane led to the development of the radiometer, an instrument whose appearance caused a sensation in England and on the Continent. The radiometer, often seen in opticians' and jewelers' display windows, consists of a set of thin vanes mounted on spokes so as to form a mill rotating about a vertical axis. The vanes of the mill are blackened on one side and silvered on the other. When this assembly is mounted inside a partially evacuated glass bulb and is exposed to sunlight the vanes will rotate in a direction away from the black surface. For this work Crookes was awarded the Royal Society's Royal Medal in 1875, although it was not until a year later that the action of the radiometer was understood, when Sir Arthur Schuster at Manchester showed it to be a consequence of the free path of the molecules of the residual gas in the enclosure.

As a next step, Crookes conducted experiments with the radiometer vanes electrically charged. These experiments then led him to the use of cathode rays and to the research that is the subject of this sketch. The work was reported to the Royal Society on November 30, 1878. He was then forty-six years old. These experiments represent the zenith of his scientific work and form the basis for his Bakerian lecture early in the following year. This lecture called the attention of the scientific world to the electrified-particle nature of the cathode rays.

Crookes's work did much to set what came to be called the "British" point of view on the rays. In discussing his experiments he speaks very often of "projected molecules." He points out, on the basis of the newly developed kinetic theory, that in these experiments the trajectories are those of single particles. In concluding the lecture he ventures a sweeping prophecy from vistas only glimpsed in the investigations—that "the phenomena in these exhausted tubes reveal to physical science a new world." He could not possibly have guessed how right his judgment would turn out to be.

Seventeen years later, Roentgen discovered X-rays emanating from the simplest kind of "Crookes" tube, as the highly evacuated cathode ray discharge tube came to be known. How was it, then, that Crookes, with his keen eye and passion for thorough investigation, missed one of the great discoveries that presaged twentieth-century physics? Had he no clues? If we may believe a long-standing rumor, the answer seems to have been in the affirmative. It was simply that Crookes had complained to the Ilford Company from time to time during his experimentation with cathode rays that batches of photographic plates sold to him were defective because on development they proved to be fogged. This is just the effect X-rays from the discharge tubes would have had on plates kept in drawers nearby! Whether the rumor is true or only a calumny we do not know, for Crookes never alluded publicly to any such phenomenon.

Following his cathode ray investigations, Crookes returned to the study of the physical properties of gases. He showed by a precise experiment that Maxwell's kinetic theory prediction—that gas viscosity is independent of the pressure over a very wide range—was completely valid.

No one who has engaged in physical research, and understands all its frustrations and disappointments, could end the catalogue of these elegant investigations without a tribute to Crookes's assistant, Charles H. Gimingham. It was Gimingham's superb skill and devotion that contributed much to the success of Crookes's work during those exciting years. For his researches Crookes was awarded almost all the scientific honors that his native country could bestow: the Davy medal of the Royal Society, 1888; presidency of the Institution of Electrical Engineers, 1890; a knighthood in 1897; presidency of the British Association for the Advancement of Science, 1898; the Copley medal of the Royal Society, 1904; an honorary degree from Cambridge University in 1908; the Order of Merit from King Edward VII in 1910; and, finally, the presidency of the Royal Society, 1913–1915.

In this brief biography nothing has been said of Crookes's interest in psychic phenomena and spiritualism. It happened in 1867, early in Crookes's career, that a younger brother Philip, to whom he was especially devoted, died as a result of yellow fever contracted in Havana. A fellow member of the Royal Society, who later became a well-known communications electrical engineer, Cromwell F. Varley, persuaded Crookes to try to communicate with his dead brother by spiritualist methods. In this way Crookes was introduced to beliefs that he held throughout his life and to phenomena that he tried to make understandable and to rationalize scientifically. He also made efforts to interest others in these phenomena as well as effects produced by various mediums, including the celebrated Daniel Home. The result of this activity was to arouse a storm of criticism and ridicule and eventually the active enmity of some influential members of the scientific community. By 1874 Crookes came to realize the hopelessness of bringing open-minded scientific opinion to spiritualist investigations and, as well, the threat they posed to his career. He therefore dropped these activities, although it is clear that he never abandoned his beliefs. Almost a quarter of a century later, in 1896, he accepted the presidency of the Society for Psychical Research and in the following year, on becoming president of the British Association for the Advancement of Science, he reiterated his belief in the reality of psychic phenomena. It is unfortunate for his reputation that in the popular mind he has been associated more with spiritualism than with science.

It must not be assumed that Crookes's latter years were unfruitful of research. The discovery of radioactivity by Becquerel in 1897 and of radium shortly after by the Curies renewed his interest. Although he was then in his mid-sixties, he began a vigorous chemical study of uranium salts to determine their radioactivity. He found that if a uranium salt was precipitated from a solution by the addition of ammonium carbonate and then treated with excess reagent, a small amount of highly radioactive residue was obtained. The active substance in the residue, the first decay product of uranium, was called uranium X (now identified as a thorium isotope and protactinium). This was followed in 1903 by the discovery that single α particles, when projected on a zinc sulfide screen, produce starlike scintillations that are clearly visible with the aid of a suitable eyepiece. This device came to be known as the spinthariscope. The discovery that individual α particles may be counted by this scintillation technique had consequences of the first importance; in the hands of Rutherford and his school it led in the period 1909–1913 to the discovery that the atom has most of its mass concentrated in a very small central nucleus, and, in 1919, to the transmutation of elements.

During World War I, although in his eighties, Crookes served as a member of the scientific advisory board to the admiralty. He also continued his own research, forwarding his last paper on scandium and its spectrum to the Royal Society in December 1918. He died four months later at the age of eighty-seven on April 4, 1919, at his home in London.

As J. J. Thomson noted in his Royal Society anniversary address of that year:

> He had a singularly independent, original and courageous mind, he looked at things in his own way and was not afraid of expressing views very different from those previously considered orthodox. In not a few cases . . . time has shown that his ideas were much more in accordance with those which are now accepted than those commonly held by his contemporaries.

When Crookes began his experiments on cathode rays, they were regarded with a great deal of mystery. The particle nature of the electric current was unknown and therefore could not shed light on the nature of the rays proceeding from the cathode of the discharge tube. To this was added the mystery of the origin of the phosphorescence of the glass brought about by the action of the rays.

Crookes's paper has the advantage of attacking the problem from the point of view of a known phenomenon—that the rays are composed of electrified particles projected at high speed from the cathode of the tube. He backs up this point of view first by showing that in discharge tubes at high exhaustions the cathode rays follow straight lines and do not bend around corners. Further, flat cathodes produce sharper shadows than point cathodes, a result to be expected from projected, mutually repelling particles, but not from light rays. If a mill is placed in the discharge tube it is observed to rotate as would be required by the impact of material particles, and a magnet in the vicinity of the tube causes the rays to deflect as charged material particles would. Focusing of the rays produces strong heating effects, agreeing with the material particle hypothesis. The green phosphorescence of the glass occurs because particles from the cathode strike the glass walls.

He concludes the paper by making use of the kinetic theory of gases whereby each of the particles in the discharge might be expected to move without collision across the tube. Under such circumstances Crookes speculated that the particles might be in an "ultra-gaseous" state with quite different properties than they exhibit at higher pressures. His own words were:

> The phenomena in these exhausted tubes reveal to physical science a new world—a world where matter may exist in a fourth state [i.e., not solid, liquid, or gas], where the corpuscular theory of light may be true, and where light does not always move in straight lines, but where we can never enter, and with which we must be content to observe and experiment from the outside.

Crookes spoke with greater prescience than he realized, for "the phenomena in these exhausted tubes" did indeed reveal to science a new world. But the revelation was not immediately forthcoming. It took the researches of J. J. Thomson in 1897 to show that the new world which the tubes revealed was the subatomic world never before suspected. The electron was the first subatomic particle discovered, but it was soon followed by a host of others and an entirely new view of the constitution of the material world.

ᴑᴑᴑᴑᴑᴑᴑᴑ

CROOKES

On the Illumination of Lines of Electrical Pressure and the Trajectory of Molecules [1]

DARK SPACE ROUND THE NEGATIVE POLE

486. When the spark from a good induction coil traverses a glass tube containing a rarefied gas, certain phenomena are observed which vary greatly with the kind of gas and the degree of exhaustion. There is one appearance, however, which is constant in all the gases which I have examined, and within very wide limits of pressure, viz.: the well-known dark space round the negative pole.

GREEN PHOSPHORESCENT LIGHT OF MOLECULAR IMPACT

510. When the exhaustion approaches 30 M, (M represents a millionth of an atmosphere) a new phenomenon makes its appearance. The dark space has spread out so much that it nearly fills the bulb; the violet light by which the focus was rendered visible has become so faint as to be difficultly traced, but with care it can be seen converging to a focus beyond the focal point noticed at lower exhaustions. At the part of the bulb on which the rays impinge, a faint spot of greenish-yellow light is observed, sharp in outline. On exhausting to 14 M, and making the cup the negative pole of the coil, the projection from the cup is represented by a brilliant green spot of light about 7 millims, diameter, and the focus can scarcely be traced. The rest of the bulb is nearly dark, but at those parts furthest removed from the negative pole the faintly luminous boundary of the dark space can still be seen. A little blue light is seen round the positive pole extending somewhat into the bulb. On reversing the poles and making the cup positive, the bulb becomes beautifully illuminated with greenish-yellow light.

511. The phosphorescent light only appears in its full intensity when the dark space surrounding the negative pole extends to the surface of the

---

[1] From Sir William Crookes, *Philosophical Transactions, 170* (1879), 135–164.

bulb. At lower exhaustions, it can be detected when specially sought for outside the luminous boundary of the dark space, but it is faint and not easily noticeable. The colour depends on the kind of glass used. Most of my apparatus are made ot soft German glass, and this gives a phosphorescent light of a greenish-yellow colour. English glass phosphoresces of a blue colour; uranium glass becomes green; a diamond became brilliantly blue.

PROJECTION OF MOLECULAR SHADOWS

524. In ordinary vacuum tubes, illuminated by the induction current, the luminous phenomena follow the tube through any amount of curves and angles; a hollow spiral becomes illuminated just as well as if the tube were in a straight line. Not so, however, the phenomena of green phosphorescence observed at these high exhaustions. The molecular ray which gives birth to green light absolutely refuses to turn a corner, and radiates from the negative pole in straight lines, casting strong and sharply-defined shadows of anything which happens to be in its path. In a U tube with poles at each end, one leg will be bright green and the other almost dark, the light being cut off sharply by the bend of the glass, a shadow being projected on the curvature. I can detect no trace of polarisation in the green phosphorescent light on the surface of the glass, except, of course, when it emerges at an angle through the side of the glass tube.

525. The projection from the negative pole of a shadow rendered visible by a sharply-defined image on the side of the glass, seemed worthy of more close examination. A tube was accordingly made, as shown in [Fig. 23–1]. In the centre, dividing the tube into nearly equal parts, is a screen of thin mica, a a, loosely fitting into a groove blown round the tube. A flat plate of uranium glass, b, about half a millimetre thick, is riveted to the mica on one side. c is a star shaped piece of aluminum foil attached to a platinum terminal, and d is a similar star made of mica. At each end of the tube are two terminals, e and h, being flat aluminum disks, and f and g aluminum points.

With this apparatus experiments were carried on during exhaustion. When the exhaustion is moderate (say 1 or 2 millims.) so as to show stratifications and the ordinary phenomena of vacuum tubes, the luminosity extends from one pole to the other. Thus, if e and g are the two poles, the light extends the whole length of the tube; if, however, e or f is one pole and c the other, the luminosity only occupies the upper part of the tube, and if e and f are the two poles, the light keeps close to the top. The whole appearance shows that both poles are at work in producing the phenomena.

526. When, however, the vacuum is sufficiently high for the dark space

round the negative pole to have swollen out to the dimensions of the tube, there is little difference in the phenomena of green phosphorescence and projection of the shadow of *c* on *b,* whichever is the positive pole, provided *e* be made the negative. The appearances are almost the same, and the shadows projected from the negative pole *e* are just as sharp and intense whether I made *f* or *h* the positive pole. The positive pole, in fact, seems to have little or nothing to do with the phenomena.

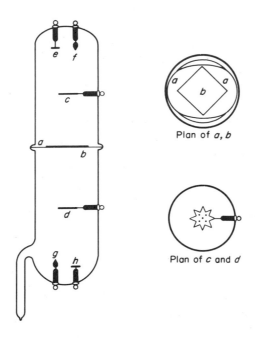

Plan of *a, b*

Plan of *c* and *d*

Fig. 23–1.

527. The best and sharpest shadows are cast by the flat disks *e* and *h.* The shadows thrown by the pointed poles *f* and *g* are faint and undecided in outline. An aluminum ring scarcely makes any shadow; a spherical pole, owing to the rays from it diverging more, gives faint and broad shadows; a square pole acts the same as a disk. Using the upper flat pole *e* as the negative, the shadow of the star *c* is thrown distinctly on the uranium plate *b,* where it is seen magnified about two diameters, but perfectly sharp in outline; either *f, g,* or *h,* and even the star itself may be made the positive pole without affecting the appearance of its shadow on *b.*

528. The whole upper part of the tube which is in the line of direct projection from the negative pole, glows with an intense yellowish-green fluorescent light. The uranium plate is still more brilliant, and of a green-

ish colour. Where the shadow of the star falls on it, no phosphorescence
whatever is visible. The mica plate a, where uncovered at the side of the
uranium plate, gives no phosphorescence, and no shadow is therefore seen
on it. When the lower pole, h, is made negative, so as to project the
shadow of the mica star d, no shadow is seen on the mica plate, neither is
any seen on the uranium plate above the mica. The thin film of mica
entirely prevents the uranium glass from becoming fluorescent under the
influence of the negative pole. Other experiments have, however, shown
that the mica star gives just as sharp and intense a shadow as the aluminum star, provided a suitable screen is used to receive it on.

529. If the aluminum star is made the positive pole, any one of the
others being the negative pole, it casts an enlarged and somewhat distorted image of itself all over the upper part of the tube. This image is
not sharply defined.

The sharpness of the shadows cast by the negative pole is slightly
affected by the intensity of the current; when the spark is very strong,
the shadow widens out a little.

530. I have already advanced the theory that the thickness of the dark
space surrounding the negative pole is the measure of the mean length of
the path of the gaseous molecules between successive collisions. The
electrified molecules are projected from the negative pole with enormous
velocity, varying, however, with the degree of exhaustion and intensity of
the induction current.

In the dark space they are few in number in comparison to what they
are at the luminous boundary. When the exhaustion is so high that the
mean path of the molecules stretches right across the tube, their velocity
is suddenly checked by the glass walls, and the production of light is the
consequence of this sudden arrest of velocity. The light actually proceeds
from the glass, and is caused by fluorescence or phosphorescence in or
on its surface, and not by an evolution of light by the molecules themselves, crowding together and striking each other on the surface of the
glass. Had this been the case—had the molecules themselves been the
lamps—they would shine equally well whatever were the arresting surface, and their light would have shown the spectral characteristics of the
gas whose residue they constituted. But no light is caused by a mica or
quartz screen, however near it may be brought to the negative pole; and
generally speaking the more fluorescent the material of the screen, the
better the luminosity.

531. The theory best supported by experiment, and the one which although new is not at all improbable in the present state of our knowledge
respecting molecules, is that the greenish-yellow phosphorescence of the
glass is caused by the direct impact of the molecules on the surface of the
glass. The shadows are not optical but molecular shadows, only they are

revealed by an ordinary illuminating effect. The sharpness of the shadow, when projected from a wide pole, proves them to be molecular. Had the projection from the negative pole radiated in all directions, after the manner of light radiating from a luminous disk, the shadows would not be perfectly sharp, but be surrounded by a penumbra. Being, however, projected material molecules in the same electrical state, they do not cross each other, but travel on in slightly divergent paths, giving perfectly sharp shadows with no penumbrae.

MECHANICAL ACTION OF PROJECTED MOLECULES

541. It was noticed that when the coil was first turned on, the thin glass film was driven back at the moment of becoming phosphorescent. This seemed to point to an actual material blow being given by the molecular impact, and the following experiment was devised to render this mechanical action more evident.

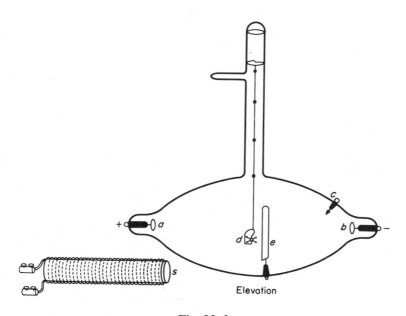

Elevation

Fig. 23–2.

A large somewhat egg-shaped bulb ([Fig. 23–2], elevation) is furnished at each end with flat aluminum poles, *a* and *b;* a pointed aluminum pole is inserted at *c*. At *d,* a little indicator is suspended from jointed glass fibers, so as to admit of being brought into any position near the middle of the bulb, by tilting the apparatus. The indicator consists of a small

radiometer fly 8 millims, in diameter, furnished with clear mica vanes 2
millims, across, and delicately supported on a glass cup and needle point.
A screen cut out of a flat aluminum plate 12 millims. wide and 30 millims.
high, is supported upright in the bulb at *e,* a little on one side of its axis,
being attached to the bulb by a platinum wire passing through the glass,
so that if needed the screen *e* can be used as a pole.

542. This apparatus was designed with a double object. The indicator
fly is not blacked on one side or favourably presented, therefore if immersed in a full stream of projected molecules, there will be no tendency
for it to turn one way rather than the other. If, however, I tilt the bulb
so as to bring the indicator half in and half out of the molecular shadow
cast by the screen, I should expect to see the fly driven round to the right
or to the left by the molecules striking one side only, thus confirming the
observation on the movement of the thin glass film under the molecular
impact.

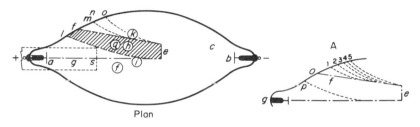

Fig. 23–3.

543. The other subject which I had in view was the following. It is
well known that a movable conductor carrying a current of electricity is
deflected under the influence of magnetic force and experiments tried very
early in this research, and repeated with the apparatus already described,
showed that the stream of molecules projected from the negative pole
obeyed in a very marked manner the power of a magnet. It was hoped
that the form of apparatus now under experiment would throw some light
on this action of magnetism on molecules.

544. The bulb being exhausted to the necessary high degree the pole *b*
is made negative, so as to cast the shadow of the screen *e* across the
tube, where it can be traced as a broad band along the lower part of the
glass. [Fig. 23–3], plan, shows the appearance, the shadow of *e* projected
by the pole *b* being enclosed within the lines *fe, ge,* shaded diagonally.

The indicator fly is first brought into position *h,* where it is entirely
screened from the molecular stream; no movement takes place. The apparatus is slightly tilted, till the fly comes into position *i,* half in and half
out of the shadow; very rapid rotation takes place in the direction of the
arrow, showing that impacts occur in the direction anticipated. The

apparatus being further tilted, so as to bring the indicator quite outside the shadow into position *j*, no movement takes place. When the indicator is brought to the other side of the shadow into position *k*, the rotation is very rapid in the direction of the arrow, opposite to what it is when at *i*.

MAGNETIC DEFLECTION OF LINES OF MOLECULAR FORCE

545. An electro-magnet is placed beneath the bulb, shown at *S* in [Fig. 23–2], elevation, and by dotted lines at *S* in [Fig. 23–3], plan. A battery of from 1 to 5 Grove's cells is connected with the magnet. The current is made to pass in such a direction that the pole under the bulb (marked *S*) is the one which would point towards the south were the magnet freely suspended.

546. The induction current being turned on, the shadow of *e* is projected straight along the tube in the position *fe, ge;* the edge of the shadow *f* is called the zero position, marked *O* on [Fig. 23–3], *A*. The electro-magnet is now excited by 1 cell. The shadow is deflected sideways to the position shown by 1, *p*, the edge *fe* now moving to 1, and the edge *ge* moving to *pe*. The lines *fe* and *ge*, when under no magnetic influence, are marked along the bottom of the bulb by perfectly straight lines, but when deflected by the magnet they are curved as at 1*e, pe*.

On increasing the number of cells actuating the electro-magnet, the deflection of the shadow likewise increases.

547. The width of the deflected shadow varies in like manner with the magnetic force. . . .

With 3 cells the position of the shadow is shown at *l m* in [Fig. 23–3], plan, shaded from left to right by diagonal lines, and with five cells the shadow is in position *n o*. . . .

On reversing the battery current passing round the magnet, the above-named deflections are obtained in the opposite direction.

548. The indicator fly is brought into position *h* ([Fig. 23–3], plan), and the induction spark passed, the pole *b* being negative. The shadow entirely envelops the indicator, and no movement is produced. The current from 3 cells is then sent round the electromagnet. This twists the shadow round to position *l e, m e,* and thereby brings half the indicator into the stream of molecules. Instantly the fly rotates with great speed in the normal direction, the same as it did at *i*. The indicator is now brought into position *q*, where it is entirely immersed in the shadow whilst deflected by the magnet. No movement occurs until battery contact is broken with the electro-magnet, when the shadow instantly returns to its normal position, and the further half of the fly being thereby left uncovered it rotates rapidly in the same direction as it did at *k*.

ALTERATION OF MOLECULAR VELOCITY—LAW
OF MAGNETIC DEFLECTION

555. It has been shown (545) that the position of the edge of the shadow is affected by varying the magnetic power used to deflect it. It became of interest to see if by keeping the magnetic power constant, the position of the edge of the shadow could be altered by any circumstance affecting the intensity of the spark, such as intercalating a Leyden jar in the circuit, or screwing the contact breaker one way or the other. If the molecules are projected from the negative pole with different velocities we might expect that under a constant magnetic deflection the higher velocities would show the flatter trajectories. With the apparatus shown at [figs 23–2 and 23–3], these variations in the trajectory of the molecules were not obtained in a decided manner, although indications of an alteration of curve by intensifying the spark were apparent.

556. Another apparatus was accordingly made in order to test this point, and also to obtain a more definite relation between the dimensions of the dark space round the negative pole, the commencement of the green phosphorescence, and the magnetic deflection under varying conditions of pressure in different gases.

I have spoken of shadows being deflected by the magnet as a convenient way of describing the phenomena observed; but it will be understood that what is really deflected is the path of the molecules driven from the negative pole and whose impact on the phosphorescent surface causes light. The shadows are the effect of a material obstacle in the way of the molecules.

In the apparatus now about to be described, a ray of light was used instead of a shadow. [Fig. 23–4] shows the arrangement.

The poles are at *a* and *b*. The negative pole *a* is a flat aluminum disk with a notch cut in it. The pole *b* is a ring of aluminum; *c* is a mica screen with a small hole in the middle about 1 millim. in diameter; *d* is a flat plate of German glass with a millimetre scale engraved on it vertically; *e* is a mica scale of millimetres. The scale *e* is to measure the thickness of the dark space as the exhaustion proceeds; the hole in *c* is to enable a spot of light to be thrown on the scale *d* from the pole *a;* the notch in the pole is to enable me to see if the spot of light projected on *d* is an image of the pole *a,* or of the hole in *c;* the scale on *d* is to enable me to measure the deflection of the ray proceeding from *a,* through *c,* to *d,* when bent by the magnet; *ff* is a vertical screen of mica in the plane of the movement of the ray, covered with a phosphorescent powder. On this the path of the ray traces itself in a straight line when the magnet is absent, and curved when the magnet is present.

576. These experiments prove several important points. In par. 559, when working with an air vacuum, it is recorded that the spot of green light is visible on the screen at a pressure of 102.6 *M* when the thickness of the dark space is only 12 millims. from the pole. Assuming, as I do, that this is a measure of the free path of the molecules before collision, it follows that some of the molecules sufficient to cause green phosphorescence on the screen, are projected the whole distance from the pole to the screen, or 102 millims., without being stopped by collisions. It is probable that this would have occurred at a still lower exhaustion, for on reference to par. 566, it is seen that the green spot was detected on the screen when the mean path in carbonic acid was 8.5 millims., and it was seen with hydrogen (570) when the mean path was only 7 millims.

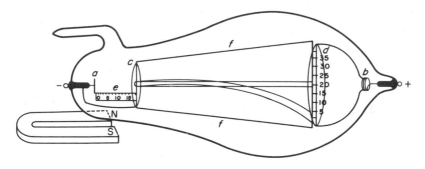

Fig. 23–4.

577. If we suppose the magnet permanently in position, and thus exerting a uniform downward pull on the molecules, it is seen that their trajectory is much curved at low exhaustions, and gets flatter as the exhaustion increases. A flatter trajectory corresponding to a higher velocity of the molecules, it follows that the molecules move quicker the better the exhaustion. This may arise from one of two causes: either the initial impulse given by the negative pole is stronger, or the collisions are less frequent. I consider the latter to be the true cause. The molecules which produce the green phosphorescence must be looked upon as in a different state from those which are arrested by frequent collisions. These impede the velocity of the free molecules and allow longer time for the magnetism to act on them; and although the deflecting force of magnetism might be expected to increase with the velocity of the molecules, Professor Stokes has pointed out that it would have to increase as the square of the velocity in order that the deflection should be as great at high as at low velocities.

Comparing the free molecules to cannon balls, the magnetic pull to the earth's gravitation, and the electrical excitation of the negative pole to the explosion of the powder in the gun, the trajectory will be quite flat when no gravitation acts, and gets curved under the influence of gravitation; it is also much curved when the ball passes through a dense resisting medium; it is less curved when the resisting medium gets rarer, and, it is seen that intensifying the induction spark, equivalent to increasing the charge of powder, gives greater initial velocity, and therefore flattens the trajectory. The parallelism is still closer if we compare the evolution of light seen when the shot strikes the target, with the phosphorescence produced in the glass screen by molecular impacts. . . .

580. Attempts to obtain continuous rotation of the ray of molecular light by means of a magnet have hitherto failed. The stream of molecules does not obey *Ampère's Law* as it would were it a perfectly flexible conductor joining the negative and positive pole. The molecules are projected from the negative pole, but the position of the positive pole, whether in front, at the side, or even behind the negative pole, has no influence on their subsequent behaviour, either in causing phosphorescence, producing mechanical effects, or in their magnetic deflection. The magnet seems to give them a spiral twist, greater or less, according to its power, but diminishing as the molecules get further off, and independent of their direction.

581. In [an] experiment described [earlier], the heating effect of the molecular bombardment is assumed to be the cause of certain phenomena. It was thought that by concentrating the molecular impacts to one point the heat produced might be rendered apparent. The experiments tried in the apparatus shown in [Fig. 23–5] prove that this supposition is correct. A polished aluminum cup *a* is made the negative pole in a properly exhausted tube. The focus is seen very sharp and distinct, as at *A*, and of a dark blue colour. The light, although blue in the centre of the tube, when it spreads out and strikes the tube at the end, illuminates it beautifully with the yellowish-green light. By means of a magnet the focus was deflected to the side of the tube, as shown at *B*, the path of the rays being beautifully curved. On the tube the appearance was that of a sharply-defined oval of a yellowish-green colour with a dark spot in the centre. To ascertain if heat were developed here I touched it with my finger and immediately raised a blister. The spot where the focus fell was nearly red hot.

582. Another apparatus was now made, as shown in [Fig. 23–6]. A nearly hemispherical cup of polished aluminum *a* is made one pole in a bulb, and a small disk of aluminum *b* is made the other pole. At *c* a strip of platinum is held by a wire passing through the glass, and forming another pole at *d*. The tip of the platinum strip is brought to the centre of curvature, and the whole is exhausted to a very high point. On first turning on the induction current, the cup being made the negative pole,

the platinum strip entered into a very rapid vibration. This soon stopped and the platinum quickly rose to a white heat, and would have melted had I not stopped the action of the coil.

The same phenomena of ignition take place if the platinum strip itself is made the positive pole.

583. Experiments in a similar tube in which a piece of charcoal is the body to be ignited, show that the ignition takes place at a less high exhaustion in hydrogen gas than it does in air.

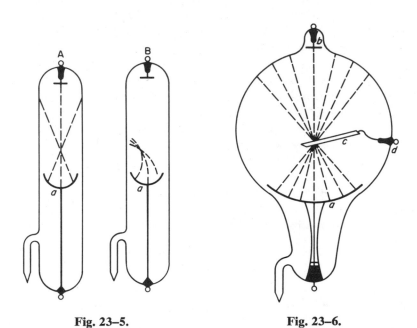

Fig. 23–5.   Fig. 23–6.

I have great pleasure in expressing my continued obligation to the great skill in glass-blowing and manipulation possessed by my friend and assistant, Mr. *C. H. Gimingham,* whose dexterity in executing complicated forms of apparatus has rendered easy a research which otherwise would have been full of difficulties.

584. I hope I may be allowed to record some theoretical speculations which have gradually formed in my mind during the progress of these experiments. I put them forward only as working hypotheses, useful, perhaps necessary, in the first dawn of new knowledge, but only to be retained as long as they are of assistance; for experimental research is necessarily and slowly progressive, and one's early provisional hypotheses have to be modified, adjusted, perhaps altogether abandoned in deference to later observations.

AN ULTRA-GASEOUS STATE OF MATTER

585. The modern idea of the gaseous state of matter is based upon the supposition that a given space of the capacity of, say, a cubic centimetre, contains millions of millions of molecules in rapid motion in all directions, each having millions of encounters in a second. In such a case the length of the mean free path of the molecules is excessively small as compared with the dimensions of the vessel, and properties are observed which constitute the ordinary gaseous state of matter, and which depend upon constant collisions. But by great rarefaction the free path may be made so long that the hits in a given time are negligible in comparison to the misses, in which case the average molecule is allowed to obey its own motions or laws withont interference; and if the mean free path is comparable to the dimensions of the vessel, the properties which constitute gaseity are reduced to a minimum, and the matter becomes exalted to an ultra-gaseous or molecular state, in which the very decided but hitherto masked properties now under investigation come into play.

The phenomena in these exhausted tubes reveal to physical science a new world—a world where matter may exist in a fourth state, where the corpuscular theory of light may be true, and where light does not always move in straight lines, but where we can never enter, and with which we must be content to observe and experiment from the outside.

24

ooooooooooo

A REMARKABLE
REGULARITY IN THE
HYDROGEN SPECTRUM

ooooooooooo

Johann Jacob Balmer (1825-1898)

In the year 1885 a remarkable paper by an obscure Swiss teacher of physics, Johann Jacob Balmer, appeared in the *Annalen der Physik und Chemie;* it was to have a profound influence on the development of atomic physics. Balmer's achievement in obtaining a mathematical formula that correctly gives the wavelengths of the spectral lines of the hydrogen atom was all the more remarkable since he based his calculations on only four lines in the visible spectrum.

Using the very accurate measurements of Ångström for the four hydrogen lines in the visible part of the spectrum, Balmer obtained a simple arithmetic formula from which the wavelengths of these lines can be calculated. The essence of Balmer's discovery is that the wavelength of any line in the spectrum of hydrogen can be obtained by multiplying a certain numerical factor, which Balmer called "the fundamental number of hydrogen," by a series of fractions. His formula is given by

$$\lambda = b \, \frac{m^2}{m^2 - n^2}$$

where b is the fundamental number and λ is the wavelength of any hydrogen line in Ångström units (10^{-8} cm). A given series of lines is determined by the choice of the integer $n,$ and the individual lines in the series by the values of m. Thus if $n = 2$ and $m = 3$, 4, 5, etc., the formula gives the series of lines in the visible hydrogen spectrum. This series is now known as the Balmer series. Other series were found later; for example, for $n = 1$,

363

and $m = 2, 3, 4$, etc. (the Lyman series); for $n = 3$, and $m = 4, 5, 6$, etc. (the Paschen series); $n = 4$, $m = 5, 6$, etc. (the Brackett series), and $n = 5$, $m = 6, 7$, etc. (the Pfund series). The physical reason for the existence of these series was first clarified by Niels Bohr's model of the hydrogen atom (see Chapter 45).

Balmer's genius and the importance of his contribution lay not so much in deducing an empirical formula that gives the correct values of wavelengths of the lines that were then known, but in generalizing the formula and showing that it can be expressed algebraically in terms of the squares of integers. Balmer pointed out that there must be other series of lines in the spectrum of hydrogen whose wavelengths can also be derived from his algebraic formula although he did not attempt to find them.

Balmer's discovery gave a great impetus to spectral theory. All subsequent investigations into the origin of atomic spectra began with the fundamental assumption that the wavelengths of the spectral lines of all atoms can be represented by simple numerical relationships involving the squares of integers. In particular, Ritz, in the year 1908, introduced what is now known as the "Ritz combination principle," which is a generalization of Balmer's discovery. The essential feature of this principle, which proved of great heuristic value, is the following:

For any atom there exists a characteristic sequence of numerical terms (the numerical values of these terms vary from one type of atom to the other) such that the frequency (the speed of light divided by the wavelength) of any line in the spectrum of this atom is equal to the difference of two of the terms of the sequence. This means that the frequency of any line in the spectrum of the atom can be expressed in terms (differences) of the frequencies of other lines in the spectrum.

Ritz then went on to show that the fundamental sequence of numerical terms for any atom is obtained by dividing a certain numerical constant (which varies from one atom type to the next) by the squares of the integers taken in turn. This remarkable sequence, which stemmed from the basic work of Balmer, was of great importance in leading finally to the Bohr model of the atom. In the case of the hydrogen spectrum, the Ritz combination principle is particularly simple since the frequency of every line radiated by hydrogen is equal to the difference of two Ritz terms.

Niels Bohr, who was born in 1885, the very year that Balmer published his fundamental paper, was undoubtedly influenced by Balmer's numerical scheme, for it was clear to him that if the wavelengths (or the frequencies) could be represented in terms of integers, some type of quantum phenomenon is involved in the emission of radiation by an atom. With this as a starting point it was not difficult for a man of Bohr's genius to see how the concept of the photon could be used to introduce integers (the quantum numbers of the Bohr orbits) into the model of the atom.

Johann Jacob Balmer was a devoted Pythagorean from his boyhood and was convinced that the explanation of the mysteries of the universe lay in the correlation of observed phenomena with the appropriate combination of integers. Thus any series of distinct events, such as the sharp emission lines in the spectrum of hydrogen, would have triggered his imagination and started him on a search for a Pythagorean relationship.

But Balmer was more than a mere numerologist, for he had an excellent educational background. He was born on May 1, 1825, in the small Swiss town of Lausen, Baselland, where he spent his early years and went to school. He later studied mathematics at the universities of Karlsruhe, Berlin, and Basel, and obtained his Doctor of Philosophy degree in mathematics at the latter university in 1869.

He was interested not only in the formal aspects of mathematics, but also in its philosophical implications and its relationship to the laws of nature. Thus, in a paper published in 1868, he dealt with the relationship of physical research to systems of world philosophy (*Naturforschung* and *Weltanschauung*) and such problems undoubtedly greatly stimulated his interest in spectroscopy. In addition, he was a reasonably good mathematician and published papers on projective geometry.

Unlike most physicists at that time, Balmer did not carry out his research at a university, for he never was appointed to a professorial chair. Although he began his academic career as a *Privatdozent* (university lecturer)—the first rung on the academic ladder—at the University of Basel, he left the university to become a teacher at a girls' secondary school, and did his famous work on hydrogen spectral lines there. This was described in a series of papers that appeared in a Basel scientific journal and in the *Annalen der Physik und Chemie* in 1884, 1885, and 1897.

Balmer died in 1898 just three years before Planck discovered the quantum of action, which was ultimately to justify Balmer's faith in the explanation of spectroscopy in terms of integers.

ooooooo

BALMER

Note on the Spectral Lines of Hydrogen [1]

USING MEASUREMENTS BY H. W. VOGEL and by Huggins of the ultraviolet lines of the hydrogen spectrum I have tried to de-

---

[1] Johann Jacob Balmer, *Annalen der Physik und Chemie*, 25 (1885), 80–85 [trans. Editors].

rive a formula which will represent the wavelengths of the different lines in a satisfactory manner. I was encouraged to take up this work by Professor E. Hagenbach. Ångström's very exact measurements of the four hydrogen lines enable one to determine a common factor for their wavelengths which is in as simple a numerical relation as possible to these wavelengths. I gradually arrived at a formula which, at least for these four lines, expresses a law by which their wavelengths can be represented with striking precision. The common factor in this formula, as it has been deduced from Ångström's measurements, is [$b = 3645.6(mm/10^7)$].

We may call this number the fundamental number of hydrogen; and if corresponding fundamental numbers can be found for the spectral lines of other elements, we may accept the hypothesis that relations which can be expressed by some function exist between these fundamental numbers and the corresponding atomic weights.

The wavelengths of the first four hydrogen lines are obtained by multiplying the fundamental number $b = 3645.6$ in succession by the coefficients 9/5; 4/3; 25/21; and 9/8. At first it appears that these four coefficients do not form a regular series; but if we multiply the numerators in the second and the fourth terms by 4 a consistent regularity is evident and the coefficients have for numerators the numbers 3^2, 4^2, 5^2, 6^2 and for denominators a number that is less by 4.

For several reasons it seems to me probable that the four coefficients which have just been given belong to two series, so that the second series includes the terms of the first series; hence I have finally arrived at the present formula for the coefficients in the more general form: $m^2/(m^2-n^2)$ in which m and n are whole numbers.

For $n = 1$ we obtain the series 4/3, 9/8, 16/15, 25/24, and so on, for $n = 2$ the series 9/5, 16/12, 25/21, 36/32, 49/45, 64/60, 81/77, 100/96, and so on. In this second series the second term is already in the first series but in a reduced form.

If we carry out the calculation of the wavelengths with these coefficients and the fundamental number 3645.6, we obtain the following numbers in 10^{-7} mm.

TABLE 24-1

According to the formula			Ångström gives	Difference
$H\alpha$ (C-line)	$= \frac{9}{5}b$	$= 6562.08$	6562.10	+0.02
$H\beta$ (F-line)	$= \frac{4}{3}b$	$= 4860.8$	4860.74	−0.06
$H\gamma$ (near G)	$= \frac{25}{21}b$	$= 4340$	4340.1	+0.1
$H\delta$ (h-line)	$= \frac{9}{8}b$	$= 4101.3$	4101.2	−0.1

The deviations of the formula from Ångström's measurements amount in the most unfavorable case to not more than 1/40000 of a wavelength, a deviation which very likely is within the limits of the possible errors of observation and is really striking evidence for the great scientific skill and care with which Ångström must have worked.

From the formula we obtained for a fifth hydrogen line $49/45 \cdot 3645.6 = 3969.65.10^{-7}$ mm. I knew nothing of such a fifth line, which must lie within the visible part of the spectrum just before H_I (which according to Ångström has a wavelength 3968.1); and I had to assume that either the temperature relations were not favorable for the emission of this line or that the formula was not generally applicable.

On communicating this to Professor Hagenbach he informed me that many more hydrogen lines are known, which have been measured by Vogel and by Huggins in the violet and the ultraviolet parts of the hydrogen spectrum and in the spectrum of the white stars; he was kind enough himself to compare the wavelengths thus determined with my formula and to send me the result.

While the formula in general gives somewhat larger numbers than those contained in the published lists of Vogel and of Huggins, the difference between the calculated and the observed wavelengths is so small that the agreement is striking in the highest degree. Comparisons of wavelengths measured by different investigators show in general no exact agreement; and yet the observations of one man may be made to agree with those of another by a slight reduction in an entirely satisfactory way.

[Here Balmer compares the wavelengths as calculated from his formula with the measurements of several observers—Editors.]

These comparisons show that the formula holds also for the fifth hydrogen line, which lies just before the first Fraunhofer H-line (which belongs to calcium). It also appears that Vogel's hydrogen lines and the corresponding Huggins lines of the white stars can be represented by the formula very satisfactorily. We may almost certainly assume that the other lines of the white stars which Huggins found farther on in the ultraviolet part of the spectrum will be expressed by the formula. I lack knowledge of the wavelengths. Using the fundamental number 3645.6, we obtain according to the formula for the ninth and the following hydrogen lines up to the fifteenth:

$$
\begin{aligned}
{}^{121}\!/_{117}b &= 3770.24 & {}^{225}\!/_{221}b &= 3711.58 \\
{}^{36}\!/_{35}b &= 3749.76 & {}^{64}\!/_{63}b &= 3703.46 \\
{}^{169}\!/_{165}b &= 3733.98 & {}^{289}\!/_{285}b &= 3696.76 \\
{}^{49}\!/_{48}b &= 3721.55
\end{aligned}
$$

Whether the hydrogen lines of the white stars agree with the formula to this point or whether other numerical relations gradually replace it can only be determined by observation.

I add to what I have said a few questions and conclusions.

Does the above formula hold only for the single chemical element hydrogen, and will not other fundamental numbers in the spectral lines of other elements be found which are peculiar to those elements? If not, we may perhaps assume that the formula that holds for hydrogen is a special case of a more general formula which under certain conditions goes over into the formula for the hydrogen lines.

None of the hydrogen lines which correspond to the formula when $n = 3$, 4, and so on, and which may be called lines of the third or fourth order, is found in any spectrum as yet known; they must be emitted under entirely new relations of temperature and pressure if they are to become perceptible.

If the formula holds for all the principal lines of the hydrogen spectrum with $n = 2$, it follows that these spectral lines on the ultraviolet side approach the wavelength 3645.6 in a more closely packed series, but they can never pass this limiting value, while the C-line also is the extreme line on the red side. Only if lines of higher orders are present can lines be found on the infrared side.

The formula has no relation, so far as can be shown, with the very numerous lines of the second hydrogen spectrum which Hasselberg has published in the *Mémoires de l'Academie des Sciences de St. Petersbourg,* 1882. For certain values of pressure and temperature hydrogen may easily change in such a way that the law of formation of its spectral lines becomes entirely different.

There are great difficulties in the way of finding the fundamental numbers for other chemical elements, such as oxygen or carbon, by means of which their principal spectral lines can be determined from the formula. Only extremely exact determinations of wavelengths of the most prominent lines of an element can give a common base for these wavelengths, and without such a base it seems as if all trials and guesses will be in vain. Perhaps by using a different graphical construction of the spectrum a way will be found to make progress in such investigations.

25

ooooooooooo

THE LUMINIFEROUS
ETHER RECEIVES
A MORTAL BLOW

ooooooooooo

Albert A. Michelson (1852-1931)

Edward W. Morley (1838-1923)

The last quarter of the nineteenth century was marked by what at that time seemed to be the final triumph of the undulatory theory of light over the corpuscular theory. With the beautiful experiments of Thomas Young and Augustin Fresnel on the interference and diffraction of light, and their brilliant theoretical analysis based on the wave theory, it appeared almost a certainty that a beam of light consisted of a periodic disturbance that was propagated through an all-pervading medium in the same way that waves are propagated across the surface of water. The nature of this light-propagating medium was not at all understood. But that some kind of medium was required to propagate light waves seemed self-evident. This idea was reinforced by Maxwell's discovery of the electromagnetic theory of light and his derivation of the wave equation for electromagnetic fields. It seemed obvious that the all-pervading medium invented by Descartes, which Maxwell called the ether, was just what was required to produce and propagate electric and magnetic displacements in space. However, it soon became evident that one would have to assign very strange and, indeed, contradictory properties to the ether to account for astronomical observations.

To begin with, it was clear that the ether had to be enormously rigid in

369

order to propagate a disturbance with the speed of light. On the other hand, it was obvious that the ether would have to permeate all material, since scientists knew that light moves through transparent solids, although at a speed slower than its speed in a vacuum. A question that naturally arose concerning the ether was what happened to it inside a body if the body was set in motion. This question was partly answered by Fresnel, who argued that in transparent bodies, at least, the ether is partly dragged along with the body when the body moves. This was verified by the experiments of Fizeau, who measured the speed of light in moving water.

However, this idea of the "ether drag" came into conflict with the aberration of starlight. If a star is observed along a line at right angles to the direction of the orbital motion of the earth, the light from the star comes to us from a slightly different direction, as though the star were somewhat displaced in the direction of the earth's orbital motion. The only way this can be explained, assuming that an ether exists, is to suppose that the earth does not drag the ether outside it. In other words, although we must suppose that the ether permeating a transparent body is partly dragged along when this body moves, we must not allow any of this drag to be communicated to the ether outside the body if we are to understand aberration. We must suppose, if an ether exists, that no matter how a body moves through this ether, the ether itself always remains at rest in the absolute space that Newton had introduced. This assumed that the ether itself must be an absolute frame of reference—relative to which the motions of bodies such as the earth can be measured. It was to test this particular point that Michelson and Morley, in 1887, devised their famous experiment to see whether a beam of light, moving at right angles to the direction of the motion of the earth, travels at a speed different from that of a beam moving parallel to the earth's motion. This experiment was therefore designed to measure the absolute motion of the earth through space, that is, relative to an absolute ether at rest in absolute space.

Albert Abraham Michelson was particularly qualified by his natural scientific ability and his training in optics to design and perform this piece of research, which was undoubtedly the most precise scientific experiment conducted up to that time. Born in Strelno, Germany, on December 19, 1852, he was brought by immigrant parents to the United States at the age of two. His father, a storekeeper, eventually settled the family in the mining town of Virginia City in Nevada, but young Albert was sent to San Francisco for his high school education. Lacking means for college, he attempted in June 1869 to obtain an appointment to the U.S. Naval Academy, but he was unsuccessful. It was at this juncture that he showed the quality of determination which was so characteristic of his later life. Deciding that he would somehow obtain a presidential appointment, he set out for Washington by any means available, for the first transcontinental railroad had just completed laying its track a month before. Once in Washington, since he had no way to obtain an interview with President Grant, he waited on the White House steps until Grant appeared for his daily stroll. The result was that young Michelson was sent to Annapolis and eventually admitted, apparently illegally, because the ten presidential appointments allowed by law were all filled. At the academy Michelson excelled in science and mathematics. Graduating in 1873 at the age of twenty, he served two years in the Caribbean before returning to the Naval Academy as instructor in physics and chemistry.

At Annapolis he became interested in optics and began the research which brought him to scientific notice and which he continued at intervals throughout his life—his measurement of the velocity of light. His first apparatus represented an improvement of Foucault's rotating mirror method and his result of 186,508 miles per second in 1879 for the velocity attracted the attention of Simon Newcomb, then president of the American Association for the Advancement of Science and an officer in the Navy Corps of Professors. Transferred to Washington, Michelson worked with Newcomb during the next year on an improved apparatus for velocity of light measurements.

Recognizing the need for further training in physics, Michelson obtained a leave of absence from the Navy and in 1880 went to Europe with his wife and children. He was abroad two years, studying at Berlin and Heidelberg in Germany and at the Collège de France and the École Polytechnique in Paris. It was while he was in Berlin that he made the first model of his famous interferometer and used it in an attempt to measure the earth's motion through the supposed all-pervading luminiferous ether. The null result aroused controversy throughout the scientific world. During this period in Europe he resigned from the Navy and accepted a position at the Case School of Applied Science in Cleveland, but postponed his return to complete his work abroad. When he returned in 1882 he was ready for the experiment that established his position in the annals of physics.

Shortly after Michelson's arrival at Case, he met Edward W. Morley, professor of chemistry at Western Reserve University, which adjoined the Case campus. They soon became devoted friends and collaborators. The pair presented an interesting contrast. Morley, deeply religious, had been trained for the ministry, but, finding no pulpit, had accepted a professorship of chemistry for which he was largely self-trained. He was energetic and talkative, and his long hair and expansive red mustache completed what can only be called a casual attitude toward dress. Michelson, on the other hand, perhaps because of his naval training, was always immaculately turned out. He had a reserved, dignified, rather handsome appearance and kept himself in trim by appropriate exercise. He was a strong individualist with an intense spirit, a strong drive, and a high opinion of his work and his worth. When crossed he could be blunt and imperious. Perhaps in keeping with his reserve he had an artistic side which found expression in music and painting. In experimental physics he had a passion for precision so that his work commanded high confidence in the scientific world. This passion was shared by Morley and made their mutual endeavors highly successful.

What is now called the Michelson-Morley experiment was begun about 1886, although previous experiments had been made by the team on the velocity of light in moving water. The idea of the experiment was essentially simple. Using Michelson's interferometer, a beam of light would be split with one part sent out *perpendicular* to the earth's motion in space, to a fixed mirror and back, and the other *parallel* to the earth's motion, to a fixed mirror at the same distance and back. If the speed of light depended on the motion of the earth through the ether, then the two beams of light should not return at the same time. If they did not return at the same time, then the wave forms of the returning beams would not fit exactly, i.e., be in the same phase, and this lack of phase would show in a displacement of the interference or fringe pattern in the field of view of the interferometer.

The difference in the time of arrival of the two light beams can be illustrated by the case of two equally fast swimmers who are sent the same distance and back again in a stream of water, with one swimmer going up and down the stream, and the other going across the stream and back. It can easily be shown algebraically that the swimmer going across stream will come back to the starting point before the swimmer moving parallel to the stream. This is what Michelson and Morley expected to find for their two beams.

To test this assumption, the interferometer apparatus was so arranged that it could be rotated in all directions, since the direction of the motion of the earth through space was not known. The results of the experiment gave no evidence at all that the earth was moving relative to the ether, since the two beams returned to the image plane of the instrument (that is, to the point at which they were focused by the observing telescope) at exactly the same time (within the limits of experimental error). As the two experimenters indicate on the last page of their paper (included in the following excerpt), the actual measured difference in the times of return of the two beams "was certainly less than the twentieth part" of the displacement to be expected from the theoretical analysis of the problem.

In the last paragraph of their paper, Michelson and Morley indicate the crisis faced by classical physics because of the negative result of their experiment. Even if one retained the concept of the ether (which seemed to be required by the Maxwell theory), the Michelson and Morley experiment proved conclusively that there could be no measurable motion of the earth relative to it. On the other hand, the explanation of the aberration of light, as given by Fresnel on the basis of the wave theory of light, required the ether to be at absolute rest, relative to which the motion of the earth should be measurable. These results were in direct contradiction to one another.

The legacy of the Michelson-Morley experiment to atomic theory was tremendous, if indirect. It was the negative result of the experiment that in part led Einstein to one of the fundamental ideas upon which the theory of relativity rests, namely, that the speed of light is the same for all observers regardless of how they may be moving. With this assumption, it is easy to see why the two beams return to their starting point at the same time; moreover, it is no longer necessary to posit the existence of a troublesome ether. However, before the theory of relativity was introduced, with its revolutionary concept of a constant speed of light, another attempt was made to explain the Michelson and Morley experiment. This *ad hoc* explanation was that the distance between the two mirrors on the line parallel to the earth's motion had decreased (because of the earth's motion) by an amount that was just big enough to enable the parallel moving beam to return at exactly the same time as the beam moving transverse to the earth's motion. This is the famous Lorentz-Fitzgerald contraction hypothesis, which Lorentz derived by picturing matter as consisting of small charged spheres (electrons) that contract in the direction of motion because of the electrical forces acting on them. This theory was not satisfactory because it tried to explain observable phenomena in terms of invisible forces and *ad hoc* hypotheses which could not be tested experimentally. Einstein's theory removed this difficulty.

The Michelson-Morley experiment was concluded when Michelson was thirty-four years old. The work placed him in the forefront of American physics and he expected that the Case trustees would recognize this fact by substantially increased support. When the support did not materialize, Michelson decided in 1889 to leave Case and accept the offer made by the new Clark University in Worcester, Massachusetts. The dissolution of the Michelson-Morley partnership was a great disappointment to Morley, who despite other offers decided to remain at Western Reserve University. Michelson's stay at Clark University was of short duration, for the University of Chicago, then being created, offered him in 1892 not only a chair but the direction of the new Ryerson Physical Laboratory. Here he was able to carry on his work on a basis which, at last, he found acceptable. Michelson remained at Chicago until his retirement at the age of seventy-seven. During that period some of his honors include the presidency of the American Physical Society (1900), election as a foreign member of the Royal Society 1902, and the receipt of the Society's highest award, the Copley medal, in 1907. In the same year he was awarded the Nobel Prize "for his optical precision instruments and for the spectroscopic and meteorological investigations made with them." He was the first American scientist so honored. Michelson's outstanding researches included a new definition of the primary standard of length in terms of the red cadmium wavelength (6,348 Å), the production of precision-ruled diffraction gratings, the echelon grating, rigidity of the earth, the diameter of Betelguese in the constellation of Orion by interferometric methods, and finally a redetermination of the velocity of light carried out with the stations at Mt. Wilson and Mt. San Antonio in California. During the course of this work, having retired from the University of Chicago and living in Pasadena, he died on May 9, 1931.

The following paper describes his greatest work, the Michelson-Morley experiment.

ооооооо

MICHELSON AND MORLEY

On the Relative Motion of the Earth and the Luminiferous Aether [1]

THE DISCOVERY OF THE ABERRATION of light was soon followed by an explanation according to the emission theory. The effect was attributed to a simple composition of the velocity of light with the velocity of the earth in its orbit. The difficulties in this apparently sufficient explanation were overlooked until after an explanation of the undulatory theory of light was proposed. This new explanation was at first almost as simple as the former. But it failed to account for the fact proved by experiment that the aberration was unchanged when observations were made with a telescope filled with water. For if the tangent of the angle of aberration is the ratio of the velocity of the earth to the velocity of light, then, since the latter velocity in water is three-fourths its velocity in a vacuum, the aberration observed with a water telescope should be four-thirds of its true value.

On the undulatory theory, according to Fresnel, first, the aether is supposed to be at rest, except in the interior of transparent media, in which,

[1] Albert A. Michelson and Edward M. Morley, *Philosophical Magazine,* 190, 449–463 (1887).

secondly, it is supposed to move with a velocity less than the velocity of the medium in the ratio $\dfrac{n^2 - 1}{n^2}$, where n is the index of refraction. These two hypotheses give a complete and satisfactory explanation of aberration. The second hypothesis, notwithstanding its seeming improbability, must be considered as fully proved, first, by the celebrated experiment of Fizeau, and secondly, by the ample confirmation of our own work. The experimental trial of the first hypothesis forms the subject of the present paper.

If the earth were a transparent body, it might perhaps be conceded, in view of the experiments just cited, that the intermolecular aether was at rest in space, notwithstanding the motion of the earth in its orbit; but we have no right to extend the conclusion from these experiments to opaque bodies. But there can hardly be any question that the aether can and does pass through metals. Lorentz cites the illustration of a metallic barometer tube. When the tube is inclined, the aether in the space above the mercury is certainly forced out, for it is incompressible. But again we have no right to assume that it makes its escape with perfect freedom, and if there be any resistance, however slight, we certainly could not assume an opaque body such as the whole earth to offer free passage through its entire mass. But as Lorentz aptly remarks: "Quoi qu'il en soit, on fera bien, à mon avis, de ne pas se laisser guider, dans une question aussi importante, par des considérations sur le degré de probabilité ou de simplicité de l'une ou de l'autre hypothèse, mais de s'addresser a l'expérience pour apprendre à connaitre l'état, de repos ou de mouvement, dans lequel se trouve l'éther à la surface terrestre."

In April, 1881, a method was proposed and carried out for testing the question experimentally.

In deducing the formula for the quantity to be measured, the effect of the motion of the earth through the aether on the path of the ray at right angles to this motion was overlooked. The discussion of this oversight and of the entire experiment forms the subject of a very searching analysis by H. A. Lorentz, who finds that this effect can by no means be disregarded. In consequence, the quantity to be measured had in fact but half the value supposed, and as it was already barely beyond the limits of errors of experiment, the conclusion drawn from the result of the experiment might well be questioned; since, however, the main portion of the theory remains unquestioned, it was decided to repeat the experiment with such modifications as would insure a theoretical result much too large to be masked by experimental errors. The theory of the method may be briefly stated as follows:

Let *sa* [Fig. 25–1] be a ray of light which is partly reflected in *ab,* and partly transmitted in *ac,* being returned by the mirrors *b* and *c* along *ba* and *ca*. *ba* is partly transmitted along *ad* and *ca* is partly reflected along *ad*. If then the paths *ab* and *ac* are equal, the two rays interfere along *ad*. Suppose now, the aether being at rest, that the whole apparatus moves in the direction *sc*, with the velocity of the earth in its orbit, the directions and distances traversed by the rays will be altered thus:—The ray *sa* is reflected along *ab* [Fig. 25–2]; the angle *bab*$_1$, being equal to the abberation $= \alpha$ is returned along *ba*$_1$, (*aba*$_1 = 2\alpha$), and goes to the focus of the telescope, whose direction is unaltered. The transmitted ray goes along *ac*, is returned along *ca*$_1$, and is reflected at *a*$_1$, making *ca*$_1$*e*, equal $90 - a$, and therefore still coinciding with the first ray. It may be remarked that the rays *ba*$_1$ and *ca*$_1$ do not now meet exactly in the same point *a*$_1$, though the difference is of the second order; this does not affect the validity of the reasoning. Let it now be required to find the difference in the two paths *aba*$_1$, and *aca*$_1$.

Let $V =$ velocity of light.

$\quad v =$ velocity of the earth in its orbit.

$\quad D =$ distance *ab* or *ac* [Fig. 25–1].

$\quad T =$ time light occupies to pass from *a* to *c*.

$\quad T_1 =$ time light occupies to return from *c* to *a*$_1$ [Fig. 25–2].

Then

$$T = \frac{D}{V - v} \qquad T_1 = \frac{D}{V + v}$$

The whole time of going and coming is

$$T + T_1 = 2D \frac{V}{V^2 - v^2},$$

and the distance travelled in this time is

$$2D \frac{V^2}{V^2 - v^2} = 2D \left(1 + \frac{v^2}{V^2}\right),$$

neglecting terms of the fourth order. The length of the other path is evidently

$$2D \sqrt{1 + \frac{v^2}{V^2}},$$

or to the same degree of accuracy,

$$2D \left(1 + \frac{v^2}{2V^2}\right).$$

The difference is therefore $D(v^2/V^2)$. If now the whole apparatus be turned through 90°, the difference will be in the opposite direction, hence the displacement of the interference fringes should be $2D(v^2/V^2)$. Considering only the velocity of the earth in its orbit, this would be $2D \times 10^{-8}$. If, as was the case in the first experiment, $D = 2 \times 10^6$ waves of yellow light, the displacement to be expected would be 0.04 of the distance between the interference-fringes.

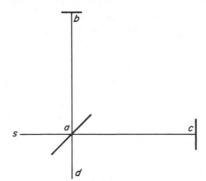

Fig. 25–1.

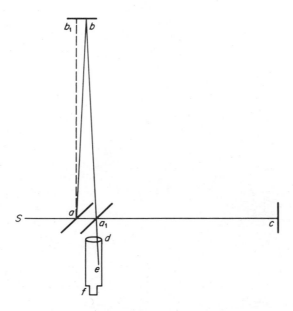

Fig. 25–2.

In the first experiment, one of the principal difficulties encountered was that of revolving the apparatus without producing distortion; and another was its extreme sensitiveness to vibration. This was so great that it was impossible to see the interference-fringes except at brief intervals when working in the city, even at two o'clock in the morning. Finally, as before remarked, the quantity to be observed, namely, a displacement of something less than a twentieth of the distance between the interference-fringes, may have been too small to be detected when masked by experimental errors.

The first-named difficulties were entirely overcome by mounting the apparatus on a massive stone floating on mercury; and the second by increasing, by repeated reflexion, the path of the light to about ten times its former value.

The apparatus is represented in perspective in [Fig. 25–3], in plan in [Fig. 25–4], and in vertical section in [Fig. 25–5]. The stone a [Fig. 25–5] is about 1.5 metre square and 0.3 metre thick. It rests on an annular wooden float bb, 1.5 metre outside diameter, 0.7 metre inside diameter, and 0.25 metre thick. The float rests on mercury contained in the cast-iron trough cc, 1.5 centimetre thick, and of such dimensions as to leave a clearance of about one centimetre around the float. A pin d, guided by arms $gggg$, fits into a socket e attached to the float. The pin may be pushed into the stocket or be withdrawn, by a lever pivoted at f. This pin keeps the float concentric with the trough, but does not bear any part of the weight of the stone. The annular iron trough rests on a bed of cement on a low brick pier built in the form of a hollow octagon.

At each corner of the stone were placed four mirrors dd ee [Fig. 25–4]. Near the centre of the stone was a plane parallel glass b. These were so disposed that light from an argand burner a, passing through a lens, fell on b so as to be in part reflected to d; the two pencils followed the paths indicated in the figure, $bdedbf$ and $bd_1e_1d_1bf$ respectively, and were ob-

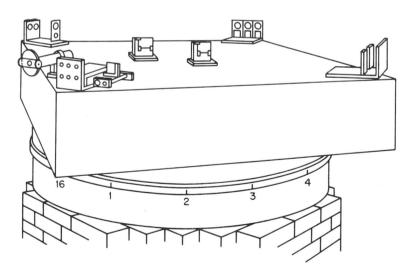

Fig. 25–3.

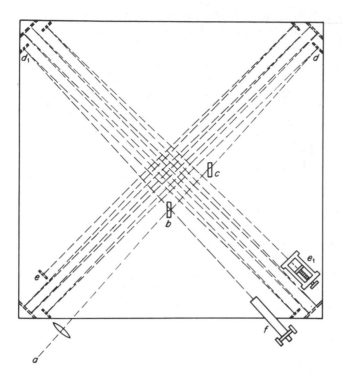

Fig. 25–4.

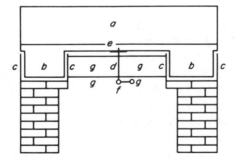

Fig. 25–5.

served by the telescope *f*. Both *f* and *a* revolved with the stone. The mirrors were of speculum metal carefully worked to optically plane surfaces five centimetres in diameter, and the glasses *b* and *c* were plane parallel of the same thickness, 1.25 centimetre; their surfaces measured 5.0 by 7.5 centimetres. The second of these was placed in the path of one of the pencils to compensate for the passage of the other through the same thickness of glass. The whole of the optical portion of the apparatus was kept covered with a wooden cover to prevent air-currents and rapid changes of temperature.

The adjustment was effected as follows:—The mirrors having been adjusted by screws in the castings which held the mirrors, against which they were pressed by springs, till light from both pencils could be seen in the telescope, the lengths of the two paths were measured by a light wooden rod reaching diagonally from mirror to mirror, the distance being read from a small steel scale to tenths of millimetres. The difference in the lengths of the two paths was then annulled by moving the mirror e_1. This mirror had three adjustments: it had an adjustment in altitude and one in azimuth, like all the other mirrors, but finer; it also had an adjustment in the direction of the incident ray, sliding forward or backward, but keeping very accurately parallel to its former plane. The three adjustments of this mirror could be made with the wooden cover in position.

The paths being now approximately equal, the two images of the source of light or of some well-defined object placed in front of the condensing lens, were made to coincide, the telescope was now adjusted for distinct vision of the expected interference-bands, and sodium light was substituted for white light, when the interference-bands appeared. These were now made as clear as possible by adjusting the mirror e_1; then white light was restored, the screw altering the length of path was very slowly moved (one turn of a screw of one hundred threads to the inch altering the path nearly 1000 wave-lengths) till the coloured interference-fringes reappeared in white light. These were now given a convenient width and position, and the apparatus was ready for observation.

The observations were conducted as follows:—Around the cast-iron trough were sixteen equidistant marks. The apparatus was revolved very slowly (one turn in six minutes) and after a few minutes the cross wire of the micrometer was set on the clearest of the interference-fringes at the instant of passing one of the marks. The motion was so slow that this could be done readily and accurately. The reading of the screw-head on the micrometer was noted, and a very slight and gradual impulse was given to keep up the motion of the stone; on passing the second mark, the same process was repeated, and this was continued till the apparatus had completed six revolutions. It was found that by keeping the apparatus in slow uniform motion, the results were much more uniform and consistent than when the stone was brought to rest for every observation; for the effects of strains could be noted for at least half a minute after the stone came to rest, and during this time effects of change of temperature came into action.

[Tabular data representing observations made at noon and near 6 P.M.

on three different days are omitted because the results are summed up in the curves presented in the following paragraph—Editors.]

The results of the observations are expressed graphically in [Fig. 25–6]. The upper is the curve for the observations at noon, and the lower that for the evening observations. The dotted curves represent *one-eighth* of the theoretical displacements. It seems fair to conclude from the figure that if there is any displacement due to the relative motion of the earth and the luminiferous aether, this cannot be much greater than 0.01 of the distance between the fringes.

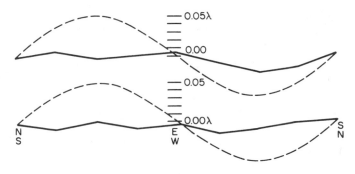

Fig. 25–6.

Considering the motion of the earth in its orbit only, this displacement should be

$$2D\,\frac{v^2}{V^2} = 2D \times 10^{-8}$$

The distance D was about eleven metres, or 2×10^7 wave-lengths of yellow light; hence the displacement to be expected was 0.4 fringe. The actual displacement was certainly less than the twentieth part of this, and probably less than the fortieth part. But since the displacement is proportional to the square of the velocity, the relative velocity of the earth and the aether is probably less than one sixth the earth's orbital velocity, and certainly less than one fourth.

In what precedes, only the orbital motion of the earth is considered. If this is combined with the motion of the solar system, concerning which but little is known with certainty, the result would have to be modified; and it is just possible that the resultant velocity at the time of the observations was small, though the chances are much against it. The experiment will therefore be repeated at intervals of three months, and thus all uncertainty will be avoided.

It appears from all that precedes reasonably certain that if there be any relative motion between the earth and the luminiferous aether, it must be small; quite small enough entirely to refute Fresnel's explanation of aberration. Stokes has given a theory of aberration which assumes the aether at the earth's surface to be at rest with regard to the latter, and only requires in addition that the relative velocity have a potential; but Lorentz shows that these conditions are incompatible. Lorentz then proposes a modification which combines some ideas of Stokes and Fresnel, and assumes the existence of a potential, together with Fresnel's coefficient. If now it were legitimate to conclude from the present work that the aether is at rest with regard to the earth's surface, according to Lorentz there could not be a velocity potential, and his own theory also fails. . . .

THE BEGINNINGS
OF MODERN
ATOMIC PHYSICS

ooooooooo

26

○○○○○○○○○○

THE DISCOVERY OF X-RAYS

○○○○○○○○○○

Wilhelm Conrad Roentgen (1845-1923)

The discovery of X-rays was made by Wilhelm Conrad Roentgen at the University of Würzburg, Germany, on November 2, 1895. From the beginning it was clear that a momentous and revolutionary find had been made but no public announcement was made until about seven weeks later when Roentgen submitted a preliminary paper entitled "On a New Kind of Rays" to the Physico-Medical Society of Würzburg on December 28. It was printed immediately in the proceedings [*Sitzungsberichte*] of the society for 1895. As might be supposed, these proceedings were not widely circulated or read, so that Roentgen, on receiving reprints, mailed them to a group of physicists and medical men in Europe, England, and America. It might have been expected that he would have sent his announcement to the *Annalen der Physik,* the leading German physical journal which had a world-wide circulation, but he did not. A reasonable explanation seems to be that Roentgen wanted not only to be very sure of his discovery but to establish the fundamental properties of the rays before others could do so. As time went on, however, the momentous character of the discovery became ever more apparent, and the necessity for communicating it the more pressing. Realizing that immediate publication could be had through a local scientific journal, it seems probable that he took advantage of this opportunity to establish his claim. Delay in announcement and caution in publication were characteristic of Roentgen. Zehnder, one of his pupils as well as one of his biographers, remarks that once Roentgen "set himself a problem he always worked at it quietly and secretly without allowing anybody a glimpse into his method of working and thinking."

385

Once the news was made public, it produced a sensation throughout the civilized world. Popular interest was greatly heightened by reports that X-ray pictures could be taken through walls and opaque screens and this caused a widespread apprehension that all privacy might be destroyed. While the penetrating property of the rays was correctly described, privacy was certainly not endangered owing to the cumbersome equipment necessary and the fact that the pictures are not taken by reflected radiation. The medical uses of the rays for photographing through the flesh and in detailing the bony structure of the body were immediately recognized. Other uses both possible and fanciful appeared in the newspapers almost daily.

Roentgen's second paper, dated March 9, 1896, also appeared in the *Würzburg Proceedings.* This second communication is reproduced with the first at the end of this article.

Roentgen's discovery of X-rays must, in most respects, be considered a lucky accident, but it must be remembered that chance favors the prepared mind. He had begun only a few weeks before to repeat some cathode ray experiments that had been reported by Lenard. In an interview in his laboratory Roentgen described the circumstances as follows:

I was working with a Crookes tube covered by a shield of black cardboard. A piece of barium platino-cyanide paper lay on the bench there. I had been passing a current through the tube and I noticed a peculiar black line across the paper. . . . The effect was one which could only be produced, in ordinary parlance, by the passage of light. No light could come from the tube, because the shield which covered it was impervious to any light known. . . . I assumed that the effect must have come from the tube, since its character indicated that it could come from nowhere else. I tested it. In a few minutes there was no doubt about it.[1]

These events occurred when he was fifty-one years old. The history of physics shows that most of the important discoveries have been made when their discoverers were relatively young. Whether age had any bearing on Roentgen's subsequent work is difficult to say, but it is interesting to note that he published only three papers dealing with the rays he discovered, two that are appended here and one other, and these were written shortly after the event. Although he had published over fifty papers before the three on X-rays, he published only three more between the latter part of 1897 and his death in 1923, and none of these was concerned with his rays.

The appended papers are translations of Roentgen's first two communications about the rays, which had appeared in the *Würzburg Sitzungs-*

---

[1] G. E. M. Jauncey, *American Journal of Physics,* 13 (1945), 360.

berichte. After describing the circumstances of the discovery, several salient properties of the rays are described. First he notes that all substances are more or less transparent to them but the denser substances, especially the heavy metals such as platinum and lead, are less so, although density is not the only factor to be considered. Next, detectors of X-rays are considered; besides fluorescence, the sensitivity of both photographic plates and films is noted. (It may be of interest to remind the reader at this juncture of Sir William Crookes's complaint to the Ilford Company regarding their photographic plates during the period when he was experimenting with cathode rays!) Roentgen goes on to say that X-rays are not ultraviolet rays because they cannot be refracted by prisms or lenses made of a variety of materials. (Later experiments were to show that a slight refraction can be observed, and that X-rays exhibit the properties of light waves of very short wavelength.) Also X-rays cannot be cathode rays because they cannot be deflected by a magnet, but they originate where cathode rays strike. Shadow pictures and pinhole photographs confirm the "ray" nature of X-rays but interference phenomena could not be produced. The first communication closes with the suggestion that X-rays are propagated as longitudinal vibrations in the ether, a guess that proved to be erroneous.

The second communication begins with the observation that X-rays make air conducting and discharge electrified bodies. Electrified bodies in dry hydrogen were also the subject of experiments with similar results. In highly exhausted spaces the discharge of a charged body proceeded much more slowly. All this, of course, is in complete accord with subsequent research which showed that the passage of X-rays through gases ionizes them, producing electrons from the gas atoms and leaving the residual atom, the ion, with a positive charge. As both charged particles are highly mobile, an electrified body attracts charges of the opposite sign and soon becomes discharged. The paper closes with some observations regarding the use of apparatus to generate X-rays and a comparison of aluminum and tungsten as sources of X-rays when they are struck with cathode rays.

Roentgen was such an interesting personality that before presenting the two papers just described, we shall briefly review his life.[2] Born at Lennep, near Düsseldorf in the Rhineland on March 27, 1845, he was the only child of a German father and a Dutch mother. Most of his childhood was spent in Holland. He received his early education in the gymnasium at Utrecht where, toward the end of his course of studies, he ran into trouble. Being caught in a youthful prank, he rather too emphatically refused to implicate others concerned. As a result he was expelled from the gym-

---

[2] The biographical sketch included here closely follows a capsule biography by G. E. M. Jauncy, *ibid.*, pp. 368–369.

nasium. This misfortune prevented his entrance to the Hochschule at Utrecht. Then, he learned that it was possible to enter the Polytechnic at Zürich, Switzerland, without a certificate. In 1863 he was accepted as a student in machine construction at Zürich, but he was hardly an eager beaver. The lake with its surrounding mountains often drew him from the laboratory on lengthy walks.

During his three years of study, he attended lectures on mathematics and on the mathematical theory of heat, the latter subject being taught by Clausius. In 1866 he obtained the diploma of mechanical engineer. But his interest was in experimental physics and he continued his studies at Zürich under Kundt, an experimental physicist. He obtained his doctorate in 1869. Along with Kundt he went to Würzburg, Bavaria, in 1870, where academic customs seemed to annoy him. In 1872 Kundt was called to Strasbourg and Roentgen accompanied him. The university had just been organized, and Roentgen was free from bothersome traditions. In 1874 he was made a *Privatdozent* at Strasbourg, and all obstacles to his career were then removed. In 1875 he became professor of mathematics and physics at the Agricultural Academy of Hohenheim. In 1876 he returned to Strasbourg as professor of theoretical physics. In 1879 he was appointed professor of physics and director of the Physical Institute at Giessen. In 1888 he was called to the chair of physics at Würzburg, as successor to Kohlrausch, and some seven years later made his discovery of X-rays.

In an obituary article in the September 1, 1923, issue of the *Physikalische Zeitschrift*, W. Friedrich of Freiburg describes Roentgen as being primarily an experimental physicist. He was the same type of physicist as Michelson, for his interest was in experiments requiring extreme precision. As noted earlier, he was reluctant to publish his results. Because he was so very careful, he never had to revise the experimental results reported in any of his papers. His attitude toward theoretical physics was similar to Faraday's in that he liked to think in terms of mechanical models. At the time of his great discovery, he believed in the elastic-solid theory of the ether. The idea of longitudinal waves in the ether were not abhorrent to him.

Friedrich states that Roentgen published a total of fifty-nine papers. Of these papers, as we have mentioned, only three cover his famous work on X-rays. His first paper was by far the most important of these. The other two are no more significant than many other contemporary reports on the rays.

Roentgen's work on X-rays was completed in a period of about eighteen months in the fifty-first and fifty-second years of his life, after which his active interest returned to those fields in which he had previously been interested. He thereafter avoided any further exploration into the new realm. We remember the names of J. J. Thomson, Barkla, W. H. and

W. L. Bragg, von Laue, and others. Roentgen was in his fifties and sixties while these men were doing such brilliant work in X-rays. The discovery of X-rays may have come too late in Roentgen's life. Thomson was not quite thirty-eight years old, and the others were even younger at the time of the discovery. The discovery might have been too iconoclastic for Roentgen's mind. There is quite a lot to be said for the view that physics is a young man's science because an open mind is a prime requirement for advance.

In 1900, Roentgen left Würzburg and became professor of experimental physics and director of the Physical Institute at Munich. A year later, he received the first Nobel Prize in physics. Friedrich says that, although Roentgen was aware of the practical value of his discovery, he held himself remote from the fast-developing technology of X-rays. Nor was it consistent with his modest scientific nature to exploit his discovery in a monetary way. According to his biographer, as Roentgen became older and his reputation grew, he turned all the more from this publicity back to the companionship of the world of nature. At Munich he spent much time in the mountain village of Weilheim, where he owned a cottage. With his colleagues, he was reserved almost to the point of unfriendliness, yet he invited his students to the cottage to chat and play ninepins. He hunted game in the mountains surrounding his cottage.

His wife died after a long illness in 1919, and he retired from his chair at Munich in the spring of 1920. On July 22, 1920, his last article—on photoconductivity—was sent to the *Annalen*. This article appears in the January 1, 1921, issue. It was written when he was seventy-five and is one of his outstanding contributions to physics. After a short illness, he died on February 10, 1923.

ooooooo

ROENTGEN

On a New Kind of Rays [3]

FIRST COMMUNICATION

1. IF THE DISCHARGE OF A fairly large induction-coil be made to pass through a Hittorf vacuum-tube, or through a Lenard tube, a Crookes tube, or other similar apparatus, which has been suf-

---

[3] Wilhelm Conrad Roentgen, trans., G. F. Barker, *Harpers Scientific Memoir* (1898); *American Journal of Physics,* 13 (1945), 284–291.

ficiently exhausted, the tube being covered with thin, black card-board which fits it with tolerable closeness, and if the whole apparatus be placed in a completely darkened room, there is observed at each discharge a bright illumination of a paper screen covered with barium platino-cyanide, placed in the vicinity of the induction-coil, the fluorescence thus produced being entirely independent of the fact whether the coated or the plain surface is turnd towards the discharge-tube. This fluorescence is visible even when the paper screen is at a distance of two metres from the apparatus.

It is easy to prove that the cause of the fluorescence proceeds from the discharge-apparatus, and not from any other point in the conducting circuit.

2. The most striking feature of this phenomenon is the fact that an active agent here passes through a black card-board envelope, which is opaque to the visible and the ultra-violet rays of the sun or of the electric arc; an agent, too, which has the power of producing active fluorescence. Hence we may first investigate the question whether other bodies also possess this property.

We soon discover that all bodies are transparent to this agent, though in very different degrees. I proceed to give a few examples: Paper is very transparent *; behind a bound book of about one thousand pages I saw the fluorescent screen light up brightly, the printers' ink offering scarcely a noticeable hindrance. In the same way the fluorescence appeared behind a double pack of cards; a single card held between the apparatus and the screen being almost unnoticeable to the eye. A single sheet of tin-foil is also scarcely perceptible; it is only after several layers have been placed over one another that their shadow is distinctly seen on the screen. Thick blocks of wood are also transparent, pine boards two or three centimetres thick absorbing only slightly. A plate of aluminum about fifteen millimetres thick, though it enfeebled the action seriously, did not cause the fluorescence to disappear entirely. Sheets of hard rubber several centimetres thick still permit the rays to pass through them.† Glass plates of equal thickness behave quite differently, according as they contain lead (flint-glass) or not; the former are much less transparent than the latter. If the hand be held between the discharge-tube and the screen, the darker shadow of the bones is seen within the slightly dark shadow-image of the hand itself. Water, carbon disulphide, and various other liquids, when they are examined in mica vessels, seem also to be transparent. That hydrogen is to any considerable degree more transparent than air I have

---

* By "transparency" of a body I denote the relative brightness of a fluorescent screen placed close behind the body, referred to the brightness which the screen shows under the same circumstances, though without the interposition of the body.

† For brevity's sake I shall use the expression "rays"; and to distinguish them from others of this name I shall call them "X-rays." (See Sec. 14.)

not been able to discover. Behind plates of copper, silver, lead, gold, and platinum the fluorescence may still be recognized, though only if the thickness of the plates is not too great. Platinum of a thickness of 0.2 millimetre is still transparent; the silver and copper plates may even be thicker. Lead of a thickness of 1.5 millimetres is practically opaque; and on account of this property this metal is frequently most useful. A rod of wood and with a square cross-section (20×20 millimetres), one of whose sides is painted white with lead paint, behaves differently according as to how it is held between the apparatus and the screen. It is almost entirely without action when the X-rays pass through it parallel to the painted side; whereas the stick throws a dark shadow when the rays are made to traverse it perpendicular to the painted side. In a series similar to that of the metals themselves their salts can be arranged with reference to their transparency, either in the solid form or in solution.

3. The experimental results which have now been given, as well as others, lead to the conclusion that the transparency of different substances, assumed to be of equal thickness, is essentially conditioned upon their density: no other property makes itself felt like this, certainly to so high a degree.

The following experiments show, however, that the density is not the only cause acting. I have examined, with reference to their transparency, plates of glass, aluminium, calcite, and quartz, of nearly the same thickness; and while these substances are almost equal in density, yet it was quite evident that the calcite was sensibly less transparent than the other substances, which appeared almost exactly alike. No particularly strong fluorescence (see Sec. 6) of calcite, especially by comparison with glass, has been noticed.

4. All substances with increase in thickness become less transparent. In order to find a possible relation between transparency and thickness, I have made photographs (see Sec. 6) in which portions of the photographic plate were covered with layers of tin-foil, varying in the number of sheets superposed. Photometric measurements of these will be made when I am in possession of a suitable photometer.

5. Sheets of platinum, lead, zinc, and aluminium were rolled of such thickness that all appeared nearly equally transparent. The following table contains the absolute thickness of these sheets measured in millimetres, the relative thickness referred to that of the platinum sheet, and their densities:

Thickness	Relative Thickness	Density
Pt 0.018 mm	1	21.5
Pb 0.05 mm	3	11.3
Zn 0.10 mm	6	7.1
Al 3.5 mm	200	2.6

We may conclude from these values that different metals possess transparencies which are by no means equal, even when the product of thickness and density is the same. The transparency increases much more rapidly than this product decreases.

6. The fluorescence of barium platino-cyanide is not the only recognizable effect of the X-rays. It should be mentioned that other bodies also fluoresce; such, for instance, as the phosphorescent calcium compounds, then uranium glass, ordinary glass, calcite, rock-salt, and so on.

Of special significance in many respects is the fact that photographic dry plates are sensitive to the X-rays. We are, therefore, in a condition to determine more definitely many phenomena, and so the more easily to avoid deception; wherever it has been possible, therefore, I have controlled, by means of photography, every important observation which I have made with the eye by means of the fluorescent screen.

In these experiments the property of the rays to pass almost unhindered through thin sheets of wood, paper, and tin-foil is most important. The photographic impressions can be obtained in a non-darkened room with the photographic plates either in the holders or wrapped up in paper. On the other hand, from this property it results as a consequence that undeveloped plates cannot be left for a long time in the neighborhood of the discharge tube, if they are protected merely by the usual covering of pasteboard and paper.

It appears questionable, however, whether the chemical action on the silver salts of the photographic plates is directly caused by the X-rays. It is possible that this action proceeds from the fluorescent light which, as noted above, is produced in the glass plate itself or perhaps in the layer of gelatin. "Films" can be used just as well as glass plates.

I have not yet been able to prove experimentally that the X-rays are able also to produce a heating action; yet we may well assume that this effect is present, since the capability of the X-rays to be transformed is proved by means of the observed fluorescence phenomena. It is certain, therefore, that all the X-rays which fall upon a substance do not leave it again as such.

The retina of the eye is not sensitive to these rays. Even if the eye is brought close to the discharge-tube, it observes nothing, although, as experiment has proved, the media contained in the eye must be sufficiently transparent to transmit the rays.

7. After I had recognized the transparency of various substances of relatively considerable thickness, I hastened to see how the X-rays behaved on passing through a prism, and to find whether they were thereby deviated or not.

Experiments with water and with carbon disulphide enclosed in mica prisms of about 30° refracting angle showed no deviation, either with the fluorescent screen or on the photographic plate. For purposes of comparison the deviation of rays of ordinary light under the same conditions was observed; and it was noted that in this case the deviated images fell on the plate about 10 or 20 millimetres distant from the direct image. By means of prisms made of hard rubber and of aluminium, also of about 30° refracting angle, I have obtained images on the photographic plate in which some small deviation may perhaps be recognized. However, the fact is quite uncertain; the deviation, if it does exist, being so small that in any case the refractive index of the X-rays in the substances named cannot be more than 1.05 at the most. With a fluorescent screen I was also unable to observe any deviation.

Up to the present time experiments with prisms of denser metals have given no definite results, owing to their feeble transparency and the consequently diminished intensity of the transmitted rays.

With reference to the general conditions here involved on the one hand, and on the other to the importance of the question whether the X-rays can be refracted or not on passing from one medium into another, it is most fortunate that this subject may be investigated in still another way than with the aid of prisms. Finely divided bodies in sufficiently thick layers scatter the incident light and allow only a little of it to pass, owing to reflection and refraction; so that if powders are as transparent to X-rays as the same substances are in mass—equal amounts of material being presupposed—it follows at once that neither refraction nor regular reflection takes place to any sensible degree. Experiments were tried with finely powdered rock-salt, with fine electrolytic silver-powder, and with zinc-dust, such as is used in chemical investigations. In all these cases no difference was detected between the transparency of the powder and that of the substance in mass, either by observation with the fluorescent screen or with the photographic plate.

From what has now been said it is obvious that the X-rays cannot be concentrated by lenses; neither a large lens of hard rubber nor a glass lens having any influence upon them. The shadow-picture of a round rod is darker in the middle than at the edge; while the image of a tube which is filled with a substance more transparent than its own material is lighter at the middle than at the edge.

8. The question as to the reflection of the X-rays may be regarded as settled, by the experiments mentioned in the preceding paragraph, in favor of the view that no noticeable regular reflection of the rays takes place from any of the substances examined. Other experiments, which I here omit, lead to the same conclusion.

One observation in this connection should, however, be mentioned, as at first sight it seems to prove the opposite. I exposed to the X-rays a photographic plate which was protected from the light by black paper, and the glass side of which was turned towards the discharge-tube giving the X-rays. The sensitive film was covered, for the most part, with polished plates of platinum, lead, zinc, and aluminium arranged in the form of a star. On the developed negative it was seen plainly that the darkening under the platinum, the lead, and particularly the zinc, was stronger than under the other plates, the aluminium having exerted no action at all. It appears, therefore, that these three metals reflect the rays. Since, however, other explanations of the stronger darkening are conceivable, in a second experiment, in order to be sure, I placed between the sensitive film and the metal plates a piece of thin aluminium-foil, which is opaque to ultra-violet rays, but is very transparent to the X-rays. Since the same result substantially was again obtained, the reflection of X-rays from the metals above named is proved.

If we compare this fact with the observation already mentioned that powders are as transparent as coherent masses, and with the further fact that bodies with rough surfaces behave like polished bodies with reference to the passage of the X-rays, as shown also in the last experiment, we are led to the conclusion already stated that regular reflection does not take place, but that bodies behave towards the X-rays as turbid media do towards light.

Since, moreover, I could detect no evidence of refraction of these rays in passing from one medium into another, it would seem that X-rays move with the same velocity in all substances; and, further, that this speed is the same in the medium which is present everywhere in space and in which the particles of matter are imbedded. These particles hinder the propagation of the X-rays, the effect being greater, in general, the more dense the substance concerned.

9. Accordingly it might be possible that the arrangement of particles in the substance exercised an influence on its transparency; that, for instance, a piece of calcite might be transparent in different degrees for the same thickness, according as it is traversed in the direction of the axis, or at right angles to it. Experiments, however, on calcite and quartz gave a negative result.

10. It is well known that Lenard came to the conclusion, from the results of his beautiful experiments on the transmission of the cathode rays of Hittorf through a thin sheet of aluminium, that these rays are phenomena of the ether, and that they diffuse themselves through all bodies. We can say the same of our rays.

In his most recent research, Lenard has determined the absorptive power of different substances for the cathode rays, and, among others, has measured it for air from atmospheric pressure to 4.10, 3.40, 3.10, referred to 1 centimetre, according to the rarefaction of the gas contained in the discharge-apparatus. Judging from the discharge-pressure as estimated from the sparking distance, I have had to do in my experiments for the most part with rarefactions of the same order of magnitude, and only rarely with less or greater ones. I have succeeded in comparing by means of the L. Weber photometer—I do not possess a better one—the intensities, taken in atmospheric air, of the fluorescence of my screen at two distances from the discharge-apparatus—about 100 and 200 millimetres; and I have found from three experiments, which agree very well with each other, that the intensities vary inversely as the squares of the distances of the screen from the discharge-apparatus. Accordingly, air absorbs a far smaller fraction of the X-rays than of the cathode rays. This result is in entire agreement with the observation mentioned above, that it is still possible to detect the fluorescent light at a distance of 2 metres from the discharge-apparatus.

Other substances behave in general like air; they are more transparent to X-rays than to cathode rays.

11. A further difference, and a most important one, between the behavior of cathode rays and of X-rays lies in the fact that I have not succeeded, in spite of many attempts, in obtaining a deflection of the X-rays by a magnet, even in very intense fields.

The possibility of deflection by a magnet has, up to the present time, served as a characteristic property of the cathode rays; although it was observed by Hertz and Lenard that there are different sorts of cathode rays, "which are distinguished from each other by their production of phosphorescence, by the amount of their absorption, and by the extent of their deflection by a magnet." A considerable deflection, however, was noted in all of the cases investigated by them; so that I do not think that this characteristic will be given up except for stringent reasons.

12. According to experiments especially designed to test the question, it is certain that the spot on the wall of the discharge-tube which fluoresces the strongest is to be considered as the main centre from which the X-rays radiate in all directions. The X-rays proceed from that spot where, according to the data obtained by different investigators, the cathode rays strike the glass wall. If the cathode rays within the discharge-apparatus are deflected by means of a magnet, it is observed that the X-rays proceed from another spot—namely, from that which is the new terminus of the cathode rays.

For this reason, therefore, the X-rays, which it is impossible to deflect, cannot be cathode rays simply transmitted or reflected without change by the glass wall. The greater density of the gas outside of the discharge-tube certainly cannot account for the great difference in the deflection, according to Lenard.

I therefore reach the conclusion that the X-rays are not identical with the cathode rays, but that they are produced by the cathode rays at the glass wall of the discharge-apparatus.

13. This production does not take place in glass alone, but, as I have

been able to observe in an apparatus closed by a plate of aluminium 2 millimetres thick, in this metal also. Other substances are to be examined later.

14. The justification for calling by the name "rays" the agent which proceeds from the wall of the discharge-apparatus I derive in part from the entirely regular formation of shadows, which are seen when more or less transparent bodies are brought between the apparatus and the fluorescent screen (or the photographic plate).

I have observed, and in part photographed, many shadow-pictures of this kind, the production of which has a particular charm. I possess, for instance, photographs of the shadow of the profile of a door which separates the rooms in which, on one side, the discharge-apparatus was placed, on the other the photographic plate; the shadow of the bones of the hand; the shadow of a covered wire wrapped on a wooden spool; of a set of weights enclosed in a box; of a galvanometer in which the magnetic needle is entirely enclosed by metal; of a piece of metal whose lack of homogeneity becomes noticeable by means of the X-rays, etc.

Another conclusive proof of the rectilinear propagation of the X-rays is a pin-hole photograph which I was able to make of the discharge-apparatus while it was enveloped in black paper; the picture is weak but unmistakably correct.

15. I have tried in many ways to detect interference phenomena of the X-rays; but, unfortunately, without success, perhaps only because of their feeble intensity.

16. Experiments have been begun, but are not yet finished, to ascertain whether electrostatic forces affect the X-rays in any way.

17. In considering the question what are the X-rays—which, as we have seen, cannot be cathode rays—we may perhaps at first be led to think of them as ultra-violet light, owing to their active fluorescence and their chemical actions. But in so doing we find ourselves opposed by the most weighty considerations. If the X-rays are ultra-violet light, this light must have the following properties:

(a) On passing from air into water, carbon disulphide, aluminium, rocksalt, glass, zinc, etc., it suffers no noticeable refraction.

(b) By none of the bodies named can it be regularly reflected to any appreciable extent.

(c) It cannot be polarized by any of the ordinary methods.

(d) Its absorption is influenced by no other property of substances so much as by their density.

That is to say, we must assume that these ultra-violet rays behave entirely different from the ultra-red, visible, and ultra-violet rays which have been known up to this time.

I have been unable to come to this conclusion, and so have sought for another explanation.

There seems to exist some kind of relationship between the new rays and light rays; at least this is indicated by the formation of shadows, the fluorescence and the chemical action produced by them both. Now, we have known for a long time that there can be in the ether longitudinal vibrations besides the transverse light-vibrations; and, according to the views of different physicists, these vibrations must exist. Their existence, it is true, has not been proved up to the present, and consequently their properties have not been investigated by experiment.

Ought not, therefore, the new rays to be ascribed to longitudinal vibrations in the ether?

I must confess that in the course of the investigation I have become more and more confident of the correctness of this idea, and so, therefore, permit myself to announce this conjecture, although I am perfectly aware that the explanation given still needs further confirmation.

SECOND COMMUNICATION

Since my work must be interrupted for several weeks, I take the opportunity of presenting in the following paper some new phenomena which I have observed.

18. It was known to me at the time of my first publication that X-rays can discharge electrified bodies; and I conjecture that in Lenard's experiments it was the X-rays, and not the cathode rays, which had passed unchanged through the aluminium window of his apparatus, which produced the action described by him upon electrified bodies at a distance. I have, however, delayed the publication of my experiments until I could contribute results which are free from criticism.

These results can be obtained only when the observations are made in a space which is protected completely, not only from the electrostatic forces proceeding from the vacuum-tube, from the conducting wires, from the induction apparatus, etc., but is also closed against air which comes from the neighborhood of the discharge-apparatus.

To secure these conditions I had a chamber made of zinc plates soldered together, which was large enough to contain myself and the necessary apparatus, which could be closed airtight, and which was provided with an opening which could be closed by a zinc door. The wall opposite the door was for the most part covered with lead. At a place near the discharge-apparatus, which was set up outside the case, the zinc wall, together with the lining of sheet-lead, was cut out for a width of 4 centimeters; and the opening was covered again air-tight with a thin sheet of aluminium. The X-rays penetrated through this window into the observation space.

I observed the following phenomena:

(*a*) Electrified bodies in air, charged either positively or negatively, are discharged if X-rays fall upon them; and this process goes on the more

rapidly the more intense the rays are. The intensity of the rays was estimated by their action on a fluorescent screen or a photographic plate.

It is immaterial in general whether the electrified bodies are conductors
or insulators. Up to the present I have not found any specific difference
in the behavior of different bodies with reference to the rate of discharge;
nor as to the behavior of positive and negative electricity. Yet it is not
impossible that small differences may exist.

(b) If the electrified conductor be surrounded not by air but by a solid
insulator, e.g. paraffin, the radiation has the same action as would result
from exposure of the insulating envelope to a flame connected to the earth.

(c) If this insulating envelope be surrounded by a close-fitting conductor which is connected to the earth, and which, like the insulator, is
transparent to X-rays, the radiation produces on the inner electrified
conductor no action which can be detected by my apparatus.

(d) The observations noted under (a), (b), (c) indicate that air
through which X-rays have passed possesses the power of discharging
electrified bodies with which it comes in contact.

(e) If this is really the case, and if, further, the air retains this property
for some time after it has been exposed to the X-rays, then it must be
possible to discharge electrified bodies which have not been themselves exposed to the rays, by conducting to them air which has thus been exposed.

We may convince ourselves in various ways that this conclusion is correct. One method of experiment, although perhaps not the simplest, I
shall describe.

I used a brass tube 3 centimetres wide and 45 centimetres long; at a
distance of some centimetres from one end a part of the wall of the tube
was cut away and replaced by a thin aluminium plate; at the other end,
through an air-tight cap, a brass ball fastened to a metal rod was introduced into the tube in such a manner as to be insulated. Between the ball
and the closed end of the tube there was soldered a side-tube which could
be connected with an exhaust-apparatus; so that when this is in action the
brass ball is subjected to a stream of air which on its way through the tube
has passed by the aluminium window. The distance from the window to
the ball was over 20 centimetres.

I arranged this tube inside the zinc chamber in such a position that the
X-rays could enter through the aluminium window of the tube perpendicular to its axis. The insulated ball lay then in the shadow, out of the range
of the action of these rays. The tube and the zinc case were connected by
a conductor, the ball was joined to a Hankel electroscope.

It was now observed that a charge (either positive or negative) given to
the ball was not influenced by the X-rays so long as the air remained at
rest in the tube, but that the charge instantly decreased considerably if

by exhaustion the air which had been subjected to the rays was drawn past the ball. If by means of storage cells the ball was maintained at a constant potential, and if the modified air was drawn continuously through the tube, an electric current arose just as if the ball were connected to the wall of the tube by a poor conductor.

(*f*) The question arises, How does the air lose the property which is given it by the X-rays? It is not yet settled whether it loses this property gradually of itself—i.e., without coming in contact with other bodies. On the other hand, it is certain that a brief contact with a body of large surface, which does not need to be electrified, can make the air inactive. For instance, if a thick enough stopper of wadding is pushed into the tube so far that the modified air must pass through it before it reaches the electrified ball, the charge on the ball remains unaffected even while the exhaustion is taking place.

If the wad is in front of the aluminium window, the result obtained is the same as it would be without the wad; a proof that it is not particles of dust which are the cause of the observed discharge.

Wire gratings act like wadding; but the gratings must be very fine, and many layers must be placed over each other if the modified air is to be inactive after it is drawn through them. If these gratings are not connected to the earth, as has been assumed, but are connected to a source of electricity at a constant potential, I have always observed exactly what I had expected; but these experiments are not yet completed.

(*g*) If the electrified bodies, instead of being in air, are placed in dry hydrogen, they are also discharged by the X-rays. The discharge in hydrogen seemed to me to proceed somewhat more slowly; yet this is still uncertain on account of the difficulty of obtaining exactly equal intensities of the X-rays in consecutive experiments.

The method of filling the apparatus with hydrogen precludes the possibility that the layer of air which was originally present, condensed on the surface of the bodies, played any important rôle.

(*h*) In spaces which are highly exhausted the discharge of a body by the direct incidence of X-rays proceeds much more slowly—in one case about seventy times more slowly—than in the same vessels when filled with air or hydrogen at atmospheric pressure.

(*i*) Experiments are about to be begun on the behavior of a mixture of chlorine and hydrogen under the influence of X-rays.

(*j*) In conclusion I would like to mention that the results of investigations on the discharging action of X-rays in which the influence of the surrounding gas is not taken into account should be received with great caution.

19. It is advantageous in many cases to include a Tesla apparatus (condenser and transformer) between the discharge-apparatus which

furnishes the X-rays and the induction-coil. This arrangement has the following advantages: first, the discharge-apparatus is less easily penetrated and is less heated; second, the vacuum maintains itself for a longer time, at least in my self-constructed apparatus; third, many discharge-tubes under these conditions give more intense X-rays. With tubes which have not been exhausted sufficiently or have been exhausted too much to be driven satisfactorily by the induction-coil alone, the addition of the Tesla transformer renders good service.

The question immediately arises—and I allow myself to mention it without being able to contribute anything to its solution at present—whether X-rays can be produced by a continuous discharge under constant difference of potential; or whether variations of this potential are essential and necessary for the production of the rays.

20. In paragraph 13 of my first memoir I announced that X-rays could originate not only in glass, but in aluminium also. In the continuation of my experiments in this direction I have not found any solid body which cannot, under the action of the cathode rays, produce X-rays. There is also no reason known to me why liquids and gases may not behave in the same manner.

Quantitative differences in the behavior of different substances have appeared, however. If, for instance, the cathode rays fall upon a plate one half of which is made of platinum 0.3 millimetre thick, the other half of aluminium 1 millimetre thick, we see on the photographic image of this double plate, taken by means of a pin-hole camera, that the platinum sends out many more X-rays from the side struck by the cathode rays (the front side) than does the aluminium from the same side. However, from the rear side the platinum emits practically no X-rays, while the aluminium sends out relatively many. These last rays are produced in the front layers of the aluminium and pass through the plate.

We can easily devise an explanation of this observation, yet it may be advisable to learn other properties of the X-rays before so doing.

It must be mentioned, however, that there is a practical importance in the facts observed. For the production of the most intense X-rays platinum is best suited, according to my experiments up to the present. I have used for some weeks with great success a discharge-apparatus in which the cathode is a concave mirror of aluminium, and the anode is a plate of platinum placed at the centre of curvature of the mirror and inclined to the axis of the mirror at an angle of 45°.

21. The X-rays proceed in this case from the anode. I must conclude, though, from experiments with apparatus of different kinds that it is entirely immaterial, so far as the intensity of the X-rays is concerned, whether the place where the rays are produced is the anode or not.

A discharge-apparatus was prepared specially for experiments with the alternating currents of the Tesla transformer; in it both electrodes were aluminium concave mirrors whose axes were at right angles; at their common centre of curvature there was placed a platinum plate to receive the cathode rays. Further information will be given later as to the usefulness of this apparatus.

27

ooooooooooo

THE DISCOVERY

OF RADIOACTiVITY

ooooooooooo

Antoine Henri Becquerel (1852-1908)

In the biography of Bernoulli, the rarity of outstanding scientific ability recurring in several generations in one family was remarked. The Bernoullis have already been cited as an exception, and to this we must add the Becquerels. The earliest of this family to distinguish himself was Antoine César. His intellectual activity extended from 1819 to 1879 and he was honored with the Royal Society's Copley medal in 1837 for his pioneer work in electrochemistry. His son Alexander Edmund authored published works extending from 1839 to 1883. Alexander Edmund's son Antoine Henri, the subject of this article and the most illustrious of the name, produced his first scientific paper in 1875 and his last in 1908. To this unequaled roster we must add Henri's son Jean Becquerel, who distinguished the family name in physics until 1953.

The first three Becquerels all contributed to the study of phosphorescence and fluorescence and Henri was acutely aware of the continuity of this research in his family. Working in the same laboratory and with the same instruments as his father and grandfather, he keenly felt the necessity of honorably discharging the responsibility of his lineage. Thus in speaking of his own work on radioactivity, of which he was the discoverer, he minimized his contribution by saying that "These discoveries are only the lineal descendants of those of my father and grandfather on phosphorescence, and without them my own discoveries would have been impossible."

Henri Becquerel was born in Paris, December 15, 1852. His early education was received at the Lycée Louis le Grand and he entered the

402

École Polytechnique at the age of nineteen, in 1872. Two years later he became a pupil at the École des Ponts et Chaussées. He was made engineer in 1877 and subsequently for ten years chief engineer. In 1876, at twenty-three, he became demonstrator at the École Polytechnique and two years later *aide-naturaliste* at the Musée d'Histoire Naturelle. In both of these positions he was subordinate to his father Edmund. He succeeded his father as professor in each of these institutions; at the Musée in 1892 where not only his father but his grandfather, as well as Gay-Lussac, had occupied the chair, and at the École Polytechnique in 1895. It is noteworthy that Henri's son Jean also succeeded to the professorship at the Musée, being the fourth in line to hold the post.

In addition to his researches on phosphorescence Henri Becquerel's early researches were concerned with the Faraday effect, i.e., the rotation of the plane of polarization of linearly polarized light under the action of a magnetic field. Subsequently he devoted his attention to spectroscopy and the absorption spectra of didymium and neodymium. Following Roentgen's announcement of the discovery of X-rays, which were associated at the time with the appearance of phosphorescence on the glass walls of Crookes tubes, Becquerel, following a suggestion of Poincaré, attacked with renewed vigor the researches which his father had made on phosphorescence with the use of uranium salts. A more fortunate choice in the search for penetrating radiations could hardly have been made. Becquerel began his work sharing the popular hunch that the penetrating X-rays were associated with phosphorescence. Using the double sulfate of uranium and potassium he exposed this salt to the sun for several hours. When the photographic plate on which it was placed was developed, the plate showed the outline of the salt, indicating the presence of a penetrating radiation. These researches led to the discovery of radioactivity, as explained in the two papers that follow this commentary. For this discovery he received the Rumford medal of the Royal Society in 1900 and the Helmholtz medal in Berlin in 1901. He was made a foreign member of the Royal Society, and of the academies in Berlin and Rome, as well as the National Academy of Sciences in Washington. Other honors were honorary degrees from the universities of Oxford and Cambridge. In 1903 he shared the Nobel Prize in physics with Pierre and Marie Curie. In 1908 he was elected president of the Academie des Sciences, an honor which he enjoyed only briefly. Accustomed to such strenuous exercise as mountain climbing and ocean swimming, he had no intimation of the heart attack from which he died on August 25, 1908, at the age of fifty-five, while on holiday at Le Croisic on the west coast of France.

ɷɷɷɷɷɷɷ

BECQUEREL

On Radiations Emitted with Phosphorescence [1]

. . . M. NIEWENGLOWSKI HAS FOUND THAT commercial phosphorescent calcium sulfide emits radiations which pass through opaque bodies. This action also occurs in several other phosphorescent bodies and in particular in the salts of uranium in which the phosphorescence is of very short duration. With the double sulfate of uranium and potassium of which I possess crystals in the form of a thin transparent crust I have made the following experiment:

A Lumière photographic plate with bromide emulsion was wrapped with two sheets of very thick black paper, such that the plate did not become clouded by exposure to the sun after a whole day.

A layer of the phosphorescent substance was placed on the outside of the paper and the combination exposed to the sun for several hours. When the photographic plate was developed, the silhouette of the phosphorescent substance appeared black on the negative. If one interposed a coin or a metal screen pierced by an openwork design between the phosphorescent substance and the paper the image of these objects appeared on the negative.

These same experiments may be repeated by interposing between the phosphorescent substance and the paper a thin glass sheet which excludes the possibility of chemical action resulting from vapors coming from the substance when heated by the sun's rays.

It is necessary to conclude from these experiments that the phosphorescent substance in question emits radiations that penetrate paper opaque to light and that reduce silver salts.

---

[1] Henri Becquerel, *Comptes Rendus*, 122 (1896) 420. Trans. Editors.

On the Invisible Radiations Emitted by Phosphorescent Bodies [2]

. . . THE EXPERIMENTS WHICH I WILL report have been made with radiations emitted by crystalline plates of the double sulfate of uranium and potassium $(SO_4(UO)K + H_2O)$, bodies whose phosphorescence is very strong and whose luminous persistence is less than one one-hundredth of a second.

[The author summarizes some experiments showing that the radiation from this uranium salt exposes a photographic plate encased in a light-tight enclosure by penetrating the enclosure walls which may be made of paper or a thin sheet of aluminum or copper—Editors.]

. . . I stress particularly the following fact which appears to me very important and outside the phenomena which one expects to see: the same crystalline lamellae placed facing the photographic plates in the same way and acting through the same screen but protected from excitation by incident radiation and kept in the dark, still produce the same photographic effects. I was led to make this observation in the following way: Among the preceding experiments, several had been prepared on Wednesday, the twenty-sixth, and Thursday, the twenty-seventh of February and as on those days the sun shone only intermittently, I kept my experiments all prepared and returned the plate holders to the darkness of the table drawer, leaving the uranium salts in place. The sun not showing itself again for several days, I developed the photographic plates on the first of March expecting to find very faint images. The silhouettes appeared on the contrary with great intensity. I thought at once that the action must go on in the dark and I arranged the following experiment.

On the bottom of an opaque cardboard box I placed a photographic plate and on the emulsion face a thin convex flake of uranium salt which touched the bromide emulsion only in a few points. Beside it, I placed on the same plate another flake of the same salt, separated from the emulsion by a thin sheet of glass. This operation performed in a dark room, the box was closed, encased in another cardboard box, then placed in a drawer.

I followed the same procedure with a holder containing a photographic plate and closed by an aluminum plate. Then on the outside I put a thin layer of uranium salt. The combination was enclosed in an opaque cardboard box, then placed in a drawer. After five hours I developed the

[2] *Ibid.*, pp. 501–503. Trans. Editors.

plates and the silhouettes of the crystalline flakes appeared black as in the preceding experiments and as if they had been made by phosphorescent light. For the salt placed directly on the emulsion, there was hardly any difference in the action between the points of contact and the different parts of the crystals which were separated by about a millimeter from the emulsion. The difference can be attributed to the different distances from the source of the active radiations. The action of the crystals placed on the sheet of glass was very slightly enfeebled but the form of the layer was very well reproduced. Finally in penetrating the aluminum sheet the effect was considerably enfeebled but still very clear.

It is important to note that the phenomena do not appear attributable to the luminous radiations emitted by phosphorescence since after about one one-hundredth of a second, these radiations became so feeble that they are hardly perceptible.

An hypothesis which naturally presents itself is to suppose that the radiations, the effects of which have a great analogy to those produced by the radiations studied by Messrs. Lenard and Roentgen, are invisible radiations emitted with phosphorescence and of which the persistence is infinitely longer than that of the luminous radiations emitted by these bodies. Nevertheless the present experiments, without being contrary to this hypothesis, do not require this formulation. The experiments which I am currently following will bring, I hope, further clarification to this new order of phenomena. . . .

Emission of New Radiations by Metallic Uranium [3]

A FEW MONTHS AGO I showed that the salts of uranium emitted radiations whose existence had not previously been recognized and that these radiations possessed remarkable properties some of which are similar to the properties of the rays studied by M. Roentgen. The radiations of the uranium salts are emitted not only when the substances are exposed to light, but also when they are kept in the dark and for more than two months the same pieces of different salts kept protected from all known exciting radiations, continued to emit, almost without perceptible enfeeblement, the new radiations. From the third of March to the third of May these substances were enclosed in an opaque cardboard box. Since the third of May, they have been in a double box of lead which did not leave the darkroom. A very simple arrangement makes it

---

[3] *Ibid.*, pp. 1086–1088. Trans. Editors.

possible to slip a photographic plate under a black paper stretched parallel to the bottom of the box on which the substance undergoing tests rests without the substance being exposed to any radiation which does not pass through the lead. . . .

Under these conditions the substances studied continued to emit the active radiations.

[The author then comments briefly on the effect of external stimulation of the salts such as that of the sun, an electric arc and the spark discharge of a Leyden jar, also, erroneously, their resemblance on refraction to light—Editors.]

They discharge electrified bodies and go through bodies opaque to light such as cardboard, aluminum, copper, and platinum. The enfeeblement of these radiations in passing through various screens is less than the enfeeblement of the rays emanating from the region of the anticathode of a Crookes tube, in passing through the same screens.

All the uranium salts that I have studied, be they phosphorescent or not under the action of light, whether crystallized, fused or in solution, have given me similar results. I have therefore been led to think that the effect is ascribable to the presence of the element uranium in these salts and that the metal would give more intense effects than its compounds.

An experiment made several weeks ago with commercial uranium powder which has been in my laboratory for a long time confirmed this expectation; the photographic effect is noticeably stronger than the impression produced by one of the uranium salts and in particular by the sulfate of uranium and potassium.

Before publishing this result, I waited until our colleague M. Moissan, whose beautiful researches on uranium have just been published, could place at my disposal some of the products that he has prepared. The results have been even more definite, and the impressions obtained on the photographic plate through black paper have been much more intense with crystallized uranium, with cast uranium, and with uranium carbide than with the double sulfate placed on the same plate as a check.

The same difference is found in the phenomena of the discharge of electrified bodies. Metallic uranium causes the dissipation of the charge at a much greater rate than the salts. . . .

[The author closes the report with quantitative data from measurements made with an electroscope—Editors.]

28

ooooooooooo

THE DISCOVERY

OF THE ELECTRON

ooooooooooo

J. J. Thomson (1856-1940)

Between the philosophical speculations of Democritus and the chemical experiments of Dalton, two thousand years of atomic theory had envisioned the smallest units of the elements as the ultimate particles of the universe. Indeed, until the classic experiments of Crookes, who glimpsed a "fourth state of matter" in his cathode ray tubes, atoms were held to be homogeneous and unshatterable. In the hands of Roentgen the magic of the Crookes tube became even more apparent with his discovery of the X-rays generated in its walls. But it was not in the spirit of magic that John Joseph Thomson, Cavendish professor of experimental physics at Cambridge University, set out to use the tubes in his study of electrical conduction in gases. Less than two years later his discovery of the electron swept away the whole fabric of atomic thought, threw a flood of light into the science of electricity, and shortly led to the invention of the electron tube which as a circuit element has produced marvels then hardly dreamed of in the wildest fantasies of fiction.

It is interesting, but rather difficult, to understand Thomson's thoughts on his discovery; he tells us in his *Recollections and Reflections,* written a few years before his death, that: "At first there were very few who believed in the existence of these bodies smaller than atoms . . . I had myself come to this explanation of my experiments with great reluctance." Why was he reluctant to be the first to peer into the world beyond the atom? We do not know, for he never seems to have explained the reasons for this remark. Thomson was in many ways a very different man than

408

many of the great scientists. There was nothing of the remote academician, secluded seer, or eccentric about him. He came from a home in moderate circumstances and his education was subsidized almost from the beginning. He always rubbed elbows with the world and maintained, in the best sense, a worldly, commonsense, and warmly human point of view. Looking back on a long, influential, and eminently successful life he had the wisdom and humility to observe: "I have had good parents, good teachers, good colleagues, good pupils, good friends, great opportunities, good luck and good health . . . had it not been for the sacrifices made by my mother, I could not have completed the course [at Owens College] or come to Cambridge. . . . The events that determined my career . . . coming to Trinity and all that it has meant to me—were sheer accidents." To this very human acknowledgment might be added the opinion of Lord Rayleigh, one of his biographers, who said of him that much of his success as director of the Cavendish Laboratory was due to his "kindly interest in his pupils and genuine enthusiasm for their success." Thomson's biography, based on his own *Recollections and Reflections* with some additions from Lord Rayleigh's writings, follows.

Joseph John Thomson was born in a suburb of Manchester on December 18, 1856, the son of Joseph James and Emma Swindells Thomson. His father, a man of Scottish descent, carried on a family business as a bookseller and publisher. When ready for regular instruction, young Thomson was sent to a small, local private school according to the prevailing custom. His father had not intended him for university training but had wanted to apprentice him to a firm of locomotive builders with the idea that he should become what we now call a mechanical engineer. Engineering in those days was learned less by formal schooling than by the apprentice method, and firms accepting apprentices generally required a substantial fee for the privilege. When young Thomson was ready for apprenticeship at fourteen, it was found that the firm had a long waiting list. In attempting to decide what should be done, his father discussed the situation with a friend, who suggested that the youngster, while waiting, might very profitably attend the local college. This, as Thomson points out, was one of the great turning points in his life, for his father accepted the advice.

Owens College, where Thomson enrolled, was a unique institution in England, having been founded by a Manchester merchant for instruction in subjects taught in the English universities but requiring no religious tests. The staff consisted of an unusual number of very able men, among whom were Thomas Barker, professor of mathematics, former senior wrangler and fellow of Trinity College, Cambridge; Balfour Stewart, whose teaching and writings inspired many students in physics; Osborne Reynolds, whose fame in engineering is perpetuated by the Reynolds number criterion in hydrodynamics; H. E. Roscoe, one of the outstanding English chemists; Stanley Jevons, author of a widely used book on logic; Adolphus Ware, professor of history and English and later vice chancellor of Cambridge University; and finally, James Bryce, professor of law, who later became Lord Bryce, ambassador to Washington, great friend of the United States and the author of the celebrated work, *The American Commonwealth.*

It was natural that a young student directed toward engineering should be most influenced by mathematics and physics. Young Thomson excelled in both of these and achieved an excellent record. At the end of his second year, the early death of his father at the age of thirty-nine completely altered the family outlook, and the large fee required to commence his intended apprenticeship was now out of the question. It was therefore decided that he should finish his last year at the college and obtain a certificate in engineering. But even this required the assistance of a scholarship, which fortunately the college awarded. By the time the year had elapsed, Professor Barker's esteem for his pupil had increased so much that he persuaded young Thomson to stay on after receiving his certificate and continue with mathematics and physics so that he might compete for an entrance scholarship at Trinity College, Cambridge. This was an idea that Thomson had never considered but one that he eagerly adopted.

His first try the following year was unsuccessful, but the next year, 1876, when nineteen, he was admitted to Trinity. As an undergraduate he was a student of the great mathematical coach E. J. Routh, and of such distinguished professors as Cayley, Adams, and Stokes. He took the tripos examinations in January of 1880 and, like Maxwell before him, came out second wrangler. Joseph Larmor, who subsequently attained eminence in physics and the Lucasian professorship at Cambridge, was first. Later in the year, Thomson took the fellowship examinations for Trinity and was elected on his first try, an unusual and unexpected accomplishment.

It was at this time that he commenced work in the Cavendish Laboratory, embarking on mathematical researches on the passage of electricity through gases and on electric charges in motion—subjects that were inspired by Crookes's experiments and that were to occupy him throughout his life. At this time, Lord Rayleigh had just assumed the direction of the laboratory as Cavendish professor, Maxwell having died the previous October. Under Rayleigh's direction, Thomson completed several papers, the most notable being the demonstration that a moving charged particle should behave as if it possessed additional mass, the added amount being in the surrounding field. Despite his absorption in these studies, Thomson joined the competition for the Adams prize in 1882. His paper, a "Treatise on the Motion of Vortex Rings," won the award. Such a subject has a strange sound today, but it must be remembered that at that time Kelvin's vortex theory of matter was the only one available to the mathematical physicist seeking to account for matter in the universe. These successes led to Thomson's election as university lecturer in 1883 and in the following year to membership in the Royal Society. In that year, Rayleigh resigned the Cavendish professorship in accordance with his original stipulation that he would serve in the post for a period of five years. Thomson, then only twenty-eight years old, sent in his name as an applicant, without, he tells us, "serious consideration of the work and the responsibility involved." To his surprise and somewhat to his dismay, he found himself the successful candidate.

As in everything else that Thomson undertook, it was soon clear that as Cavendish professor he would be outstandingly successful. The number of science students in the university increased rapidly. Thomson's own stature was greatly enhanced in 1893 by the publication of his book, *Recent Researches in Electricity and Magnetism,* a work that spread his reputation throughout the scientific world. But the event that provided him with the opportunity to develop one of the great schools of physics and to bring world renown to the Cavendish Laboratory was the institution of a new policy at Cambridge in 1895. It provided that graduates of any other university in England or abroad were eligible for admission as "Research Students," and after two years' residence and the submission of an approved thesis, were eligible for the B.A. degree. The introduction of this rule produced a profound effect on the excellence of the laboratory for it brought many able students from overseas who made substantial contributions to research. In fact, there appeared in the first group to be admitted a talented and industrious student who likewise was destined to create for himself an outstanding place in the history of physics. This young man, Ernest Rutherford from Christchurch, New Zealand, would follow Thomson as Cavendish professor.

It must be remembered that the year 1895 was one of the epoch-making years in physics. In November of that year, Roentgen announced his discovery of X-rays—a discovery that began the era of modern physics. Thomson immediately began experimenting with gases exposed to X-rays and discovered the conductivity that the radiation engendered. He studied the formation of ions, the saturation current, ion mobilities, and recombination. But his most important research was the investigation of the nature of the cathode rays that appeared when the gas discharge occurred at low pressures.

In this study he was only one of the many who were immensely stimulated by the mystery surrounding both cathode rays and X-rays. One of the first investigators to report on the nature of cathode rays was Jean Perrin in Paris, who showed that the cathode-ray beam carried negative charges and that a magnetic field deflected the beam, as would be expected for such charges. By actually catching the negative charges in a Faraday cage, he had gone one step further than Crookes, whose magnetic deflection of the rays agreed with the presence of negatively charged particles.

What Perrin did not show was that the cathode rays and the negative charges were one and the same thing. It remained for Thomson not only to clinch this fact but to take the immensely more significant step of demonstrating that the negative particles were the same in all the gases used in generating cathode rays and that these particles, or "corpuscles" as he called them, were subatomic particles. These demonstrations constitute the discovery of the electron and are all clearly developed in Thomson's paper, which follows this biography.

The discovery of the electron in 1897 required a complete revision of the physical view of matter—the nature of the positive charge, the constancy or the range of variation of atomic charges, and the disposition of positive and negative charges in the atom. These were only some of the larger questions raised by the discovery. To clarify some of them, Thomson and his students set about the determination of the charge carried by ions, using C. T. R. Wilson's cloud method. The cloud method was later refined by Robert Millikan to become the famous oil drop experiment. X-ray scattering experiments by Charles Barkla eventually showed that the number of electrons in the light elements was about half the atomic number; finally, Thomson himself developed a model for the atom that is known by his name. In it, the electrons were embedded at equilibrium positions in a sphere of uniformly distributed positive charge. These were the principal researches that occupied him until 1906, when he was awarded the Nobel Prize.

Following these investigations, Thomson turned to the study of the positive charges occurring in the gas discharge. In order to study the positive rays, he found it convenient to change the crossed electric and magnetic field arrangement used in the isolation of the electron to one in which these fields were parallel. Under such conditions, the positive ions produce parabolic traces on a sensitive plate placed at right angles to the original path of the rays. The first gas analyzed was neon; among the traces produced were those corresponding to elements of mass 20 and 22, but no trace was found corresponding to 20.2, the chemical atomic weight of neon. Careful investigation led to the conclusion that the particles producing traces at mass 20 and 22 indeed came from the neon gas in the tube. Soddy had already showed as a result of his radioactivity researches that atoms of stable lead existed as chemically similar particles but with different atomic weights. These particles he designated as isotopes (equal place). Thomson's experiments now showed that isotopes were not limited to the radioactive series, but the advent of World War I made it impossible to continue the researches.

During the period 1914–1918, Thomson served in advisory and committee work with the Board of Inventions and Research under Lord Fisher. In 1915 he was elected president of the Royal Society, succeeding Crookes, the man who had so greatly influenced his whole life's work. Early in 1918, Dr. H. Montague Butler, the master of Trinity College, died, leaving the position vacant. Trinity is the only one of the Cambridge colleges in which the master is not elected by the fellows but is appointed by the Crown. The Prime Minister, then Lloyd George, offered the post to Thomson, who accepted. The following year, at the age of sixty-three, Thomson relinquished his Cavendish professorship after thirty-five years of service, during which he had made the Cavendish Laboratory one of the most outstanding centers of physics in the world. As Lord Rayleigh suggests, his success in this endeavor was the result of "his personality, fertility in suggestion, kindly interest in pupils and genuine enthusiasm for their success."

His retirement as Cavendish professor and the assumption of the mastership of Trinity did not sever his connection with physics, for he continued his university lectures and his contributions to research throughout his life. Most of his later papers deal with the properties of the electron. It is remarkable that he found time in the midst of his administrative responsibilities to keep abreast of the rapidly expanding developments in physics, which, in the mid-twenties, through the researches of de Broglie, Heisenberg, and Schroedinger, brought a completely altered concept of matter—the wave nature of particles. Thomson readily championed this point of view and it is interesting that its experimental confirmation in 1927 was made by his son G. P. Thomson and by Davisson and Germer in the United States. His little monograph *Beyond the Electron* which dealt with the wave nature of matter was published in 1929. His last paper, written in 1939, one year before his death, was entitled "Electron Waves." During his lifetime he published more than two hundred research papers. He wrote sixteen books, eleven under his own name alone, one with his son, and four textbooks with J. H. Poynting. Through generations of research students at "The Cavendish" his influence in physics spread around the world. In the years that followed no fewer than eighty-one of his students held professorships in universities throughout the British Isles, Europe, Canada, the United States, Russia, South Africa and India. What it meant to work under his direction is perhaps best described by Professor F. W. Aston, who wrote:

Working under him never lacked thrills. When results were coming out well his boundless, indeed childlike, enthusiasm was contagious and occasionally embarrassing. Negatives just developed had actually to be hidden away for fear he would handle them while they were still wet. Yet when hitches occurred, and the exasperating vagaries of an apparatus had reduced the man who had designed, built and worked with it to baffled despair, along would shuffle this remarkable being, who, after cogitating in a characteristic attitude over his funny old desk in the corner, and jotting down a few figures and formulae in his tiny tidy handwriting, on the back of somebody's Fellowship thesis, or on an old envelope, or even the laboratory cheque book, would produce a luminous suggestion, like a rabbit out of a hat, not only revealing the cause of the trouble, but also the means of cure. This intuitive ability to comprehend the inner working of intricate apparatus without the trouble of handling it appeared to me then, and still appears to me now, as something verging on the miraculous, the hall-mark of a great genius.*

His personal characteristics, especially in his later years, are perhaps best described by Lord Rayleigh, who said of him:

> He had no undue fear of giving himself away and was quite ready to express opinions offhand which had not been carefully matured. His readiness of speech and stimulating personality made him very much in demand as a speaker. . . .
>
> He had no command of foreign languages and indeed refused to make any attempt to converse even in French. In this matter he relied on the help of Lady Thomson. He had of course complete facility in reading French and German, but never wrote or spoke in these languages. . . .
>
> As master of Trinity, his relations with the junior members of the college were very easy. He took the keenest delight in their athletic performances and nothing delighted him more than the opportunity of going to a good football match or watching the performance of Trinity men on the river. He was sincerely pleased to be asked as a guest to an informal luncheon club by undergraduates, and he almost seemed to think more of the honour of being asked to this than of the many and impressive dignities which had been conferred upon him by universities and learned bodies all over the world.[1]

Before Thomson had begun his study of the cathode rays, electrical discharges through low-pressure gases had been studied for a number of years; with the improvement of vacuum techniques it became possible to study discharges between electrodes that could be considered as being surrounded by a vacuum. Under these conditions, the discharge from the cathode presented itself as a well-defined beam, and one of the most

---

* F. W. Aston: *The Times,* London, Sept. 4, 1940, p. 9.
[1] Lord Rayleigh, Obituary Notices of Fellows of the Royal Society, Vol. 3, 587–597, 1941.

important questions that faced physicists in the mid-1890's concerned the nature of this beam.

Thomson himself clearly stated the problem in the opening paragraph of his paper "Cathode Rays," which is printed following this commentary. That very competent physicists were aligned on each side of the corpuscular-wave controversy over cathode rays is evidence that there must have been serious difficulties in arriving at the final decision. Thomson himself was convinced that these rays were negatively charged corpuscles. He refers first to the work of Jean Perrin, who showed that when cathode rays pass into an electroscope, the electroscope becomes charged. Thomson repeated these experiments of Perrin's in such a way that there could be no doubt that the cathode rays consisted of negatively charged particles. In this paper his most important contribution is the determination of the ratio of the electric charge on the cathode ray particles to the mass of these particles. This he accomplished by first deflecting the particles in an electric field directed at a right angle to the beam. He then brought the beam back to its original direction by subjecting it to a magnetic field at right angles to the electric field. Since the effect of the electric field is just balanced by that of the magnetic field, a mathematical relationship can be found for the ratio of the charge to the mass in terms of the geometry of the tube and the known electric and magnetic fields.

Thomson investigated a number of different gases and found that the ratio of the charge to the mass of these particles was independent of the chemical nature of the gas in the tube and the chemical nature of the cathode that was used. The immediate consequence of Thomson's discovery was the recognition that the ratio of the mass to the charge of these cathode particles is smaller by a factor of about 2,000 than this same ratio for the lightest known ion, namely, the hydrogen ion in electrolysis. To Thomson this signified only one thing: that these particles in the cathode rays were a new form of matter that did not fit anywhere in the table of elements. He correctly interpreted the cathode rays as "matter in a new state, a state in which the subdivision of matter is carried much further than in the ordinary gaseous state: a state in which all matter . . . is of one and the same kind; this matter being the substance from which all chemical elements are built up."

His paper, describing the existence of particles smaller than the atom, follows.

○○○○○○○

THOMSON

Cathode Rays [2]

THE EXPERIMENTS DISCUSSED IN THIS paper
were undertaken in the hope of gaining some information as to the
nature of the Cathode Rays. The most diverse opinions are held as to
these rays; according to the almost unanimous opinion of German
physicists they are due to some process in the æther to which—inasmuch
as in a uniform magnetic field their course is circular and not rectilinear—
no phenomenon hitherto observed is analogous: another view of these rays
is that, so far from being wholly ætherial, they are in fact wholly material, and that they mark the paths of particles of matter charged with
negative electricity. It would seem at first sight that it ought not to be
difficult to discriminate between views so different, yet experience shows
that this is not the case, as amongst the physicists who have most deeply
studied the subject can be found supporters of either theory.

The electrified-particle theory has for purposes of research a great
advantage over the ætherial theory, since it is definite and its consequences
can be predicted; with the ætherial theory it is impossible to predict what
will happen under any given circumstances, as on this theory we are
dealing with hitherto unobserved phenomena in the æther, of whose laws
we are ignorant.

The following experiments were made to test some of the consequences
of the electrified-particle theory.

CHARGE CARRIED BY THE CATHODE RAYS

If these rays are negatively electrified particles, then when they enter
an enclosure they ought to carry into it a charge of negative electricity.
This has been proved to be the case by Perrin, who placed in front of a
plane cathode two coaxial metallic cylinders which were insulated from
each other: the outer of these cylinders was connected with the earth,
the inner with a gold-leaf electroscope. These cylinders were closed except

---

[2] J. J. Thomson, *Philosophical Magazine,* 44 (1897), 293–311.

for two small holes, one in each cylinder, placed so that the cathode rays could pass through them into the inside of the inner cylinder. Perrin found that when the rays passed into the inner cylinder the electroscope received a charge of negative electricity, while no charge went to the electroscope when the rays were deflected by a magnet so as no longer to pass through the hole.

This experiment proves that something charged with negative electricity is shot off from the cathode, travelling at right angles to it, and that this something is deflected by a magnet; it is open, however, to the objection that it does not prove that the cause of the electrification in the electroscope has anything to do with the cathode rays. Now the supporters of

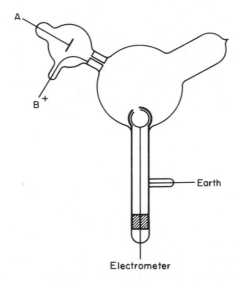

Fig. 28–1.

the ætherial theory do not deny that electrified particles are shot off from the cathode; they deny, however, that these charged particles have any more to do with the cathode rays than a rifle-ball has with the flash when a rifle is fired. I have therefore repeated Perrin's experiment in a form which is not open to this objection. The arrangement used was as follows: —Two coaxial cylinders [Fig. 28–1] with slits in them are placed in a bulb connected with the discharge-tube; the cathode rays from the cathode A pass into the bulb through a slit in a metal plug fitted into the neck of the tube; this plug is connected with the anode and is put to earth. The cathode rays thus do not fall upon the cylinders unless they are deflected by a magnet. The outer cylinder is connected with the earth, the inner with the electrometer. When the cathode rays (whose path was traced by the phosphorescence on the glass) did not fall on the slit, the electrical charge sent to the electrometer when the induction-coil producing the rays was set in action was small and irregular; when, however, the rays were bent by a magnet so as to fall on the slit there was a large charge of negative electricity sent to the electrometer. I was surprised at the magnitude of the charge; on some occasions enough negative electricity went through the narrow slit into the inner cylinder in one second to alter the potential of a capacity of $1 \cdot 5$ microfarads by 20 volts. If the rays were so much bent by the magnet that they overshot the slits in the cylinder, the charge passing into the cylinder fell again to a very small fraction of its value when the aim was true. Thus this experiment shows that however we twist and deflect the cathode rays by magnetic forces, the negative electrification follows the same path as the rays, and that this negative electrification is indissolubly connected with the cathode rays.

When the rays are turned by the magnet so as to pass through the slit into the inner cylinder, the deflexion of the electrometer connected with this cylinder increases up to a certain value, and then remains stationary although the rays continue to pour into the cylinder. This is due to the fact that the gas in the bulb becomes a conductor of electricity when the cathode rays pass through it, and thus, though the inner cylinder is perfectly insulated when the rays are not passing, yet as soon as the rays pass through the bulb the air between the inner cylinder and the outer one becomes a conductor, and the electricity escapes from the inner cylinder to the earth. Thus the charge within the inner cylinder does not go on continually increasing; the cylinder settles down into a state of equilibrium in which the rate at which it gains negative electricity from the rays is equal to the rate at which it loses it by conduction through the air. If the inner cylinder has initially a positive charge it rapidly loses that charge and acquires a negative one; while if the initial charge is a negative one, the cylinder will leak if the initial negative potential is numerically greater than the equilibrium value.

DEFLEXION OF THE CATHODE RAYS BY AN ELECTROSTATIC FIELD

An objection very generally urged against the view that the cathode rays are negatively electrified particles, is that hitherto no deflexion of the rays has been observed under a small electrostatic force, and though the rays are deflected when they pass near electrodes connected with sources of large differences of potential, such as induction-coils or electrical machines, the deflexion in this case is regarded by the supporters of the ætherial theory as due to the discharge passing between the electrodes, and not primarily to the electrostatic field. Hertz made the rays travel between two parallel plates of metal placed inside the discharge-tube, but found that they were not deflected when the plates were connected with a battery of storage-cells; on repeating this experiment I at first got the same result, but subsequent experiments showed that the absence of deflexion is due to the conductivity conferred on the rarefied gas by the cathode rays. On measuring this conductivity it was found that it diminished very rapidly as the exhaustion increased; it seemed then that on trying Hertz's experiment at very high exhaustions there might be a chance of detecting the deflexion of the cathode rays by an electrostatic force.

The apparatus used is represented in [Fig. 28–2].

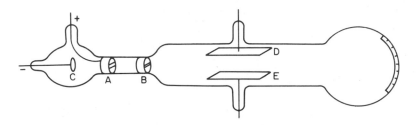

Fig. 28–2.

The rays from the cathode C pass through a slit in the anode A, which is a metal plug fitting tightly into the tube and connected with the earth; after passing through a second slit in another earth-connected metal plug B, they travel between two parallel aluminium plates about 5 cm. long by 2 broad and at a distance of $1 \cdot 5$ cm. apart; they then fall on the end of the tube and produce a narrow well-defined phosphorescent patch. A scale pasted on the outside of the tube serves to measure the deflexion of this patch. At high exhaustions the rays were deflected when the two aluminium plates were connected with the terminals of a battery of small storage-cells; the rays were depressed when the upper plate was connected with the negative pole of the battery, the lower with the positive, and raised when the upper plate was connected with the positive, the lower with the negative pole. The deflexion was proportional to the difference of potential between the plates, and I could detect the deflexion when the potential-difference was as small as two volts. It was only when the vacuum was a good one that the deflexion took place, but that the absence of deflexion is due to the conductivity of the medium is shown by what takes place when the vacuum has just arrived at the stage at which the deflexion begins. At this stage there is a deflexion of the rays when the plates are first connected with the terminals of the battery, but if this connexion is maintained the patch of phosphorescence gradually creeps back to its undeflected position. This is just what would happen if the space between the plates were a conductor, though a very bad one, for then the positive and negative ions between the plates would slowly diffuse, until the positive plate became coated with negatives ions, the negative plate with positive ones; thus the electric intensity between the plates would vanish and the cathode rays be free from electrostatic force. . . .

[A description of the details of electrostatic deflection under various conditions is omitted—Editors.]

MAGNETIC DEFLEXION OF THE CATHODE RAYS IN DIFFERENT GASES

The deflexion of the cathode rays by the magnetic field was studied with the aid of the apparatus shown in [Fig. 28–3]. The cathode was placed in a side-tube fastened on to a bell-jar; the opening between this tube and the

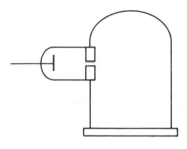

Fig. 28–3.

bell-jar was closed by a metallic plug with a slit in it; this plug was connected with the earth and was used as the anode. The cathode rays passed through the slit in this plug into the bell-jar, passing in front of a vertical plate of glass ruled into small squares. The bell-jar was placed between two large parallel coils arranged as a Helmholtz galvanometer. The course of the rays was determined by taking photographs of the bell-jar when the cathode rays were passing through it; the divisions on the plate enabled the path of the rays to be determined. Under the action of the magnetic field the narrow beam of cathode rays spreads out into a broad fan-shaped luminosity in the gas. The luminosity in this fan is not uniformly distributed, but is condensed along certain lines. The phosphorescence on the glass is also not uniformly distributed; it is much spread out, showing that the beam consists of rays which are not all deflected to the same extent by the magnet. The luminosity on the glass is crossed by bands along which the luminosity is very much greater than in the adjacent parts.

These bright and dark bands are called by Birkeland, who first observed them, the magnetic spectrum. The brightest spots on the glass are by no means always the terminations of the brightest streaks of luminosity in the gas; in fact, in some cases a very bright spot on the glass is not connected with the cathode by any appreciable luminosity, though there may be plenty of luminosity in other parts of the gas. One very interesting point brought out by the photographs is that in a given magnetic field, and with a given mean potential-difference between the terminals, the path of the rays is independent of the nature of the gas. Photographs were taken of the discharge in hydrogen, air, carbonic acid, methyl iodide, *i.e.,* in gases whose densities range from 1 to 70, and yet, not only were the paths of the most deflected rays the same in all cases, but even the details, such as the distribution of the bright and dark spaces, were the same; in fact, the photographs could hardly be distinguished from each other. It is to be noted that the pressures were not the same; the pressures in the different gases were adjusted so that the mean potential-differences between the cathode and the anode were the same in all the gases. When the pressure of a gas is lowered, the potential-difference between the terminals increases, and the deflexion of the rays produced by a magnet diminishes, or at any rate the deflexion of the rays when the phosphorescence is a maximum diminishes. If an airbreak is inserted an effect of the same kind is produced.

In the experiments with different gases, the pressures were as high as was consistent with the appearance of the phosphorescence on the glass, so as to ensure having as much as possible of the gas under consideration in the tube.

As the cathode rays carry a charge of negative electricity, are deflected by an electrostatic force as if they were negatively electrified, and are acted on by a magnetic force in just the way in which this force would act on a negatively electrified body moving along the path of these rays, I can see no escape from the conclusion that they are charges of negative electricity carried by particles of matter. The question next arises, What are these particles? are they atoms, or molecules, or matter in a still finer state of subdivision? To throw some light on this point, I have made a series of measurements of the ratio of the mass of these particles to the charge carried by it. To determine this quantity, I have used two independent methods. The first of these is as follows:—Suppose we consider a bundle of homogeneous cathode rays. Let m be the mass of each of the particles, e the charge carried by it. Let N be the number of particles passing across any section of the beam in a given time; then Q the quantity of electricity carried by these particles is given by the equation

$$Ne = Q.$$

We can measure Q if we receive the cathode rays in the inside of a vessel connected with an electrometer. When these rays strike against a solid body, the temperature of the body is raised; the kinetic energy of the moving particles being converted into heat; if we suppose that all this energy is converted into heat, then if we measure the increase in the temperature of a body of known thermal capacity caused by the impact of these rays, we can determine W, the kinetic energy of the particles, and if v is the velocity of the particles,

$$\tfrac{1}{2}Nmv^2 = W.$$

If ρ is the radius of curvature of the path of these rays in a uniform magnetic field H, then

$$\frac{mv}{e} = H\rho = I,$$

where I is written for $H\rho$ for the sake of brevity. From these equations we get

$$\frac{1}{2}\frac{m}{e}v^2 = \frac{W}{Q}.$$

$$v = \frac{2W}{QI},$$

$$\frac{m}{e} = \frac{I^2Q}{2W}.$$

Thus, if we know the values of Q, W, and I, we can deduce the values of v and m/e. . . .

[Thomson used this method to determine v and m/e. The description of the apparatus and results are omitted because the alternative method which follows proved to be more accurate—Editors.]

I shall describe another method of measuring the quantities m/e and v of an entirely different kind from the preceding; this method is based upon the deflexion of the cathode rays in an electrostatic field. If we measure the deflexion experienced by the rays when traversing a given length under a uniform electric intensity, and the deflexion of the rays when they traverse a given distance under a uniform magnetic field, we can find the values of m/e and v in the following way:—

Let the space passed over by the rays under a uniform electric intensity F be l, the time taken for the rays to traverse this space is l/v, the velocity in the direction of F is therefore

$$\frac{Fe}{m}\frac{l}{v},$$

so that θ, the angle through which the rays are deflected when they leave the electric field and enter a region free from electric force, is given by the equation

$$\theta = \frac{Fe}{m} \frac{l}{v^2}.$$

If, instead of the electric intensity, the rays are acted on by a magnetic force H at right angles to the rays, and extending across the distance l, the velocity at right angles to the original path of the rays is

$$\frac{Hev}{m} \frac{l}{v},$$

so that ϕ, the angle through which the rays are deflected when they leave the magnetic field, is given by the equation

$$\phi = \frac{He}{m} \frac{l}{v}.$$

From these equations we get

$$v = \frac{\phi}{\theta} \frac{F}{H}$$

and

$$\frac{m}{e} = \frac{H^2\theta . l}{F\phi^2}.$$

In the actual experiments H was adjusted so that $\phi = \theta$; in this case the equations become

$$v = \frac{F}{H},$$

$$\frac{m}{e} = \frac{H^2 l}{F\theta}.$$

The apparatus used to measure v and m/e by this means is that represented in [Fig. 28–2]. The electric field was produced by connecting the two aluminum plates to the terminals of a battery of storage-cells. The phosphorescent patch at the end of the tube was deflected, and the deflexion measured by a scale pasted to the end of the tube. As it was necessary to darken the room to see the phosphorescent patch, a needle coated with luminous paint was placed so that by a screw it could be moved up and down the scale; this needle could be seen when the room was darkened, and it was moved until it coincided with the phosphorescent patch. Thus, when light was admitted, the deflexion of the phosphorescent patch could be measured.

The magnetic field was produced by placing outside the tube two coils whose diameter was equal to the length of the plates; the coils were placed so that they covered the space occupied by the plates, the distance between the coils was equal to the radius of either. The mean value of the magnetic force over the length l was determined in the following way: a narrow coil C whose length was l, connected with a ballistic galvanometer, was placed between the coils; the plane of the windings of C was parallel to the planes of the coils; the cross section of the coil was a rectangle 5 cm. by 1 cm. A given current was sent through the outer coils and the kick α of the galvanometer observed when this current was reversed. The coil C was then placed at the centre of two very large coils, so as to be in a field of uniform magnetic force: the current through the large coils was reversed and the kick β of the galvanometer again observed; by comparing α and β we can get the mean value of the magnetic force over a length $l;$ this was found to be

$$60 \times i,$$

where i is the current flowing through the coils.

A series of experiments was made to see if the electrostatic deflexion was proportional to the electric intensity between the plates; this was found to be the case. In the following experiments the current through the coils was adjusted so that the electrostatic deflexion was the same as the magnetic:—

TABLE 28-1

Gas.	θ.	H.	F.	l.	m/e.	v.
Air	8/100	5·5	$1 \cdot 5 \times 10^{10}$	5	$1 \cdot 3 \times 10^{-7}$	$2 \cdot 8 \times 10^{9}$
Air	9·5/100	5·4	$1 \cdot 5 \times 10^{10}$	5	$1 \cdot 1 \times 10^{-7}$	$2 \cdot 8 \times 10^{9}$
Air	13/110	6·6	$1 \cdot 5 \times 10^{10}$	5	$1 \cdot 2 \times 10^{-7}$	$2 \cdot 3 \times 10^{9}$
Hydrogen	9/110	6·3	$1 \cdot 5 \times 10^{10}$	5	$1 \cdot 5 \times 10^{-7}$	$2 \cdot 5 \times 10^{9}$
Carbonicacid	11/110	6·9	$1 \cdot 5 \times 10^{10}$	5	$1 \cdot 5 \times 10^{-7}$	$2 \cdot 2 \times 10^{9}$
Air	6/110	5	$1 \cdot 8 \times 10^{10}$	5	$1 \cdot 3 \times 10^{-7}$	$3 \cdot 6 \times 10^{9}$
Air	7/110	3·6	1×10^{10}	5	$1 \cdot 1 \times 10^{-7}$	$2 \cdot 8 \times 10^{9}$

The cathode in the first five experiments was aluminium, in the last two experiments it was made of platinum; in the last experiment Sir William Crookes's method of getting rid of the mercury vapour by inserting tubes of pounded sulphur, sulphur iodide, and copper filings between the bulb and the pump was adopted. In the calculation of m/e and v no allowance has been made for the magnetic force due to the coil in the region outside the plates; in this region the magnetic force will be in the opposite direction to that between the plates, and will tend to bend the cathode rays in the opposite direction: thus the effective value of H will be smaller than the value used in the equations, so that the values of m/e are larger and those of v less than they would be if this correction were applied. The method of determining the values of m/e and v is much less laborious and probably more accurate than the former method; it cannot, however, be used over so wide a range of pressures.

From these determinations we see that the value of m/e is independent of the nature of the gas, and that its value 10^{-7} is very small compared with the value 10^{-4}, which is the smallest value of this quantity previously known, and which is the value for the hydrogen ion in electrolysis.

Thus for the carriers of the electricity in the cathode rays m/e is very small compared with its value in electrolysis. The smallness of m/e may be due to the smallness of m or the largeness of e, or to a combination of these two. That the carriers of the charges in the cathode rays are small compared with ordinary molecules is shown, I think, by Lenard's results as to the rate at which the brightness of the phosphorescence produced by these rays diminishes with the length of path traveled by the ray. If we regard this phosphorescence as due to the impact of the charged particles, the distance through which the rays must travel before the phosphorescence fades to a given fraction (say $1/e$, where $e = 2\cdot71$) of its original intensity, will be some moderate multiple of the mean free path. Now Lenard found that this distance depends solely upon the density of the medium, and not upon its chemical nature or physical state. In air at atmospheric pressure the distance was about half a centimetre, and this must be comparable with the mean free path of the carriers through air at atmospheric pressure. But the mean free path of the molecules of air is a quantity of quite a different order. The carrier, then, must be small compared with ordinary molecules.

The two fundamental points about these carriers seem to me to be (1) that these carriers are the same whatever the gas through which the discharge passes, (2) that the mean free paths depend upon nothing but the density of the medium traversed by these rays.

It might be supposed that the independence of the mass of the carriers of the gas through which the discharge passes was due to the mass concerned being the quasi mass which a charged body possesses in virtue of the electric field set up in its neighbourhood; moving the body involves the production of a varying electric field, and, therefore, of a certain amount of energy which is proportional to the square of the velocity. This causes the charged body to behave as if its mass were increased by a quantity, which for a charged sphere is $\frac{1}{5} e^2/\mu a$ ("Recent Researches in Electricity and Magnetism"), where e is the charge and a the radius of the sphere. If we assume that it is this mass which we are concerned with in the cathode rays, since m/e would vary as e/a, it affords no clue to the explanation of either of the properties (1 and 2) of these rays. This is not by any means the only objection to this hypothesis, which I only mention to show that it has not been overlooked.

The explanation which seems to me to account in the most simple and straightforward manner for the facts is founded on a view of the constitution of the chemical elements which has been favourably entertained by many chemists: this view is that the atoms of the different chemical elements are different aggregations of atoms of the same kind. In the form in which this hypothesis was enunciated by Prout, the atoms of the different elements were hydrogen atoms; in this precise form the hypothesis is not tenable, but if we substitute for hydrogen some unknown primordial substance X, there is nothing known which is inconsistent with this hypothesis. . . .

If, in the very intense electric field in the neighbourhood of the cathode, the molecules of the gas are dissociated and are split up, not into the ordinary chemical atoms, but into these primordial atoms, which we shall for brevity call corpuscles; and if these corpuscles are charged with electricity and projected from the cathode by the electric field, they would behave exactly like the cathode rays. They would evidently give a value of m/e which is independent of the nature of the gas and its pressure, for the carriers are the same whatever the gas may be. . . .

Thus we have in the cathode rays matter in a new state, a state in which the subdivision of matter is carried very much further than in the ordinary gaseous state: a state in which all matter—that is, matter derived from different sources such as hydrogen, oxygen, &c.—is of one and the same kind; this matter being the substance from which all the chemical elements are built up.

29

ooooooooooo

THE DISCOVERY
OF POLONIUM
AND RADIUM

ooooooooooo

Pierre Curie (1859-1906)

Marie Sklodovska Curie (1867-1934)

No one can read the life story of Pierre and Marie Curie without being deeply impressed by the almost superhuman dedication each brought to their partnership in science. Before their marriage in 1895, Pierre had already achieved a name in physics by his discovery, some fourteen years earlier with his brother Jacques, of the phenomenon of piezoelectricity. This effect is the appearance of positively and negatively charged surfaces on certain properly prepared crystals, such as quartz, when the crystal is placed under compression or tension. Conversely, if such a quartz crystal is placed between metal plates with opposite electrical charges, a mechanical stress is induced in the crystal. If an alternating voltage is applied to such plates, and the free period of vibration of the crystal is the same as the applied voltage, then resonance is produced. This stable resonating arrangement has found widespread application in controlling the frequency of vacuum tube oscillators, and thus is of the greatest importance in the broadcasting and communications industries.

In addition to this discovery, Pierre published one of the most useful researches in the history of magnetism, dealing with the temperature variation of the magnetic susceptibility of a wide range of substances. Although many scattered susceptibility measurements had been made on a variety of substances, no general conclusions could be drawn from the results, and the temperature variation of the susceptibility of magnetic materials was little known. As a result of Pierre Curie's investigations it became clear that dia- and paramagnetism were distinctly different phenomena and ferromagnetism was somehow related to paramagnetism since the former passed into the latter at a fixed temperature which is now called the Curie temperature.

Pierre was born in Paris May 15, 1859, the son of a physician. He received his early education at home and then at the Sorbonne. Between the ages of nineteen and twenty-three he was an assistant in the laboratory of the Faculté des Sciences. Following that, he was appointed chief of the laboratory at the School of Physics and Chemistry of the city of Paris. It was here that he carried out his research on magnetism, without assistants and with the most meager facilities. Pierre was an idealist and a dreamer and completely immersed in his work. His love of physics was for its own sake, with no eye either to professorships or awards. Thus, when proposed by the director of the School of Physics for a decoration he wrote, "If you obtain this distinction for me, you will put me under the obligation of refusing it, for I have quite decided never to accept any decorations of any sort." [1] Such was the situation when early in 1894 Pierre met Marie Sklodovska, a student of physics at the Sorbonne.

Marie, the daughter of Polish schoolteachers, was born in Warsaw on November 7, 1867, the youngest in a family of four girls and one boy. From the beginning she showed outstanding intelligence. As a result of family financial reverses it was necessary for her at the age of fifteen to seek a position upon completion of her secondary school training. For six years, from September 1885 to September 1891, she served as a governess in order to save money for a university education.

At that time, Polish laws forbade the higher education of women. Marie had a married sister, Bronya Dluski, practicing medicine in Paris, and arranged to live with her and her husband to continue her study of physics and mathematics at the Sorbonne. But the hoped-for arrangement proved impossible—the interruptions to her studies were frequent and the distance she traveled to reach the Sorbonne was too great. To solve the problem she moved into the cheapest quarter near the university on a budget of 100 francs a month, a sum which had to cover everything, including university fees. The only solution was to spend practically nothing for food, or for her coal stove, even in the bitterest months of winter. More than once she fainted from hunger. Yet nothing mattered to her except learning. Her resolution carried her through to July 1893 when, at

---

[1] Eve Curie, *Madame Curie* (New York: Doubleday Doran & Co., 1937), p. 126.

the end of her strength, she took first place in the master's examination in physics. She then went home to Poland to recuperate.

The following fall, Marie was able to return to the Sorbonne with a small scholarship to complete a master's degree in mathematics. It was during this time that she met Pierre Curie. A year later they were married, and marriage meant the opportunity for both to work at Pierre's laboratory at the School of Chemistry and Physics—an arrangement that was only interrupted for a short time in 1897 by the birth of their daughter Irène.

Becquerel's discovery and his initial researches in the field of radioactivity appeared in publications covering the brief span of three months—from late February to late May 1886. Following this, he seems to have returned to investigations in magnetooptics. Inexplicably, this new field lay quiescent for about a year and a half. But the mystery of the rays intrigued Marie and early in 1898 she began studying the invisible radiations from uranium.

It must be remembered that Becquerel had arrived at the correct conclusion that the rays originated in uranium regardless of the state of chemical combination of the metal. Although he had tested other phosphorescent sulfides, including those of calcium, strontium, and zinc, and found no activity, it had not occurred to him or to anyone else to make a systematic search of the elements to determine whether or not uranium was unique in emitting penetrating and ionizing rays. But the idea of a systematic search *did* occur to Marie and she soon discovered that thorium and its compounds behaved in the same manner as uranium. Her tests were made by placing a uniform layer of the material in question on the lower of two parallel plates spaced 3 cm. apart. The potential difference between the plates was kept at 100 volts and the current between them, resulting from the activity, was measured with an electrometer. A few days after her paper appeared announcing the radioactive nature of thorium, the same discovery was reported by G. C. Schmidt in Germany.

Turning next to an examination of the ores of uranium and thorium, she found that two uranium ores, pitchblende and chalcolite (a hydrous uranium copper phosphate), showed an activity greater than that attributable to the uranium that each contained. Evidently an unknown active element was present in the ore. At this point husband and wife joined forces to find the source of the unknown activity.

As the first of the following papers shows, the research was guided by the activity of the chemically separated substances as determined in their plate apparatus. Pitcheblende, more active than uranium, was submitted to chemical treatment and the high activity was found to accompany bismuth sulfide. The most effective method found for separating the active element from the inert bismuth was to heat the mixture *in vacuo* at

700° C. The active part—four hundred times more active than uranium—tended to deposit on the cooler part of the tube. They proposed the name polonium for it in honor of Marie's native country.

In the course of the chemical separations, another activity was found to be even stronger than that associated with bismuth—an activity accompanying an element showing chemical properties resembling barium. This element, the subject of the second of the following papers, was eventually named radium. Their research was completed with the help of an assistant, G. Bemont, at the end of 1898.

But in the initial researches the presence of polonium and radium had only been inferred from the intensity of the radioactivity in a chemical precipitate. In order to clinch the discovery it was necessary to isolate each of the elements and determine their atomic weight. This could only be accomplished by concentrating the very small percentages of the active substances contained in the pitchblende ore. To obtain finite amounts of the new elements it was necessary to begin with tons of material, but tons of pitchblende delivered in Paris would cost much more than they could afford. This difficulty was overcome by an initial gift from the Joachimsthal mine in Bohemia of a ton of pitchblende residue after the uranium had been extracted.

Once the ore was obtained its processing required a large laboratory to carry out all the necessary chemical treatments. A search showed that no laboratory space was available except an abandoned wooden shed with leaking skylights situated across the courtyard from the tiny laboratory which Marie had been using at the School of Chemistry and Physics. It was in these quarters, stifling hot in summer and freezing cold in winter, that the fanatically dedicated couple endured forty-five months of almost unremitting labor to prepare a sample of pure radium chloride and to determine its atomic weight. This success was achieved in 1902, but its price was almost complete exhaustion for Pierre and Marie, especially since both, while continuing the research, had taken on new teaching duties in order to obtain sufficient income for their own and their child's support.

It should be of special interest to students of physics and chemistry that Marie Curie had begun her work on radioactivity in order to present a thesis at the Sorbonne for her doctor's degree. In her four years of epoch-making work on radioactivity and radium, there had been no time to go through the formalities of such an application. At last, in June 1903, the examination was taken and the degree conferred. Six months later Marie and Pierre Curie shared the distinction of winning the Nobel Prize in physics with Henri Becquerel, the discoverer of radioactivity. Marie was too ill to go to Stockholm to receive the prize, so neither was present at the ceremonial session. Characteristically, they refused all invitations for lectures or for ceremonial honors; they avoided receptions and social functions. Only official scientific occasions could bring them out.

Following the award of the Nobel Prize, the Curies continued their research on the properties of radium. In December 1904, their second child Eve was born. Pierre, long unsuccessful in seeking a chair in physics at the Sorbonne, now had one created for him in 1905. His election to the Academy of Sciences, denied earlier, was voted, but still the election, strangely enough, was a close contest with a relatively unknown scientist. In the midst of success and the brightest outlook for the future, Pierre was killed on April 19, 1906, in a street accident. Crossing the street in the rain he was struck by a heavy horse-drawn van. He was then forty-six years old.

Marie succeeded to Pierre's chair at the Sorbonne and continued the work they had begun together. In 1911 she was awarded an unprecedented second Nobel Prize, this time in chemistry. Until recent years she was the only person to achieve this double honor. Such recognition evidently required from French academic circles a tangible act to provide adequately for her scientific work. Consequently, the Institut du Radium came into being in July 1914. World War I precluded official work in the physics section of the institute and it was not until 1919 that research was begun. At that time Marie was joined by her elder daughter Irène, who later became the wife of Frédéric Joliot. With Joliot, Irène shared the 1935 Nobel Prize in chemistry for induced radioactivity.

Marie Curie continued her selfless devotion to science almost to the end. Overtaken by pernicious anemia induced by years of overwork and radiation exposure, this greatest woman of science died peacefully on July 4, 1934.

Einstein, in a moving tribute, said of her:

Her strength, her purity of will, her austerity toward herself, her objectivity, her incorruptible judgment—all these were of a kind seldom found joined in a single individual . . . The greatest scientific deed of her life—proving the existence of radioactive elements and isolating them—owes its accomplishment not merely to bold intuition but to a devotion and tenacity in execution under the most extreme hardships imaginable, such as the history of experimental science has not often witnessed.[2]

---

[2] Albert Einstein, *Out of My Later Years* (New York: Philosophical Library, 1950), pp 227–228.

ᴏᴏᴏᴏᴏᴏᴏ

PIERRE AND MARIE CURIE

On a New Radioactive Substance Contained in Pitchblende [3]

CERTAIN MINERALS CONTAINING URANIUM and thorium (pitchblende, chalcolite, uranite) are very active from the point of view of the emission of Becquerel rays. In a previous paper, one of us (Mme. Curie) has shown that their activity is even greater than that of uranium and thorium, and has expressed the opinion that this effect was attributable to some other very active substance included in small amounts in these minerals.

The study of uranium and thorium compounds has shown in fact that the property of emitting rays which make the air conducting and which affect photographic plates, is a specific property of uranium and thorium that occurs in all compounds of these metals, being weaker in proportion as the active metal in the compound is diminished. The physical state of the substances appears to have an entirely secondary importance. Various experiments have shown that the state of mixture of these substances seems to act only to vary the proportions of the active bodies and the absorption produced by the inert substances. Certain causes (such as the presence of impurities) which have so great an effect on the phosphorescence or fluorescence are here entirely without effect. It is therefore very probable that if certain minerals are more active than uranium and thorium, it is because they contain a substance more active than these metals.

We have sought to isolate this substance in pitchblende and experiment has just confirmed the preceding conjectures.

Our chemical researches have been guided constantly by a check of the radiant activity of the separated products in each operation. Each product was placed on one of the plates of a condenser and the conductivity acquired by the air was measured with the aid of an electrometer and a

---

[3] Pierre and Marie Curie, trans. Editors, *Comptes Rendus,* 127 (1898), pp. 175–178.

piezoelectric quartz, as in the work cited above. One has thus not only an indication but a number which gives a measure of the strength of the product in the active substance.

The pitchblende which we have analysed was approximately two and a half times more active than uranium in our plate apparatus. We have treated it with acids and have treated the solutions obtained with hydrogen sulfide. Uranium and thorium remain in solution. We have verified the following facts:

The precipitated sulphides contain a very active substance together with lead, bismuth, copper, arsenic, and antimony. This substance is completely insoluble in the ammonium sulphide which separates it from arsenic and antimony. The sulphides insoluble in ammonium sulphide being dissolved in nitric acid, the active substance may be partially separated from lead by sulphuric acid. On washing lead sulfate with dilute sulphuric acid, most of the active substance entrained with the lead sulphate is dissolved.

The active substance present in solution with bismuth and copper is precipitated completely by ammonia [along with bismuth] which separates it from copper. Finally the active substance remains with bismuth.

We have not yet found any exact procedure for separating the active substance from bismuth by a wet method. We have, however, effected incomplete separations as judged by the following facts:

When the sulphides are dissolved by nitric acid, the least soluble portions are the least active. In the precipitation of the salts from water [solution] the first portions precipitated are by far the most active. We have observed that on heating pitchblende one obtains by sublimation some very active products. This observation led us to a separation process based on the difference in volatility between the active sulphide and bismuth sulphide. [For this purpose] the sulphides are heated in vacuum to about 700° in a tube of Bohemian glass. The active sulphide is deposited in the form of a black coating in those regions of the tube which are at 250° to 300°, while the bismuth sulphide stays in the hotter parts.

More and more active products are obtained by repetition of these different operations. Finally we obtained a substance whose activity is about four hundred times greater than that of uranium. We have sought again among the known substances to determine if this is the most active. We have examined compounds of almost all the elementary substances; thanks to the kindness of several chemists we have had samples of the rarest substances. Uranium and thorium only are naturally active, perhaps tantalum may be very feebly so.

We believe therefore that the substance which we have removed from pitchblende contains a metal not yet reported [and] close to bismuth in its analytical properties. If the existence of this new metal is confirmed, we propose to call it *polonium* from the name of the country of origin of one of us.

M. Demarcay has been kind enough to examine the spectrum of the substance which we studied. He was not able to distinguish any characteristic line apart from those ascribable to impurities. This fact is not favourable to the idea of the existence of a new metal. However, M. Demarcay called our attention to the fact that uranium, thorium, and tantalum exhibit spectra formed of innumerable very fine lines difficult to resolve. . . .

ᴐᴑᴑᴑᴑᴑᴑᴐ

PIERRE AND MARIE CURIE AND BEMONT

On a New Substance Strongly Radioactive, Contained in Pitchblende [4]

TWO OF US HAVE SHOWN that by purely chemical processes one can extract from pitchblende a strongly radioactive substance. This substance is closely related to bismuth in its analytical properties. We have stated the opinion that pitchblende may possibly contain a new element for which we have proposed the name polonium.

The investigations which we are now following are in accord with the first results obtained, but in the course of these researches we have found a second substance strongly radioactive and entirely different in its chemical properties from the first. In fact, polonium is precipitated out of acid solutions by hydrogen sulphide, its salts are soluble in acids, and water precipitates them from these solutions; polonium is completely precipitated by ammonia.

The new radioactive substance that we have just found has all the chemical aspects of nearly pure barium: It is precipitated neither by hydrogen sulphide, nor ammonium sulphide, nor by ammonia: the sulphate is insoluble in acids and water, the carbonate is insoluble in water, the chloride very soluble in water is insoluble in concentrated hydrochloric

---

[4] Pierre Curie, Marie Curie, and G. Bemont, *op. cit.*, pp. 1215–1217. Trans. Editors.

acid and in alcohol. Finally this substance shows the easily recognized spectrum of barium.

We believe nevertheless that this substance, although constituted for the greater part by barium, contains in addition a new element which gives it its radioactivity and which moreover is very close to barium in its chemical properties. The following are the reasons which argue in favour of this view:

1. Barium and its compounds are not ordinarily radioactive but one of us has shown that radioactivity appears to be an atomic property, persisting in all the chemical and physical states of the material. From this point of view, if the radioactivity of our substance is not due to barium, it must be attributed to another element.

2. The first preparations which have been obtained, in the form of the hydrated chloride, have a radioactivity sixty times stronger than that of metallic uranium (the radioactive intensity being evaluated by the conductivity of the air in our plate apparatus). In dissolving these chlorides in water and in precipitating a part with alcohol, the part precipitated is much more active than the part remaining in solution. Based on this fact, one ought to be able to effect a series of fractionations, securing chlorides more and more active. We have thus obtained chlorides having an activity nine hundred times greater than that of uranium. We have been stopped by the lack of material but, from the progress of the work, it is anticipated that the activity would have increased much more if we had been able to continue. These facts may be understood in terms of the presence of a radioactive element whose chloride is less soluble in a water solution of alcohol than that of barium.

3. M. Demarcay has examined the spectrum of our material so obligingly that we cannot thank him enough. The results of his examination are set forth in a special note following ours. M. Demarcay has found in the spectrum a line which does not appear to belong to any known element. This line, hardly visible with the chloride sixty times more active than uranium, is considerably stronger when the chloride is enriched by fractionation to nine hundred times that of uranium. The intensity of this line thus increases at the same time as the radioactivity and this we think is a very weighty reason for attributing the radioactive part of our substance to it.

The various reasons which we have just enumerated lead us to believe that the new radioactive substance contains a new element to which we propose to give the name radium.

We have determined the atomic weight of our active barium by titrating chlorine in the anhydrous chloride. We have found values which differ very slightly from those obtained in a parallel manner with inactive barium chloride; however, the values for the active barium are always a little higher but the difference is of the order of magnitude of the experimental errors.

The new radioactive substance certainly contains a large proportion of barium, despite the fact that the radioactivity is considerable. The radioactivity of radium ought therefore to be enormous.

Uranium, thorium, polonium, radium, and their compounds make the air a conductor of electricity and expose photographic plates. From these two points of view, polonium and radium are considerably more active than uranium and thorium. On photographic plates one obtains good images with radium and polonium in a half-minute exposure; it takes several hours to obtain the same results with uranium or thorium.

The rays emitted by the compounds of polonium and radium make barium platinocyanide fluorescent. Their action from this point of view is analogous to that of Roentgen rays, but considerably weaker.

30

○○○○○○○○○○○

THE DISCOVERY OF THE α - AND β -RAYS FROM URANIUM

○○○○○○○○○○○

Ernest Rutherford (1871-1937)

Becquerel's discovery that uranium emits a penetrating radiation or radiations was quickly followed by the recognition of similar properties in thorium by Mme. Curie and by Schmidt and shortly after by the isolation of polonium and radium by the Curies. But the nature of the radioactive radiations remained obscure. Ernest Rutherford, a young graduate student from New Zealand, working with Prof. J. J. Thomson at the Cavendish Laboratory, Cambridge, was intrigued by the mystery and began researches to solve the problem. Becquerel had shown that the radiations make the air that they traverse conducting, in the same manner as X-rays. But the conduction of the air resulting from the passage of X-rays was just the problem that Rutherford had been studying under Thomson's direction. He was therefore well fitted to apply his knowledge to the solution of the uranium problem.

In the paper that follows Rutherford first discusses the comparative merits of photographic and electrical methods for making his investigations. He attempts next to see if the rays from uranium are refracted in passing through a prism of glass, aluminum, or paraffin wax in a manner analogous to light rays through a glass prism. A photographic plate was used to determine if any bending of the rays could be detected. No effect was observed and the details of these observations in his paper are omitted. He next describes the process of ionization, showing what kind

437

of results should be obtained if uranium radiation makes the air conducting by this process. The results confirmed the ionization theory.

To test the complexity of the radiation he made use of the apparatus set up to prove the ionization theory. He found that by placing successively an increasing number of sheets of very thin aluminum foil over the uranium source, the ionization current produced in the contiguous air continually decreased by a constant ratio, a result that follows when there is absorption of a homogeneous radiation. Using thicker sheets of foil, the same result was secured until a thickness of 0.002 cm was reached. At this point the addition of another 0.004 cm was shown to have only a small effect. The conclusion was therefore drawn that the radiation was not homogeneous, at least two different kinds being present. The first radiation, having a high absorbability or a low penetrating power, he called the α-radiation, and the second, more penetrating, he called the β-radiation. Each of the separate radiations was found to be homogeneous. The nature of the α- and the β-radiations, however, was not discovered. This section of the paper concludes with the observation that "the cause and origin of the radiation continuously emitted by uranium and its salts still remain a mystery."

Because Rutherford was one of the greatest experimental physicists of all time we shall attempt to present the main facts of his life serially as we present the various papers which describe his great discoveries. The reader desiring a deeper understanding of this great man should consult the magnificent biography entitled simply *Rutherford,* written by his friend, Prof. A. S. Eve, who later, like Rutherford, was also McDonald professor at McGill University. The biographical material that follows is based on Eve's book and will be devoted to Rutherford's early life and training—up to the time of his discovery of the α- and β-rays from uranium.

Ernest Rutherford was born on August 30, 1871, at Brightwater about a dozen miles south of Nelson, one of the principal towns on the north coast of South Island, New Zealand. Both his parents, James Rutherford and Martha Thompson, had been brought to New Zealand from Scotland as children. The couple, as was common then, had a large family, seven sons and five daughters. Ernest was the fourth child and second son. Four years after his birth, the family moved to the town of Foxhill, about ten miles from Brightwater, where his schooling began. This period of residence lasted seven years, until 1882, when the family moved again, this time to Havelock on the northeast coast. Young Rutherford was then eleven years old. At Havelock he won a scholarship for his outstanding marks, and the award made it possible for him to go to Nelson College. This scholarship was the deciding event in his life. Nelson College had excellent teachers, especially one W. S. Littlejohn, a Scot who taught Rutherford science and mathematics. It was not only in these studies that Rutherford excelled: he was soon first in his class in all subjects. But about this time Rutherford's family, having suffered tragedy and reverses at Havelock, moved to Pungarehu on the North Island, where the elder Rutherford began a profitable flax-growing and exporting business. In 1889, shortly after this move, the eighteen-year-old Ernst won a scholarship to Canterbury College, a part of the University of New Zealand at Christchurch. Here he spent five years, earning a B.A. and then an M.A. degree, the latter with a first both in mathematics and physical science. In his fifth year, deeply impressed with Hertz's experimental discovery of electromagnetic waves, he set up a Hertz oscillator and a receiver equipped with a magnetic detector of his own design in the college basement. With this apparatus he was able to detect electromagnetic waves over a distance of about sixty feet with building walls intervening.

It was just at this time that Cambridge University opened its doors to research students. By attending for two years and writing an acceptable thesis, a student could obtain the Cambridge B.A. degree. One of the 1851 Exhibition Scholarships at Cambridge was open to students at the University of New Zealand and Rutherford had the good fortune to win it. Eve's biography notes that "when his mother came to tell him of his good fortune, he was digging potatoes. He flung away his spade with a laugh, exclaiming: 'That's the last potato I'll dig."

Thus in September 1895, when he had just turned twenty-four, Rutherford arrived in Cambridge as the first of the new research students at the Cavendish Laboratory and the first such student to be accepted by Prof. J. J. Thomson. Rutherford continued with his electromagnetic-wave researches begun at Christchurch and improved his apparatus sufficiently to transmit signals a distance of more than a half mile. This attracted a great deal of favorable attention and earned him a reputation as an outstanding research student in a very few months.

In the spring of 1896 he began studying with Thomson the ionization of the air produced by the passage of X-rays. Later this investigation was extended to ions produced by the action of ultraviolet light on zinc. This work continued during 1897 and into 1898. Toward the latter part of this period he became interested, as noted previously, in the manner in which uranium produces conductivity in the air. The paper that follows presents the results of his research. Before he completed this paper, he was offered in the summer of 1898 the position as McDonald professor of physics at McGill University in Montreal, Canada. He decided to accept, and left Cambridge early in September to take up his new responsibilities. The following paper was submitted from McGill University.

ଡ଼ଡ଼ଡ଼ଡ଼ଡ଼ଡ଼ଡ଼

RUTHERFORD

Uranium Radiation and the Electrical Conduction Produced by It [1]

THE REMARKABLE RADIATION EMITTED BY uranium and its compounds has been studied by its discoverer, Becquerel, and the results of his investigations on the nature and properties of the radiation have been given in a series of papers in the *Comptes Rendus*.[2] He showed that the radiation, continuously emitted from uranium compounds, has the power of passing through considerable thicknesses of metals and other opaque substances; it has the power of acting on a photographic plate and of discharging positive and negative electrification to an equal degree. The gas through which the radiation passes is made a temporary conductor of electricity and preserves its power of discharging electrification for a short time after the source of radiation has been removed.

The results of Becquerel showed that Roentgen and uranium radiations were very similar in their power of penetrating solid bodies and producing conduction in a gas exposed to them; but there was an essential difference between the two types of radiation. He found that uranium radiation could be refracted and polarized, while no definite results showing polarization or refraction have been obtained for Roentgen radiation.

It is the object of the present paper to investigate in more detail the nature of uranium radiation and the electrical conduction produced. . . .

§1. COMPARISON OF METHODS OF INVESTIGATION

The properties of uranium radiation may be investigated by two methods, one depending on the action on a photographic plate and the other on the discharge of electrification. The photographic method is

---

[1] Ernest Rutherford, *Philosophical Magazine*, 47 (1899), 109–116.
[2] Henri Becquerel, *Comptes Rendus*, 122 (1896), 420–423, 501–603, 1086–1088.

very slow and tedious, and admits of only the roughest measurements. Two or three days' exposure to the radiation is generally required to produce any marked effect on the photographic plate. In addition, when we are dealing with very slight photographic action, the fogging of the plate, during the long exposures required, by the vapours of substances is liable to obscure the results. On the other hand the method of testing the electrical discharge caused by the radiation is much more rapid than the photographic method, and also admits of fairly accurate quantitative determinations.

The question of polarization and refraction of the radiation can, however, only be tested by the photographic method.

[In Section 2, Rutherford explains that an attempt to refract the radiation using prisms of glass, pieces of aluminum, and paraffin wax were unsuccessful. Attempts to detect polarization using parallel and crossed tourmaline plates also yielded negative results—Editors.]

§3. THEORY OF IONIZATION

To explain the conductivity of a gas exposed to Roentgen radiation, the theory has been put forward that the rays in passing through the gas produce positively and negatively charged particles in the gas, and that the number produced per second depends on the intensity of the radiation and the pressure.

These carriers are assumed to be so small that they will move with a uniform velocity through a gas under a constant potential gradient. The term ion was given to them from analogy with electrolytic conduction, but in using the term it is not assumed that the ion is necessarily of atomic dimensions; it may be a multiple or submultiple of the atom.

Suppose we have a gas between two plates exposed to the radiation and that the plates are kept at a constant difference of potential. A certain number of ions will be produced per second by the radiation and the number produced will in general depend on the pressure of the gas. Under the electric field the positive ions travel towards the negative plate and the negative ions towards the other plate, and consequently a current will pass through the gas. Some of the ions will also recombine, the rate of recombination being proportional to the square of the number present. The current passing through the gas for a given intensity of radiation will depend on the difference of potential between the plates, but when the potential-difference is greater than a certain value the current will reach a maximum. When this is the case all the ions are removed by the electric field before they can recombine.

The positive and negative ions will be partially separated by the electric field, and an excess of ions of one sign may be blown away, so that a charged gas will be obtained. If the ions are not uniformly distributed between the plates, the potential gradient will be disturbed by the movement of the ions.

If energy is absorbed in producing ions, we should expect the absorption to be proportional to the number of ions produced and thus depend on the pressure. If this theory be applied to uranium radiation we should expect to obtain the following results:—

(1) Charged carriers produced through the volume of the gas.

(2) Ionization proportional to the intensity of the radiation and the pressure.

(3) Absorption of radiation proportional to pressure.

(4) Existence of saturation current.

(5) Rate of recombination of the ions proportional to the square of the number present.

(6) Partial separation of positive and negative ions.

(7) Disturbance of potential gradient under certain conditions between two plates exposed to the radiation.

The experiments now to be described sufficiently indicate that the theory does form a satisfactory explanation of the electrical conductivity produced by uranium radiation.

In all experiments to follow, the results are independent of the sign of the charged plate, unless the contrary is expressly stated.

§4. COMPLEX NATURE OF URANIUM RADIATION

Before entering on the general phenomena of the conduction produced by uranium radiation, an account will be given of some experiments to decide whether the same radiation is emitted by uranium and its compounds and whether the radiation is homogeneous. Roentgen and others have observed that the X-rays are in general of a complex nature, including rays of wide differences in their power of penetrating solid bodies. The penetrating power is also dependent to a large extent on the stage of exhaustion of the Crookes tube.

In order to test the complexity of the radiation, an electrical method was employed. The general arrangement is shown in [Fig. 30–1].

The metallic uranium or compound of uranium to be employed was powdered and spread uniformly over the centre of a horizontal zinc plate A, 20 cm. square. A zinc plate B, 20 cm. square, was fixed parallel to A and 4 cm. from it. Both plates were insulated. A was connected to one pole of a battery of 50 volts, the other pole of which was to earth; B was connected to one pair of quadrants of an electrometer, the other pair of which was connected to earth.

Under the influence of the uranium radiation there was a rate of leak between the two plates A and B. The rate of movement of the electrometer needle, when the motion was steady, was taken as a measure of the current through the gas.

Successive layers of thin metal foil were then placed over the uranium compound and the rate of leak determined for each additional sheet. [Table 30–1] shows the results obtained for thin Dutch metal.

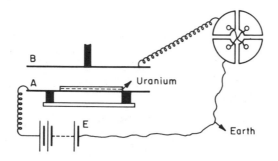

Fig. 30–1.

In the third column the ratio of the rates of leak for each additional thickness of metal leaf is given. Where two thicknesses were added at once, the square root of the observed ratio is taken, for three thicknesses the cube root. The table shows that for the first ten thicknesses of metal the rate of leak diminished approximately in a geometrical progression as the thickness of the metal increased in arithmetical progression.

TABLE 30–1 *Thickness of Metal Leaf ·00008 cm. Layer of Uranium Oxide on Plate.*

Number of Layers	Leak per min. in scale-divisions	Ratio for each layer
0	91	
1	77	·85
2	60	·78
3	49	·82
4	42	·86
5	33	·79
6	24·7	·75
8	15·4	·79
10	9·1	·77
13	5·8	·86

It will be shown later that the rate of leak between two plates for a saturating voltage is proportional to the intensity of the radiation after passing through the metal. The voltage of 50 employed was not sufficient to saturate the gas, but it was found that the comparative rates of leak under similar conditions for 50 and 200 volts between the plates were nearly the same. When we are dealing with very small rates of leak, it is advisable to employ as small a voltage as possible, in order that any small changes in the voltage of the battery should not appreciably affect the result. For this reason the voltage of 50 was used, and the comparative rates of leak obtained are very approximately the same as for saturating electromotive forces.

Since the rate of leak diminishes in a geometrical progression with the thickness of metal, we see from the above statement that the intensity of the radiation falls off in a geometrical progression, *i.e.* according to an ordinary absorption law. This shows that the part of the radiation considered is approximately homogeneous.

With increase of the number of layers the absorption commences to diminish. This is shown more clearly by using uranium oxide with layers of thin aluminium leaf [see Table 30–2].

T A B L E   3 0 – 2   *Thickness of Aluminium Foil ·0005 cm.*

Number of Layers of Aluminium foil	Leak per min. in scale-divisions	Ratio
0	182	
1	77	·42
2	33	·43
3	14·6	·44
4	9·4	·65
12	7	

It will be observed that for the first three layers of aluminium foil, the intensity of the radiation falls off according to the ordinary absorption law, and that, after the fourth thickness, the intensity of the radiation is only slightly diminished by adding another eight layers.

The aluminium foil in this case was about ·0005 cm. thick, so that after the passage of the radiation through ·002 cm. of aluminium the intensity of the radiation is reduced to about $\frac{1}{20}$ of its value. The addition of a thickness of ·001 cm. of aluminium has only a small effect in cutting down the rate of leak. The intensity is, however, again reduced to about half of its value after passing through an additional thickness of ·05 cm., which corresponds to 100 sheets of aluminium foil.

These experiments show that the uranium radiation is complex, and that there are present at least two distinct types of radiation—one that is very readily absorbed, which will be termed for convenience the α radiation, and the other of a more penetrative character, which will be termed the β radiation.

The character of the β radiation seems to be independent of the nature of the filter through which it has passed. It was found that radiation of the same intensity and of the same penetrative power was obtained by cutting off the α radiation by thin sheets of aluminium, tinfoil, or paper. The β radiation passes through all the substances tried with far greater facility than the α radiation. For example, a plate of thin cover-glass placed over the uranium reduced the rate of leak to ⅟₃₀ of its value; the β radiation, however, passed through it with hardly any loss of intensity.

Some experiments with different thicknesses of aluminium seem to show, as far as the results go, that the β radiation is of an approximately homogeneous character. [Table 30–3] gives some of the results obtained for the β radiation from uranium oxide:

T A B L E   3 0 – 3   *β Radiation*

Thickness of Aluminium	Rate of Leak
·005	1
·028	·68
·051	·48
·09	·25

The rate of leak is taken as unity after the α radiation has been absorbed by passing through ten layers of aluminium foil. The intensity of the radiation diminishes with the thickness of metal traversed according to the ordinary absorption law. It must be remembered that when we are dealing with the β radiation alone, the rate of leak is in general only a few per cent. of the leak due to the α radiation, so that the investigation of the homogeneity of the β radiation cannot be carried out with the same accuracy as for the α radiation. As far, however, as the experiments have gone, the results seem to point to the conclusion that the β radiation is approximately homogeneous, although it is possible that other types of radiation of either small intensity or very great penetrating power may be present. . . . The cause and origin of the radiation continuously emitted by uranium and its salts still remain a mystery.

31

○○○○○○○○○○

THE DISCOVERY OF γ-RAYS

○○○○○○○○○○

Paul Villard (1860-1934)

Paul Villard was born in Lyon, France, on September 28, 1860. He was the only son of parents of English origin; his father was an artist and musician. As a youth, young Villard was allowed considerable freedom, so that he found his early education at the lycée in Lyon confining and irksome. This attitude carried over into his later education at the École Normale Supérieure in Paris, which he entered at the age of twenty-one. After receiving his certificate from the École Normale he taught at several lycées before accepting a post in the faculty of sciences at the University of Montpellier. His work at Montpellier greatly encouraged his interest in science and, having a small income sufficient to meet his needs, he soon resigned his appointment to devote his full energies to advanced study in chemistry at the École Normale Supérieure in Paris.

After obtaining his doctorate he continued at the École, more and more completely immersed in research. He never married and his life was centered about his laboratory work. He was active in the study of cathode rays and X-rays. It was in the course of investigating the radiations from radium to see whether or not a penetrating radiation like X-rays might be emitted that he discovered γ-rays, as his paper (which follows) shows. Villard was active also in invention but sought no financial reward from his labor. The honor that he most prized was election to membership in the French Academy of Sciences in 1908.

During his later years he suffered from ill-health, apparently related to his exposure to radiation against which he seems not to have taken sufficient precaution. He died in Bayonne on January 13, 1934.

As the title of the paper partly reproduced below indicates, Villard was engaged in investigating the properties of reflected and refracted cathode rays and of the similar rays obtained from a radium source. The first part

446

of the report, which is omitted, deals with the behavior of a cathode ray beam incident on a thin insulated metallic plate, as well as the nature of the reflected radiation.

Villard then used a very thin foil of aluminum (0.02 mm) to obtain a "refracted" beam, i.e., radiation emerging from the face opposite to the incident radiation. This emerging radiation he characterized as an apparent refraction, but he considered that the phenomenon was actually a new emission, or "secondary" radiation. Next he examined the refraction using the rays from radium as a source but with a much thicker (0.3 mm) metal plate as the refracting material. It was in this part of the experiment that he discovered that radium emits a very penetrating radiation that was not deflected by a magnetic field. Hence the rays carried no electric charge. These rays soon came to be known as γ-rays, and were found later to be of the nature of very penetrating X-rays.

ᴑᴑᴑᴑᴑᴑᴑ

VILLARD

On the Reflection and Refraction of Cathode Rays and Deviable Rays of Radium[1]

REFRACTION OF RADIUM RAYS

[The first two sections of the paper deal with experiments on the reflection and refraction of cathode rays and are omitted—Editors.]

THE DEVIABLE RAYS FROM RADIUM behave like the cathode rays in Crookes tubes; the experiment was made in the following manner.

A small quantity of radium-bearing barium chloride enclosed in a thin glass ampoule was placed in a lead tube, one of the ends of which, completely open, allowed a cone of rays of about 20° spread to emerge. At 2 or 3 mm in front of this opening there was fixed a small aluminum plate, 0.3 mm thick, inclined at 45° to the axis of the tube and placed in such a way as to intercept half the beam. All of this was placed on a photographic plate wrapped in a double sheet of black paper which re-

---

[1] Paul Villard, *Comptes Rendus,* 130 (1900), 1010–1012. Trans. Editors.

ceived the emerging beam at almost grazing incidence. The impression produced on the photographic plate showed that the half-beam which had struck the aluminum, instead of continuing its path in a straight line and remaining symmetrical with the non-intercepted half-beam, followed a direction clearly normal to the aluminum sheet. This refraction is accompanied by a strong scattering. Except for the greater thickness of metal traversed, the phenomenon is the same as in Crookes tubes.

REMARK ON THE RADIATION FROM RADIUM

On repeating the preceding experiment under different conditions, I have almost always observed that there is superposed on the refracted beam a rectilinearly propagated beam which sometimes made the negatives difficult to interpret. It occurred to me that this effect was due to the presence of non-deviable rays less absorbable than those described by M. Curie. The magnetic analysis of the radiation has shown that this supposition is justified.

The rays emitted from a small glass tube filled with active material pass through a rectangular opening 6 mm wide cut in a lead bar, and cross a magnetic field. A photographic plate 13 by 18 (cm) placed at almost grazing incidence recorded the trajectories. Under these conditions one observes that the rays admitted to the field divide into two distinct groups which become separated after traveling a few centimeters.

One of these groups is deviated in the expected direction, the other formed by the non-deviable rays, propagates rectilinearly across the whole length of the plate. This non-deviated beam is sufficiently penetrating to make an impression on a sensitive plate protected by several sheets of black paper and a foil of aluminum at a distance of 25 cm; it can even penetrate a lead sheet 0.2 mm thick.

The complete results that I have observed can be explained without difficulty; the beam which in my experiments went through the inclined aluminum foil without refraction corresponds to the non-deviable rays. Indeed the experiment has shown that the beam is not affected by the magnetic field. The deviable rays on the contrary behave like cathode rays and emerge normal to the foil traversed.

I propose to repeat these experiments with pure deviable rays.

The preceding facts lead to the conclusion that the non-deviable part of the emission from radium contains very penetrating radiations capable of traversing metal foils, these radiations being revealed by the photographic method.

32

ᴏᴏᴏᴏᴏᴏᴏᴏᴏᴏ

THE TRANSFORMATION
OF THE ELEMENTS

ᴏᴏᴏᴏᴏᴏᴏᴏᴏᴏ

Ernest Rutherford (1871-1937)

Frederick Soddy (1877-1956)

Early experiments gave no indication that the emission of α and β particles from radioactive elements produced any chemical change in these elements or that the activity decreased with time. Then late in 1899 the Curies discovered "excited radioactivity," produced by radium on nearby bodies. Early in 1900 Ernest Rutherford discovered thorium emanation, an active gas, and noted that the same "excited radioactivity," or "active deposit," as it came to be called, could be traced to this thorium gas. But a new and surprising fact was uncovered by Rutherford; the activity decreased exponentially with the time!

Following these investigations Rutherford left Canada in April for New Zealand to visit his parents and to marry his fiancée Mary Newton. An event of considerable significance in the study of radioactivity occurred during Rutherford's visit to New Zealand. In May 1900, Sir William Crookes announced the discovery of uranium-X. He prepared it by first treating a uranium solution with ammonium carbonate, then dissolving the precipitated uranium carbonate in an excess of the ammonium carbonate. A final light precipitate resulted. This was filtered and constituted uranium-X, a substance that appeared at the time to have all the activity of the original uranium. The chemistry of radioactive substances thus began to be of fundamental importance.

On his return to Montreal in the autumn, Rutherford realized that he

449

would need an able collaborator to assist him with chemical analyses. His extraordinary luck, which has often been commented upon, came to his aid. A very able young chemist, Frederick Soddy, had been added to the chemistry staff during the summer. Soddy, a vigorous and adventurous young man of twenty-three, trained at Oxford, had applied for a professorship which had become vacant at the University of Toronto. Not content with waiting to hear the outcome of his application he had impulsively decided to appear in Toronto in person to bolster his candidacy. On arriving in New York from his ocean crossing he started at once by train for Canada. On the way he was chagrined to read in the newspaper that the vacancy had been filled. Later, by the merest chance, he decided to stop briefly in Montreal to have a look at the new McDonald laboratories at McGill University. Here the senior professor of chemistry showed him the chemistry facilities and offered him a demonstratorship on the spot; Soddy accepted. It was in this way that Soddy became associated with McGill, and very shortly thereafter with Rutherford.

Early in 1901 Soddy gave up his appointment to spend full time on the radioactivity research. The paper that follows is one of the results of this collaboration. In it is the epochal announcement of the instability of atoms, which chemistry had always considered immutable, and the transformation theory of the radioactive elements; i.e., the change of uranium and thorium atoms by radioactivity into other chemical elements. These daughter substances are also radioactive, and decay in activity exponentially, and have a definite half-life.

The essence of the paper begins with the demonstration that thorium nitrate when treated with ammonia yields a precipitate, thorium hydroxide, and a filtrate, ammonium nitrate. If the precipitate is treated with nitric acid, thorium nitrate is produced in water solution. This thorium nitrate is again reacted with ammonia producing a purer thorium hydroxide and ammonium nitrate. Chemically the processes may be written as follows:

$$Th(NO_3)_4 + 4\,NH_4OH = Th(OH)_4 + 4\,NH_4NO_3$$
$$Th(OH)_4 + 4\,HNO_3 = Th(NO_3)_4 + 4\,H_2O$$

After drying the filtrate, the ammonium salts were driven off by ignition and the residue was found, on a weight basis, to be several thousand times as active as the thorium from which it was derived. This active substance was designated Th-X. Its activity was found to decay according to the graph in Fig. 32–1 and, neglecting the activity in the first two days, to decay exponentially as shown in Fig. 32–2. As shown in the same figure, the thorium hydroxide was found to recover its activity with time. Subsequently the thorium hydroxide that had recovered its activity was converted to the nitrate and precipitated with ammonia. Examination of the filtrate showed that Th-X of the original level of activity was obtained; therefore the investigators inferred that this substance was continuously generated by the disintegration of thorium. The paper gives supporting evidence for this conclusion, including the measurement of the rate of production of Th-X. The latter, in turn, was considered to decay to thorium emanation and this to the "excited radioactivity." The activity of thorium itself was also investigated.

From their experiments, Rutherford and Soddy reached the general conclusion that radioactivity is a manifestation of subatomic change—a phrase that seems prophetic in view of the nuclear atom, which Rutherford was to propose nine years later. Thus if radioactivity occurs because of a change in the atom, i.e., by the expulsion of an α- or β-particle, the atom itself changes and a new substance is born, a fact that was proved chemically. Consequently, all radioactive elements were considered as undergoing spontaneous transformation into new elements; the atom could no longer be viewed as the immutable entity that chemistry had hitherto considered it. Thus the most sweeping changes in the contemporary outlook on matter were introduced.

○○○○○○○○

RUTHERFORD AND SODDY

The Cause and Nature of Radioactivity [1]

INTRODUCTION

THE FOLLOWING PAPERS GIVE THE results of a detailed investigation of the radioactivity of thorium compounds which has thrown light on the questions connected with the source and maintenance of the energy dissipated by radioactive substances. Radioactivity is shown to be accompanied by chemical changes in which new types of matter are being continuously produced. These reaction products are at first radioactive, the activity diminishing regularly from the moment of formation. Their continuous production maintains the radioactivity of the matter producing them at a definite equilibrium-value. The conclusion is drawn that these chemical changes must be sub-atomic in character.

---

[1] From Ernest Rutherford and Frederick Soddy, *Philosophical Magazine*, 4 (1902), 370–396.

The present researches had as their starting-point the facts that had come to light with regard to thorium radioactivity. Besides being radio-active in the same sense as the uranium compounds, the compounds of thorium continuously emit into the surrounding atmosphere a gas which possesses the property of temporary radioactivity. This "emanation," as it has been named, is the source of rays, which ionize gases and darken the photographic film.*

The most striking property of the thorium emanation is its power of exciting radioactivity on all surfaces with which it comes into contact. A substance after being exposed for some time in the presence of the emanation behaves as if it were covered with an invisible layer of an intensely active material. If the thoria is exposed in a strong electric field, the excited radioactivity is entirely confined to the negatively changed surface. In this way it is possible to concentrate the excited radioactivity on a very small area. The excited radioactivity can be removed by rubbing or by the action of acids, as, for example, sulphuric, hydrochloric, and hydrofluoric acids. If the acids be then evaporated, the radioactivity re-mains on the dish.

The emanating power of thorium compounds is independent of the surrounding atmosphere, and the excited activity it produces is independ-ent of the nature of the substance on which it is manifested. These proper-ties made it appear that both phenomena were caused by minute quanti-ties of special kinds of matter in the radioactive state, produced by the thorium compound.

The next consideration in regard to these examples of radioactivity, is that the activity in each case diminishes regularly with the lapse of time, the intensity of radiation at each instant being proportional to the amount of energy remaining to be radiated. For the emanation a period of one minute, and for the excited activity a period of eleven hours, causes the activity to fall to half its value. . . . The radioactivity of thorium at any time is the resultant of two opposing processes—

(1) The production of fresh radioactive material at a constant rate by the thorium compound;

(2) The decay of the radiating power of the active material with time.

The normal or constant radioactivity possessed by thorium is an equilibrium value, where the rate of increase of radioactivity due to the production of fresh active material is balanced by the rate of decay of radioactivity of that already formed. It is the purpose of the present paper to substantiate and develope this hypothesis.

---

* If thorium oxide be exposed to a white heat its power of giving an emanation is to a large extent destroyed. Thoria that has been so treated is referred to throughout as "de-emanated."

THE RATES OF RECOVERY AND DECAY
OF THORIUM RADIOACTIVITY

A quantity of the pure thorium nitrate was separated from ThX . . . by several precipitations with ammonia. The radioactivity of the hydroxide so obtained was tested at regular intervals to determine the rate of recovery of its activity. For this purpose the original specimen of ·5 gram was left undisturbed throughout the whole series of measurements on the plate over which it had been sifted, and was compared always with ·5 gram of ordinary de-emanated thorium oxide spread similarly on a second plate and also left undisturbed. The emanation from the hydroxide was prevented from interfering with the results by a special arrangement for drawing a current of air over it during the measurements.

The active filtrate from the preparation was concentrated and made up to 100 c.c. volume. One quarter was evaporated to dryness and the ammonium nitrate expelled by ignition in a platinum dish, and the radioactivity of the residue tested at the same intervals as the hydroxide to determine the rate of decay of its activity. The comparison in this case was a standard sample of uranium oxide kept undisturbed on a metal plate, which repeated work has shown to be a perfectly constant source of radiation. The remainder of the filtrate was used for other experiments.

[A table of data, plotted in Fig. 32–1, is omitted—Editors.]

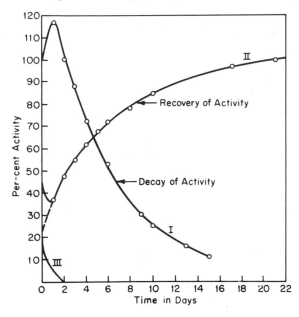

Fig. 32–1.

[Fig. 32–1] shows the curves obtained by plotting the radioactivities as ordinates, and the time in days as abscissæ. Curve II. illustrates the rate of recovery of the activity of thorium, curve I. the rate of decay of activity of ThX. It will be seen that neither of the curves is regular for the first two days. The activity of the hydroxide at first actually diminished and was at the same value after two days as when first prepared. The activity of the ThX, on the other hand, at first increases and does not begin to fall below the original value till after the lapse of two days. . . . These results cannot be ascribed to errors of measurement, for they have been regularly observed whenever similar preparations have been tested. The activity of the residue obtained from thorium oxide by the second method of washing decayed very similarly to that of ThX, as shown by the above curve.

If for present purposes the initial periods of the curve are disregarded and the later portions only considered, it will be seen at once that the time taken for the hydroxide to recover one half of its lost activity is about equal to the time taken by the ThX to lose half its activity, viz., in each case about 4 days, and speaking generally the percentage proportion of the lost activity regained by the hydroxide over any given interval is approximately equal to the percentage proportion of the activity lost by the ThX during the same interval. If the recovery curve is produced backwards in the normal direction to cut the vertical axis, it will be seen to do so at a minimum of about 25 per cent., and the above result holds even more accurately if the recovery is assumed to start from this constant minimum, as indeed, it has been shown to do under suitable conditions. . . .

This is brought out by [Fig. 32–2], which represents the recovery curve of thorium in which the percentage amounts of activity recovered, reckoned from this 25 per cent. minimum, are plotted as ordinates. In the same figure the decay curve after the second day is shown on the same scale.

The activity of ThX decreases very approximately in a geometrical progression with the time, i.e. if I_0 represent the initial activity and I_t the activity after time t.

$$\frac{I_t}{I_0} = e^{-\lambda t}, \tag{1}$$

where λ is a constant and e the base of natural logarithms.

The experimental curve obtained with the hydroxide for the rate of rise of its activity from a minimum to a maximum value will therefore be approximately expressed by the equation

$$\frac{I_t}{I_0} = 1 - e^{-\lambda t}, \tag{2}$$

where I_0 represents the amount of activity recovered when the maximum is reached, and I_t the activity recovered after time t, λ *being the same constant as before.*

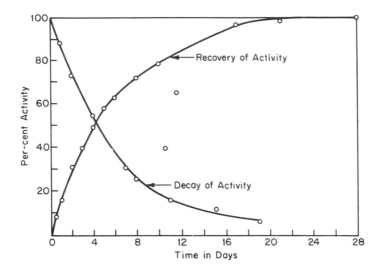

Fig. 32–2.

Now this last equation has been theoretically developed in other places to express the rise of activity to a constant maximum of a system consisting of radiating particles in which

(1) The rate of supply of fresh radiating particles is constant.

(2) The activity of each particle dies down geometrically with the time according to equation (1).

It therefore follows that if the initial irregularities of the curves are disregarded and the residual activity of thorium is assumed to possess a *constant* value, the experimental curve obtained for the recovery of activity will be explained if two processes are supposed to be taking place:

(1) That the active constituent ThX is being produced at a constant rate;

(2) That the activity of the ThX decays geometrically with time.

Without at first going into the difficult questions connected with the initial irregularities and the residual activity, the main result that follows from the curves given can be put to experimental test very simply. The primary conception is that the major part of the radioactivity of thorium is not due to the thorium at all, but to the presence of a non-thorium substance in minute amount which is being continuously produced.

CHEMICAL PROPERTIES OF THX

The fact that thorium on precipitation from its solutions by ammonia leaves the major part of its activity in the filtrate does not of itself prove that a material *constituent* responsible for this activity has been chemically separated. It is possible that the matter constituting the non-thorium part of the solution is rendered temporarily radioactive by its association with thorium, and this property is retained through the processes of precipitation, evaporation, and ignition, and manifests itself finally on the residue remaining.

This view, however, can be shown to be quite untenable, for upon it any precipitate capable of removing thorium completely from its solution should yield active residues similar to those obtained from ammonia. Quite the reverse, however, holds.

When thorium nitrate is precipitated by sodium or ammonium carbonate, the residue from the filtrate by evaporation and ignition is free from activity, and the thorium carbonate possesses the normal value for its activity.

The same holds true when oxalic acid is used as the precipitant. This reagent even in strongly acid solution precipitates almost all of the thorium. When the filtrate is rendered alkaline by ammonia, filtered, evaporated, and ignited, the residue obtained is inactive.

In the case where sodium phosphate is used as the precipitant in ordinary acid solution, the part that comes down is more or less free from ThX. On making the solution alkaline with ammonia, the remainder of the thorium is precipitated as phosphate, and carries with it the whole of the active constituent, so that the residue from the filtrate is again inactve.

In fact ammonia is the only reagent of those tried capable of separating ThX from thorium.

The result of Sir William Crookes with uranium, which we have confirmed with the electrical method, may be here mentioned. UrX is completely precipitated by ammonia together with uranium, and the residue obtained by the evaporation of the filtrate is quite inactive.

There can thus be no question that both ThX and UrX are distinct types of matter with definite chemical properties. Any hypothesis that attempts to account for the recovery of activity of thorium and uranium with time must of necessity start from this primary conception.

THE CONTINUOUS PRODUCTION OF THX

If the recovery of the activity of thorium with time is due to the production of ThX, it should be possible to obtain experimental evidence of the process. The first point to be ascertained is how far the removal of

ThX by the method given reduces the total radioactivity of thorium. A preliminary trial showed that the most favourable conditions for the separation are by precipitating in hot dilute solutions by dilute ammonia. A quantity of 5 grams of thorium nitrate, as obtained from the maker, was so precipitated by ammonia, the precipitate being redissolved in nitric acid and reprecipitated under the same conditions successively *without lapse of time.*

The removal of ThX was followed by measuring the activity of the residues obtained from the successive filtrates. The activity of the ThX from the first filtrate was equivalent to 4·25 grams of thoria, from the second to 0·33 gram, and from the third to 0·07 gram. It will be seen that by two precipitations practically the whole of the ThX is removed. The radioactivity of the separated hydroxide was 48 per cent. of that of the standard de-emanated sample of thoria.

Rate of Production of ThX

A quantity of thorium nitrate solution that had been freed from ThX about a month before, was again subjected to the same process. The activity of the residue from the filtrate in an experiment in which 10 grams of this nitrate had been employed was equivalent to 8·3 grams of thorium oxide. This experiment was performed on the same day as the one recorded above, in which 5 grams of new nitrate had been employed, and it will be seen that there is no difference in the activity of the filtrate in the two cases. In one month the activity of the ThX in a thorium compound again possesses its maximum value.

If a period of 24 hours is allowed to elapse between the successive precipitations, the activity of the ThX formed during that time corresponds to about one-sixth of the maximum activity of the total thorium employed. In three hours the activity of the amount produced is about one-thirtieth. The rate of production of ThX worked out from those figures well agrees with the form of the curve obtained for the recovery of activity of thorium, if the latter is taken to express the continuous production of ThX at a constant rate and the diminution of the activity of the product in geometrical progression with the time.

By using the sensitive electrometer, the course of production of ThX can be followed after extremely short intervals. Working with 10 grams of thorium nitrate, the amount produced in the minimum time taken to carry out the successive precipitations is as much as can be conveniently measured. If any interval is allowed to lapse the effect is beyond the range of the instrument, unless the sensitiveness is reduced to a fraction of its ordinary value by the introduction of capacities into the system. Capacities of ·01 and ·02 microfarad, which reduce the sensitiveness to less than one two-hundredth of the normal, were frequently employed in dealing with these active residues.

The process of the production of ThX is continuous, and no alteration was observed in the amount produced in a given time after repeated separations. In an experiment carried out for another purpose after 23 successive precipitations extending over 9 days, the amount formed during the last interval was as far as could be judged no less than what occurred at the beginning of the process.

The phenomenon of radioactivity, by means of the electrometer as its measuring instrument, thus enables us to detect and measure changes occurring in matter after a few minutes' interval, which have never yet been detected by the balance or suspected of taking place.

THE CAUSE AND NATURE OF RADIOACTIVITY

The foregoing conclusions enable a great generalization to be made in the subject of radioactivity. Energy considerations require that the intensity of radiation from any source should die down with time unless there is a constant supply of energy to replace that dissipated. This has been found to hold true in the case of all known types of radioactivity with the exception of the "naturally" radioactive elements—to take the best established cases, thorium, uranium, and radium. It will be shown later that the radioactivity of the emanation produced by thorium compounds decays geometrically with the time under all conditions, and is not affected by the most drastic chemical and physical treatment. The same has been shown by one of us to hold for the excited radioactivity produced by the thorium emanation. This decays at the same rate whether on the wire on which it is originally deposited, or in solution of hydrochloric or nitric acid. The excited radioactivity produced by the radium emanation appears analogous. All these examples satisfy energy considerations. In the case of the three naturally occurring radioactive elements, however, it is obvious that there must be a continuous replacement of the dissipated energy, and no satisfactory explanation has yet been put forward.

The nature of the process becomes clear in the light of the foregoing results. The material constituent responsible for the radioactivity, when it is separated from the thorium which produces it, then behaves in the same way as the other types of radioactivity cited. Its activity decays geometrically with the time, and the rate of decay is independent of the molecular conditions. The normal radioactivity is, however, maintained at a constant value by a chemical change which produces fresh radioactive material at a rate also independent of the conditions. The energy required to maintain the radiations will be accounted for if we suppose that the energy of the system after the change has occurred is less than it was before.

The work of Crookes and Becquerel on the separation of UrX and the recovery of the activity of the uranium with time, makes it appear extremely probable that the same explanation holds true for this element. The work of M. and Mme. Curie, the discoverers of radium, goes to show that this body easily suffers a temporary decrease of its activity by chemical treatment, the normal value being regained after the lapse of time, and this can be well interpreted on the new view. All known types of radioactivity can thus be brought under the same category.

SUMMARY OF RESULTS

The foregoing experimental results may be briefly summarized. The major part of the radioactivity of thorium—ordinarily about 54 per cent.—is due to a non-thorium type of matter, ThX, possessing distinct chemical properties, which is temporarily radioactive, its activity falling to half value in about four days. The constant radioactivity of thorium is maintained by the production of this material at a constant rate. Both the rate of production of the new material and the rate of decay of its activity appear to be independent of the physical and chemical condition of the system.

The ThX further possesses the property of exciting radioactivity on surrounding inactive matter, and about 21 per cent. of the total activity under ordinary circumstances is derived from this source. Its rate of decay and other considerations make it appear probable that it is the same as the excited radioactivity produced by the thorium emanation, which is in turn produced by ThX. There is evidence that, if from any cause the emanation is prevented from escaping in the radioactive state, the energy of its radiation goes to augment the proportion of excited radioactivity in the compound.

[The sections on which the following conclusions were based have been omitted—Editors.]

Thorium can be freed by suitable means from both ThX and the excited radioactivity which the latter produces, and then possesses an activity about 25 per cent. of its original value, below which it has not been reduced. This residual radiation consists entirely of rays non-deviable by the magnetic field, whereas the other two components comprise both deviable and non-deviable radiation. Most probably this residual activity is caused by a second non-thorium type of matter produced in the same change as ThX, and it should therefore prove possible to separate it by chemical methods.

GENERAL THEORETICAL CONSIDERATIONS

Turning from the experimental results to their theoretical interpretation, it is necessary to first consider the generally accepted view of the nature of radioactivity. It is well established that this property is the function of the atom and not of the molecule. Uranium and thorium, to take the most definite cases, possess the property in whatever molecular condition they occur, and the former also in the elementary state. So far as the radioactivity of different compounds of different density and states of division can be compared together, the intensity of the radiation appears to depend only on the quantity of active element present. It is not at all dependent on the source from which the element is derived, or the process of purification to which it has been subjected, provided sufficient time is allowed for the equilibrium point to be reached. It is not possible to explain the phenomena by the existence of impurities associated with the radioactive elements, even if any advantage could be derived from the assumption. For these impurities must necessarily be present always to the same extent in different specimens derived from the most widely different sources, and, moreover, they must persist *in unaltered amount* after the most refined processes of purification. This is contrary to the accepted meaning of the term impurity.

All the most prominent workers in this subject are agreed in considering radioactivity an atomic phenomenon. M. and Mme. Curie, the pioneers in the chemistry of the subject, have recently put forward their views. They state that this idea underlies their whole work from the beginning and created their methods of research. M. Becquerel, the original discoverer of the property for uranium, in his announcement of the recovery of the activity of the same element after the active constituent had been removed by chemical treatment, points out the significance of the fact that uranium is giving out cathode-rays. These, according to the hypothesis of Sir William Crookes and Prof. J. J. Thomson, are *material* particles of mass one thousandth of the hydrogen atom.

Since, therefore, radioactivity is at once an atomic phenomenon and accompanied by chemical changes in which new types of matter are produced, these changes must be occurring within the atom, and the radioactive elements must be undergoing spontaneous transformation. The results that have so far been obtained, which indicate that the velocity of this reaction is unaffected by the conditions, make it clear that the changes in question are different in character from any that have been before dealt with in chemistry. It is apparent that we are dealing with phenomena outside the sphere of known atomic forces. Radioactivity may therefore be considered as a manifestation of subatomic chemical change.

The changes brought to knowledge by radioactivity, although undeniably material and chemical in nature, are of a different order of magnitude from any that have before been dealt with in chemistry. The course of the production of new matter which can be recognized by the electrometer, by means of the property of radioactivity, after the lapse of a few hours or even minutes, might conceivably require geological epochs to attain to quantities recognized by the balance. However, the well-defined chemical properties of both ThX and UrX are not in accordance with the view that the actual amounts involved are of this extreme order of minuteness. On the other hand, the existence of radioactive elements at all in the earth's crust is an *à priori* argument against the magnitude of the change being anything but small.

Radioactivity as a new property of matter capable of exact quantitative determination thus possesses an interest apart from the peculiar properties and powers which the radiations themselves exhibit. Mme. Curie, who isolated from pitchblende a new substance, radium, which possessed distinct chemical properties and spectroscopic lines, used the property as a means of chemical analysis. An exact parallel is to be found in Bunsen's discovery and separation of cæsium and rubidium by means of the spectroscope.

The present results show that radioactivity can also be used to follow *chemical changes occurring in matter*. The properties of matter that fulfil the necessary conditions for the study of chemical change without disturbance to the reacting system are few in number. It seems not unreasonable to hope, in the light of the foregoing results, that radioactivity, being such a property, affords the means of obtaining information of the processes occurring within the chemical atom, in the same way as the rotation of the plane of polarization and other physical properties have been used in chemistry for the investigation of the course of molecular change.

33

○○○○○○○○○○

THE QUANTUM THEORY
OF RADIATION

○○○○○○○○○○○

Max Planck (1858-1947)

BORN

Max Karl Ernst Ludwig Planck [1]

ALMOST HALF A CENTURY HAS elapsed since Max Planck's discovery of the quantum of action, a time sufficiently long to estimate its importance for science and, more generally, for the development of human thought. There is no doubt that it was an event of the first order, comparable with the scientific revolutions brought about by Galileo and Newton, Faraday and Maxwell. Like these it has changed the whole aspect of physics and deeply influenced all neighbouring sciences, from chemistry to biology. Its philosophical implications reach far beyond the epistemology of science itself into the deepest roots of metaphysics.

What kind of man was he who initiated this great movement? . . . my best help must be the memory of years of personal contact and friendship, which have left an unforgettable impression.

Planck came from an old family of lawyers, public servants and scholars. One of his ancestors was a minister in Suabia who later became a professor of Divinity at Göttingen. One of the grandchildren of this man was

---

[1] Max Born, *Obituary Notices of Fellows of the Royal Society,* 6, 1948, 161–180.

to become a celebrated jurist, professor of law at Göttingen, distinguished as the founder of the German Civil Code (*Deutsches Bürgerliches Gesetzbuch*). The Planck-Strasse, where I later lived for several years, was called after him. He lost his sight at an early age, and I remember the venerable figure of the blind old "Excellency" from my own student days. He and Max Planck's father were cousins; the latter also a distinguished jurist and professor of law at Kiel University. In 1867 he was called to Munich, and is said to have enjoyed the confidence of his colleagues and played an important part in the administration of the university.

This ancestry of excellent, reliable, incorruptible, idealistic and generous men, devoted to the service of the Church and State, must be remembered if one wishes to understand the character of Max Planck and the roots of his success. For his work was directed by just the same traits combined with a sincere belief in the simplicity of nature and an absolute confidence in logical reasoning from facts.

Max Karl Ernst Ludwig Planck was born at Kiel on 23 April 1858. Here he spent his early childhood. When he was nine years old the family moved to Munich. He became a pupil of the Maximilian Gymnasium (Grammar School), where he received his first scientific inspiration from his mathematics teacher, Herman Müller, an ingenious and sharp-witted man who knew how to demonstrate the laws of physics from simple, forceful examples.

In his autobiography Planck says about these beginnings: "What led me to my science and from my youth filled me with enthusiasm, is the fact—not at all self-evident—that our laws of thinking conform with the lawfulness in the passage of impressions which we receive from the outer world, thus making it possible for man to gain information about that lawfulness by mere thinking. In this it is of the highest significance that the outer world represents something independent of us and absolute with which we are confronted, and the search for the laws which govern this absolute has appeared to me as the most fascinating work of a lifetime."

These ideas are characteristic of Planck's whole attitude to science, and it was Müller who encouraged and assisted him in developing them.

The principle of conservation of energy was welcomed by Planck "like a gospel" as the first of those "absolute" laws.

When it came to the choice of a profession there were, however, other competing interests. He considered for a time the study of classical philology. He tried his musical gifts in composition, but came to the conviction that they did not suffice for original production. In the end physics prevailed. Music, however, remained an essential part of his life. He became an excellent pianist and found in playing deep enjoyment and recreation.

Planck studied for three years at the University of Munich. There were no chairs of theoretical physics at that time, so he attended the lectures on mathematics by Gustav Bauer and Ludwig Seidel, and on physics by Ph. von Jolly. They gave him a solid foundation of knowledge, but the wide horizon of science was opened to him only when he went to Berlin, where he studied one year under Helmholtz and Kirchhoff. However, so he reports, it was not from their lectures that he benefited. Helmholtz was never properly prepared, he improvised with the help of a little notebook and made mistakes in the calculations on the blackboard, so that his students felt that he was just as bored as they themselves. Kirchhoff's lectures on the other hand, were carefully worked out, each sentence well considered, but the whole was dry and monotonous. It was when Planck turned to their writings that he was fascinated. His main interest was still the principle of conservation of energy. Soon he discovered a new source of enlightenment in the publications of Clausius, which made a deep impression on him through their clear language and lucid explanations. Here he learned for the first time to distinguish between the two fundamental theorems, as formulated by Clausius, and from this time on his whole scientific thinking was rooted in the conceptions of thermodynamics.

His doctor's thesis, Munich 1879, is the first of his papers dealing with the second theorem. He was not satisfied with Clausius' definition of irreversibility, namely that a process is irreversible if it cannot be made to go in the opposite direction, like the conduction of heat; Planck regards this as insufficient, as it does not exclude the possibility of reversing the result of the process in an indirect way, which is just what should be excluded. So he suggests that a process should be called irreversible, or as he prefers to say "natural," if it cannot be completely undone without compensation. Entropy is a measure of the "predilection" of nature for the final state and it increases in all "natural" processes.

Planck's expectation of a favourable reception of his paper was not fulfilled. Helmholtz was indifferent, Kirchhoff objected that entropy was only measurable by reversible processes and should therefore not be applied to irreversible ones. An attempt to get in personal contact with Clausius in Bonn failed, and a correspondence with Carl Neumann in Leipzig remained futile.

But Planck was not discouraged. He continued his work on thermodynamics in a series of papers from 1880 to 1892, the first of which was used as thesis for the admission as *Privatdozent* (habilitation) at Munich University, which he obtained in 1880.

If one reads these articles now, one has the feeling of meeting old acquaintances. Everything seems to be familiar, the definitions, demonstrations, even the symbols. The reason is that we have all been nursed with Planck's book on thermodynamics, in which he has condensed the result of his previous work. So systematic was his mind, so well considered every word, every formula he wrote, that hardly anything had to be changed in the final compilation. This book *Vorlesungen über Thermodynamik* appeared first in 1897 and has since had numerous new editions.

Planck's interest in physics had always a philosophical background, namely, his fundamental belief formulated above, that the human mind can penetrate into the mysteries of nature by pure thinking because of a harmony between the laws of mind and the laws of nature. Therefore, he always preferred deductive, sometimes even axiomatic methods. This is quite obvious in his thermodynamical work. Once he was convinced of the general and universal law of the increase of entropy he tried to deduce from it as much as possible. Equilibria are then characterized by maxima of entropy, or by equivalent extrema of other thermodynamical potentials. These extremal principles of thermodynamics formed therefore the basis of his work, in contrast to the usual methods of the physico-chemists who preferred special cyclic processes which appealed to their intuition. Planck did not know at the time that his extremal principles had already been discovered and applied by Willard Gibbs, and it is only natural that he felt a certain disappointment when he found this out. He was still *Privat-dozent* at the University of Munich and waited with some impatience for the offer of a professorial chair. Yet the chances were slight since theoretical physics was not an acknowledged academic subject.

In order to make himself better known in the scientific world Planck decided to compete for the prize for 1887 of the Philosophical Faculty of Göttingen, demanding a thesis on the conception of energy. Before this paper was finished Planck was offered a chair as "extraordinary" (i.e. not full, or "ordinary") professor of theoretical physics at the University of Kiel, the place of his birth. He has told us in his autobiography that the day when he received this call was one of the happiest of his life; for although he was living quite comfortably in the house of his parents, he yearned for independence and a house of his own. Now it became his ambition to justify the confidence shown to him by his colleagues in Kiel. He quickly finished his work for Göttingen and was successful against two competitors, though he was awarded only the second prize. The report of the Faculty contains a paragraph criticizing his attitude to Weber's law of electro-dynamic interaction. Wilhelm Weber, then Professor of Physics at Göttingen, was involved in a sharp controversy with Helmholtz. If Planck's siding with the latter cost him the first prize at Göttingen, he was soon compensated by the interest which the Berlin physicists took in the young scholar.

Planck now returned to his favourite subject and wrote four big papers with the common title "On the Principle of the Increase of Entropy" (1887, 1891). The first of these, where again instead of "irreversible" the term "natural" processes is used, contains the introduction of thermo-dynamical potentials and the derivation of their extremal properties, al-ready mentioned above. Planck calls the expression $w = u + pv - Ts$ "Massieu's function" which to-day goes under the name of Gibbs' Poten-tial. The equilibrium of different phases is discussed and a general outline of the theory of chemical equilibrium given. The following papers fill this frame with detail. For obtaining concrete results explicit expressions for the thermodynamical potentials must be known. Planck made simple and natural assumptions, for instance that in a dilute solution the thermo-dynamic potential is a linear function of the concentration of the dis-solved particles. In this way he developed a formal apparatus which he applied to deducing observable facts.

This was a period when the newly established science of physical chem-istry produced discoveries and theories in abundance. The law of mass action was established by Guldberg and Waage; the properties of dilute solutions were studied by Van't Hoff and those of electrolytes by Arrhenius. Planck deduced many of these results from his principles, sometimes independently of and even prior to the chemists. He gave a thermodynamical derivation of the dissociation of gases, of the osmotic pressure and of the lowering of the freezing point in solutions. Discussing the observed values of the freezing point in many solutions of salts, he arrived at the conclusion that the salts in solution must be dissociated. He saw in this result a thermodynamical foundation of the theory of electro-lytic dissociation which Svante Arrhenius had developed about the same time from a large amount of experimental material. Arrhenius however rejected Planck's thermodynamical reasoning because he believed that the ionic state was essential for his hypothesis. Planck insisted that the thermodynamical laws are equally applicable to charged and neutral particles—which is certainly right; yet the actual form of the laws may well depend on the charge, as modern investigations have shown (Debye and Hückel). To-day we can therefore say that none of the adversaries was quite right. If Planck resented the misunderstanding of his work there is no trace of it in his publications. He welcomes the agreement of con-clusions reached by so widely different methods and sees in it a confirma-tion of his belief in the fundamental character of the second law of thermodynamics.

After Kirchhoff's death the Philosophical Faculty of Berlin, apparently under Helmholtz's influence, offered in 1899 the Chair of Theoretical Physics to Planck. It was an "extraordinary" Professorship which how-ever in 1892 was converted into an "ordinary" one. Planck describes the subsequent years as a most important period which widened his scientific horizon by bringing him, for the first time in his life, in personal contact with leading men in his field. Helmholtz, whose works he had admired, won also his personal veneration by his simplicity, dignity and kindness. A word of appreciation from him made him happy. Planck was also on excellent terms with Helmholtz' successor, A. Kundt, and a close friendship developed later with H. Rubens.

In the first period of Planck's life in Berlin he suspended his thermodynamical work for another task, which attracted his musical interest.

A big harmonium with numerous keys, built on Helmholtz' suggestion in pure tuning, was at that time delivered to the Department of Physics. Planck learned to play this complicated instrument and studied the effect of the pure tuning as compared with the tempered one introduced by Bach; he found the unexpected result, published in a special paper (1893), that our ear prefers decidedly the tempered scales.

At that time there had grown, under the leadership of Wilhelm Ostwald, a school of "energetics" which proclaimed that the law of energy was a sufficient basis for the derivation of the whole of physics and chemistry. Boltzmann took up this challenge and was soon involved in a sharp controversy with this group. Planck came to his assistance in an article (1896) which revealed, for the first time, his polemic gifts. Ostwald distinguished three different types of energy corresponding to the three dimensions of space: energy of distance, of surface and of volume. Planck replied that there are cases where no volume energy in Ostwald's sense exists, as for instance in the case of an ideal gas where the energy depends only on temperature and not at all on the volume. Another point of controversy was the failure of the energetics school to understand Clausius' Second Theorem. They compared the flow of energy from a higher level of temperature to a lower with the falling of a weight without taking into account the irreversibility of the process. This superficial analogy was violently opposed by Planck. Although the principle of conservation of energy was, right from the beginning, foremost in his mind, he was perfectly clear that it alone was an insufficient foundation on which to build up mechanics and that a much more powerful principle, such as that of least action, was needed. With regard to thermodynamics he defended Clausius' distinction between reversible and irreversible processes.

Planck complains in his autobiography that in this case, as in many others, he did not succeed in convincing his colleagues by arguments which seemed to him, though theoretical, perfectly valid. In fact, the defeat of the energetics' school was eventually due to Boltzmann's atomistic theory which Planck, at that time, did not fully appreciate.

Boltzmann's investigations on the kinetic theory of gases had led him to the construction of a certain quantity H, depending on the velocity distribution of the molecules, which he could prove was continuously decreasing in time. By identifying $-H$ with the entropy he obtained a kinetic interpretation of Clausius' second law. This atomistic conception of irreversibility made a profound impression and was generally accepted.

Planck confesses himself that to begin with he was not only indifferent but somewhat doubtful about Boltzmann's statistical views. The reason is that he believed the law of the increase of entropy to be just as general and free from exception as the law of conservation of energy while in Boltzmann's theory it appeared only as a probable law: the quantity H might occasionally increase, the entropy decrease.

E. Zermelo, a young and temperamental pupil of Planck, attacked Boltzmann's statistical ideas, using a theorem of Poincaré according to which any mechanical system is quasi-periodic; how then could a quantity defined in terms of mechanical variables, like Boltzmann's H, permanently decrease? It was not difficult for Boltzmann to refute this argument by showing that the definition of his function H involved probability and that therefore the theorem of its decrease had to be understood statistically. The controversy was carried on from both sides with considerable heat; Boltzmann brought into play his sarcastic wit, hitting also Planck himself who had backed his pupil. From that time on the relation between the two men was not too friendly, until the atomistic derivation of the radiation law by Planck mellowed Boltzmann's mind. In fact, nobody has done more to foster and spread Boltzmann's ideas than Planck; his theory of radiation is completely built on them and modelled on their analogy, and one of its main results was the determination from radiation data, of the constant k in Boltzmann's fundamental relation $S = k \log P$ between entropy S and probability P.

Discussing this question in his autobiography Planck expresses a slight resentment at the usual nomenclature "Boltzmann's constant" for this factor k, pointing out that Boltzmann had neither introduced it nor ever thought of determining it numerically, leaving this task to his colleague Loschmidt. This indicates that the quarrel with Boltzmann had left traces in his mind which still were discernible in his old age when he wrote those lines.

Planck's interest in heat radiation was roused by the experimental work done at the Physikalisch-Technische Reichsanstalt (National Physical Laboratory) in Berlin-Charlottenburg on the spectral distribution of the radiation emitted by a "black body." There were two prominent teams at work, Lummer and Pringsheim, Rubens and Kurlbaum. Their measurements directed Planck's attention to Kirchhoff's theoretical investigations of the properties of the radiation of a "black body," that is to say, the radiation in a cavity bounded by perfectly reflecting walls and containing arbitrary emitting and absorbing substances. He had shown that an equilibrium is established in the course of time where all substances have the same temperature and the radiation in all its properties, including the spectral distribution (energy per unit wave-length), is independent of the bodies and only a function of temperature. This so-called "normal spectrum" is therefore something "absolute," a great attraction for Planck, whose philosophical mind was always directed towards the search for the "absolute." Henceforward the explanation of this law was his aim which he pursued from 1896 on with amazing persistency, always in contact with the parallel experimental investigations of the Reichsanstalt. The series of papers (1897–1901) exclusively dealing with this problem and ending with complete success are a testimony not only to Planck's skill and ingenuity, but also to his character, his unbending will and untiring industry, his cautious patience combined with greatest audacity. His was, by nature, a conservative mind; he had nothing of the revolutionary and was thoroughly sceptical about speculations. Yet his belief in the compelling force of logical reasoning from facts was so strong that he did not flinch from announcing the most revolutionary idea which ever has shaken physics.

Maxwell's electromagnetic theory of light was at that time beginning to conquer the continent. Planck accepted and used it for his purpose. As according to Kirchhoff the nature of the emitting and absorbing substances was irrelevant for black body radiation, Planck chose a simple model, namely linear oscillators with different proper frequencies and small damping. He expected to find that the exchange of energy by emission and absorption of radiation would lead automatically to a final equilibrium state in agreement with Kirchhoff's results. The first step in this direction consisted in the calculation of the averaged emission and absorption of an oscillator situated in a given radiation field. To represent the latter, the electromagnetic field components were expanded in Fourier series with arbitrary amplitudes and phases. This is now a standard method of theoretical physics and so well known that few physicists will realize the effort needed to invent it. This effort is still discernible in Planck's book on the theory of radiation which appeared much later and contains a condensed form of the calculations. The main result was a relation between the mean energy u of an oscillator of a given frequency v and the mean energy density ρ of the surrounding radiation in stationary (statistical) equilibrium,

$$\rho = \frac{8\pi v^2}{c^3} u.$$

This relation is independent of the damping of the oscillator, a fact which meant a considerable simplification of the problem; for it was thus reduced to the study of the system of oscillators, each of which had only one degree of freedom. On the other hand, Planck's original hope, that the oscillators would produce an exchange of energy between different frequencies and thus lead directly to the establishment of the normal spectrum, was disappointed, as each oscillator was found to be sensitive only to the radiation of its own frequency.

Here again a controversy with Boltzmann developed. The latter denied that the interaction of the oscillators with the radiation was irreversible and pointed out that every single process considered by Planck could just as well go in the opposite direction, even the emission of a spherical wave by an oscillator; for in a stationary state to each expanding wave there corresponds a contracting wave which transfers energy to the oscillator. This is formally correct, but nevertheless Planck was perfectly right and showed a deeper insight in a matter of statistical physics even than Boltzmann. Just as in a gas the mechanical reversibility can only be transformed into thermodynamical irreversibility through the introduction of the hypothesis of molecular disorder (i.e. by replacing rigorous expressions by averaged ones) one has in the case of radiation to introduce a corresponding assumption which Planck called the hypothesis of "natural radiation." It consists in averaging the phases and amplitudes of the simple harmonic waves into which the radiation can be decomposed. Thus this dispute was not futile but led Planck to greater clarity about his own procedure.

After the failure of his first attempt Planck looked for another way of attack and found it in the use of thermodynamical conceptions and finally in the application of the statistical methods due to his adversary Boltzmann.

Planck had the idea that he would obtain simple results by investigating the relation of energy U to entropy S, not to temperature T. For a system in a fixed volume one has the thermodynamical formula $T dS = dU$, from which one easily obtains

$$\frac{d^2 S}{dU^2} = \frac{-1}{T^2 \dfrac{dU}{dT}} \cdot$$

If the energy U is a known function of the temperature, the right-hand side can be regarded as a given function of U; hence one has a differential equation to determine $S(U)$.

Now at that time W. Wien had published a law for the spectral distribution of radiation of the form $U(T) = A e^{-B/T}$ (B proportional to the frequency), which was attractive by reason of its similarity to Boltzmann's statistical distribution law and also well confirmed by experiment in a wide spectral region. If it is introduced into the previous formula one finds

$$\frac{d^2 S}{dU^2} = -\frac{1}{BU} \cdot$$

a result so surprisingly simple that Planck first believed it would be generally correct. At this point Planck's close connexion with the experimentalists of the Reichsanstalt was decisive. Through the measurements of Lummer and Pringsheim and still more those of Rubens and Kurlbaum, it became more and more clear, that Wien's radiation law, though very satisfactory for short waves and low temperatures, was not in agreement with the facts for long waves and higher temperatures, where it had to be replaced by another law, namely that the energy per frequency interval is proportional to the temperature, $U(T) = CT$. This law is now known under the name of Rayleigh-Jeans; in fact Lord Rayleigh showed about the same time, in 1900, that it is a necessary consequence of ordinary statistical mechanics applied to radiation, and this point of view was stressed by Jeans again in 1909. One finds in this case

$$\frac{d^2S}{dU^2} = -\frac{C}{U^2},$$

again a surprisingly simple result.

Thus Planck had two limiting cases to ponder about. In describing this period Planck says that fate was kind to him. He had often been pained by the lack of interest of his colleagues in his work; but now this turned to his advantage; nobody else had the idea to consider the entropy as the crucial quantity, and he was allowed to follow his plan to its end without interference or competition. The next problem was to combine the two expressions into one, that they appear as the limiting cases for large and for small U. Planck noticed at once that this is achieved by taking the reciprocal of d^2S/dU^2 and adding the two expressions $-BU$ and $-U^2/C$; taking again the reciprocal he found the differential equation

$$\frac{d^2S}{dU^2} = \frac{-C}{U(U + BC)}.$$

This adding up was one of the most fateful and significant interpolations ever made in the history of physics; it reveals an almost uncanny physical intuition. Five years later it became much more comprehensible and natural by an interpretation due to Einstein (made in the same paper where he correlated Planck's quanta with the photoelectric effect); he remarked that the reciprocal of d^2S/dU^2 has a simple physical meaning: it represents the mean square fluctuation of energy $\overline{\Delta U^2}$; and it is well known that mean square fluctuations are additive, if due to independent causes. This argument was then used by Einstein as an indication of the independent existence of light quanta; but that is beyond the scope of this article.

The combined formula, which contains two constants, can now be integrated and leads directly to the new radiation formula, which Planck submitted to the Berliner Physikalische Gesellschaft on 19 October 1900.

He tells us that the next morning his colleague Rubens appeared to inform him that in the same night, after the meeting, he had compared Planck's formula with his own measurements and found everywhere satisfactory agreement. Lummer and Pringsheim believed first that there were deviations but discovered soon that these were due to an error in computation. Many later experiments have been made to check Planck's formula, with the result that the agreement has been found to become more and more perfect with the improvement of methods of measurement.

Yet it was only an interpolation, a real physical meaning had to be found. At this point Planck's attention was directed to Boltzmann's fundamental relation between entropy and probability, $S = k \log P$. Hence he investigated the question whether the expression of P obtained by substituting for S the value corresponding to the new radiation law could be interpreted as a probability. In a lecture given to the German Physical Society on 14 December 1900, he announced the result that this interpretation is possible indeed. Apart from the constant k which was recognized to be the absolute gas constant per gram-molecule, there appeared a new constant of the dimensions (energy $\times$ time) which he called the "elementary quantum of action" and denoted by h, now always quoted as Planck's constant. Planck, right from the beginning, saw the essential feature of his discovery in this "quantum of action." His contemporaries were more stirred by the "quantum of energy" $\epsilon_0 = h\nu$, and by Planck's contention that the energy of the emitting and absorbing oscillators was "atomistic," always a multiple of ϵ_0. It was this assumption which led Planck to the expression for the mean energy of a system of oscillators; using Boltzmann's distribution law one has

$$u = \frac{\sum\limits_{n=1}^{\infty} n\, \epsilon_0 e^{-n\epsilon_0/kT}}{\sum\limits_{n=0}^{\infty} e^{-n\epsilon_0/kT}} = \frac{\epsilon_0}{e^{\epsilon_0/kT} - 1}, \quad \epsilon_0 = h\nu,$$

and, with the help of Planck's previous result concerning the relation of radiation and oscillators, one finds the expression for the radiation density

$$\rho = \frac{8\pi\nu^2}{c^3}\, u = \frac{\dfrac{8\pi h}{c^3}\nu^3}{e^{h\nu/kT} - 1}.$$

This formula contains all previously known radiation laws, the law of Stephan and Boltzmann for the total radiation, Wein's displacement law and, of course, the two limiting laws of Rayleigh-Jeans for large T and of Wien for small T. From the known constants of these Planck derived numerical values for his two constants k and h. From k he calculated the number N of atoms per gramme molecule (Avogadro's or Loschmidt's number), and, with the help of Faraday's law, the elementary electric charge e; his values were much more reliable than all known before and were later confirmed by many other methods.

Planck was perfectly clear about the importance of his discovery. We have not only the testimony of his wife but also an account of his son Erwin, given to and reported by Professor Bavink. It was in 1900 when his father, on a walk in the Grunewald, near Berlin, said to him: "To-day I have made a discovery as important as that of Newton." Planck has, of course, never said anything like that in public. His modest and reluctant way of speaking about his work has caused the impression that he did himself not quite believe in his result. Therefore, the opinion spread, especially outside Germany, that Planck "did not seem to know what he had done when he did it," that he did not realize the range of his discovery. That this is wrong can clearly be seen from his autobiography; though it was written in his old age, we have no reason to doubt that it correctly reflects his thoughts in the years following his discovery. Planck reports that he tried hard to fit the quantum of action into the frame of classical theory, but with no success. Then he continues: "But this quantity (the constant h) proved to be unwieldy and resistive against all attempts of this kind. As long as it could be regarded as infinitely small, i.e. for larger energies and longer periods, everything was in good order. But in the general case there appeared somewhere a cleavage which became the more conspicuous, the faster the vibrations considered. The failure of all attempts to bridge this gulf, soon removed all doubt that the quantum of action plays a fundamental part in atomic physics, and that with its appearance a new epoch of physical science has begun. For it forebodes something unheard-of destined to reform thoroughly our physical thinking which since the invention of the infinitesimal calculus through Leibniz and Newton was based on the assumption of continuity of all causal relations."

It has been generally acknowledged that the year 1900 of Planck's discovery marks indeed the beginning of a new epoch in physics. Yet during the first years of the new century very little happened. It was the time of my own student days, and I remember that Planck's idea was hardly mentioned in our lectures, and if so as a kind of preliminary "working hypothesis" which ought of course to be eliminated. Planck himself turned to other fields of work. But that he never forgot his quanta is shown by the publication, in 1906, of his book *Vorlesungen über die Theorie der Wärmestrahlung* which made a profound impression by the masterly presentation of the successive steps which led to the quantum hypothesis.

A year earlier Einstein's paper, already quoted, had appeared in that famous volume (1905) of *Annalen der Physik,* which contains also two other fundamental articles of Einstein, one on relativity and one on the Brownian movement. Einstein showed that the quanta were not a feature of radiating heat, but of radiation in general, and he produced experimental and theoretical evidence for a corpuscular interpretation of light. A series of phenomena like the photo-electric effect, the excitation of X-rays by the impact of electrons on the target, Stokes' rule of fluorence could be simply explained in terms of 'light quanta' $h\nu$. Now the interest of the experimentalists was roused and progress became quicker. From the standpoint of the theory a decisive step was made again by Einstein in 1907, when he applied Planck's formula for the mean energy u of a system of oscillators (given above) to the vibrations of atoms, molecules and solids, explaining in particular the deviations of the specific heat of solids from the classical law of Dulong and Petit. This initiated a great amount of experimental research, for instance the investigations of Nernst and his school on the specific heat at very low temperatures. But I cannot follow up the history of quantum theory in general as this would mean a description of the greatest part of modern physics; I must confine myself to Planck's own contribution.

There is a publication of his in 1910 where he summarizes the situation. He discusses a number of papers by J. J. Thomson, Larmor, Stark and Einstein which use the quantum hypothesis for explaining divers phenomena; but he is very cautious in regard to Einstein's revival of the corpuscular theory of light. Its main argument is the existence of electrostatic fields which from Einstein's standpoint would be something completely different from radiation fields. Can one abandon the unification due to Maxwell of all electromagnetic fields in view of the existing evidence? His conclusion is that electrodynamics is very probably right, but physical statistics possibly wrong.

In his lecture to the Solvay Congress 1911, he made a decided attempt to develop a modified statistical mechanics by assuming the phase space of Gibbs divided up in finite cells of the size h for each pair of conjugate variables p, q. At the same time he changed his assumption about absorption and emission; absorption was supposed to be continuous, emission discontinuous (1911). This strange hypothesis seemed to him the only way out of the dilemma between quantum effects and electromagnetic theory. Many physicists, particularly those of the younger generation, regarded Planck's "second quantum theory" as a weak compromise. It is to-day hardly worthwhile to discuss its pro and contra. But one must not forget that it led to a most important result, the zero point energy $\frac{1}{2}h\nu$ per oscillator. It appears formally when one expands Planck's formula for the resonator energy for large temperatures

$$ u = \frac{\epsilon_0}{e^{\epsilon_0/kT}-1} = kT - \frac{\epsilon_0}{2} + \ldots\ , $$

where the terms indicated by dots vanish for $T \to \infty$. This expression shows that Planck's formula does not precisely tend to the equipartition value kT (which corresponds to Rayleigh-Jeans' formula for ρ) but differs from it by $\frac{1}{2}\epsilon_0 = \frac{1}{2}h\nu$. Planck's new statistics leads to a value for u which is larger than that given above by $\frac{1}{2}\epsilon_0$ and tends therefore exactly towards kT for $T \to \infty$. In this way he found a new approach to Nernst's theorem and the zero point entropy of gases (1916). Later research has demonstrated the reality of the zero point energy, for instance by its influence on the scattering of X-rays in crystals. Planck himself regarded his second quantum hypothesis as so important that he made it the basis of the second edition of his book *Wärmestrahlung,* which appeared in 1913. Another modification of the theory is contained in a series of papers (1915, 1917) where he replaced the oscillators by rotators. Here he used a method first introduced by Einstein in his theory of Brownian motion and later improved and applied to radiation by Fokker; it describes the changes in time and space of a distribution of particles subject to small irregular impulses with the help of a partial differential equation containing as coefficients the mean displacement and the mean square displacement for a given small time. This formula is now generally quoted as the Fokker-Planck equation, and its full range of application seems to be not at all exhausted yet.

The year 1913 marks a turning point in quantum theory as there appeared Niels Bohr's first papers on the quantum theory of the electronic structure of atoms. A straight development in which Planck took an active part, led from here to modern quantum mechanics. But in the intermediate period he turned his mind to many other subjects of which a short account must be given.

His investigations on radiation convinced him that the electromagnetic field showed statistical features similar to those of a gas; the amplitudes and phases of the elementary waves are arbitrary and may be distributed at random. In this way he came to his theory of "natural" or "white" light (1902), which later was taken up by his pupil Max von Laue. Then he became interested in ordinary optics, in particular in Drude's theory of dispersion in which he introduced radiation damping of the oscillators (1902, 1903, 1904, 1905). He calculated the extinction of light in an optically homogeneous medium of normal dispersion and compared his results with an older theory of Lord Rayleigh concerning the propagation of light in a vacuum in which numerous non-conducting particles are dispersed; he found the same law for the extinction coefficient as had Rayleigh, although the dispersion law is completely different for the two models. The experiments made by Hagen and Rubens on the optical properties of metals induced Planck to a theoretical study of this subject (1905).

He returned to the theory of gases (1908) and generalized Boltzmann's method in such a way that it could take into account van der Waal's corrections due to the finite volume of the molecules.

But the subject that caught Planck's imagination more than anything else was Einstein's theory of relativity, published in 1905. In Planck's scientific autobiography is a remarkable page where he explains how his search for "the absolute," the main spring of his scientific activity, is compatible with his interest in the principle of relativity. "One might regard this as a contradiction. . . . This presumption is based on a fundamental error. For everything 'relative' presupposes something 'absolute,' it has only significance if it is opposed to some absolute. The often quoted sentence 'Everything is relative' is just as misleading as thoughtless. So at the bottom of the so-called theory of relativity there is something absolute, namely the metric of the space-time continuum, and it is just a particularly attractive problem, to discover the Absolute which lends a meaning to a given Relative. . . ." He found the attraction of relativity in the search for those invariants which represent the "absolute." The velocity of light which in classical physics has only a relative meaning becomes in relativity an absolute invariant. The next important invariant is the action integral of mechanics; the laws of motion can be obtained by the principle of least action in relativity.

Planck applied this idea first to a mass point (1906) and found the relativistic form of the mechanical equations, a little earlier than Minkowski. He discussed Kaufmann's measurements of the deflexion of β-rays in regard to their bearing on the principle of relativity (1906, 1907). In 1908 he published a long paper on the general dynamics of moving systems, in which he expands the thesis of his pupil K. v. Mosengeil (published by Planck in 1907 after the young author's untimely death). As relativity teaches that mass is proportional to energy, and as the energy of a body depends on its heat content, a separation of mechanics and thermodynamics is impossible. Planck develops a combined theory based on the relativistic invariance of the principle of least action and obtains the transformation laws for energy, momentum, entropy and temperature; with the help of these the expression of these quantities in terms of the velocity can be obtained from their values in the rest system. If one supposes that these expressions derived for steady motion also hold for acceleration, one can write down the equations of motion. This paper contains a most remarkable section (§ 18) in which he predicts the possibility of utilization of "atomic energy." He is perfectly clear that every body contains, in [its] rest-mass, a colossal amount of "latent" energy, and says: "Though the actual production of such a 'radical' process might have appeared extremely small only a decade ago, it is now in the range of the possible, through the discovery of radioactive elements and their transmutation, and in fact the observation of continuous production of heat of radioactive substances is direct evidence for the assumption that the source of this heat is just nothing else than the latent energy of the atoms."

The Prussian Academy, mainly on the instigation of Planck, Nernst and Haber, created a special chair for Einstein which allowed him to pursue his ideas unhampered by teaching and routine work. Now for many years Planck and Einstein met at regular intervals at the Berlin Academy, and a friendship developed which went far beyond the exchange of scientific ideas. Yet it is difficult to imagine two men of more different attitudes to life: Einstein a citizen of the whole world, little attached to the people around him, independent of the emotional background of the society in which he lived—Planck deeply rooted in the traditions of his family and nation, an ardent patriot, proud of the greatness of German history and consciously Prussian in his attitude to the state. Yet what did all these differences matter in view of what they had in common—the fascinating interest in the secrets of nature, similar philosophical convictions, and a deep love of music. They often played chamber music together, Planck at the piano and Einstein fiddling, both perfectly absorbed and happy. Planck was an excellent pianist and could play on demand almost any piece of classical music, a great many by heart. He also liked to improvise either on a theme given to him, or on old German folk-songs which he dearly loved.

The collaboration of Planck and Einstein made Berlin, in the years preceding the first World War, the greatest centre of theoretical physics in the world. I was also fortunate to be called to Berlin. Planck wished to be freed from a part of his duties in routine teaching and persuaded the Prussian Minister of Education to found a new (extraordinary) Chair at the University of Berlin. This was offered to me, but alas, on the day of mobilization, 2 August 1914. There was not much of teaching and peaceful research for me during the following four years of war, yet I was in Berlin for long periods and saw Einstein and Planck frequently. A short walk brought me from my own house to Planck's, a villa in the suburb of Grunewald. I remember his studio, the walls covered with books, simple furniture, among which a high desk (like those found in old-fashioned offices) where he used to work standing upright. I had never been his pupil, not even attended one of his courses; I knew his papers and books, I had seen him from a distance at scientific meetings and perhaps exchanged a few words with him. He was at that time already a great and famous man, and I approached him with some shyness. But his kindness, his lovable expression, the hospitality of his house removed very quickly the barrier of age and experience. We had many fascinating discussions on physics and the topics of the day. He had very definite views and expressed them frankly, even if he did not expect agreement, but never in an offending way. The same systematic order, tidiness and clarity which distinguish his writings, were also characteristic of his attitude to the small and big questions of ordinary life. During the years of the war a great change came over him; sorrow darkened his friendly expression. It was not only the general suffering, the catastrophic end of the struggle which hurt his patriotic feeling deeply, but terrible personal loss. Planck's first wife, Marie Merck, had died in 1909. He had married again, Marga von Hoesslin. Three of the four children of his first marriage died during the war period. His eldest son Karl was killed in action near Thiaumont, France, in 1916. The two daughters, Emma and Margarete, were twins. One of them married Professor Ferdinand Fehling; she died in 1917 in childbirth; her sister took charge of the orphan baby and later married the widower. A year later exactly the same thing happened to her; she died after her first confinement, while the child lived. Both children were partly educated in the grandfather's house. Only one son, Erwin, of his first wife was left, and a young son, Hermann, of his second marriage. More tragedy was to come.

In spite of all this worry and sorrow Planck continued his scientific work, returning to his long neglected quantum theory, which through Bohr's papers of 1913, had suddenly become the focus of interest in the world of physics. Bohr's method of quantization was extremely successful for the one-electron problem; how could it be generalized for a system of many electrons? This problem was almost simultaneously solved by Sommerfeld, Epstein and Planck (1915, 1916). The methods differ in form but lead in all practical cases to essentially the same results. While Sommerfeld considers multi-periodic systems for which a separation of the Hamiltonian in independent pairs of co-ordinates and momenta is possible, Planck's method consists in a division of the total "phase space" of all co-ordinates and momenta into cells, with the help of pairs of surfaces nh apart ($n = 1, 2, \ldots$) which are invariant integrals of the equations of motion. In this way he obtained for instance the energy in terms of quantum numbers for the rotator, the symmetric top, the ordinary and relativistic Kepler motion, etc. He even tackled the asymmetric top (1918). Then he applied the results to the optical problem of the rotational spectra of molecules (1917). There he had to overcome a particular difficulty connected with his method of quantization; this allowed for each set of quantum numbers small but finite domains in the phase space, while the observations showed rather sharp lines. The way in which he removed this apparent contradiction has to-day only historical interest like all the work done in this period. Therefore it suffices to mention some other papers which show that he always tried to attack the most interesting problems of the day. He calculated the heat of dissociation of the hydrogen molecule according to the "ring model" suggested by Bohr and Debye (1919). He tried to solve Gibb's paradox of statistical mechanics by a careful determination of the free energy of gas molecules with arbitrary velocity distribution (1922). Several papers under different titles deal with the fluctuations of energy in the black body radiation (1923, 1924). He discussed a difficulty concerning the free energy of atomic hydrogen gas; as Bohr had already noticed the partition function taken over the discontinuous states diverges in this case as the energy values approach zero like $-n^{-1}$. Planck's solution consists essentially in cutting off the discrete spectrum where the radius of the orbit reaches the linear dimensions of the vessel; he does not however neglect the remainder but shows that in these states the electron can be treated as a free particle.

One paper entitled "A New Statistical Definition of Entropy" (1925) contains a general formulation of Boltzmann's and Gibb's statistical expression of the entropy $S = k \log P$ for quantum systems; Planck defines P as the number of stationary states for which the energy does not exceed a given value E (instead of taking the sum over all states in a given narrow energy interval) and he shows that this leads to the correct expression for a system of oscillators and for a monatomic gas.

When the war ended I left Berlin. Max von Laue, Planck's celebrated pupil, wished to return to Berlin and to be near his master; so he offered me an exchange of my Berlin position (Extraordinariat) with his full professorship in Frankfurt-on-Main, and as Planck agreed, I accepted. From 1919 on Berlin enjoyed this constellation of three most-brilliant theoretical physicists, Planck, Einstein, v. Laue, which was soon to be enhanced by a fourth, Schrödinger. He had published in 1926 his paper on wave mechanics which made an immediate impression everywhere, even more than Planck's discovery in 1900; for the world of physics was prepared for this step by the work done during the preceding twenty-five years and in particular by the publications of de Broglie and the Göttingen school.

So it was only natural, that in 1928 when Planck reached his seventieth year and had to resign his Chair, Schrödinger became his successor. Planck, however, did not retire into inactivity. He remained permanent secretary to the mathematical physical class of the Berlin Academy and continued his scientific work and publications, free from the burden of lecturing to students.

Planck had never had a research school, like Sommerfeld in Munich, and the number of pupils who wrote a thesis under his direction is small. I have already mentioned K. von Mosengeil, E. Zermelo and M. von Laue; then there are Max Abraham, known through his book on Maxwell's theory of electricity, F. Reiche who wrote one of the first books on quantum theory, E. Lamla, H. Kallmann and a few others. Lise Meitner was Planck's assistant for a considerable time.

But large numbers of students have attended his lectures and studied his books. His normal course of lectures was published in 1930 in five volumes, corresponding to five semesters (2½ years) lecturing. The first four contain mechanics of points and rigid bodies, mechanics of continuous substances, electricity and magnetism, optics; the last volume gives a condensed account of thermodynamics, the theory of radiation and quantum theory. They are the prototype of similar lectures given at all German universities. An English translation has spread their influence over a wider area. Planck has edited books and lectures by Clausius and Kirchhoff. In 1910 he published a series of eight lectures given by him the previous year at Columbia University, New York; in 1922 a book entitled *Physikalische Rundblicke,* and more recently, 1943, a collection of his speeches and addresses in two volumes under the title *Wege zur physikalischen Erkenntnis.*

The last period of his scientific life is that of quantum mechanics. What he expected from the work of his successor is revealed in the address, with which he, as Secretary of the Academy, replied to Schrödinger's inaugural lecture (1929). Planck welcomed wave mechanics as the solution of a crisis threatening physics, namely the sceptical attitude towards the universal validity of the law of causality.

I quote the last words of this address: "You were the first to show how the spatio-temporal process in an atomic system can in fact be completely determined, though only under the supposition that one regards as their elements not the motions of particles but of material waves; and how the mysterious discontinuous proper values of the energy of the system can be calculated with absolute accuracy from your differential equation together with natural boundary conditions, while the question about the physical significance of the waves can be left undecided."

This crisis of causality occupied his mind very much, as is seen from his numerous popular writings and addresses. Before speaking of these it must be mentioned that up to his very old age he continued to publish papers on special subjects, mainly those on which he had worked in earlier periods. There is a series (1930, 1931, 1933) on the boundary layers of dilute electrolytes, one on the principle of le Chatelier and Braun (1934), one on the production of electricity in electrolytes. Most remarkable are three papers with the title "Attempt at a Synthesis between Undulatory and Corpuscular Mechanics" written in 1940, when he was above eighty years of age. They contain a careful consideration of the transition from wave mechanics to particle mechanics through the limiting process $h \to o$. He shows that to obtain this transition an additional condition must be fulfilled, and he postulates this condition to hold rigorously, instead of the usual boundary conditions of the Schrödinger equation. Translated into the language of optics it means the exclusion of all solutions which correspond to diffraction phenomena, as Wessel has pointed out. I do not share Planck's hope that his "modified wave mechanics" will bridge the gap between quantum and classical physics; but it shows clearly how deeply Planck was worried by the logical hardships which his own work has imposed on the physicists. This brings me to a short account of his philosophical writings which became more and more numerous with increasing age and predominate in his last period.

It is hardly possible to attach to Planck's work a label with one of the traditional philosophical systems; it has strains of rationalism, idealism, empiricism. But there is one school which he emphatically and repeatedly rejected: positivism. His spirited controversy with Ernst Mach is still worth reading. Planck started it in 1909 with an article on "The Unit of the Physical Picture of the World," published in the *Physikalische Zeitschrift*. The next volume (1910) of this periodical contains Mach's strongly ironical reply and a final article of Planck which is not less pointed and peppered. Mach defends his idea that all science is due to the principle of economy of thinking which itself can only be understood in the frame of Darwin's biological theory, and he claims to have thus found a basis for science free from all metaphysics. Planck's main answer is that this principle of economy itself is certainly metaphysical. There are many other points of disagreement. Mach was sceptical about the existence of atoms, he declared Boltzmann's kinetic theory, even the absolute zero of temperature, to be unproved hypothesis, and he attacked the Newtonian concept of absolute rotation, anticipating in some vague way Einstein's theory of general relativity. But this is the only point where he was right, in all other questions at issue Planck's physical intuition was confirmed by the later development of physics.

In 1930 Planck renewed his attack against the anti-metaphysical school in a lecture, "Positivism and the Real External World," in which he presents his arguments in a less caustic but most convincing way. I quote a paragraph containing the essence of this paper:

"The basis given to physics by positivism, though well founded, is too narrow, it has to be widened by an additional statement, whose importance is this: it frees science as far as possible from the incidences produced by the relation to human individuals. And this is achieved through a fundamental step into metaphysics, not imposed by formal logics but by common sense; namely through the hypothesis, that our personal experiences do not form the physical world, but that they only bring us messages from another world which lies beyond them and which is independent of them; in other words, that there exists a real external world."

The same idea appears in many of his philosophical lectures and articles. Their general tendency is to show that science is nothing but developed and refined common sense.

Meanwhile Planck's own child, quantum theory, had grown beyond all expectation and now dominated the whole of physics; but it had taken a direction which led straight away from Planck's fundamental convictions. Causality and strict determinism, even the assumption of an external objective world independent of ourselves became problematic. Planck discussed these questions in numerous publications, always maintaining the essence of his principles and trying to reconcile them with the facts of physics. Some of these articles culminate in a consideration of the paradoxes connected with the conception of free will in a deterministic world. Planck's solution is this: Determinism holds without exception, and we can use it for predicting not only events in inorganic nature, but even the behavior of other human beings—though never our own behavior. For by thinking about our possible decisions we influence them and can therefore not predict them. Hence there is no contradiction between the belief in free will and rigorous causality. An English version of Planck's ideas can be found in the Guthrie Lecture of the Physical Society, London, which he gave in 1932 under the title "The Concept of Causality," published in the *Proceedings of the Physical Society* and discussed in *Nature* (1932, p. 45). Planck was a religious man and several of his articles deal with the relation of science and faith (1930, 1947). He believed that science could contribute not only to material progress but also to the moral and spiritual development of mankind. There was no gap in his mind between his scientific and religious convictions.

Planck enjoyed good health up to his old age. This was certainly due to the simplicity and regularity of his life and to his custom of having real holidays. He spent the vacations mostly in the Alps, staying some weeks in lonely mountain villages near the high peaks, and then at his little property near Tegernsee. He loved the mountains and was a trained and hardened mountaineer. I visited him once in Trafoi when he was well over sixty; he had just returned from climbing the Ortler, a summit of 12,000 feet.

I was soon to meet him again in South Tyrol under different circumstances. After having been dismissed by Hitler in April 1933, my family and I left Germany at once for a little house in the Dolomites which we had rented for the summer. Planck spent the summer in a neighbouring valley, where I visited him. He told me then that in his capacity as President of the Kaiser Wilhelm Gesellschaft he had to pay a visit to Hitler and tried on this occasion to intervene in favour of his colleague Fritz Haber without whose method of fixing nitrogen from the air the First World War would have been lost by Germany from the beginning. Hitler's reaction was a violent outburst against the Jews in general. He finally brought himself into such a rage that Planck could do nothing but listen silently and take his leave. He later, in 1947, described the scene in *Physikalische Blätter*. After the failure of this attempt to plead for reason and restraint Planck seems to have given up all hope of changing the course of events, and he kept an outward peace with the powers in being. Yet there is no doubt about his true feelings, and the Nazis knew it. Goebbels wrote in his *Diary* (English edition by L. P. Lochner, p. 295): "It was a great mistake that we failed to win science over to support the new state. That men such as Planck are reserved, to put it mildly, in their attitude towards us, is the fault of Rust (the Minister of Education) and is irremediable." Planck continued to serve at the Academy, the Kaiser Wilhelm Gesellschaft and other public institutions, with the hope of saving German science and learning from total destruction. The Prussian tradition of service to the state and allegiance to the Government was deeply rooted in him. I think he trusted that violence and oppression would subside in time and everything return to normal. He did not see that an irreversible process was going on.

Planck has been in this country on several occasions and has had many friends here. In 1937 he came to Scotland to receive an Honorary degree at Glasgow and the honorary membership of the Royal Society of Edinburgh. He and his wife stayed in my house; it was the last time that we discussed matters scientific, political and personal. When I met him after the war at the Newton celebrations of the Royal Society in 1946 he was only a shadow of his former self, tired and frail, yet with his kindly smile unchanged. His house in Grunewald was destroyed in one of the big air raids on Berlin, and he lost everything, including his library. His son Erwin, the only surviving one of the four children of his first marriage, who held a high post in the Government, was involved in the July plot of 1944 against Hitler and was killed by the Nazis.

I know little about Planck's life during the war. He and his wife had found a refuge on the estate of a friend in Rogätz, on the river Elbe, near Magdeburg. There they came between the lines of the retiring Germans and of the advancing Allied armies, the battle raged around them for days. When Pohl, the physicist in Göttingen, heard of their plight he induced the Americans to send a military car and take them to the safety of Göttingen.

Planck bore his Job-like fate with quiet fortitude, resigning himself to the will of God. In this his deterministic philosophy may have helped him as well as his faith. He made his last home in Göttingen, but under-took long and tedious journeys when he was invited to lecture. On one of these occasions he fell seriously ill at Bonn but miraculously recovered from double pneumonia in spite of his eighty-eight years. So it could be hoped that he would reach his ninetieth birthday for which a great cele-bration was being prepared. Yet a few months before this date he began to fail and died on 4 October 1947 in Göttingen. The planned birthday celebration was changed into a memorial service which took place on 23 April 1948. It was attended by representatives of numerous scientific institutions in Germany and in many other countries.

The list of those institutions which have honoured Planck by awarding him a degree or by electing him a member is too long to be reproduced here. A few only may be mentioned. He had the German degrees of Dr. rer. nat. h.c., Dr. ing. h.c., Dr. med. h.c., also honorary degrees of several British universities, including Cambridge. He was a member of all the German and Austrian Academies (Berlin, Munich, Dresden, Göttin-gen, Vienna) and of many others (Britain, Denmark, Eire, Finland, Greece, Holland, Hungary, Italy, Russia, Sweden, Ukraine, United States). The Royal Society of London elected him a Foreign Member in 1926. He received the Nobel Prize in 1919. One of the small planets was "given" to him as a present on his eightieth birthday by the astronomers and called Planckiana. In 1930 he became President and in 1946 honorary President of the Kaiser Wilhelm Gesellschaft which has now been renamed "Max Planck Gesellschaft."

A Planck Medal has been founded by the German Physical Society, which he was the first to receive. He was awarded the Goethe-Preis of the city of Frankfurt-on-Main in 1946 and was appointed honorary mem-ber and "knight" of an American Mark Twain Society.

Thus his greatness has been acknowledged by his contemporaries. Will posterity confirm this judgment? We who have witnessed the incredible transformation of science which his work has brought about in less than half a century, have no doubt it will.

ⓞⓞⓞⓞⓞⓞⓞ

Max Born's excellent biographical sketch of Max Planck, originally published as an obituary by the Royal Society after Planck's death in 1947, is included in this volume because of its importance as a historical document. Born indicates the catholicity of Planck's interests, discussing his revolutionary contributions to atomism and physics as a whole. In our own commentary, we restrict our discussion to Planck's quantum theory of radiation, the most significant of his discoveries. Planck's Nobel Prize address of 1919, on the quantum of action, is presented after this commentary. The award, given in 1919, honored Planck for work done at the turn of the century.

As Born suggests in the previous essay, near the close of the nineteenth century, physicists were almost unanimous in the conviction that all the fundamental laws had been discovered and that there remained only mopping-up actions in the form of more precise experiments. It was genuinely felt that no matter how refined experimental apparatus became, there would be no serious departures from the theories known at the time. Thus it was taken for granted that ultimately all astronomical observations would take their proper place in the Newtonian gravitational system, even though at that moment the motion of the planet Mercury could not be accurately accounted for. Likewise, it was assumed that all the problems concerning radiation would one day yield to the laws of Maxwell. Although no one had any notion about the way radiation and matter are related or by what process matter emits and absorbs radiation, no one had any doubts that these questions would be answered in time by the proper application of Newton's laws of motion and Maxwell's theory of the electromagnetic field.

At this same time, physicists were encountering special difficulties in trying to understand the nature of the energy emitted in hollow enclosures by the walls surrounding such enclosures. This problem, which at first sight may have seemed uninteresting, became the rock upon which the ship of classical physics foundered.

In solving this problem, Planck was led to the discovery of the quantum of action and the concept of the photon. To understand the difficulty of the problem, we first note that when a body is heated it radiates energy; as its temperature rises, not only does the amount of energy emitted per second increase rapidly, but the quality of the emitted radiation changes visibly. For example, when the temperature is low, the emitted energy is concentrated mostly in the long wavelengths and the body glows with a cherry-red color; as the temperature of the body increases, the cherry-red color gives way to a yellow and finally to a blue-white color.

Now the late nineteenth- and early twentieth-century physicists, such as Gustav Kirchhoff, Lord Rayleigh, James H. Jeans, and Willy Wien, had explained most of the observed data relating to this type of radiation in terms of the classical electromagnetic and thermodynamic principles. But one observation stubbornly refused to yield to classical physics. This was the spectral distribution of the total amount of emitted energy. It was found that if one separated the emitted radiation into its various component colors by means of a spectroscope, the results obtained (the amount of radiant energy in each color) did not agree with the predictions of the theory. It was in dealing with this flaw in classical theory that Planck presented his revolutionary idea of the quantum of energy. In his Nobel address, which is reproduced here, he outlines the way in

which he was led to the conception of the quantum of energy and ultimately to that of the quantum of action.

To study the properties of the radiant energy in an enclosure, he
started out by picturing the material in the walls as being composed of
simple harmonic oscillators, because Heinrich Hertz had already shown
how such bodies emit and absorb energy. As he notes in his address, he
was justified in doing this, since Kirchhoff had proved that the nature of
the radiation in an enclosure does not in any way depend on the material of the walls, but only on their temperature. Using this simple model,
Planck analyzed the way in which such oscillators would emit into and
absorb energy from the enclosure. This energy—referred to as "black-
body radiation" because it is the same as the energy emitted by a perfectly black body—is distributed in a definite way among all possible
wavelengths. A certain fraction of the total radiant energy is concentrated
in each color. The exact amount depends only on the temperature of the
enclosure and the wavelength being considered.

The problem that Planck faced was to determine the mathematical form
of the relationship between the concentration of energy in a particular
color, the temperature of the walls, and the wavelength of the particular
color being considered. As Planck notes in his address, he expected to
discover this law for the distribution of black-body radiation within the
framework of classical electrodynamics. This was his anticipation, in
spite of his knowledge that previous similar attempts to achieve the
same results by other physicists had failed. Planck proceeded by developing the most general laws of the emission and absorption of a linear
harmonic oscillator. He saw at once, however, that there was nothing
about the classical electrical properties of an oscillator that would cause
it to absorb and emit radiation in such a way as to give a result that
agreed with experiment.

We may understand the nature of the difficulty if we consider a
harmonic oscillator vibrating with a definite frequency. It emits and
absorbs electromagnetic radiation of this same frequency, according to
classical electromagnetic theory. As a result, Planck could not account
for the distribution of the total energy among the various frequencies,
since he could see no way in which two oscillators vibrating at different
frequencies could influence one another and establish a condition of
equilibrium that depended only on the temperature. However much he
tried to invent some method by which this might be achieved, he found
himself up against the fact that each oscillator must interact in a reversible
manner with the radiation field. Thus, a distribution of the radiation over
the entire spectrum could not occur since this would mean that the oscillator would have to re-emit radiation of all frequencies even though it
could absorb only one frequency.

In other words, Planck had first tried to find some asymmetrical relationship between the rate at which an oscillator emits energy and the rate at which it absorbs energy. He felt that if he then expressed this relationship in terms of the temperature, he would obtain the condition for equilibrium between the oscillators and the radiation—and that then the energy-distribution formula would drop into his lap. This, however, proved to be a vain hope, since, as Ludwig Boltzmann pointed out, all the effects considered by Planck could, according to the laws of classical mechanics, work in exactly the reverse direction, so that emission and absorption are completely symmetrical. This led Planck finally to discard the electromagnetic approach to the problem (that is, the approach through the laws of radiation) and to consider the laws of thermodynamics, with which, as he says ". . . I felt more at home. . . ." Since Planck had done a good deal of research into the second law of thermodynamics, he decided to attack the problem from that direction, that is, with the aid of the concept of *entropy*.

The second law of thermodynamics is essentially a qualification of the first law of thermodynamics, which itself is an extension of the principle of the conservation of energy to include heat as well as mechanical energy. The second law does not deny that there must always be an energy balance under all conditions, but it severely restricts the conditions under which heat can be turned into mechanical energy, that is, work. It is, of course, always possible to change work completely into heat; the reverse, however, it is not true, and heat can never be changed completely into work without leaving some kind of compensating change elsewhere in the universe. This means that there are irreversible processes in nature—so that a system left to itself evolves only along certain directions and not along others; certain processes are completely excluded.

The second law defines the directions in which a system may move or the states that it will reach if left to itself; these states are calculated by introducing a function of the state of the system that is called *entropy*. This important quantity, as Boltzmann first pointed out, is a measure of the probability that a system will evolve in a certain way; the higher the entropy of a particular state is, the greater is the likelihood of ultimately finding the system in that state. To say of a system composed of two bodies in contact that the entropy increases when heat flows spontaneously from the hotter to the cooler body, is the same as saying that heat must always flow spontaneously to the cooler body in such a system.

The entropy of a system is similar to the energy of a system in that one cannot give it an absolute value (at least this was the case when the entropy was first introduced). One can only determine the difference between the entropy of a system in some standard or reference state and the entropy in another state. In fact, when the concept of entropy was introduced, it was defined mathematically as the change in the energy that takes place in a system, divided by the absolute temperature at which the

change occurs. Since the entropy is thus related to the energy change
within a system, Planck felt that he could deal with the energy distribution
of the radiation emitted by harmonic oscillators by starting with the
entropy of a collection of such oscillators. His belief was reinforced by
the work of W. Wien, who at just about the same time had discovered a
law for the spectral distribution of the radiation emitted by a black body,
which agrees very well with the observations for the high frequencies,
or short-wavelength end of the spectrum. Planck was convinced that he
could find a universal and simple relationship that would express the most
general distribution law, if he could relate the entropy of the radiation to
the energy by means of Wien's law.

Planck found, by combining Wien's law with the mathematical expression for entropy, that a certain simple quantity (the R in the text of his
talk, which follows) varies directly with the energy, that is, it is a linear
function of the energy. Planck at first thought that this was the universal
law that he was seeking. But it turned out that Wien's law disagreed with
the data for black-body radiation for the long wavelengths. Thus, Planck
realized that he would have to look further. He was aided in his search
by the experimental work of Rubens and Kurlbaum, which showed that
the quantity R for long wavelengths varies as the square of the energy, instead of directly as the energy. A classical formula giving this result for
long wavelengths had already been derived by Lord Rayleigh. Planck
therefore decided to set up an algebraic formula for R, consisting of a sum
of two terms; one term was to depend on the first power of the energy,
and the other on the second power with two coefficients that were to be
determined. He determined these coefficients by choosing them so that
the new formula went smoothly into (that is, became) the Wien formula
for the short wavelengths, and the Rayleigh formula for long wavelengths.
If the wavelength in Planck's formula is allowed to become very small,
the formula approaches the Wien formula. As the wavelength becomes
large the Planck formula approaches the Rayleigh formula.

Although the formula he thus obtained agreed with the distribution of
the energy in black-body radiation over the entire spectrum, he was not
entirely happy with it since, as he said, ". . . even if this radiation
formula should prove to be absolutely accurate, it would after all be
only an interpolation formula found by happy guesswork and would thus
leave one rather unsatisfied." He therefore was concerned from the day
of its discovery with the problem of giving it physical meaning.

To do this, Planck started again from the concept of entropy. But this
time he related it to the probability that a certain state would occur in a
system. In the case of radiation, this was the probability for the distribution of the energy emitted by a black body among the various frequencies of the spectrum. This relationship between probability and

entropy had already been treated by Boltzmann, who had formulated the principle that entropy is a measure of the physical probability of finding a system in a given state.

To use this relationship between entropy and probability to obtain the general law of black-body radiation, it was necessary to start with a formula for the absolute entropy. But up to that time, as already noted, only *differences* of entropy were considered to have any meaning. This absolute definition of entropy was now introduced by Planck in such a way that the constant in the usual formula for the entropy of a system goes to zero as the absolute temperature of the system approaches zero. The application of this absolute formula to the determination of the spectral distribution of black-body radiation led to the formula that Planck had previously obtained by his empirical *ad hoc* methods. But there were two constants in the final radiation formula that had to be properly interpreted before the entire procedure could be given physical meaning.

One constant was fairly easy to interpret, since it turned out to be just twice the average kinetic energy of a harmonic oscillator divided by the absolute temperature of the ensemble of oscillators that were in equilibrium with the black-body radiation. This constant, k, which is called the Boltzmann constant (we have seen that Planck felt this to be ironic), plays a very important role in the kinetic theory of gases and is equal to two-thirds the average kinetic energy of molecules in a gas divided by the absolute temperature of the gas. This constant also plays a very important role in the relationship between probability and entropy; it is just the ratio of the entropy of a system in a given state to the logarithm of the probability of the system's being in that state.

The second universal constant that appears in Planck's formula required a good deal more thought on Planck's part before he properly interpreted it. The initial difficulty arose because he attempted to fit this constant into the framework of classical physics and the wave properties of radiation. He soon realized, however, that he could not do this without completely destroying the results of his theory and therefore the agreement that he had found with the observational data. He finally, and quite reluctantly, concluded that this new constant represented a drastic departure from classical physics and would have to be explained in terms of an atomism in radiation that was quite revolutionary.

This universal constant h, known as Planck's constant, has the very small numerical value 6.6×10^{-27}; it has the dimensional properties of an energy multiplied by a time so that it must be related to what is called "action" in classical physics. The importance of this concept for a given system in classical physics lies in the assumption that all systems tend to move along paths for which the total action, as with the planets, is a minimum. Moreover, in classical physics the action is always assumed to vary continuously, representing a continuous change in the system as it moves along its orbit. But the existence of the constant h indicated to Planck that in the future one would have to revise one's entire thinking concerning the way in which events occur in nature. Instead of a classical construction based upon the assumption that there exists a "continuity of all causal chains of events," one would have to introduce a quantum description of nature based upon the concept that action itself is atomistic and therefore quantized or discontinuous.

When Planck obtained his quantum formula of radiation, few physicists were prepared to accept its full implications; namely, that the wave picture of electromagnetic radiation as it had been developed by Maxwell was not complete and that it would have to be replaced by a wave-corpuscular picture.

The full significance of the quantum of action h is only now apparent when we see that it appears in all atomic, nuclear, and high energy processes. The presence of h in Planck's formula distinguishes it from the classical radiation formula and we find in general that all quantum formulae are characterized by the presence of this constant. Just as Planck's formula changes into Rayleigh's classical law as h goes to zero, so all atomic formulas become classical formulas as h goes to zero. Thus, in a universe in which h decreased steadily, ultimately becoming zero, quantum phenomena (the discontinuous structure of radiation, of action, and of energy in general) would disappear and classical science would be valid. From all that we know today, it is clear that the variegated structure of the atom and such stable structures as the electron and the photon are possible because h is finite. Thus, if h were zero, atoms as we know them could not exist and such things as organic chemistry and life itself would disappear. The importance of the quantum of action h for life processes is indicated by the continuity and remarkable stability of the gene. If action were not quantized, even small environmental changes would change the genetic structure, but the existence of a quantum of action means that genes retain their structures unless enough energy, let us say in the form of a high-energy photon, is absorbed to disrupt this structure. Thus genes can only change their structure discontinuously and not gradually.

That h is a very small number indicates that the discontinuities in nature are very minute. To the unaided eye, therefore, action (defined by the physicist as the momentum of a body multiplied by the distance it moves with the same momentum), energy, radiation, all appear continuous. Only to the physicist who peers deeply into matter and observes the behavior of the tiny individual components of matter (electrons, atoms, protons, neutrons) are the discontinuities apparent, and the need for a finite h and a quantum theory obvious.

The atomicity of action means that the emission and absorption of radiation by matter is discontinuous. Thus radiation of frequency v can be absorbed or emitted only in bundles (or quanta) hv. The larger the frequency is (the bluer the light), that is, the shorter the wavelength, the more energy there is concentrated in a bundle. Thus, in the emission and absorption of black-body radiation by oscillators at a given temperature, the very high-frequency oscillators play a very small role because a great deal of energy per quantum is required to excite such an oscillator. Precisely because the roles of the high-energy oscillators are practically eliminated in black-body radiation by the quantum of action does Planck's theory give the correct spectral distribution of black-body radiation.

The last paragraph in Planck's Nobel address indicates his hesitancy in extending his quantum concept beyond what was required to give his radiation formula. He was sure that energy is emitted and absorbed in little packets but was not convinced that the packets are permanent features of radiation.

We shall see, in our commentary on Einstein's theory of the photon, that Einstein answered this and other questions fully. Energy is not only emitted and absorbed in bundles, but these "photons," as Einstein called them, exist as unchanging entities after they have been emitted.

ｏｏｏｏｏｏｏ

PLANCK

The Origin and Development of the Quantum Theory [2]

. . . WHEN I RECALL THE DAYS of twenty years ago, when the conception of the physical quantum of "action" was first beginning to disentangle itself from the surrounding mass of available experimental facts, and when I look back upon the long and tortuous road which finally led to its disclosure, this development strikes me at times as a new illustration of Goethe's saying, that "man errs, so long as he is striving." And all the mental effort of an assiduous investigator must in-

[2] Max Planck, Nobel Prize in Physics Award Address, 1919. By permission of the Nobel Foundation.

deed appear vain and hopeless, if he does not occasionally run across striking facts which form incontrovertible proof of the truth he seeks, and show him that after all he has moved at least one step nearer to his objective. The pursuit of a goal, the brightness of which is undimmed by initial failure, is an indispensable condition, though by no means a guarantee, of final success.

In my own case such a goal has been for many years the solution of the question of the distribution of energy in the normal spectrum of radiant heat. The discovery by Gustav Kirchhoff that the quality of the heat radiation produced in an enclosure surrounded by any emitting or absorbing bodies whatsoever, all at the same temperature, is entirely independent of the nature of such bodies, established the existence of a universal function, which depends only upon the temperature and the wavelength, and is entirely independent of the particular properties of the substance. And the discovery of this remarkable function promised a deeper insight into the relation between energy and temperature, which is the principal problem of thermodynamics and therefore also of the entire field of molecular physics. The only road to this function was to search among all the different bodies occurring in nature, to select one of which the emissive and absorptive powers were known, and to calculate the energy distribution in the heat radiation in equilibrium with that body. This distribution should then, according to Kirchhoff's law, be independent of the nature of the body.

A most suitable body for this purpose seemed H. Hertz's rectilinear oscillator (dipole) whose laws of emission for a given frequency he had just then fully developed. If a number of such oscillators be distributed in an enclosure surrounded by reflecting walls, there would take place, in analogy with sources and resonators in the case of sound, an exchange of energy by means of the emission and reception of electro-magnetic waves, and finally what is known as black-body radiation corresponding to Kirchhoff's law should establish itself in the vacuum-enclosure. I expected, in a way which certainly seems at the present day somewhat naïve, that the laws of classical electrodynamics would suffice, if one adhered sufficiently to generalities and avoided too special hypotheses, to account in the main for the expected phenomena and thus lead to the desired goal. I thus first developed in as general terms as possible the laws of the emission and absorption of a linear resonator, as a matter of fact by a rather circuitous route which might have been avoided had I used the electron theory which had just been put forward by H. A. Lorentz. But as I had not yet complete confidence in that theory I preferred to consider the energy radiating from and into a spherical surface of a suitably large radius drawn around the resonator. In this connexion we need to consider only processes in an absolute vacuum, the knowledge of which, however, is all that is required to draw the necessary conclusions concerning the energy changes of the resonator.

The outcome of this long series of investigations of which some could be tested and were verified by comparison with existing observations, e.g. the measurements of V. Bjerknes on damping, was the establishment of a general relation between the energy of a resonator of a definite free frequency and the energy radiation of the corresponding spectral region in the surrounding field in equilibrium with it. The remarkable result was obtained that this relation is independent of the nature of the resonator, and in particular of its coefficient of damping—a result which was particularly welcome since it introduced the simplification that the energy of the radiation could be replaced by the energy of the resonator so that a simple system of one degree of freedom could be substituted for a complicated system having many degrees of freedom.

But this result constituted only a preparatory advance towards the attack on the main problem, which now towered up in all its imposing height. The first attempt to master it failed: for my original hope that the radiation emitted by the resonator would differ in some characteristic way from the absorbed radiation, and thus afford the possibility of applying a differential equation, by the integration of which a particular condition for the composition of the stationary radiation could be reached, was not realized. The resonator reacted only to those rays which were emitted by itself, and exhibited no trace of resonance to neighboring spectral regions.

Moreover, my suggestion that the resonator might be able to exert a one-sided, i.e. irreversible, action on the energy of the surrounding radiation field called forth the emphatic protest of Ludwig Boltzmann, who with his more mature experience in these questions succeeded in showing that according to the laws of the classical dynamics every one of the processes I was considering could take place in exactly the opposite sense. Thus a spherical wave emitted from a resonator when reversed shrinks in concentric spherical surfaces of continually decreasing size on to the resonator, is absorbed by it, and so permits the resonator to send out again into space the energy formerly absorbed in the direction from which it came. And although I was able to exclude such singular processes as inwardly directed spherical waves by the introduction of a special restriction, to wit the hypothesis of "natural radiation," yet in the course of these investigations it became more and more evident that in the chain of argument an essential link was missing which should lead to the comprehension of the nature of the entire question.

The only way out of the difficulty was to attack the problem from the opposite side, from the standpoint of thermodynamics, a domain in which I felt more at home. And as a matter of fact my previous studies on the second law of thermodynamics served me here in good stead, in that my first impulse was to bring not the temperature but the entropy of the resonator into relation with its energy, more accurately not the entropy itself but its second derivative with respect to the energy, for it is this differential coefficient that has a direct physical significance for the irreversibility of the exchange of energy between the resonator and the radiation. But as I was at that time too much devoted to pure phenomenology to inquire more closely into the relation between entropy and probability, I felt compelled to limit myself to the available experimental results. Now, at that time, in 1899, interest was centred on the law of the distribution of energy, which had not long before been proposed by W. Wien, the experimental verification of which had been undertaken by F. Paschen in Hanover and by O. Lummer and E. Pringsheim of the Reichsanstalt, Charlottenburg. This law expresses the intensity of radiation in terms of the temperature by means of an exponential function. On calculating the relation following from this law between the entropy and energy of a resonator the remarkable result is obtained that the reciprocal value of the above differential coefficient, which I shall here denote by R, is proportional to the energy. This extremely simple relation can be regarded as an adequate expression of Wien's law of the distribution of energy; for with the dependence on the energy that of the wave-length is always directly given by the well-established displacement law of Wien.

Since this whole problem deals with a universal law of nature, and since I was then, as to-day, pervaded with a view that the more general and natural a law is the simpler it is (although the question as to which formulation is to be regarded as the simpler cannot always be definitely and unambiguously decided), I believed for the time that the basis of the law of the distribution of energy could be expressed by the theorem that the value of R is proportional to the energy. But in view of the results of new measurements this conception soon proved untenable. For while Wien's law was completely satisfactory for small values of energy and for short waves, on the one hand it was shown by O. Lummer and E. Pringsheim that considerable deviations were obtained with longer waves, and on the other hand the measurements carried out by H. Rubens and F. Kurlbaum with the infra-red residual rays (*Reststrahlen*) of fluorspar and rock salt disclosed a totally different, but, under certain circumstances, a very simple relation characterized by the proportionality of the value of R not to the energy but to the square of the energy. The longer the waves and the greater the energy the more accurately did this relation hold.

Thus two simple limits were established by direct observation for the function R: for small energies proportionality to the energy, for large energies proportionality to the square of the energy. Nothing therefore seemed simpler than to put in the general case R equal to the sum of a term proportional to the first power and another proportional to the square of the energy, so that the first term is relevant for small energies and the second for large energies; and thus was found a new radiation formula which up to the present has withstood experimental examination fairly satisfactorily. Nevertheless it cannot be regarded as having been experimentally confirmed with final accuracy, and a renewed test would be most desirable.

But even if this radiation formula should prove to be absolutely accurate it would after all be only an interpolation formula found by happy guesswork, and would thus leave one rather unsatisfied. I was, therefore, from the day of its origination, occupied with the task of giving it a real physical meaning, and this question led me, along Boltzmann's line of thought, to the consideration of the relation between entropy and probability; until after some weeks of the most intense work of my life clearness began to dawn upon me, and an unexpected view revealed itself in the distance.

Let me here make a small digression. Entropy, according to Boltzmann, is a measure of a physical probability, and the meaning of the second law of thermodynamics is that the more probable a state is, the more frequently will it occur in nature. Now what one measures are only the differences of entropy, and never entropy itself, and consequently one cannot speak, in a definite way, of the absolute entropy of a state. But nevertheless the introduction of an appropriately defined absolute magnitude of entropy is to be recommended, for the reason that by its help certain general laws can be formulated with great simplicity. As far as I can see the case is here the same as with energy. Energy, too, cannot itself be measured; only its differences can. In fact, the concept used by our predecessors was not energy but work, and even Ernst Mach, who devoted much attention to the law of conservation of energy but at the same time strictly avoided all speculations exceeding the limits of observation, always abstained from speaking of energy itself. Similarly in the early days of thermochemistry one was content to deal with heats of reaction, that is to say again with differences of energy, until Wilhelm Ostwald emphasized that many complicated calculations could be materially shortened if energies instead of calorimetric numbers were used. The additive constant which thus remained undetermined for energy was later finally fixed by the relativistic law of the proportionality between energy and inertia.

As in the case of energy, it is now possible to define an absolute value of entropy, and thus of physical probability, by fixing the additive constant so that together with the energy (or better still, the temperature) the entropy also should vanish. Such considerations led to a comparatively simple method of calculating the physical probability of a given distribution of energy in a system of resonators, which yielded precisely the same expression for entropy as that corresponding to the radiation law; and it gave me particular satisfaction, in compensation for the many disappointments I had encountered, to learn from Ludwig Boltzmann of his interest and entire acquiescence in my new line of reasoning.

To work out these probability considerations the knowledge of two universal constants is required, each of which has an independent meaning, so that the evaluation of these constants from the radiation law could serve as an a posteriori test whether the whole process is merely a mathematical artifice or has a true physical meaning. The first constant is of a somewhat formal nature; it is connected with the definition of temperature. If temperature were defined as the mean kinetic energy of a molecule in a perfect gas, which is a minute energy indeed, this constant would have the value $\frac{2}{3}$. But in the conventional scale of temperature the constant assumes (instead of $\frac{2}{3}$) an extremely small value, which naturally is intimately connected with the energy of a single molecule, so that its accurate determination would lead to the calculation of the mass of a molecule and of associated magnitudes. This constant is frequently termed Boltzmann's constant, although to the best of my knowledge Boltzmann himself never introduced it (an odd circumstance, which no doubt can be explained by the fact that he, as appears from certain of his statements, never believed it would be possible to determine this constant accurately). Nothing can better illustrate the rapid progress of experimental physics within the last twenty years than the fact that during this period not only one, but a host of methods have been discovered by means of which the mass of a single molecule can be measured with almost the same accuracy as that of a planet.

While at the time when I carried out this calculation on the basis of the radiation law an exact test of the value thus obtained was quite impossible, and one could scarcely hope to do more than test the admissibility of its order of magnitude, it was not long before E. Rutherford and H. Geiger succeeded, by means of a direct count of the α-particles, in determining the value of the electrical elementary charge as $4 \cdot 65.10^{-10}$, the agreement of which with my value $4 \cdot 69.10^{-10}$ could be regarded as a decisive confirmation of my theory. Since then further methods have been developed by E. Regener, R. A. Millikan, and others, which have led to a but slightly higher value.

Much less simple than that of the first was the interpretation of the second universal constant of the radiation law, which, as the product of energy and time (amounting on a first calculation to $6 \cdot 55.10^{-27}$ erg. sec.) I called the elementary quantum of action. While this constant was absolutely indispensable to the attainment of a correct expression for entropy —for only with its aid could be determined the magnitude of the "elementary region" or "range" of probability, necessary for the statistical treatment of the problem—it obstinately withstood all attempts at fitting it, in any suitable form, into the frame of the classical theory. So long as it could be regarded as infinitely small, that is to say for large values of energy or long periods of time, all went well; but in the general case a difficulty arose at some point or other, which became the more pronounced the weaker and the more rapid the oscillations. The failure of all attempts to bridge this gap soon placed one before the dilemma: either the quantum of action was only a fictitious magnitude, and, therefore, the entire deduction from the radiation law was illusory and a mere juggling with formulae, or there is at the bottom of this method of deriving the radiation law some true physical concept. If the latter were the case, the quantum would have to play a fundamental rôle in physics, heralding the advent of a new state of things, destined, perhaps, to transform completely our physical concepts which *since* the introduction of the infinitesimal calculus by Leibniz and Newton have been founded upon the assumption of the *continuity* of all *causal* chains of *events*.*

Experience has decided for the second alternative. But that the decision should come so soon and so unhesitatingly was due not to the examination of the law of distribution of the energy of heat radiation, still less to my special deduction of this law, but to the steady progress of the work of those investigators who have applied the concept of the quantum of action to their researches.

The first advance in this field was made by A. Einstein, who on the one hand pointed out that the introduction of the quanta of energy associated with the quantum of action seemed capable of explaining readily a series of remarkable properties of light action discovered experimentally, such as Stokes's rule, the emission of electrons, and the ionization of gases, and on the other hand, by the identification of the expression for the energy of a system of resonators with the energy of a solid body, derived a formula for the specific heat of solid bodies which on the whole represented it correctly as a function of temperature, more especially exhibiting its decrease with falling temperature. A number of questions were thus thrown out in different directions, of which the accurate and many-sided investigations yielded in the course of time much valuable material. It is not my task to-day to give an even approximately complete report of the successful work achieved in this field; suffice it to give the most important and characteristic phase of the progress of the new doctrine.

First, as to thermal and chemical processes. With regard to specific heat of solid bodies, Einstein's view, which rests on the assumption of a single free period of the atoms, was extended by M. Born and Th. von Karman to the case which corresponds better to reality, viz. that of several free periods; while P. Debye, by a bold simplification of the assumptions

* Editors' italics.

as to the nature of the free periods, succeeded in developing a comparatively simple formula for the specific heat of solid bodies which excellently represents its values, especially those for low temperatures obtained by W. Nernst and his pupils, and which, moreover, is compatible with the elastic and optical properties of such bodies. But the influence of the quanta asserts itself also in the case of the specific heat of gases. At the very outset it was pointed out by W. Nernst that to the energy quantum of vibration must correspond an energy quantum of rotation, and it was therefore to be expected that the rotational energy of gas molecules would also vanish at low temperatures. This conclusion was confirmed by measurements, due to A. Eucken, of the specific heat of hydrogen; and if the calculations of A. Einstein and O. Stern, P. Ehrenfest, and others have not as yet yielded completely satisfactory agreement, this no doubt is due to our imperfect knowledge of the structure of the hydrogen atom. That "quantized" rotations of gas molecules (i.e. satisfying the quantum condition) do actually occur in nature can no longer be doubted, thanks to the work on absorption bands in the infra-red of N. Bjerrum, E. v. Bahr, H. Rubens and G. Hettner, and others, although a completely exhaustive explanation of their remarkable rotation spectra is still outstanding.

Since all affinity properties of a substance are ultimately determined by its entropy, the quantic calculation of entropy also gives access to all problems of chemical affinity. The absolute value of the entropy of a gas is characterized by Nernst's chemical constant, which was calculated by O. Sackur by a straightforward combinatorial process similar to that applied to the case of the oscillators, while H. Tetrode, holding more closely to experimental data, determined by a consideration of the process of vaporization, the difference of entropy between a substance and its vapour.

While the cases thus far considered have dealt with the states of thermodynamical equilibrium, for which the measurements could yield only statistical averages for large numbers of particles and for comparatively long periods of time, the observation of the collisions of electrons leads directly to the dynamic details of the processes in question. Therefore the determination, carried out by J. Franck and G. Hertz, of the so-called resonance potential or the critical velocity which an electron impinging upon a neutral atom must have in order to cause it to emit a quantum of light, provides a most direct method for the measurement of the quantum of action. Similar methods leading to perfectly consistent results can also be developed for the excitation of the characteristic X-ray radiation discovered by C. G. Barkla, as can be judged from the experiments of D. L. Webster, E. Wagner, and others.

The inverse of the process of producing light quanta by the impact of electrons is the emission of electrons on exposure to light-rays, or X-rays, and here, too, the energy quanta following from the action quantum and the vibration period play a characteristic rôle, as was early recognized from the striking fact that the velocity of the emitted electrons depends not upon the intensity but only on the colour of the impinging light. But quantitatively also the relations to the light quantum, pointed out by Einstein, have proved successful in every direction, as was shown especially by R. A. Millikan, by measurements of the velocities of emission of electrons, while the importance of the light quantum in inducing photo-chemical reactions was disclosed by E. Warburg.

Although the results I have hitherto quoted from the most diverse chapters of physics, taken in their totality, form an overwhelming proof of the existence of the quantum of action, the quantum hypothesis received its strongest support from the theory of the structure of atoms (Quantum Theory of Spectra) proposed and developed by Niels Bohr. For it was the lot of this theory to find the long-sought key to the gates of the wonderland of spectroscopy which since the discovery of spectrum analysis up to our days had stubbornly refused to yield. And the way once clear, a stream of new knowledge poured in a sudden flood, not only over this entire field but into the adjacent territories of physics and chemistry. Its first brilliant success was the derivation of Balmer's formula for the spectrum series of hydrogen and helium, together with the reduction of the universal constant of Rydberg to known magnitudes; and even the small differences of the Rydberg constant for these two gases appeared as a necessary consequence of the slight wobbling of the massive atomic nucleus (accompanying the motion of electrons around it). As a sequel came the investigation of other series in the visual and especially the X-ray spectrum aided by Ritz's resourceful combination principle, which only now was recognized in its fundamental significance.

But whoever may have still felt inclined, even in the face of this almost overwhelming agreement—all the more convincing, in view of the extreme accuracy of spectroscopic measurements—to believe it to be a coincidence, must have been compelled to give up his last doubt when A. Sommerfeld deduced, by a logical extension of the laws of the distribution of quanta in systems with several degrees of freedom, and by a consideration of the variability of inert mass required by the principle of relativity, that magic formula before which the spectra of both hydrogen and helium revealed the mystery of their "fine structure" as far as this could be disclosed by the most delicate measurements possible up to the present, those of F. Paschen—a success equal to the famous discovery of the planet Neptune, the presence and orbit of which were calculated by Leverrier [and Adams] before man ever set eyes upon it. Progressing along the same road, P. Epstein achieved a complete explanation of the Stark effect of the electrical splitting of spectral lines, P. Debye obtained a simple interpretation of the K-series of the X-ray spectrum investigated by

Manne Siegbahn, and then followed a long series of further researches which illuminated with greater or less success the dark secret of atomic structure.

After all these results, for the complete exposition of which many famous names would here have to be mentioned, there must remain for an observer, who does not choose to pass over the facts, no other conclusion than that the quantum of action, which in every one of the many and most diverse processes has always the same value, namely $6 \cdot 52.10^{-27}$ erg. sec., deserves to be definitely incorporated into the system of the universal physical constants. It must certainly appear a strange coincidence that at just the same time as the idea of general relativity arose and scored its first great successes, nature revealed, precisely in a place where it was the least to be expected, an absolute and strictly unalterable unit, by means of which the amount of action contained in a space-time element can be expressed by a perfectly definite number, and thus is deprived of its former relative character.

Of course the mere introduction of the quantum of action does not yet mean that a true Quantum Theory has been established. Nay, the path which research has yet to cover to reach that goal is perhaps not less long than that from the discovery of the velocity of light by Olaf Römer to the foundation of Maxwell's theory of light. The difficulties which the introduction of the quantum of action into the well-established classical theory has encountered from the outset have already been indicated. They have gradually increased rather than diminished; and although research in its forward march has in the meantime passed over some of them, the remaining gaps in the theory are the more distressing to the conscientious theoretical physicist. In fact, what in Bohr's theory served as the basis of the laws of action consists of certain hypotheses which a generation ago would doubtless have been flatly rejected by every physicist. That with the atom certain quantized orbits [i.e. picked out on the quantum principle] should play a special rôle could well be granted; somewhat less easy to accept is the further assumption that the electrons moving on these curvilinear orbits, and therefore accelerated, radiate no energy. But that the sharply defined frequency of an emitted light quantum should be different from the frequency of the emitting electron would be regarded by a theoretician who had grown up in the classical school as monstrous and almost inconceivable.

But numbers decide, and in consequence the tables have been turned. While originally it was a question of fitting in with as little strain as possible a new and strange element into an existing system which was generally regarded as settled, the intruder, after having won an assured position, now has assumed the offensive; and it now appears certain that it is about to blow up the old system at some point. The only question now is, at what point and to what extent this will happen. If I may express at the present time a conjecture as to the probable outcome of this desperate struggle, everything appears to indicate that out of the classical theory the great principles of thermodynamics will not only maintain intact their central position in the quantum theory, but will perhaps even extend their influence. The significant part played in the origin of the classical thermodynamics by mental experiments is now taken over in the quantum theory by P. Ehrenfest's hypothesis of the adiabatic invariance; and just as the principle introduced by R. Clausius, that any two states of a material system are mutually interconvertible on suitable treatment by reversible processes, formed the basis for the measurement of entropy, just so do the new ideas of Bohr show a way into the midst of the wonderland he has discovered.

There is one particular question the answer to which will, in my opinion, lead to an extensive elucidation of the entire problem. What happens to the energy of a light-quantum after its emission? Does it pass outwards in all directions, according to Huygens's wave theory, continually increasing in volume and tending towards infinite dilution? Or does it, as in Newton's emanation theory, fly like a projectile in one direction only? In the former case the quantum would never again be in a position to concentrate its energy at a spot strongly enough to detach an electron from its atom; while in the latter case it would be necessary to sacrifice the chief triumph of Maxwell's theory—the continuity between the static and the dynamic fields—and with it the classical theory of the interference phenomena which accounted for all their details, both alternatives leading to consequences very disagreeable to the modern theoretical physicist.

34

ooooooooooo

MASS CHANGES

WITH VELOCITY

ooooooooooo

Walter Kaufmann (1871-1947)

With the discovery that cathode rays consist of negatively charged particles (electrons, as they came to be called), physicists began an intensive study of the properties of these particles; one of the most interesting and important questions dealt with their mass. With the equipment that was available immediately after the electron had been discovered, only the ratio of its charge to its mass could be measured directly. Only after Millikan had measured the charge on the electron first with charged water drops in 1909 and then with his famous oil-drop experiment in 1910–1911 was it possible to obtain a precise value for the mass of the electron.

Although the electronic mass could not be measured directly, some important observational conclusions could be drawn, particularly since the various applicable theories pointed to some unusual properties of the mass. The problem that arose in connection with the mass of the electron is essentially the following one.

Since an electron has an electrostatic field surrounding it because of its own charge, we must picture this field as moving along with the electron. Moreover, if the electrostatic field is set moving, it should, in principle, be accompanied by a magnetic field according to Maxwell's electromagnetic theory. Indeed, Rowland in 1878 had demonstrated experimentally that a moving charge is accompanied by a magnetic field whose lines of force form concentric circles about the line of motion of the charge. From this we can see at once that setting an electron in motion requires a greater push than setting an uncharged particle in motion, if we consider

502

the situation in terms of Newton's laws of motion and Maxwell's electromagnetic theory.

Let us consider an electron and an uncharged particle of the same mass at rest, and let us accelerate these particles by applying the same force to both of them. According to Newton's second law of motion, the force applied to either of these particles, divided by the acceleration imparted to this particle by the force, is the mass of the particle. In the case of the uncharged particle, this ratio (that is, the way a particle responds to a force) was referred to as the "true" mass of the particle.

The situation for the charged particle is much more complicated because of the electrostatic and the magnetic field. The same force that imparts a given acceleration to the uncharged particle cannot impart the same acceleration to the electron because, to begin with, the entire electrostatic field of the electron must also be set moving. Moreover, the moving electron immediately finds itself surrounded by a magnetic field that (according to the laws of induction) is always so directed as to oppose the force acting to accelerate the electron. In other words, the electron behaves as though it were more massive when it is set moving than when it is at rest. When Kaufmann undertook his experiments on the variation of the mass of an electron with velocity, physicists differentiated between what they called the "true" mass and the "apparent" mass of the electron. The "true" mass referred to the mass of the electron when it was not in motion and the "apparent" mass to its mass in virtue of its motion.

A theoretical investigation by J. J. Thomson had indicated that the mass of a moving charge should depend on its velocity and that the "apparent" mass should increase with velocity. In 1897, Searle, using a special model of the electron, according to which the charge is pictured as distributed over an infinitely thin surface shell, obtained a simple expression for the "apparent" mass as a function of the velocity. Another question which arose in connection with this was whether or not the so-called "true" mass was not itself entirely of an electromagnetic nature. As Kaufmann points out in his paper on the variation of mass with speed, the theoretical conclusions about the relative contribution of "true" and "apparent" mass to the total mass depend on the model of the electron that one uses. Today questions concerning the "true" and "apparent" mass do not arise, since only the total mass of the electron has physical significance.

When Kaufmann performed his experiments in 1901 on the change of mass of the electron with velocity, the theory of relativity had not yet been developed, but the electron theory of H. A. Lorentz had yielded, as early as 1895, the same relation later obtained by Einstein. But this was entirely a theoretical result and it was not certain that the speed of light was the maximum attainable speed for any object. Nevertheless, physicists such as Kaufmann knew that the speed of light played some kind of limiting role in the behavior of charged particles, for he states that "electrons cannot move with speeds in excess of that of light, at least over a path that is large compared to their dimensions because during such motion the electrons would radiate energy until their speeds were reduced to that of light." After Kaufmann demonstrated that the "apparent" mass of the electron increases with speed, he remarked that his results showed that the "increase in apparent mass is such that it approaches infinity as the speed approaches the speed of light," a completely correct conclusion.

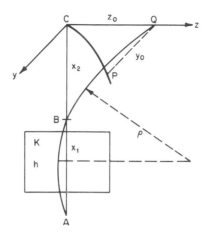

Fig. 34–1. Schematic arrangement of Kaufmann's apparatus showing undeflected and deflected electron paths.

Since Kaufmann had no high-energy accelerators to obtain electron speeds sufficiently high to show an appreciable increase of the mass, he used Becquerel rays, the electrons emitted by radioactive atoms, now called β-rays. These were much more energetic than the cathode rays that were available to him. In the first few paragraphs of his paper, he gives arguments in support of the belief that Becquerel rays are the same as cathode rays despite their much higher speeds. Then he outlines his experiment and describes his apparatus. The theoretical aspects of the experiment are discussed in terms of the arrangement of Fig. 34–1 taken from Kaufmann's paper.

We shall use this figure for a brief description of his experiment. A speck of radium bromide was placed at A, just below a pair of closely spaced and electrically insulated square metal plates K. A difference of potential of approximately 7,000 volts could be applied to the plates to produce a strong electric field. The whole region represented by Fig. 34–1 could also be subjected to a uniform magnetic field generated by an electromagnet, the field direction being perpendicular to and into the plane of the paper. The vertical line x_1x_2 determined by A and a fine circular opening at B, terminates on a photographic plate lying in the xy plane at C. In the absence of the electric and magnetic fields β-rays (electrons) from the radium bromide source could reach the photographic plate only along x_1x_2. Thus C on the photographic plate was a reference point for the undeflected rays. When only the magnetic field was applied electrons of the proper velocity initially directed along x_1 were forced along the circular arc ABQ of radius ρ, by the action of the field. When both electric and magnetic fields were applied simultaneously, the path of all the electrons that could get through the hole B, terminated on the curve CP on the photographic plate. Thus the point P lying in the yz plane has coordinates y_0 and z_0. From his measurements Kaufmann deduced values of e/m for electrons of five different velocities. These values are listed in Table 34–1. It is clear that as the velocity of the electrons increased, the value of e/m decreased, thus showing that since the electronic charge e is constant, the mass of the electron increased with velocity. If the ratio $\dfrac{M + m_0 \cdot \eta}{M + m_0}$ is calculated from Kaufmann's data for his given values of v and plotted against the corresponding values of $\beta = v/c$, the open circles shown in Fig. 34–2 result. This figure appears at the end of the paper. It is evident that the mass of the electron is tending to very large values as v approaches the speed of light. For reference, the full line in this figure is the graph of the Lorentz-Einstein relation. The dots on the lower part of the curve are the values of m/m_0 found by Bucherer in his experiments eight years later.

Before reading the paper, let us look briefly at Walter Kaufmann's life. He was born on June 5, 1871 in Elberfeld, Germany, where he spent his early schooldays. When he was ready for advanced instruction he entered the University of Munich. He continued there until 1894, earning his Ph.D. degree at the age of twenty-three. Leaving Munich, he went to the University of Berlin, then to Göttingen, and from there to Bonn. It was during his period at Göttingen that he did his most important experimental work, in particular the experiment which yielded the dependence of the mass of the electron on its speed, a classic investigation that after sixty years is still cited in the textbooks of modern physics. His research was marked by great proficiency in experimentation, especially in the techniques for obtaining the high vacuums necessary for cathode ray discharge tubes. His most notable contribution to this art was the construction of the first rotary high-vacuum pump; it was very artfully made of loops of glass tubing through which separate columns of mercury forced trapped volumes of gas out of the vacuum space. Although the pump was extremely fragile, unwieldy, and temperamental, Kaufmann used it with great success in his celebrated electron mass research.

In 1908, at the age of thirty-seven, he was appointed professor of experimental physics at the University of Königsberg. Here he devoted his principal efforts to lecturing and writing; from his presentation of advanced material it is clear that he was a skillful and excellent teacher.

On his retirement from Königsberg in 1935, he went to Freiberg as guest professor, remaining there until his death on January 1, 1947.

ၜၜၜၜၜၜ

KAUFMANN

Magnetic and Electric Deflectability of the Becquerel Rays and the Apparent Mass of the Electron [1]

1.) THE QUESTION AS TO WHETHER the "mass" of the electron calculated from the experiments on cathode rays or from the Zeeman effect is the "true" or "apparent" mass has recently been discussed quite extensively, although no direct experiments have yet been proposed in this direction. Now investigations into Becquerel rays have shown that these are deflected by electric and magnetic fields, and a rough measurement has given values for ϵ/μ (ϵ, charge; μ, mass) as well as for the velocity v, which are of the same order of magnitude as for cathode rays. It must therefore be all the more striking that the Becquerel rays are quantitatively so different from cathode rays. The magnetic deflection of the former is much smaller and their ability to penetrate solids much larger than the latter. Since previous experiments on cathode rays have shown that with increasing speed the deflectability decreases and the penetrability increases, it was reasonable to conclude that the Becquerel rays have much higher speeds than the cathode rays. If the cathode rays have speeds anywhere from $\frac{1}{3}$ to $\frac{1}{5}$ the speed of light, we must assume that the Becquerel rays have speeds only slightly different from that of light. It is impossible for these rays to exceed the speed of light, at least in a path length large with respect to the size of the "electron" (as these ray particles are now called) because during such a motion energy is radiated until the speed is reduced to the speed of light.

---

[1] Walter Kaufmann, trans. Editors, *Göttingen Nachrichten* (1901), 143–155.

2.) The purpose of the following experiments is to determine the speed as well as the ratio ϵ/μ as accurately as possible for Becquerel rays and also from the degree of dependence of ϵ/μ on v to determine the relation between "actual" and "apparent" mass.

3.) By using a very small radioactive source of rays and a tiny hole as a diaphragm, a small beam was separated out, which produced a point image on a photographic plate placed at right angles to the beam. Magnetic deflection changed the image into a line; simultaneous electric deflection in a direction normal to that of the magnetic deflection gave a curve as an image, each point of which corresponded to a definite v and a definite ϵ/μ. We thus obtained on a single plate a whole series of observations from which the dependence of ϵ/μ on v can be read off directly. . . .

7.) Let P be a point of the curve on the photographic plate, Q its projection of the direction of the magnetic deflection (z), $z_0 = \overline{CQ}$ the magnetic, and $y_0 = \overline{PQ}$ the electric deflection. Let a be the source of the rays, B the diaphragm, K one of the condenser plates. Let the X-direction be that of the undeflected beam. We consider the projection of the beam path on the X-Z-plane. If v_x is the projection of the velocity on this plane, ρ the radius of curvature of the path projection in the constant magnetic field, H, then

$$\frac{v_x^2}{\rho} = \frac{\epsilon}{\mu} v_x H \quad \text{or} \quad \frac{1}{\rho} = \frac{\epsilon}{\mu v_x} H \tag{2}$$

where ϵ is the charge and μ is the mass of the electron.

Further, if F is the electric field intensity, and if the condenser plates are symmetrical to a and B, then the rays leave B at an angle α to the X-Z-plane and their tangents can be obtained as follows: At the point B we have

$$\frac{dy}{dt} = \frac{\epsilon}{\mu} F \frac{t}{2}, \tag{3}$$

where t is the time during which the electrons were in the electric field. Now

$$dt = \frac{ds}{v_x} \quad \text{and} \quad \frac{t}{2} = \frac{s_1}{v_x},$$

where s_1 is the projection of half the path traversed in the electric field; hence

$$\tan \alpha = \frac{dy}{ds} = \frac{\epsilon F s_1}{\mu v_x^2} \tag{4}$$

If s_2 is the projection of the path from B to Q, the electric deflection is

$$y_0 = \frac{\epsilon F s_1 s_2}{\mu v_x^2}. \tag{5}$$

If we know the distance x_1 from the ray source to the diaphragm and the distance x_2 from the diaphragm to the plate, we can easily obtain an approximate relationship between ρ and the magnetic deflection z_0

$$\rho = \frac{z_0^2 + x_2^2 + x_1 x_2}{2z_0} - \frac{x_1^2 z_0}{4z_0^2 + x_2^2 + x_1 x_2} \tag{6}$$

or, since $x_1 = 2.07$ cm and $x_2 = 2$ cm:

$$\rho = \frac{z_0^2 + 8.15}{2z_0} - \frac{4.29 z_0}{4z_0^2 + 8.15}. \tag{7}$$

Moreover, the height of the condenser plates is $h = 1.775$ cm so that

$$\left\{ \begin{array}{l} s_1 = \rho \text{ arc sin } \dfrac{1.775}{2\rho} \\[3mm] s_2 = 2\rho \text{ arc sin } \dfrac{\sqrt{4 + z_0^2}}{2\rho} \end{array} \right. \tag{8}$$

From (2) and (5) we obtain

$$v_x = \frac{F s_1 s_2}{y_0 \rho H} \tag{9}$$

$$\epsilon/\mu = \frac{v_x}{\rho H}. \tag{10}$$

Finally, we easily see that the true velocity along the trajectory, which is exactly as large at B as it is at a, is given by

$$v = v_x \left(1 + \tfrac{1}{2} \frac{y_0^2}{s_2^2} \right). \tag{11}$$

Since y_0/s_2 is very small, we may place $v_x = v$.

8.) Results:

The experimental data are the following: Exposure time twice 48 hours; separation of condenser plates $\delta = 0.1525$ cm; potential difference $\Phi = 6750$ volts $= 6750 \times 10^8$ CGS [centimeter-gram-second] units.

Further, the mean value of the magnetic field

$$H = 299; \ \frac{H_{max} - H_{min}}{H} \times 100 = 7.5\%$$

Whatever the accuracy of the results may be, the relative accuracy of the individual numbers is, in any case, much larger than the absolute accuracy, since the latter depends on a much larger series of individual measurements. Nevertheless, the error in the absolute measurements is certainly no worse than 5%.

9.) True and apparent mass:

We see from [Table 34–1] that velocities of the fastest particles that can be measured are only slightly smaller than the speed of light. From the curve for v it appears that the speeds of the rays that are deflected only

TABLE 34–1*

z_0	y_0	ρ	s_1	s_2	$v \cdot 10^{-10}$	$\epsilon/\mu \cdot 10^{-7}$
0.271	0.0621	15.1	0.888	2.02	2.83	0.63
0.348	0.0839	11.7	0.888	2.03	2.72	0.77
0.461	0.1175	8.9	0.889	2.06	2.59	0.975
0.576	0.1565	7.1	0.889	2.09	2.48	1.17
0.688	0.198	6.0	0.890	2.13	2.36	1.31

* All numbers in absolute units.

weakly in the magnetic field converge toward the speed of light. In the observed range of speeds ϵ/μ varies very strongly; with increasing v the ratio ϵ/μ decreases very markedly, from which one may infer the presence of a not inconsiderable fraction of "apparent mass" which increases with speed in such a way as to become infinite at the speed of light.

A rigorous formula for the field energy of a rapidly moving electron has been derived by Searle under the assumption that an electron is equivalent to an infinitely thin, charged, spherical shell. If a is the radius of the shell, c the speed of light, v the speed of the electron, ϵ its charge in electromagnetic units, the field energy (electrostatic plus electromagnetic energy)

$$W = \frac{\epsilon^2 c^2}{2a} \left[\frac{1}{\beta} \log \frac{1 + \beta}{1 - \beta} - 1 \right] \tag{12}$$

where $\beta = v/c$.

From this we obtain for the apparent mass

$$m = \frac{1}{v}\frac{dW}{dv} = \frac{\epsilon^2}{2a}\frac{1}{\beta^2}\left[\frac{1}{\beta}\log\frac{1-\beta}{1+\beta} + \frac{2}{1-\beta^2}\right] \tag{13}$$

or, using a series expansion

$$m = \frac{2}{3}\frac{\epsilon^2}{a}\left[1 + \frac{3}{2}\cdot\frac{4}{5}\beta^2 + \frac{3}{2}\cdot\frac{6}{7}\beta^4 + \frac{3}{2}\cdot\frac{8}{9}\beta^6. \quad\cdot\quad\cdot\quad\cdot\right] \tag{14}$$

For very small β we have

$$m = m_0 = \frac{2}{3}\frac{\epsilon^2}{a}, \tag{15}$$

so that we obtain

$$\eta = \frac{m}{m_0} = \frac{3}{4\beta^2}\left[\frac{1}{\beta}\log\frac{1-\beta}{1+\beta} + \frac{2}{1-\beta^2}\right] \tag{16}$$

$$= 1 + \frac{3}{2}\cdot\frac{4}{5}\beta^2 + \frac{3}{2}\cdot\frac{6}{7}\beta^4 + \quad\cdot\quad\cdot\quad\cdot$$

Let M be the true mass of the electron, μ the total mass so that

$$\mu = M + m = M + m_0\eta \tag{17}$$

and

$$\epsilon/\mu = \epsilon/(M + m_0\eta). \tag{18}$$

If v is known, η is also known and we can determine the most probable value of M/ϵ and m_0/ϵ by a least square solution.

[let $M' = M/\epsilon$, $m'_0 = m_0/\epsilon$, $\mu' = \mu/\epsilon$]

We obtain from [Table 34–1] the most probable values,

$$\begin{aligned}M' &= 0.39 \times 10^{-7}\\ m'_0 &= 0.122 \times 10^{-7}\end{aligned} \tag{19}$$

Hence, for very slow rays

$$1/\mu' = \frac{1}{M' + m'_0\eta} = 1.95 \times 10^7 \tag{20}$$

a value which agrees quite well with that found for cathode rays (1.865×10^7).

[Table 34–2] gives a summary of the observed values and values calculated from equations (16), (18), and (19).

TABLE 34–2

$10^{-10}v$	β	η	$10^7\mu'$ Obs.	Calc.	Diff. %
2.83	0.945	12.5	1.59	1.91	
2.72	0.907	7.41	1.30	1.29	+0.8
2.59	0.864	4.88	1.025	0.99	+3.5
2.48	0.827	3.85	0.855	0.86	−0.6
2.36	0.787	3.13	0.765	0.77	−0.6

With the exception of the values in the first row which are experimentally uncertain, the formula gives the observed values quite well. The ratio of apparent to true mass for speeds that are small with respect to the speed of light is

$$\frac{m_0}{M} = \frac{m'_0}{M'} = \frac{0.122}{0.39} = 0.313 \text{ or about } \tfrac{1}{3}. \tag{21}$$

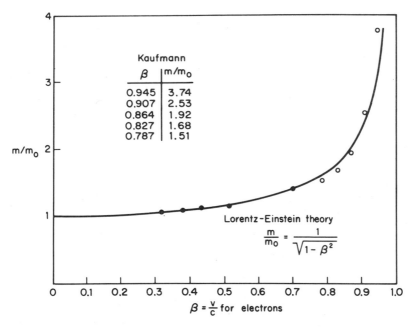

Fig. 34–2. Variation of electron mass with velocity. Open circles give Kaufmann's results; dots give later measurements of Bucherer (1909). Full line is prediction from Lorentz and Einstein.

Even if this value has an appreciable error in it (an error of 10% in the parameters that determine the magnetic deflection would make the true mass negligibly small) we can assert on the basis of the above results *that the apparent mass is of the same order of magnitude as the true mass and for the two fastest Becquerel rays the apparent mass is appreciably larger than the true mass.*

We must point out that the above development depends on the assumption that the charge of the electron is distributed over an infinitely thin spherical shell. Since we know nothing about the constitution of the electron and we are not justified *a priori* in applying to the electron the laws of electrostatics which we seek to derive from the properties of the electron itself, it is quite possible that the energy relationships of the electron can be derived from other charge distributions, and that there may be distributions which, when applied to the above analysis, give a zero true mass. [A plot of m/m_0 from Kaufmann's data appears as Fig. 34–2—Editors.]

35

ooooooooooo

THE ELECTRON THEORY
OF MATTER

ooooooooooo

Henrik Anton Lorentz (1853-1928)

The physics of the late nineteenth and early twentieth century was dominated by the investigations and writings of a few giants, among them Lord Kelvin, Lord Rayleigh, Sir J. J. Thomson, Planck, and Einstein. Near the very top of the list was the great Dutch physicist H. A. Lorentz, who laid the basis for modern electron theory. A section of the first chapter of his book, *The Theory of Electrons,* follows this commentary. One of the great classics of scientific literature, it has served many generations of students as the bridge between the macroscopic world of the electromagnetic field and the microscopic world of the electron.

Henrik Anton Lorentz was born on July 18, 1853, at Arnhem in Holland, the son of Gerrit Frederik Lorentz and Geertruida van Ginkel, whose first husband had died shortly after the birth of her first son. Although Henrik's mother died when he was four years old, she left a deep impression on him; he visited her grave whenever he was in Arnhem. Fortunately, his stepmother was kind so that his boyhood was a happy one.

Although the Lorentz family was fairly prosperous and cultured, there was only one children's book in the household and this became Henrik's most precious possession; on each page he carefully placed his initials H. A. L. When he began school at the age of six, his teachers quickly became aware of his unusual qualities, for he ranked first in all of his classes. He progressed so rapidly (partly because he taught himself) that at the age of nine he mastered logarithms by studying a table that he had bought in the marketplace with his own money.

He carried over his excellence in scholarship to his work in high school,

513

where he was an outstanding student, doing everything he undertook with such ease and assurance that he never considered this period of his life as anything but a very happy one. The natural, calm self-assurance that he developed never left him.

Lorentz at this time developed a great interest in history and in the humanities. He spent many hours in the pleasant hills of Arnhem discussing the Reformation with his friends and teachers, and he read extensively, mostly English authors; he was particularly found of Macaulay, Carlyle, Scott, Thackeray, and Dickens. Since he had an excellent memory, he knew Dickens practically word for word. His remarkable memory and analytical powers helped him master the many languages that he soon learned (Dutch, English, French, German, Greek, and Latin) although his English teacher felt that his English sounded a bit too much like Dickens. He had the amazing ability of being able to discover the grammatical rules and idiomatic usages of a language just by careful reading, without any formal instruction. In German he read Goethe and Schiller, and in French he spent many hours with Voltaire. His interest in learning French led him to attend a French church regularly.

It is evident from the course of his studies in these early years that he developed his great gifts in mathematics and physics without the help of anyone, for he had no one to turn to until he entered Leyden University in 1870, where many had already heard of his skill and were waiting to see and meet this "highly gifted, dark little person."

Lorentz passed his examination for the degree of Candidate in Mathematics and Physics (equivalent of our B.A. degree) *summa cum laude* at the age of eighteen, but Professor Van Geer, who administered the preliminary oral examination in mathematics, although satisfied with Lorentz's performance, expressed some disappointment. On being questioned about this, it turned out that Van Geer had mistakenly examined Lorentz for the Doctor's degree.

Lorentz left Leyden and returned to Arnhem in the following year to become a high school teacher. At the same time, he prepared himself for the Doctor's examination, studying all the necessary subjects on his own. He passed this examination *summa cum laude* in June 1873. During this study period he immersed himself in the work of Maxwell and this influenced the rest of his scientific life. He devoured Maxwell's original papers as soon as he could lay his hands on them, and that he mastered them completely is evident from his superb doctoral thesis, *On the Reflection and Refraction of Light,* which he defended publicly at Leyden on December 11, 1875, at the age of twenty-two. This dissertation shows that Lorentz had not only mastered Maxwell's theory but had learned how to use and apply it as a powerful tool. There is no doubt that this work convinced Lorentz that Maxwell's theory could give a description of nature only if it were complemented by an electrical theory of matter which would show how the electromagnetic field of Maxwell interacts with matter. This was the germ of his electron theory, which we discuss in our commentary.

Because of this excellent dissertation a new chair of theoretical physics was created for Lorentz at Leyden and after giving his inaugural address, "Concerning Molecular Theories of Physics" on January 25, 1878, he assumed his teaching duties and at the age of twenty-five became the first professor of theoretical physics in the Netherlands.

Lorentz was not only happy in his academic work but also in his personal and family life. After marrying the pretty Aletta Kaiser in 1881 he settled down to a very happy and fruitful life. Two daughters and two sons, one of whom died in infancy, were born to the couple and contributed greatly to Lorentz's joy of life.

Lorentz was an excellent and sympathetic teacher, completely devoted to his students. To work under him meant being assured of a doctoral degree in a relatively short time; he worked right along with each student, directing the research and even helping to write the final thesis as well. Understandably, he was revered by his students.

He was as kind as he was brilliant and helped people whenever he found them in need. It did not matter whether it was the famous Professor Kamerlingh Onnes, whose lectures Lorentz took over when the former became ill, or a young bricklayer apprentice whom Lorentz helped to become a master-mason—all shared his kindness.

Once Lorentz settled down to his career, great scientific achievements followed each other in rapid succession and hardly any branch of physics was left untouched by his remarkable contributions. His greatness as a physicist and human being was quickly recognized and every honor in the scientific world, including the Nobel Prize, was awarded to him. His collected works, issued in nine volumes between 1934 and 1939, epitomize one of the great transitional periods of physics and are still an exciting intellectual adventure to the student of physics.

On February 4, 1928, in his seventy-sixth year, this genius died in Haarlem, and all the world mourned. In the words of the physicist Paul Ehrenfest, who spoke the funeral oration, we see his greatness.

> Hendrik Antoon Lorentz dead! Since death was powerful enough to close the eyes of Lorentz, the ancient question arises in our hearts: "What after all may be the meaning of our human lives?"

After Maxwell had offered his equations of the electromagnetic field and Heinrich Hertz had verified them experimentally, physicists began to investigate the relationship of the electromagnetic field to the matter from which it emanates. Until the profound investigations of Lorentz, the approach to this problem had been a macroscopic one: the electromagnetic field was pictured as being coupled to matter through certain macroscopic parameters, such as the dielectric constant of a substance, the conductivity, the magnetic permeability, and so on. In this way, physicists were able to treat many problems, such as the behavior of light in a refractive medium, electromagnetic induction, and electric currents in matter. But, as Lorentz remarked, this procedure could "no longer be considered as satisfactory when we wish to obtain a deeper insight into the nature of the phenomena."

Lorentz obtained a deeper insight into this relationship by postulating the existence in the interior of matter of large numbers of extremely small charged particles, electrons. According to this picture, which, from our modern point of view, is quite naïve, the electron is understood to be a small hard sphere with an electric charge distributed uniformly over its entire surface. Aside from their being charged spheres, the electrons of Lorentz were to be treated like any other particles, and the same mechanical laws were to apply to them as apply to ordinary bits of matter. In particular, they were supposed to move, when acted upon by a force, according to Newton's laws of motion: if a force were applied to an electron, it was supposed to experience an acceleration proportional to the force and inversely proportional to its mass.

Lorentz went beyond merely picturing the electron as a particle that would behave in an electromagnetic field according to the accepted laws of motion. He ascribed definite properties to the interior of this particle, and introduced the assumption that the state within such an electron is similar to the conditions found outside it. Indeed, to derive some of the results he was seeking, he postulated that the interior of the electron is permeated by the ether and that electromagnetic fields exist in its interior just as they do in the space surrounding it. Lorentz was very careful to point out that the application of electron theory to the analysis of the behavior of matter in its interaction with radiation was in the nature of an adventuresome approach to the solution of these problems, but that this was in the tradition and, indeed, an extension of molecular and atomic theory that had proved so fruitful in chemistry and molecular physics.

We must remember that when Lorentz advanced his theory, the existence of electrons had not yet been universally accepted by physicists, in spite of J. J. Thomson's investigations into the conduction of electricity through gases. These developments had come at a time when some outstanding physicists were still skeptical about the existence of atoms and molecules, so that the introduction of a theory of electrons was a very bold step, indeed.

Lorentz's electron was drastically different in concept from the amorphous, imprecise wave-particle that we now have in mind when we speak of an electron. According to Lorentz, the electron was to be considered as an electric-charge distribution, in which the charge density is pictured as having a definite value in the interior of the electron and as sinking gradually to zero across a thin outer surrounding shell. The noteworthy property of the Lorentz electron is its description in terms of ordinary geometrical concepts that make it possible to speak of its interior.

Since Maxwell's electromagnetic theory says nothing about the existence or the properties of electrons, Lorentz found it necessary to extend Maxwell's theory to take the electron into account. This he did by simply adding some terms to Maxwell's equations. Thus, wherever Maxwell's equations contain the time rate of change of the electric field, Lorentz added to this the product of the charge density of the electron and its velocity. He altered the Maxwell equation, which states that the lines of force in an electric field must all be closed loops, by imposing the condition that such lines of force must begin and end on an electron. To study the motion of an electron in an electromagnetic field, Lorentz had to introduce an additional formula—his famous expression (the Lorentz force) for the force exerted by the electromagnetic field on a moving electron. This consists of two terms, one giving the action of the electric field on the electron and the other giving the action of the magnetic field. With these two simple changes in Maxwell's equations and the expression for the force, Lorentz forged an extremely powerful tool for the analysis of the interaction of radiation and matter.

Lorentz's procedure was so effective that with it he explained such diverse effects as the dispersion of light, the absorption and emission of radiation, and the various Zeeman effects; he also used it to derive the famous Einstein-Lorentz transformation equations. One other remarkable result that he obtained with the aid of this simple theory was the expression for the force of an electron on itself; that is, "the force to which an electron is subjected on account of its own field." Lorentz did this by picturing each point of the electron as exerting a force on a point P "of the ether occupied by the particle (electron) at the time t for which we wish to calculate the force." The remarkable part about this Lorentz force of the electron on itself is that it still endures even though its derivation is based on a model of the electron, which physicists now recognize as incompatible with modern quantum theory.

In his treatise on the electron, Lorentz first presented the hypothesis that had also been proposed by Fitzgerald to explain the negative result of the Michelson-Morley experiment. As already noted, the Michelson-Morley experiment indicates that the speed of light, as measured by an observer on the earth, is independent of the motion of the earth. This contradicts the long-accepted Newtonian concepts of space and time. To explain this result, Fitzgerald had suggested that the arm of the Michelson interferometer lying parallel to the direction of motion of the earth contracted by just the right amount to give the null effect that had been observed.

Lorentz showed that his theory of the electron would quite naturally lead to the contraction hypothesis, since he had demonstrated that an electron in motion changes its shape from a sphere to an ellipsoid, with the long axis of the ellipsoid perpendicular to the direction of motion of the electron. Having obtained this result for the electron, Lorentz generalized it further to include the spacings between molecules in a solid structure. As he says,

> We can understand the possibility of the assumed change of dimensions, if we keep in mind that the form of a solid body depends on the forces between molecules, and that, in all probability, these forces are propagated by the intervening ether in a way more or less resembling that in which electromagnetic actions are transmitted through this medium. From this point of view it is natural to suppose that just like the electromagnetic forces, the molecular attractions and repulsions are somewhat modified by a translation imparted to the body, and this may very well result in a change in dimensions.

It must be noted that Lorentz considered the contraction of an electron in motion (which he assumed led to the contraction of all bodies in motion) as a very real physical shrinkage and not merely the result of a change in the way space and time appear to moving observers. According to Lorentz, then, the contraction in the size of an electron occurs as the result of the electron's motion and not as a result of the relative motion between electron and observer. With the development of the theory of relativity, this one-sided way of looking at the effect of motion on spatial dimensions had to be discarded and replaced by a symmetrical picture in which only relative motion is important.

Yet through the idea of a contracting electron Lorentz established a very important criterion for the introduction of physical theories and hypotheses. This criterion concerns the legitimacy of introducing a hypothesis, however unlikely and strange it may appear, to further the development of science—just so long as the hypothesis is not *known* to be wrong. He remarks, after considering certain objections that had been raised against a contracting electron: "Notwithstanding all of this, it would, in my opinion, be quite legitimate to maintain the hypothesis of the contracting electron, if by its means we could really make some progress in the understanding of phenomena."

He then goes on to assert a belief that has not found acceptance in modern physics, namely, that the electron may possess some complex internal structure. He says,

> In speculating on the structure of these minute particles we must not forget that there may be many possibilities not dreamed of at present: It may very well be that other internal forces serve to insure the stability of the system, and perhaps, after all, we are wholly on the wrong track when we apply to parts of an electron our ordinary notion of force.

Although no internal structure of the electron has yet been found, it is becoming more and more evident that the next great development in our knowledge of the nature of matter will deal with precisely this question.

Lorentz used the theory of electrons to obtain another very important result, which is now referred to as the Lorentz transformations. Since a great many of the problems that arose during the years that Lorentz was pursuing his investigations dealt with the effect of the earth's motion on the behavior of light, Lorentz proposed to treat these problems by transforming the electromagnetic equations of the electron to a coordinate system not attached to the earth—but to one moving with the electron. In carrying out these transformations, Lorentz found it necessary, in discussing the behavior of an electron in the moving system, to picture a change as taking place not only in the dimensions of the electron, but also in time as measured by a clock moving with the electron. Lorentz called the time associated with a moving electron the "local" or "proper" time of the electron. By doing this he obtained a set of transformation equations that Einstein later obtained independently from a more general point of view; these are the basic equations of the special theory of relativity. These transformation equations were introduced by Lorentz in order to keep Maxwell's electromagnetic equations the same in a fixed and a moving coordinate system.

The remarkable thing about Lorentz's theory of the electron is that by means of simple classical procedures he obtained results still correct today, to a high order of approximation. However, it is precisely because of some higher-order disagreements between the simple Lorentz theory of electrons and observation that today's more sophisticated theories had to be introduced. Aside from the fact that Lorentz explained many experimental phenomena by means of electron theory, his work is important as a significant departure from all previous treatments of the interaction between charged particles. Before him, charged particles had been assumed to be capable of acting on each other at a distance, with the forces depending on the distances between these particles as well as on their charges and their state of motion. The Lorentz treatment, however, uses the idea of the medium or field. The electrons are pictured as interacting with each other, not directly, but rather locally with the medium or field in which they are embedded. Local interaction with the field is then pictured as being propagated in all directions with a definite speed. According to Lorentz, the medium, or the field (in a sense it is equivalent to the Maxwellian ether) is unaffected by the motions of the electrons and is essentially ordinary space with certain additional electrodynamic properties.

The way in which this electrodynamic space differs from the older idea of the ether is that each point in this space is characterized by four quantities—three components of a vector (the vector potential) and a scalar (the scalar potential)—which completely define the electromagnetic field at that point.

In 1905, Lorentz was invited to give a series of lectures at Columbia University, which were later published under the title *The Theory of Electrons*. The selection that follows is from Chapter 1 of this book.

ɷɷɷɷɷɷɷ

LORENTZ

The Theory of Electrons [1]

GENERAL PRINCIPLES. THEORY OF FREE ELECTRONS.

THE THEORY OF ELECTRONS, ON which I shall have the honor to lecture before you, already forms so vast a subject, that it will be impossible for me to treat it quite completely. Even if I confine myself to a general review of this youngest branch of the science of electricity, to its more important applications in the domain of light and radiant heat, and to the discussion of some of the difficulties that still remain, I shall have to express myself as concisely as possible, and to use to the best advantage the time at our disposal.

In this, as in every other chapter of mathematical physics, we may distinguish on the one hand the general ideas and hypotheses of a physical nature involved, and on the other the array of mathematical formulae and developments by which these ideas and hypotheses are expressed and worked out. I shall try to throw a clear light on the former part of the sub-

---

[1] From Henrik Anton Lorentz, *The Theory of Electrons* (2nd ed.; New York: Dover, 1915), Chapter 1.

ject, leaving the latter part somewhat in the background and omitting all lengthy calculations, which indeed may better be presented in a book than in a lecture.

1. As to its physical basis, the theory of electrons is an offspring of the great theory of electricity to which the names of Faraday and Maxwell will be for ever attached.

You all know this theory of Maxwell, which we may call the general theory of the electromagnetic field and in which we constantly have in view the state of the matter or the medium by which the field is occupied. While speaking of this state, I must immediately call your attention to the curious fact that, although we never lose sight of it, we need by no means go far in attempting to form an image of it and, in fact, we cannot say much about it. It is true that we may represent to ourselves internal stresses existing in the medium surrounding an electrified body or a magnet, that we may think of electricity as of some substance or fluid, free to move in a conductor and bound to positions of equilibrium in a dielectric, and that we may also conceive a magnetic field as the seat of certain invisible motions, rotations for example around the lines of force. All this has been done by many physicists and Maxwell himself has set the example. Yet, it must not be considered as really necessary; we can develop the theory to a large extent and elucidate a great number of phenomena, without entering upon speculations of this kind. Indeed, on account of the difficulties into which they lead us, there has of late years been a tendency to avoid them altogether and to establish the theory on a few assumptions of a more general nature.

The first of these is, that in an electric field there is a certain state of things which gives rise to a force acting on an electrified body and which may therefore be symbolically represented by the force acting on such a body per unit of charge. This is what we call the *electric force,* the symbol for a state in the medium about whose nature we shall not venture any further statement. The second assumption relates to a magnetic field. Without thinking of those hidden rotations of which I have just spoken, we can define this by the so called *magnetic force,* i.e. the force acting on a pole of unit strength.

After having introduced these two fundamental quantities, we try to express their mutual connexions by a set of equations which are then to be applied to a large variety of phenomena. The mathematical relations have thus come to take a very prominent place, so that Hertz even went so far as to say that, after all, the theory of Maxwell is best defined as the system of Maxwell's equations. . . .

We shall further find it convenient to use a simple kind of vector analysis and to distinguish vectors and scalar quantities by different sorts

of letters. Conforming to general usage, I shall denote scalars by ordinary
Latin or Greek letters. As to the vectors, I have, in some former publications, represented them by German letters. On the present occasion,
however, it seems to me that Latin letters, either capital or small ones,
of the so called Clarendon type, e.g. **A**, **P**, **c** etc. are to be preferred. I
shall denote by $\mathbf{A}_h$ the component of a vector **A** in the direction $h,$ by
$\mathbf{A}_x$, $\mathbf{A}_y$, $\mathbf{A}_z$ its components parallel to the axes of coordinates, by $\mathbf{A}_s$ the
component in the direction of a line s and finally by $\mathbf{A}_n$ that along the
normal to a surface.

The magnitude of a vector **A** will be represented by $|\mathbf{A}|$. For its square
however we shall simply write $\mathbf{A}^2$. . . .

In many cases we have to consider a scalar quantity φ or a vector **A**
which is given at every point of a certain space. If φ is a continuous function of the coordinates, we can introduce the vector having for its components

$$\frac{\partial \phi}{\partial x}, \ \frac{\partial \phi}{\partial y}, \ \frac{\partial \phi}{\partial z}.$$

This can easily be shown to be perpendicular to the surface

$$\phi = \text{const.}$$

and we may call it the *gradient* of ϕ, which, in our formulae, we shall
shorten to „grad ϕ".

A space at every point of which a vector **A** has a definite direction and
a definite magnitude may be called a vector field, and the lines which at
every point indicate the direction of **A** may be spoken of as vector- or
direction-lines. In such a vector field, if $\mathbf{A}_x$, $\mathbf{A}_y$, $\mathbf{A}_z$ are continuous functions of the coordinates, we can introduce for every point a certain scalar
quantity and a certain new vector, both depending on the way in which **A**
changes from point to point, and both having the property of being independent of the choice of the axes of coordinates. The scalar quantity is
called the *divergence* of **A** and defined by the formula

$$\text{div } \mathbf{A} = \frac{\partial \mathbf{A}_x}{\partial x} + \frac{\partial \mathbf{A}_y}{\partial y} + \frac{\partial \mathbf{A}_z}{\partial z}.$$

The vector is called the *rotation* or the *curl* of **A**; its components are

$$\frac{\partial \mathbf{A}_z}{\partial y} - \frac{\partial \mathbf{A}_y}{\partial z}, \ \frac{\partial \mathbf{A}_x}{\partial z} - \frac{\partial \mathbf{A}_z}{\partial x}, \ \frac{\partial \mathbf{A}_y}{\partial x} - \frac{\partial \mathbf{A}_x}{\partial y},$$

and it will be represented by the symbol „rot **A**".

. . . In order to complete our list of notations, I have only to add that the symbol Δ is an abbreviation for

$$\frac{\partial^2}{\partial x^2} + \frac{\partial^2}{\partial y^2} + \frac{\partial^2}{\partial z^2},$$

and that not only scalars but also vectors may be differentiated with respect to the coordinates or the time. For example, $\frac{\partial \mathbf{A}}{\partial x}$ means a vector whose components are

$$\frac{\partial \mathbf{A}_x}{\partial x}, \ \frac{\partial \mathbf{A}_y}{\partial x}, \ \frac{\partial \mathbf{A}_z}{\partial x},$$

and $\frac{\partial \mathbf{A}}{\partial t}$ has a similar meaning. A differentiation with respect to the time t will be often represented by a dot, a repeated differentiation of the same kind by two dots, etc.

3. We are now prepared to write down the fundamental equations for the electromagnetic field in the form which they take for the ether. We shall denote by $\mathbf{d}$ the electric force, the same symbol serving for the dielectric displacement, because in the ether this has the same direction and, on account of the choice of our units, the same numerical magnitude as the electric force. We shall further represent by $\mathbf{h}$ the magnetic force and by c a constant depending on the properties of the ether. A third vector is the current $\mathbf{c}$, which now consists only of the displacement current of Maxwell. It exists wherever the dielectric displacement $\mathbf{d}$ is a function of the time, and is given by the formula

$$\mathbf{c} = \dot{\mathbf{d}}. \tag{1}$$

In the form of differential equations, the formulae of the electromagnetic field may now be written as follows:

$$\operatorname{div} \mathbf{d} = 0, \tag{2}$$

$$\operatorname{div} \mathbf{h} = 0, \tag{3}$$

$$\operatorname{rot} \mathbf{h} = \frac{1}{c}\,\mathbf{c} = \frac{1}{c}\,\dot{\mathbf{d}}, \tag{4}$$

$$\operatorname{rot} \mathbf{d} = -\frac{1}{c}\,\dot{\mathbf{h}}. \tag{5}$$

The third equation, conjointly with the second, determines the magnetic field that is produced by a given distribution of the current $\mathbf{c}$. As to the last equation, it expresses the law according to which electric forces are called into play in a system with a variable magnetic field, i. e. the law of what is ordinarily called electromagnetic induction. The formulae (1), (4) and (5) are vector equations and may each be replaced by three scalar equations relating to the separate axes of coordinates.

Thus (1) is equivalent to

$$\mathbf{c}_x = \frac{\partial \mathbf{d}_z}{\partial t}, \ \mathbf{c}_y = \frac{\partial \mathbf{d}_y}{\partial t}, \ \mathbf{c}_z = \frac{\partial \mathbf{d}_x}{\partial t},$$

and (4) to

$$\frac{\partial \mathbf{h}_z}{\partial y} - \frac{\partial \mathbf{h}_y}{\partial z} = \frac{1}{c} \frac{\partial \mathbf{d}_x}{\partial t}, \text{ etc.}$$

The state of things that is represented by our fundamental equations consists, generally speaking, in a propagation with a velocity c. Indeed, of the six quantities $\mathbf{d}_x$, $\mathbf{d}_y$, $\mathbf{d}_z$, $\mathbf{h}_x$, $\mathbf{h}_y$, $\mathbf{h}_z$ five may be eliminated, and we then find for the remaining one ψ an equation of the form

$$\Delta \psi - \frac{1}{c^2} \frac{\partial^2 \psi}{\partial t^2} = 0. \tag{6}$$

This is the typical differential equation for a disturbance of the state of equilibrium, travelling onwards with the speed c.

Though all the solutions of our equations have this general character, yet there are a very large variety of them. The simplest corresponds to a system of polarized plane waves. For waves of this kind, we may have for example

$$\mathbf{d}_y = a \cos n \left(t - \frac{x}{c} \right), \ \mathbf{h}_z = a \cos n \left(t - \frac{x}{c} \right). \tag{7}$$

all other components of $\mathbf{d}$ and $\mathbf{h}$ being 0.

I need not point out to you that really, in the state represented by these formulae, the values of $\mathbf{d}_y$ and $\mathbf{h}_z$, which for a certain value of t exist at a point with the coordinate x, will after a lapse of time δt be found in a point whose coordinate is $x + c\delta t$. The constant a is the amplitude and n is the frequency, i. e. the number of vibrations in a time 2π. If n is high enough, we have to do with a beam of plane polarized light, in which, as you know already, the electric and the magnetic vibrations are perpendicular to the ray as well as to each other. . . .

The formulae for the ether constitute the part of electromagnetic theory that is most firmly established. Though perhaps the way in which they are deduced will be changed in future years, it is hardly conceivable that the equations themselves will have to be altered. It is only when we come to consider the phenomena in ponderable bodies, that we are led into uncertainties and doubts.

4. There is one way of treating these phenomena that is comparatively safe and, for many purposes, very satisfactory. In following it, we simply start from certain relations that may be considered as expressing, in a condensed form, the more important results of electromagnetic experiments. We have now to fix our attention on *four* vectors, the electric force **E**, the magnetic force **H**, the current of electricity **C** and the magnetic induction **B**. These are connected by the following fundamental equations:

$$\text{div } \mathbf{C} = 0, \tag{8}$$

$$\text{div } \mathbf{B} = 0, \tag{9}$$

$$\text{rot } \mathbf{H} = \frac{1}{c}\,\mathbf{C}, \tag{10}$$

$$\text{rot } \mathbf{E} = -\frac{1}{c}\,\dot{\mathbf{B}}, \tag{11}$$

presenting the same form as the formulae we have used for the ether.

In the present case, however, we have to add the relation between **E** and **C** on the one hand, and that between **H** and **B** on the other. Confining ourselves to isotropic bodies, we can often describe the phenomena with sufficient accuracy by writing for the dielectric displacement

$$\mathbf{D} = \epsilon \mathbf{E}, \tag{12}$$

a vector equation which expresses that the displacement has the same direction as the electric force and is proportional to it. The current in this case is again Maxwell's displacement current

$$\mathbf{C} = \dot{\mathbf{D}}. \tag{13}$$

In conducting bodies on the other hand, we have to do with a current of conduction, given by

$$\mathbf{J} = \sigma \mathbf{E}, \tag{14}$$

where σ is a new constant. This vector is the only current and therefore identical to what we have called **C**, if the body has only the properties of a conductor. In some cases, however, one has been led to consider bodies endowed with the properties of both conductors and dielectrics. If, in a substance of this kind, an electric force is supposed to produce a dielectric

displacement as well as a current of conduction, we may apply at the same
time (12) and (14), writing for the total current

$$\mathbf{C} = \dot{\mathbf{D}} + \mathbf{J} = \epsilon\mathbf{E} + \sigma\mathbf{E}. \tag{15}$$

Finally, the simplest assumption we can make as to the relation between
the magnetic force and the magnetic induction is expressed by the formula

$$\mathbf{B} = \mu\mathbf{H}, \tag{16}$$

in which μ is a new constant.

5. Though the equations (12), (14) and (16) are useful for the treatment of many problems, they cannot be said to be applicable to all cases.
Moreover, even if they were so, this general theory, in which we express
the peculiar properties of different ponderable bodies by simply ascribing
to each of them particular values of the dielectric constant ϵ, the conductivity σ and the magnetic permeability μ, can no longer be considered as satisfactory, when we wish to obtain a deeper insight into the nature of the
phenomena. If we want to understand the way in which electric and magnetic properties depend on the temperature, the density, the chemical
constitution or the crystalline state of substances, we cannot be satisfied
with simply introducing for each substance these coefficients, whose values
are to be determined by experiment; we shall be obliged to have recourse
to some hypothesis about the mechanism that is at the bottom of the
phenomena.

It is by this necessity, that one has been led to the conception of
electrons, i. e. of extremely small particles, charged with electricity, which
are present in immense numbers in all ponderable bodies, and by whose
distribution and motions we endeavor to explain all electric and optical
phenomena that are not confined to the free ether. My task will be to treat
some of these phenomena in detail, but I may at once say that, according
to our modern views, the electrons in a conducting body, or at least a
certain part of them, are supposed to be in a free state, so that they can
obey an electric force by which the positive particles are driven in one,
and the negative electrons in the opposite direction. In the case of a non-
conducting substance, on the contrary, we shall assume that the electrons
are bound to certain positions of equilibrium. If, in a metallic wire, the
electrons of one kind, say the negative ones, are travelling in one direction,
and perhaps those of the opposite kind in the opposite direction, we have
to do with a current of conduction, such as may lead to a state in which
a body connected to one end of the wire has an excess of either positive
or negative electrons. This excess, the charge of the body as a whole, will,

in the state of equilibrium and if the body consists of a conducting substance, be found in a very thin layer at its surface.

In a ponderable dielectric there can likewise be a motion of the electrons. Indeed, though we shall think of each of them as having a definite position of equilibrium, we shall not suppose them to be wholly immovable. They can be displaced by an electric force exerted by the ether, which we conceive to penetrate all ponderable matter, a point to which we shall soon have to revert. Now, however, the displacement will immediately give rise to a new force by which the particle is pulled back towards its original position, and which we may therefore appropriately distinguish by the name of *elastic force*. The motion of the electrons in non-conducting bodies, such as glass and sulphur, kept by the elastic force within certain bounds, together with the change of the dielectric displacement in the ether itself, now constitutes what Maxwell called the displacement current. A substance in which the electrons are shifted to new positions is said to be electrically polarized.

Again, under the influence of the elastic forces, the electrons can vibrate about their positions of equilibrium. In doing so, and perhaps also on account of other more irregular motions, they become the centres of waves that travel outwards in the surrounding ether and can be observed as light if the frequency is high enough. In this manner we can account for the emission of light and heat. As to the opposite phenomenon, that of absorption, this is explained by considering the vibrations that are communicated to the electrons by the periodic forces existing in an incident beam of light. If the motion of the electrons thus set vibrating does not go on undisturbed, but is converted in one way or another into the irregular agitation which we call heat, it is clear that part of the incident energy will be stored up in the body, in other terms that there is a certain absorption. Nor is it the absorption alone that can be accounted for by a communication of motion to the electrons. This optical resonance, as it may in many cases be termed, can likewise make itself felt even if there is no resistance at all, so that the body is perfectly transparent. In this case also, the electrons contained within the molecules will be set in motion, and though no vibratory energy is lost, the oscillating particles will exert an influence on the velocity with which the vibrations are propagated through the body. By taking account of this reaction of the electrons we are enabled to establish an electromagnetic theory of the refrangibility of light, in its relation to the wave-length and the state of the matter, and to form a mental picture of the beautiful and varied phenomena of double refraction and circular polarization.

On the other hand, the theory of the motion of electrons in metallic bodies has been developed to a considerable extent. Though here also much remains to be done, new questions arising as we proceed, we can already mention the important results that have been reached by Riecke, Drude and J. J. Thomson. The fundamental idea of the modern theory of the thermic and electric properties of metals is, that the free electrons in these bodies partake of the heat-motion of the molecules of ordinary matter, travelling in all directions with such velocities that the mean kinetic energy of each of them is equal to that of a gaseous molecule at the same temperature. If we further suppose the electrons to strike over and over again against metallic atoms, so that they describe irregular zigzag-lines, we can make clear to ourselves the reason that metals are at the same time good conductors of heat and of electricity, and that, as a general rule, in the series of the metals, the two conductivities change in nearly the same ratio. The larger the number of free electrons, and the longer the time that elapses between two successive encounters, the greater will be the conductivity for heat as well as that for electricity.

6. This rapid review will suffice to show you that the theory of electrons is to be regarded as an extension to the domain of electricity of the molecular and atomistic theories that have proved of so much use in many branches of physics and chemistry. Like these, it is apt to be viewed unfavourably by some physicists, who prefer to push their way into new and unexplored regions by following those great highways of science which we possess in the laws of thermodynamics, or who arrive at important and beautiful results, simply by describing the phenomena and their mutual relations by means of a system of suitable equations. No one can deny that these methods have a charm of their own, and that, in following them, we have the feeling of treading on firm ground, whereas in the molecular theories the too adventurous physicist often runs the risk of losing his way and of being deluded by some false prospect of success. We must not forget, however, that these molecular hypotheses can boast of some results that could never have been attained by pure thermodynamics, or by means of the equations of the electromagnetic field in their most general form, results that are well known to all who have studied the kinetic theory of gases, the theories of dilute solutions, of electrolysis and of the genesis of electric currents by the motion of ions. Nor can the fruitfulness of these hypotheses be denied by those who have followed the splendid researches on the conduction of electricity through gases of J. J. Thomson and his fellow workers.

7. I have now to make you acquainted with the equations forming the foundation of the mathematical theory of electrons. Permit me to introduce them by some preliminary remarks.

In the first place, we shall ascribe to each electron certain finite dimensions, however small they may be, and we shall fix our attention not only on the exterior field, but also on the interior space, in which there is room for many elements of volume and in which the state of things may vary from one point to another. As to this state, we shall suppose it to be of the same kind as at outside points. Indeed, one of the most important of our fundamental assumptions must be that the ether not only occupies all space between molecules, atoms or electrons, but that it pervades all these particles. We shall add the hypothesis that, though the particles may move, *the ether always remains at rest.* We can reconcile ourselves with this, at first sight, somewhat startling idea, by thinking of the particles of matter as of some local modifications in the state of the ether. These modifications may of course very well travel onward while the volume-elements of the medium in which they exist remain at rest.

Now, if within an electron there is ether, there can also be an electromagnetic field, and all we have got to do is to establish a system of equations that may be applied as well to the parts of the ether where there is an electric charge, i. e. to the electrons, as to those where there is none. As to the distribution of the charge, we are free to make any assumption we like. For the sake of convenience we shall suppose it to be distributed over a certain space, say over the whole volume occupied by the electron, and we shall consider the volume-density ρ as a continuous function of the coordinates, so that the charged particle has no sharp boundary, but is surrounded by a thin layer in which the density gradually sinks from the value it has within the electron to 0. Thanks to this hypothesis of the continuity of ρ, which we shall extend to all other quantities occurring in our equations, we have never to trouble ourselves about surfaces of discontinuity, nor to encumber the theory by separate equations relating to these. Moreover, if we suppose the difference between the ether within and without the electrons to be caused, at least so far as we are concerned with it, only by the existence of the volume-density in the interior, the equations for the external field must be got from those for the internal one by simply putting $\rho = 0$, so that we have only to write down *one* system of differential equations.

Of course, these must be obtained by a suitable modification, in which the influence of the charge is expressed, of the equations (2)–(5) which we have established for the free, i. e. for the uncharged ether. It has been found that we can attain our object by the slightest modification imaginable, and that we can assume the following system

$$\text{div } \mathbf{d} = \rho, \tag{17}$$

$$\text{div } \mathbf{h} = 0, \tag{18}$$

$$\text{rot } \mathbf{h} = \frac{1}{c}\,\mathbf{c} = \frac{1}{c}\,(\dot{\mathbf{d}} + \rho\mathbf{v}), \tag{19}$$

$$\text{rot } \mathbf{d} = -\frac{1}{c}\,\dot{\mathbf{h}}, \tag{20}$$

in which the first and the third formula are the only ones that have been altered. . . .

8. There is one more equation to be added, in fact one that is of equal importance with (17)–(20). It will have been noticed that I have carefully abstained from saying anything about the nature of the electric charge represented by ρ. Speculations on this point, or attempts to reduce the idea of a charge to others of a different kind, are entirely without the scope of the present theory; we do not pretend to say more than this, that ρ is a quantity, belonging to a certain point in the ether and connected with the distribution of the dielectric displacement in the neighbourhood of that point by the equation (17). We may say that the ether can be the seat of a certain state, determined by the vector **d** which we call the dielectric displacement, that in general this vector is solenoidally distributed, but that there are some places which form an exception to this rule, the divergence of **d** having a certain value ρ, different from 0. In such a case, we speak of an electric charge and understand by its density the value of div **d**.

As to the statement that the charges can move through the ether, the medium itself remaining at rest, if reduced to its utmost simplicity, it only means that the value of div **d** which at one moment exists at a point P, will the next moment be found at another place P'.

Yet, in order to explain electromagnetic phenomena, we are obliged to go somewhat further. It is not quite sufficient to consider ρ as merely the symbol for a certain state of the ether. On the contrary, we must invest the charges with a certain degree of substantiality, so far at least that we recognize the possibility of *forces* acting on them and producing or modifying their motion. The word „force" is here taken in the ordinary sense it has in dynamics, and we should easily become accustomed to the idea of forces acting on the charges, if we conceived these latter as fixed to what we are accustomed to call matter, or as being a property of this matter. This is the idea underlying the name of „charged particle" which we have already used and shall occasionally use again for an electron. We shall see later on that, in some cases at least, the fitness of the name is somewhat questionable.

However this may be, we must certainly speak of such a thing as the force acting on a charge, or on an electron, on charged matter, whichever appellation you prefer. Now, in accordance with the general principles of Maxwell's theory, we shall consider this force as caused by the state of the ether, and even, since this medium pervades the electrons, as exerted by the ether on all internal points of these particles where there is a charge. If we divide the whole electron into elements of volume, there will be a force acting on each element and determined by the state of the ether existing within it. We shall suppose that this force is proportional to the charge of the element, so that we only want to know the force acting per unit charge. This is what we can now properly call *the electric force*. We shall represent if by **f**. The formula by which it is determined, and which is the one we still have to add to (17)–(20), is as follows:

$$\mathbf{f} = \mathbf{d} + \frac{1}{c}\,[\mathbf{v}\cdot\mathbf{h}]. \tag{23}$$

Like our former equations, it is got by generalizing the results of electromagnetic experiments. The first term represents the force acting on an electron in an electrostatic field; indeed, in this case, the force per unit of charge must be wholly determined by the dielectric displacement. On the other hand, the part of the force expressed by the second term may be derived from the law according to which an element of a wire carrying a current is acted on by a magnetic field with a force perpendicular to itself and the lines of force, an action, which in our units may be represented in vector notation by

$$\mathbf{F} = \frac{s}{c}\,[\mathbf{i}\cdot\mathbf{h}],$$

where **i** is the intensity of the current considered as a vector, and s the length of the element. According to the theory of electrons, **F** is made up of all the forces with which the field **h** acts on the separate electrons moving in the wire. Now, simplifying the question by the assumption of only one kind of moving electrons with equal charges e and a common velocity **v**, we may write

$$s\mathbf{i} = N e \mathbf{v},$$

if N is the whole number of these particles in the element s. Hence

$$\mathbf{F} = \frac{N e}{c}\,[\mathbf{v}\cdot\mathbf{h}],$$

so that, dividing by Ne, we find for the force per unit charge

$$\frac{1}{c}\,[\mathbf{v}\cdot\mathbf{h}].$$

As an interesting and simple application of this result, I may mention the explanation it affords of the induction current that is produced in a wire moving across the magnetic lines of force. The two kinds of electrons having the velocity **v** of the wire, are in this case driven in opposite directions by forces which are determined by our formula.

9. After having been led in one particular case to the existence of the force **d**, and in another to that of the force $\frac{1}{c}$ [**v** · **h**], we now combine the two in the way shown in the equation (23), going beyond the direct result of experiments by the assumption that in general the two forces exist at the same time. If, for example, an electron were moving in a space traversed by Hertzian waves, we could calculate the action of the field on it by means of the values of **d** and **h**, such as they are at the point of the field occupied by the particle. . . .

10. While I am speaking so boldly of what goes on in the interior of an electron, as if I had been able to look into these small particles, I fear one will feel inclined to think I had better not try to enter into all these details. My excuse must be that one can scarcely refrain from doing so, if one wishes to have a perfectly definite system of equations; moreover, as we shall see later on, our experiments can really teach us something about the dimensions of the electrons. In the second place, it may be observed that in those cases in which the internal state of the electrons can make itself felt, speculations like those we have now entered upon, are at all events interesting, be they right or wrong, whereas they are harmless as soon as we may consider the internal state as a matter of little importance.

It must also be noticed that our assumptions by no means exclude the possibility of certain distributions of charge which we have not at first mentioned. By indefinitely diminishing the thickness of the transition layer in which ρ passes from a finite value at 0, we can get as a limiting case that of an electron with a sharp boundary. We can also conceive the charge to be present, not throughout the whole extent of the particle, but only in a certain layer at its surface, whose thickness may be made as small as we like, so that after all we can speak of a surface-charge. Indeed, in some of our formulae we shall have in view this special case.

11. Since our equations form the real foundation-stones of the structure we are going to build, it will be well to examine them somewhat more closely, so that we may be sure that they are consistent with each other. They are easily shown to be so, provided only the charge of an element of volume remain constant during its motion. If we regard the electrons as rigid bodies, as we shall almost always do, this of course means that ρ is constant at every point of a particle. However, we might also suppose the electrons to change their shape and volume; only, in this case, the value of ρ for an element of volume ought to be considered as varying in the inverse ratio as the magnitude of the element. . . .

36

○○○○○○○○○○

EINSTEIN'S LEGACY

○○○○○○○○○○

Albert Einstein (1879-1955)

For the man in the street, the name of Einstein is a byword for the ultimate in intellectual capacity. At a slightly more sophisticated level, his name is synonymous with the theory of relativity; but what this theory asserts still remains a mystery to the majority of men. Perhaps it is easiest to say that in the educated imagination Einstein has become the modern Newton—the pre-eminent physicist. The comparison is very apt, for both Newton and Einstein looked at the physical world in the most fundamental terms, and both produced a profound reorganization of the scientific outlook.

There are other parallels, for in their youths both were unlikely candidates for the laurels of genius. Newton was a farm boy whose intellectual stature was evident only after he had completed his undergraduate study at Cambridge. At one point in his life, Einstein was what we would today call a high-school "drop-out." His remarkable abilities went unrecognized in the university, and he remained an unknown entity until he began to publish the profound ideas on which his fame now rests. Newton as an undergraduate also seems to have been almost unknown, yet he made a deep impression on Isaac Barrow, Lucasian professor of mathematics at Cambridge. In a few years Barrow understood his pupil's genius so well that he resigned his chair, recommending Newton as his successor. Einstein, on the other hand, seems to have impressed no one. He was not offered an appointment even as an assistant—the lowest rung on the academic ladder. His epoch-making paper on relativity, published in 1905,

---

Note: The reader's attention is called to the similarity between the italic vee, v, used to represent velocity and volume and the Greek letter ν used to denote frequency and the number of particles per unit volume.

when he was twenty-six, was appreciated by the scientific world only after a lapse of years. If the story is true, it was an obscure professor in the old Polish University of Kracow who first recognized the significance of this work. Calling the paper to the attention of his students, he announced: "A new Copernicus has been born."

Albert Einstein's parents, Hermann and Pauline Koch Einstein, were freethinking German Jews of modest means living in the small city of Ulm. Here Albert was born on March 14, 1879. A year later the family moved to Munich, where his father operated an electrochemical business. It was in Munich that the boy grew up. As a child he was backward and took so long in learning to speak that his parents feared that he was not normal. Not only did his speaking come late, but he was a silent, dreamy child averse to physical play and characterized by a certain slowness that was irritating to many of his elders. His parents, indifferent to religion, began his schooling by sending him to a nearby Catholic elementary school where he was the only Jew in his class. But the discipline of the German classroom, standing at attention when spoken to, and the mechanical drill, all irritated the boy and he found school unpleasant. At ten he entered the Luitpold Gymnasium, but liked it no better. Here, however, he had the second intellectual experience of his youth (the first was the wonder instilled by a magnetic compass which his father had given him at age five)—the discovery of geometry in a book that he read entirely by himself at the age of twelve before the subject was presented at school. For Einstein, the orderliness and the logic of the theorems made an impression that was never lost.

When Albert was fifteen, his father's business failed. In the belief that Milan offered better opportunities, it was decided that the family—father, mother and Albert's younger sister Maya—would move there. Because Albert had not completed Gymnasium and a diploma was necessary for university admission, he was left behind to live in the care of orthodox cousins. Unhappy at school, without close friends, and in a home atmosphere in which he could not be at ease, he soon found his situation unbearable. The direct action of leaving school and presenting himself to his family in Italy would have been a decisive move entirely foreign to his nature. Instead, he decided to ask a doctor to state that he had suffered a nervous breakdown and must return to his parents.

As it turned out, this ruse was unnecessary; one of his instructors advised him that he would never amount to anything and that he ought to leave school because his indifference was demoralizing both to his teachers and to the other students. And so it was with vast relief that Albert, released from his unhappy situation, set out for Italy and temporary freedom.

But his father was hardly more successful in Milan than in Munich. Consequently, Einstein was soon forced to think about supporting himself.

His interest in science and mathematics suggested an eventual teaching career, and with financial assistance from more affluent relatives he applied for entrance to the famed Swiss Federal Institute of Technology in Zurich. Having no diploma, it was necessary to take the entrance examination, a step that produced another failure. Thus he was entered in the high school at Aarau to make up his deficiencies. From there he was able to enter the Polytechnic Institute without further trouble.

Once admitted and with courses dealing almost completely with mathematics and physics, one might expect that Einstein might have outdistanced all his fellow students. But this was not the case. Finding in the roster of subjects such a multitude of mathematics courses that he was unable to decide which were fundamental, he solved the problem by foreseeing no pressing need for higher mathematics. Physics, too, was greatly subdivided, but here he was able to make his way. Once again he found the discipline of classes irksome, so he read in his room. A friend who did attend classes took notes; with their aid Einstein was able to pass the required examinations.

Graduating in 1900, he started looking for employment as a teacher. What he desired most was a position as assistant in the institute, but he found no professor sufficiently impressed with what he had done, nor were other regular teaching positions available. He lived by doing the odd jobs of the intellectual world—substitute teaching and tutoring backward students. After two years, he was rescued from this precarious existence by the help of his good friend Marcel Grossman, who had supplied him with the lecture notes at the institute. Through Grossman's family, a job was found for him as a junior patent examiner in the Swiss Patent Office at Berne. Here at last Einstein found a satisfactory haven, time to think and to work at his own pace. Since the pay was sufficient to support a family, he married a former fellow student with whom he had studied physics, a reserved and rather stolid Hungarian woman, Mileva Maritsch. He was then twenty-three years old.

In the next three years, Einstein prepared three remarkable papers all of which appeared in the *Annalen der Physik* early in 1905. The first of these revived the corpuscular theory of light by introducing the revolutionary idea of the free photon—the atom of light—as an explanation for radiation phenomena (other than black-body radiation) and especially as an explanation for the photoelectric effect. His ideas in this latter field were verified by Millikan's experiments between 1912 and 1915. The second paper was a mathematical theory of the Brownian motion that provided a further proof of the reality of gas molecules on the basis that particles suspended in a fluid should behave as large gas molecules. This prediction was verified by the beautiful experiments of Perrin in 1909. Finally, the third paper, his first publication on the theory of relativity, dealt with that branch of the subject now called the special theory, which has been most useful in atomic physics. Commentaries on the contents of these papers precede their reproduction in the following pages. The papers on radiation and special relativity presented new and revolutionary approaches to physics and it is remarkable that Einstein developed these ideas entirely on his own and without the benefit of discussion with academic colleagues. Long after these papers were published he remarked that until he was about thirty he had "never seen a real theoretical physicist." He did not seem to need to test his ideas in the academic arena, nor did he ever seem uncertain as to the validity of his revolutionary innovations.

In 1909, as his work began to be recognized, he was appointed professor extraordinary at his old school in Zurich after a short apprenticeship as *Privatdozent* at Berne. The following year he was appointed to the chair of theoretical physics in Prague. His wife, however, disliked Prague; when he was offered a promotion to return to the Polytechnic in Zurich, he returned there in 1912. This appointment, too, was short-lived, for the following year he accepted (with many misgivings because of his unhappy youth in Germany) the post as director of the Kaiser Wilhelm Physical Institute in Berlin. With this move came a disruption in his family life, for the austere Mileva divorced Einstein and with their two sons remained in Switzerland.

The following year Germany was engaged in World War I and only Swiss citizenship saved Einstein from being regarded as a traitor for his refusal to participate in any effort connected with the war and for his determined pacifism. About this time he married his cousin Elsa, a union which for both was destined to be a lasting and happy relationship. Despite the war he continued with his work and in 1916 published his general theory of relativity. Owing to the hostilities it was impossible to carry out the measurements needed to provide a test of the theory. Thus, the prediction that light from distant stars would be deflected in the gravitational field of the sun had to wait until eclipse expeditions could be formed in 1919. The favorable results gained him world-wide renown. The Nobel Prize in physics was conferred on him in 1921, not for the theory of relativity but for "his contributions to mathematical physics and especially for his discovery of the law of the photoelectric effect." Although Einstein gained fame principally for his theory of relativity, this citation was necessary because of the clause in Nobel's will stipulating that the prizes were to be awarded for discoveries conferring great benefit on mankind.

In 1921 Einstein visited the United States to further the Zionist movement for a Jewish national home in Palestine and for the establishment of the Hebrew National University in Jerusalem. In 1922 he traveled to the

Far East and in 1925 to South America. In the winters of 1930–1931 and 1932–1933 he was visiting professor at the California Institute of Technology. Following this last visit, the consolidation of the Hitler movement in Germany made it inadvisable for him to return to Berlin, and he and his wife settled temporarily at Ostend, Belgium. It was fortunate that he did not re-enter Germany, for in a short time all of his property was confiscated, and it seems probable that he would have been arrested. In the autumn of 1933 he accepted a professorship at the Institute for Advanced Study at Princeton, where he remained until his death in 1955. One of his most significant acts during this period was his famous letter to President Roosevelt, written largely on the urging of Leo Szilard, advising the president of the feasibility of a superbomb made from uranium and the danger of a German lead in this awesome endeavor. Ironically it was this man of peace who paved the way for the development of nuclear explosives, which increasingly threaten all mankind.

Any appraisal of Einstein must acknowledge his greatness as a man as well as his greatness as a physicist. He was the supreme humanist, standing on the side of justice for all men regardless of the cost to himself. He believed deeply in the worth and dignity of every human being, and he fought against the evils that men everywhere are called to suffer at the hands of those who misuse power. One of his biographers has remarked that Einstein was a man of the sort who appears but once in a century—as a physicist it would be more realistic to say once in two centuries, for this was the approximate time that separated Newton and Einstein.

No man, with the possible exception of Newton, has so influenced the science of an era as Einstein influenced the physics of the twentieth century. His papers, whose full significance for the structure of the atom only became evident many years after they were published, are models of excellence and simplicity, with much of the development based a good deal more on physical reasoning than on mathematical formulation. Although at first sight the relationship between his work and the course of atomism is not always evident, a closer analysis shows that much of what we accept today about atoms would be untenable if any of Einstein's basic discoveries were discarded.

Thus, without his concept of the photon as an unchanging entity, such phenomena as the photoelectric effect, the photoionization of atoms, fluorescence, photoluminescence, could not be understood. Without the special theory of relativity such things as nuclear energy, the electron spin, the fine structure of spectral lines, positrons, and antimatter, in general, could not be understood. Today physicists are beginning to feel, more and more strongly, that a complete picture of the structure of matter is possible only if Einstein's general theory of relativity, published fifty years ago, is properly incorporated into atomic theory.

Before we go into a detailed discussion of Einstein's paper on the photon, we shall sketch briefly the chronology of his work.

He began with a series of papers, between 1902 and 1904, in which he developed the essential features of statistical mechanics, without fore-knowledge of the similar work that Willard Gibbs had already completed in 1901. In 1905, he applied his statistical mechanics to the analysis of Brownian motion, using the kinetic theory of gases. In the same year and in the same journal, the *Annalen der Physik,* two more of Einstein's fundamental papers appeared. In one, he developed the theory of the photon, which we shall discuss presently, and used it to explain the photo-electric effect, Stokes's law, and photoluminescence, among other phe-nomena. In the second, he began his series of famous papers on the theory of relativity. In the ensuing ten years, Einstein presented his theory of specific heats, in which, for the first time, the quantum theory was made to account for the observed behavior of the specific heats of solids as the absolute temperature approaches zero. In this same creative period, he published his proof that energy and mass are equivalent, deriving the famous equation $E = mc^2$. He also published an analysis indicating that the equivalence of gravitational and inertial mass is not a mere accident of nature, but the basis of a profound physical principle that leads to a new theory of gravity. He also extended the application of statistical mechanics to all physical systems and showed that the relationship of statistical mechanics to thermodynamics is valid under the most general conditions. Shortly thereafter, he published his general theory of rela-tivity, his general statistical derivation of Planck's law of radiation, in which only atomic processes of absorption and emission are assumed, and his first paper on cosmology, which ushered in modern cosmology. Finally, he recognized the importance of the wave properties of particles and the need to consider these properties in the statistical mechanics of such particles.

The remarkable thing about all Einstein's investigations is that they are all of a fundamental nature. In some cases, they opened up totally new realms in science. His papers demonstrated an uncanny ability to pene-trate to the heart of the most obscure problem. There seems never to have been any doubt in his mind that he had the correct answers, even when confronting the most profound questions that disturbed his con-temporaries. His principal concern, it appears, was to supply the answers in an understandable manner, with as little formalism as possible. All of these papers are marked by bold departures from the accepted paths and by confident applications of new and untried ideas. Thus, in his papers on the specific heats of solids, he departs immediately from the idea, ac-cepted until then, that the atomic vibrators composing these solids obey the ordinary classical laws of mechanics; instead he assumes that they are governed by the quantum theory. This was, indeed, a revolutionary step of the first magnitude, since it had previously been thought that quantum effects were to be ascribed to radiation only. Because Einstein obtained more nearly correct results for the specific heats of solids with the quantum theory (impossible with classical physics), physicists realized that the quantum theory would have to be applied to all atomic processes. The next great advance in this direction was made by Bohr in his monumental work on atomic spectra.

Had Einstein restricted himself to any one of the fields listed above, his contributions would still have marked him as one of the great physicists of our time. Although most people suppose that he was awarded the Nobel Prize for his theory of relativity, the prize was actually given for his paper of photons and the explanation of the photoelectric effect. The same paper, "Concerning a Heuristic Point of View about the Creation and Transformation of Light," is reproduced at the end of this commentary. It is remarkable because, although it deals with one of the most puzzling problems that physicists had to cope with, it is amazingly free of complex mathematical formulas. Indeed, except for one or two equations in the entire paper, the analysis is carried out with elementary algebra that can be followed by a good third-year high-school student. This paper is also of special interest because it shows that statistical mechanics, which up to then had been applied only to systems of particles, can also be applied to radiation in a container. Such radiation acts in many respects like a perfect gas. By carrying out the analogy between the statistics of molecules in a gas and the statistics of radiation in a container, Einstein established the existence of photons as unchanging entities under all conditions.

Although Planck had introduced the quantum of action to account for the spectral distribution of black-body radiation, the concept of the photon as a real entity was not a very popular one and was rejected by most physicists at the time. Planck himself felt very uncomfortable about the photon, and considered it more or less as a useful device to derive the correct radiation equations. He was inclined to picture the photon as having reality (if it had any at all) only during the processes of absorption and emission. At all other times, then, radiation had only a wave structure and character. Einstein departed completely from this tentative position that sought a compromise between classical physics and the new quantum hypothesis. He went over entirely to the quantum theory. He states his position very early in the paper that we are discussing and accepts the concept in the following words: "It appears to me, in fact, that the observations . . . can be understood better on the assumption that the energy in light is distributed discontinuously in space." Having stated this revolutionary position unequivocally, Einstein demonstrated the correctness of his assumption by applying to a container of black-body radiation, at the absolute temperature T, the statistical laws of Boltzmann and Maxwell, and those that he himself had developed in connection with the behavior of systems of particles. He carries through the analysis in two broad steps. He first considers freely moving particles, electrons and molecules, bound resonators, and harmonic oscillators in the light of the classical laws of thermodynamics and statistical mechanics, intermingled with the radiation in the container and interacting with it, as well as interacting among themselves. All are in dynamic equilibrium. He treats this ensemble of radiation, particles, and resonators according to the classical electromagnetic theory of Maxwell— the continuous distribution of energy in black-body radiation—and the classical theory of the electron. Therefore, since thermal equilibrium exists in this ensemble (the temperature is constant), it follows (from the classical laws of thermodynamics and statistical mechanics) that the mean kinetic energy of the resonators must equal that of the free particles, the molecules and electrons. The kinetic energy of the free particles is given by the equation $E = \frac{3}{2}kT$, (k being the Boltzmann constant) and hence is proportional to the absolute temperature T. In this derivation there is implicit the concept that each oscillator can have all possible energies consistent with the condition that it be in equilibrium with the freely moving molecules at the given temperature. By equilibrium we mean that, on the average, each molecule and each resonator has the same energy.

Einstein next considers the interaction of the *radiation* and the resonators when equilibrium exists; he assumes that Maxwell's theory governs this interaction. Therefore, the resonators can absorb and emit radiant energy continuously, that is, classically. Under these conditions the mean energy of a resonator of frequency ν must be directly proportional to the energy density of the radiation of that frequency and inversely proportional to the square of the frequency itself.

On equating this result for the mean energy of a resonator with that found by the methods of the previous paragraph, he finds that the energy density of the radiation in the container is proportional to the absolute temperature and the square of the frequency of the radiation.

Einstein points out that this is clearly incorrect, since the density of radiant energy in the higher frequencies would grow larger and larger if the frequency were continually increased, which is contrary to the observed facts. It is clear, then, that the idea of a continuous distribution of radiant energy in the container, in accordance with Maxwell's theory, is incorrect, although, as Einstein shows later in the paper, this is approximately true for very high temperatures and long wavelengths, that is, for large radiation densities.

To show that this result for the long wavelengths becomes more and more accurate with increasing absolute temperature, Einstein starts out from the correct Planck formula for the radiation density and considers it for large values of the absolute temperature divided by the frequency of the radiation. Under these conditions he shows that Planck's formula is the same as the one developed from the classical theory of Maxwell, that is, it is proportional to the square of the frequency and the absolute temperature. This leads to two conclusions: first, that the classical theory of radiation (that is, the wave theory with the continuous distribution of energy) is valid if we are dealing with dense quantities of radiation of long wavelength; second, the constants appearing in Planck's formula must be related to the gas constant and Avogadro's number since these constants appear in the classical formula. In fact, by equating the classical formula for the density of the radiation to that obtained from the Planck formula for high temperatures and long wavelengths, Einstein derives the mass of the hydrogen atom, that is, the reciprocal of Avogadro's number. This, to Einstein, was a clear indication that Planck's formula is correct and that the classical formula is only a correct approximation under certain conditions.

In the next part of the paper, Einstein considers the more important question of the nature of radiation when the density of the radiation is small and when the wavelength is very short. Under these conditions, one may replace Planck's formula by a somewhat simpler one, which was first introduced by Wien but which, in Einstein's words, "is completely satisfied experimentally for large values of v/T" (with v the frequency and T the temperature).

Einstein now compares the behavior of the radiation in this case with that of a perfect gas by introducing the entropy of the radiation which he can easily calculate from the Wien formula. He then shows that the entropy of the radiation expressed in terms of the volume of the radiation is of exactly the same mathematical form as the formula for the entropy of a perfect gas. To obtain the entropy of the gas in the form that is suitable for comparison with the entropy of the radiation, Einstein applies to the gas an important principle that was first stated by Boltzmann, viz.: that the entropy of a system is related to the probability for the state of the system. In so doing, Einstein gave a definite physical meaning to Boltzmann's equation relating entropy and probability; he defined the probability of a state as the length of time during which the system remains in this state, relative to some standard time.

In form, the equation Einstein derived for the entropy of an ideal gas is identical, in its dependence on volume, with the formula he derived for the entropy of monochromatic radiation in a container. Therefore, he concludes that the chance of finding, at any given moment, in some smaller volume of the container its total monochromatic radiation is expressed in a formula that is the same in form as the probability that the molecules in a perfect gas, distributed throughout a volume v_0, all will be found in a smaller volume v at any given moment.

Einstein's formula for the entropy of a dilute, short-wavelength, monochromatic radiation gas of frequency v leads, via Boltzmann's relationship between probability and entropy, to the probability $(v/v_0)^{E/hv}$. This is the probability for finding all the radiation in the smaller volume v_0, where E is the energy of the radiation and h is Planck's constant of action. Since the probability for finding all the molecules, n, of a perfect gas in the volume v_0 at any time is $(v/v_0)^n$, Einstein concludes that the two exponents, E/hv and n, in these two formulas must be the same. Since n is the number of molecules in the gas, it follows from this that E/hv is the number of distinct particles (quanta or photons) of radiation in the radiation. Since E is the total energy of the radiation, it follows that each quantum or particle of radiation has an amount of energy hv.

This is exactly the content of Planck's quantum hypothesis, but Einstein's results go further than Planck's hypothesis in that they show that radiation always consists of quanta or photons. Einstein states in his paper that follows:

> *Monochromatic radiation of small energy density (within the validity range of the Wien radiation formula) behaves in thermodynamic theoretical relationships as though it consisted of distinct independent* energy quanta of magnitude hv—[Editors' italics].

In the last part of the paper Einstein applies these conclusions to the explanation of two effects: Stokes's rule and the photoelectric effect. We shall consider here only the second of these two phenomena. It had been known for a number of years before Einstein's work, as the result of Heinrich Hertz's experiments and observations, that when light strikes a metal surface electrons are emitted. This is known as the photoelectric effect. The energy of the emitted electrons does not depend on the intensity of the light used, but only on the color of the light. This cannot be understood on the basis of Maxwell's classical electromagnetic theory. According to this theory, the intensity of the beam incident on the metal surface should determine the energy of the ejected electrons, which is proportional to the square of the speed with which each electron comes off the surface.

Einstein explained the phenomenon very easily, however, by means of his photon hypothesis (as will be seen in his paper) in the following words:

> According to the concept that the exciting radiation consists of energy quanta with energy content hv, the production of cathode rays by light can be understood as follows. Quanta of energy penetrate into the surface layer of the body and their energy, at least in part, is transformed into kinetic energy of electrons. The simplest explanation is that a quantum transfers all its energy to a single electron. . . . If each quantum of energy of the exciting light gives up its energy to an electron independently of all the other

quanta, then the velocity distribution of the electrons, that is, the quality of the produced cathode ray, is independent of the intensity of the exciting radiation; on the other hand, the number of electrons leaving the body, all other conditions being the same, will depend on the intensity of the exciting radiation.

During the next three years Einstein came back to the problem of the nature of radiation and, in a series of papers as brilliant and simple as the one discussed above, established the existence of the photon beyond any doubt.

At the same time, he showed that the statistical methods that worked so well in the analysis of the Brownian motion can be applied with the same success to radiation. He used these statistical methods to analyze the statistical fluctuations of radiation in a volume. If one considers a small part of a large volume containing radiation, the energy of the radiation in this small volume fluctuates from moment to moment. Einstein calculated this fluctuation using Planck's formula for the energy density of the radiation.

He showed that if E is the mean energy of the radiation of frequency v in a volume, then the square of the fluctuation of this energy is equal to

$$hv \left(\frac{E}{V}\right) + \left(\frac{8\pi v^2 dv}{c^3}\right)^{-1} \left(\frac{E}{V}\right)^2$$

where dv is the frequency range and V is the total volume of the radiation. This is a very remarkable result, as Einstein first pointed out, for it can be shown that although the second term $\left(\frac{8\pi v^2 dv}{c^3}\right)^{-1} \left(\frac{E}{V}\right)^2$ in this expression can be derived from classical electromagnetic theory, the first term, $hv \left(E/V\right)$, cannot be so derived and can only be accounted for by assuming that radiation has particle properties.

Einstein had thus indicated mathematically when energy can be expected to behave as a group of particles and when as a wave. The two terms in this expression show that the wave properties are dominant when the frequency is small (long wavelengths) and the energy density E/V is large. On the other hand, the first term (hence, the particle properties of radiation) dominates when E/V is small (dilute radiation) and the frequency is large (short wavelengths).

Not content with this analysis alone, Einstein went on to consider a small mirror suspended freely in black-body radiation and analyzed its motion as though it were a Brownian particle in a gas. As the mirror is bombarded by photons from all sides, it fluctuates back and forth and carries out a Brownian motion. Again Einstein found that this motion consists of two parts, one of which can be explained by means of Maxwell's classical electrodynamic theory. But the other effect can only be understood if one accepts the quantum hypothesis.

ၥၥၥၥၥၥၥ

EINSTEIN

Concerning a Heuristic Point of View about the Creation and Transformation of Light [1]

THERE IS A PROFOUND FORMAL difference between the theoretical representations of gases and other ponderable bodies which physicists have constructed and Maxwell's theory of electromagnetic processes in so-called empty space. Whereas we may consider the state of a body as being completely determined by the positions and velocities of, to be sure, a very large but finite number of atoms and electrons, we must use continuous, spatial functions to specify the electromagnetic state of a region, so that a finite number of parameters cannot be considered as sufficient to describe completely the electromagnetic state of a region of space. According to Maxwell's theory in all cases of pure electromagnetic phenomena, hence in the case of light, the energy must be considered as a continuous spatial function, whereas the energy of a ponderable body, according to the current concepts of physicists, can be represented by a sum taken over the atoms and electrons. The energy of a ponderable body can break up into arbitrarily many, arbitrarily small parts, whereas the energy of a ray of light emitted by a point source of light distributes itself continuously throughout an ever-increasing volume of space according to Maxwell's theory (or, more generally, according to any wave theory).

The wave theory, operating with continuous spatial functions, has proved to be correct in representing purely optical phenomena and will probably not be replaced by any other theory. One must, however, keep in mind that the optical observations are concerned with temporal mean values and not with instantaneous values, and it is possible, in spite of the complete experimental verification of the theory of diffraction, reflection, refraction, dispersion, and so on, that the theory of light that operates with continuous spatial functions may lead to contradictions with observa-

---

[1] Albert Einstein, trans. Editors, *Annalen der Physik,* 17 (1905), 132–148.

tions if we apply it to the phenomena of the generation and transformation of light.

It appears to me, in fact, that the observations on "black-body radiation," photoluminescence, the generating of cathode rays with ultraviolet radiation, and other groups of phenomena related to the generation and transformation of light can be understood better on the assumption that the energy in light is distributed discontinuously in space. According to the presently proposed assumption the energy in a beam of light emanating from a point source is not distributed continuously over larger and larger volumes of space but consists of a finite number of energy quanta, localized at points of space, which move without subdividing and which are absorbed and emitted only as units.

In what follows, I want to present the thinking and indicate the facts that have led me along the present path in the hope that the point of view associated with these ideas may prove useful to some researchers in their investigations.

I. CONCERNING CERTAIN DIFFICULTIES IN THE THEORY OF BLACK-BODY RADIATION

We begin by adopting the point of view of Maxwell's theory and the electron theory and consider the following case. We suppose that a volume of space completely enclosed by perfectly reflecting walls contains a number of gas molecules and electrons, which move about freely and exert conservative forces on each other when they get close to each other, that is, they can collide with one another like gas molecules according to the kinetic theory of gases. Further let a number of electrons be anchored at widely separated points by forces which are directed to these points and which are proportional to the displacements from the points. These electrons also are to be in conservative interaction with the free electrons and molecules when these free particles get very close to them. We call the anchored electrons "resonators"; they emit and absorb electromagnetic waves of definite period.

According to the current point of view about the emission of light, the radiation in the enclosed volume, which for the case of dynamical equilibrium is present on the basis of Maxwell's theory, must be identical with the "black-body radiation," at least when resonators of all frequencies that are to be considered are present.

We disregard for the moment the radiation that is absorbed and emitted by the resonators and investigate the condition for dynamical equilibrium for interactions [collisions] among the gas molecules and the electrons. The kinetic theory of gases gives as this condition that the mean energy of a resonator electron must equal the mean kinetic energy of the translational motion of a gas molecule. If we resolve the motion of a resonator electron into three mutually perpendicular components, we find for the mean value of the energy of such a linear vibratory motion

$$\overline{E} = R/N\,T$$

where R is the gas constant, N is the number of real molecules in a gram equivalent, and T is the absolute temperature. Because of the equality of the time average of the kinetic and potential energy of a resonator, the energy $\overline{E}$ is $\frac{2}{3}$ as large as the kinetic energy of a monatomic gas molecule. If through some cause—in our case through radiative processes—the mean energy of the resonator were larger than E, the collisions with the free electrons and gas molecules would lead, on the average, to a transfer to, or an absorption from, the gas of a non-zero amount of energy. We see then that in our case dynamical equilibrium is possible only when each resonator has a mean energy $\overline{E}$.

We carry through a similar analysis relative to the interaction of the resonators and the radiation in the container. Planck has derived the condition for dynamical equilibrium in this case under the assumption that the radiation can be considered as the most random phenomenon possible. He found

$$\overline{E}_\nu = \frac{L^3}{8\pi\nu^2}\,\rho_\nu;$$

$\overline{E}_\nu$ is here the mean energy of a resonator of proper frequency ν (per oscillatory component or degree of freedom), L the speed of light, ν the frequency, and $\rho_\nu d\nu$ the energy per unit volume of the radiation in the frequency range from ν to $\nu + d\nu$.

If the radiation energy of frequency ν is neither to increase nor to decrease continuously on the whole, we must have

$$\frac{R}{N}T = \overline{E} = \overline{E}_\nu = \frac{L^3}{8\pi\nu^2}\cdot\rho_\nu$$

$$\rho_\nu = \frac{R}{N}\cdot\frac{8\pi\nu^2}{L^3}\cdot T.$$

This relationship obtained as the condition for dynamical equilibrium not only does not agree with observation, but it also states that in our picture there can be no talk of a definite distribution of energy between ether and matter. The larger the frequency range that is chosen for the resonators, the larger is the radiation energy in the container, and in the limit we obtain

$$\int_0^\infty \rho_\nu d\nu = \frac{R}{N}\cdot\frac{8\pi}{L^3}\cdot T\int_0^\infty \nu^2 d\nu = \infty$$

II. PLANCK'S DERIVATION OF THE ELEMENTARY QUANTA

We wish to demonstrate in what follows that Planck's derivation of the elementary quanta is to a certain degree independent of his theory of "black radiation."

Planck's formula for ρ_ν which satisfies all the conditions required up to now reads

$$\rho_\nu = \frac{\alpha \nu^3}{e^{\frac{\beta \nu}{T}} - 1}$$

where

$$\alpha = 6.10 \times 10^{-56} = \frac{8\pi h}{L^3}$$

$$\beta = 4.866 \times 10^{-11} = \left(\frac{h}{k}\right).$$

For large values of T/ν, that is, long wavelengths and large radiation densities, this formula in the limit goes over into the following one

$$\rho_\nu = \frac{\alpha}{\beta} \nu^2 T$$

We see that this formula is the same as the one in Section I developed from the Maxwell and the electron theory. By equating the coefficients in both formulae we obtain

$$\frac{R}{N} \times \frac{8\pi}{L^3} = \frac{\alpha}{\beta}$$

or

$$N = \frac{\beta}{\alpha} \cdot \frac{8\pi R}{L^3} = 6.17 \times 10^{23}$$

that is, a hydrogen atom has a mass of $\frac{1}{N}$ grams $= 1.62 \times 10^{-24}$ grams.

This is precisely the value found by Planck, which agrees very satisfactorily with the value of this constant found in other ways.

We thus arrive at the following conclusion: The larger the energy density and the wavelength of any radiation, the more applicable are the theoretical principles we have used; for small wavelengths and small energy densities, however, these principles break down completely.

In the following we shall consider the "black radiation" and its observed characteristics without introducing a model for the emission and propagation of radiation.

III. CONCERNING THE ENTROPY OF RADIATION

The following considerations are contained in a famous paper of W. Wien and are included here only for the sake of completeness.

Let us consider radiation which occupies a volume V. We assume that the observable characteristics of this radiation are fully known when the energy density $\rho(\nu)$ is given for all frequencies. Since radiations of different frequencies may be considered as separable from each other without doing work or introducing heat, the entropy of the radiation may be written in the form

$$S = V \int_0^\infty \phi(\rho, \nu) \, d\nu$$

where ϕ is a function of the variables ρ and ν. ϕ can be reduced to a function of only one variable by expressing in formulae the statement that the entropy of radiation is unaltered by compressing it adiabatically between perfectly reflecting walls. However, we do not want to go into this here but instead consider at once how the function ϕ is to be determined from the radiation law of black bodies.

For "black radiation" ρ is such a function of ν that the entropy is a maximum for a given energy, that is, that

$$\delta \int_0^\infty \phi(\rho, \nu) \, d\nu = 0$$

if

$$\delta \int_0^\infty \rho \, d\nu = 0,$$

From this it follows that for every choice of $\delta\rho$ as a function of ν

$$\int_0^\infty \left(\frac{\partial \phi}{\partial \rho} - \lambda \right) \delta\rho \, d\nu = 0,$$

where λ is independent of ν. Thus for "black radiation" $\frac{\partial \phi}{\partial \rho}$ is independent of ν.

For a temperature increase dT of black radiation of volume $V = 1$ we have the equation

$$dS = \int_{\nu = 0}^{\nu = \infty} \frac{\partial \phi}{\partial \rho} \, d\rho \, d\nu,$$

or, since $\frac{\partial \phi}{\partial \rho}$ is independent of ν,

$$dS = \frac{\partial \phi}{\partial \rho} \, dE.$$

Since dE is equal to the heat supplied to the radiation and the process is reversible, we have

$$dS = \frac{1}{T} \, dE.$$

By comparing these two formulae we find

$$\frac{\partial \phi}{\partial \rho} = \frac{1}{T}.$$

This is the law of black radiation. We thus can obtain the law of black radiation from the function ϕ and conversely if we know this law we can find ϕ by integration, keeping in mind that ϕ vanishes if $\rho = 0$.

IV. LIMITING LAW OF THE ENTROPY OF MONOCHROMATIC RADIATION FOR SMALL RADIATION DENSITY

From the considerations up to now about "black radiation," it follows that the original law proposed by W. Wien

$$\rho = \alpha \nu^3 e^{-\frac{\beta \nu}{T}}$$

is not precisely correct. However, it is satisfied experimentally for large values of $\frac{\nu}{T}$. We shall base our analysis on this formula but keep in mind that our results are valid only within certain limits.

From this formula we first see that

$$\frac{1}{T} = -\frac{1}{\beta \nu} \log \frac{\rho}{\alpha \nu^3}$$

and further, by taking into account the relationship obtained in the previous paragraph

$$\phi(\rho,\nu) = -\frac{\rho}{\beta\nu}\left\{\log\frac{\rho}{\alpha\nu^3} - 1\right\}.$$

We consider now radiation of energy E whose frequency lies between
ν and $\nu + d\nu$. Let this radiation occupy the volume V. The entropy of this
radiation is

$$S = V\phi(\rho,\nu)d\nu = -\frac{E}{\beta\nu}\left\{\log\frac{E}{V\alpha\nu^3 d\nu} - 1\right\}.$$

If we limit ourselves to considering the dependence of the entropy on the
volume of the radiation and designate the entropy of the radiation as S_0
when its volume is V_0, we obtain

$$S - S_0 = \frac{E}{\beta\nu}\log\left(\frac{V}{V_0}\right).$$

This equation shows that the entropy of monochromatic radiation of
sufficiently small density varies with volume like the entropy of an ideal
gas or like a very dilute solution. The relationship just obtained will be
interpreted in what follows on the basis of the principle introduced into
physics by Boltzmann, according to which the entropy of a system is a
function of the probability of its state.

V. MOLECULAR THEORETIC INVESTIGATION INTO THE DEPENDENCE OF THE ENTROPY OF GASES AND DILUTE SOLUTIONS ON THEIR VOLUMES

In calculating the entropy by molecular theoretic methods the word
"probability" is often given a meaning which does not correspond to the
definition of probability as it is given in the calculus of probability.

In particular, "cases of equal probability" are often determined hypo-
thetically in situations where the applied theoretical pictures are definite
enough to permit a deduction instead of the hypothetical method. I shall
demonstrate in a separate paper that in dealing with thermal processes we
can manage completely with the so-called "statistical probability" and
hope thereby to overcome a logical difficulty which still stands in the
way of carrying out the Boltzmann principle. Here, however, we shall
concern ourselves only with its general formulation and its application to
quite special cases.

If there is any meaning attached to talking of the probability of the state of a system, if, further, each entropy increase is to be taken as a transition to a more probable state, then the entropy S, of a system is a function of the probability W, of the momentary state. If, then, there are two noninteracting systems S_1 and S_2, we can set

$$S_1 = \phi_1(W_1)$$
$$S_2 = \phi_2(W_2).$$

If we consider these two systems as forming a single system of entropy S and probability W, we have

$$S = S_1 + S_2 = \phi(W)$$

and

$$W = W_1 W_2.$$

The last relationship states that the states of the two systems are phenomena that are independent of each other.

From these equations we obtain

$$\phi(W_1 W_2) = \phi_1(W_1) + \phi_2(W_2),$$

and from this, finally

$$\phi_1(W_1) = C \log W_1 + \text{const.}$$
$$\phi_2(W_2) = C \log W_2 + \text{const.}$$
$$\phi(W) = C \log W + \text{const.}$$

The constant C is thus a universal constant; from the kinetic theory of gases its value is found to be R/N where R and N have the same meanings as above. If S_0 is the entropy of a given system in its initial state and W is the relative probability in a state of entropy S, we have in general

$$S - S_0 = \frac{R}{N} \log W.$$

We treat first the following special case. In a volume V_0 let there be a number (n) of moving points (for example, molecules upon which we shall carry out our considerations). Besides these, there may also be present other moving points of any arbitrary kind. We shall assume nothing about the law that governs the motion of these points except to specify that the motion shall be such that no region of space (nor direction) shall be preferred above any other. The number of specified (the first mentioned) moving points shall further be so small that we may neglect the interaction of one of these points with another.

This system, which, for example, may be an ideal gas or a dilute solution has an entropy S_0. We consider a part V of the volume V_0 and suppose that all n moving points are transferred to the volume V without any other change in the system. This state of the system obviously has a different value of the entropy (S) and we shall now calculate the entropy difference by means of Boltzmann's principle.

We ask: How large is the probability of this last considered state relative to the initial state? Or, how large is the probability that at some particular moment all n independently moving particles in the given volume V_0 are found (by chance) in the volume V.

For this probability, which is a statistical probability, we find clearly the value

$$W = \left(\frac{V}{V_0}\right)^n.$$

We obtain from this by applying the Boltzmann principle

$$S - S_0 = R\left(\frac{n}{N}\right) \log\left(\frac{V}{V_0}\right).$$

It is remarkable that for the derivation of this equation, from which the law of Boyle–Gay-Lussac and the equivalent law of osmotic pressure can be easily derived by thermodynamics, we had to make no assumption about the law governing the motion of the molecules.

VI. INTERPRETATION OF THE EXPRESSION FOR THE DEPENDENCE OF THE ENTROPY OF MONOCHROMATIC RADIATION ON THE VOLUME ACCORDING TO THE BOLTZMANN PRINCIPLE

In Section IV we obtained the expression

$$S - S_0 = \frac{E}{\beta\nu} \log\left(\frac{V}{V_0}\right)$$

for the dependence of the entropy of monochromatic radiation on its volume. If we write this formula in the form

$$S - S_0 = \frac{R}{N} \log\left[\left(\frac{V}{V_0}\right)^{\frac{N}{R}\frac{E}{\beta\nu}}\right]$$

and compare it with the general formula expressing Boltzmann's principle

$$S - S_0 = \frac{R}{N} \log W,$$

we reach the following conclusion:

If monochromatic radiation of frequency ν and energy E is enclosed in the volume V_0 (by perfectly reflecting walls), then the probability that at any moment all the radiation energy will be found in the partial volume V of the volume V_0 is given by

$$W = \left(\frac{V}{V_0}\right)^{\frac{N}{R} \frac{E}{\beta\nu}}.$$

From this we conclude further:

Monochromatic radiation of small energy density (within the validity range of the Wien radiation formula) behaves in thermodynamic theoretical relationships as though it consisted of distinct independent energy quanta of magnitude $R\beta\dfrac{\nu}{N}$.

We wish further to compare the mean energy of the energy quanta of "black radiation" with the mean kinetic energy of the center of mass motion of a molecule for a given temperature. The latter is $\frac{3}{2}(R/N)T$, whereas using Wien's formula, we obtain for the mean energy of the energy-quanta

$$\frac{\displaystyle\int_0^\infty \alpha\nu^3 e^{-\frac{\beta\nu}{T}}\, d\nu}{\displaystyle\int_0^\infty \frac{N}{R\beta\nu}\cdot \alpha\nu^3 e^{-\frac{\beta\nu}{T}}\, d\nu} = 3\frac{R}{N}\cdot T.$$

If then as far as the dependence of entropy on volume goes, monochromatic radiation (of sufficiently small density) behaves like a discontinuous medium consisting of energy-quanta of magnitude $R\beta\nu/N$, it is reasonable to inquire if the laws of emission and transformation of light are so constituted as though the light were composed of these same energy-quanta. We shall concern ourselves with this question in the next section.

VII. ON STOKES'S RULE

Let monochromatic light be transformed by photoluminescence into light of a different frequency and, in accordance with the result just derived, let the exciting as well as the excited radiation consist of energy quanta of magnitude $\left(\dfrac{R}{N}\right)\beta\nu$, where ν is the frequency of the radiation. The transformation process is then to be understood as follows:

Each exciting quantum of frequency ν_1 is absorbed and gives—at least for sufficiently small density distribution of the exciting energy quanta— by itself an opportunity for the emission of a quantum of frequency ν_2; eventually it is possible after the absorption of the exciting quantum also for quanta of frequencies ν_3, ν_4, and so on, as well as other kinds of energy (e.g., heat) to be emitted simultaneously. It is not essential for these end results to determine what the intermediate processes are. If we are not to look upon the photoluminescing material as an unending source of energy, then according to the energy principle, the energy of an excited quantum cannot exceed the energy of the exciting light quantum; the following relationship must therefore be valid

$$\frac{R}{N}\,\beta\nu_2 \leqq \frac{R}{N}\,\beta\nu_1$$

or

$$\nu_2 \leqq \nu_1$$

This is the well-known Stokes's law.

In particular one must emphasize that for weak irradiation, the emitted amount of light, all other things being equal, must be proportional to the intensity of the exciting light since each exciting energy quantum generates an elementary process of the kind described above, independently of the action of the other exciting energy quanta. In particular there is no lower limit for the intensity of the exciting light below which the light is unable to excite light emission.

Departures from Stokes's law are conceivable according to the above picture of the process in the following cases:

1. if the number per unit volume of simultaneously transformed energy-quanta is so large that an energy-quantum of the excited light can receive its energy from many exciting energy quanta.

2. if the exciting (or excited) light is not of the same energy constitution as that of "black radiation" in the range where Wien's law is valid; if, for example, the exciting light is emitted by a body of so high a temperature that the pertinent wavelengths are no longer governed by Wien's law.

This last possibility deserves special interest. According to the concepts developed here one may not exclude the possibility that a "non-Wien type of radiation" may differ in its energetic behavior from that of "black radiation" in the region where Wien's law is valid.

VIII. ON THE PRODUCTION OF CATHODE RAYS BY IRRADIATING SOLID BODIES

The traditional view that the energy of light is distributed continuously through the region illuminated by the light runs into great difficulty in trying to explain photoelectric phenomena, as was outlined in a trail-blazing paper by Lenard.

According to the concept that the exciting radiation consists of energy quanta with energy content $\left(\dfrac{R}{N}\right) \beta\nu$, the production of cathode rays by light can be understood as follows: Quanta of energy penetrate into the surface layer of the body and their energy, at least in part is transformed into kinetic energy of electrons. The simplest explanation is that a quantum transfers all its energy to a single electron; we shall assume that this occurs. We shall, however, not exclude the possibility that electrons can absorb only parts of the energy of light quanta. An interior electron with kinetic energy will have lost some of this kinetic energy by the time it reaches the surface. Besides this we must assume that each electron will have to do some work (an amount characteristic of the body) when it leaves the body. The electrons lying right at the surface of the body will leave the body with the greatest velocity normal to the surface. The kinetic energy of such electrons is

$$\frac{R}{N} \beta\nu - P.$$

If the body is charged to the positive potential Π and surrounded by conductors at zero potential, and if Π is large enough to prevent a discharge of the body, then we must have

$$\Pi\epsilon = \frac{R}{N} \beta\nu - P,$$

Where ϵ is the electric charge of the electron, or

$$\Pi E = R\beta\nu - P',$$

where E is the charge of a gram equivalent of a single charged ion and P' is the potential of this amount of negative charge relative to the body.

If we place $E = 9.6 \times 10^3$, then $\Pi \cdot 10^{-8}$ is the potential in volts that the body acquires on being irradiated in a vacuum.

In order to see at first if the derived relationship is of the right order of magnitude as obtained empirically we place $P' = 0$, $\nu = 1.03 \times 10^{15}$ (corresponding to the ultraviolet limit of the solar spectrum) and $\beta = 4.866 \times 10^{-11}$, we obtain $\Pi \cdot 10^7 = 4.3$ volts which agrees in order of magnitude with the results of Lenard.

If the derived formula is correct, then π must be a linear function of the frequency whose slope depends on the nature of the material being studied.

Our point of view, as far as I can see, does not contradict Lenard's observed properties of the photoelectric phenomena. If each quantum of energy of the exciting light gives up its energy to an electron independently of all the other quanta, then the velocity distribution of the electrons, that is, the characteristic of the produced cathode ray, is independent of the intensity of the exciting radiation; on the other hand the number of electrons leaving the body, all other conditions being the same, will depend on the intensity of the exciting radiation.

Concerning the probable domain of validity of the above laws we may make the same observations as for Stokes's rule.

In the above we assumed that the energy of at least a part of the quantum of the exciting light is given completely to one electron. If we do *not* make this reasonable assumption, we obtain in place of the above equation the following:

$$\Pi E + P' \leqq R\beta\nu.$$

For cathode luminescence, which is the inverse of the process discussed above, we obtain by analogous reasoning

$$\Pi E + P' \geqq R\beta\nu.$$

For the substances investigated by Lenard PE is significantly larger than $R\beta\nu$ since the potential through which the cathode rays had to move, just to emit visible light, equaled hundreds of volts in some cases, and thousands of volts in other cases. We may thus assume that the kinetic energy of an electron is used to produce numerous light quanta.

IX. ON THE IONIZATION OF GASES WITH ULTRAVIOLET LIGHT

We assume that in the ionization of a gas by ultraviolet light, one quantum of energy ionizes just one molecule. From this it follows, first of all, that the ionization energy (that is, the theoretical work needed to ionize) of a molecule cannot exceed the energy of the absorbed quantum that is effective in ionizing the molecule. If J is the (theoretical) ionization energy per gram equivalent, we must have

$$R\beta\nu \geqq J.$$

But according to Lenard's measurements, the longest effective wavelength for air is about 1.9×10^{-5} cm, so that

$$R\beta\nu = 6.4 \times 10^{12} \text{ erg} \gtrsim J.$$

We can also obtain an upper bound for the ionization energy in attenuated gases. According to J. Stark, the smallest measured ionization potential (for platinum anodes) is about 10 volts for air. We thus obtain 9.6×10^{12} as the upper bound for J which is very nearly the same as the value found above. There is another consequence, the experimental verification of which appears to me to be of great importance. If each quantum ionizes just one molecule, then the relationship $j = L/R\beta\nu$ must hold between the quantity of light L and the number, j, of gram molecules ionized by this amount of light. If our picture is correct, this equation must hold for every gas which (for the given frequency) shows no appreciable absorption unaccompanied by ionization.

ⲟⲟⲟⲟⲟⲟⲟ

Max Born, in an essay honoring Einstein on his seventieth birthday, wrote that Vol. 17 of the *Annalen der Physik* of 1905 is "one of the most remarkable volumes in the whole scientific literature. It contains three papers by Einstein, each dealing with a different subject and each today acknowledged to be a masterpiece, the source of a new branch of physics. These three subjects, in order of pages, are: theory of photons, Brownian motion, and relativity." When these papers were published, Einstein was still a clerk in the Swiss patent office, and his only contact with the main stream of physics and the great physicists of that period was through some of their original papers and the standard treatises by such men as Mach, Kirchhoff, Helmholtz, Hertz, and others that were available at the time.

Considering the magnitude of Einstein's achievement in writing any one of the three papers mentioned by Born, we are amazed that this could have been done without direct contact with other physicists of that period. If one reads Einstein's *Autobiographical Notes,* excerpts of which are presented in this section, it becomes somewhat clearer as to just why he departed from the classical approach to space and time and how he arrived at his theory of relativity. Remaining outside the influence of the dominant physicists of the late nineteenth and early twentieth century, Einstein was free to speculate to his heart's desire and to wander along forbidden intellectual paths. Moreover, he was fortunate in beginning to probe at a time when serious disagreement existed between classical theory and experimental data and when the old mechanistic ideas (that all the phenomena of nature could be explained by means of Newtonian mechanics) were being challenged by the success of Maxwell's theory.

The work of Faraday, Maxwell, and Hertz had introduced into man's concept of the universe an entity that could exist in space quite independently of palpable matter, namely, the radiation field. As Einstein remarked in 1949,

> The factor which finally succeeded, after long hesitation, to bring the physicists slowly around to give up the faith in the possibility that all of physics could be founded upon Newton's mechanics, was the electrodynamics of Faraday and Maxwell. For this theory and its confirmation by Hertz's experiment showed that there are electromagnetic phenomena which by their very nature are detached from every ponderable matter—namely the waves in empty space which consist of electromagnetic fields. If mechanics was to be maintained as the foundation of physics, Maxwell's equations had to be interpreted mechanically. This was zealously but fruitlessly attempted, while the equations were proving themselves fruitful in mounting degree. One got used to operating with those fields as independent substances without finding it necessary to give one's self an account of their mechanical nature; thus mechanics as the basis of physics was being abandoned, almost unnoticeably, because its adaptability to the facts presented itself finally as hopeless.[2]

It was precisely in analyzing the incompatibility between electromagnetic phenomena, or light, and the classical laws of mechanics that Einstein realized that a fundamental change was necessary in our concepts of space and time. His primary interest in pursuing this analysis was to understand the manner in which light interacts with rapidly moving media. Put differently, how would an observer moving with a very great speed see radiative processes unfold themselves?

Most remarkable about Einstein's work was his willingness to give up the most cherished ideas of physicists, to set out boldly along new paths, and to reformulate problems in terms of the most elementary ideas. He states in his autobiographical notes that he realized shortly after 1900, i.e., after Planck's trail-blazing work, that . . .

> neither mechanics nor thermodynamics could (except in limiting cases) claim exact validity. By and by I despaired of the possibility of discovering the true laws by means of constructive efforts based on the known facts. The longer and the more despairingly I tried, the more I came to the conviction that only the discovery of a universal formal principle could lead us to as-

[2] Einstein, "Autobiographical Notes," in Paul Schilpp, *Albert Einstein, Philosopher-Scientist* ("The Library of Living Philosophers"; Evanston, Ill.: Library of Living Philosophers, 1949), Vol. 7, pp. 25, 27.

sured results. The example I saw before me was thermodynamics. The general principle was there given in terms of the theorem: the laws of nature are such that it is impossible to construct a *perpetuum mobile* (of the first and second kind). How then could such a universal principle be found? After ten years of reflection such a principle resulted from a paradox upon which I had already hit at the age of sixteen.[3]

And here Einstein describes the first of a series of *Gedanken* (carried out in the mind of the scientist) experiments for which he is famous. These experiments, although extremely simple, were powerful tools in his hands and revealed to him the basic physical ideas involved in the phenomenon he was analyzing. The *Gedanken* experiment that occurred to Einstein at the age of sixteen dealt with the way in which a beam of light would appear to an observer traveling with the speed of light. He says,

> If I pursue a beam of light with the velocity [of light in a vacuum], I should observe such a beam of light as a spatially oscillatory electromagnetic field at rest. However, there seems to be no such thing, whether on the basis of experience or according to Maxwell's equations. From the very beginning it appeared to me intuitively clear that, judging from the standpoint of such an observer, everything would have to happen according to the same laws as for an observer who, relative to the earth, was at rest.[4]

This is the beginning of the principle of invariance (the laws of nature should appear the same to all observers moving with uniform speed with respect to each other) that Einstein was to make the basis of all his work in relativity. In this *Gedanken* experiment, Einstein had already formulated the idea that an observer could not travel with the speed of light, for if he did so, he would observe a stationary electromagnetic field.

A more profound analysis of the unique role of the speed of light in nature finally convinced him that this feature of light could be understood only if one revised one's concepts of space and time. He states it very clearly in the following paragraph:

> One sees that in this paradox [the way a beam of light would appear to an observer traveling with the speed of light] the germ of the special theory of relativity is already contained. Today everyone knows, of course, that all attempts to clarify this paradox satisfactorily were condemned to failure as long as the axiom of the absolute character of time, viz., of simultaneity, unrecognizedly was anchored in the unconscious. Clearly to recognize this axiom and its arbitrary character really implies already the solution of the problem. The type of critical reasoning which was required for the discovery

---

[3] *Ibid.*, p. 53.
[4] *Ibid.*, p. 53.

of this central point was decisively furthered, in my case, especially by the reading of David Hume's and Ernst Mach's philosophical writings.[5]

Einstein eventually realized that further progress could be made in resolving the above paradox only by first carefully analyzing such apparently simple ideas as the distance and the time interval between two events.

In classical physics, that is, before the advent of the special theory of relativity, two observers moving with uniform speed with respect to each other could compare their separate descriptions of events in the universe by means of simple mathematical formulas that connected their two coordinate systems (transformation of coordinates). Thus, any law of nature expressed mathematically by one observer in terms of his coordinate system could be translated into the mathematical language of the other observer by means of these transformations. Since all observers moving with uniform speed with respect to each other must be taken as equal in the eyes of nature, the transformation of a law from one coordinate system to another should leave the law unaltered (principle of relativity or the principle of invariance); yet these transformation equations do not leave an experimentally verified law, namely, the constancy of the speed of light (based upon the Michelson-Morley experiment and Einstein's *Gedanken* experiment) unaltered when one passes from one system to another. In other words, the constancy of the speed of light for all observers, regardless of the speed with which they are moving with respect to the earth, is in direct contradiction to the transformation equations of classical physics.

Einstein became aware of this and realized that if one accepted the constancy of the speed of light as an experimentally and, in terms of Maxwell's equations, a theoretically established law of nature, then one would have to replace the classical transformation equations by "relations of a new type (Lorentz transformation)." Einstein saw further that any set of relations (that is, transformation equations) that enables one to pass from a description of the laws of nature and events in one coordinate system to a description in another coordinate system involves a very definite concept of space and time; it has meaning only in terms of the specific way in which the measurements of distance and time are introduced.

The Newtonian way of looking at space and time, as absolute and independent entities in our universe, was based upon a very definite way of interpreting measuring rods and clocks. As long as one insisted on the correctness of this classical picture, it was impossible to fit the constancy of the speed of light into the framework in which the laws of nature are taken as independent of the choice of the inertial frame of reference. The only way these two ideas can be made compatible is by introducing a new

---

[5] *Ibid.,* p. 53.

hypothesis concerning "the actual behavior of moving measuring-rods and clocks, which can be experimentally validated or disproved." Einstein was led to a reevaluation of the role of measuring rods and clocks in establishing the laws of physics and of how our knowledge of their behavior in motion would be affected if we accept the constancy of the speed of light.

In classical physics it was taken as an a priori truth that if different observers in the universe were to order the events of history along a time axis and were to specify their positions and the distances between them, then this would always be the same arrangement regardless of how the observers were moving with respect to each other. According to this picture space and time are pictured as entirely independent of each other. Einstein's great contribution was to demonstrate that the constancy of the speed of light brought with it a new picture of space and time in which the two are fused into a single continuum with the space and time parts having different aspects for different observers.

By combining the space and the time intervals between two events into a single space-time interval, Einstein showed how the classical transformation equations would give way to the Lorentz transformations. All these developments were presented in a small book by Einstein written in 1916 entitled *Relativity, the Special and the General Theory*. Excerpts taken from this book that present the salient features of the development of special relativity are reproduced later in this chapter. The transformation equations Einstein obtained (they are the basis of the special theory of relativity) from this general analysis of space and time are identical with those Lorentz obtained by analyzing the behavior of his theoretical electrons. But the Lorentz derivation did not lead to a revision of the concepts of space and time, since Lorentz always considered his equations applicable only to electrons; indeed, from the way Lorentz derived these equations there was no justification for drawing more comprehensive conclusions from them. Lorentz, in fact, long persisted in the idea that his transformation equations were a peculiarity of electronic behavior and that the classical transformations were valid in the general case.

ooooooo

Autobiographical Notes [6]

. . . The most fascinating subject at the time that I was a student was Maxwell's theory. What made this theory appear revolutionary was the transition from forces at a distance to fields as fundamental variables.

---

[6] *Ibid.*, pp. 33–53.

The incorporation of optics into the theory of electromagnetism, with its relation of the speed of light to the electric and magnetic absolute system of units as well as the relation of the refraction coëfficient to the dielectric constant, the qualitative relation between the reflection coëfficient and the metallic conductivity of the body—it was like a revelation. Aside from the transition to field-theory, i.e., the expression of the elementary laws through differential equations, Maxwell needed only one single hypothetical step—the introduction of the electrical displacement current in the vacuum and in the dielectrica and its magnetic effect, an innovation which was almost prescribed by the formal properties of the differential equations. In this connection I cannot suppress the remark that the pair Faraday-Maxwell has a most remarkable inner similarity with the pair Galileo-Newton—the former of each pair grasping the relations intuitively, and the second one formulating those relations exactly and applying them quantitatively.

What rendered the insight into the essence of electromagnetic theory so much more difficult at that time was the following peculiar situation. Electric or magnetic "field intensities" and "displacements" were treated as equally elementary variables, empty space as a special instance of a dielectric body. *Matter* appeared as the bearer of the field, not *space*. By this it was implied that the carrier of the field could have velocity, and this was naturally to apply to the "vacuum" (ether) also. Hertz's electrodynamics of moving bodies rests entirely upon this fundamental attitude.

It was the great merit of H. A. Lorentz that he brought about a change here in a convincing fashion. In principle a field exists, according to him, only in empty space. Matter—considered as atoms—is the only seat of electric charges; between the material particles there is empty space, the seat of the electromagnetic field, which is created by the position and velocity of the point charges which are located on the material particles. Dielectricity, conductivity, etc., are determined exclusively by the type of mechanical tie connecting the particles, of which the bodies consist. The particle-charges create the field, which, on the other hand, exerts forces upon the charges of the particles, thus determining the motion of the latter according to Newton's law of motion. If one compares this with Newton's system, the change consists in this: action at a distance is replaced by the field, which thus also describes the radiation. Gravitation is usually not taken into account because of its relative smallness; its consideration, however, was always possible by means of the enrichment of the structure of the field, i.e., expansion of Maxwell's law of the field. The physicist of the present generation regards the point of view achieved by Lorentz as the only possible one; at that time, however, it was a surprising and audacious step, without which the later development would not have been possible.

If one views this phase of the development of theory critically, one is struck by the dualism which lies in the fact that the material point in Newton's sense and the field as continuum are used as elementary concepts side by side. Kinetic energy and field-energy appear as essentially different things. This appears all the more unsatisfactory inasmuch as, according to Maxwell's theory, the magnetic field of a moving electric charge represents inertia. Why not then *total* inertia? Then only field-energy would be left, and *the particle would be merely an area of special density of field-energy.** In that case one could hope to deduce the concept of the mass-point together with the equations of the motion of the particles from the field equations—the disturbing dualism would have been removed.

H. A. Lorentz knew this very well. However, Maxwell's equations did not permit the derivations of the equilibrium of the electricity which constitutes a particle. Only other, nonlinear field equations could possibly accomplish such a thing. But no method existed by which this kind of field equations could be discovered without deteriorating into adventurous arbitrariness. In any case one could believe that it would be possible by and by to find a new and secure foundation for all of physics upon the path which had been so successfully begun by Faraday and Maxwell.

Accordingly, the revolution begun by the introduction of the field was by no means finished. Then it happened that, around the turn of the century, independently of what we have just been discussing, a second fundamental crisis set in, the seriousness of which was suddenly recognized due to Max Planck's investigations into heat radiation (1900). The history of this event is all the more remarkable because, at least in its first phase, it was not in any way influenced by any surprising discoveries of an experimental nature.

On thermodynamic grounds Kirchhoff had concluded that the energy density and the spectral composition of radiation in a *Hohlraum,* surrounded by impenetrable walls of the temperature T, would be independent of the nature of the walls. That is to say, the nonchromatic density of radiation ρ is a universal function of the frequency v and of the absolute temperature T. Thus arose the interesting problem of determining this function $\rho(v,T)$. What could theoretically be ascertained about this function? According to Maxwell's theory the radiation had to exert a pressure on the walls, determined by the total energy density. From this Boltzmann concluded, by means of pure thermodynamics, that the entire energy density of the radiation ($\int\rho dv$) is proportional to T^4. In this way he found a theoretical justification of a law which had previously been discovered empirically by Stefan, i.e., in this way he connected this empirical law with the basis of Maxwell's theory. Thereafter, by way of an ingenious thermo-

---

* Editors italics.

dynamic consideration, which also made use of Maxwell's theory, W. Wien found that the universal function ρ of the two variables v and T would have to be of the form

$$\rho \approx v^3 f\left(\frac{v}{T}\right),$$

whereby $f(v/T)$ is a universal function of one variable v/T only. It was clear that the theoretical determination of this universal function f was of fundamental importance—this was precisely the task which confronted Planck. Careful measurements had led to a very precise empirical determination of the function f. Relying on those empirical measurements, he succeeded in the first place in finding a statement which rendered the measurements very well indeed:

$$\rho = \frac{8\pi h v^3}{c^3} \frac{1}{\exp\,(hv/kT) - 1},$$

whereby h and k are two universal constants, the first of which led to quantum theory. Because of the denominator this formula looks a bit queer. Was it possible to derive it theoretically? Planck actually did find a derivation, the imperfections of which remained at first hidden, which latter fact was most fortunate for the development of physics. If this formula was correct, it permitted, with the aid of Maxwell's theory, the calculation of the average energy E of a quasi-monochromatic oscillator within the field of radiation:

$$E = \frac{hv}{\exp\,(hv/kT) - 1}.$$

Planck preferred to attempt calculating this latter magnitude theoretically. In this effort, thermodynamics, for the time being, proved no longer helpful, and neither did Maxwell's theory. The following circumstance was unusually encouraging in this formula. For high temperatures (with a fixed v) it yielded the expression

$$E = kT.$$

This is the same expression as the kinetic theory of gases yields for the average energy of a mass-point which is capable of oscillating elastically in one dimension. For in kinetic gas theory one gets

$$E = (R/N)T,$$

whereby R means the constant of the equation of state of a gas and N the number of molecules per mol, from which constant one can compute the absolute size of the atom. Putting these two expressions equal to each other one gets

$$N = R/k.$$

The one constant of Planck's formula consequently furnishes exactly the correct size of the atom. The numerical value agreed satisfactorily with the determinations of N by means of kinetic gas theory, even though these latter were not very accurate.

This was a great success, which Planck clearly recognized. But the matter has a serious drawback, which Planck fortunately overlooked at first. For the same considerations demand in fact that the relation $E = kT$ would also have to be valid for low temperatures. In that case, however, it would be all over with Planck's formula and with the constant h. From the existing theory, therefore, the correct conclusion would have been: the average kinetic energy of the oscillator is either given incorrectly by the theory of gases, which would imply a refutation of [statistical] mechanics; or else the average energy of the oscillator follows incorrectly from Maxwell's theory, which would imply a refutation of the latter. Under such circumstances it is most probable that both theories are correct only at the limits, but are otherwise false; this is indeed the situation, as we shall see in what follows. If Planck had drawn this conclusion, he probably would not have made his great discovery, because the foundation would have been withdrawn from pure deductive reasoning.

Now back to Planck's reasoning. On the basis of the kinetic theory of gases Boltzmann had discovered that, aside from a constant factor, entropy is equivalent to the logarithm of the "probability" of the state under consideration. Through this insight he recognized the nature of courses of events which, in the sense of thermodynamics, are "irreversible." Seen from the molecular-mechanical point of view, however, all courses of events are reversible. If one calls a molecular-theoretically defined state a microscopically described one, or, more briefly, micro-state, and a state described in terms of thermodynamics a macro-state, then an immensely large number (Z) of states belong to a macroscopic condition. Z then is a measure of the probability of a chosen macro-state. This idea appears to be of outstanding importance also because of the fact that its usefulness is not limited to microscopic description on the basis of mechanics. Planck recognized this and applied the Boltzmann principle to a system which consists of very many resonators of the same frequency v. The macroscopic situation is given through the total energy of the oscillation of all resonators, a micro-condition through determination of the (instantaneous) energy of each individual resonator. In order then to be able to express the number of the micro-states belonging to a macro-state by means of a finite number, he [Planck] divided the total energy into a large but finite number of identical energy-elements ϵ and asked: in how many ways can these energy-elements be divided among the resonators. The logarithm of this number, then, furnishes the entropy and thus (via thermodynamics) the temperature of the system. Planck got his radiation-formula if he chose his energy-elements ϵ of the magnitude $\epsilon = h\nu$. The decisive element in doing this lies in the fact that the result depends on taking for ϵ a definite finite value, i.e., that one does not go to the limit $\epsilon = 0$. This form of reasoning does not make obvious the fact that it contradicts the mechanical and electrodynamic basis, upon which the derivation otherwise depends. Actually, however, the derivation presupposes implicitly that energy can be absorbed and emitted by the individual resonator only in "quanta" of magnitude $h\nu$, i.e., that the energy of a mechanical structure capable of oscillations as well as the energy of radiation can be transferred only in such quanta—in contradiction to the laws of mechanics and electrodynamics. The contradiction with dynamics was here fundamental; whereas the contradiction with electrodynamics could be less fundamental. For the expression for the density of radiation-energy, although it is *compatible* with Maxwell's equations, is not a necessary consequence of these equations. That this expression furnishes important average-values is shown by the fact that the Stefan-Boltzmann law and Wien's law, which are based on it, are in agreement with experience.

All of this was quite clear to me shortly after the appearance of Planck's fundamental work; so that, without having a substitute for classical mechanics, I could nevertheless see to what kind of consequences this law of temperature-radiation leads for the photo-electric effect and for other related phenomena of the transformation of radiation-energy, as well as for the specific heat of (especially) solid bodies. All my attempts, however, to adapt the theoretical foundation of physics to this [new type of] knowledge failed completely. It was as if the ground had been pulled out from under one, with no firm foundation to be seen anywhere, upon which one could have built. That this insecure and contradictory foundation was sufficient to enable a man of Bohr's unique instinct and tact to discover the major laws of the spectral lines and of the electron-shells of the atoms together with their significance for chemistry appeared to me like a miracle—and appears to me as a miracle even today. This is the highest form of musicality in the sphere of thought.

My own interest in those years was less concerned with the detailed consequences of Planck's results, however important these might be. My major question was: What general conclusions can be drawn from the radiation-formula concerning the structure of radiation and even more generally concerning the electro-magnetic foundation of physics? Before I take this up, I must briefly mention a number of investigations which relate to the Brownian motion and related objects (fluctuation-phenomena) and which in essence rest upon classical molecular mechanics. Not acquainted with the earlier investigations of Boltzmann and Gibbs, which had appeared earlier and actually exhausted the subject, I developed the statistical mechanics and the molecular-kinetic theory of thermodynamics which was based on the former. My major aim in this was to find facts which would guarantee as much as possible the existence of atoms of definite finite size. In the midst of this I discovered that, according to atomist theory, there would have to be a movement of suspended microscopic particles open to observation, without knowing that observations concerning the Brownian motion were already long familiar. The simplest derivation rested upon the following consideration. If the molecular-kinetic theory is essentially correct, a suspension of visible particles must possess the same kind of osmotic pressure fulfilling the laws of gases as a solution of molecules. This osmotic pressure depends upon the actual magnitude of the molecules, i.e., upon the number of molecules in a gram-equivalent. If the density of the suspension is inhomogeneous, the osmotic pressure is inhomogeneous, too, and gives rise to a compensating diffusion, which can be calculated from the well-known mobility of the particles. This diffusion can, on the other hand, also be considered as the result of the random displacement—unknown in magnitude originally—of the suspended particles due to thermal agitation. By comparing the amounts obtained for the diffusion current from both types of reasoning one reaches quantitatively the statistical law for those displacements, i.e., the law of the Brownian motion. The agreement of these considerations with experience together with Planck's determination of the true molecular size from the law of radiation (for high temperatures) convinced the sceptics, who were quite numerous at that time (Ostwald, Mach) of the reality of atoms. The antipathy of these scholars towards atomic theory can indubitably be traced back to their positivistic philosophical attitude. This is an interesting example of the fact that even scholars of audacious spirit and fine instinct can be obstructed in the interpretation of facts by philosophical prejudices. The prejudice—which has by no means died out in the meantime—consists in the faith that facts by themselves can and should yield scientific knowledge without free conceptual construction. Such a misconception is possible only because one does not easily become aware of the free choice of such concepts, which, through verification and long usage, appear to be immediately connected with the empirical material.

The success of the theory of the Brownian motion showed again conclusively that classical mechanics always offered trustworthy results whenever it was applied to motions in which the higher time derivatives of velocity are negligibly small. Upon this recognition a relatively direct method can be based which permits us to learn something concerning the constitution of radiation from Planck's formula. One may conclude in fact that, in a space filled with radiation, a (vertically to its plane) freely moving, quasi-monochromatically reflecting mirror would have to go through a kind of Brownian movement, the average kinetic energy of which equals $\frac{1}{2}(R/N)T$ (R = constant of the gas-equation for one gram-molecule, N equals the number of the molecules per mol, T = absolute temperature). If radiation were not subject to local fluctuations, the mirror would gradually come to rest, because, due to its motion, it reflects more radiation on its front than on its reverse side. However, the mirror must experience certain random fluctuations of the pressure exerted upon it due to the fact that the wave-packets, constituting the radiation, interfere with one another. These can be computed from Maxwell's theory. This calculation, then, shows that these pressure variations (especially in the case of small radiation-densities) are by no means sufficient to impart to the mirror the average kinetic energy $\frac{1}{2}(R/N)T$. In order to get this result one has to assume rather that there exists a second type of pressure variations, which can not be derived from Maxwell's theory, which corresponds to the assumption that radiation energy consists of indivisible point-like localized quanta of the energy $h\nu$ (and of momentum ($h\nu/c$), (c — velocity of light)), which are reflected undivided. This way of looking at the problem showed in a drastic and direct way that a type of immediate reality has to be ascribed to Planck's quanta, that radiation must, therefore, possess a kind of molecular structure in energy, which of course contradicts Maxwell's theory. Considerations concerning radiation which are based directly on Boltzmann's entropy-probability-relation (probability taken equal to statistical temporal frequency) also lead to the same result. This double nature of radiation (and of material corpuscles) is a major property of reality, which has been interpreted by quantum-mechanics in an ingenious and amazingly successful fashion. This interpretation, which is looked upon as essentially final by almost all contemporary physicists, appears to me as only a temporary way out; a few remarks to this [point] will follow later.

Reflections of this type made it clear to me as long ago as shortly after 1900, i.e., shortly after Planck's trail-blazing work, that neither mechanics nor thermodynamics could (except in limiting cases) claim exact validity. By and by I despaired of the possibility of discovering the true laws by means of constructive efforts based on known facts. The longer and the more despairingly I tried, the more I came to the conviction that only the discovery of a universal formal principle could lead us to assured results. The example I saw before me was thermodynamics. The general principle was there given in the theorem: the laws of nature are such that it is impossible to construct a *perpetuum mobile* (of the first and second kind). How, then, could such a universal principle be found? After ten years of reflection such a principle resulted from a paradox upon which I had already hit at the age of sixteen: If I pursue a beam of light with the velocity *c* (velocity of light in a vacuum), I should observe such a beam of light as a spatially oscillatory electromagnetic field at rest. However, there seems to be no such thing, whether on the basis of experience or according to Maxwell's equations. From the very beginning it appeared to me intuitively clear that, judged from the standpoint of such an observer, everything would have to happen according to the same laws as for an observer who, relative to the earth, was at rest. For how, otherwise, should the first observer know, i.e., be able to determine that he is in a state of fast uniform motion?

One sees that in this paradox the germ of the special relativity theory is already contained. Today everyone knows, of course, that all attempts to clarify this paradox satisfactorily were condemned to failure as long as the axiom of the absolute character of time, viz., of simultaneity, unrecognizedly was anchored in the unconscious. Clearly to recognize this axiom and its arbitrary character really implies already the solution of the problem. . . .

The Special Theory of Relativity [7]

SPACE AND TIME IN CLASSICAL MECHANICS

THE PURPOSE OF MECHANICS IS to describe how bodies change their position in space with "time." I should load my conscience with grave sins against the sacred spirit of lucidity were I to formulate the aims of mechanics in this way, without serious reflection and detailed explanations. Let us proceed to disclose these sins.

It is not clear what is to be understood here by "position" and "space." I stand at the window of a railway carriage which is travelling uniformly, and drop a stone on the embankment, without throwing it. Then, disregarding the influence of the air resistance, I see the stone descend in a straight line. A pedestrian who observes the misdeed from the footpath notices that the stone falls to earth in a parabolic curve. I now ask: Do the "positions" traversed by the stone lie "in reality" on a straight line or on a parabola? Moreover, what is meant here by motion "in space"? . . . The

---

[7] Einstein, *Relativity: The Special and General Theory*, trans. R. W. Lawson (New York: Henry Holt, 1920), pp. 9–56.

answer is self-evident. In the first place we entirely shun the vague word "space," of which, we must honestly acknowledge, we cannot form the slightest conception, and we replace it by "motion relative to a practically rigid body of reference." . . . If instead of "body of reference" we insert "system of coordinates," which is a useful idea for mathematical description, we are in a position to say: The stone traverses a straight line relative to a system of coordinates rigidly attached to the carriage, but relative to a system of coordinates rigidly attached to the ground (embankment) it describes a parabola. With the aid of this example it is clearly seen that there is no such thing as an independently existing trajectory, but only a trajectory relative to a particular body of reference.

In order to have a *complete* description of the motion, we must specify how the body alters its position *with time; i.e.* for every point on the trajectory it must be stated at what time the body is situated there. These data must be supplemented by such a definition of time that, in virtue of this definition, these time-values can be regarded essentially as magnitudes (results of measurements) capable of observation. If we take our stand on the ground of classical mechanics, we can satisfy this requirement for our illustration in the following manner. We imagine two clocks of identical construction; the man at the railway-carriage window is holding one of them, and the man on the footpath the other. Each of the observers determines the position of his own reference-body occupied by the stone at each tick of the clock he is holding in his hand. In this connection we have not taken account of the inaccuracy involved by the finiteness of the velocity of propagation of light. With this and with a second difficulty prevailing here we shall have to deal in detail later.

THE PRINCIPLE OF RELATIVITY (IN THE RESTRICTED SENSE)

In order to attain the greatest possible clearness, let us return to our example of the railway carriage supposed to be travelling uniformly. We call its motion a uniform translation ("uniform" because it is of constant velocity and direction, "translation" because although the carriage changes its position relative to the embankment yet it does not rotate in so doing). Let us imagine a raven flying through the air in such a manner that its motion, as observed from the embankment, is uniform and in a straight line. If we were to observe the flying raven from the moving railway carriage, we should find that the motion of the raven would be one of different velocity and direction, but that it would still be uniform and in a straight line. Expressed in an abstract manner we may say: If a mass m is moving uniformly in a straight line with respect to a coordinate system K, then it will also be moving uniformly and in a straight line relative to a second coordinate system K', provided that the latter is executing a uniform translatory motion with respect to K. In accordance with the discussion contained in the preceding section,[8] it follows that:

If K is a Galileian coordinate system, then every other coordinate system K' is a Galileian one, when, in relation to K, it is in a condition of uniform motion of translation. Relative to K' the mechanical laws of Galilei-Newton hold good exactly as they do with respect to K.

We advance a step farther in our generalisation when we express the tenet thus: If, relative to K, K' is a uniformly moving coordinate system devoid of rotation, then natural phenomena run their course with respect to K' according to exactly the same general laws as with respect to K. This statement is called the *principle of relativity* (in the restricted sense).

As long as one was convinced that all natural phenomena were capable of representation with the help of classical mechanics, there was no need to doubt the validity of this principle of relativity. But in view of the more recent development of electrodynamics and optics it became more and more evident that classical mechanics affords an insufficient foundation for the physical description of all natural phenomena. At this juncture the question of the validity of the principle of relativity became ripe for discussion, and it did not appear impossible that the answer to this question might be in the negative.

Nevertheless, there are two general facts which at the outset speak very much in favour of the validity of the principle of relativity. Even though classical mechanics does not supply us with a sufficiently broad basis for the theoretical presentation of all physical phenomena, still we must grant it a considerable measure of "truth," since it supplies us with the actual motions of the heavenly bodies with a delicacy of detail little short of wonderful. The principle of relativity must therefore apply with great accuracy in the domain of *mechanics*. But that a principle of such broad generality should hold with such exactness in one domain of phenomena, and yet should be invalid for another, is *a priori* not very probable.

We now proceed to the second argument, to which, moreover, we shall return later. If the principle of relativity (in the restricted sense) does not hold, then the Galileian coordinate systems K, K', K'', etc., which are moving uniformly relative to each other, will not be *equivalent* for the description of natural phenomena. In this case we should be constrained to believe that natural laws are capable of being formulated in a particularly simple manner, and of course only on condition that, from amongst all possible Galileian coordinate systems, we should have chosen *one* (K_0) of a particular state of motion as our body of reference. We should then

---

[8] This section, a discussion of classical coordinate systems, is not included in this excerpt—Editors.

be justified (because of its merits for the description of natural phenomena) in calling this system "absolutely at rest," and all other Galileian
systems K "in motion." If, for instance, our embankment were the system
K_0, then our railway carriage would be a system K, relative to which less
simple laws would hold than with respect to K_0. This diminished simplicity
would be due to the fact that the carriage K would be in motion (*i.e.*
"really") with respect to K_0. In the general laws of nature which have
been formulated with reference to K, the magnitude and direction of the
velocity of the carriage would necessarily play a part. We should expect,
for instance, that the note emitted by an organ-pipe placed with its axis
parallel to the direction of travel would be different from that emitted if
the axis of the pipe were placed perpendicular to this direction. Now in
virtue of its motion in an orbit around the sun, our earth is comparable
with a railway carriage travelling with a velocity of about 30 kilometres
per second. If the principle of relativity were not valid we should therefore
expect that the direction of motion of the earth at any moment would
enter into the laws of nature, and also that physical systems in their behaviour would be dependent on the orientation in space with respect to the
earth. For owing to the alteration in direction of the velocity of revolution
of the earth in the course of a year, the earth cannot be at rest relative to
the hypothetical system K_0 throughout the whole year. However, the most
careful observations have never revealed such anisotropic properties in
terrestrial physical space, *i.e.* a physical non-equivalence of different directions. This is a very powerful argument in favour of the principle of
relativity.

THE RELATIVITY OF SIMULTANEITY

Up to now our considerations have been referred to a particular body of
reference, which we have styled a "railway embankment." We suppose a
very long train travelling along the rails with the constant velocity v and
in the direction indicated in [Fig. 36–1]. People travelling in this train will
with advantage use the train as a rigid reference-body (coordinate system);
they regard all events in reference to the train. Then every event which
takes place along the line also takes place at a particular point of the train.
Also the definition of simultanity can be given relative to the train in
exactly the same way as with respect to the embankment. As a natural consequence, however, the following question arises:

Are two events (*e.g.* the two strokes of lightning A and B) which are
simultaneous *with reference to the railway embankment* also simultaneous
relatively to the train? We shall show directly that the answer must be in
the negative.

When we say that the lightning strokes A and B are simultaneous with respect to the embankment, we mean: the rays of light emitted at the places *A* and *B*, where the lightning occurs, meet each other at the mid-point *M* of the length *A* → *B* of the embankment. But the events *A* and *B* also correspond to positions *A* and *B* on the train. Let *M'* be the mid-point of the distance *A* → *B* on the travelling train. Just when the flashes * of lightning occur, this point *M'* naturally coincides with the point *M*, but it moves towards the right in the diagram with the velocity *v* of the train. If an observer sitting in the position *M'* in the train did not possess this velocity, then he would remain permanently at *M*, and the light rays emitted by the flashes of lightning *A* and *B* would reach him simultaneously, *i.e.* they would meet just where he is situated. Now in reality (considered with reference to the railway embankment) he is hastening towards the beam of light coming from *B*, whilst he is riding on ahead of the beam of light com-

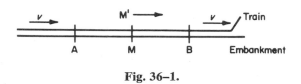

Fig. 36–1.

ing from *A*. Hence the observer will see the beam of light emitted from *B* earlier than he will see that emitted from *A*. Observers who take the railway train as their reference-body must therefore come to the conclusion that the lightning flash *B* took place earlier than the lightning flash *A*. We thus arrive at the important result:

Events which are simultaneous with reference to the embankment are not simultaneous with respect to the train, and *vice versa* (relativity of simultaneity). Every reference-body (coordinate system) has its own particular time; unless we are told the reference-body to which the statement of time refers, there is no meaning in a statement of the time of an event.

Now before the advent of the theory of relativity it had always tacitly been assumed in physics that the statement of time had an absolute significance, *i.e.* that it is independent of the state of motion of the body of reference. But we have just seen that this assumption is incompatible with the most natural definition of simultaneity; if we discard this assumption, then the conflict between the law of the propagation of light *in vacuo* and the principle of relativity disappears.

. . . We concluded that the man in the carriage, who traverses the distance *w per second* relative to the carriage, traverses the same distance also with respect to the embankment *in each second* of time. But, according to the foregoing considerations, the time required by a particular occurrence

---

* As judged from the embankment.

with respect to the carriage must not be considered equal to the duration of the same occurrence as judged from the embankment (as reference-body). Hence it cannot be contended that the man in walking travels the distance *w* relative to the railway line in a time which is equal to one second as judged from the embankment. . . .

THE LORENTZ TRANSFORMATION

. . . The apparent incompatibility of the law of propagation of light with the principle of relativity has been derived by means of a consideration which borrowed two unjustifiable hypotheses from classical mechanics; these are as follows:

(1) The time-interval (time) between two events is independent of the condition of motion of the body of reference.

(2) The space-interval (distance) between two points of a rigid body is independent of the condition of motion of the body of reference.

If we drop these hypotheses, then . . . [the] possibility presents itself that the law of the propagation of light *in vacuo* may be compatible with the principle of relativity, and the question arises: . . . How are we to find the place and time of an event in relation to the train, when we know the place and time of the event with respect to the railway embankment? Is there a thinkable answer to this question of such a nature that the law of transmission of light *in vacuo* does not contradict the principle of relativity? In other words: Can we conceive of a relation between place and time of the individual events relative to both reference-bodies, such that every ray of light possesses the velocity of transmission *c* relative to the embankment and relative to the train? This question leads to a quite definite positive answer, and to a perfectly definite transformation law for the space-time magnitudes of an event when changing over from one body of reference to another.

Before we deal with this, we shall introduce the following incidental consideration. Up to the present we have only considered events taking place along the embankment, which had mathematically to assume the function of a straight line. In the manner indicated [earlier] we can imagine this reference-body supplemented laterally and in a vertical direction by means of a framework of rods, so that an event which takes place anywhere can be localised with reference to this framework. Similarly, we can imagine the train travelling with the velocity *v* to be continued across the whole of space, so that every event, no matter how far off it may be, could also be localised with respect to the second framework. Without committing any fundamental error, we can disregard the fact that in reality these frameworks would continually interfere with each other, owing to the impenetrability of solid bodies. In every such framework we imagine three surfaces perpendicular to each other marked out, and designated as "coordinate planes" ("coordinate system"). A coordinate system K then corresponds to the embankment, and a coordinate system K' to the train. An event, wherever it may have taken place, would be fixed in space with respect to K by the three perpendiculars x, y, z on the coordinate planes, and with regard to time by a time-value t. Relative to K', *the same event* would be fixed in respect of space and time by corresponding values x', y', z', t', which of course are not identical with x, y, z, t. It has already been set forth in detail how these magnitudes are to be regarded as results of physical measurements.

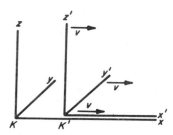

Fig. 36–2.

Obviously our problem can be exactly formulated in the following manner. What are the values x', y', z', t' of an event with respect to K', when the magnitudes x, y, z, t, of the same event with respect to K are given? The relations must be so chosen that the law of the transmission of light *in vacuo* is satisfied for one and the same ray of light (and of course for every ray) with respect to K and K'. For the relative orientation in space of the coordinate systems indicated in the diagram [Fig. 36–2], this problem is solved by means of the equations:

$$x' = \frac{x - vt}{\sqrt{1 - \frac{v^2}{c^2}}}$$

$$y' = y$$
$$z' = z$$

$$t' = \frac{t - \frac{v}{c^2} \cdot x}{\sqrt{1 - \frac{v^2}{c^2}}}.$$

This system of equations is known as the "Lorentz transformation."

If in place of the law of transmission of light we had taken as our basis the tacit assumptions of the older mechanics as to the absolute character of times and lengths, then instead of the above we should have obtained the following equations:

$$x' = x - vt$$
$$y' = y$$
$$z' = z$$
$$t' = t.$$

This system of equations is often termed the "Galilei transformation." The Galilei transformation can be obtained from the Lorentz transformation by substituting an infinitely large value for the velocity of light c in the latter transformation.

Aided by the following illustration, we can readily see that, in accordance with the Lorentz transformation, the law of the transmission of light *in vacuo* is satisfied both for the reference-body K and for the reference-body K'. A light-signal is sent along the positive x-axis, and this light-stimulus advances in accordance with the equation

$$x = ct,$$

i.e. with the velocity c. According to the equations of the Lorentz transformation, this simple relation between x and t involves a relation between x' and t'. In point of fact, if we substitute for x the value ct in the first and fourth equations of the Lorentz transformation, we obtain:

$$x' = \frac{(c - v)t}{\sqrt{1 - \dfrac{v^2}{c^2}}}$$

$$t' = \frac{\left(1 - \dfrac{v}{c}\right)t}{\sqrt{1 - \dfrac{v^2}{c^2}}},$$

from which, by division, the expression

$$x' = ct'$$

immediately follows. If referred to the system K', the propagation of light takes place according to this equation. We thus see that the velocity of transmission relative to the reference-body K' is also equal to c. The same result is obtained for rays of light advancing in any other direction whatsoever. Of course this is not surprising, since the equations of the Lorentz transformation were derived conformably to this point of view.

GENERAL RESULTS OF THE THEORY

It is clear from our previous considerations that the (special) theory of relativity has grown out of electrodynamics and optics. In these fields it has not appreciably altered the predictions of theory, but it has considerably simplified the theoretical structure, *i.e.* the derivation of laws, and—what is incomparably more important—it has considerably reduced the number of independent hypotheses forming the basis of theory. The special theory of relativity has rendered the Maxwell-Lorentz theory so plausible, that the latter would have been generally accepted by physicists even if experiment had decided less unequivocally in its favour.

Classical mechanics required to be modified before it could come into line with the demands of the special theory of relativity. For the main parts, however, this modification affects only the laws of rapid motions, in which the velocities of matter v are not very small as compared with the velocity of light. We have experience of such rapid motions only in the case of electrons and ions; for other motions the variations from the laws of classical mechanics are too small to make themselves evident in practice. We shall not consider the motion of stars until we come to speak of the general theory of relativity. In accordance with the theory of relativity the kinetic energy of a material point of mass m is no longer given by the well-known expression

$$m \frac{v^2}{2},$$

but by the expression

$$\frac{mc^2}{\sqrt{1 - \frac{v^2}{c^2}}}.$$

This expression approaches infinity as the velocity v approaches the velocity of light c. The velocity must therefore always remain less than c, however great may be the energies used to produce the acceleration. If we develop the expression for the kinetic energy in the form of a series, we obtain

$$mc^2 + m \frac{v^2}{2} + \frac{3}{8} m \frac{v^4}{c^2} + \ldots .$$

When $\dfrac{v^2}{c^2}$ is small compared with unity, the third of these terms is always
small in comparison with the second, which last is alone considered in classical mechanics. The first term mc^2 does not contain the velocity, and requires no consideration if we are only dealing with the question as to how the energy of a point-mass depends on the velocity. We shall speak of its essential significance later.

The most important result of a general character to which the special theory of relativity has led is concerned with the conception of mass. Before the advent of relativity, physics recognised two conservation laws of fundamental importance, namely, the law of the conservation of energy and the law of the conservation of mass; these two fundamental laws appeared to be quite independent of each other. By means of the theory of relativity they have been united into one law. We shall now briefly consider how this unification came about, and what meaning is to be attached to it.

The principle of relativity requires that the law of the conservation of energy should hold not only with reference to a coordinate system K, but also with respect to every coordinate system K' which is in a state of uniform motion of translation relative to K, or, briefly, relative to every "Galileian" system of coordinates. In contrast to classical mechanics, the Lorentz transformation is the deciding factor in the transition from one such system to another.

By means of comparatively simple considerations we are led to draw the following conclusion from these premises, in conjunction with the fundamental equations of the electrodynamics of Maxwell: A body moving with the velocity v, which absorbs * an amount of energy E_0 in the form of radiation without suffering an alteration in velocity in the process, has, as a consequence, its energy increased by an amount

$$\frac{E_0}{\sqrt{1 - \dfrac{v^2}{c^2}}}.$$

In consideration of the expression given above for the kinetic energy of the body, the required energy of the body comes out to be

$$\frac{\left(m + \dfrac{E_0}{c^2}\right) c^2}{\sqrt{1 - \dfrac{v^2}{c^2}}}.$$

* E_0 is the energy taken up, as judged from a coordinate system moving with the body.

Thus the body has the same energy as a body of mass

$$\left(m + \frac{E_0}{c^2}\right)$$

moving with the velocity v. Hence we can say: If a body takes up an amount of energy E_0, then its inertial mass increases by an amount E_0/c^2; the inertial mass of a body is not a constant, but varies according to the change in the energy of the body. The inertial mass of a system of bodies can even be regarded as a measure of its energy. The law of the conservation of the mass of a system becomes identical with the law of the conservation of energy, and is only valid provided that the system neither takes up nor sends out energy. Writing the expression for the energy in the form

$$\frac{mc^2 + E_0}{\sqrt{1 - \frac{v^2}{c^2}}},$$

we see that the term mc^2, which has hitherto attracted our attention, is nothing else than the energy possessed by the body * before it absorbed the energy E_0.

A direct comparison of this relation with experiment is not possible at the present time, owing to the fact that the changes in energy E_0 to which we can subject a system are not large enough to make themselves perceptible as a change in the inertial mass of the system. E_0/c^2 is too small in comparison with the mass m, which was present before the alteration of the energy. It is owing to this circumstance that classical mechanics was able to establish successfully the conservation of mass as a law of independent validity.

Let me add a final remark of a fundamental nature. The success of the Faraday-Maxwell interpretation of electromagnetic action at a distance resulted in physicists becoming convinced that there are no such things as instantaneous actions at a distance (not involving an intermediary medium) of the type of Newton's law of gravitation. According to the theory of relativity, action at a distance with the velocity of light always takes the place of instantaneous action at a distance or of action at a distance with an infinite velocity of transmission. This is connected with the fact that the velocity c plays a fundamental rôle in this theory.

ooooooo

---

* As judged from a coordinate system moving with the body.

One of the most important consequences of the special theory of relativity is the equivalence of mass and energy, which Einstein expressed in his famous equation $E = mc^2$. This equation states that if an amount of mass m is transformed into energy by some process or other (for example, by thermonuclear reactions such as occur in stellar interiors or in the explosion of a hydrogen bomb) the amount of energy released is equal to the amount of mass that disappears multiplied by the square of the speed of light. This means we get vast amounts of energy by destroying only small amounts of mass. Of course, every time we obtain energy from any type of chemical reaction, e.g. the burning of coal, some mass is destroyed, but the amount is much too small to be measured. To see how much energy is released when mass is transformed into energy, imagine that just one gram is destroyed. The energy released is 900 million trillion ergs or 20 trillion calories; enough heat to melt about one billion pounds of ice.

In stellar interiors energy is released by a series of thermonuclear reactions in which the nuclei of the light elements are built up into heavier nuclei with a transformation of mass into energy. Thus inside the sun four and a half million tons of mass are transformed into energy every second as the result of a thermonuclear process in which hydrogen is continuously being transformed into helium. But Einstein's mass-energy equivalence relationship is important not only for an understanding of energetic processes, but also for all branches of atomic, nuclear, and high-energy-particle physics. It is interesting, therefore, to see just how this basic equation is derived from fundamental principles.

One can obtain this equation from a straightforward application of the principles of relativistic mechanics to a moving particle, and this is how Einstein derived it originally, shortly after he published his first paper on relativity in 1905. We can see, without going into a detailed, rigorous analysis, why such a relationship between mass and energy must exist if we note that radiation, that is, energy, as has been observed experimentally, exerts a pressure when it strikes a surface. In other words, it exerts a push against the surface. We know from Newton's laws of motion that a push is equivalent to the transference of momentum to the surface at a certain rate. In other words, energy exerts a pressure against a surface because this energy carries momentum with it. But we know that energy and momentum are related to each other through the speed at which the energy moves. This simply means, in the case of light, that its energy divided by its speed (the speed of light c) is just equal to the momentum of the light, which we may write as the mass of the light multiplied by its speed. If we equate these two expressions, we then obtain the mass-energy equation. This, of course, is not a rigorous derivation, but it does indicate the direction of Einstein's thinking when he derived the formula.

In the excerpt from Einstein's later writings he gives a very simple and elegant derivation of the mass-energy formula, which is based on a few elementary properties of light. Among these are the conservation of momentum for light and the aberration of light. This last effect is merely the apparent change in the direction of motion of a beam of light as seen by a moving observer. If an observer is moving at right angles to the direction of propagation of a beam of light, the observer sees the light approaching him from a direction that is slightly tilted (with respect to the true direction of the light) in the direction of the observer's motion. We observe the same phenomenon when running in the rain. If we stand still, and if the rain comes down vertically, we hold our umbrella upright, but if we are running, we must tilt our umbrella forward because the rain appears to come from a slightly forward direction.

To derive the mass-energy equation Einstein considers two pulses of radiation (equal in energy content) impinging from opposite directions on the opposite faces of an absorbing body. He then analyzes the absorption as viewed by an observer fixed with respect to the body and one moving perpendicular to the direction of motion of the radiation. For the fixed observer nothing happens because the actions of the two pulses of light are equal and opposite. But for the moving observer, the aberration of the light introduces a net transfer of momentum to the body at right angles to the motion of the light. However, since the speed of the body as seen by the moving observer must be the same before and after the radiation pulses are absorbed, the transfer of momentum must mean that the mass of the absorbing body is increased to give the additional momentum after the absorption. (Momentum can be increased by either increasing speed or mass.) Thus mass and energy are equivalent. The equation is obtained by applying the principle of the conservation of momentum.

ᴑᴑᴑᴑᴑᴑᴑ

An Elementary Derivation of the Equivalence of Mass and Energy [9]

THE FOLLOWING DERIVATION OF THE law of equivalence, which has not been published before, has two advantages. Although it makes use of the principle of special relativity, it does not presume the formal machinery of the theory but uses only three previously known laws:

---

[9] Einstein, *Out of My Later Years* (New York: Philosophical Library, 1950), pp. 116–119.

(1) The law of the conservation of momentum.
(2) The expression for the pressure of radiation; that is, the momentum of a complex of radiation moving in a fixed direction.
(3) The well-known expression for the aberration of light (influence of the motion of the earth on the apparent location of the fixed stars —Bradley).

We now consider the following system [see Fig. 36–3]. Let the body B rest freely in space with respect to the system K_0. Two complexes of radiation S. S' each of energy $\dfrac{E}{2}$ move in the positive and negative x_0 direction respectively and are eventually absorbed by B. With this absorption the energy of B increases by E. The body B stays at rest with respect to K_0 by reasons of symmetry. [See Fig. 36–4.]

Now we consider this same process with respect to the system K, which moves with respect to K_0 with the constant velocity v in the negative Z_0 direction. With respect to K the description of the process is as follows [see Fig. 36–5]: The body B moves in the positive z direction with velocity v. The two complexes of radiation now have directions with respect to K which make an angle α with the x axis. The law of aberration states that in the first approximation $\alpha = \dfrac{v}{c}$, where c is the velocity of light. From the consideration with respect to K_0 we know that the velocity v of B remains unchanged by the absorption of S and S' [see Fig. 36–6].

Now we apply the law of conservation of momentum with respect to the z direction to our system in the coordinate-frame K.

I. *Before the absorption* let M be the mass of B; Mv is then the expression of the momentum of B (according to classical mechanics). Each of the complexes has the energy $\dfrac{E}{2}$ and hence, by a well-known conclusion of Maxwell's theory, it has the momentum $\dfrac{E}{2c}$. Rigorously speaking this is the momentum of S with respect to K_0. However, when v is small with respect to c, the momentum with respect to K is the same except for a quantity of second order of magnitude $\left(\dfrac{v^2}{c^2} \text{ compared to } 1 \right)$. The z-component of this momentum is $\dfrac{E}{2c} \sin \alpha$ or with sufficient accuracy (except for quantities of higher order of magnitude)

$$\frac{E}{2c} \, \alpha \text{ or } \frac{E}{2} \cdot \frac{v}{c^2}$$

S and S' together therefore have a momentum

$$E \, \frac{v}{c^2}$$

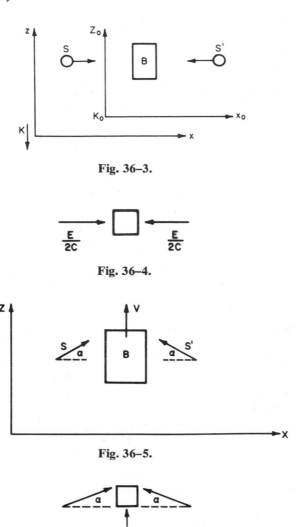

Fig. 36–3.

Fig. 36–4.

Fig. 36–5.

Fig. 36–6.

in the z direction. The total momentum of the system before absorption is therefore

$$Mv + \frac{E}{c^2} \cdot v$$

II. *After the absorption* let M′ be the mass of B. We anticipate here the possibility that the mass increased with the absorption of the energy

E (this is necessary so that the final result of our consideration be consistent). The momentum of the system after absorption is then

$$M'v.$$

We now assume the law of the conservation of momentum and apply it with respect to the z direction. This gives the equation

$$Mv + \frac{E}{c^2} v = M'v$$

or

$$M' - M = \frac{E}{c^2}.$$

This equation expresses the law of the equivalence of energy and mass. The energy increase E is connected with the mass increase $\frac{E}{c^2}$. Since energy according to the usual definition leaves an additive constant free, we may so choose the latter that $E = Mc^2$.

ooooooo

In 1905, when Einstein published the first in his series of great papers on molecular physics, he had just completed the examinations for his doctorate and had already written two other papers on the foundation of thermodynamics and statistical mechanics. At that period of his life, while he was still working as an examiner in the Swiss patent office, he was interested in three branches of physics: molecular physics, radiation theory, and theories of space and time. Although he was out of touch with his contemporaries, and, indeed, with the mainstream of physics, he unerringly surmised that some of the greatest discoveries in physics were to be made in these three fields.

While working on his theory of the photon and on his papers on the special theory of relativity, Einstein saw quite clearly that a deep insight into the behavior of molecular systems could be gained most easily by analyzing such systems statistically. He realized that even without any particular model of a molecule, one can derive the known (observed) macroscopic behavior of molecular systems by applying the laws of statistics to such systems. This field of physics, now called statistical mechanics (of which kinetic theory of gases is a special case) had already been applied by Maxwell and by Boltzmann to gaseous systems; Willard Gibbs had written down the basic equations for systems of particles in liquids as well as the general equations of statistical mechanics. Einstein, however, was not aware of the papers of Gibbs, which had been published in

1901 in a rather obscure journal, and so before doing his work on Brownian motions, he developed the principles of statistical mechanics *ab initio* in two fundamental papers.

In undertaking his analysis of Brownian motion, even before he knew that such notions had been observed long ago, Einstein was prompted by his desire to relate the existence of molecules to some directly observable phenomena that can be explained only in terms of the random motions of molecules. Although kinetic theory had been used by both Maxwell and Boltzmann to derive the laws of perfect gases, there were still many physicists who rejected the molecular concept since there was no direct experimental evidence for the existence of molecules.

Einstein saw in the Brownian motion a way of proving the existence of molecules directly, although when he wrote his first paper on the subject he was not too certain about the exact nature of Brown's discovery.

After the botanist Robert Brown had published his observations of the erratic, irregular motions of fine pollen grains dispersed in water, various theories were advanced to explain this motion, but only M. Gouey in 1888 and F. M. Exner in 1900 attempted precise investigations of the Brownian phenomenon. Although both of these men ascribed the motion to molecular action, their analyses were inadequate and incorrect.

Einstein reasoned that if the observed Brownian motion was caused by the submicroscopic thermal motions of the molecules and that, if this Brownian motion could then be explained by applying statistical laws to molecular motions, two important goals could be achieved: on the one hand, one would have a means of determining the domain of applicability of classical thermodynamics (down to what size particles); on the other hand, one would also have a means of determining, exactly, molecular and atomic dimensions. As Einstein noted in his first paper, ". . . had the prediction of this movement proved to be incorrect a weighty argument would be provided against the molecular-kinetic concept of heat."

In the first paper, Einstein considers the state of equilibrium of suspended particles irregularly dispersed in a liquid. They are subject to a constant force in a given direction, and move about irregularly, owing to the uneven molecular bombardment. He then shows, by applying to the system the second law of thermodynamics (the entropy principle), that the suspended particles can be in equilibrium only if the applied constant force is balanced by the osmotic pressure. From this Einstein concludes that particles suspended in a liquid differ from the molecules of substances dissolved in the liquid only by their size and in no other observable way. Hence, suspended particles diffuse in a liquid just as the molecules of a solute do. By applying this type of reasoning, Einstein then derives an expression for the coefficient of diffusion of the Brownian particles in terms of the coefficient of viscosity of the liquid. He also derives the equation of diffusion, and from this equation expresses the mean displacement of a suspended particle (under the bombardment of the molecules of the liquid) in terms of the coefficient of diffusion.

By introducing the coefficient of diffusion into this expression for the average displacement, he obtains an expression for the average displacement in terms of Avogadro's number (the number of molecules in one mole of substance), the viscosity of the liquid, and the size of a suspended particle. In this way Avogadro's number can be measured directly from the observed viscosity, the observed average displacement of the suspended particles, and the observed sizes of the particles. This was the first observational determination of Avogadro's number.

In later papers, Einstein applied his theory of Brownian motion to various problems in molecular physics, such as the determination of molecular dimensions, problems of diffusion, the departure of the motion of suspended bodies from classical thermodynamics, and so on. All of these papers are marked by their extreme simplicity and deep physical insight. In all the cases that Einstein considered, his results are in complete agreement with observation. These papers were of great importance in the development of physics since they showed quite clearly how powerful the statistical approach is. Einstein used this same statistical analysis later in his theory of the photon and his derivation of the Planck radiation formula, setting a pattern and precedent for his contemporaries and those who followed him.

In this volume we have included an elementary discussion of Brownian motion that Einstein published in 1908 for the benefit of chemists who did not know enough mathematics to follow the original technical papers. He uses elementary algebra and the simple expression for the osmotic pressure—exerted against a membrane by molecules dissolved in a liquid—given by the perfect gas law. Thus, the dissolved molecules are treated like the free molecules of a gas colliding against the semipermeable membrane. Einstein first obtains an expression for the osmotic force exerted on a unit volume of the solute in terms of the temperature and the density gradient of the dissolved molecules. This force is just proportional to the absolute temperature of the solution and the density gradient of the dissolved molecules in the solution. This is equation (1) of Einstein's paper.

This, of course, is what one expects from simple, logical physical arguments, for it is clear that the higher the temperature, the more violent is the random motion of the dissolved molecules; the greater the variation in density in a direction at right angles to the surface of the membrane, the greater will be the drift in that direction. These two factors multiplied together then give the osmotic force.

Einstein next considers the velocity imparted to the dissolved molecules by the osmotic force and obtains an expression for this velocity in terms of the osmotic force. He thus obtains two relationships involving the osmotic force. By dividing one of these equations by the other, he obtains an expression, his equation (4), for the velocity (drift, not random) of the dissolved molecules. He then relates this velocity to the coefficient of diffusion and obtains an expression for the latter, equation (5a), in terms of the viscosity of the solution, the size of the dissolved molecule, and the absolute temperature. From this expression, one can determine the size of a dissolved molecule by measuring the viscosity of the liquid and the rate of diffusion of the solute.

Using the same simple reasoning, Einstein derives an expression for the mean displacement of a molecule in random motion, his equation (8a), and then points out that this same expression gives the displacement of a suspended particle in Brownian motion, since a suspended particle and a dissolved molecule differ only in size.

This paper is an excellent example of Einstein's physical approach to a problem and his remarkable ability to go straight to the heart of a problem with a minimum of mathematical formalism.

ᴓᴓᴓᴓᴓᴓᴓᴓ

The Elementary Theory of the Brownian * Motion [10]

PROF. R. LORENTZ HAS CALLED to my attention that an elementary theory of the Brownian motion would be welcomed by a number of chemists. Acting on this invitation, I present in the following a simple theory of this phenomenon. The train of thought is briefly as follows.

First we investigate how the process of diffusion in an undissociated dilute solution depends on the distribution of osmotic pressure in the solution and on the mobility of the dissolved substance compared to that of the solvent. We thus obtain, if a molecule of the dissolved substance is large compared to that of the solvent, an expression for the coefficient of diffusion which, except for the viscosity of the solute and the diameter of the dissolved molecules, contains no quantities depending on the nature of the solution.

After this we relate the process of diffusion to the irregular motions of the dissolved molecules, and find how the average magnitude of these

---

* We mean by Brownian motion that irregular movement which small particles of microscopic size carry out when suspended in a liquid.

[10] Einstein, *Zeitschrift für Elektrochemie,* 14 (1908), 235–239.

irregular motions of the dissolved molecules can be calculated from the diffusion-coefficient, and therefore, with the help of the results indicated above, from the viscosity of the solvent and the size of the dissolved molecules. The result so obtained holds not only for actual dissolved molecules, but also for any small particles suspended in the liquid.

DIFFUSION AND OSMOTIC PRESSURE

Suppose the cylindrical vessel Z [Fig. 36–7] filled with a dilute solution. The interior of Z is divided by a movable semi-permeable piston k, into two parts A and B. If the concentration of the solution in A is greater than that in B, an exterior force, directed towards the left, must be applied to the piston in order to retain it in equilibrium; this force is in fact equal to the difference of the two osmotic pressures which the dissolved substance exerts on the piston on the left and on the right side

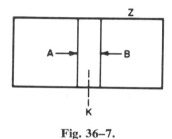

Fig. 36–7.

respectively. If no external force is applied to the piston, it will move under the influence of the greater osmotic pressure of the solution in A so far to the right that the concentrations in A and B no longer differ. From this it follows that the forces of osmotic pressure equalize the concentrations in diffusion; for we can prevent diffusion, that is, an equalization of concentration, by balancing the osmotic differences, which correspond to the differences of concentration, by external forces acting on semi-permeable partitions. It has long been realized that the osmotic pressure can be looked upon as the driving force in diffusion phenomena. Nernst made this the foundation of his investigations into the connection between the ionic mobility diffusion-coefficient, and the E.M.F. in electrolytic cells.

Suppose a diffusion process is taking place within the cylinder Z [Fig. 36–8] of unit cross-section area in the direction of the axis of the cylinder. We investigate first the osmotic forces arising from the motion of diffusion of the dissolved substance between the planes E and E' separated by the infinitesimal distance dx. The osmotic force p acts on the surface E

of the layer from left to right, the force p' acts on the surface E' from right to left; the resultant force is therefore

$$p - p'$$

We now call x the distance of the surface E from the left end of the vessel, $x + dx$ the distance of the surface E' from that end; then dx is the volume of the layer of liquid in question. Since $p - p'$ is the osmotic pressure which acts on the volume dx of the dissolved substance, then

$$K = \frac{p - p'}{dx} = -\frac{p' - p}{dx} = -\frac{dp}{dx}$$

is the osmotic pressure, which acts on the dissolved substance per unit volume. Since, further, the osmotic pressure is given by the equation

$$p = RT\nu$$

where R is the constant of the gas-equation ($8 \cdot 31 \; . \; 10^7$), T the absolute temperature, and ν the number of gram-molecules of solute per unit vol-

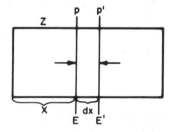

Fig. 36–8.

ume, we get, finally, for the osmotic force K acting on the dissolved substance per unit volume the expression

$$K = -RT\frac{d\nu}{dx}. \tag{1}$$

Now, to calculate the motions of diffusion, which these active forces can induce, we must know how great a resistance the solvent offers to movements of the dissolved molecules. If a force K acts on a molecule, it imparts to the molecule a proportional velocity v, according to the equation

$$v = \frac{K}{R}, \tag{2}$$

where **R** is a constant, which we call the frictional resistance of the molecule. This frictional resistance cannot in general be deduced theoretically. But if the dissolved molecule may be taken approximately to be a sphere, which is large compared with a molecule of the solvent, we may ascertain the frictional resistance of the solute molecule according to the methods of ordinary hydrodynamics, which do not take account of the molecular constitution of the liquid. Within the limits of valid application of ordinary hydrodynamics, for a sphere moving in a liquid the equation (2) holds, where we put

$$\mathbf{R} = 6\pi\eta\rho \tag{3}$$

Here η denotes the coefficient of viscosity of the liquid, ρ the radius of the sphere. If we may assume that the molecules of a solute are approximately spherical and are large compared with the molecules of the solvent, equation (3) may be applied to the individual dissolved molecules.

We can now estimate the mass of solute diffusing across the cylinder per unit of time since there are ν gram-molecules in the unit volume, there are νN molecules in this volume where N is the number of molecules in a gram-molecule. If a force K is distributed over these νN molecules, it imparts to these a νN-times smaller velocity than it is able to impart to a single molecule, if acting on the latter alone. Reverting to equation (2): for the velocity v, which the force K is able to impart to the νN molecules, we obtain the expression

$$v = \frac{1}{\nu N} \cdot \frac{K}{\mathbf{R}}$$

In the case under consideration, K is equal to the osmotic force previously calculated, which acts on the νN molecules in a unit volume; we thus obtain from the above, using equation (1),

$$v\nu = -\frac{RT}{N} \cdot \frac{1}{\mathbf{R}} \cdot \frac{d\nu}{dx} \tag{4}$$

On the left-hand side we have the product of the concentration ν of the solute, and of the velocity, with which the latter is moved forward by the process. This product therefore gives the mass of the dissolved substance (in gram-molecules) which is carried per second by diffusion across a unit area of the piston. The multiplier of $d\nu/dx$ on the right-hand side of this equation is therefore (*) just the coefficient of diffusion D of the solution in question. We have, therefore, in general

$$D = \frac{RT}{N} \cdot \frac{1}{\mathbf{R}} \tag{5}$$

* It is to be noted that the numerical value of the coefficient of diffusion is independent of the unit taken for concentration.

and if the diffusing molecules may be taken as spherical, and large compared to the molecules of the solvent, introducing equation (3),

$$D = \frac{RT}{N} \cdot \frac{1}{6\pi\eta\rho} \qquad (5a)$$

In the last case, therefore, the coefficient of diffusion depends upon no constants characteristic of the substance in question other than the viscosity η of the solvent and the radius ρ of the molecule.*

DIFFUSION AND IRREGULAR MOTION OF THE MOLECULES

The molecular theory of heat affords a second point of view, from which the process of diffusion can be considered. The irregular molecular motion which we conceive of as the heat-content of a substance is such that the individual molecules of a liquid alter their positions in the most irregular manner thinkable. This wandering about of the molecules of the solute—fortuitous to a certain extent—in a solution gradually changes an originally non-uniform distribution of concentration of the solute into a uniform one.

We now examine this process somewhat more intimately, whilst we confine ourselves again to the case considered in [the first section], fixing our attention on the diffusion in one direction only, namely, in the direction of the axis (x-axis) of the cylinder Z.

We imagine that we know the x co-ordinates of all solute molecules at a certain time t, and also at the time $t + \tau$, where τ is so short that the concentration of our solution alters only very slightly during this interval. During this time τ the x co-ordinate of the first solute molecule will have changed, through the irregular thermal motion, by a certain amount Δ_1, that of the second molecule by Δ_2, etc. These displacements, Δ_1, Δ_2, etc., are partly negative (towards the left), partly positive (towards the right). The magnitudes of these displacements are in general different for the individual molecules. But since, as before, we presuppose a dilute solution, each displacement is determined only by the surrounding solvent, and not to a sensible extent by the rest of the solute molecules; hence, in parts of the solution with different concentrations these displacements Δ

---

* From this equation we can deduce the radius of large molecules approximately from the coefficient of diffusion, when the latter is known; thus

$$\rho = \frac{RT}{6\pi N\eta} \cdot \frac{1}{D}$$

where $R = 8\cdot31 . 10^7$, $N = 6 . 10^{23}$. Of course, a degree of uncertainty of some 50 per cent is involved in the value of N. This relation should be of importance for the determination of the approximate dimensions of the molecules in colloidal solutions.

are on the average of equal magnitude, and just as frequently positive as negative.

We shall now see how large a mass of solute diffuses in the time τ through unit cross-section area of a solution, when the magnitude of the displacement Δ in the direction of the axis of the cylinder, which the solute molecules experience on an average is known. To simplify this investigation, we assume that all the molecules experience an equally large displacement Δ, with one-half of the molecules having the displacement $+\Delta$ (i.e. to the right), and the other half the displacement $-\Delta$ (i.e. to the left). We therefore replace the individual displacements Δ_1, Δ_2, etc., by their mean value Δ.

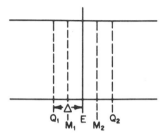

Fig. 36–9.

With these simplified assumptions, only those solute molecules can pass from left to right across a plane E or our cylinder [Fig. 36–9] during the time τ, which before the time τ were situated to the left of E, at a distance from E less than Δ. These molecules all lie between the planes Q_1 and E [Fig. 36–9]. But since only half of these molecules experience the displacement $+\Delta$, only half of them pass across the plane E. Half the solute situated between Q_1 and E when expressed in gram-molecules, is equal to

$$\frac{1}{2} \nu_1 \Delta,$$

where ν_1 is the mean concentration in the volume Q_1E, i.e. the concentration in the middle layer M_1. Since the cross-section is unity, Δ is the volume included between Q_1 and E, which, when multiplied by the mean concentration, gives the amount of the solute in gram-molecules in this volume.

By similar reasoning, it follows that the mass of solute which passes across E from right to left in the time τ is equal to

$$\frac{1}{2} \nu_2 \Delta$$

where v_2 is the concentration in the middle layer M_2. The quantity of substance which diffuses across from left to right during the time τ is then obviously equal to the difference of these two expressions, therefore equal to

$$\frac{1}{2}\Delta(v_1 - v_2) \tag{6}$$

v_1 and v_2 are the concentrations in two cross-sections which are separated by the very small distance Δ. Again, if we denote by x the distance of a cross-section from the left cylinder-end, we have

$$\frac{v_2 - v_1}{\Delta} = \frac{dv}{dx}$$

or

$$v_1 - v_2 = -\Delta\frac{dv}{dx}$$

so that the quantity of the substance which diffuses across E during time τ is also equal to

$$-\frac{1}{2}\Delta^2\frac{dv}{dx} \tag{6a}$$

The amount of solute (expressed in gram-molecules) which diffuses across E in a unit of time is therefore

$$-\frac{1}{2}\frac{\Delta^2}{\tau}\frac{dv}{dx}$$

We have thereby obtained a second value for the coefficient of diffusion D. It is

$$D = \frac{1}{2}\frac{\Delta^2}{\tau}, \tag{7}$$

where Δ signifies the length of path described on the average (*) by a solute molecule during the time τ in the direction of the x-axis.

Solving equation (7) for Δ, we obtain

$$\Delta = \sqrt{2D}\sqrt{\tau} \tag{7a}$$

---

* More accurately, Δ should be put equal to the square root of the mean of the squares of the individual displacements $\Delta_1{}^2$, $\Delta_2{}^2$, etc. We should therefore write, with greater accuracy, $\sqrt{\overline{\Delta^2}}$ in place of Δ.

MOVEMENT OF THE SINGLE MOLECULES: BROWNIAN MOTION

If in equation (7a) we substitute the value of D from equation (5), we obtain,

$$\Delta = \sqrt{\frac{2RT}{NR}} \; \sqrt{\tau} \tag{8}$$

We see from this formula that the path described by a molecule on the average is not proportional to the time, but proportional to the square root of the time. This follows because the paths described during two consecutive unit time-intervals are not always to be added, but just as frequently have to be subtracted. We can now calculate the displacement of the molecule resulting on an average from the irregular molecular motion: either from equation (7a) using the coefficient of diffusion, or from equation (8) using the resistance $\mathbf{R}$ which is offered to force motion of velocity $v = 1$.

If the solute molecule is spherical and large compared to the molecule of the solvent, we can put the value of $\mathbf{R}$ given in equation (3) in equation (8), and obtain

$$\Delta = \sqrt{\frac{RT}{N} \cdot \frac{1}{3\pi\eta\rho}} \; \sqrt{\tau} \tag{8a}$$

With this equation we can calculate the mean displacement Δ * from the temperature T, the viscosity of the solute η, and the radius ρ of the molecule.

According to the molecular kinetic conception, there is no essential difference between a solute molecule and a suspended particle. We therefore consider equation (8a) as also valid for any kind of small suspended spherical particles.

We calculate the length of path Δ which a particle of 1μ diameter describes on the average in one second in a certain direction in water at room temperature. We have to put

$$
\begin{array}{ll}
R = 831 \times 10^7 & \eta = 0.0135 \\
T = 290 & \rho = 0.5 \cdot 10^{-4} \\
N = 6 \cdot 10^{23} & \tau = 1.
\end{array}
$$

We obtain

$$\Delta = 0.8 \times 10^{-4} \text{cm} = 0.8\mu$$

---

* More accurately the square root of the mean value of Δ^2.

This number is subject to an error of some $\pm$ 25 per cent. on account of the limited degree of accuracy with which N is known.

It is of interest to compare the mean individual motions of microscopic particles calculated in this manner, with those of solute molecules and of ions respectively. For an undissociated dissolved substance, whose co-efficient of diffusion is known, we can calculate Δ from equation (7a). For sugar at room temperature

$$D = \frac{0.33}{24 \cdot 60 \cdot 60}.$$

Hence we obtain from equation (7a) for $\tau = 1$

$$\Delta = 27.6\mu.$$

One can deduce from the number N and the molecular volume of solid sugar that the diameter of a molecule of sugar is of the order of magnitude of 1 $\mu\mu$, therefore about a thousand times smaller than the diameter of the particle considered above. From the equation (8a) we must therefore expect that Δ for sugar will be about $\sqrt{1000}$ times greater than for the particles of 1 μ diameter. This is actually approximately correct, as can be seen.

From the equation (8) we can calculate the value of l for ions from their velocity of migration. l is equal to the quantity of electricity in coulombs, which passes across a square centimeter in one second for a concentration $v = 1$ of the ion in question, and for a potential gradient of 1 volt per centimeter. In our case the velocity v of the ionic motion (in cm./sec.) is evidently determined by the equation

$$l = v \cdot 96,000.$$

Since, further, 1 volt is equivalent to 10^8 electromagnetic units, and the charge of a (univalent) ion is equal to $9600/N$ electromagnetic units, the force K acting on one ion in this case is

$$K = \frac{10^8 \cdot 9600}{N}.$$

If we put in equation (2) this value of K, and the value of v obtained in the former equation,

$$v = \frac{l}{96,000}.$$

we get

$$\mathbf{R} = \frac{K}{v} = \frac{10^8 \cdot 9600 \cdot 96{,}000}{lN}.$$

This expression also holds, with the usual definition of l, for polyvalent ions. Introducing this value for $\mathbf{R}$ in equation (8), we get

$$\Delta = 4.25 \cdot 10^{-5} \sqrt{lT\tau}$$

The formula gives for room temperature, and $\tau = 1$. [See Table 36–1.]

TABLE 36–1

Ion	l	s
H	300	125μ
K	65	58μ
Diisoamyl-ammonium, $C_{10}H_{24}N$	24	35μ

ⴰⴰⴰⴰⴰⴰⴰ

Although the gravitational force is the weakest of all the forces known in nature and therefore plays a negligible role in the dynamics of an atom, we have included a discussion of general relativity in this volume because it must ultimately be taken into account if a correct picture of the structure of fundamental particles, such as electrons and protons, is to be obtained. In spite of its being so small, the gravitational force is the most ubiquitous of all the forces and is a property, not only of material particles such as electrons, but also of photons and neutrinos. Moreover, as we penetrate into a particle, we may expect the gravitational force to become more and more important, and finally to dominate all other forces and play a very important role in the particle's interior.

In addition to this, there is a cosmological aspect of the structure of matter which can be understood only if the gravitational properties of the universe are understood. Many physicists have long felt that the existence of electrons and protons is but one aspect of the much larger problem of the structure of the universe, and that these basic particles must, somehow or other, be derivable from a single unified theory which gives not only the gravitational field, but all the other force fields associated with the known particles of nature.

Finally, the argument that the gravitational force is small, and therefore need not be considered in atomic theories, is valid only to the extent that one wishes to obtain numbers from the theory that are in good agreement with present observations. But we know from the previous crises in physics that new conceptual developments must be sought at the very borderline of the observations. In time, as observational techniques improve, we may hope to detect the contribution of the gravitational force to the dynamics of the atom; any departure of observation from theory will be an important indicator of the new direction that theory will have to take. Even now, physicists are introducing a quantum-mechanical version of Einstein's gravitational field equations. In what follows we discuss Einstein's theory of gravitation (the general theory of relativity) from the classical point of view, as it was originally proposed by Einstein, and not from the quantum-mechanical viewpoint.

Of the many remarkable theories concerning the nature of matter and the structure of the universe that have been developed in the twentieth century, the most astounding is probably the general theory of relativity as propounded by Einstein. As the creation of a single mind, it is undoubtedly the highest intellectual achievement of mankind. For the first time in the history of science the geometry of space-time and the laws of nature were demonstrated as interdependent. That the theory was immediately recognized as an amazing departure from the traditions of physics is indicated by Arnold Sommerfeld's reaction to a letter he received one day from Einstein. In this letter, Einstein communicates great excitement on discovering that he could deduce the observed perihelion motion of Mercury, which could never be explained by Newtonian theory, as well as Newton's theory of gravitation itself, as a first approximation from a non-Euclidean description of space-time in the neighborhood of matter. On reading this, Sommerfeld was amazed. He wrote back that he was incredulous and could hardly believe such a result possible. To this letter, Einstein sent the following reply, on a postcard dated February 1916:

"Of the General Theory of Relativity you will be convinced, once you have studied it. Therefore I am not going to defend it with a single word."

The great mathematician Hermann Weyl stated in the preface of his book *Space, Time and Matter* that "Einstein's Theory of Relativity has advanced our ideas of the structure of the cosmos a step further. It is as if a wall which separated us from Truth has collapsed."

Weyl's statement was quite prophetic, for already the general theory has unraveled many snarls in the realm of cosmology and has given us a consistent and powerful means of investigating the nature and structure of the universe. Moreover, it is becoming increasingly obvious that Einstein's theory is indispensable in studying the extreme states of matter that are found in very dense stars such as white dwarfs and the so-called hyperon stars. It has become evident that no acceptable scheme of the structure of fundamental particles, such as electrons, can be depicted without ultimately introducing the concept of general relativity.

Let us now examine the basis of the General Theory of Relativity and just what led Einstein to this geometrical formulation of one of the most important laws of nature—the law of gravity. First, we should reconsider the Special Theory of Relativity and see why Einstein found it necessary to extend or generalize this earlier statement of the principle of relativity. In the special theory, Einstein pointed out that if no gravitational fields are present and if the observers under consideration are not accelerated, all inertial frames of reference (that is, all frames of reference that are moving with constant velocities with respect to one another) are equivalent and equally permissible for expressing the laws of nature. In other words, there can be no absolute frame of reference, such as a stationary ether, in our universe in which the laws of nature assume an especially simple or correct form. This means, taken together with the constancy of the speed of light, that absolute time, absolute space, and absolute motion must be discarded. Only the space-time continuum described by a four-dimensional space-time geometry is absolute.

From this, we begin to see why Einstein called this the Special or Restricted Theory of Relativity and why he found it necessary to develop a more general version. According to the special theory, all inertial frames of reference are equivalent to the eyes of nature. Yet these inertial frames, as a group, are singled out from all other frames of reference, such as those of accelerated systems, as the correct ones in which to formulate the laws of physics. Now since inertial frames alone are employed, one should be able to formulate the law of gravity so that it is the same in all such frames.

But Einstein quickly saw that this is impossible. The special theory shows that the inertial mass of a body, that is, the mass that resists the action of forces and is also responsible for the apparent "inertial forces" that arise from acceleration, varies with speed so that it is different in different inertial frames. But we know from experiment that the inertial mass of a body is exactly equal to its gravitational mass (the mass that is responsible for the weight of a body). This means that the gravitational mass of a body varies from inertial frame to inertial frame, and, since the gravitational force depends on the gravitational masses of bodies, there is no way to formulate a law of gravity that has the same form in all inertial systems. Einstein therefore gave up the attempt to incorporate the gravitational field into special relativity, and set out to extend his principle so that gravitational forces could be incorporated into it.

In this attempt to generalize, he was guided by the very condition that made special relativity invalid for gravitation, namely, the equality of inertial and gravitational mass. This equality leads to the famous principle of equivalence, which is the starting point of Einstein's derivation of the General Theory of Relativity. We recall that as long as inertial frames of reference are given special preference in nature, gravity cannot be represented in the framework of relativity; this is because the gravitational field induces accelerations in bodies, so that there is no inertial frame in which a body in a gravitational field can be considered as moving with uniform motion. Einstein therefore saw the need to generalize the theory so that no particular frame of reference or set of frames would be given preference over other frames. We shall now see how Einstein used the principle of equivalence to do this.

If noninertial frames of reference, such as accelerated frames (rotating coordinates, for example), are to be put on a par with inertial frames in describing nature, then there should be no physical way of distinguishing between inertial frames and accelerated frames. This at once seems contrary to our experience. For everybody knows when he is in an accelerated system; he can feel himself being "pushed or pulled" as the velocity of the frame of reference, let us say a train, changes as the result of the acceleration. The principle of equivalence allowed Einstein to solve this enigma. He reasoned that since inertial mass and gravitational mass are equal, all bodies in a gravitational field behave as though they were really not in a gravitational field, but instead were reacting inertially to the acceleration of a noninertial frame of reference; whereas all bodies reacting inertially in accelerated systems behave as though they were not in accelerated systems but in gravitational fields.

In other words, the equality of inertial and gravitational mass implies that inertial and gravitational forces are indistinguishable; therefore, according to Einstein, these forces must be treated as equals as long as we are dealing with very small regions of space. Thus, in any small enclosure there is no experimental way of distinguishing between gravitational forces and forces arising from accelerations of the entire enclosure. This may be interpreted in another way by saying that in any small region of space it is always possible to eliminate a gravitational field through an appropriate acceleration of the system (for example, by means of a freely falling elevator or an orbiting space capsule). This is the famous principle of equivalence.

Therefore, in small regions of a gravitational field, objects may behave as they do in a region free of gravitation if one introduces in place of an inertial coordinate system a coordinate system that is accelerated with respect to the inertial system. Conversely, by means of acceleration one can reproduce in a field-free space the effects that are found in an inertial system at rest in a gravitational field. Therefore both frames of reference are equally valid for the description of nature. Indeed, this means not only that inertial and noninertial frames of reference are equally valid, but that the concept of absolute acceleration and that of a gravitational force are no longer tenable, since what one observer may take as a gravitational force is just as validly perceived as an inertial force by another observer. Therefore the basic demand of the special theory of relativity, invariance of the laws under the Lorentz transformation, is too narrow. Invariance of the laws must be postulated relative to non-linear transformations of the coordinates in the four-dimensional continuum.

Einstein acknowledges that the condition imposed by his special theory of relativity is invalid. He had assumed that mathematical descriptions of nature were to be taken as laws only if their forms remain unchanged in going from one inertial frame of reference to another by way of a Lorentz transformation. But he recognized that this was not the case when one deals with gravitational fields or accelerated—for example, rotating—systems. To take into account gravitational fields and accelerated systems, one must require that the mathematical expressions for the laws of nature remain unchanged if we pass from one frame of reference to any other frame by the most general type of coordinate transformation we can imagine.

To see how this led Einstein to his mathematical formulation of the general theory we shall consider first the physical significance of the principle of equivalence and the principle of general covariance, that is, the invariance of the laws of nature under general transformations. Since the principle of equivalence asserts that no distinction can be made between an observer in an inertial frame in a gravitational field and an observer in an accelerated frame in field-free space, the whole idea of an absolute gravitational force between two bodies is untenable, so that gravity must be treated in some other way. For if we discard the idea of gravitational forces, we run into difficulty with Newton's laws of motion: we know that a body moving in a gravitational field does not travel in a straight line, and hence, according to Newton's first law of motion, must be under the action of a force. But the principle of equivalence denies the existence of such a force, so that Einstein appears to be up against a contradiction.

Einstein overcame this obstacle by altering Newton's first law of motion; he removed from it any reference to forces. We remember that Newton's first law states that a body moves in a straight line with constant speed unless a force acts on it. In other words, the presence of a force acting on a body is indicated by the departure from straight-line motion. But we can get away from the difficulty by stating that the departure from straight-line motion (straight in the Euclidean sense) is not due to a force but to a difference in the geometry. In other words, we replace the usual statement of Newton's first law by the statement that a body that is free to move, that is, not in contact with any other body or subjected to electromagnetic forces, will move in a "straight line" characteristic of the geometry of the space in which it is moving. If a gravitational field is present, the geometry of the space is not Euclidean and a straight path is curved as represented in Euclidean space. This means that what Newton called a gravitational force is to be considered as the manifestation of the non-Euclidean character of space. In this way Einstein was led to his geometrical interpretation of gravitation.

In carrying out his program of geometrizing gravitation, Einstein was guided by what he had already done in special relativity, for he knew that the general theory would have to be an extension of the special theory. Moreover, he was aided by the analogy between what he planned and Gauss's theory of surfaces. The Special Theory of Relativity grew out of the need to replace the hitherto separate three-dimensional space manifold and the one-dimensional time manifold by a single four-dimensional space-time manifold (a space-time interval) that is the same for all observers moving in inertial frames of reference. Time and space in special relativity theory are merged into a single four-dimensional space-time manifold by a natural extension of the theorem of Pythagoras from three to four dimensions. This was done by considering the separation between two events in space and time and merging these separate space and time intervals into a single space-time interval in four-dimensional geometry.

If, then, one is treating conditions governed by the special theory (inertial frames of reference and no gravitational fields), the space-time interval that one obtains is essentially the theorem of Pythagoras in four-dimensional Euclidean space, so that we may say that the Special Theory of Relativity is given by the geometry of four-dimensional Euclidean, or flat space. Recognizing this, Einstein at once suspected that one could obtain a general theory of relativity that would take into account gravitational fields and accelerated frames of reference by replacing the four-dimensional Euclidean geometry of space-time by a suitable four-dimensional non-Euclidean geometry. In this he was guided by the following consideration. If we consider a flat two-dimensional surface and allow a particle to move freely on it, the particle will move along a straight line. However, if we have a two-dimensional curved surface along which a particle is constrained to move, the particle naturally moves in a curved orbit, following the curvature of the surface itself. It follows, then, that we may compare a particle moving freely (relative to an inertial frame) in space free of gravitational fields to the particle on the flat surface, and a particle moving freely in a gravitational field, or relative to a noninertial frame, to the particle moving on the curved surface. All that was required then, for a generalization of the theory that would account for gravitational fields and noninertial frames, was to replace the four-dimensional Euclidean space-time interval of special relativity theory with a non-Euclidean four-dimensional space-time interval.

To do this, Einstein used the theory of surfaces that had been developed by Gauss and then extended to many dimensions by one of Gauss's most famous students, Riemann. Einstein showed that by using the appropriate mathematics (the tensor calculus) it is possible to obtain a set of geometrical quantities in four-dimensional space that describes the non-Euclidean properties of this space and at the same time describes the behavior of masses in gravitational fields or in accelerated frames of reference. The mathematical properties of the real gravitational field or of fields generated by accelerated frames of reference (for example, a rotating frame of reference) are contained in a set of tensor equations that are referred to as Einstein's field equations. Einstein showed that, to a first approximation, these field equations give Newton's law of gravity.

Although one must solve Einstein's field equations to see exactly how a mass moves in a gravitational field (this was first done in 1917 by K. Schwarzschild for planetary motion around the sun), Einstein derived the various effects by applying the principle of equivalence. In the excerpt from his book reproduced here, Einstein applies the principle of equivalence to a rotating disk to show that for an observer on such a disk the geometry is of the hyperbolic non-Euclidean kind. It is easy to see why this is so since rods and clocks placed at various points on the disk travel at different speeds and thus contract and slow down by different amounts.

In the case of a body in a gravitational field, the principle of equivalence can also be applied, since gravitational fields can be duplicated by appropriately accelerated frames of reference. One sees what happens in a gravitational field by simply applying the contraction of rods and the slowing down of clocks to observers in frames of reference that are allowed to fall freely in gravitational fields. In this way, such things as the bending of beams of light, the slowing down of clocks, the shrinking of rulers, and so on in gravitational fields can be derived.

To see how the principle of equivalence is used, we apply it to a ray of light grazing the sun. Since, according to this principle, the gravitational field of the sun may be reproduced by an elevator being accelerated away from the sun with the same acceleration that a freely falling body has on the sun, we may see how the gravitational field of the sun affects the ray of light by allowing it to pass through the accelerated elevator.

An observer in this elevator would see the light entering one side of the elevator at a certain height above the floor. But, by the time the light moved across the elevator, the elevator would have accelerated upward, so that to the observer it would appear that the light had accelerated— that is, had fallen downward. Thus, light must fall in a gravitational field. Hence, the sun bends a ray of light that is grazing it. This has been verified in many solar eclipses.

What is remarkable about Einstein's treatment of the gravitational problem is not the brilliance of the mathematics or the clever and sophisticated use of physics, but rather his deep insight into the very heart of the matter and his intuitive knowledge that the gravitational field must be related to non-Euclidean geometry. As in all of his papers, here, too, where a very sophisticated type of mathematics is required for a rigorous analysis of the problem, Einstein obtained his final results with a simple algebraic analysis of elementary physical processes. One is always amazed, and particularly so in this case, at the daring qualities of Einstein's generalizations and his unerring penetration to the heart of a problem.

ᴑᴑᴑᴑᴑᴑᴑᴑ

The General Theory of Relativity [11]

ALL OF THE PREVIOUS CONSIDERATIONS[12] have been based upon the assumption that all inertial systems are equivalent for the description of physical phenomena, but that they are preferred, for the formulation of the laws of nature, to spaces of reference in a different state of motion. We can think of no cause for this preference for definite states of motion to all others, according to our previous considerations, either in the perceptible bodies or in the concept of motion; on the contrary, it must be regarded as an independent property of the space-time continuum. The principle of inertia, in particular, seems to compel us to ascribe physically objective properties to the space-time continuum. Just as it was consistent from the Newtonian standpoint to make both the statements, *tempus est absolutum, spatium est absolutum,* so from the standpoint of the special theory of relativity we must say, *continuum spatii et temporis est absolutum.* In this latter statement *absolutum* means not only "physically real," but also "independent in its physical properties, having a physical effect, but not itself influenced by physical conditions."

As long as the principle of inertia is regarded as the keystone of physics,

---

[11] Einstein, *The Meaning of Relativity* (Princeton, N. J.: Princeton University Press, 1953), pp. 55–63.

[12] Here Einstein refers to the considerations that led to the Special Theory.

this standpoint is certainly the only one which is justified. But there are two serious criticisms of the ordinary conception. In the first place, it is contrary to the mode of thinking in science to conceive of a thing (the space-time continuum) which acts itself, but which cannot be acted upon. This is the reason why E. Mach was led to make the attempt to eliminate space as an active cause in the system of mechanics. According to him, a material particle does not move in unaccelerated motion relatively to space, but relatively to the centre of all the other masses in the universe; in this way the series of causes of mechanical phenomena was closed, in contrast to the mechanics of Newton and Galileo. In order to develop this idea within the limits of the modern theory of action through a medium, the properties of the space-time continuum which determine inertia must be regarded as field properties of space, analogous to the electromagnetic field. The concepts of classical mechanics afford no way of expressing this. For this reason Mach's attempt at a solution failed for the time being. We shall come back to this point of view later. In the second place, classical mechanics exhibits a deficiency which directly calls for an extension of the principle of relativity to spaces of reference which are not in uniform motion relatively to each other. The ratio of the masses of two bodies is defined in mechanics in two ways which differ from each other fundamentally; in the first place, as the reciprocal ratio of the accelerations which the same motive force imparts to them (inert mass), and in the second place, as the ratio of the forces which act upon them in the same gravitational field (gravitational mass). The equality of these two masses, so differently defined, is a fact which is confirmed by experiments of very high accuracy (experiments of Eötvös), and classical mechanics offers no explanation for this equality. It is, however, clear that science is fully justified in assigning such a numerical equality only after this numerical equality is reduced to an equality of the real nature of the two concepts.

That this object may actually be attained by an extension of the principle of relativity, follows from the following consideration. A little reflection will show that the law of the equality of the inert and the gravitational mass is equivalent to the assertion that the acceleration imparted to a body by a gravitational field is independent of the nature of the body. For Newton's equation of motion in a gravitational field, written out in full, is

$$\text{(Inert mass)} \cdot \text{(Acceleration)} = \text{(Intensity of the gravitational field)} \cdot \text{(Gravitational mass)}.$$

It is only when there is numerical equality between the inert and gravitational mass that the acceleration is independent of the nature of the body. Let now K be an inertial system. Masses which are sufficiently far from each other and from other bodies are then, with respect to K, free from acceleration. We shall also refer these masses to a system of coordinates K', uniformly accelerated with respect to K. Relatively to K' all the masses have equal and parallel accelerations; with respect to K' they behave just as if a gravitational field were present and K' were unaccelerated. Overlooking for the present the question as to the "cause" of such a gravitational field, which will occupy us later, there is nothing to prevent our conceiving this gravitational field as real, that is, the conception that K' is "at rest" and a gravitational field is present we may consider as equivalent to the conception that only K is an "allowable" system of coordinates and no gravitational field is present. The assumption of the complete physical equivalence of the systems of coordinates, K and K', we call the "principle of equivalence;" this principle is evidently intimately connected with the law of the equality between the inert and the gravitational mass, and signifies an extension of the principle of relativity to coordinate systems which are in non-uniform motion relatively to each other. In fact, through this conception we arrive at the unity of the nature of inertia and gravitation. For according to our way of looking at it, the same masses may appear to be either under the action of inertia alone (with respect to K) or under the combined action of inertia and gravitation (with respect to K'). The possibility of explaining the numerical equality of inertia and gravitation by the unity of their nature gives to the general theory of relativity, according to my conviction, such a superiority over the conceptions of classical mechanics, that all the difficulties encountered must be considered as small in comparison with this progress.

What justifies us in dispensing with the preference for inertial systems over all other coordinate systems, a preference that seems so securely established by experience? The weakness of the principle of inertia lies in this, that it involves an argument in a circle: a mass moves without acceleration if it is sufficiently far from other bodies; we know that it is sufficiently far from other bodies only by the fact that it moves without acceleration. Are there at all any inertial systems for very extended portions of the space-time continuum, or, indeed, for the whole universe? We may look upon the principle of inertia as established, to a high degree of approximation, for the space of our planetary system, provided that we neglect the perturbations due to the sun and planets. Stated more exactly, there are finite regions, where, with respect to a suitably chosen space of reference, material particles move freely without acceleration, and in which the laws of the special theory of relativity, which have been developed above, hold with remarkable accuracy. Such regions we shall call "Galilean regions." We shall proceed from the consideration of such regions as a special case of known properties.

The principle of equivalence demands that in dealing with Galilean regions we may equally well make use of non-inertial systems, that is, such coordinate systems as, relatively to inertial systems, are not free from acceleration and rotation. If, further, we are going to do away completely with the vexing question as to the objective reason for the preference of certain systems of coordinates, then we must allow the use of arbitrarily moving systems of coordinates. As soon as we make this attempt seriously we come into conflict with that physical interpretation of space and time to which we were led by the special theory of relativity. For let K' be a system of coordinates whose z'-axis coincides with the z-axis of K, and which rotates about the latter axis with constant angular velocity. Are the configurations of rigid bodies, at rest relatively to K', in accordance with the laws of Euclidean geometry? Since K' is not an inertial system, we do not know directly the laws of configuration of rigid bodies with respect to K', nor the laws of nature, in general. But we do know these laws with respect to the inertial system K, and we can therefore infer their form with respect to K'. Imagine a circle drawn about the origin in the $x'y'$ plane of K', and a diameter of this circle. Imagine, further, that we have given a large number of rigid rods, all equal to each other. We suppose these laid in series along the periphery and the diameter of the circle, at rest relatively to K'. If U is the number of these rods along the periphery, D the number along the diameter, then, if K' does not rotate relatively to K, we shall have

$$\frac{U}{D} = \pi.$$

But if K' rotates we get a different result. Suppose that at a definite time t, of K we determine the ends of all the rods. With respect to K all the rods upon the periphery experience the Lorentz contraction, but the rods upon the diameter do not experience this contraction (along their lengths!).* It therefore follows that

$$\frac{U}{D} > \pi.$$

It therefore follows that the laws of configuration of rigid bodies with respect to K' do not agree with the laws of configuration of rigid bodies that are in accordance with Euclidean geometry. If, further, we place two similar clocks (rotating with K'), one upon the periphery, and the other at the centre of the circle, then, judged from K, the clock on the periphery

---

* These considerations assume that the behavior of rods and clocks depends only upon velocities, and not upon accelerations, or at least, that the influence of acceleration does not counteract that of velocity.

will go slower than the clock at the centre. The same thing must take place, judged from K', if we do not define time with respect to K' in a wholly unnatural way, (that is, in such a way that the laws with respect to K' depend explicitly upon the time). Space and time, therefore, cannot be defined with respect to K' as they were in the special theory of relativity with respect to inertial systems. But, according to the principle of equivalence, K' may also be considered as a system at rest, with respect to which there is a gravitational field (field of centrifugal force, and force of Coriolis). We therefore arrive at the result: the gravitational field influences and even determines the metrical laws of the space-time continuum. If the laws of configuration of ideal rigid bodies are to be expressed geometrically, then in the presence of a gravitational field the geometry is not Euclidean.

The case that we have been considering is analogous to that which is presented in the two-dimensional treatment of surfaces. It is impossible in the latter case also, to introduce coordinates on a surface (e.g. the surface of an ellipsoid) which have a simple metrical significance, while on a plane the Cartesian coordinates, x_1, x_2, signify directly lengths measured by a unit measuring rod. Gauss overcame this difficulty, in his theory of surfaces, by introducing curvilinear coordinates which, apart from satisfying conditions of continuity, were wholly arbitrary, and only afterwards these coordinates were related to the metrical properties of the surface. In an analogous way we shall introduce in the general theory of relativity arbitrary coordinates, x_1, x_2, x_3, x_4, which shall number uniquely the space-time points, so that neighbouring events are associated with neighbouring values of the coordinates; otherwise, the choice of coordinates is arbitrary. We shall be true to the principle of relativity in its broadest sense if we give such a form to the laws that they are valid in every such four-dimensional system of coordinates, that is, if the equations expressing the laws are covariant with respect to arbitrary transformations.

The most important point of contact between Gauss's theory of surfaces and the general theory of relativity lies in the metrical properties upon which the concepts of both theories, in the main, are based. In the case of the theory of surfaces, Gauss's argument is as follows. Plane geometry may be based upon the concept of the distance ds, between two infinitely near points. The concept of this distance is physically significant because the distance can be measured directly by means of a rigid measuring rod. By a suitable choice of Cartesian coordinates this distance may be expressed by the formula $ds^2 = dx_1^2 + dx_2^2$. We may base upon this quantity the concepts of the straight line as the geodesic ($\delta \int ds = 0$), the interval, the circle, and the angle, upon which the Euclidean plane geometry is built. A geometry may be developed upon another continuously curved surface, if we observe that an infinitesimally small portion of the surface may be regarded as plane, to within relatively infinitesimal quantities. There are Cartesian coordinates, X_1, X_2, upon such a small portion of the surface, and the distance between two points, measured by a measuring rod, is given by

$$ds^2 = dX_1{}^2 + dX_2{}^2.$$

If we introduce arbitrary curvilinear coordinates, x_1, x_2, on the surface, then dX_1, dX_2, may be expressed linearly in terms of dx_1, dx_2. Then everywhere upon the surface we have

$$ds^2 = g_{11}dx_1{}^2 + 2g_{12}dx_1dx_2 + g_{22}dx_2{}^2$$

where g_{11}, g_{12}, g_{22} are determined by the nature of the surface and the choice of coordinates; if these quantities are known, then it is also known how networks of rigid rods may be laid upon the surface. In other words, the geometry of surfaces may be based upon this expression for ds^2 exactly as plane geometry is based upon the corresponding expression.

There are analogous relations in the four-dimensional space-time continuum of physics. In the immediate neighbourhood of an observer, falling freely in a gravitational field, there exists no gravitational field. We can therefore always regard an infinitesimally small region of the space-time continuum as Galilean. For such an infinitely small region there will be an inertial system (with the space coordinates, X_1, X_2, X_3, and the time coordinate X_4) relatively to which we are to regard the laws of the special theory of relativity as valid. The quantity which is directly measurable by our unit measuring rods and clocks,

$$dX_1{}^2 + dX_2{}^2 + dX_3{}^2 - dX_4{}^2$$

or its negative,

$$ds^2 = -dX_1{}^2 - dX_2{}^2 - dX_3{}^2 + dX_4{}^2$$

is therefore a uniquely determinative invariant for two neighbouring events (points in the four-dimensional continuum), provided that we use measuring rods that are equal to each other when brought together and superimposed, and clocks whose rates are the same when they are brought together. In this the physical assumption is essential that the relative lengths of two measuring rods and the relative rates of two clocks are independent, in principle, of their previous history. But this assumption is certainly warranted by experience; if it did not hold there could be no sharp spectral lines, since the single atoms of the same element certainly do not have the same history, and since—on the assumption of relative variability of the single atoms depending on previous history—it would be absurd to suppose that the masses or proper frequencies of these atoms ever had been equal to one another.

Space-time regions of finite extent are, in general, not Galilean, so that a gravitational field cannot be done away with by any choice of coordinates in a finite region. There is, therefore, no choice of coordinates for which the metrical relations of the special theory of relativity hold in a finite region. But the invariant *ds* always exists for two neighbouring points (events) of the continuum. This invariant *ds* may be expressed in arbitrary coordinates. If one observes that the local dX_ν may be expressed linearly in terms of the coordinate differentials dx_ν, ds^2 may be expressed in the form

$$ds^2 = g_{\mu\nu}dx_\mu dx_\nu.$$

The functions $g_{\mu\nu}$ describe, with respect to the arbitrarily chosen system of coordinates, the metrical relations of the space-time continuum and also the gravitational field. As in the special theory of relativity, we have to discriminate between time-like and space-like line elements in the four-dimensional continuum; owing to the change of sign introduced, time-like line elements have a real, space-like line elements an imaginary *ds*. The time-like *ds* can be measured directly by a suitably chosen clock. . . .

PART

VII

ooooooooooo

NEW IDEAS AND NEW MEASUREMENTS

ooooooooooo

37

ooooooooooo

THE "THOMSON" ATOM

ooooooooooo

J. J. Thomson (1856-1940)

Following the discovery of the electron it was clear that a complete revision of atomic theory was required. The atom could no longer be regarded as the ultimate unit of matter because Thomson's experiments had shown that, regardless of the gases used to produce the cathode ray discharge, the same subatomic particle, the electron, always appeared. Since this particle carries a negative electric charge and the atom as a whole is uncharged, questions immediately arose as to the number of electrons per atom, the nature of the positive charge, and the spatial relation of the latter to the electron or electrons present.

The very small electronic mass determined by Thomson's experiments, approximately 1/1,000 the mass of the hydrogen atom, at first suggested that the hydrogen atom might contain some 1,000 electrons. This contemporary thinking was clearly set forth in the closing pages of Rutherford's book, *Radioactive Transformations,* published in 1906. Rutherford points out that atom models had already been suggested, the first by Lord Kelvin.

Kelvin proposed, in 1902, an atom model consisting of a sphere of uniformly distributed positive electricity in which discrete electrons were embedded so that equilibrium was obtained when these charges were at rest. A year later J. J. Thomson published calculations on the stability of a model in which electrons, arranged uniformly around a circle within the positive sphere, rotated at high speed. A further paper by Thomson appeared early in 1904, which reexamined Kelvin's static atom model at considerable length. Much of this paper, with additions, appeared in Thomson's book, *The Corpuscular Theory of Matter,* published in 1907; our excerpt is from this book. Here static electrons are placed one by one in a positive sphere and the stability is examined. Somehow Kelvin's pro-

613

prietary claim to this atomic scheme was lost, so that in later years the arrangement became known as "the Thomson atom."

But while Thomson was examining, and elaborating the original Kelvin scheme, Kelvin himself went on to other and more complicated models. Finally, in December 1905, he proposed a Boscovichian atom that had alternating shells of "vitreous and resinous" electricity with "the total vitreous greater than the resinous." The electrons were embedded in the vitreous (positive) shells, and could therefore, if unstable, be ejected with varying speeds as demanded of electrons issuing from radioactive atoms. Still another model, proposed in 1904, was that of Nagaoka, who, harking back to Maxwell's paper on Saturn's rings, suggested that the atom might consist of a number of electrons revolving with nearly the same velocity in a ring about a positively charged center. Rutherford noted this suggestion in his famous paper of 1911, in which he proposed the nuclear atom. All of these atom models had varying degrees of plausibility; they would account qualitatively for various atomic properties but not for all. Thomson, however, was perhaps most persistent in his search for a model that would give both qualitative and some quantitative agreement with experiment.

Suppose one begins with the question: How many electrons are there per atom? Thomson obtained an answer to this question from several sources. The first came from experiments on the scattering of electrons made to pass through thin sheets of metal. (Lenard, for instance, had shown some years previously that cathode rays can pass through thin metal windows and ionize the air outside the tube in which they were generated.) By comparing a computed value of electron scattering with that observed experimentally, Thomson found that the number of electrons per atom needed to produce the observed scattering should be approximately the same as the atomic weight of the scattering material assuming unit atomic weight for hydrogen. (Except for hydrogen, this result was approximately two times too large.) The second source of information was the dispersion of light by hydrogen. Here a calculation showed that the number of dispersion electrons per atom of hydrogen must be closely equal to unity. The third source was X-ray scattering experiments. When a beam of X-rays passes through matter, the atoms both absorb and scatter the rays; hence, the amount transmitted decreases as the thickness of the material increases. From early X-ray scattering measurements the number of electrons per atom was found to be of the order of the atomic weight. Later, more accurate measurements by Barkla showed that for the light atoms, except hydrogen, it was more nearly half the atomic weight. As a consequence of all this evidence, it was apparent that hydrogen, the least massive of all the atoms, consisted probably of *one* electron, and an equal amount of positive charge. Heavier atoms were presumably obtained by adding one electron for every unit of positive charge.

Results from kinetic theory had shown that the diameter of an atom was of the order of 10^{-8} cm. From the scattering experiments it was known that an electron was not much deflected by passing through thin foils many atoms thick, so the conclusion was reached that the "density" of positive charge must be low. Accordingly, Thomson, in making a model for hydrogen, the simplest atom, had some basis other than Kelvin's proposal for assuming that positive charge, equal to that of the electron, occupied the *whole* atomic volume with uniform density.

Having made these tentative choices, the question of stability demanded examination. Where was the electron in such an atom? Elementary electrical theory shows that if the electron is assumed to be at the center of the positive sphere, any displacement of it will result in vibrations about the center. These would continue indefinitely if the electron did not lose energy; but since a vibratory motion about the center is an accelerated motion, and classical electromagnetic theory required that accelerated electrons must radiate energy, the electron would naturally be brought to rest. Hence, the undisturbed atom would be a static atom, and if disturbed, would produce dynamically stable vibrations, dying away with time. If the disturbances were sufficiently violent, the electron would be ejected, resulting in a hydrogen ion. All this seemed in accord with experience. But a little further investigation showed that despite its good beginning, the model had at least one serious defect. The radiation emitted by the vibrating electron should, according to theory, consist of light of a single wavelength appropriate to the far-ultraviolet region of the spectrum. Experimentally, one observed quite unaccountably a spectrum in the visible region consisting of several discrete wavelengths. Other series of lines also existed in the infrared and ultraviolet.

Despite this defect, Thomson went ahead to examine the stability of the multielectron atom. From stability considerations he shows in his paper that, proceeding to the atom containing two electrons, stability is obtained by keeping the size of the sphere of positive electricity constant. As regards the two electrons placed inside the sphere, equilibrium is obtained when they are on a line through the center of the sphere and equidistant from it, the distance being half the radius of the sphere. As the number of electrons increases to four, the electrons can no longer be in static equilibrium in a planar arrangement; instead they are located at the corners of a regular tetrahedron. Stable arrangements with greater numbers of electrons up to 100 are then discussed. Thomson was also able to show that the electron arrangements in his scheme of "atom-building" suggested an explanation of the periodic properties of the chemical elements. This section of his paper is not reproduced here.

The stability of experimental configurations, using magnetized needles thrust through corks and floated on water, iron spheres floating on mercury, and elongated conductors floating vertically in water, is then briefly noted as a result of the work of other investigators. These experiments support the idea that a number of corpuscles, if confined to a plane, will arrange themselves in a series of rings as Thomson's calculations indicated.

One of the main props for the Thomson atom was its support of α-particle-scattering experiments. It is ironic that this aspect of his model on closer investigation led to its downfall!

ଚଚଚଚଚଚଚ

THOMSON

The Arrangement of Corpuscles in the Atom [1]

WE HAVE SEEN THAT CORPUSCLES are always of the same kind whatever may be the nature of the substance from which they originate; this, in conjunction with the fact that their mass is much smaller than that of any known atom, suggests that they are a constituent of all atoms; that, in short, corpuscles are an essential part of the structure of the atoms of the different elements. This consideration makes it important to consider the ways in which groups of corpuscles can arrange themselves so as to be in equilibrium. Since the corpuscles are all negatively electrified, they repel each other, and thus, unless there is some force tending to hold them together, no group in which the distances between the corpuscles is finite can be in equilibrium. As the atoms of the elements in their normal states are electrically neutral, the negative electricity on the corpuscles they contain must be balanced by an equivalent amount of positive electricity; the atoms must, along with the corpuscles, contain positive electricity. The form in which this positive electricity occurs in the atom is at present a matter about which we have very little information. No positively electrified body has yet been found having a mass less than that of an atom of hydrogen. All the positively electrified systems in gases at low pressures seem to be atoms which, neutral in their normal state, have become positively charged by losing a corpuscle. In

---

[1] From J. J. Thomson, *The Corpuscular Theory of Matter* (New York: Charles Scribner's Sons, 1907), pp. 103–167.

default of exact knowledge of the nature of the way in which positive electricity occurs in the atom, we shall consider a case in which the positive electricity is distributed in the way most amenable to mathematical calculation, *i.e.,* when it occurs as a sphere of uniform density, throughout which the corpuscles are distributed. The positive electricity attracts the corpuscles to the centre of the sphere, while their mutual repulsion drives them away from it; when in equilibrium they will be distributed in such a way that the attraction of the positive electrification is balanced by the repulsion of the other corpuscles.

Let us now consider the problem as to how $1 \ldots 2 \ldots 3 \ldots n$ corpuscles would arrange themselves if placed in a sphere filled with positive electricity of uniform density, the total negative charge on the corpuscles being equivalent to the positive charge in the sphere.

When there is only one corpuscle the solution is very simple: the corpuscle will evidently go to the centre of the sphere. The potential energy possessed by the different arrangements is a quantity of considerable importance in the theory of the subject. We shall call Q the amount of work required to remove each portion of electricity to an infinite distance from its nearest neighbour; thus in the case of the single corpuscle we should have to do work to drag the corpuscle out of the sphere and then carry it away to an infinite distance from it; when we have done this we should be left with the sphere of positive electricity, the various parts of which would repel each other; if we let these parts recede from each other until they were infinitely remote we should gain work. The difference between the work spent in removing the negative from the positive and that gained by allowing the positive to scatter is Q the amount of work required to separate completely the electrical charges. When there is only one corpuscle we can easily show that

$$Q = \frac{9}{10} \frac{e^2}{a},$$

where e is the charge on a corpuscle measured in electrostatic units and a is the radius of the sphere.

When there are two corpuscles inside a sphere of positive electricity they will, when in equilibrium, be situated at two points A and B, in a straight line with O the center of the sphere and such that

$$OA = OB = \frac{a}{2},$$

where a is the radius of the sphere. We can easily show that in this position the repulsion between A and B is just balanced by the attraction of the positive electricity and also that the equilibrium is stable. We may point out that A B the distance between the corpuscles is equal to the radius of the sphere of positive electrification. In this case we can show that

$$Q = \frac{21}{10}\frac{e^2}{a}.$$

Thus if the radius of the sphere of positive electrification remained constant, Q for a system containing two corpuscles in a single sphere would be greater than Q for the arrangement in which each corpuscle is placed in a sphere of positive electrification of its own, for in the latter case we have seen that

$$Q = 2 \times \frac{9}{10}\frac{e^2}{a}$$

and this is less than

$$\frac{21}{10}\frac{e^2}{a}.$$

Thus the arrangement with the two corpuscles inside one sphere is more than that where there are two spheres with a single corpuscle inside each: thus if we had a number of single corpuscles each inside its own sphere, they would not be so stable as if they were to coagulate and form systems each containing more than one corpuscle. There would therefore be a tendency for a large number of systems containing single corpuscles to form more complex systems. This result depends upon the assumption that the size of the sphere of positive electrification for the system containing two corpuscles is the same as that of the sphere containing only one corpuscle. If we had assumed that when two systems unite the volume of the sphere of positive electricity for the combined system is the sum of the volumes of the individual systems, then a for the combined system would be $2\frac{1}{3}$ or $1 \cdot 25$ times a for the single system. Taking this into account, we find that Q for the combined system is less than the sum of the values of Q for the individual system; in this case the system containing two corpuscles would not be so stable as two systems each containing one corpuscle, so that the tendency now would be towards dissociation rather than association.

Three corpuscles inside a single sphere will be in stable equilibrium when at the corners of an equilateral triangle whose centre is at the centre of the sphere and whose side is equal in length to the radius of that sphere; thus for three as for two corpuscles the equilibrium position is determined by the condition that the distance between two corpuscles is equal to the radius of the sphere of positive electrification.

For the case of three corpuscles $Q = \dfrac{36}{10}\dfrac{e^2}{a}$, and thus again we see that
if the radius of the sphere of positive electricity is invariable, the arrangement with three corpuscles inside one sphere is more stable than three single corpuscles each inside its own sphere, or than one corpuscle inside one sphere and two corpuscles inside another sphere; thus again the tendency would be towards aggregation. If, however, the positive electricity instead of being invariable in size were invariable in density, we see that the tendency would be for the complex system to dissociate into the simpler ones.

Four corpuscles if at rest cannot be in equilibrium when in one plane, although the co-planar arrangement is possible and stable when the four are in rapid rotation. When there is no rotation the corpuscles, when in stable equilibrium, are arranged at the corners of a regular tetrahedron whose centre is at the centre of the sphere of positive electrification and whose side is equal to the radius of that sphere; thus we again have the result that the distance between the corpuscles is equal to the radius of the positive sphere.

For four corpuscles

$$Q = \frac{e^2}{a}\frac{54}{10}.$$

We see that the values of Q per corpuscle are for the arrangements of 1, 2, 3, 4 corpuscles in the proportion of 6 : 7 : 8 : 9 if the radius of the positive sphere is invariable.

Six corpuscles will be in stable equilibrium at the corners of a regular octahedron, but it can be shown that the equilibrium of eight corpuscles at the corners of a cube is unstable. The general problem of finding how n corpuscles will distribute themselves inside the sphere is very complicated, and I have not succeeded in solving it; we can, however, solve the special case where the corpuscles are confined to a plane passing through the centre of the sphere, and from the results obtained from this solution we may infer some of the properties of the more general distribution. The analytical solution of the problem when the motion of the corpuscles is confined to one plane is given in a paper by the author in the *Philosophical Magazine* for March, 1904; we shall refer to that paper for the analysis and quote here only the results.

If we have n corpuscles arranged at the corners of a regular polygon with n sides with its centre at the centre of the sphere of positive electrification, each corpuscle being thus at the same distance r from the centre of this sphere, we can find a value of r, so that the repulsion exerted by the $(n-1)$ corpuscles on the remaining corpuscle is equal to the attraction of the positive electricity on that corpuscle; the ring of corpuscles would then be in equilibrium. But it is shown in the paper referred to that if n is greater than 5 the equilibrium is unstable and so cannot exist; thus 5 is the greatest number of corpuscles which can be in equilibrium as a single ring. It is shown, however, that we *can* have a ring containing more than five corpuscles in equilibrium if there are other corpuscles inside the ring. Thus, though a ring of six corpuscles at the corners of a regular hexagon is unstable by itself, it becomes stable when there is another corpuscle placed at the centre of the hexagon and rings of seven and eight corpuscles are also made stable by placing one corpuscle inside them. To make a ring of nine corpuscles stable, however, we must have two corpuscles inside it, and the number of corpuscles required inside a ring to keep it stable increases very rapidly with the number of corpuscles in the ring. This is shown by [Table 37–1], where n represents the number of corpuscles in the ring and i the number of corpuscles which must be placed inside the ring to keep it in stable equilibrium.

T A B L E   3 7 – 1

n	5.	6.	7.	8.	9.	10.	12.	13.	15.	20.	30.	40.
i	0.	1.	1.	1	2.	3.	8.	10.	15.	39.	101.	232.

When n is large i is proportional to n^3. We thus see that in the case when the corpuscles are confined to one plane they will arrange themselves in a series of concentric rings.

[Thomson then gives the details of the calculation by which the equilibrium of a number of corpuscles in a planar arrangement may be calculated—Editors.]

[Table 37–2] giving the various rings for corpuscles ranging in number from 1 to 100 has been calculated in this way; the first row contains the numbers for which there is only one ring, the second those with two rings, the third those with three, and so on.

We can investigate the equilibrium of corpuscles in one plane by experiment as well as by analysis, using a method introduced for a different purpose by an American physicist, Professor Mayer. The problem of the arrangement of the corpuscles is to find how a number of bodies which repel each other with forces inversely proportional to the square of the distance between them will arrange themselves when under the action of an attractive force tending to drag them to a fixed point. For the experimental method the corpuscles are replaced by magnetised needles pushed through cork discs and floating on water. Care should be taken that the needles are equally magnetised. These needles, having their poles all pointing in the same way, repel each other like the corpuscles. The attractive

TABLE 37–2

NUMBERS OF CORPUSCLES IN ORDER

```
 1  2  3  4  5
 5  6  7  8  8  8  9 10 10 10 11
 1  1  1  2  3  3  3  4  5  5

11 11 11 12 12 12 13 13 13 13 13 14 14 15 15
 5  6  7  7  8  8  8  8  9 10 10 10 10 10 11
 1  1  1  1  1  2  3  3  3  4  4  5  5  5

15 15 15 16 16 16 16 16 16 16 17 17 17 17 17 17 17
11 11 11 11 12 12 12 13 13 13 13 13 13 14 14 15 15
 5  6  7  7  7  8  8  8  8  9  9 10 10 10 10 10 11
 1  1  1  1  1  1  2  2  3  3  3  3  4  4  5  5  5

17 18 18 18 18 18 19 19 19 19 20 20 20 20 20 20 20 20 20 21 21
15 15 15 15 16 16 16 16 16 16 16 16 16 17 17 17 17 17 17 17 17
11 11 11 11 11 12 12 12 12 13 13 13 13 13 13 13 14 14 15 15 15
 5  5  6  7  7  7  7  8  8  8  8  9  9 10 10 10 10 10 10 10 11
 1  1  1  1  1  1  1  1  2  2  2  3  3  3  3  4  4  5  5  5  5

21 21 21 21 21 21 21 21 22 22 22 22 22 22 22 22 23 23 23 23 23 23 24
17 18 18 18 18 18 19 19 19 19 19 20 20 20 20 20 20 20 20 20 21 21 21
15 15 15 15 16 16 16 16 16 16 16 16 16 16 17 17 17 17 17 17 17 17 17
11 11 11 11 11 12 12 12 12 12 13 13 13 13 13 13 13 13 14 14 15 15 15 15
 5  5  6  7  7  7  7  8  8  8  8  8  9  9 10 10 10 10 10 10 10 10 11 11
 1  1  1  1  1  1  1  1  1  2  2  2  3  3  3  3  3  4  4  5  5  5  5  5

24 24 24 24 24 24 24
21 21 21 21 21 21 21
17 18 18 18 18 18 19
15 15 15 15 16 16 16
11 11 11 11 11 12 12
 5  5  6  7  7  7  7
 1  1  1  1  1  1  1
```

force is produced by a large magnet placed above the surface of the water, the lower pole of this magnet being of the opposite sign to that of the upper poles of the floating magnets. The component along the surface of the water of the force due to this magnet is directed to the point on the surface vertically below the pole of the magnet, and is approximately proportional to the distance from this point. The forces acting on the magnets are thus analogous to those acting on the corpuscles.

If we throw needle after needle into the water we shall find that they will arrange themselves in definite patterns, three needles at the corners of a triangle, four at the corners of a square, five at the corners of a pentagon; when, however, we throw in a sixth needle this sequence is broken; the six needles do not arrange themselves at the corners of a hexagon, but five go to the corners of a pentagon and one goes to the middle. When we throw in a seventh needle we get a ring of six with one at the centre; thus a ring of six, though unstable when hollow, becomes stable as soon as one is put in the inside. This is an example of a fundamental principle in the stable configurations of corpuscles; the structure must be substantial; we cannot have a great display of corpuscles on the outside and nothing in the inside. If, however, we have a good foundation of corpuscles—if, for example, we tie a considerable number of needles together for the inside—we can have a ring containing a large number of corpuscles in stable equilibrium around it, although five is the greatest number of corpuscles that can be in equilibrium in a hollow ring. By the aid of these floating magnets we can illustrate the configurations for considerable numbers of corpuscles, and verify [Table 37–2].

Another method, due to Professor R. W. Wood, is to replace the magnets floating on water by iron spheres floating on mercury; these spheres get magnetised by induction by the large magnet placed above them and repel each other—though in this case the repulsive force does not vary inversely as the square of the distance—while they are attracted by the external magnet; the iron spheres arrange themselves in patterns analogous to those formed by the magnets. Dr. Monckman used, instead of magnets, elongated conductors floating vertically in water; these were electrified by induction by a charged body held above the surface of the water; the conductors, being similarly electrified, repelled each other and were attracted towards the electrified body; under these forces they formed patterns similar to those formed by the floating magnets.

We see from this experimental illustration, as well as by the analytical investigation, that a number of corpuscles will, if confined to one plane, arrange themselves in a series of rings, the number of corpuscles in the ring increasing as the radius of the ring increases.

If we refer to the arrangements of the different numbers of corpuscles [see Table 37–2], we see that the numbers which come in the same vertical columns are arranged in patterns which have much in common, for each arrangement is obtained by adding another storey to the one above it. Thus, to take the first column, we have the pattern 5, 1, the one below it is 11, 5, 1; the one below this 15, 11, 5, 1; the one below this 17, 15, 11, 5, 1; then 21, 17, 15, 11, 5, 1; and then 24, 21, 17, 15, 11, 5, 1. We should expect the properties of the atoms formed of such arrangements of corpuscles to have many points of resemblance. Take, for example, the vibrations of the corpuscles; these may be divided into two sets. The first set consists of those arising from the rotation of the corpuscles around their orbits. If all the corpuscles in an atom have the same angular velocity, the frequency of the vibrations produced by the rotation of the ring of corpuscles is proportional to the number of corpuscles in the ring; and thus in the spectrum of each of the elements corresponding to the arrangements of corpuscles found in a vertical column in [Table 37–2], there would be a series of lines whose frequencies would be in a constant ratio to each other, this ratio being the ratio of the numbers of corpuscles in the various rings.

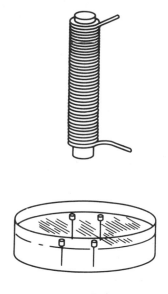

Fig. 37–1.

The second set of vibrations are those corresponding to the displacement of a ring from its circular shape. If the distance of a corpuscle from the nearest member in its own ring is small compared with its distance from its nearest neighbour on another ring, the effect of the outer ring will only "disturb" the vibrations of the ring without altering their fundamental character. Thus we should expect the various elements in a vertical column to give corresponding groups of associated lines. We might, in short, expect the various elements corresponding to the arrangements of the corpuscles contained in the same vertical column, to have many properties, chemical as well as physical, in common. If we suppose that the atomic weight of an element is proportional to the number of corpuscles contained in its atom,—and we shall give later on evidence in favour of this view,—we may regard the similarity in properties of these arrangements of corpuscles in the same vertical column as similar to a very striking property of the chemical elements, *i.e.,* the property expressed by the periodic law. We know that if we arrange the elements in the order of their atomic weights, then as we proceed to consider the elements in this order, we come across an element—say lithium—with a certain property; we go on, and after passing many elements which do not resemble lithium, we come to another, sodium, having many properties in common with lithium; then, as we go on we lose these properties for a time, coming across them again when we arrive at potassium, and so on. We find here just the same recurrence of properties at considerable intervals that we should get if the atoms contained numbers of corpuscles proportional to their atomic weight. Consider a series of atoms, such that the atom of the pth member is formed from that of the $(p-1)$th by the addition of a single ring, *i.e.,* is a compound, so to speak, of the $(p-1)$th atom with a fresh ring. Such a series would belong to elements which are in the same group according to the periodic law, *i.e.,* these elements form a series which, if arranged according to Mendeléef's table would all be in the same vertical column. [The remainder of the paper discusses the stability and electrochemical properties of atoms starting with 20 corpuscles in the outer ring and 59 or more in the inner ring—Editors.]

38

○○○○○○○○○○

THE DETERMINATION OF
AVOGADRO'S NUMBER

○○○○○○○○○○○

Jean Perrin (1870-1942)

Jean Baptiste Perrin was born at Lille, France, on September 30, 1870. After his early education in Lille, he attended the École Normale Supérieure in Paris and became a teacher of physics there from 1894 to 1897. At the age of twenty-six he was awarded the degree of Dr. es Science from the University of Paris and was also appointed a lecturer in physical chemistry. He became professor of physical chemistry at forty in 1910 and held this post for thirty years, except for the period of World War I, during which he served as an officer with the engineers. He was elected a foreign member of the Royal Society in 1918. In 1923 he became a member of the French Academy and in 1926 was awarded the Nobel Prize in physics. He was then fifty-six years old. Because of his eminence he became, ten years later, Under Secretary of State for scientific research in the government of Premier Léon Blum. Two years afterward he was elected president of the Academie des Sciences and in the same year president of the department of scientific research in the French government. He retired in 1940, and after the German invasion of France lived in Lyon. In December 1941 he came to the United States to teach in the Free French University in New York. At that time he made his home with his son, Dr. Francis Perrin, who was then visiting professor of physics and mathematics at Columbia University. His work in the United States lasted only a few months, being terminated by his death in New York on April 17, 1942.

It was not until after the beginning of this century that Einstein's theory of the Brownian motion and Jean Perrin's application of the kinetic-

625

theory law of isothermal atmospheres provided new ways to establish Avogradro's constant for determining the number of molecules in a gram-molecular weight of an element or compound, for example, in 32 grams of oxygen. Perrin's method and the details of his experimental work which follow are excerpted from his paper "Brownian Motion and Molecular Reality." The paper is a model of scientific writing and deserves to be read not only for its importance but for its admirable clarity and direct style.

Once the importance of Avogrado's number had been established by Cannizzaro, it became increasingly urgent to ascertain its exact numerical value.

Perrin's method is simple in principle, and may be readily explained. The kinetic theory of gases predicts that in a stagnant atmosphere maintained at a constant temperature T, the number of molecules, each of mass m, composing the atmosphere will decrease with height above the earth's surface according to the relation:

$$n = n_0 e^{-\frac{mgh}{kT}}$$

In this expression n_0 is the number of molecules per unit volume at the earth's surface; n is the corresponding number at any given height h; e is the base of natural logarithms; g the acceleration of gravity; k the Boltzmann constant; T the absolute temperature.

The Boltzmann constant k is defined as the ratio of the ideal gas constant per mole, R, and Avogadro's number, N. It should be recognized that mgh represents potential energy of a molecule at a height h above the earth's surface. Since $3kT/2$ is the mean kinetic energy W of the molecules, kT is given by $2W/3$. By taking the logarithm of both sides of the equation, and rearranging and making the substitution for W, we get one of the relations noted in Perrin's paper:

$$\tfrac{2}{3} W \, log \, \frac{n_0}{n} = mgh$$

Since experimentation at various heights in the atmosphere is difficult, and the realization of an isothermal atmosphere highly improbable, it is necessary to simulate the conditions for experiment. It occurred to Perrin that particles much larger than a molecule, but small enough to show Brownian motion when immersed in a fluid at constant temperature, might behave as molecules do; they might show the same height-density characteristics as required by the theory. Accordingly, he carried out experiments, using emulsions containing microscopic particles of gum-mastic or gum-gamboge, obtained by centrifuging solutions of these materials. The particles were found to remain in suspension and to be distributed exponentially with height when counted using a microscope focused in the liquid.

It was thus possibl ewith such emulsions to use th eisothermal-atmosphere theory to determine N. Only one modification was necessary to the foregoing equation. Gum particles suspended in a liquid are buoyed up by it so that the net downward force is the difference between the gravitational force and the buoyant force. If ϕ represents the volume of the uniform particles, Δ their density, and δ the density of the solution, the net downward force is given by $\phi(\Delta - \delta)g$. Making this substitution, we obtain the equation given by Perrin:

$$\tfrac{2}{3} W \log \frac{n_0}{n} = \phi(\Delta - \delta)gh$$

In order to compute Avogadro's number, the quantity W is expressed in terms of R/N instead of k, viz., $3RT/2N$. If we also change the indicated natural logarithm to the base 10, we finally get:

$$2 \cdot 303 \frac{RT}{N} \log_{10} \frac{n_0}{n} = \frac{4}{3} \pi a^3 g (\Delta - \delta) h,$$

where a is now the radius of the gum particles. The final result obtained, using this relation, was 7.05×10^{23} (or 70.5×10^{22}, as Perrin gives it). This is substantially larger than the presently accepted value of 6.025×10^{23} because of the error associated with the many different measurements that must be made with this method.

Referring to the formula above, used to calculate N, two factors appear to be especially susceptible to relatively large errors, namely, the value of a, the radius of a gum particle, and the ratio n_0/n of the number of particles at different heights. Perrin's paper lists three methods for finding the radius of the particles. Only the one that he considers best is included in the excerpt from his paper, but a reading of this method will show that it contains uncertainties not easy to estimate. The same is true of the determination of n_0/n. Both of these quantities in the ratio involve small numbers of particles which must be identified at a glance (when the visual method is used) as clearly in the focal plane. Another way of expressing the same uncertainty is to say that the height h used for determining a given value of n_0 is not accurately known.

The value of Avogadro's number as now accepted is obtained from the relation that essentially defines the quantity of electricity called the Faraday. This is the product of the electronic charge and Avogadro's number, i.e., $Ne = F$. Now F can be determined with good precision by measuring the amount of charge necessary to deposit 1 gram mole of univalent ion in electrolysis. Dividing this number by the measured value of the electronic charge yields N. The electronic charge was determined by Millikan around 1912 (as will be shown in a later article in this anthology) very soon after Perrin's determination. Using Millikan's value in the expression for the Faraday, N was found to be 6.062×10^{23} with an estimated precision of 0.1 per cent. Despite all of Perrin's care in his experiment the difference between his value and the presently accepted one would indicate how difficult it is to use detailed indirect measurements and obtain high precision. Actually, Millikan's value for the electronic charge had small errors also, so that the present value of N is taken to be 6.025×10^{23}.

ooooooo

PERRIN

Brownian Motion and Molecular Reality [1]

THE SINGULAR PHENOMENON DISCOVERED BY Brown . . . remained for a long time ignored by the majority of physicists, and it may be supposed that those who had heard of it thought it analogous to the movement of the dust particles, which can be seen dancing in a ray of sunlight, under the influence of feeble currents of air which set up small differences of pressure or temperature. When we reflect that this apparent explanation was able to satisfy even thoughtful minds, we ought the more to admire the acuteness of those physicists, who have recognised in this, supposed insignificant, phenomenon a fundamental property of matter.

Besides, as happens most frequently when it is sought to unravel the genesis of a great directing idea, it is difficult to fix precisely how the hypothesis, which ascribes the Brownian movement to molecular agitation, first appeared and how it was developed.

The first name which calls for reference in this respect is, perhaps, that of Wiener, who declared at the conclusion of his observations, that the movement could not be due to convection currents, that it was necessary to seek for the cause of it in the liquid itself, and who, finally, almost at the

---

[1] Jean Perrin, *Brownian Motion and Molecular Reality*, trans. F. Soddy (London: Taylor and Francis, 1908), pp. 1–48.

commencement of the development of the kinetic theory of heat, divined that molecular movements were able to give the explanation of the phenomenon.

Some years later Fathers Delsaulx and Carbonnelle published in the *Royal Microscopical Society* and in the *Revue des Questions scientifiques,* from 1877 to 1880, various Notes on the *Thermodynamical Origin of the Brownian Movement.* In a note by Father Delsaulx, for example, one may read: "the agitation of small corpuscles in suspension in liquids truly constitutes a general phenomenon," that it is "henceforth natural to ascribe a phenomenon having this universality to some general property of matter," and that "in this train of ideas, the internal movements of translation which constitute the calorific state of gases, vapours and liquids, can very well account for the facts established by experiment." . . .

These remarkable reflections unfortunately remained as little known as those of Wiener. Besides it does not appear that they were accompanied by an experimental trial sufficient to dispel the superficial explanation indicated a moment ago; in consequence, the proposed theory did not impress itself on those who had become acquainted with it.

On the contrary, it was established by the work of M. Gouy (1888), not only that the hypothesis of molecular agitation gave an admissible explanation of the Brownian movement, but that no other cause of the movement could be imagined, which especially increased the significance of the hypothesis. This work immediately evoked a considerable response, and it is only from this time that the Brownian movement took a place among the important problems of general physics.

In the first place, M. Gouy observed that the Brownian movement is not due to vibrations transmitted to the liquid under examination, since it persists equally, for example, at night on a sub-soil in the country as during the day near a populous street where heavy vehicles pass. Neither is it due to the convection currents existing in fluids where thermal equilibrium has not been attained, for it does not appreciably change when plenty of time is given for equilibrium to be reached. Any comparison between Brownian movement and the agitation of dust-particles dancing in the sunlight must therefore be set aside. In addition, in the latter case, it is easy to see that the neighbouring dust-particles move in general in the same sense, roughly tracing out the form of the common current which bears them along, whereas the most striking feature of the Brownian movement is the absolute independence of the displacements of neighbouring particles, so near together that they pass by one another. Lastly, neither can the unavoidable illumination of the preparation be suspected, for M. Gouy was able abruptly to reduce it a thousand times, or to change its colour considerably, without at all modifying the phenomenon observed. All the other causes from time to time imagined have as little influence; even the nature of the particles does not appear to be of any importance, and henceforward it was difficult not to believe that these articles simply serve to reveal an internal agitation of the fluid, the better the smaller they are, much as a cork follows better than a large ship the movements of the waves of the sea. . . .

THE KINETIC MOLECULAR HYPOTHESIS

I have said that the Brownian movement is explained, in the theory of M. Gouy and his predecessors, by the incessant movements of the molecules of the fluid, which striking unceasingly the observed particles, drive about these particles irregularly through the fluid except in the case where these impacts exactly counterbalance one another. It has, to be sure, been long recognised, especially in explanation of the facts of diffusion, and of the transformation of motion into heat, not only that substances in spite of their homogeneous appearance, have a discontinuous structure and are composed of separate *molecules,* but also that these molecules are in incessant agitation, which increases with the temperature and only ceases at absolute zero.

Instead of taking this hypothesis ready made and seeing how it renders account of the Brownian movement, it appears preferable to me to show that, possibly, it is logically suggested by this phenomenon alone, and this is what I propose to try.

What is really strange and *new* in the Brownian movement is, precisely, that it never stops. At first that seems in contradiction to our every-day experience of friction. If for example, we pour a bucket of water into a tub, it seems natural that, after a short time, the motion possessed by the liquid mass disappears. Let us analyse further how this apparent equilibrium is arrived at: all the particles had at first velocities almost equal and parallel; this co-ordination is disturbed as soon as certain of the particles, striking the walls of the tub, recoil in different directions with changed speeds, to be soon deviated anew by their impacts with other portions of the liquid. So that, some instants after the fall, all parts of the water will be still in motion, but it is now necessary to consider quite a small portion of it, in order that the speeds of its different points may have about the same direction and value. It is easy to see this by mixing coloured powders into a liquid, which will take on more and more irregular relative motions.

What we observe, in consequence, so long as we can distinguish anything, is not a cessation of the movements, but that they become more and more chaotic, that they distribute themselves in a fashion the more irregular the smaller the parts. . . .

The Brownian movement is permanent at constant temperature: that is an experimental fact. The motion of the molecules which it leads us to imagine is thus itself also permanent. If these molecules come into collision like billiard balls, it is necessary to add that they are perfectly elastic, and this expression can, indeed, be used to indicate that in the molecular collisions of a thermally isolated system the sum of the energies of motion remains definitely constant.

In brief the examination of Brownian movement alone suffices to suggest that every fluid is formed of elastic molecules, animated by a perpetual motion. . . .

Let us now consider a particle a little larger still, itself formed of several molecules, in a word a *dust*. Will it proceed to react towards the impact of the molecules encompassing it according to a new law? Will it not comport itself simply as a very large molecule, in the sense that its mean energy has still the same value as that of an isolated molecule? This cannot be averred without hesitation, but the hypothesis at least is sufficiently plausible to make it worth while to discuss its consequences.

Here we are then taken back again to the observation of the particles of an emulsion and to the study of this wonderful movement which most directly suggests the molecular hypothesis. But at the same time we are led to render the theory precise by saying, not only that each particle owes its movement to the impacts of the molecules of the liquid, but further that the energy maintained by the impacts is on the average equal to that of any one of these molecules. . . . We are led to regard the mean energy of translation of a molecule as equal to that possessed by the granules of an emulsion.

EXTENSION OF THE LAWS OF GASES TO DILUTE EMULSIONS

Let us suppose that it is possible to obtain an emulsion, with the granules all identical, an emulsion which I shall call, for shortness, *uniform*. It appeared to me at first intuitively, that the granules of such an emulsion should distribute themselves as a function of the height in the same manner as the molecules of a gas under the influence of gravity. Just as the air is more dense at sea-level than on a mountain-top, so the granules of an emulsion, whatever may be their initial distribution, will attain a permanent state where the concentration will go on diminishing as a function of the height from the lower layers, and the law of rarefaction will be the same as for the air.

A closer examination confirms this conception and gives the law of rarefaction. . . .

Let us imagine a uniform emulsion in equilibrium, which fills a vertical cylinder of cross section s. The state of a horizontal slice contained between the levels h and $h + dh$ would not be changed if it were enclosed between two pistons, permeable to the molecules of water, but impermeable to the granules (membranes of parchment-paper or of collodion could effectively play this part). Each of these semi-permeable pistons is subjected by the impact of the granules which it stops to an osmotic pressure. If the emulsion is dilute, this pressure can be calculated by the same reasoning as for a gas or a dilute solution, in the sense that, if at level h there are n granules per unit volume, the osmotic pressure P will be equal to $2/3nW$, if W signifies the mean granular energy; it will be $2/3(n + dn)$ W at the level $h + dh$. Now the slice of granules under consideration does not fall: for this it is necessary that there should be equilibrium between the difference of the osmotic pressures, which urges it upward, and the total weight of the granules, diminished by the buoyancy of the liquid, which urges them downwards. Hence, calling ϕ the volume of each granule, Δ its density, and δ that of the intergranular liquid, we see that

$$-\frac{2}{3} sW dn = ns \, dh \, \phi(\Delta - \delta)g,$$

or

$$-\frac{2}{3} W \frac{dn}{n} = \phi(\Delta - \delta)g \cdot dh,$$

which, by an obvious integration, involves the following relation between the concentrations n_0 and n at two points for which the difference of level is h:

$$\frac{2}{3} W \log \frac{n_0}{n} = \phi(\Delta - \delta)gh,$$

a relation which may be termed *the equation of distribution* of the emulsion. It shows clearly that *the concentration of the granules of a uniform emulsion decreases in an exponential manner as a function of the height,* in the same way as the barometric pressure does as a function of the altitude.*

If it is possible to measure the magnitudes other than W which enter

---

* I indicated this equation at the time of my first experiments (*Comptes rendus,* May 1908). I have since learnt that Einstein and Smoluchowski, independently, at the time of their beautiful theoretical researches of which I shall speak later, had already seen that the exponential distribution is a necessary consequence of the equipartition of energy. Beyond this it does not seem to have occurred to them that in this sense an *experimentum crucis* could be obtained, deciding for or against the molecular theory of the Brownian movement.

into this equation, one can see whether it is verified and whether the value it indicates for W is the same as that which has been approximately assigned to the molecular energy. In the event of an affirmative answer, the origin of the Brownian movement will be established, and the laws of gases, already extended by Van't Hoff to solutions, can be regarded as still valid even for emulsions with visible granules.

EMULSIONS SUITABLE FOR THE RESEARCHES

Previous observations do not afford any information as to the equilibrium distribution of the granules of an emulsion. It is only known that a large number of colloidal solutions will clarify in their upper part when they are left undisturbed for several weeks or months.

I have made some trials without result upon these colloidal solutions (sulphate of arsenic, ferric hydroxide, collargol, etc.). On the other hand, after some trials, I have been enabled to carry out measurements on emulsions of gamboge, then (with the assistance of M. Dabrowski) on emulsions of mastic.

The *gamboge,* which is used for a water-colour, comes from the desiccation of the latex secreted by *Garcinia morella* (*guttier* of Indo-China). A piece of this substance rubbed with the hand under a thin film of distilled water (as *soapsuds* can be made from a piece of soap) dissolves little by little, giving a beautiful opaque emulsion of a bright yellow colour, in which the microscope shows a swarm of yellow granules of various sizes, all perfectly spherical. These yellow granules can be separated from the liquid in which they are contained by energetic centrifuging, in the same manner as the red corpuscles may be separated from blood serum. They then collect at the bottom of the vessel centrifuged as a yellow mud, above which is a cloudy liquid which is decanted away. The yellow mud diluted anew (by shaking) with distilled water gives the mother emulsion which will serve for the preparation of the uniform emulsions intended for the measurements.

Instead of so using the natural granules the gamboge may be treated with methyl alcohol which entirely dissolves the yellow material (about four-fifths of the raw material) leaving a mucilaginous residue, to the properties of which I shall perhaps have to revert. This alcoholic solution, which is quite transparent and very similar to a solution of bichromate, changes suddenly, on the addition of much water, into a yellow opaque emulsion of the same appearance as the natural emulsion, and like it, composed of spherical granules. They can be separated again by centrifuging from the weak alcoholic liquid which contains them, then diluted with pure water, which gives, as in the preceding case, a mother emulsion which consists of granules of very different sizes. . . .

[Several sections dealing with the preparation of emulsions containing particles of uniform size and the determination of their density are omitted—Editors.]

Let us suppose that a very thin glass plate bored with a large hole has been cemented in a fixed position upon a glass slide [Fig. 38–1]. Thus will be formed a shallow cylindrical vessel of which the height H will be, for example, about 100μ ($0\cdot1$ mm.).*

At the centre of this vessel is placed a drop of the emulsion, which is immediately flattened by the cover-glass, and the latter, sticking to the upper face of the perforated glass plate, completely closes the cell. In addition, to prevent all evaporation, the edges of the cover-glass are covered with paraffin or varnish, which admits of a preparation being kept under observation during several days or even weeks.

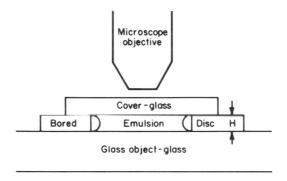

Fig. 38–1.

The preparation is then put on to the stage of a good microscope, which has been carefully levelled. The objective used, being of a very high magnifying power, has a small depth of focus, and only those granules can be seen clearly at the same time which are present in a very thin horizontal layer, the thickness of which is of the order of a micron. By raising or lowering the microscope the granules in another layer can be seen.

The vertical distance between these two layers corresponds to a height h which enters into the equation of distribution, and this must be exactly known. We obtain it by multiplying the displacement h' of the microscope by the relative refractive index of the two media which the cover-glass separates. As the intergranular liquid is water, h will be equal to $\frac{4}{3} h'$, if a dry objective is employed, and simply equal to h' if, as I have most frequently done, a water immersion is used. As for the displacement h', it is

* These requirements are quite satisfied by the *cells for enumeration of the blood corpuscles* (Zeiss), which I have employed.

read off directly on the graduated disc, fixed to the micrometer screw actuating the motion of the microscope (the screw of the Zeiss instrument reads to at least the quarter of a micron).

COUNTING THE GRANULES

It is now necessary that we should be able to determine the ratio $\frac{n_0}{n}$ of the concentration of the granules at two different levels. This ratio is obviously equal to the mean ratio of the number of granules visible in the microscope at these two levels. It remains to find these numbers.

That does not at first sight appear to be easy: it is not a question of counting fixed objects, and when the eye is placed to the microscope and some hundreds of granules are seen moving in every direction, besides disappearing unceasingly while at the same time new granules make their appearance, one is soon convinced of the uselessness of attempts to estimate even roughly the mean number of granules present in the layer under observation.

The simplest course appears to be to take instantaneous photographs of this layer, to obtain the number of sharp images of granules there, and, if the emulsion is so dilute that the number is small, to repeat the process until the mean number of granules obtained on the plate can be considered known to the desired degree of approximation, for example, 1 per cent. I have, indeed, employed this procedure for the relatively large granules, as will appear later. For granules of diameter less than $0 \cdot 5 \, \mu$ I have not been able to obtain good images, and I have had recourse to the following device: I placed in the focal plane of the eyepiece an opaque screen of foil pierced with a very small round hole by means of a dissecting-needle. The field of vision is thus very much diminished, and the eye can take in at a glance the exact number of granules visible at a definite instant, determined by a short signal, or during the very short period of illumination which can be obtained by means of a photographic shutter. It is necessary for this that the number does not exceed 5 or 6.

Operating thus at regular intervals, every 15 seconds for example, a series of numbers is noted down of which the mean value approaches more and more nearly a limit which gives the mean frequency of granules at the level studied, in the small cylindrical layer upon which the microscope is set. Recommencing at another level, the mean frequency is there redetermined for the same volume, and the quotient of these two numbers gives the ratio of the concentrations sought. As well understood, instead of making all the readings relating to one level continuously it is better to alternate the readings, making for example 100 at one level, then 100 at another level, then again 100 at the first level, and so on.

Some thousands of readings are required if some degree of accuracy is aimed at. To take an example, I have copied below the numbers given by 50 consecutive readings at two levels 30 μ apart in one of the emulsions I have used:

3	2	0	3	2	2	5	3	1	2
3	1	1	0	3	3	4	3	4	4
0	3	1	3	1	4	2	2	1	3
1	1	2	2	3	0	1	3	4	3
0	2	2	1	0	2	1	3	2	4

for the lower level, and

2	1	0	0	1	1	3	1	0	0
0	2	0	0	0	0	1	2	2	0
2	1	3	3	1	0	0	0	3	0
1	0	2	1	0	0	1	0	1	0
1	1	0	2	4	1	0	1	0	1

for the upper level.

DETERMINATION OF THE RADIUS OF THE GRANULES

Second Method

This radius would be obtained in a very certain manner, if it were possible to find how many granules (immediately after shaking) there were in a known *titrated* volume of emulsion. That would give the mass of a granule and in consequence, since its density is known, the radius. It would be sufficient for this to count all the granules present in a cylinder of the emulsion having, as height, the height of the preparation (about 100 μ) and, as base, a surface of known area, engraved previously on the microscope slide, which is done in the *cells for the enumeration of corpuscles,* the bottom of which is divided into squares of 50 μ side. But the counting (or integration), layer by layer, of all the granules present in the height of the preparation carries with it much uncertainty. It is necessary in fact to know exactly the depth of each layer, which is of the order of a micron,* not to speak of other difficulties.

Happily I have had occasion in another connection to notice that in a feebly acid medium (for example 0·01 gram-molecule per litre) the granules of gamboge or of mastic collect on the walls of the glass which

---

* We do not need to know this thickness when, in order to obtain the ratio of the concentrations at two different levels, we take the ratio of the number of granules visible at these two levels: it is sufficient for our purpose that the depth of the field, whatever it may be, has the same value for these two levels.

holds the preparation. At a perceptible distance from the walls the Brownian movement is in no way modified; but as soon as the chances of the movement bring a granule into contact with the slide or cover-glass, the granule becomes motionless and does not leave the wall. The emulsion is thus progressively impoverished and, after some hours, all the granules it contained are affixed to the walls. Only those, however, can be counted which are fixed in distinct positions and which do not form part of a clotted mass (partial coagulation of the colloid). Without being able to insist upon it here, I am content to say that very minute quantities of a *protecting* colloid, precisely such as is present in the natural latex of gamboge, added to the emulsion studied, prevent the granules from caking together in water acidulated by pure hydrochloric acid. On this account one may operate as follows:—

The uniform emulsion under observation, which has been previously titrated, is shaken, and a known volume of it is mixed with a known volume of feebly acidulated water, and again shaken: a drop of the mixture is taken and arranged on the microscope slide, and at once flattened by a cover-glass, the edges of which are then paraffined, taking care not to displace it, for all parts at first moistened and then abandoned by the liquid carry away the granules. This done, the preparation is left on the stage of the microscope until all the granules have become attached to the walls. A *camera lucida* is then fitted to the microscope and, focussing on the bottom of the preparation, the contour which corresponds to one of the squares engraved upon the slide is drawn: the image of each of the granules fixed inside this square is marked by a point: then, adjusting the microscope until the granules fixed to the upper face are sharply defined, the images of these granules within the same contour are marked in the same way, which correspond in consequence to the same right prism of emulsion. The points on the drawing obtained can be subsequently counted at leisure, and their number is equal to the number of granules sought.

The same work is then recommenced upon another portion of the preparation, and so on until the mean value of the number of granules marked in each square can be considered well known. An obvious calculation then permits the number of granules contained in unit volume of the primary titrated emulsion to be found and gives in consequence the required radius, by a *second method* into which the law of Stokes does not enter. . . .

The use of the *camera lucida,* fatiguing in other respects, would have been avoided by directly photographing the granules fixed to the walls. But the eye is more sensitive than the photographic plate as regards the visibility of very small clear granules on a bottom almost equally clear (it must not be forgotten that the granules are transparent spheres), and I have only been able to employ photography for granules having a diameter exceeding a demimicron.

THE PROGRESSIVE RAREFACTION AS A FUNCTION OF THE HEIGHT

Let us consider a vertical cylinder of emulsion. . . . At first, after the shaking which necessarily accompanies the manipulation, the granules of this emulsion have an almost uniform distribution. But, if our kinetic theory is exact, this distribution will change from the time the preparation is left at rest, will attain a limiting state, and in this state the concentration will decrease in an exponential manner as a function of the height.

This is just what experiment verifies. At first practically as many granules are visible in the upper layers as in the lower layers of the emulsion. A few minutes suffice for the lower layers to become manifestly richer in granules than the upper layers. If then the counting of the granules at two different levels is commenced, the ratio $\frac{n_0}{n}$ of the concentrations at these levels is found to have a value gradually increasing for some time, but more and more slowly, and which ends by showing no systematic variation. With the emulsions I have employed three hours is sufficient for the attainment of a well-defined limiting distribution in an emulsion left at rest, for practically the same values are found after 3 hours as after 15 days. Those emulsions which have not been rendered aseptic are occasionally invaded by elongated and very active protozoa, which, by stirring up the emulsion like fishes agitating the mud of a pond, much diminish the inequality of distribution between the upper and lower layers. But if one has patience to wait until these microbes, through lack of food, die and fall inert to the bottom of the preparation, which takes two or three days, it will be found that the initial limiting redistribution is exactly regained, and this possesses all the characters of the distribution of a permanent regime.

Once this permanent state is attained, it is easy to see whether the concentration decreases in an exponential manner as a function of the height. The following measurements show that it is so.

At first I worked on granules of gamboge of radius approximately equal to $0 \cdot 14 \mu$, which were studied in a cell having a height of 110μ. The concentrations of the granules were determined in five equidistant planes, the lowest plane being taken 5μ above the bottom of the preparation (to eliminate the possible influence of the boundary), the distance between two consecutive planes being 25μ, so that the uppermost plane was 5μ below the surface.

The numbers found were between themselves as

$$100, \quad 116, \quad 146, \quad 170, \quad 200,$$

whereas the numbers

100, 119, 142, 169, 201,

which do not differ from the preceding by more than the limits of experimental error, are in geometrical progression. The distribution of the granules is thus quite exponential, as is the case for a gas in equilibrium under the influence of gravity. Only the diminution of the concentration to one-half, which for the atmosphere is produced by a height of about 6 kilometres, is produced here in a height of $0 \cdot 1$ millimetre.

But this fall of concentration is still too feeble for the exponential character of the decrease to be quite manifest. I have therefore tried to secure with larger granules a more rapid fall of concentration.

My most careful series has been done with granules of gamboge having a radius of $0 \cdot 212 \mu$. The readings have been made, in a cell having a height of 100μ, in four equidistant horizontal planes cutting the vessel at the levels

5μ, 35μ, 65μ, 95μ.

These readings, made by direct counting through a needle-hole, relate to 13,000 granules and give, respectively for these levels, concentrations proportional to the numbers

100, 47, 22·6, 12,

which are practically equal to the numbers

100, 48, 23, 11·1,

which again are exactly in a geometrical progression.

Thus the exponential distribution cannot be doubted, each elevation of 30μ here decreasing the concentration to about half its value.

It may be interesting to observe that the largest of the granules, for which I have found the laws of perfect gases followed, are already visible in sunlight under a strong lens. They behave as the molecules of a perfect gas, of which the gram-molecule would weigh *200,000 tons*.

PRECISE DETERMINATION OF AVOGADRO'S CONSTANT

Recapitulating, equal granules distribute themselves in a dilute emulsion as heavy molecules obeying the laws of perfect gases, and the equation of their distribution, since W may now be replaced by $\dfrac{3}{2}\dfrac{RT}{N}$, can be written

$$2 \cdot 303 \, \frac{RT}{N} \, \log_{10} \frac{n_0}{n} = \frac{4}{3} \pi a^3 g(\Delta - \delta)h.$$

Once this has been well established, this same equation affords a means for determining the constant N, and the constants depending upon it, which is, it appears, *capable of an unlimited precision*. The preparation of a uniform emulsion and the determination of the magnitudes other than N which enter into the equation can in reality be pushed to whatever degree of perfection desired. It is simply a question of patience and time; nothing limits *a priori* the accuracy of the results, and the mass of the atom can be obtained, if desired, with the same precision as the mass of the Earth. I scarcely need observe, on the other hand, that even perfect measurements of compressibility might not be able to prevent an uncertainty of perhaps 40 per cent. in the value of N, deduced from the equation of Van der Waals, by means of hypotheses which we know are certainly not completely exact.

The values found for N by the five series of experiments detailed give a rough mean of 69 . 10^{22}; the most careful of the series is the one made with *mastic* (dotting upon photographic plates) which gives 70 . 10^{22}.

I have made, with *gamboge,* a sixth series already mentioned above on various occasions, which I consider considerably more accurate still. The mean radius of the granules of the emulsion employed was found equal to $0 \cdot 212 \, \mu$, by counting 11,000 granules of a titrated emulsion, and to $0 \cdot 213 \, \mu$ by application of the law of Stokes. The difference of density between the material of the granules and the intergranular water was $0 \cdot 2067$ at 20°, the temperature to which the measurements refer. 13,000 granules were counted at different heights (direct observation through a needle-hole), and it was verified that the distribution was quite exponential, each elevation of 30 μ lowering the concentration to about half of its value (exact figures are given in No. 22). The value resulting from these measurements is $70 \cdot 5 \times 10^{22}$. . . . . Thus, then, one is led to adopt for Avogadro's constant the value

$$N = 70 \cdot 5 \times 10^{22}.$$

39

ooooooooooo

THE -PARTICLE AND
HELIUM

ooooooooooo

Ernest Rutherford (1871-1937)

Rutherford's desire to be closer to the center of science than a position at McGill University afforded was realized in 1907 when Professor Arthur Schuster, head of physics at Manchester, retired in Rutherford's favor. Manchester was to be the site of Rutherford's greatest triumph, the discovery of the nuclear atom, and from the beginning he found everything there to his liking.

One of the finest researches that Rutherford completed at Manchester in collaboration with T. Royds, a research student, was the proof that α particles are indeed ionized helium atoms. This had been suspected for some time and correspondence of Rutherford's as early as 1905 expresses this conviction. Various lines of evidence had indicated the correctness of this point of view, including charge-to-mass ratio (e/m) measurements. The direct proof was still lacking, however, until the elegant and simple experiment, described in the following paper, was made. It consisted of compressing a small quantity of the emanation of radium into a closed glass capillary surrounded by a glass enclosure tipped with a spark discharge tube. The walls of the capillary were sufficiently thin to allow the α particles emitted by the emanation to shoot through them but they were nevertheless quite gas-tight to the passage of helium itself.

The α particles entering the evacuated glass enclosure surrounding the capillary were stopped by the thicker walls of the enclosure. Tests on the discharge tube located on top of the enclosure were made to ensure the absence of helium. After several days spark tests showed faintly visible yellow helium lines and after six days most of the visible helium spectrum

641

was present in the discharge. The precautions taken to show that the helium could have come only from the α particles are described.

०००००००

R U T H E R F O R D   and   R O Y D S

The Nature of the α Particle from Radioactive Substances [1]

THE EXPERIMENTAL EVIDENCE COLLECTED during the last few years has strongly supported the view that the α particle is a charged helium atom, but it has been found exceedingly difficult to give a decisive proof of the relation. In recent papers, Rutherford and Geiger have supplied still further evidence of the correctness of this point of view. The number of α particles from one gram of radium have been counted, and the charge carried by each determined. The values of several radioactive quantities, calculated on the assumption that the α particle is a helium atom carrying two unit charges, have been shown to be in good agreement with the experimental numbers. In particular, the good agreement between the calculated rate of production of helium by radium and the rate experimentally determined by Sir James Dewar, is strong evidence in favour of the identity of the α particle with the helium atom.

The methods of attack on this problem have been largely indirect, involving considerations of the charge carried by the helium atom and the value of e/m of the α particle. The proof of the identity of the α particle with the helium atom is incomplete until it can be shown that the α particles, accumulated quite independently of the matter from which they are expelled, consist of helium. For example, it might be argued that the appearance of helium in the radium emanation was a result of the expulsion of the α particle, in the same way that the appearance of radium A is a consequence of the expulsion of an α particle from the emanation. If one atom of helium appeared for each α particle expelled, calculation and experiment might still agree, and yet the α particle itself might be an atom of hydrogen or of some other substance.

---

[1] Ernest Rutherford and T. Royds, *Philosophical Magazine*, 17 (1909), 281–286.

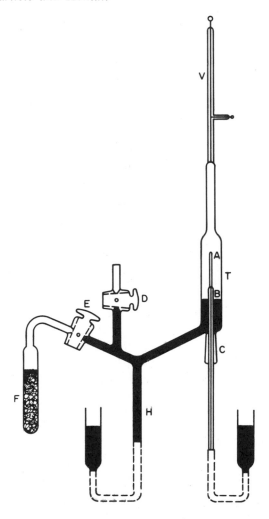

Fig. 39–1.

We have recently made experiments to test whether helium appears in a vessel into which the α particles have been fired, the active matter itself being enclosed in a vessel sufficiently thin to allow the α particles to escape, but impervious to the passage of helium or other radioactive products.

The experimental arrangement is clearly seen in [Fig. 39–1]. The equilibrium quantity of emanation from about 140 milligrams of radium was purified and compressed by means of a mercury-column into a fine glass tube A about 1·5 cms. long. This fine tube, which was sealed on a larger capillary tube B, was sufficiently thin to allow the α particles from the emanation and its products to escape, but sufficiently strong to withstand atmospheric pressure. After some trials, Mr. Baumbach succeeded in blowing such fine tubes very uniform in thickness. The thickness of the wall of the tube employed in most of the experiments was less than $\frac{1}{100}$ mm., and was equivalent in stopping power of the α particle to about 2 cms. of air. Since the ranges of the α particles from the emanation and its products radium A and radium C are 4·3, 4·8, and 7 cms. respectively, it is seen that the great majority * of the α particles expelled by the active matter escape through the walls of the tube. The ranges of the α particles after passing through the glass were determined with the aid of a zinc-sulphide screen. Immediately after the introduction of the emanation the phosphorescence showed brilliantly when the screen was close to the tube, but practically disappeared at a distance of 3 cms. After an hour, bright phosphorescence was observable at a distance of 5 cms. Such a result is to be expected. The phosphorescence initially observed was due mainly to the α particles of the emanation and its product radium A (period 3 mins.). In the course of time the amount of radium C, initially zero, gradually increased, and the α radiations from it of range 7 cms. were able to cause phosphorescence at a greater distance.

The glass tube A was surrounded by a cylindrical glass tube T, 7·5 cms. long and 1·5 cms. diameter, by means of a ground glass joint C. A small vacuum-tube V was attached to the upper end of T. The outer glass tube T was exhausted by a pump through the stopcock D, and the exhaustion completed with the aid of the charcoal tube F cooled by liquid air. By means of a mercury column H attached to a reservoir, mercury was forced into the tube T until it reached the bottom of the tube A.

Part of the α particles which escaped through the walls of the fine tube were stopped by the outer glass tube and part by the mercury surface. If the α particle is a helium atom, helium should gradually diffuse from the glass and mercury into the exhausted space, and its presence could then be detected spectroscopically by raising the mercury and compressing the gases into the vacuum-tube.

In order to avoid any possible contamination of the apparatus with helium, freshly distilled mercury and entirely new glass apparatus were used. Before introducing the emanation into A, the absence of helium was confirmed experimentally. At intervals after the introduction of the emanation the mercury was raised, and the gases in the outer tube spectroscopically examined. After 24 hours no trace of the helium yellow line was seen; after 2 days the helium yellow [line] was faintly visible; after 4 days the helium yellow and green lines were bright; and after 6 days all the

---

* The α particles fired at a very oblique angle to the tube would be stopped in the glass. The fraction stopped in this way would be small under the experimental conditions.

stronger lines of the helium spectrum were observed. The absence of the neon spectrum shows that the helium present was not due to a leakage of air into the apparatus.

There is, however, one possible source of error in this experiment. The helium may not be due to the α particles themselves, but may have *diffused* from the emanation through the thin walls of the glass tube. In order to test this point the emanation was completely pumped out of A, and after some hours a quantity of helium, about 10 times the previous volume of the emanation, was compressed into the same tube A.

The outer tube T and the vacuum-tube were removed and a fresh apparatus substituted. Observations to detect helium in the tube T were made at intervals, in the same way as before, but no trace of the helium spectrum was observed over a period of eight days.

The helium in the tube A was then pumped out and a fresh supply of emanation substituted. Results similar to the first experiment were observed. The helium yellow and green lines showed brightly after four days.

These experiments thus show conclusively that the helium could not have diffused through the glass walls, but must have been derived from the α particles which were fired through them. In other words, the experiments give a decisive proof that the α particle after losing its charge is an atom of helium.

OTHER EXPERIMENTS

We have seen that in the experiments above described helium was not observed in the outer tube in sufficient quantity to show the characteristic yellow line until two days had elapsed. Now the equilibrium amount of emanation from 100 milligrams of radium should produce helium at the rate of about ·03 c.mm. per day. The amount produced in one day, if present in the outer tube, should produce a bright spectrum of helium under the experimental conditions. It thus appeared probable that the helium fired into the glass must escape very slowly into the exhausted space, for if the helium escaped at once, the presence of helium should have been detected a few hours after the introduction of the emanation.

In order to examine this point more closely the experiments were repeated, with the addition that a cylinder of thin sheet lead of sufficient thickness to stop the α particles was placed over the fine emanation tube. Preliminary experiments, in the manner described later, showed that the lead-foil did not initially contain a detectable amount of helium. Twenty-four hours after the introduction into the tube A of about the same amount of emanation as before, the yellow and green lines of helium showed brightly in the vacuum-tube, and after two days the whole helium spectrum was observed. The spectrum of helium in this case after one day was of about the same intensity as that after the fourth day in the experiments without the lead screen. It was thus clear that the lead-foil gave up the helium fired into it far more readily than the glass.

In order to form an idea of the rapidity of escape of the helium from the lead some further experiments were made. The outer cylinder T was removed and a small cylinder of lead-foil placed round the thin emanation-tube surrounded the air at atmospheric pressure. After exposure for a definite time to the emanation, the lead screen was removed and tested for helium as follows. The lead-foil was placed in a glass tube between two stopcocks. In order to avoid a possible release of the helium present in the lead by pumping out the air, the air was displaced by a current of pure electrolytic oxygen.* The stopcocks were closed and the tube attached to a subsidiary apparatus similar to that employed for testing for the presence of neon and helium in the gases produced by the action of the radium emanation on water (Phil. Mag. Nov. 1908). The oxygen was absorbed by charcoal and the tube then heated beyond the melting-point of lead to allow the helium to escape. The presence of helium was then spectroscopically looked for in the usual way. Using this method, it was found possible to detect the presence of helium in the lead which had been exposed for only four hours to the α rays from the emanation. After an exposure of 24 hours the helium yellow and green lines came out brightly. These experiments were repeated several times with similar results.

A number of blank experiments were made, using samples of the lead-foil which had not been exposed to the α rays, but in no case was any helium detected. In a similar way, the presence of helium was detected in a cylinder of tinfoil exposed for a few hours over the emanation-tube.

These experiments show that the helium does not escape at once from the lead, but there is on the average a period of retardation of several hours and possibly longer.

The detection of helium in the lead and tin foil, as well as in the glass, removes a possible objection that the helium might have been in some way present in the glass initially, and was liberated as a consequence of its bombardment by the α particles.

The use of such thin glass tubes containing emanation affords a simple and convenient method of examining the effect on substances of an intense α radiation quite independently of the radioactive material contained in the tube.

We can conclude with certainty from these experiments that the α particle after losing its charge is a helium atom. Other evidence indicates that the charge is twice the unit charge carried by the hydrogen atom set free in the electrolysis of water.

---

* That the air was completely displaced was shown by the absence of neon in the final spectrum.

40

○○○○○○○○○○○

ATOMS OF ELECTRICITY

○○○○○○○○○○○

Robert Andrews Millikan
(1868-1953)

The idea that electricity, like matter, might be composed of discrete units seems to have originated with Benjamin Franklin about 1750. He wrote that "The electrical matter consists of particles extremely subtile, since it can permeate common matter, even the densest, with such freedom and ease as not to receive any appreciable resistance." Despite this categorical statement, it must be noted that no experimental evidence existed for this point of view until Faraday's discovery of the laws of electrolysis more than eighty years later. Then it was found that the transference of a fixed quantity of electricity through a given electrolyte, regardless of its concentration, always caused the appearance of a definite amount of material at the cathode of the electrolytic cell. The complete significance of this discovery could not then be appreciated because the atomic theory of matter was not on a firm basis, despite the demonstrated value of Dalton's theory in advancing the science of chemistry. Moreover, Faraday himself was very cautious about the atomic theory; if he entertained the theory at all, he thought of atoms as proposed by Boscovitch, i.e., as point centers of force. The idea of a fundamental electric charge appears to have been foreign to Faraday's thinking and it certainly was to the great master of electrical theory who followed him, James Clerk Maxwell. In fact, in speaking of the discrete charge explanation of electrolysis, Maxwell states that "it is extremely improbable that . . . we shall retain in any form the theory of molecular charges. . . ."

Nevertheless, the hypothesis of discrete charges was not completely neglected. G. Johnstone Stoney, in particular, emphasized it in 1881 and not only estimated the size of the fundamental unit as 3×10^{-11} esu (electrostatic units) (more than ten times too small) but also designated this quantity of charge as the "electron." Indeed, he went further and proposed as basic units of measurement, not length, mass, and time, but the (presumably) more basic natural units, the velocity of light, the co-efficient of universal gravitation, and the elementary electric charge. Inasmuch as Faraday's laws of electrolysis cannot do more than make statements about the *average* charge of the great number which must pass through an electrolytic cell in order to deposit appreciable amounts of matter, Stoney's hypothesis of an elementary electric charge could not have been taken too seriously. As an example of how wrong he could have been the reader need only recall the constancy of atomic weight determinations together with Dalton's dictum that the atoms of a given substance were "all alike in weight, figure, mass, etc." and compare it with what was found when isotopes were discovered.

Even the discovery of the electron by Thomson did not require that there be a single fixed elemental electric charge. His experiments measured the ratio of charge to mass, e/m, of the cathode ray particles; the fact that particles appeared in all gases with the same charge-to-mass ratio did not exclude some compensating adjustment of charge and mass, however unlikely that might be. While it was assumed that the charge e (as well as the mass m) of all the particles was constant, direct experimental measurements were needed not only to show the constancy of the charge but also to find its value. Once the magnitude of e was determined, then the mass of the electron could be deduced from the known value of the e/m ratio. The knowledge of both these constants was of the utmost importance for the further understanding of atomic structure and the development of atomic theory.

The necessity of determining the value of e was, of course, immediately clear to Thomson following the e/m measurements. He, as well as others in the Cavendish Laboratory, made several attempts to determine its value. All were based on the application of C. T. R. Wilson's discovery that a sudden expansion of air in a chamber saturated with water vapor will produce a cloud, the droplets of which condense around ions present in the moist air (see Chapter 42). In an experiment by H. A. Wilson in 1903, the ions were produced by X-ray irradiation of the saturated air. The top of the cloud produced by the expansion in the cloud chamber was timed as it fell between two horizontal metal plates, first under the action of gravity alone and then under the combined action of gravity and an imposed electric field acting on the ions. From this a value of e was deduced but its precision was low, the separate determinations fluctuating between 2.0×10^{-10} and 4.4×10^{-10} electrostatic units (esu of charge).

Attracted by the possibilities of greatly improving the accuracy of the measurement of e and thus finding m, and of the importance of the whole problem, Robert A. Millikan took up the experiment at the University of Chicago in 1909. His original idea was to use Wilson's method but to reduce some inaccuracies by including a measurement in which the top of the cloud was held steady by the application of a sufficiently high voltage. This required the building of a 10,000-volt small cell storage battery which at that time was an undertaking of some difficulty. When the experiment was repeated with the application of this high voltage the workers found that instead of holding the cloud steady, it forced the immediate disappearance of the cloud. The ions in the cloud were, of course, pulled to the charged plates by the strong electric field. However, instead of destroying the experiment, this event unexpectedly disclosed a much more accurate way of carrying it out, for it was found that in the field of the observing telescope, a few drops remained for some time and appeared to be suspended almost motionless in the field of view. These were the few for which the upward force of the electric field just balanced the downward pull of gravity. Thus instead of experimenting on a cloud of drops it was possible to make measurements on a *single* charged drop and to keep this drop under observation for some time. This change in the experimental procedure ultimately made it possible to show unambiguously that nature supplies electric charge only in one fixed size, that all charges, no matter where they may occur, are only multiples of this charge, and that electric charges of any other magnitude do not exist.

To see how this fundamental electronic charge is determined, we shall review Millikan's method very briefly. Suppose that oil droplets (water droplets evaporate) are sprayed into the air space between two parallel horizontal metal plates. Once in this space the droplet is a free body and will fall in the normal way under the influence of gravity. However, since the droplet is very small it will soon reach a terminal velocity v_1 because of air resistance, and its subsequent downward motion will be at constant speed. In fact, the motion of any object moving at low speed in a resisting medium assumes a speed proportional to the force driving it. In the case of the oil droplet, the driving force in free fall is its weight w_1, which by Newton's second law is given by $w = mg$, where m is the mass of the droplet and g the acceleration of gravity. Suppose next that the plates are charged so that the upper of the two has positive polarity and the droplet negative. The electric field F between the plates then acts to drive the droplet upward, the net upward force being $Fe_n - mg$, where e_n is the number of electronic charges carried by the drop. This force determines an upward terminal velocity v_2.

Since in this range of speeds the "constant" of proportionality between force and terminal speed is, in fact, constant, the two proportional relations $mg \sim v_1$ and $Fe_n - mg \sim v_2$ may be divided, giving $v_1/v_2 =$

$mg/(Fe_n - mg)$. If this equation is solved for e_n we find $e_n = (mg/Fv_1)$ $(v_1 + v_2)$. This is Millikan's equation (9) in the following article. If now the drop changes its charge by capturing a charged ion, then

$$e'_n = \frac{mg}{Fv_1} (v_1 + v'_2).$$

Hence the value of the charge on the ion e_i is the difference of the last two relations or

$$e_i = e'_n - e_n = \frac{mg}{Fv_2} (v'_2 - v_2).$$

Since in a given experiment mg and Fv_1 are constants, the value of e_i is proportional to $(v'_2 - v_2)$. The latter quantity was found to have a minimum value of which all other values were multiples. It thus became clear that ionic electric charge was somehow regulated by the laws of nature to occur in the afore-mentioned single fixed size. The following chapter, taken from Millikan's book on the electron, gives a clear account of some of the facets of this fascinating research.

The main work on the determination of the electronic charge was finished in 1912, although subsidiary investigations to increase its accuracy were continued until 1917 when Millikan left his academic work at Chicago to devote his energies to organizing scientific work for the United States government during World War I. During the 1912–1917 period he also carried out another important major research, the verification of Einstein's photoelectric equation, together with a determination of Planck's constant. Einstein's photon theory was not taken very seriously at that time and this research did much to convince physicists of its importance.

Millikan served the United States government during World War I as one of the chief organizers of scientific effort on war problems, the most important of which was the organization of antisubmarine research. He ultimately became Chief of Science and Research, Division of the Signal Corps, U. S. Army. He was also instrumental during the war period in founding the National Research Council. Following the war, he returned briefly to the University of Chicago but a very strong bid for his services was made by the California Institute of Technology; in September 1921 he took the position there as director of the Norman Bridge Laboratory. He was then fifty-three years old and had been at Chicago for twenty-five years. At Cal Tech he had practically a free hand but, of necessity, much of his time was devoted to administration. Through his contact with physicists both in the United States and in Europe he was able to build an outstanding physics department, strengthened by the addition of Einstein, Lorentz, Sommerfeld, and others as visiting professors. In 1923 Millikan was awarded the Nobel Prize in recognition of his work on the electronic charge and the photoelectric effect. In these years, he began research in the then new field of cosmic rays. Perhaps the high point in his cosmic ray work came in 1932, when Carl D. Anderson, working under Millikan's direction, discovered the positive electron, or positron. This was followed a few years later by Anderson's discovery, with S. H. Neddermeyer, of the first of the heavy electrons, the muon.

Millikan continued at Cal Tech until his retirement in 1945. He died in Pasadena at the age of eighty-five on December 19, 1953. His influence on American physics was profound and reflects his personal characteristics of independence, vigor, and industry, qualities that were instilled in him as a youth. He was a man of great self-assurance and conveyed the impression of an able and forceful business executive. These qualities were so evident that an amusing canard circulated about him among the graduate students in physics in several of the country's leading universities. It was said that the unit of pomposity was the "kan" but that this unit was so large as to be impractical for ordinary use. Therefore the practical unit was taken as $\frac{1}{1000}$ of this value or the "millikan."

Millikan was born in Morrison, Illinois, on March 22, 1868, the son of a struggling Protestant country minister. When he was five the family moved briefly to McGregor, Iowa, and again in 1875 to Maquoketa, Iowa, where he grew up with two brothers and three sisters in the typical fashion of small-town life of that period. He finished high school at seventeen and went to Oberlin College in 1886. In his sophomore year he was entrusted with the teaching of physics, a subject which he had never studied. He continued teaching until 1893 when he took his M.A. degree two years after graduation. He was then twenty-five years old.

Having been offered a fellowship in physics, Millikan spent the next two years at Columbia University and obtained his Ph.D. there in 1895. After three terms of postdoctoral study in Germany at Jena, Berlin, and Göttingen, he returned to take a position as assistant to Michelson at the University of Chicago in September 1896. His first twelve years there, from 1896 to 1908, were spent largely in teaching, textbook writing, and getting several research problems under way, none of which yielded very promising results. In 1909 he began his outstanding work on determining the electronic charge. A description of some of this work follows.

ଡ଼ଡ଼ଡ଼ଡ଼ଡ଼ଡ଼ଡ଼ଡ଼

MILLIKAN

The Atomic Nature of Electricity [1]

ISOLATION OF INDIVIDUAL IONS AND MEASUREMENT OF THEIR RELATIVE CHARGES

IN ORDER TO COMPARE THE charges on different ions, the procedure adopted was to blow with an ordinary commercial atomizer an oil spray into the chamber C [Fig. 40–1]. The air with which this spray was blown was first rendered dust-free by passage through a tube containing glass wool. The minute droplets of oil constituting the spray, most of them having a radius of the order of a one-thousandth of a millimeter, slowly fell in the chamber C, and occasionally one of them would find its way through the minute pinhole p in the middle of the circular brass plate M, 22 cm. in diameter, which formed one of the plates of the air condenser. The other plate, N, was held 16 mm. beneath it by three ebonite posts a. By means of the switch S these plates could be charged, the one positively and the other negatively, by making them the terminals of a 10,000-volt storage battery B, while throwing the switch the other way (to the left) short-circuited them and reduced the field between them to zero. The oil droplets which entered at p were illuminated by a powerful beam of light which passed through diametrically opposite windows in the encircling ebonite strip c. As viewed through a third window in c on the side toward the reader, it appeared as a bright star on a black background. These droplets which entered p were found in general to have been strongly charged by the frictional process involved in blowing the spray, so that when the field was thrown on in the proper direction they would be pulled up toward M. Just before the drop under observation could strike M the plates would be short-circuited and the drop allowed to fall under gravity until it was close to N, when the direction of motion would be again reversed by throwing on the field. In this way the drop would be kept traveling back and forth between the plates. The first time the experiment was tried an ion was caught within a few

---

[1] From Robert Millikan, *The Electron* (2nd ed.; Chicago: University of Chicago Press, 1924) Chapter 6, pp. 67–85.

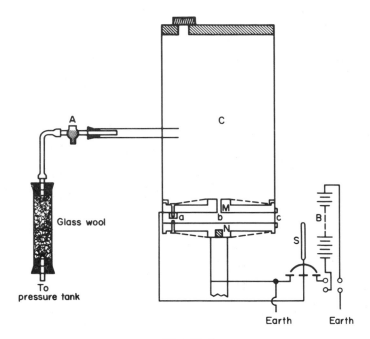

Fig. 40–1.

minutes, and the fact of its capture was signaled to the observer by the change in the speed with which it moved up when the field was on. The significance of the experiment can best be appreciated by examination of the complete record of one of the early experiments when the timing was done merely with a stop watch [see Table 40–1].

The column headed t_g gives the successive times which the droplet required to fall between two fixed cross-hairs in the observing telescope whose distance apart corresponded in this case to an actual distance of fall of .5222 cm. It will be seen that these numbers are all the same within the limits of error of a stop-watch measurement. The column marked t_F gives the successive times which the droplet required to rise under the influence of the electrical field produced by applying in this case 5,051 volts of potential difference to the plates M and N. It will be seen that after the second trip up, the time changed from 12.4 to 21.8, indicating, since in this case the drop was positive, that a negative ion had been caught from the air. The next time recorded under t_F, namely, 34.8, indicates that another negative ion had been caught. The next time, 84.5, indicates the capture of still another negative ion. This charge was held for two trips, when the speed changed back again to 34.6, showing that a positive ion had now been caught which carried precisely the same charge as the negative ion which before caused the inverse change in time, i.e., that from 34.8 to 84.5.

In order to obtain some of the most important consequences of this and other similar experiments we need make no assumption further than this, that the velocity with which the drop moves is proportional to the

TABLE 40 – 1

t_g	t_F
13.6	12.5
13.8	12.4
13.4	21.8
13.4	34.8
13.6	84.5
13.6	85.5
13.7	34.6
13.5	34.8
13.5	16.0
13.8	34.8
13.7	34.6
13.8	21.9
13.6	
13.5	
13.4	
13.8	
13.4	
Mean 13.595	

force acting upon it and is independent of the electrical charge which it carries. Fortunately this assumption can be put to very delicate experimental test, as will presently be shown, but introducing it for the time being as a mere assumption, as Townsend, Thomson, and Wilson had done before, we get

$$\frac{v_1}{v_2} = \frac{mg}{Fe_n - mg} \text{ or } e_n = \frac{mg}{Fv_1} (v_1 + v_2) \tag{9}$$

The negative sign is used in the denominator because v_2 will for convenience be taken as positive when the drop is going up in the direction of F, while v_1 will be taken as positive when it is going down in the direction of g. e_n denotes the charge on the drop, and must not be confused with the charge on an ion. If now by the capture of an ion the drop changes its charge from e_n to e_n^1, then the value of the captured charge e_i is

$$e_i = e_n^1 - e_n = \frac{mg}{Fv_1} (v_2' - v_2) \qquad (10)$$

and since

$$\frac{mg}{Fv_1}$$

is a constant for this drop, any charge which it may capture will always be proportional to $(v_2' - v_2)$, that is, to the change produced in the velocity in the field F by the captured ion. The successive values of v_2 and of $(v_2' - v_2)$, these latter being obtained by subtracting successive values of the velocities given under v_2, are shown in [Table 40–2].

TABLE 40–2

v_2	$(v_2' - v_2)$
$\frac{.5222}{12.45} = .04196$	.01806 ÷ 2 = .00903
$\frac{.5222}{21.5} = .02390$	.00885 ÷ 1 = .00885
$\frac{.5222}{34.7} = .01505$	.00891 ÷ 1 = .00891
$\frac{.5222}{85.0} = .006144$	.00891 ÷ 1 = .00891
$\frac{.5222}{34.7} = .01505$	.01759 ÷ 2 = .00880
$\frac{.5222}{16.0} = .03264$	.01759 ÷ 2 = .00880
$\frac{.5222}{34.7} = .01505$	.00891 ÷ 1 = .00891
$\frac{.5222}{21.85} = .02390$	

It will be seen from the last column that within the limits of error of a stop-watch measurement, all the charges captured have exactly the same value save in three cases. In all of these three the captured charges were just twice as large as those appearing in the other changes. Relationships of exactly this sort have been found to hold absolutely without exception, no matter in what gas the drops have been suspended or what sort of droplets were used upon which to catch the ions. In many cases a given drop has been held under observation for five or six hours at a time and has been seen to catch not eight or ten ions, as in the experiment above, but hundreds of them. Indeed, I have observed, all told, the capture of many thousands of ions in this way, and in no case have I ever found one the charge of which, when tested as above, did not have either exactly the value of the smallest charge ever captured or else a very small multiple of that value. *Here, then, is direct, unimpeachable proof that the electron is not a "statistical mean," but that rather the electrical charges found on ions all have either exactly the same value or else small exact multiples of that value.*

PROOF THAT ALL STATIC CHARGES BOTH ON CONDUCTORS AND INSULATORS ARE BUILT UP OF ELECTRONS

The foregoing experiment leads, however, to results of much more fundamental importance than that mentioned in the preceding section. The charge which the droplet had when it first came under observation had been acquired, not by the capture of ions from the air, but by the ordinary frictional process involved in blowing the spray. If then ordinary static charges are built up of electrons, this charge should be found to be an exact multiple of the ionic charge which had been found from the most reliable measurement shown in [Table 40–2] to be proportional to the velocity .00891. This initial charge e_n on the drop is seen from equations (9) and (10) to bear the same relation to $(v_1 + v_2)$ which the ionic charge $e'_n - e_n$ bears to $(v'_2 - v_2)$. Now, $v_1 = .5222/13 \cdot 595 = .03842$, hence $v_1 + v_2 = .03842 + .04196 = .08038$. Dividing this by 9 we obtain .008931, which is within about one-fifth of 1 per cent of the value found in the last column of [Table 40–2] as the smallest charge carried by an ion. *Our experiment has then given us for the first time a means of comparing a frictional charge with the ionic charge, and the frictional charge has in this instance been found to contain exactly 9 electrons.* A more exact means of making this comparison will be given presently, but suffice it to say here that experiments like the foregoing have now been tried on thousands of drops in different media, some of the drops being made of non-conductors like oil, some of semi-conductors like glycerin, some of excellent metallic conductors like mercury. In every case, without a single exception, the initial charge placed upon the drop by the frictional process, and all of the dozen or more charges which have resulted from the capture by the drop of a larger or smaller number of ions, have been found to be exact multiples of the smallest charge caught from the air. Some of these drops have started with no charge at all, and one, two, three, four, five, and six elementary charges or electrons have been picked up. Others have started with seven or eight units, others with twenty, others with fifty, others with a hundred, others with a hundred and fifty elementary units, and have picked up in each case a dozen or two of elementary charges on either side of the starting-point, so that, in all, drops containing every possible number of electrons between one and one hundred and fifty have been observed and the number of electrons which each drop carried has been accurately counted by the method described. When the number is less than fifty there is not a whit more uncertainty about this count than there is in counting one's own fingers and toes. It is not found possible to determine with certainty the number of electrons in a charge containing more than one hundred or two hundred of them, for the simple reason that the method of measurement used fails to detect the difference between 200 and 201, that is, we cannot measure $v'_2 - v_2$ with an accuracy greater than one-half of 1 per cent. But it is quite inconceivable that large charges such as are dealt with in commercial applications of electricity can be built up in an essentially different way from that in which the small charges whose electrons we are able to count are found to be. Furthermore, since it has been definitely proved that an electrical current is nothing but the motion of an electrical charge over or through a conductor, it is evident that the experiments under consideration furnish not only the most direct and convincing of evidence that all electrical charges are built up out of these very units which we have been dealing with as individuals in these experiments, but that all electrical currents consist merely in the transport of these electrons through the conducting bodies.

In order to show the beauty and precision with which these multiple relationships stand out in all experiments of this kind, a table corresponding to much more precise measurements than those given heretofore is here introduced [Table 40–3]. The time of fall and rise shown in the first and second columns were taken with a Hipp chronoscope reading to one-thousandth of a second. The third column gives the reciprocals of these times. These are used in place of the velocities v_2 in the field, since distance of fall and rise is always the same. The fourth column gives the successive changes in speed due to the capture of ions. These also are expressed merely as time reciprocals. For reasons which will be explained in the next section, each one of these changes may correspond to the capture of not merely one but of several distinct ions. The numbers in the fifth column represent simply the small integer by which it is found that the numbers in the fourth column must be divided in order to obtain the numbers in the sixth column. These will be seen to be exactly alike

TABLE 40-3

t_g Sec.	t_F Sec.	$\frac{1}{t_F}$	$\left(\frac{1}{t'_F} - \frac{1}{t_F}\right)$	n'	$\frac{1}{n'}\left(\frac{1}{t'_F} - \frac{1}{t_F}\right)$	$\left(\frac{1}{t_g} + \frac{1}{t_F}\right)$	n	$\frac{1}{n}\left(\frac{1}{t_g} + \frac{1}{t_F}\right)$
11.848	80.708	.01236				.09655	18	.005366
11.890	22.366 }		} .03234	6	.005390			
11.908	22.390 }	.04470				.12887	24	.005371
11.904	22.368 }		} .03751	7	.005358			
11.882	140.565 }	.007192 }				.09138	17	.005375
11.906	79.600 }	.01254 }	} .005348	1	.005348	.09673	18	.005374
11.838	34.748 }		} .01616	3	.005387			
11.816	34.762 }	.02870				.11289	21	.005376
11.776	34.846 }							
11.840	29.286 }	.03414				.11833	22	.005379
11.904	29.236 }		} .026872	5	.005375			
11.870	137.308	.007268 }	} .021572	4	.005393	.09146	17	.005380
11.952	34.638	.02884 }				.11303	21	.005382
11.860			} .01623	3	.005410			
11.846	22.104 }	.04507				.12926	24	.005386
11.912	22.268 }		} .04307	8	.005384			
11.910	500.1	.002000				.08619	16	.005387
11.918	19.704 }	.05079	} .04879	9	.005421			
11.870	19.668 }					.13498	25	.005399
11.888	77.630 }	.01285	} .03794	7	.005420			
11.894	77.806 }					.09704	18	.005390
11.878	42.302	.02364	} .01079	2	.005395	.10783	20	.005392
11.880			Means		.005386			.005384

Duration of exp. = 45 min.	Pressure	= 75.62 cm.
Plate distance = 16 mm.	Oil density	= .9199
Fall distance = 10.21 mm.	Air viscosity	− 1,824 × 10⁻⁷
Initial volts = 5,088.8	Radius (a)	= .000276 cm.
Final volts = 5,081.2	$\frac{l}{a}$	= .034
Temperature = 22.82° C.	Speed of fall	= .08584 cm./sec.

$$e_1 = 4.991 \times 10^{-10}$$

within the limits of error of the experiment. The mean value at the bottom of the sixth column represents, then, the smallest charge ever caught from the air, that is, it is the elementary *ionic* charge. The seventh column gives the successive values of $v_1 + v_2$ expressed as reciprocal times. These numbers, then, represent the successive values of the *total* charge carried by the droplet. The eighth column gives the integers by which the numbers in the seventh column must be divided to obtain the numbers in the last column. These also will be seen to be invariable. The mean at the bottom of the last column represents, then, *the electrical unit out of which the frictional charge on the droplet was built up, and it is seen to be identical with the ionic charge represented by the number at the bottom of the sixth column.*

It may be of interest to introduce one further table [Table 40–4] arranged in a slightly different way to show how infallibly the atomic structure of electricity follows from experiments like those under consideration.

TABLE 40–4

n	$4.917 \times n$	Observed Charge	n	$4.917 \times n$	Observed Charge
1	4.917		10	49.17	49.41
2	9.834		11	54.09	53.91
3	14.75		12	59.00	59.12
4	19.66	19.66	13	63.92	63.68
5	24.59	24.60	14	68.84	68.65
6	29.50	29.62	15	73.75	
7	34.42	34.47	16	78.67	78.34
8	39.34	39.38	17	83.59	83.22
9	44.25	44.42	18	88.51	

In this table 4.917 is merely a number obtained precisely as above from the change in speed due to the capture of ions and one which is proportional in this experiment to the ionic charge. The column headed $4.917 \times n$ contains simply the whole series of exact multiples of this number from 1 to 18. The column headed "Observed Charge" gives the successive observed values of $(v_1 + v_2)$. It will be seen that during the time of observation, about four hours, this drop carried all possible multiples of the elementary charge from 4 to 18, save only 15. *No more exact or more consistent multiple relationship is found in the data which chemists have amassed on the combining powers of the elements and on which the atomic theory of matter rests than is found in the foregoing numbers.*

Such tables as these—and scores of them could be given—place beyond all question the view that an electrical charge wherever it is found, whether on an insulator or a conductor, whether in electrolytes or in metals, has a definite granular structure, that it consists of an exact number of specks of electricity (electrons) all exactly alike, which in static phenomena are scattered over the surface of the charged body and in current phenomena are drifting along the conductor. Instead of giving up, as Maxwell thought we should some day do, the "provisional hypothesis of molecular charges," we find ourselves obliged to make all our interpretations of electrical phenomena, *metallic as well as electrolytic,* in terms of it.

MECHANISM OF CHANGE OF CHARGE OF A DROP

All of the changes of charge shown in [Table 40–1] were spontaneous changes, and it has been assumed that all of these changes were produced by the capture of ions from the air. When a negative drop suddenly increases its speed in the field, that is, takes on a larger charge of its own kind than it has been carrying, there seems to be no other conceivable way in which the change can be produced. But when the charge suddenly *decreases* there is no a priori reason for thinking that the change may not be due as well to the direct loss of a portion of the charge as to the neutralization of this same amount of electricity by the capture of a charge of opposite sign. That, however, the changes do actually occur, when no X-rays or radioactive rays are passing between the plates, only by the capture of ions from the air, was rendered probable by the fact that drops not too heavily charged showed the same tendency on the whole to increase as to decrease in charge. This should not have been the case if there were two causes tending to decrease the charge, namely, direct loss and the capture of opposite ions, as against one tending to increase it, namely, capture of like ions. The matter was very convincingly settled, however, by making observations when the gas pressures were as low as 2 or 3 mm. of mercury. Since the number of ions present in a gas is in general directly proportional to the pressure, spontaneous changes in charge should almost never occur at these low pressures; in fact, it was found that drops could be held for hours at a time without changing. The frequency with which the changes occur decreases regularly with the pressure, as it should if the changes are due to the capture of ions. For the number of ions formed by a given ionizing agent must vary directly as the pressure.

Again, the changes do not, in general, occur when the electrical field is on, for then the ions are driven instantly to the plates as soon as formed, at a speed of, say, 10,000 cm. per second, and so do not have any opportunity to accumulate in the space between them. When the field is off, however, they do so accumulate, until, in ordinary air, they reach the number of, say, 20,000 per cubic centimeter. These ions, being endowed with the kinetic energy of agitation characteristic of the temperature, wander rapidly through the gas and become a part of the drop as soon as they impinge upon it. It was thus that all the changes recorded in [Table 40–1] took place.

It is possible, however, so to control the changes as to place electrons of just such sign as one wishes, and of just such number as one wishes, within limits, upon a given drop. If, for example, it is desired to place a positive electron upon a given drop the latter is held with the aid of the field fairly close to the negative plate, say the upper plate; then an ionizing agent—X-rays or radium—is arranged to produce uniform ionization in the gas between the plates. Since now all the positive ions move up while the negatives move down, the drop is in a shower of positive ions, and if the ionization is intense enough the drop is sure to be hit. In this way a positive charge of almost any desired strength may be placed upon the drop.

Similarly, in order to throw a negative ion or ions upon the drop it is held by the field close to the lower, i.e., to the positive, plate in a shower of negative ions produced by the X-rays. It was in this way that most of the changes shown in [Table 40–3] were brought about. This accounts for the fact that they correspond in some instances to the capture of as many as six electrons.

When X-rays are allowed to fall directly upon the drop itself the change in charge may occur, not merely because of the capture of ions, but also because the rays eject beta particles, i.e., negative electrons, from the molecules of the drop. That changes in charge were actually produced in this way in our experiments was proved conclusively in 1910 by the fact that when the pressure was reduced to a very low value and X-rays were allowed to pass through the air containing the drop, the latter would change readily in the direction of increasing positive or decreasing negative charge, but it could almost never be made to change in the opposite direction. This is because at these low pressures the rays can find very few gas molecules to ionize, while they detach negative electrons from the drop as easily as at atmospheric pressure. *This experiment proved directly that the charge carried by an ion in gases is the same as the charge on the beta or cathode-ray particle.*

When it was desired to avoid the direct loss of negative electrons by the drop, we arranged lead screens so that the drop itself would not be illuminated by the rays, although the gas underneath it was ionized by them.

DIRECT OBSERVATION OF THE KINETIC ENERGY OF AGITATION OF A MOLECULE

I have already remarked that when a drop carries but a small number of electrons it appears to catch ions of its own sign as rapidly as those of opposite signs—a result which seems strange at first, since the ions of opposite sign must be attracted, while those of like sign must be repelled. Whence, then, does the ion obtain the energy which enables it to push itself up against this electrostatic repulsion and attach itself to a drop already strongly charged with its own kind of electricity? It cannot obtain it from the field, since the phenomenon of capture occurs when the field is not on. It cannot obtain it from any explosive process which frees the ion from the molecule at the instant of ionization, since in this case, too, ions would be caught as well, or nearly as well, when the field is on as when it is off. Here, then, is an absolutely direct proof that the ion must be endowed with a kinetic energy of agitation which is sufficient to push it up to the surface of the drop against the electrostatic repulsion of the charge on the drop.

This energy may easily be computed as follows: Let us take a drop, such as was used in one of these experiments, of radius .000197 cm. The potential at the surface of a charged sphere can be shown to be the charge divided by the radius. The value of the elementary electrical charge obtained from the best observations of this type is 4.774×10^{-10} absolute electrostatic units. Hence the energy required to drive an ion carrying the elementary charge e up to the surface of a charged sphere of radius r, carrying 16 elementary charges, is

$$\frac{16e^2}{r} = \frac{16 \times (4.774 \times 10^{-10})^2}{.000197} = 1.95 \times 10^{-14} \text{ ergs}$$

Now, the kinetic energy of agitation of a molecule as deduced from the value of e herewith obtained, and the kinetic theory equation, $p = \frac{1}{3}nmc^2$, is 5.75×10^{-14} ergs. According to the Maxwell-Boltzmann law of the partition of energy, which certainly holds in gases, this should also be the kinetic energy of agitation of an ion. It will be seen that the value of this energy is approximately three times that required to push a single ion up to the surface of the drop in question. Hence the electrostatic forces due to 16 electrons on the drop are too weak to exert much influence upon the motion of an approaching ion. But if it were possible to load up a drop with negative electricity until the potential energy of its charge were about three times as great as that computed above for this drop, then the phenomenon here observed of the catching of new negative ions by such a negatively charged drop should not take place, save in the exceptional case in which an ion might acquire an energy of agitation considerably larger than the mean value. Now, as a matter of fact, it was regularly observed that the heavily charged drops had a very much smaller tendency to pick up new negative ions than the more lightly charged drops, and, in one instance, we watched for four hours another negatively charged drop of radius .000658 cm., which carried charges varying from 126 to 150 elementary units, and which therefore had a potential energy of charge (computed as above on the assumption of uniform distribution) varying from 4.6×10^{-14} to 5.47×10^{-14}. In all that time this drop picked up but one single negative ion when the field was off, and that despite the fact that the ionization was several times more intense than in the case of the drop [observed earlier]. Positive ions too were being caught at almost every trip down under gravity. (The strong negative charge on the drop was maintained by forcing on negative ions by the field as explained above.)

POSITIVE AND NEGATIVE ELECTRONS EXACTLY EQUAL

The idea has at various times been put forth in connection with attempts to explain chemical and cohesive forces from the standpoint of electrostatic attractions that the positive and negative charges in a so-called neutral atom may not after all be exactly equal, in other words, that there is really no such thing as an entirely neutral atom or molecule. As a matter of fact, it is difficult to find decisive tests of this hypothesis. The present experiments, however, make possible the following sort of test. I loaded a given drop first with negative electrons and took ten or twelve observations of rise and fall, then with the aid of X-rays, by the method indicated in the last section, I reversed the sign of the charge on the drop and took a corresponding number of observations of rise and fall, and so continued observing first the value of the negative electron and then that of the positive. [Table 40–5] shows a set of such observations taken in air with a view to subjecting this point to as rigorous a test as possible. Similar, though not quite so elaborate, observations have been made in hydrogen with the same result. The table shows in the first column the sign of the charge; in the second the successive values of the time of fall under gravity; in the third the successive times of rise in the field F; in the fourth the number of electrons carried by the drop for each value of t_F; and in the fifth the number, characteristic of this drop, which is proportional to the charge of one electron. This number is obtained precisely as in the two preceding tables by finding the greatest common divisor of the successive values of $(v_1 + v_2)$ and then multiplying this by an arbitrary constant which has nothing to do with the present experiment and hence need not concern us here. . . .

It will be seen that though the times of fall and of rise, even when the same number of electrons is carried by the drop, change a trifle because of a very slight evaporation and also because of the fall in the potential of the battery, yet the mean value of the positive electron, namely, 6.697, agrees with the mean value of the negative electron, namely, 6.700, to within less than 1 part in 2,000. Since this is about the limit of the experimental error (the probable error by least squares is 1 part in 1,500), *we*

TABLE 40 – 5

Sign of Drop	t_g (fall) Sec.	t_F (rise) Sec.	n	e
	63.118			
	63.050			
	63.186	41.728	8	
	63.332	41.590		
−	62.328			$e_1 = 6.713$
	62.728	25.740		
	62.926	25.798	11	
	62.900	25.510		
	63.214	25.806		
	Mean = 62.976			
	63.538	22.694	12	
	63.244	22.830		
	63.114	25.870		
	63.242	25.876	11	
	63.362	25.484		
+	63.136	10.830		$e_1 = 6.692$
	63.226	10.682		
	63.764	10.756		
	63.280	10.778	22	
	63.530	10.672		
	63.268	10.646		
	Mean = 63.325			
	63.642			
	63.020	71.664	6	
	62.820	71.248		
	63.514	52.668		
+	63.312	52.800	7	$e_1 = 6.702$
	63.776	52.496		
	63.300	52.860		
	63.156	71.708	6	
	63.126			
	Mean = 63.407			

TABLE 40 – 5 (*continued*)

Sign of Drop	t_g (fall) Sec.	t_r (rise) Sec.	n	e
	63.228	42.006 ⎫		
	63.294	41.920 ⎬ 8		
	63.184	42.108 ⎭		
	63.260	53.210 ⎫		
—	63.478	52.922	7	
	63.074	53.034		$e_1 = 6.686$
	63.306	53.438 ⎭		
	63.414	12.888 ⎫		
	63.450	12.812	19	
	63.446	12.748		
	63.556	12.824 ⎭		
	Mean = 63.335			

Duration of experiment 1 hr. 40 min.   Mean $e+$ = 6.697
Initial volts = 1723.5   Mean $e-$ = 6.700
Final volts = 1702.1
Pressure   =   53.48 cm.

may with certainty conclude that there are no differences of more than this amount between the values of the positive and negative electrons. This is the best evidence I am aware of for the exact neutrality of the ordinary molecules of gases. Such neutrality, if it is actually exact, would seem to preclude the possibility of explaining gravitation as a result of electrostatic forces of any kind. The electromagnetic effect of moving charges might, however, still be called upon for this purpose.

TWO FAR-REACHING

DISCOVERIES

ooooooooooo

41

 o o o o o o o o o o o

THE DISCOVERY OF

COSMIC RAYS

o o o o o o o o o o o

Viktor F Hess (1883-1964)

When we look at the stars on a clear night, we might conclude that most of the energy in interstellar space consists of electromagnetic waves, because the stars constantly pour out such energy. But our conclusion would be wrong because in each cubic centimeter of space there is about as much energy in the form of very energetic charged particles as there is in the form of light. When these ions reach the earth, we call them cosmic rays.

There are many unsolved mysteries about these particles, among which are their origin, their age, and their relationship to the stars and galaxies. We know today that these rays appear to strike the earth in equal intensities from all directions of space, and with energies ranging up to a billion trillion electron volts, far larger than any other known energies in nature.

The history of the study of cosmic rays goes back to the work of the late Viktor F. Hess, a Viennese physicist who was puzzled by certain discrepancies in the behavior of γ rays emitted by radioactive sources in the earth's crust and in its atmosphere. He suggested, in a paper written in 1911, that most of the penetrating radiation observed at the earth's surface is γ radiation emitted by terrestrial radioactive atoms; he pointed out, though, that not all of it could come from the earth because its intensity appeared to fall off only very gradually with increasing distance from the terrestrial source, as measured in balloon flights. Although Hess felt quite certain about his hypothesis, he decided, before pursuing it further, to check the absorption of γ radiation by the earth's atmosphere, for the

669

could not exclude entirely the possibility that γ radiation was not absorbed as effectively by air as he had thought. A smaller absorption coefficient than had been assumed would give a greater radioactive γ-ray intensity with increasing distance from the earth's surface than that calculated from the assumed coefficient.

His absorption measurements, in agreement with those made by previous investigators, showed that the penetrating γ radiation from the earth's radioactive material falls off very quickly with increasing height (at 500 meters only a small per cent of this terrestrial radiation survives). Hess decided that it was worthwhile to check his hypothesis by a series of balloon-flight measurements. In 1912, the results of these measurements were reported in a classic paper "Penetrating Radiation in Seven Free Balloon Flights," in *Physikalische Zeitschrift,* parts of which have been translated and reproduced in this volume.

To measure the cosmic radiation, Hess used three ionization chambers. Two of these had walls with thicknesses of 2 mm, so that such things as β rays and soft—that is, nonpenetrating—γ rays and X-rays were excluded. The third chamber was made of very thin walls to check on any soft rays and β rays (electrons) that might have been present.

The data from all the balloon flights were consistent in showing that, after one deducts from the measurements the contribution to the radiation of the earth's radioactive material, the intensity of the "penetrating radiation" increases with height. Hess further demonstrated that the intensity of this penetrating radiation is the same at night time as during the day, and does not decrease during an eclipse. He therefore concluded, correctly, that it does not originate in the sun but that it comes from regions beyond the solar system.

Since Hess's discovery of cosmic rays, a great deal of work has been done in this field. Originally, the exact nature of these rays was not known, but we now know that they are mostly very energetic protons intermixed with small quantities of heavy positive ions and electrons and positrons. When these very energetic particles strike the earth's atmosphere, they give rise to vast showers of other atomic and subatomic particles. Thus they create positron-electron pairs, mesons of all kinds, and many of the strange particles, so puzzling to physicists today, called hyperons. They also create proton-antiproton and neutron-antineutron pairs.

Since, for many years, the energies of cosmic ray particles far exceeded anything that could be produced in laboratories on the earth, people interested in high-energy physics quite naturally worked with cosmic rays. Thus Carl Anderson discovered the positron and the μ-meson by analyzing the various tracks on cloud chamber photographs, and the π-meson was discovered in cosmic rays in 1947 by C. F. Powell and G. P.

Occhialini. Other new particles have also been discovered in these rays, but today, with the use of high-energy accelerators, physicists are turning more and more to the laboratory for detailed studies of new particles.

The origin of cosmic rays is still pretty much of an unsolved problem, although various theories have been advanced to account for these. Thus, Fermi proposed the theory that positively charged particles, such as protons, in the Milky Way continually collide with clouds of gas-carrying magnetic fields and are thus accelerated to very high energies. It has been suggested, also, that cosmic rays arise from supernovae explosions and other very energetic distant events such as quasars (sources of high-frequency radio waves). Finally, some physicists and astrophysicists believe that cosmic rays were born with the universe itself.

Victor Franz Hess, who discovered cosmic rays, was born June 24, 1883, in Waldstein Castle near Peggan in Steiermark, Austria; his father Vinzens Hess was a forester in the household of Prince Öttingen-Wallerstein. After studying at the Gymnasium in Graz, Hess entered the University of Graz and received his doctorate in 1910. He began research in the field of radiation at the Physical Institute in Vienna under Professor Von Schweidler.

The techniques and instruments needed for the study of radioactivity were also suitable for the detection of cosmic rays. It was quite natural, therefore, that Hess progressed from the study of radioactivity to cosmic rays. Since the entire earth is radioactive, any attempt to assess its total radioactivity leads inevitably to the detection of cosmic radiation. Thus, shortly after beginning his work in radioactivity, Hess, in 1911, began to measure cosmic radiation and, in 1912, conclusively demonstrated, through tests made during balloon flights, that these penetrating rays come from interstellar space.

From 1910 to 1920, Hess was assistant at the Institute of Radium Research of the Viennese Academy of Sciences. In 1919 he received the Lieben prize for his discovery of cosmic rays and a year later became assistant professor of experimental physics at the University of Graz. Hess remained at Graz for only a year and then took a leave of absence for two years to work in the United States, where he became Director of Research for the U.S. Radium Corporation in New Jersey. At the same time, he acted as a consulting physicist for the Bureau of Mines of the U.S. Department of the Interior in Washington, D.C.

Upon completion of this work he returned to Graz where he was appointed full professor of experimental physics in 1925. Six years later, Hess accepted the chair at Innsbruck University and, at the same time, became director of the newly established Institute of Radiology. Under his guidance and initiative, the station at Hafelekar Mountain was founded for the further study of cosmic rays. Just before World War II Hess came to the United States and was appointed professor of physics at Fordham University. He became a United States citizen in 1944 and remained at Fordham until his death in 1964.

ၜၜၜၜၜၜၜ

HESS

Penetrating Radiation in Seven Free Balloon Flights [1]

LAST YEAR I HAD THE opportunity to investigate the penetrating radiation during two balloon flights. I reported on the first of these to the scientific meeting of Karlsruhe. In both flights no essential variation in the radiation could be observed up to heights of 1,100 meters.

Gockel, also, in two balloon flights, was unable to detect the expected diminution in intensity of the radiation with height. From this it was concluded that besides the γ radiation from the radioactive element in the earth's crust there must be another source of penetrating radiation.

Two Wulf radiation apparatuses of 3 mm. wall thickness were used for the observations.

Apparatus No. 1 had an ionization cell with a volume of 2039 cc and a capacity of 1.597 cm. Apparatus No. 2 had a volume of 2970 cc and a capacity of 1.097 cm.

A charge loss corresponding to a decrease of 1 volt per hour thus represented an intensity of ionization of $q = 1.56$ ions per cc per second in Apparatus No. 1 and $q = 0.7355$ ions per cc per second in Apparatus No. 2.

Whereas all observers of the penetrating radiation on the top of towers have always confirmed a decrease of the penetrating radiation, Gockel and I in balloon flights could not detect such a decrease with certainty. In order to obtain reliable mean values it was necessary to carry out observations in long-lasting flights at modest heights. Parallel observations with a third thin-wall apparatus were accordingly undertaken to determine if the soft rays behave like the intrinsic radiation.

Further attention had also to be given to the fluctuations of the radiation. Pocini, making parallel observations with two Wulf radiation apparatuses, detected during single hour reading intervals undoubted

---

[1] Viktor F. Hess, trans. Editors, *Physikalische Zeitschrift,* 13 (1912), 1084–1091.

simultaneous fluctuations of the rate of discharge over land as well as over the sea. The cause of the fluctuations therefore clearly lay outside the apparatus and in the radiation itself. It was therefore very important to determine whether this kind of simultaneous fluctuation can also be observed in balloon flights. Since such observations can be carried out with the least difficulty in long-lasting balloon flights at the same height, I have made the major part of the observations during night flights.

The last and most important objective of this investigation was the measurement of the radiation at the greatest possible height. In the six flights orginating in Vienna the low-load capacity of the gases used as well as the poor meteorological conditions prevented us from achieving this objective. In a hydrogen flight from Aussig a.d. Elbe succeeded in carrying out measurements to a height of 5350 meters.

Before each flight, control observations were made for several hours with the three sets of instruments. In this procedure the instruments were attached to the balloon cabin in the same manner as during the flight.

In [Table 41–1] q_1, q_2, q_3 are the readings in ions per cc per second of the penetrating radiation made with the instruments 1, 2, and 3, respectively.

T A B L E 4 1 – 1 Trip (26–27 April 1912).
Balloon: "Excelsior."
Pilot: Hauptmann W. Hoffory.
Observer: V. F. Hess.

Nr.	Time	Mean Height abso-lute m	rela-tive m	Apparatus 1 q_1	Apparatus 2 q_2	q_3	Apparatus 3 q_3 (reduced)	
1	16ʰ 40–17ʰ 40	156	0	15,6	11,5	—	—	from the
2	17ʰ 40–18ʰ 40	156	0	18,7	11,8	21,0	21,0	take-off
3	18ʰ 40–21ʰ —	156	0	17,8	11,6	19,5	19,5	point in
4	21ʰ 30–22ʰ 30	156	0	17,8	11,3	20,0	20,0	the Klub-
5	23ʰ 26– 0ʰ 26	300	140	14,4	9,6	19,4	19,8	platz,
6	0ʰ 26– 1ʰ 26	350	190	16,2	9,9	17,4	17,9	Vienna
7	1ʰ 26– 2ʰ 26	300	140	14,4	10,1	17,7	18,1	
8	2ʰ 26– 3ʰ 32	330	160	15,0	9,6	18,2	18,7	
9	3ʰ 32– 4ʰ 32	320	150	14,4	9,8	18,5	19,0	
10	4ʰ 32– 5ʰ 35	300	70	17,2	13,2	20,6	21,0	
11	5ʰ 35– 6ʰ 35	540	240	17,8	11,8	19,6	20,8	
12	6ʰ 35– 7ʰ 35	1050	800	17,6	10,0	18,1	20,3	
13	7ʰ 35– 8ʰ 35	1400	1200	12,2	8,8	17,3	20,3	
14	8ʰ 35– 9ʰ 35	1800	1600	17,5	10,9	17,3	21,3	

The mean height of the balloon during any particular observing interval (as a rule, about an hour) was determined graphically from the barometric trace. A mean value for the height was then obtained from altitude above sea level of the particular spot under the balloon.

[Table 41–1] shows first of all that for small heights above the ground the radiation is really weaker than at the ground itself. If we compute mean values we obtain [Table 41–2].

TABLE 41–2

	App. No. 1	App. No. 2	App. No. 3
Before ascent	$q_1 = 17.5$	$q_2 = 11.55$	$q_3 = 20.2$ ions/cc/second
140 to 190 meters above ground	$q_1 = 14.7$	$q_2 = 9.8$	$q_3 = 18.7$ ions/cc/second

The ion count differences are 2.6, 1.8, and 1.5. The mean difference is thus about 2 ions. This decrease of about 2 ions in the radiation is clearly due to the absorption by the air of γ rays of the radioactive material in the earth's crust. The above-mentioned difference of 2 ions represents about three quarters of the total ionizing power arising from the γ rays of the radioactive material in the earth's crust. The total γ radiation from the earth's crust must thus give rise to about 3 ions per cc per second in the zinc container.

(For the small height of 160 meters we may disregard the possible increase of radiation coming from above.)

[The data for several balloon flights are omitted—Editors.]

In order to get an over-all picture of the variation of the penetrating radiation with heights as given by the mean values, I have arranged all the 88 balloon observations that I have made of radiation intensities in vertical steps. Since in this procedure each mean value for a given height is computed from several individual values which were obtained under different conditions and which may be influenced by the temporal fluctuations already discussed, we must not expect at this point to obtain a very exact picture of the variation of the radiation with increasing height. . . .

[A discussion of some minor variations of the ion count near the earth's surface is omitted—Editors.]

We see that the γ radiation from the surface of the earth and the air layers close to the earth accounts for the excitation in the zinc containers of about 3 ions per cc per second.

At heights of more than 2,000 meters there is a marked increase in the radiation. It reaches 4 ions from 3,000 to 4,000 meters and 16 to 18 ions from 4,000 to 5,200 meters in two counters. The increase is even stronger in the thin-walled counter No. 3.

What is the source of this penetrating radiation which is observed simultaneously in the three counters? . . .

[Here Hess gives various reasons and cogent arguments for dismissing the earth's radioactivity as the source—Editors.]

The discoveries revealed by the observations here given are best explained by assuming that radiation of great penetrating power enters our atmosphere from the outside and engenders ionization even in counters lying deep in the atmosphere. The intensity of this radiation appears to vary hourly. Since I found no diminution of this radiation for balloon flights during an eclipse or at night time we can hardly consider the sun as its source.

42

ooooooooooo

THE CLOUD CHAMBER

ooooooooooo

Charles Thomson Rees Wilson (1869-1959)

It would seem hardly credible that researches in atmospheric physics dealing with the formation of clouds and mist should lead to the invention of one of the most important tools of atomic physics. Nevertheless it was in pursuit of studies on the formation of clouds that C.T.R. Wilson, starting in 1894, began the development of a most wonderful instrument that became known as the Wilson cloud chamber. With this device some sixteen years later the marvel of seeing the path of charged atomic particles and of atomic collisions was realized through the trails of foglike droplets that the particles left in their wakes. Even more important than seeing such events, the apparatus can depict them photographically, and once photographed tracks left by the particles in the chamber are recorded for future careful study.

In the hands of skillful experimenters the cloud chamber became a powerful tool for studying atomic collisions and analyzing the results of such collisions. It was the instrument by which much of the science of cosmic radiation was unraveled, and it was through such studies that Carl D. Anderson discovered the positive electron or "positron" in 1933. A few years later, with S. H. Neddermeyer, his cloud-track studies disclosed the first of the heavy electrons—the muon.

By the same device another prophecy of quantum physics, pair production—the generation of an electron-positron pair from the conversion of a high-energy photon—was made evident. These phenomena represent only a sampling of the highly useful results achieved by the use of the cloud chamber. It is therefore no wonder that Rutherford once characterized the instrument as "the most original and wonderful in scientific history."

676

But as is the case with most inventions, technological advance led to improved ways of performing old tasks; consequently, the cloud chamber has given way in modern high-energy physics to the bubble chamber and the spark chamber. But whatever path improvements may take, it is to the pioneer who showed the way that most honor should be given and it is in this spirit that all physicists honor the memory of C.T.R. Wilson.

"C.T.R.," as he came to be called, was the son of John Wilson, a sheep-farmer whose family had lived on the land for generations in the neighborhood of Edinburgh, Scotland. His mother, Annie Harper Wilson of Glasgow, was John Wilson's second wife; Charles, their son, was the youngest of eight children and was born on February 14, 1869. When he was four his father died and the family moved to Manchester. In 1884, at the age of fifteen, he entered Owens College, from which he graduated at the age of eighteen. After an additional year at Owens he entered Sidney Sussex College, Cambridge, on a scholarship, and decided to study physics instead of medicine, which had been his previous interest. He took his Cambridge degree at twenty-two and remained at the University for another year as a demonstrator in chemistry and physics. Then, feeling that his prospects at Cambridge were uncertain, he accepted a position as assistant master at the Bradford Grammar School.

Before leaving for this post he spent a few weeks at the Meteorological Observatory at the summit of Ben Nevis, the highest of the Scottish hills. Here, in September 1894, he saw the wonderful optical phenomenon of the sun playing on the clouds around the hilltop and their changing forms in various kinds of weather. Wilson was so impressed that he resolved to study cloud formation in the laboratory, a decision that determined the course of his life's work in physics.

Although he enjoyed his relations with the students in his new secondary school position, he soon came to realize that such work was incompatible with his urge to do research. Even though he had no prospect of employment, he left the school and returned to Cambridge. Fortunately he soon obtained a demonstratorship, and a connection with the Cavendish Laboratory where he enjoyed the advice and guidance of its director,, J. J. Thomson. Early in 1895 Wilson assembled an apparatus for expanding moist air under controlled conditions in which the expansion ratios could be measured. The formation of clouds and drops was then investigated as a function of the expansion ratios.

Early in 1896, following the news of the discovery of X-rays, he found that the cloud chamber would produce a fog that took many minutes to fall when exposed to the rays. It became clear from this experiment that ions would act as condensation nuclei for moisture in the chamber. Other experiments in succeeding years with "uranium rays" and ultraviolet light produced similar results. In support of the ion-condensation theory it was also found that if the ions were removed with an electric field, no cloud was formed.

The quality of Wilson's work must have deeply impressed his seniors, for he was elected a fellow of the Royal Society in 1900, as well as fellow of Sidney Sussex College and University lecturer and demonstrator. He was then thirty-one years old.

Not until the spring of 1911 did the idea occur to him that the condensation of droplets on ions might be used to show the path of an ionizing particle. An α-particle projected through the air dislodges electrons from atoms in or close to its path. In the cloud chamber these electrons, as well as the positive ions formed by their detachment, act as condensation centers for water vapor if the degree of supersaturation is sufficient. This supersaturation is achieved by suddenly expanding saturated air through a valve connected to the volume of the chamber cylinder or by using a retractable piston in the cylinder. The sudden expansion produces a temperature drop in the chamber air without immediate precipitation, thus supersaturating the volume. The apparatus is generally arranged so that a photograph is taken of the cylinder directly following the expansion; the mobilities of the ions are sufficiently small so that in this time the tracks do not become diffuse. An electric field maintained in the chamber volume sweeps out the ion droplets clearing the chamber for the next expansion. Wilson, in his Nobel lecture, noted his immediate success: "The first test was made with x-rays" . . . and . . . "the cloud chamber filled with little wisps and threads of cloud," showing the path of electrons ejected from the atoms of air by the rays. The description of the apparatus and some pictures (see figures 42–1 – 42–7) obtained with its use are presented in the following paper. This was the high point of his work in physics.

He continued his teaching and research at Cambridge until his retirement at sixty-five in 1934. During these years he was honored with the award of the Hughes medal in 1911, the Royal medal in 1922, and the Copley medal in 1935. In 1925 he was appointed Jacksonian professor of natural philosophy and in 1927 shared the Nobel Prize in physics with Arthur H. Compton.

In 1908, at the age of thirty-nine, Wilson married Jessie Fraser Dick. The couple had three children, a boy and two girls. To those who knew C.T.R. at Cambridge, perhaps his most notable characteristics were his patience and even temper. He was essentially a lone worker; unlike other leaders in Cambridge research, he had no students until well into the 1920's. His unassuming manner and angular features, particularly in his later years, suggested his descent from the generations who had lived on the Scottish land before him. Indifferent to acclaim and honors, he was a gentle and serene man, whose work proceeded from a genuine love of the natural world and from the revelation that he had experienced at Ben Nevis in his youth.

Two years after his retirement at Cambridge, C.T.R. returned to Scotland, settling in the village of Carlops in the region of his birthplace near Edinburgh. Here he enjoyed a vigorous and healthful old age. He died at ninety, after a brief illness, on November 15, 1959.

ༀༀༀༀༀༀༀ

WILSON

On an Expansion Apparatus for Making Visible the Tracks of Ionising Particles in Gases and Some Results Obtained by Its Use [1]

IN A RECENT COMMUNICATION I described a method of making visible the tracks of ionising particles through a moist gas by condensing water upon the ions immediately after their liberation. At that time I had only succeeded in obtaining photographs of the clouds condensed on the ions produced along the tracks of α-particles and of the corpuscles set free by the passage of X-rays through the gas. The interpretation of the photographs was complicated to a certain extent by distortion arising from the position which the camera occupied.

The expansion apparatus and the method of illuminating the clouds have both been improved in detail, and it has now been found possible to photograph the tracks of even the fastest β-particles, the individual ions being rendered visible. In the photographs of the X-ray clouds the drops in many of the tracks are also individually visible; the clouds found in the α-ray tracks are generally too dense to be resolved into drops. The photographs are now free from distortion. The cloud chamber has been greatly increased in size; it is now wide enough to give ample room for the longest α-ray, and high enough to admit of a horizontal beam of X-rays being sent through it without any risk of complications due to the proximity of the roof and floor.

---

[1] Charles T. R. Wilson, *Proceedings of the Royal Society* (London), Series A, 87 (1912), 277–289.

THE EXPANSION APPARATUS

The essential features of the expansion apparatus are shown in [Fig. 42–1]. The cylindrical cloud chamber A is 16·5 cm. in diameter and 3·4 cm. high; the roof, walls and floor are of glass, coated inside with gelatine, that on the floor being blackened by adding a little Indian ink. The plate glass floor is fixed on the top of a thin-walled brass cylinder (the "plunger"), 10 cm. high, open below, and sliding freely within an outer brass cylinder (the "expansion cylinder") of the same height and about 16 cm. in internal diameter. The expansion cylinder supports the

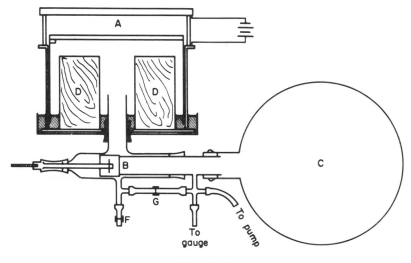

Fig. 42–1.

walls of the cloud chamber and rests on a thin sheet of indiarubber lying on a thick brass disc, which forms the bottom of a shallow receptacle containing water to a depth of about 2 cm. The water separates completely the air in the cloud chamber from that below the plunger. The base plate rests on a wooden stand, not shown on the diagram.

The expansion is effected by opening the valve B and so putting the air space below the plunger in communication with the vacuum chamber C through wide glass connecting tubes of about 2 cm. in diameter. The floor of the cloud chamber, in consequence, drops suddenly until brought to a sudden stop, when the plunger strikes the indiarubber-covered base plate, against which it remains firmly fixed by the pressure of the air in the cloud chamber. To reduce the volume of air passing through the connecting tubes at each expansion the wooden cylinder D was inserted within the air space below the plunger.

The valve is opened by the fall of a weight W released by a trigger . . . On closing the valve and opening communication with the atmosphere through the pinch-cock F, the plunger rises and so reduces the volume of the air in the cloud chamber. By means of the two pinch-cocks F and G (the latter on a tube communicating with the vacuum chamber), the plunger may be adjusted to give any desired initial volume v_1 between the upper limit v_2—the maximum volume of the cloud chamber—and the lower limit reached when the pressure below the plunger is that of the atmosphere.

The final volume v_2 is always the same (about 750 cc.), the expansion ratio v_2/v_1 depending only on the initial volume. A scale attached to the side of the cloud chamber enables the position of the top of the plunger to be read, and hence the initial volume to be determined, the area of the cross-section of the plunger and the maximum volume v_2 of the cloud chamber being known.

In setting up the apparatus, the plunger is placed on the rubber-covered base plate, and the expansion cylinder slipped over it, a hole in the side of the cloud chamber being open at this stage to allow of the imprisoned air escaping. Then, by blowing in air through F, momentarily opened for the purpose, the plunger is driven up to a height sufficient to allow of the largest desired expansions being made. The aperture in the wall of the cloud chamber is then closed, and the mass of imprisoned air remains unchanged during subsequent operations.

The gelatine layer under the roof of the cloud chamber is connected, through a ring of tinfoil cemented between the cylindrical wall and the roof, with one terminal of a battery of cells of which the other terminal is connected, through the brass expansion cylinder and plunger, with the layer of blackened gelatine on the floor of the cloud chamber. An approximately uniform vertical electric field of any desired intensity may thus be maintained in the cloud chamber.

The gelatine lining of the roof and walls is formed by pouring into the cloud chamber, before attaching it to the expansion cylinder, a hot solution containing about 4 per cent. of gelatine and $0\cdot1$ per cent. of boracic acid and allowing the surplus to drain away by inverting the vessel. The thin coating of gelatine which remains is allowed to dry over calcium chloride. The cloud chamber is cemented to the expansion cylinder by means of gelatine.

A comparatively thick layer (about 1 mm.) of a solution containing 15 per cent. of gelatine, 2 per cent. of boracic acid, and 3 per cent. of Indian ink is poured on to the glass plate which forms the floor of the cloud chamber, the brass walls of the plunger being prolonged for about 1 mm. above the upper surface of the plate, thus forming a shallow receptacle for the gelatine and making an efficient electric contact with it. The blackened gelatine is not allowed to dry, but at once covered to prevent evaporation and to protect it from dust till ready for use. The gelatine is in all cases previously sterilised by heat.

METHOD OF ILLUMINATING AND PHOTOGRAPHING THE CLOUDS

As in the experiments described in my last paper, a Leyden jar discharge through mercury vapour at atmospheric pressure is used for the instantaneous illumination of the clouds resulting from the expansion. A horizontal silica tube about 15 cm. long, and having an internal diameter of about 1 mm., is filled with mercury and enclosed, for the central 4 cm. of its length, by a close-fitting silver tube about 2 mm. thick, and having a slot about 1 mm. wide extending from end to end. The silver tube when heated by a small flame serves to keep the enclosed portion of the silica tube at a nearly uniform temperature high enough to vaporise the mercury, and thus form a mercury-vapour spark-gap. Connection with the Leyden jars is made through platinum wires fused through the ends of glass tubes filled with mercury and inserted into the ends of the silica tube.

The silica tube is first filled with mercury, the end pieces inserted, and a small flame placed under the silver tube. When the mercury occupying the portion of the silica tube which is surrounded by the silver jacket has all been vaporised (the excess of mercury escaping from the ends of the tube) no further change takes place and the spark-gap is ready for use. The very considerable capillary forces set up when the mercury is forced into the narrow space between the glass end pieces and the surrounding silica tube effectually prevent the violent oscillatory motions which are apt to be the principal source of trouble in the use of a mercury spark-gap of this type.

For firing the spark the arrangement used is essentially that which has generally been employed in instantaneous photography by the Leyden jar discharge. The outer coatings of two sets of 4 or 5 "gallon" Leyden jars, standing on the floor of the room, are connected to the terminals of the illuminating spark. The inner coatings are connected to the terminals of a Wimshurst machine and to two brass balls separated by a space of about 5 cm. which forms the primary spark-gap. The jars having been charged almost to sparking potential, a metal ball is allowed to fall between the terminals of the primary spark-gap, causing a spark to pass at both gaps. The ball whose fall causes the spark is hung by a fine thread, just strong enough to carry it, from the weight W which works the valve of the expansion apparatus. . . .

In the experiments described in this paper, the camera lens has always occupied one of the two positions indicated diagrammatically in [Fig. 42–2], (a) and (b). In (a) the small circle represents a transverse section of a narrow horizontal beam of ionising rays crossing a diameter of the cloud chamber. The camera looks in a horizontal direction normal to the ionising beam. The mercury spark-gap is at S, at the principal focus of a cylindrical lens about 20 cm. long and 2 cm. wide, and having a focal length of about 3 cm. With this arrangement the whole of the cloud produced by a considerable length of the ionising beam is illuminated, while the direction of the incident light makes a comparatively small angle (about 25°) with the axis of the camera.

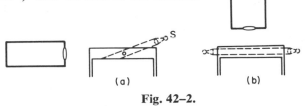

Fig. 42–2.

Arrangement (b) has been used chiefly with the α-rays, which give clouds of sufficient density to scatter a large amount of light at right angles to the illuminating beam. The camera lens is vertically over the centre of the cloud chamber; and by means of two similar mercury spark-gaps (arranged in series), each at the principal focus of a cylindrical lens like that used in (a), a horizontal stratum of about 2 cm. in vertical thickness and extending across the whole area of the vessel, is illuminated.

IONISATION BY α-RAYS

[Fig. 42–3] is a typical photograph of the cloud obtained on expansion when a minute quantity of radium is placed on the tip of a wire projecting into the cloud chamber. A potential difference of 40 volts was maintained between the roof and floor, the roof being at the higher potential. The camera was placed with its axis vertical, and a horizontal section of the cloud chamber, about 2 cm. in depth, was illuminated [arrangement (b)

Fig. 42–3.

of [Fig. 42–2]. The β-rays are not visible in the photographs obtained with this mode of illumination.

The narrow, sharply defined rays of these photographs are clouds condensed along the tracks of α-particles which have traversed the supersaturated air after the expansion, so that there has been very little time for the ions to diffuse before losing their mobility through condensation of water upon them. The diffuse rays are clouds condensed upon ions set free by α-particles which have traversed the air before its expansion, so that there has been time for diffusion of the ions before the formation of the cloud. The weaker the electric field the greater is the maximum possible age, and consequent diffuseness, of the tracks which may be present; with a potential difference of only two or three volts, wide finger-like clouds are formed on expansion.

α-Rays which pass after the expansion can only leave visible trails if the degree of supersaturation still remains sufficient to cause water to condense on the ions. In the immediate neighbourhood of the cloud already condensed on an older track, the supersaturation remaining may be insufficient to cause condensation, although elsewhere the α-particle may leave a visible trail. This is doubtless the explanation of the fact that most of the sharply defined trails only seem to begin at some considerable distance from the radium, the diffuse cloud trails formed at the moment of expansion being so closely packed near the source of the rays that there is little chance of an α-particle, ejected after the expansion, finding the supersaturation necessary for rendering its trail visible, until it has travelled for some distance. . . .

As will be seen from the photographs, the α-rays are generally straight over the greater part of their length, but they nearly all are bent, often abruptly, in the last 2 mm. of their course. Abrupt bends through considerable angles are seen much earlier in the course of some of the rays.

In [Fig. 42–4] is shown an enlargement of a particularly interesting trail. Here there are two absolutely abrupt bends—the first through about $10\frac{1}{2}°$, the second through about 43°. There is a very well-marked spur at the second bend, which it is difficult to interpret otherwise than as being due to ionisation by the recoil of the atom, by collision with which the course of the α-particle has been abruptly changed. (But for the spur this α-ray shows an astonishingly close resemblance to one in a diagram constructed by Prof. Bragg to illustrate what he considered to be likely forms of α-ray paths.)

Apart from these sudden bends a certain amount of curvature is apparent in some of the tracks. In some cases, where the curvature occurs close to the walls of the cloud chamber, it is certainly a spurious effect, due to displacement of the tracks by air motions or to optical distortion arising from a thickening of the gelatine around the circumference of the roof. Where, however, it appears at no great distance from the centre of the cloud chamber it is probably genuine, indicating deviation of the α-particle by repeated small deflections. There is generally unmistakably genuine curvature in the last millimetre of the track.

The photographs thus furnish evidence of two distinct ways in which α-particles are "scattered" in passing through air, what Rutherford has called "single" and "compound" scattering respectively. And, as Rutherford has contended, the scattering of [a] large amount is in the case of α-particles mainly due to the former process, that is to say, it is the result of single deflections through considerable angles and not a cumulative effect due to a very large number of minute deviations.

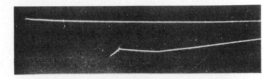

Fig. 42–4.

Fig. 42–5.

When the α-rays arise from the emanation it is possible to photograph the complete track of an α-particle, including the beginning and end. The latter is at once recognisable by its characteristic bend or hook. In [Fig. 42–5] is shown the track of an α-particle, which has completed its course in the illuminated layer; the beginning of the trail is seen to be marked by an enlarged head in which the cloud is of greater density than elsewhere. This may represent ionisation by the recoil of the atom from which the α-particle has escaped. The same characteristic head appears at what is presumably the beginning of other, obviously foreshortened, tracks whose ends lie outside the illuminated layer.

Of two complete α-ray tracks from the emanation [photographed on this and on another plate not shown] one has a length (when reduced to

760 mm. and 15° C.) of 4·3 cm., in good agreement with the usually accepted value of the range. The other is apparently somewhat shorter,
about 3·8 cm., the low value being probably due to foreshortening.

Some photographs of α-ray trails were obtained with the camera in the
lateral position and with oblique illumination—arrangement (a) of [Fig.
42–2]. The radium tipped wire was surrounded by a glass tube about
1 mm. wide open at the end and projecting for about 1 cm. beyond the
radium, the object being to confine the rays to a moderately narrow pencil
with its axis in the plane for which the camera was focussed.

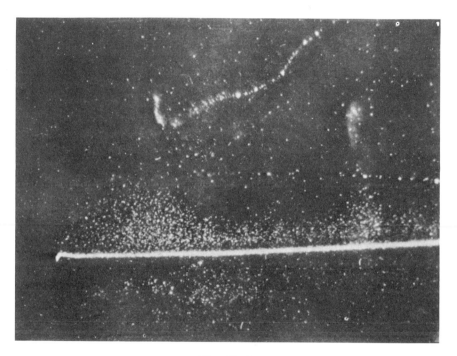

Fig. 42–6.

An example of one of the photographs obtained in this way is shown
in [Fig. 42–6], which is an enlargement of the original negative. The track
of an α-particle is seen near the bottom of the picture. Some of the ions
appear to have retained their mobility in the supersaturated atmosphere
long enough to enable them to travel some distance under the action of
the electric field before growing into drops, thus giving rise to a vertical
sheet or curtain of drops. The effect is most marked above the main track,
i.e. on the side to which the negative ions would travel. . . .

It will be noticed [the upper track in Fig. 42–6] that the β-rays photographed do not show abrupt deflections like the α-rays, but, except while

the velocity remains very high, they show gradual bending resulting in large deviations. The scattering of the β-rays is thus mainly or entirely of the cumulative or "compound" type, being due to a large number of successive deflections, each in itself inappreciable.

IONISATION BY RÖNTGEN RAYS

The X-ray bulb was excited by a Leyden jar discharge, in most cases so timed that the rays traversed the cloud chamber immediately after the expansion, while the gas was in the supersaturated condition. The ions had thus extremely little time in which to diffuse before being fixed by the condensation of water upon them. . . .

A photograph of a typical X-ray cloud is shown in [Fig. 42–7]. In all cases [except one] the rays traversed the supersaturated gas, the order of events being: (1) Production of the supersaturated condition by sudden expansion; (2) Leyden jar discharge through the Crookes tube, causing ionisation within the cloud chamber; (3) condensation of water upon the ions; (4) passage of the illuminating spark, giving a photograph of the cloud condensed on the ions.

The potential difference between the top and bottom of the cloud chamber was in some vases 40 volts, in others only 4 volts, the top being always positive.

In most cases the expansion ratio was between $1 \cdot 33$ and $1 \cdot 36$; *i.e.* it considerably exceeded the minimum (approximately $1 \cdot 31$) required to cause condensation on the positive as well as the negative ions (the minimum for the latter is $1 \cdot 25$), but less than is required to give dense clouds in the absence of ions ($v_2/v_1 = 1 \cdot 38$). Under these conditions, as the photographs show, the tracks of the cathode- or β-particles produced in the gas by the X-rays are very sharply defined, the ions being fixed by condensation of water upon them before they have had time to diffuse, or travel under the action of the electric force, for any appreciable distance.

The following are among the more striking features of the photographs, of which [Fig. 42–7 is a typical] example out of a considerable number obtained under these conditions.

1. Cathode or β-rays are seen to start from within the track of the primary X-ray beam, many of them extending to some distance outside it.

2. There is no indication of any effect of the X-rays on the gas other than the production of the corpuscular radiation; the track of the primary X-ray beam is not distinguishable otherwise than as being the region in which the β-rays have their origin. In some photographs, it is true, there appear scattered throughout the region illuminated by the spark drops which might be taken to represent ions set free by the X-rays, but these

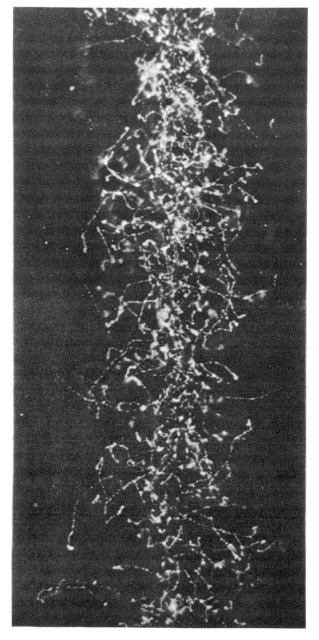

Fig. 42-7.

show no concentration along the path of the primary beam, and, moreover, they appear in equal numbers in comparison photographs taken under conditions otherwise identical but without any X-ray discharge. There is no doubt, I think, that these scattered drops are condensed upon uncharged nuclei similar in nature to those produced by weak ultra-violet light and certain metals, which require a similar expansion to catch them. They appear to be due to a chemical action in which some trace of impurity plays an essential part, as they are much more numerous when the air in the apparatus has recently been renewed.

Ionisation by X-rays appears therefore to be, as Bragg has suggested, entirely a secondary process, except in so far as each cathode ray produced in the gas may be said to indicate the formation of one pair of ions by the X-radiation.

3. The number of cathode rays produced in air in a known length of a limited beam of X-rays can readily be counted by this method.

4. The X-radiation thus far used has been heterogeneous. It is to be expected therefore that the cathode rays should be of varying length. Reduced to atmospheric pressure, a frequent length, measured along the path, was from ¾ to 1 cm., or measured in a straight line from beginning to end of the path, about half these amounts. Tracks as long as 2 cm. were, however, met with.

5. The rays show two distinct kinds of deflection as a result of their encounters with the atoms of the gas—Rutherford's "single" and "compound" scattering. The gradual or cumulative deviation due to successive deflections of very small amount is evidently, however, in this case much the more important factor in causing scattering, all the rays showing a large amount of curvature, while quite a small proportion show abrupt bends. When abrupt deflections occur they are frequently through large angles, 90° or more.

6. The rays tend to become more and more bent as the end is approached, the actual end of each cloud trail being also enlarged into a kind of head, possibly owing to the path of the corpuscle finally becoming extremely irregular in form.

7. In many of the photographs there are cloud trails sufficiently sharply in focus over at least a portion of their length to show the individual drops and, therefore, allow of the ions on which they have condensed being counted. . . . Out of 12 counts of this kind, the smallest number obtained is 150 pairs per cm. (at atmospheric pressure)—this is at the beginning of a ray—the largest 2160 pairs per cm. in the last ½ mm. of a ray.

8. The cathode rays appear to start in all directions. I have not yet attempted any systematic statistical study such as would be required to determine the relative frequency of different initial directions of the rays with respect to the direction of propagation of the Röntgen radiation. . . .

THE NUCLEAR ATOM

ooooooooooo

43

○○○○○○○○○○○

STRANGE RESULTS FROM
α-PARTICLE SCATTERING

○○○○○○○○○○○

Hans Geiger (1882-1945)
Ernest Marsden (b. 1889)

Entirely new vistas into the structure of matter were opened in October 1897 by J. J. Thomson's discovery of the electron. This sub-atomic particle, less massive than hydrogen, the lightest known element, somehow had to be a part of all atoms. But if it were a part of all atoms, then these atoms must have a structure. It was the task of physics to puzzle out what this structure might be. The first suggestion that appeared in the scientific journals came from Lord Kelvin in 1902; it envisioned an arrangement in which diffuse positive electricity was spread homogeneously through the volume of the spherical atom. The exact nature of this positive electricity was not delineated, but it seems to have been pictured as a kind of viscous material resembling jelly. In this sphere of positive charge, the small discrete negative charges, the electrons, were supposed to be embedded; moreover, the positive charge was of such magnitude as to exactly counterbalance the negative charges of the electrons so that the whole atom was electrically neutral.

This arrangement was investigated more carefully the following year by J. J. Thomson and the stability calculated in detail for various numbers of electrons. As a consequence the model came to be called the "Thomson atom" and has generally been known by this name since then.

It must be clear, however, that no direct physical experiments on atoms led to this model; instead it was a product of the sophisticated imagina-

693

tion and was shaped to fulfill criteria of mechanical and electrical stability. One of the ways in which its credibility could be tested was to use the recently discovered α- and β-particles from radioactive atoms. If a stream of these particles was projected at a piece of metal foil, physically thin but in reality many atoms thick, the particles incident on the foil would have to be deflected by the atoms or pass through them. An analysis of the scattering could then be made to provide information on the structure of the foil atoms.

Upon his arrival in Manchester Rutherford found in the laboratory a young German, Hans Geiger, who had come to work for a few years in England. Geiger was a very able experimental physicist and, at Rutherford's suggestion, began work on an electrical device to count individual charged particles. Out of this came the famous Geiger counter which contributed so much to experimental atomic physics, to particle physics, and to the study of the cosmic rays in the years that followed. Another problem that was attacked was a suitable α-ray source to provide a fine beam for scattering experiments from thin foils. A young undergraduate, Ernest Marsden, assisted in the scattering experiments; Geiger and Marsden's first experiment is described in the following paper. Fig. 43–1 shows the simple arrangement by which it was possible to obtain results very quickly.

Radium emanation enclosed in a conical glass tube capped with a piece of thin mica supplied α-particles which were directed, at an angle, to a thin metal foil. Those α-particles deflected by the foil so that they emerged on the same side as the incident particles, i.e., at about 90° to the original direction, were intercepted by a zinc-sulfide screen. A thick lead plate prevented particles from the source from reaching the screen directly. Each α-particle impact on the screen could be detected by the scintillation it produced. By observing the screen with a low-power microscope the scintillations could be counted, and the dependence of the number thus deflected on the atomic weight of the atoms of the foil noted.

Several results were immediately apparent: First, large deflections of α-particles did occur; second, the number so deflected increased as the atomic weight of the foil increased. The effect of increasing the thickness of the scattering foil was then examined and it was found, as was known for β-rays, that the scattering was not a surface but a volume effect. The fact that a thickness of 6×10^{-5} cm of gold was sufficient to produce a deflection of 90° or more was a matter of great surprise. Finally, with an altered arrangement, the *number* of particles scattered by a platinum foil through an angle of 90° or more was determined. The result showed that about 1 in 8,000 was so deflected.

Geiger next carried out an experiment (not reproduced in this anthology) which was aimed at determining the average deflection of α-particles which traversed various thin metallic foils whose absorption was equivalent to several centimeters of air. As was expected, the average deflection measured was only a few degrees.

Nevertheless, the large deflections found in the Geiger and Marsden experiment disturbed Rutherford; as Marsden notes in his remarks at the Rutherford Jubilee International Conference at Manchester in 1961, "he thought over these remarkable results for many weeks." Rutherford knew that such deflections were too big to be consistent with the Thomson model of the atom, and he began looking for an alternative to explain the data. The conclusions that he drew will be presented following this paper of Geiger and Marsden.

Hans Geiger was born in 1882 in Neustadt, Germany. He was the son of a professor of Indo-Germanic languages at the University of Munich and grew up in an academic atmosphere. His Ph.D. research, under Wiedemann at the University of Erlangen, was concerned with the conduction of electricity in gases and his doctorate was awarded in 1906. He then went to Manchester to work with Schuster; following Rutherford's arrival there in 1907, he entered into a most fruitful collaboration on the latter's researches. In the five years of their association, Geiger wrote papers on the statistical nature of radioactive decay, the determination of the number of α-particles emitted per second from a gram of radium, the Geiger range law for charged particles passing through matter, the well-known Geiger-Nuttall relation between the decay constant of a radioactive nucleus and the range of the emitted α-particles, as well as the paper on scattering experiment, conducted with Marsden, which appears in Chapter 44.

He was thirty years old when he left Manchester in 1912 to become director of the newly established laboratory of radioactivity at the Physikalische-Technischen Reichsanstalt in Berlin. Geiger remained in this position until 1925 when he accepted the chair in physics at the University of Kiel. It was here, in 1928, that he developed, with his student W. Müller, the famous instrument that has become a household word, the "Geiger counter." In 1929, he went from Kiel to Tübingen, where he began research on cosmic rays. In 1936 he moved again, this time to the Institute of Technology in Berlin; he remained there until rheumatoid arthritis caused his death at sixty-three on September 24, 1945.

Geiger was a man of warm and humane feeling, with a genuine concern for the students who worked under his direction. The testimony of his students indicates that working under him was both an exciting and heartwarming experience. He was not only a leader in research but he lectured widely on many different scientific topics for popular audiences. In 1937 he became editor of the *Zeitschrift für Physik,* one of the outstanding physical journals of that time. He was a devoted man of science who left his mark on the history of physics.

Sir Ernest Marsden, who collaborated with Geiger in the two experiments that first suggested the nuclear atom and then provided its proof, was born on February 19, 1889. He was educated at the Queen Elizabeth School, Blackburn, and at Victoria University, Manchester, commencing work on radioactivity as an undergraduate and on the scattering of α-particles as assistant to Geiger. After completing graduate study at Manchester, he became lecturer in physics at the University of London, then was invited to return to Manchester to help Geiger check Rutherford's theory. The results of that research are embodied in their joint paper which follows in Chapter 44.

In 1914, after completing this investigation, he accepted a position as Professor of Physics at Victoria University College in Wellington, New Zealand, and remained there until 1922. During the next five years he was Assistant Director of Education for New Zealand. In 1927 he was appointed secretary of the New Zealand Department of Scientific and Industrial Research, a post which he held until 1947. He was elected a fellow of the Royal Society of London in 1946 and was knighted in 1958. He has held the chairmanship of the New Zealand Defense Science Advisory Council and the presidency of the Royal Society of New Zealand, and has received honorary degrees from Oxford and Manchester universities. At the present time, he is living in Wellington, New Zealand.

ooooooo

GEIGER and MARSDEN

On a Diffuse Reflection of the α-Particles [1]

WHEN β-PARTICLES FALL ON A plate, a strong radiation emerges from the same side of the plate as that on which the β-particles fall. This radiation is regarded by many observers as a secondary radiation, but more recent experiments seem to show that it consists mainly of primary β-particles, which have been scattered inside the material to such an extent that they emerge again at the same side of the plate. For α-particles a similar effect has not previously been observed,

---

[1] Hans Geiger and Ernest Marsden, *Proceedings of the Royal Society* (London), 82 (1909), 495–499.

and is perhaps not to be expected on account of the relatively small scattering which α-particles suffer in penetrating matter.

In the following experiments, however, conclusive evidence was found of the existence of a diffuse reflection of the α-particles. A small fraction of the α-particles falling upon a metal plate have their directions changed to such an extent that they emerge again at the side of incidence. To form an idea of the way in which this effect takes place, the following three points were investigated:—

(I) The relative amount of reflection from different metals.
(II) The relative amount of reflection from a metal of varying thickness.
(III) The fraction of the incident α-particles which are reflected.

For the observation of the reflected particles the scintillation method was used in all experiments. . . .

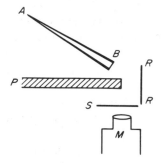

Fig. 43–1.

On account of the fact that the amount of reflection is very small, it was necessary to use a very intense source of α-rays. A tube was employed similar to that which has been proved to be a suitable source in the scattering experiments of one of us. This source consisted of a glass tube AB [Fig. 43–1], drawn down conically and filled with radium emanation, the end B of the tube being closed airtight by means of a mica window. The thickness of the mica was equivalent to about 1 cm. of air, so that the α-particles could easily pass through it.

Since it is of importance that the gas pressure inside this tube should be as low as possible, the emanation was purified according to the methods developed by Prof. Rutherford. The tube contained an amount of emanation equivalent to about 20 milligrammes $RaBr_2$ at a pressure of a few centimeters. The number of α-particles expelled per second through the window was, therefore, very great, and, on account of the small pressure inside the tube, the different ranges of the α-particles from the three products (*i.e.* emanation, RaA, and RaC) were sharply defined.

The zinc sulphide screen S [Fig. 43–1] was fixed behind the lead plate P, in such a position that no α-particles could strike it directly. When a reflector was placed in the position RR at about 1 cm. from the end of the tube, scintillations were at once observed. At the same time the screen brightened up appreciably on account of the reflected β-particles.

By means of a low power microscope, the number of scintillations per minute on a definite square millimetre of the screen was counted for reflectors of different materials. Care was taken that the different reflectors were always placed in exactly the same position.

It is, of course, to be expected that the number of α-particles reflected from the plate would be different in different directions, and would also depend on the angle of incidence. In our arrangement, however, no appreciable difference was found for different angles. This is due to the fact that, owing to the necessity of having the tube very near to the reflector, the angle of incidence varied very much. An investigation of the variation of the effect with the angles of incidence and emergence would necessitate a parallel and very intense source of homogeneous α-rays, which can, however, not easily be realised.

In [Table 43–1] the number of scintillations observed per minute are given in column 3; in column 4 the ratio to the atomic weight is calculated, and it can be seen that this ratio decreases with decreasing atomic weight. The case of lead appears to be an exception which may be due to slight impurities in the lead.

Even in the absence of any reflector about one scintillation per minute was observed. It was easy to show that this was due to a reflection from

TABLE 43–1

1. Metal.	2. Atomic weight, A.	3. Number of scintillations per minute, Z.	4. A/Z.
Lead	207	62	30
Gold	197	67	34
Platinum	195	63	33
Tin	119	34	28
Silver	108	27	25
Copper	64	14·5	23
Iron	56	10·2	18·5
Aluminium	27	3·4	12·5

the air through which the α-particles passed. The numbers on the table are corrected for this effect.

It is interesting to note here that for β-particles the number of re- flected particles also decreases with the atomic weight of the reflector. But while for β-particles the number reflected from gold is only about twice as great as for aluminium, for α-particles the same ratio amounts to about twenty.

(II) We have already pointed out that the diffuse reflection of the α-particles is a consequence of their scattering. According to this point of view, the number of particles reflected must vary with the thickness of the reflecting screen. Since gold can be obtained in very thin and uniform

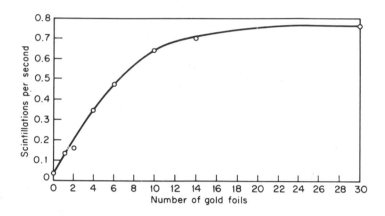

Fig. 43–2.

foils, different numbers of these foils were used as reflectors. Each foil was equivalent in stopping power to about 0·4 mm. of air. It was neces- sary to mount the foils on glass plates, but the number reflected from the glass itself was found to be very small compared even with the number from one gold foil. The curve [Fig. 43–2] gives the result of the meas- urements.

The number of scintillations which were due to the reflection from the air is subtracted from each reading. The first point on the curve represents the number of scintillations observed for a glass plate alone as reflector; the last point (marked 30) gives the number of scintillations when a thick gold plate was used.

The curve is similar to those which have been obtained for the reflec- tion of the β-particles. It brings out clearly that the reflection is not a surface but a volume effect.

Compared, however, with the thickness of gold which an α-particle can penetrate, the effect is confined to a relatively thin layer. In our experi-

ment, about half of the reflected particles were reflected from a layer
equivalent to about 2 mm. of air. If the high velocity and mass of the
α-particle be taken into account, it seems surprising that some of the
α-particles, as the experiment shows, can be turned within a layer of
6×10^{-5} cm. of gold through an angle of 90°, and even more. To produce a similar effect by a magnetic field, the enormous field of 10^9 absolute units would be required.

(III) In the next experiment, an estimate of the total number of particles reflected was aimed at. For this purpose the emanation tube used in
the previous experiments was unsuitable, firstly, on account of the difficulty of correctly ascertaining the number of α-particles emerging from
the tube; and secondly, on account of the different ranges of the α-par-

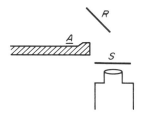

Fig. 43–3.

ticles from the three products: emanation, radium A, and radium C.
Consequently, as radiating source, radium C, deposited on a plate of small
dimensions, was used. The arrangement, which is sketched in [Fig. 43–3],
was such that the α-particles from the plate A fell upon the platinum reflector R, of about 1 square centimetre area, at an average angle of 90°.
The reflected particles were counted on different points of the screen S.

No appreciable variation of the number was found with different
angles of emergence, the reason of which has already been explained
above.

The amount of radium C deposited on the plate was determined by its
γ-ray activity. Assuming that $3 \cdot 4 \times 10^{10}$ particles are expelled per second from an amount of RaC equivalent to 1 gramme Ra, the number of
α-particles expelled per second from the active plate was determined. The
number falling on the platinum reflector was then easily calculated from
its known distance and area. To find the whole number of reflected particles, it was assumed that they were distributed uniformly round a half
sphere with the middle of the reflector as centre.

Three different determinations showed that of the incident α-particles
about 1 in 8000 was reflected, under the described conditions.

[The paper concludes with a short discussion of effects which produce
errors in the results—Editors.]

44

oOoooooooOo

THE NUCLEAR ATOM

ooOooooooOo

Ernest Rutherford (1871-1937)

By the time Rutherford was ready to leave McGill University to come to Manchester, his research into the nature of the emanations from radioactive atoms and his theories of radioactivity had made him quite famous. Not only was he invited to give technical lectures at the outstanding American universities, but he was also in great demand as a popular lecturer and as an author of popular articles. Although, as he stated in various letters to his mother, he tried to discourage these requests because they were a drain on his time, he seldom denied them, and he took great delight in entertaining his audiences. He enjoyed counting the house and, in one letter to his mother, remarked that, "I had the largest audience they had ever raised at McGill. They were stored everywhere, including some who were looking through a ventilator in the top of the roof."

In 1904 he was invited to give the famous Bakerian lecture to the Royal Society of London; during this lecture he expounded his theory of the chain reaction of radioactive products and laid down the basic principles of the arrangement of elements in radioactive families. While in England during that year, he gave a lecture to a full audience of the Royal Institution, where he proposed the radioactive method of estimating the age of the earth and demonstrated that Lord Kelvin, at that time the grand old man of British physics, was wrong in concluding that the earth was only a few million years old and could, at most, exist for another hundred million years. Lord Kelvin had arrived at his result on the assumption that all the energy from the sun came from gravitational contraction, which Rutherford knew was false. On seeing Lord Kelvin in his audience, Rutherford, on the spur of the moment, softened his blow to

701

Kelvin's analysis by stating that Kelvin had based his theory on the hypothesis that "no new source of energy would be discovered. That prophetic utterance refers to what we are considering tonight, radium." In telling the story of this lecture later, Rutherford remarked that Kelvin, who had been asleep up to that point of the lecture, "sat up and beamed upon me."

In that same year, Rutherford received the Rumford Medal of the Royal Society for his theory of radioactive decay. He was happy about this, for not only was it a great distinction, but it also carried a monetary award of £70, which was quite welcome at a time when professors' salaries were not much to speak of.

Following upon these honors, he was invited to give the Silliman lectures at Yale, which meant that he would have to be away from his wife three more weeks than he had meant to be. In an amusing letter to her, he then asked whether she preferred an additional 2,500 dollars or three more weeks of his company. Two years later, in 1906, he was awarded his first honorary degree by the University of Philadelphia. In writing to his mother about it, he remarked that he was rather youthful for such honors "as they are usually the special perquisites of septuagenarians. They [honorary degrees] don't worry me much I can assure you, but one is supposed to value them very highly—I imagine the esteem is largely dependent on whether you feel you deserve them or not."

During this period of intense scientific and academic work, Rutherford always found time for play. He was not the sort of man who did nothing but physics in every waking moment of his life. He enjoyed many activities and was an omnivorous reader. He was fond of light reading and while at McGill kept four libraries busy supplying him with novels, detective stories, historical fiction, biographies, and books of general interest. He was also fond of bridge and golf, and he thrived on open-air activities. He felt that spending all one's time at a desk was stultifying, and he would often be heard advising his colleagues to leave their offices and "go home and think."

On May 20, 1905, two years before he left McGill, Rutherford received a letter from Sir William Ramsay of University College, London, supporting the application of a young German physicist, Dr. Otto Hahn, for a research position at McGill. Rutherford welcomed Hahn to McGill and introduced him to the research techniques in radioactivity that were later, in 1939, to lead Hahn to the discovery of uranium fission.

In 1907, when Rutherford decided to accept the Langworthy chair of Professor of Physics at the University of Manchester, he was recognized by the greatest physicists of the time as their equal. He had already published about fifty papers, each of which was of first-rate importance. But his greatest achievements at Manchester were yet to come. He was very happy to be in Manchester, which was then one of the great centers of scientific research, and his constant contact with the top physicists of the day was a source of great inspiration to him as well as to them. Arriving at Manchester, Rutherford immediately pitched into his research, teaching, and lecturing activities, most of which stemmed from his work on radioactivity. This was just the kind of life that Rutherford wanted. In a letter to his mother dated October 29, 1907, he reported that everyone was kind to him and that he was enjoying his life thoroughly with a good many "outside lectures in hand."

Shortly after coming to Manchester, in fact six months after his arrival in 1908, his great scientific achievements were recognized by the Turin Academy of Sciences, which awarded him the Bressa Prize for his discovery of the "mutability of matter and of the evolution of the atom." This was followed by an honorary degree from Trinity College, Dublin, and then, in 1908, the Nobel Prize for chemistry, which is certainly one of the great ironies in the history of physics and chemistry. In his acceptance speech in Stockholm, Rutherford declared that he had dealt with many kinds of radioactive transformations with different periods of time, but that the quickest transformation he had met was his own—a transformation from a physicist to a chemist in a single moment.

After returning from Stockholm, Rutherford became interested in the properties of the thorium family of radioactive elements, which was the principal subject of Hahn's experimental investigations. Hahn was at Berlin then, and he had working with him at that time a young assistant, Fräulein Lise Meitner, who was also to play a prominent role some thirty years later in the uranium-fission problem. Rutherford and Hahn exchanged a series of letters on the properties of the thorium family, and Rutherford, as usual, was greatly interested in the emanations from these radioactive atoms. He became greatly engrossed at that time in the passage of α particles through matter and was very much impressed with the ease with which these particles passed through thin foils of metal of very thin glass. It was at this time, two years before he published his paper on the nuclear atom, that his ideas on the structure of matter began to crystallize. The passage of α particles through matter clearly indicated to him the possibility of using α particles as a probe and also suggested to him the possibility that the atom itself was mostly empty space. This was in 1909, a period of great happiness for Rutherford who went calmly along his way enjoying his research work, his teaching, his lecturing, his family life, and his regular correspondence with his mother, whom he kept informed about most of his activities. At this point in his life, Rutherford became interested in a new form of recreation—motoring. He bought a Wolseley-Siddeley automobile and spent many hours with his family driving around the countryside.

Once Rutherford became convinced of the possibility of probing the structure of an atom with α particles, he followed the work of Geiger on the large-angle scattering of α particles with great interest and began to formulate his theory of the nuclear atom. Although he ultimately accepted the picture of a positively charged nucleus, he was at first inclined to the idea of a negatively charged nucleus. As he stated in a letter to Bragg, "I am beginning to think that the central core is negatively charged . . . ," but soon after that he changed his mind. In 1911, he had worked out most of the details of his theory of scattering of α particles from a nuclear atom and communicated his ideas in a general form in a letter to Bragg. In this letter, he also discounts Crowther's analysis, which arrived at scattering results in agreement with the J. J. Thomson atom. Rutherford puts this down to the "use of imagination and the failure to grasp where the theory was inapplicable."

The thing that impressed Rutherford most about the α-particle scattering was that some of the α particles, even though only a few, returned almost back toward their source, behaving the way a bullet might if it bounced directly back when fired at a sheet of paper. To him this could mean only one thing: there was an enormous force in the atom. He announced this idea at a Sunday supper at his house in Manchester in 1911, when he was dining with a few scientists, including the theoretical physicist, C. G. Darwin, who later recounted that he was present "half an hour after the nucleus was born." Here Rutherford presented the idea that it would take one hundred electron charges on the gold nucleus to give the observed result.

Darwin goes on to say, in his recollection of this event, that he was surprised at Rutherford's mathematics and the way he worked out his results, for Rutherford was neither a mathematician nor a theoretical physicist. In looking for some kind of picture that would show him the effect of a large force on a body, he probably thought of a gravitationally controlled comet swinging around the sun and coming directly back again— just like the α particles. This naturally led him to the idea of a hyperbolic orbit and possibly first suggested the idea of a negative nucleus attracting the positive α particle the way the sun attracts a comet. Of course, he soon saw that the only important thing in the dynamics of the problem was the inverse square law of force and that the orbit of the α particle must be a conic section whether the force was attractive or repulsive. There is evidence that at this stage of his analysis he went back to Newton's *Principia* and used Newtonian mathematics to obtain his final results.

Having conceived the idea of a hyperbolic orbit for the α particles, he recalled a theorem in geometrical conics which he had learned at school. This theorem relates the eccentricity (that is, the shape) of the hyperbola to the angle between the asymptotes. This is the content of equation (1) in Rutherford's paper on the scattering of α and β particles. Using this mathematical relation and the principles of conservation of momentum and energy, he then obtained a complete solution of the α-particle scattering problem.

That very day Rutherford asked Darkwin to check his conclusions and also to work out the results if the law of repulsion were an inverse cube law. Rutherford was particularly interested in the question, "How close to the nucleus can an alpha particle approach?" He got this answer from his theory and the measurements of the scattered α particles. The answer, 3×10^{-10} cm., showed him how small and compact a nucleus is, and thus the nuclear atom was born.

Rutherford was supremely confident of his conclusions and was sure that he had the right answer, which not only explained the scattering of α particles, but also gave a correct picture of the structure of the atom. This is evident in Geiger's account of events. One day, in 1911, Rutherford, very sprightly and happy, came into Geiger's laboratory and informed Geiger that he knew what the atom looked like and how to explain the large deflections of the α particles. Geiger began his crucial experiments to test Rutherford's analysis on that same day and thus verified one of the greatest contributions to physics. This must be considered as the very peak of Rutherford's research and is certainly to be counted among the greatest of all scientific achievements.

An interesting insight into the general attitude of British physicists of that period toward new scientific theories is given by Rutherford's remarks about the theory of relativity at the Brussels conference in 1910. When, at a luncheon, Rutherford was teasing Willy Wien about relativity, Wien, after explaining that Newton's law of the addition of velocities was wrong, remarked that "no Anglo-Saxon can understand relativity." "No!" laughed Rutherford, "they have too much sense." Later, Rutherford's attitude changed, for he welcomed the great contributions to physics stemming from the theories of Planck, Einstein, and Bohr without which his own theory of the atom would collapse. We give below, after a brief commentary, the most important excerpts from Rutherford's great paper on the scattering of α particles.

In the Thomson model of the atom the positive electricity was considered to be somewhat like a jelly in which the discrete electrons were embedded. The electrons were held stationary in their equilibrium positions by the attraction of the positive electrical fluid surrounding them and the repulsion of the other electrons. Radiation from such an atomic model occurred whenever the atom was disturbed because the electrons would be forced out of their equilibrium positions and set vibrating. As they vibrated they radiated energy until they came to rest again. This picture is in complete accord with the classical electromagnetic theory of the electron as developed by Maxwell and Lorentz, and for this reason the Thomson model was favorably received by Thomson's contemporaries.

Thomson's purpose in developing this model was to explain the "scattering of electrified particles in passing through small thicknesses of matter." In scattering experiments, the crucial criterion for the atom model is the angle through which a charged particle is deflected from its original direction of motion as it passes through a metal foil used as the scatterer. Thomson assumed that the angle of deviation suffered by the charged particle was always caused by a large number of collisions with many atoms. Any single collision played only a minimal role in the total deviation, which was a cumulative effect. It can be shown that on the basis of the Thomson model the total deviation is not the average deviation produced in a single collision multiplied by the total number of collisions; rather, the multiplicand is the *square root* of this sum of collisions. Thus, if each collision resulted on the average in a deviation of 1°, 100 collisions would give rise to a net deviation of only 10°.

Rutherford pointed out the importance of this fact by calling attention to the observations of Geiger and Marsden. They had found, in their experiments with α particles passing through a layer of gold foil about 0.00006 cm thick, that they could be scattered through an angle of 90° or more. If only small deviations occurred in each encounter, the α particle would have had to undergo about 10,000 of the lesser collisions to produce such a large total deviation. This was highly improbable, as Rutherford pointed out, because of the extreme thinness of the gold foil. Rutherford contended that such large deviations must have been caused, therefore, by single direct collisions. He then proceeded to analyze the theory of single collisions on the basis of a model of the atom that is radically different from the Thomson model.

In this Rutherford model the positive electricity is not distributed over a large volume but instead is concentrated in a very small nucleus at the center of the atom. As Rutherford points out in the paper that follows, the actual analysis is the same whether one assumes that the positive charge is concentrated at the nucleus and the electrons are on the outside, or vice versa.

A model of this sort cannot be in static equilibrium, since the electrons would all be dragged into the nucleus if they were not moving in stable orbits around this nucleus. Yet this kind of dynamical equilibrium is in serious contradiction with classical electrodynamics. Rutherford was aware of this, but chose to ignore the difficulty for the time being. He stated that the "question of the stability of the atom proposed need not be considered at this stage. . . ."

By very simple but elegant arguments and with the most elementary mathematics, Rutherford showed that his model of the atom gives rise to the kind of deviations during single collisions that Geiger and Marsden had observed. The paper itself is exemplary in its simplicity, yet so profound that none could doubt that Rutherford's ideas must serve as the basis of a new and correct picture of the structure of matter.

We should note, however, that the picture of the atom that Rutherford drew was still very tentative and vague. He speculates that not all of the positive charge is in the nucleus; that "a small fraction of the positive charge may be carried by satellites extending some distance from the center." Although the values he obtained for the charge on the nuclei of different metals are all too large, for example, 100 for gold, he correctly concludes that the nuclear charge should be "approximately proportional" to the atomic weight of the atom. But Rutherford was not sure that this would hold for the light elements and indicated that for such elements his simple theory of atomic collisions is no longer applicable.

Although throughout most of the paper he does not specifically mention the planetary theory of the atom, it is clear from his reference to the work of Nagaoka that Rutherford had this planetary model in mind, and it is here that we have the starting point of modern atomic theory.

It has often happened in the past that authors in referring to this paper of Rutherford's speak of his experiments on the scattering of α particles; however, the experiments used by Rutherford were not his own but those of Geiger and Marsden. Rutherford's great contribution lay in showing that the Thomson model of the atom cannot possibly explain the large number of large-angle scatterings, whereas the nuclear model can.

٥٥٥٥٥٥٥٥

RUTHERFORD

The Scattering of α and β Particles by Matter and the Structure of the Atom [1]

IT IS WELL KNOWN THAT the α and β particles suffer deflexions from their rectilinear paths by encounters with atoms of matter. This scattering is far more marked for the β than for the α particle on account of the much smaller momentum and energy of the former particle. There seems to be no doubt that such swiftly moving particles pass

---

[1] Ernest Rutherford, *Philosophical Magazine,* 21 (1911), 669–688.

through the atoms in their path, and that the deflexions observed are due to the strong electric field traversed within the atomic system. It has generally been supposed that the scattering of a pencil of α or β rays in passing through a thin plate of matter is the result of a multitude of small scatterings by the atoms of matter traversed. The observations, however, of Geiger and Marsden on the scattering of α rays indicate that some of the α particles must suffer a deflexion of more than a right angle at a single encounter. They found, for example, that a small fraction of the incident α particles, about 1 in 20,000, were turned through an average angle of 90° in passing through a layer of gold-foil about ·00004 cm. thick, which was equivalent in stopping-power of the α particle to 1·6 millimetres of air. Geiger showed later that the most probable angle of deflexion for a pencil of α particles traversing a gold-foil of this thickness was about 0°·87. A simple calculation based on the theory of probability shows that the chance of an α particle being deflected through 90° is vanishingly small. In addition, it will be seen later that the distribution of the α particles for various angles of large deflexion does not follow the probability law to be expected if such large deflexions are made up of a large number of small deviations. It seems reasonable to suppose that the deflexion through a large angle is due to a single atomic encounter, for the chance of a second encounter of a kind to produce a large deflexion must in most cases be exceedingly small. A simple calculation shows that the atom must be a seat of an intense electric field in order to produce such a large deflexion at a single encounter.

Recently Sir J. J. Thomson has put forward a theory to explain the scattering of electrified particles in passing through small thicknesses of matter. The atom is supposed to consist of a number N of negatively charged corpuscles, accompanied by an equal quantity of positive electricity uniformly distributed throughout a sphere. The deflexion of a negatively electrified particle in passing through the atom is ascribed to two causes— (1) the repulsion of the corpuscles distributed through the atom, and (2) the attraction of the positive electricity in the atom. The deflexion of the particle in passing through the atom is supposed to be small, while the average deflexion after a large number m of encounters was taken as $\sqrt{m} \cdot \theta$, where θ is the average deflexion due to a single atom. It was shown that the number N of the electrons within the atom could be deduced from observations of the scattering of electrified particles. The accuracy of this theory of compound scattering was examined experimentally by Crowther in a later paper. His results apparently confirmed the main conclusions of the theory, and he deduced, on the assumption that the positive electricity was continuous, that the number of electrons in an atom was about three times its atomic weight.

The theory of Sir J. J. Thomson is based on the assumption that the scattering due to a single atomic encounter is small, and the particular structure assumed for the atom does not admit of a very large deflexion of an α particle in traversing a single atom, unless it be supposed that the diameter of the sphere of positive electricity is minute compared with the diameter of the sphere of influence of the atom.

Since the α and β particles traverse the atom, it should be possible from a close study of the nature of the deflexion to form some idea of the constitution of the atom to produce the effects observed. In fact, the scattering of high-speed charged particles by the atoms of matter is one of the most promising methods of attack of this problem. The development of the scintillation method of counting single α particles affords unusual advantages of investigation, and the researches of H. Geiger by this method have already added much to our knowledge of the scattering of α rays by matter.

We shall first examine theoretically the single encounters * with an atom of simple structure, which is able to produce large deflexions of an α particle, and then compare the deductions from the theory with the experimental data available.

Consider an atom which contains a charge $\pm$ Ne at its centre surrounded by a sphere of electrification containing a charge $\mp$Ne supposed uniformly distributed throughout a sphere of radius R. e is the fundamental unit of charge, which in this paper is taken as $4 \cdot 65 \times 10^{-10}$ E.S. unit. We shall suppose that for distances less than 10^{-12} cm. the central charge and also the charge on the α particle may be supposed to be concentrated at a point. It will be shown that the main deductions from the theory are independent of whether the central charge is supposed to be positive or negative. For convenience, the sign will be assumed to be positive. The question of the stability of the atom proposed need not be considered at this stage, for this will obviously depend upon the minute structure of the atom, and on the motion of the constituent charged parts.

In order to form some idea of the forces required to deflect an α particle through a large angle, consider an atom containing a positive charge Ne at its centre, and surrounded by a distribution of negative electricity Ne uniformly distributed within a sphere of radius R. The electric force X and the potential V at a distance r from the centre of an atom for a point inside the atom, are given by

$$X = Ne \left(\frac{1}{r^2} - \frac{r}{R^3} \right)$$

$$V = Ne \left(\frac{1}{r} - \frac{3}{2R} + \frac{r^2}{2R^3} \right).$$

* The deviation of a particle throughout a considerable angle from an encounter with a single atom will in this paper be called "single" scattering. The deviation of a particle resulting from a multitude of small deviations will be termed "compound" scattering.

Suppose an α particle of mass m and velocity u and charge E shot directly towards the centre of the atom. It will be brought to rest at a distance b from the centre given by

$$\tfrac{1}{2}mu^2 = NeE\left(\frac{1}{b} - \frac{3}{2R} + \frac{b^2}{2R^3}\right).$$

It will be seen that b is an important quantity in later calculations. Assuming that the central charge is $100\ e$, it can be calculated that the value of b for an α particle of velocity $2 \cdot 09 \times 10^9$ cms. per second is about $3 \cdot 4 \times 10^{-12}$ cm. In this calculation b is supposed to be very small compared with R. Since R is supposed to be of the order of the radius of the atom, viz. 10^{-8} cm., it is obvious that the α particle before being turned back penetrates so close to the central charge, that the field due to the uniform distribution of negative electricity may be neglected. In general, a simple calculation shows that for all deflexions greater than a degree, we may without sensible error suppose the deflexion due to the field of the central charge alone. Possible single deviations due to the negative electricity, if distributed in the form of corpuscles, are not taken into account at this stage of the theory. It will be shown later that its effect is in general small compared with that due to the central field.

Consider the passage of a positive electrified particle close to the centre of an atom. Supposing that the velocity of the particle is not appreciably changed by its passage through the atom, the path of the particle under the influence of a repulsive force varying inversely as the square of the distance will be an hyperbola with the centre of the atom S as the external focus. Suppose the particle to enter the atom in the direction PO [Fig. 44–1], and that the direction of motion on escaping the atom is OP'. OP and OP' make equal angles with the line SA, where A is the apse of the hyperbola. $p = SN =$ perpendicular distance from centre on direction of initial motion of particle.

Let angle POA $= \theta$.

Let V $=$ velocity of particle on entering the atom, v its velocity at A, then from consideration of angular momentum

$$pV = SA \cdot v.$$

From conservation of energy

$$\tfrac{1}{2}mV^2 = \tfrac{1}{2}mv^2 + \frac{NeE}{SA},$$

$$v^2 = V^2\left(1 - \frac{b}{SA}\right).$$

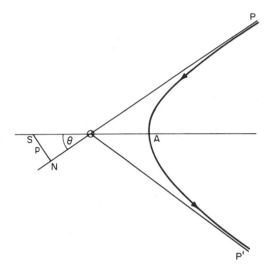

Fig. 44–1.

Since the eccentricity is sec θ,

$$SA = SO + OA = p \operatorname{cosec} \theta(1 + \cos \theta)$$

$$= p \cot \theta/2,$$

$$p^2 = SA(SA - b) = p \cot \theta/2 (p \cot \theta/2 - b),$$

$$\therefore \ b = 2p \cot \theta.$$

The angle of deviation ϕ of the particle is $\pi - 2\theta$ and

$$\cot \phi/2 = \frac{2p}{b} \ ^* \tag{1}$$

This gives the angle of deviation of the particle in terms of b, and the perpendicular distance of the direction of projection from the centre of the atom.

For illustration, the angle of deviation ϕ for different values of p/b are shown in the following table:—

p/b	10	5	2	1	·5	·25	·125
ϕ	5°·7	11°·4	28°	53°	90°	127°	152°

---

* A simple consideration shows that the deflexion is unaltered if the forces are attractive instead of repulsive.

PROBABILITY OF SINGLE DEFLEXION THROUGH ANY ANGLE

Suppose a pencil of electrified particles to fall normally on a thin screen of matter of thickness t. With the exception of the few particles which are scattered through a large angle, the particles are supposed to pass nearly normally through the plate with only a small change of velocity. Let n = number of atoms in unit volume of material. Then the number of collisions of the particle with the atom of radius R is $\pi R^2 nt$ in the thickness t.

The probability m of entering an atom within a distance p of its centre is given by

$$m = \pi p^2 nt.$$

Chance dm of striking within radii p and $p + dp$ is given by

$$dm = 2\pi pnt \cdot dp = \frac{\pi}{4} ntb^2 \cot \phi/2 \operatorname{cosec}^2 \phi/2 \, d\phi, \qquad (2)$$

since

$$\cot \phi/2 = 2p/b.$$

The value of dm gives the *fraction* of the total number of particles which are deviated between the angles ϕ and $\phi + d\phi$.

The fraction ρ of the total number of particles which are deflected through an angle greater than ϕ is given by

$$\rho = \frac{\pi}{4} ntb^2 \cot^2 \phi/2. \qquad (3)$$

The fraction ρ which is deflected between the angles ϕ_1 and ϕ_2 is given by

$$\rho = \frac{\pi}{4} ntb^2 \left(\cot^2 \frac{\phi_1}{2} - \cot^2 \frac{\phi_2}{2} \right) \qquad (4)$$

It is convenient to express the equation (2) in another form for comparison with experiment. In the case of the α rays, the number of scintillations appearing on a *constant* area of a zinc sulphide screen are counted for different angles with the direction of incidence of the particles. Let r = distance from point of incidence of α rays on scattering material, then if Q be the total number of particles falling on the scattering material, the

number y of α particles falling on unit area which are deflected through
an angle ϕ is given by

$$y = \frac{Qdm}{2\pi r^2 \sin \phi \cdot d\phi} = \frac{ntb^2 \cdot Q \cdot \text{cosec}^4 \phi/2}{16r^2} \tag{5}$$

Since

$$b = \frac{2NeE}{mu^2},$$

we see from this equation that a number of α particles (scintillations) per
unit area of zinc sulphide screen at a given distance r from the point of
incidence of the rays is proportional to

(1) $\text{cosec}^4 \phi/2$ or $1/\phi^4$ if ϕ be small;
(2) thickness of scattering material t provided this is small;
(3) magnitude of central charge Ne;
(4) and is inversely proportional to $(mu^2)^2$, or to the fourth power of
     the velocity if m be constant.

In these calculations, it is assumed that the α particles scattered through
a large angle suffer only one large deflexion. For this to hold, it is essential
that the thickness of the scattering material should be so small that the
chance of a second encounter involving another large deflexion is very
small. If, for example, the probability of a single deflexion ϕ in passing
through a thickness t is $1/1000$, the probability of two successive deflexions each of value ϕ is $1/10^6$, and is negligibly small.

The angular distribution of the α particles scattered from a thin metal
sheet affords one of the simplest methods of testing the general correctness of this theory of single scattering. This has been done recently for α
rays by Dr. Geiger, who found that the distribution for particles deflected
between $30°$ and $150°$ from a thin gold-foil was in substantial agreement
with the theory. A more detailed account of these and other experiments
to test the validity of the theory will be published later.

ALTERATION OF VELOCITY IN AN ATOMIC ENCOUNTER

It has so far been assumed that an α or β particle does not suffer an
appreciable change of velocity as the result of a single atomic encounter
resulting in a large deflexion of the particle. The effect of such an encounter in altering the velocity of the particle can be calculated on certain
assumptions. It is supposed that only two systems are involved, viz., the
swiftly moving particle and the atom which it traverses supposed initially

at rest. It is supposed that the principle of conservation of momentum and of energy applies and that there is no appreciable loss of energy or momentum by radiation.

Let m be mass of the particle,
  v_1 = velocity of approach,
  v_2 = velocity of recession,
  M = mass of atom,
  V = velocity communicated to atom as result of encounter.

Let OA [Fig. 44–2] represent in magnitude and direction the momentum mv_1 of the entering particle, and OB the momentum of the receding particle which has been turned through an angle AOB = ϕ. Then BA represents in magnitude and direction the momentum MV of the recoiling atom.

$$(MV)^2 = (mv_1)^2 + (mv_2)^2 - 2m^2 v_1 v_2 \cos \phi. \tag{1}$$

By the conservation of energy

$$MV^2 = mv_1{}^2 - mv_2{}^2 \tag{2}$$

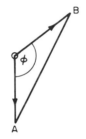

Fig. 44–2.

Suppose M$/m$ = K and $v_2 = \rho v_1$, where ρ is < 1.
From (1) and (2),

$$(K + 1)\rho^2 - 2\rho \cos \phi = K - 1,$$

or

$$\rho = \frac{\cos \phi}{K + 1} + \frac{1}{K + 1} \sqrt{K^2 - \sin^2 \phi}.$$

Consider the case of an α particle of atomic weight 4, deflected through an angle of 90° by an encounter with an atom of gold of atomic weight 197.

Since K = 49 nearly,

$$\rho = \sqrt{\frac{K-1}{K+1}} = \cdot 979,$$

or the velocity of the particle is reduced only about 2 per cent. by the encounter.

In the case of aluminium K = 27/4 and for $\phi = 90°$, $\rho = \cdot 86$.

It is seen that the reduction of velocity of the α particle becomes marked on this theory for encounters with the lighter atoms. Since the range of an α particle in air or other matter is approximately proportional to the cube of the velocity, it follows that an α particle of range 7 cms. has its range reduced to $4 \cdot 5$ cms. after incurring a single deviation of 90° in traversing an aluminium atom. This is of a magnitude to be easily detected experimentally. Since the value of K is very large for an encounter of a β particle with an atom, the reduction of velocity on this formula is very small.

Some very interesting cases of the theory arise in considering the changes of velocity and the distribution of scattered particles when the α particle encounters a light atom, for example a hydrogen or helium atom. A discussion of these and similar cases is reserved until the question has been examined experimentally. . . .

[The section on the comparison of single and compound scattering is omitted—Editors.]

COMPARISON OF THEORY WITH EXPERIMENTS

On the present theory, the value of the central charge Ne is an important constant, and it is desirable to determine its value for different atoms. This can be most simply done by determining the small fraction of α or β particles of known velocity falling on a thin metal screen, which are scattered between ϕ and $\phi + d\phi$ where ϕ is the angle of deflexion. The influence of compound scattering should be small when this fraction is small.

Experiments in these directions are in progress, but it is desirable at this stage to discuss in the light of the present theory the data already published on scattering of α and β particles.

The following points will be discussed:—

(a) The "diffuse reflexion" of α particles, *i.e.* the scattering of α particles through large angles (Geiger and Marsden).

(b) The variation of diffuse reflexion with atomic weight of the radiator (Geiger and Marsden).

(c) The average scattering of a pencil of α rays transmitted through a thin metal plate (Geiger).

(d) The experiments of Crowther on the scattering of β rays of different velocities by various metals.

(a) In the paper of Geiger and Marsden on the diffuse reflexion of α particles falling on various substances it was shown that about 1/8000 of the α particles from radium C falling on a thick plate of platinum are scattered back in the direction of the incidence. This fraction is deduced on the assumption that the α particles are uniformly scattered in all directions, the observations being made for a deflexion of about 90°. The form of experiment is not very suited for accurate calculation, but from the data available it can be shown that the scattering observed is about that to be expected on the theory if the atom of platinum has a central charge of about 100 e.

(b) In their experiments on this subject, Geiger and Marsden gave the relative number of α particles diffusely reflected from thick layers of different metals, under similar conditions. The numbers obtained by them are given in [Table 44–1] below, where z represents the relative number of scattered particles, measured by the number of scintillations per minute on a zinc sulphide screen.

TABLE 44–1

Metal.	Atomic weight. A	z.	$z/A^{3/2}$
Lead	207	62	208
Gold	197	67	242
Platinum	195	63	232
Tin	119	34	226
Silver	108	27	241
Copper	64	14·5	225
Iron	56	10·2	250
Aluminium	27	3·4	243

Average 233

On the theory of single scattering, the fraction of the total number of α particles scattered through any given angle in passing through a thickness t is proportional to n. A^2t, assuming that the central charge is proportional to the atomic weight A. In the present case, the thickness of matter from which the scattered α particles are able to emerge and affect the zinc sulphide screen depends on the metal. Since Bragg has shown that the stopping power of an atom for an α particle is proportional to the square root of its atomic weight, the value of nt for different elements is proportional to $1/\sqrt{A}$. In this case t represents the greatest depth from which the scattered α particles emerge. The number z of α particles scattered back from a thick layer is consequently proportional to $A^{3/2}$ or $z/A^{3/2}$ should be a constant.

To compare this deduction with experiment, the relative values of the latter quotient are given in the last column. Considering the difficulty of the experiments, the agreement between theory and experiment is reasonably good.*

The single large scattering of α particles will obviously affect to some extent the shape of the Bragg ionization curve for a pencil of α rays. This effect of large scattering should be marked when the α rays have traversed screens of metals of high atomic weight, but should be small for atoms of light atomic weight.

(*c*) Geiger made a careful determination of the scattering of α particles passing through thin metal foils, by the scintillation method, and deduced the most probable angle through which the α particles are deflected in passing through known thicknesses of different kinds of matter.

A narrow pencil of homogeneous α rays was used as a source. After passing through the scattering foil, the total number of α particles deflected through different angles was directly measured. The angle for which the number of scattered particles was a maximum was taken as the most probable angle. The variation of the most probable angle with thickness of matter was determined, but calculation from these data is somewhat complicated by the variation of velocity of the α particles in their passage through the scattering material. A consideration of the curve of distribution of the α particles given in the paper . . . shows that an angle through which half the particles are scattered is about 20 per cent greater than the most probable angle.

We have already seen that compound scattering may become important when about half the particles are scattered through a given angle, and it is difficult to disentangle in such cases the relative effects due to the two kinds of scattering. An approximate estimate can be made in the following way:— . . . [T]he relation between the probabilities p_1 and p_2 for compound and single scattering respectively is given by

$$p_2 \log p_1 = -\cdot 721.$$

The probability q of the combined effects may as a first approximation be taken as

$$q = (p_1^2 + p_2^2)^{1/2}.$$

---

* The effect of change of velocity in an atomic encounter is neglected in this calculation.

If $q = \cdot 5$ it follows that

$$p_1 = \cdot 2 \quad \text{and} \quad p_2 = \cdot 46.$$

We have seen that the probability p_2 of a single deflexion greater than ϕ is given by

$$p_2 = \frac{\pi}{4} n \cdot t \cdot b^2 \cot^2 \phi/2.$$

Since in the experiments considered ϕ is comparatively small

$$\frac{\phi \sqrt{\overline{p_2}}}{\sqrt{\pi n t}} = b = \frac{2NeE}{mu^2}.$$

Geiger found that the most probable angle of scattering of the α rays in passing through a thickness of gold equivalent in stopping power to about $\cdot 76$ cm. of air was $1° \ 40'$. The angle ϕ through which half the α particles are turned thus corresponds to $2°$ nearly.

$$t = \cdot 00017 \text{ cm.}; n = 6 \cdot 07 \times 10^{22};$$
$$u \text{ (average value)} = 1 \cdot 8 \times 10^9.$$
$$E/m = 1 \cdot 5 \times 10^{14} . \text{ E.S. units}; e = 4 \cdot 65 \times 10^{-10}.$$

Taking the probability of single scattering $= \cdot 46$ and substituting the above values in the formula, the value of N for gold comes out to be 97.

For a thickness of gold equivalent in stopping power to $2 \cdot 12$ cms. of air, Geiger found the most probable angle to be $3° \ 40'$. In this case $t = \cdot 00047$, $\phi = 4° \cdot 4$, and average $u - 1 \cdot 7 \times 10^9$, and N comes out to be 114.

Geiger showed that the most probable angle of deflexion for an atom was nearly proportional to its atomic weight. It consequently follows that the value of N for different atoms should be nearly proportional to their atomic weights, at any rate for atomic weights between gold and aluminium.

Since the atomic weight of platinum is nearly equal to that of gold, it follows from these considerations that the magnitude of the diffuse reflexion of α particles through more than $90°$ from gold and the magnitude of the average small angle scattering of a pencil of rays in passing through gold-foil are both explained on the hypothesis of single scattering by supposing the atom of gold has a central charge of about $100 \ e$.

[A section on the scattering of β rays is omitted—Editors.]

The scattering data for the β rays, as well as for the α rays, indicate that the central charge in an atom is approximately proportional to its atomic weight. This falls in with the experimental deductions of Schmidt. In his theory of absorption of β rays, he supposed that in traversing a thin sheet of matter, a small fraction α of the particles are stopped, and a small fraction β are reflected or scattered back in the direction of incidence. From comparison of the absorption curves of different elements, he deduced that the value of the constant β for different elements is proportional to nA^2 where n is the number of atoms per unit volume and A the atomic weight of the element. This is exactly the relation to be expected on the theory of single scattering if the central charge on an atom is proportional to its atomic weight.

GENERAL CONSIDERATIONS

In comparing the theory outlined in this paper with the experimental results, it has been supposed that the atom consists of a central charge supposed concentrated at a point, and that the large single deflexions of the α and β particles are mainly due to their passage through the strong central field. The effect of the equal and opposite compensating charge supposed distributed uniformly throughout a sphere has been neglected. Some of the evidence in support of these assumptions will now be briefly considered. For concreteness, consider the passage of a high speed α particle through an atom having a positive central charge Ne, and surrounded by a compensating charge of N electrons. Remembering that the mass, momentum, and kinetic energy of the α particle are very large compared with the corresponding values for an electron in rapid motion, it does not seem possible from dynamic considerations that an α particle can be deflected through a large angle by a close approach to an electron, even if the latter be in rapid motion and constrained by strong electrical forces. It seems reasonable to suppose that the chance of single deflexions through a large angle due to this cause, if not zero, must be exceedingly small compared with that due to the central charge.

It is of interest to examine how far the experimental evidence throws light on the question of the extent of the distribution of the central charge. Suppose, for example, the central charge to be composed of N unit charges distributed over such a volume that the large single deflexions are mainly due to the constituent charges and not to the external field produced by the distribution. It has been shown that the fraction of the α particles scattered through a large angle is proportional to $(NeE)^2$, where Ne is the central charge concentrated at a point and E the charge on the deflected particle. If, however, this charge is distributed in single units, the fraction of the α particles scattered through a given angle is proportional to Ne^2 instead of N^2e^2. In this calculation, the influence of mass of the constituent particle has been neglected, and account has only been taken of its electric field. Since it has been shown that the value of the central point charge for gold must be about 100, the value of the distributed charge required to produce the same proportion of single deflexions through a large angle should be at least 10,000. Under these conditions the mass of the constituent particle would be small compared with that of the α particle, and the difficulty arises of the production of large single deflexions at all. In addition, with such a large distributed charge, the effect of compound scattering is relatively more important than that of single scattering. For example, the probable small angle of deflexion of a pencil of α particles passing through a thin gold-foil would be much greater than that experimentally observed by Geiger. The large and small angle scattering could not then be explained by the assumption of a central charge of the same value. Considering the evidence as a whole, it seems simplest to suppose that the atom contains a central charge distributed through a very small volume, and that the large single deflexions are due to the central charge as a whole, and not to its constituents. At the same time, the experimental evidence is not precise enough to negative the possibility that a small fraction of the positive charge may be carried by satellites extending some distance from the centre. Evidence on this point could be obtained by examining whether the same central charge is required to explain the large single deflexions of α and β particles; for the α particle must approach much closer to the centre of the atom than the β particle of average speed to suffer the same large deflexion.

The general data available indicate that the value of this central charge for different atoms is approximately proportional to their atomic weights, at any rate for atoms heavier than aluminium. It will be of great interest to examine experimentally whether such a simple relation holds also for the lighter atoms. In cases where the mass of the deflecting atom (for example, hydrogen, helium, lithium) is not very different from that of the α particle, the general theory of single scattering will require modification, for it is necessary to take into account the movements of the atom itself. . . .

It is of interest to note that Nagaoka has mathematically considered the properties of a "Saturnian" atom which he supposed to consist of a central attracting mass surrounded by rings of rotating electrons. He showed that such a system was stable if the attractive force was large. From the point of view considered in this paper, the chance of large deflexion would practically be unaltered, whether the atom is considered to be a disk or a sphere. It may be remarked that the approximate value found for the central charge of the atom of gold ($100\ e$) is about that to be expected if the atom of gold consisted of 49 atoms of helium, each carrying a charge $2\ e$. This may be only a coincidence, but it is certainly suggestive in view of the expulsion of helium atoms carrying two unit charges from radioactive matter.

The deductions from the theory so far considered are independent of the sign of the central charge, and it has not so far been found possible to obtain definite evidence to determine whether it be positive or negative. It may be possible to settle the question of sign by consideration of the difference of the laws of absorption of the β particle to be expected on the two hypotheses, for the effect of radiation in reducing the velocity of the β particle should be far more marked with a positive than with a negative centre. If the central charge be positive, it is easily seen that a positively charged mass, if released from the centre of a heavy atom, would acquire a great velocity in moving through the electric field. It may be possible in this way to account for the high velocity of expulsion of α particles without supposing that they are initially in rapid motion within the atom.

Further consideration of the application of this theory to these and other questions will be reserved for a later paper, when the main deductions of the theory have been tested experimentally. Experiments in this direction are already in progress by Geiger and Marsden.

ooooooo

The preceding paper by Rutherford sets forth his theory of the scattering of α particles by atoms composed of a small, centrally located, positively charged nucleus surrounded by a sphere of equal but uniformly distributed negative charge whose effect on the scattering of the particles is negligible. The orders of magnitude envisioned were, roughly, for the nuclear radius about 10^{-12} cm, and for the whole atom about 10^{-8} cm. If one imagines that discrete negative electrons were present instead of a distribution of negative charge, then the nuclear atom would be mostly empty space.

Rutherford's scattering formula (see the previous paper, equation [5]) predicted that the fraction of the α particles scattered by a thin foil should be proportional to: (1) the inverse $\sin^4 \phi/2$, where ϕ is the angle through which the α particle is deflected by its encounter with an atom of the foil; (2) the thickness of the scattering foil, provided this is small; (3) the square of the nuclear charge Ne; (4) the inverse fourth power of the velocity v of the bombarding α particles.

Fig. 44–3 in Geiger and Marsden's paper, which follows, shows the very simple apparatus that they set up to examine the theoretical predictions enumerated above. Essentially the device consists of a scattering foil *F*, upon which α particles from the source R, drawn into a stream of parallel trajectories by a diaphragm at D, strike at right angles. The box B, which carries the viewing microscope M, rotates around the axis of the foil F by means of the ground-glass joint C. A cap over the end of the microscope carries a zinc-sulfide screen S that produces a scintillation of light if struck by an α particle. These scintillations are viewed through the microscope. By turning the plate A, the microscope is moved around the foil F, and thus intercepts particles scattered through various angles. The cover P acts as an air-tight lid for the box B, in which a vacuum is achieved by pumping the air away through the space T.

The results of the experiment appear in several tables. Reference to equation (5) in Rutherford's paper shows us that if the characteristics of the foil and the velocity of the α particles are unvaried in the tests, the number of particles falling on the zinc-sulfide screen depends only on the angle of deflection ϕ. (Hence if the number of particles N deflected through the angle ϕ is multiplied by $\sin^4\phi/2$, the right-hand side of the equation becomes constant. Table 44–3, columns IV and VI, lists values of $N \sin^4\phi/2$ —the columns are mislabeled as the "quotient" for silver and gold foils, respectively. The numbers, within the limits of error, are constant.) The variation with thickness and atomic weight of the foil and with the velocity of the α particles was found by experiment to verify the formula also. It was shown that at least from the standpoint of scattering, atoms behaved as though most of their mass was concentrated in a very small nucleus, although the Rutherford model did not distinguish whether this nucleus was positively or negatively charged. It soon became evident from many lines of evidence that the nucleus did indeed have a positive charge, that the nuclear model was in accord with other experiments, and that the electrons were charges of approximately the same size as the nucleus but moving in orbits such that the diameter of the atom was of the order of 10^{-8} cm. Thus was the nuclear atom discovered.

๑๑๑๑๑๑๑๑

GEIGER and MARSDEN

The Laws of Deflexion of α Particles through Large Angles [2]

IN A FORMER PAPER ONE of us has shown that in the passage of α particles through matter the deflexions are, on the average, small and of the order of a few degrees only. In the experiments a

---

[2] Hans Geiger and Ernest Marsden, *Philosophical Magazine*, 25 (1913), 604–623.

narrow pencil of α particles fell on a zinc-sulphide screen in vacuum, and the distribution of the scintillations on the screen was observed when different metal foils were placed in the path of the α particles. From the distribution obtained, the most probable angle of scattering could be deduced, and it was shown that the results could be explained on the assumption that the deflexion of a single α particle is the resultant of a large number of very small deflexions caused by the passage of the α particle through the successive individual atoms of the scattering substance.

In an earlier paper, however, we pointed out that α particles are sometimes turned through very large angles. This was made evident by the fact that when α particles fall on a metal plate, a small fraction of them, about 1/8000 in the case of platinum, appears to be diffusely reflected. This amount of reflexion, although small, is, however, too large to be explained on the above simple theory of scattering. It is easy to calculate from the experimental data that the probability of a deflexion through an angle of 90° is vanishingly small, and of a different order to the value found experimentally.

Professor Rutherford has recently developed a theory to account for the scattering of α particles through these large angles, the assumption being that the deflexions are the result of an intimate encounter of an α particle with a single atom of the matter traversed. In this theory an atom is supposed to consist of a strong positive or negative central charge concentrated within a sphere of less than about 3×10^{-12} cm. radius, and surrounded by electricity of the opposite sign distributed throughout the remainder of the atom of about 10^{-8} cm. radius. In considering the deflexion of an α particle directed against such an atom, the main deflexion-effect can be supposed to be due to the central concentrated charge which will cause the α particle to describe an hyperbola with the centre of the atom as one focus.

The angle between the directions of the α particle before and after deflexion will depend on the perpendicular distance of the initial trajectory from the centre of the atom. The fraction of the α particles whose paths are sufficiently near to the centre of the atom will, however, be small, so that the probability of an α particle suffering a large deflexion of this nature will be correspondingly small. Thus, assuming a narrow pencil of α particles directed against a thin sheet of matter containing atoms distributed at random throughout its volume, if the scattered particles are counted by the scintillations they produce on a zinc-sulphide screen distance r from the point of incidence of the pencil in a direction making an angle ϕ with it, the number of α particles falling on unit area of the screen per second is deduced to be equal to

$$\frac{Qntb^2 \operatorname{cosec}^4 \phi/2}{16r^2},$$

where Q is the number of α particles per second in the original pencil, n the number of atoms in unit volume of the material, and t the thickness of the foil. The quantity

$$b = \frac{2NeE}{mu^2},$$

where Ne is the central charge of the atom, and m, E, and u are the respective mass, charge, and velocity of the α particle.

The number of deflected α particles is thus proportional to (1) $\operatorname{cosec}^4 \phi/2$, (2) thickness of scattering material t if the thickness is small, (3) the square of the central charge Ne of the atoms of the particular matter employed to scatter the particles, (4) the inverse fourth power of the velocity u of the incident in α particles.

At the suggestion of Prof. Rutherford, we have carried out experiments to test the main conclusions of the above theory. The following points were investigated:—

(1) Variation with angle.
(2) Variation with thickness of scattering material.
(3) Variation with atomic weight of scattering material.
(4) Variation with velocity of incident α particles.
(5) The fraction of particles scattered through a definite angle.

The main difficulty of the experiments has arisen from the necessity of using a very intense and narrow source of α particles owing to the smallness of the scattering effect. All the measurements have been carried out by observing the scintillations due to the scattered α particles on a zinc-sulphide screen, and during the course of the experiments over 100,000 scintillations have been counted. It may be mentioned in anticipation that all the results of our investigation are in good agreement with the theoretical deductions of Prof. Rutherford, and afford strong evidence of the correctness of the underlying assumption that an atom contains a strong charge at the centre of dimensions, small compared with the diameter of the atom.

VARIATION OF SCATTERING WITH ANGLE

We have already pointed out that to obtain measurable effects an intense pencil of α particles is required. It is further necessary that the path of the α particles should be in an evacuated chamber to avoid complications due to the absorption and scattering of the air. The apparatus used is shown in [Fig. 44–3], and mainly consisted of a strong cylindrical metal box B, which contained the source of α particles R, the scattering foil F, and a microscope M to which the zinc-sulphide screen S was rigidly attached. The box was fastened down to a graduated circular platform A, which could be rotated by means of a conical airtight joint C. By rotating the platform the box and microscope moved with it, whilst the scattering foil and radiating source remained in position, being attached to the tube T, which was fastened to the standard L. The box B was closed by the ground-glass plate P, and could be exhausted through the tube T.

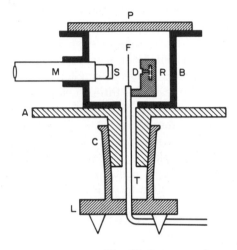

Fig. 44–3.

The source of α particles employed was similar to that used originally by Rutherford and Royds in their experiments on the nature of the α particle. It consisted of a small thin-walled glass tube about 1 mm. in diameter, containing a large quantity of well purified radium emanation. The α particles emitted by the emanation and its active deposit could pass through the glass walls without much reduction of range. For these experiments the unhomogeneity of the source, due to the different α particles from the emanation, Ra A and Ra C, does not interfere with the application of the law of scattering with angle as deduced from the theory, as each group of α particles is scattered according to the same law.

By means of a diaphragm placed at D, a pencil of α particles was directed normally on to the scattering foil F. By rotating the microscope the α particles scattered in different directions could be observed on the screen S. Although over 100 millicuries of radium emanation were available for the experiments, the smallness of the effect for the larger angles of deflexion necessitated short distances of screen and source from the scattering foil. In some experiments the distance between the source and scattering foil was 2·5 cm., and the screen moved in a circle of 1·6 cm. radius, while in other experiments these distances were increased. Observations were taken in various experiments for angles of deflexion from 5° to 150°. When measuring the scattering through large angles the zinc-sulphide screen had to be turned very near to the source, and the β and γ rays produced a considerable luminescence on it, thus making countings of the scintillations difficult. The effect of the β rays was reduced as far as possible by enclosing the source in a lead box shown shaded in the diagram. The amount of lead was, however, limited by considerations of the space taken up by it, and consequently observations could not be made for angles of deflexion between 150° and 180°.

In the investigation of the scattering through relatively small angles the distances of source and screen from the scattering foil were increased considerably in order to obtain beams of smaller solid angle.

The number of particles scattered through different angles was found to decrease extremely rapidly with increase of angle, and as it is not possible to count with certainty more than 90 scintillations per minute or less than about 5 per minute, measurements could only be made over a relatively small range of angles at the same time. The number of α particles scattered through large angles was first measured, and as the emanation decayed it was possible to take measurements for smaller and smaller angles, and from the known decay of the emanation measurements taken at different times could be corrected for the decrease of activity.

Even when no scattering foil was used a few scintillations were always observed on the screen. They were obviously due to scattered radiation from the walls of the vessel and from the edge of the diaphragm limiting the beam. The effect was reduced as far as possible by lining the box with paper and by using a substance of low atomic weight, viz. aluminium, for the diaphragm. The number of stray α particles was determined for different positions of the microscope by removing the scattering foil so that the necessary corrections could be applied with certainty.

In order to make the best use of the emanation available, measurements were made simultaneously with different foils. These foils were attached to frames which fitted into a slot in the tube T in such a way that they could be exchanged and accurately replaced in position. [Table 44–2] gives an example of a particular set of countings, when a silver foil was used to scatter the α particles.

In this set about 2500 scintillations were counted. After a few days had elapsed the measurements for the smaller angles were repeated and the range of angles extended. Proceeding in this way the whole range of angles was investigated in the course of a few weeks. When measuring relatively large angles of deflexion a wide beam of about 15° radius had to be used in order to obtain a suitable number of scintillations, but for the smaller angles the aperture of the diaphragm confining the beam was reduced considerably, so that the angle at which the scintillations were counted was always large compared with the angular radius of the beam. When changing over from one diaphragm to another comparative measurements for different angles were made so as to obtain an accurate value of the reduction constant.

TABLE 44-2 *Variation of Scattering with Angle. (Example of a set of measurements)* *

Angle ϕ.	Scintillations per minute.				$\dfrac{1}{\sin^4 \phi/2}$.	$N \times \sin^4 \phi/2$.
	Without foil.	With foil.	Corrected for effect without foil.	Corrected for decay, N.		
150°	0·2	4·95	4·75	6·95	1·15	6·0
135	2·6	8·3	5·7	8·35	1·38	6·1
120	3·8	10·3	6·5	9·5	1·79	5·3
105	0·6	10·6	10·0	14·6	2·53	5·8
75	0·0	28·6	28·6	41·9	7·25	5·8
60	0·3	69·2	68·9	101	16·0	6·3

* Silver foil. Time elapsed since filling of emanation tube, 51 hours. Correction for decay, 0·683.

[Table 44–3] gives the collected results for two series of experiments with foils of silver and gold. The thicknesses of the foils were in the first series equivalent to 0·45 and 0·3 cm. air, and in the second series 0·45 and 0·1 cm. air for silver and gold respectively. Col. I. gives the values of the angles ϕ between the direction of the beam and the direction in which the scattered α particles were counted. Col. II. gives the values of

$$\frac{1}{\sin^4 \phi/2}.$$

In Cols. III. and V. the numbers of scintillations are entered which were observed for the silver and gold respectively. Corrections are made for the decay of the emanation, for the natural effect, and for change of diaphragm. For the smaller angles corrections have been applied (in no case exceeding 20 per cent.) owing to the fact that the beam of α particles was of finite dimensions and not negligible compared with the angle of deflexion. These corrections were calculated from geometrical

TABLE 44–3   *Variation of Scattering with Angle. (Collected results.)*

I.	II.	III.	IV.	V.	VI.
		SILVER		GOLD.	
Angle of deflexion, ϕ.	$\dfrac{1}{\sin^4 \phi/2}$	Number of scintillations, N.	$\dfrac{N}{\sin^4 \phi/2}$	Number of scintillations, N.	$\dfrac{N}{\sin^4 \phi/2}$
150°	1·15	22·2	19·3	33·1	28·8
135	1·38	27·4	19·8	43·0	31·2
120	1·79	33·0	18·4	51·9	29·0
105	2·53	47·3	18·7	69·5	27·5
75	7·25	136	18·8	211	29·1
60	16·0	320	20·0	477	29·8
45	46·6	989	21·2	1435	30·8
37·5	93·7	1760	18·8	3300	35·3
30	223	5260	23·6	7800	35·0
22·5	690	20300	29·4	27300	39·6
15	3445	105400	30·6	132000	38·4
30	223	5·3	0·024	3·1	0·014
22·5	690	16·6	0·024	8·4	0·012
15	3445	93·0	0·027	48·2	0·014
10	17330	508	0·029	200	0·0115
7·5	54650	1710	0·031	607	0·011
5	276300			3320	0·012

considerations. In Cols. IV. and VI. the ratios of the numbers of scintillations to

$$\frac{1}{\sin^4 \phi/2}$$

are entered. It will be seen that in both sets the values are approximately constant. The deviations are somewhat systematic, the ratio increasing with decreasing angle. However, any slight asymmetry in the apparatus and other causes would affect the results in a systematic way so that, fitting on the two sets of observations and considering the enormous variation in the numbers of scattered particles, from 1 to 250,-000, the deviations from constancy of the ratio are probably well within the experimental error. The experiments, therefore, prove that the number of α particles scattered in a definite direction varies as $\operatorname{cosec}^4 \phi/2$.

VARIATION WITH THICKNESS
OF MATERIAL

In investigating the variation of scattering with thickness of material, it seemed necessary to use a homogeneous source of α particles, for according to the theory the effect of the change of velocity with increasing thickness will be very appreciable for α particles of low velocity. In the experiments on "compound scattering" by one of us, a source was used consisting of Ra C deposited from radium emanation *in situ* in a small conical tube fitted with a mica window, the emanation being withdrawn when measurements were taken by expanding into a large volume connected to it. In our first experiments we used such a source, but the observations eventually showed it to be unsuitable. After expansion some emanation remains clinging to the walls of the glass tube. This emanation and the Ra A associated with it gives α particles of considerably lower velocity than the α particles of Ra C, and although the number of α particles so contributed was of the order of only a few per cent. of the number from Ra C, yet owing to the fact that the amount of scattering increases very rapidly with decreasing velocity, the disturbances caused by the slower α particles were so large as to render the source unsuitable for the present work.

. . . About 80 millicuries of radium emanation were very highly purified and pressed into the conical end of the glass tube T of about 1 mm. internal diameter. After the emanation had remained in position for a sufficient time to attain equilibrium with Ra C, it was expanded into a bulb below, and a small part of the capillary tube was drawn off. . . . About 1 mm. of the end of the tube which was coated with the Ra C was then cut off . . . and freed from occluded emanation by washing with alcohol and by heating. The resulting source of Ra C was used in the experiments, and with due care its decay was found to be in agreement with theory, at least for the first 80 minutes. . . .

[The arrangement used for this experiment is omitted—Editors.]

In [Table 44–4] the results of an experiment with gold foils are tabulated. Column I. gives the number of foils and column II. the thicknesses expressed as the stopping power of α particles in centimetres of air as determined by the scintillation method. The figures given in column III. represent the number of scintillations observed on the zinc-sulphide screen. These figures are corrected for the variation of activity with time of the source. A slight correction has been made due to the increase of scattering on account of the decrease of velocity of the α particles in passing through the foils. The magnitude of this correction . . . amounted to 9 per cent. in this experiment for the thickest foil used. The last column of

TABLE 44–4   *Gold.—Variation of Scattering with Thickness.*

I.	II.	III.	IV.
Number of foils.	Air equivalent. T in cm.	Number N of scintillations per minute.	Ratio $\frac{N}{T}$.
1	0·11	21·9	200
2	0·22	38·4	175
5	0·51	84·3	165
8	0·81	121·5	150
9	0·90	145	160

the table gives the ratio of the corrected number of scintillations to the thickness. The values are constant within the limits of the experimental error. The variations exhibited by the figures are well within the probability errors, owing to the relatively small number of scintillations which could be counted in the time available.

Similar experiments were carried out with foils of tin, silver, copper, and aluminium. In each set about 1000 scintillations were counted. The results are plotted in [Fig. 44–4], where the abscissæ represent the thickness of the scattering foil expressed in centimetres of air equivalent and the ordinates the number of scattered particles. Similar corrections of the above have been introduced in each case.

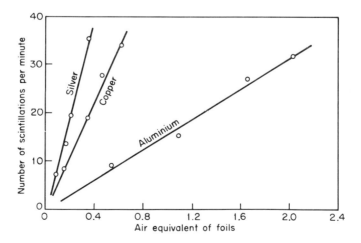

Fig. 44–4.

For all the metals examined the points lie on straight lines which pass through the origin. The experiments therefore prove that for small thicknesses of matter the scattering is proportional to the thickness. . . .

VARIATION WITH ATOMIC WEIGHT

Assuming that the magnitude of the central charge of the atom is proportional to the atomic weight A, Professor Rutherford has shown that the number of α particles scattered by different foils containing the same number of atoms should be proportional to A^2. With the thin foils which had to be used experimentally, it was found impracticable to calculate the number of atoms per unit area by weighing the foils. It proved much more reliable to deduce the required number of atoms from the air equivalent as found by the reduction of the range of α particles by the scintillation method. This method had the advantage that the thickness was determined at the exact part of the foil which served to scatter the α particles, thus eliminating any errors due to variations in the thickness of the foils. Bragg and others have given numbers connecting the thicknesses of foils of various materials and their stopping power, and it has been shown that for different foils of the same air equivalent the numbers of atoms per unit area are inversely proportional to the square roots of the atomic weights. Consequently if the scattering per atom of atomic weight A is proportional to A^2, the scattering per centimetre air equivalent will be proportional to $A^2 \times A^{-\frac{1}{2}}$, i.e. to $A^{\frac{3}{2}}$.

In the experimental investigation the same apparatus was used as in the previous experiments on the variation of scattering with thickness of material. . . . A number of different sets of experiments were made, the foils being varied in each experiment. . . .

The combined results of four experiments are given in [Table 44–5]. In the last column are given the ratios of the numbers of scintillations per centimetre equivalent to $A^{\frac{3}{2}}$. This ratio should be constant according to theory. The experimental values show a slight increase with decreasing atomic weight. . . .

[The section on scattering as a function of the velocity of the α-particles is omitted—Editors.]

. . . Using a gold foil of air equivalent 1 mm. (actual thickness $2 \cdot 1 \times 10^{-5}$ cm.), the fraction of incident Ra C α particles ($v = 2 \cdot 06 \times 10^9$ cm./sec.) scattered through an angle of 45° and observed on an area of 1 sq. mm. placed normally at a distance of 1 cm. from the point of incidence of the beam, was $3 \cdot 7 \times 10^{-7}$. Substituting this value in the equation given at the commencement of this paper, it can be calculated that the value of the number of elementary electric charges composing the central charge of the gold atom is about half the atomic weight. This result is probably correct to 20 per cent., and agrees with the deduction of Prof. Rutherford from the less definite data given in our previous paper.

From the results of this and the previous sections it is possible to calculate the probability of an α particle being scattered through any angle under any specified conditions. For materials of atomic weight greater than that of aluminium, it is sufficiently accurate to put N equal to half the atomic weight in the equation given at the commencement of the paper.

T A B L E   4 4 – 5   *Variation of Scattering with Atomic Weight. (Collected results using Ra C.)*

Substance.	Total number of scintillations counted for each material.	$A^{3/2}$.	Ratio of scintillations per cm. air equivalent to $A^{3/2}$ *.
Gold	850	2770	95
Platinum	200	2730	99
Tin	700	1300	96
Silver	800	1120	98
Copper	600	507	104
Aluminium	700	144	110

* *Note* 1.—Since these experiments were carried out, Richardson and one of us (*Phil. Mag.* vol. xxv. p. 184 (1913)) have determined the masses per unit area per cm. air equivalent for different metals, using the scintillation method. Introducing the results, and calculating the values of the ratio of the scattering per atom divided by A^2, the following are obtained:—Au 3·4, Pt 3·2, Sn 3·3, Ag 3·6, Cu 3·7, Al 3·6. These numbers show better agreement than those in the last column above, which are calculated on the assumption of Bragg's law.

It will be seen that the laws of "single scattering" found in this paper are quite distinct from the laws of "compound scattering" previously deduced by Geiger. It must be remembered, however, that the experiments are not directly comparable. In the present paper we are dealing with very thin sheets of matter, and are measuring the very small fraction of α particles which are deflected by single collisions through relatively large angles. The experiments of Geiger, however, deal with larger thicknesses of scattering foils and angles of deflexion of a few degrees only. Under these conditions the scattering is due to the combination of a large number of deflexions not only by the central charges of the atoms, but probably also by the electronic charges distributed throughout the remainder of their volumes.

SUMMARY

The experiments described in the foregoing paper were carried out to test a theory of the atom proposed by Prof. Rutherford, the main feature of which is that there exists at the centre of the atom an intense highly concentrated electrical charge. The verification is based on the laws of scattering which were deduced from this theory. The following relations have been verified experimentally:

(1) The number of α particles emerging from a scattering foil at an angle ϕ with the original beam varies as $1/\sin^4 \phi/2$, when the α particles are counted on a definite area at a constant distance from the foil. This relation has been tested for angles varying from 5° to 150°, and over this range the number of α particles varied from 1 to 250,000 in good agreement with the theory.

(2) The number of α particles scattered in a definite direction is directly proportional to the thickness of the scattering foil for small thicknesses. For larger thicknesses the decrease of velocity of the α particles in the foil causes a somewhat more rapid increase in the amount of scattering.

(3) The scattering per atom of foils of different materials varies approximately as the square of the atomic weight. This relation was tested for foils of atomic weight from that of carbon to that of gold.

(4) The amount of scattering by a given foil is approximately proportional to the inverse fourth power of the velocity of the incident α particles. This relation was tested over a range of velocities such that the number of scattered particles varied as 1 : 10.

(5) Quantitative experiments show that the fraction of α particles of Ra C, which is scattered through an angle of 45° by a gold foil of 1 mm. air equivalent ($2 \cdot 1 \times 10^{-5}$ cm.), is $3 \cdot 7 \times 10^{-7}$ when the scattered particles are counted on a screen of 1 sq. mm. area placed at a distance of 1 cm. from the scattering foil. From this figure and the foregoing results, it can be calculated that the number of elementary charges composing the centre of the atom is equal to half the atomic weight. . . .

45

ooooooooooo

ATOMIC STRUCTURE

ooooooooooo

Niels Bohr (1885-1962)

Niels Bohr, at various periods of his life, was referred to as the "Great Dane," the "spirit of modern physics," the "symbol of modern physics," the "main architect of our work," and so on, in recognition of his outstanding contributions, which dwarfed all but those of Einstein. We may, indeed, refer to these two figures as the two great masters, whose work formed the basis of most phases of modern physics. Bohr was more than a mere discoverer of new theories; he was a great teacher, a source of new ideas, a penetrating critic, a bold innovator, and a stimulating companion, who probably inspired more scientific papers for his students and visiting scientists than any other physicist.

Physics and Bohr were both fortunate in the date of his birth, October 7, 1885, for he reached maturity and began his research career in 1905, just when the new and exciting concepts of the quantum theory and the theory of relativity were emerging from the tentative pen of Planck and the bold imagination of Einstein. For physics, what a heroic and golden time the fifty-seven years of Bohr's scientific career spanned. In this period the atomic theory as we now know it was created, mostly through his efforts and inspiration, and the causal approach of classical mechanics was replaced by the Bohr complementarity scheme of quantum mechanics.

Niels Henrik David Bohr was born in Copenhagen, the son of an outstanding professor of physiology at the University of Copenhagen. He grew up in an environment of great learning and culture, surrounded by people devoted to science, humanism, and mankind. Such outstanding men as the physicist Christiansen, the philosopher Hoffding, and the philologist Thomsen were constant visitors at the Bohr home; Niels was a devoted listener to the four-way conversations that were held almost every Friday night. This early exposure to humanistic tenets unquestionably did much to influence Bohr's later warm regard for his fellow men. In the words of Prof. J. Rud Nielson, one of his closest associates, Bohr was one of the "wisest and most lovable of men."

When Bohr began his high-school studies, Planck had just announced the quantum theory. By the time Bohr entered the university in 1903, he was already grappling with these challenging new ideas. But he was by no means the sedentary student who devotes himself entirely to books. He was much too restless and active for such a life and was very fond of bicycling, sailing, skiing, and soccer. Indeed, he and his younger brother Harald, who was to become a first-rate mathematician, were both outstanding soccer players.

Bohr never quite finished with a problem regardless of how long he worked on it or how many papers he published. He pursued each subject year after year, with dogged tenacity, looking at the questions from every angle, and considering the same points over and over again, until he had polished away the rough edges and achieved what, at least momentarily, appeared to be a finished product, only to come back to it again a few months or a few years later. This approach to his research work was already evident in the first paper that he published, in 1906 at the age of twenty-one. This paper was of both a theoretical and experimental nature, and he could not pull himself away from the laboratory to write up his results. Each time he completed some phase of the work, he saw some new features of the problem that he felt he must understand. Finally, his father sent him away from Copenhagen to his grandparents; here Bohr wrote the paper. The paper dealt with the surface tension of water, and it won him the gold medal of the Danish Academy of Science.

John A. Wheeler, with whom Bohr collaborated on the very important problems of nuclear structure and nuclear fission just before World War II, describes this persistence of Bohr as follows:

> This place [a special room in Bohr's beautiful home] satisfied his definition of a work room, "a place where nobody can keep you from working." One of the most delightful features was a set of drawers, about 25 in number. Each was perhaps an inch deep and contained a draft manuscript having to do with one or another issue of physics. Each topic ripened from draft to draft—sometimes over many years—until the point was reached where, in Bohr's judgment, publication was at last appropriate. Among the manuscripts for which the basic idea reached far into the past, one of the most celebrated dealt with angular momentum and its exchange in atomic and nuclear transformation processes. It never reached the point of publication. However, it, like other drafts in this collection, defined conclusions and stated issues, and it furnished the starting point for the development of new ideas.[1]

---

[1] John A. Wheeler, *Physics Today,* 16 (1963), 44.

After Bohr had received his doctor's degree in 1911 for a brilliant dissertation on the electron theory of metals he went to Cambridge to work with J. J. Thomson and a few months later to Manchester to work with Rutherford. He remained in Manchester until 1913, the year in which he published the first of his epochal papers on atomic and molecular structure. He then returned to Copenhagen to begin his family life, for he had married Margarethe Nølund the year before; he lectured at the university, having been appointed a docent.

The scientific climate in Denmark at that time was not conducive to the full flowering of Bohr's genius; little was heard of his work and few of the top physicists were interested in what he was doing. Professor Knudsen, who had verified the kinetic theory experimentally, on being asked to explain Bohr's theory, remarked that he could not because he had not read Bohr's papers. Bohr must have felt this lack of interest for he returned to Manchester in the fall of 1914 as reader in mathematical physics.

In 1916 Bohr again return to Copenhagen, this time to stay. A professorship in theoretical physics had been created for him. From that time on, the level and general tone of physics in Denmark improved steadily. Although he had to work in a small room, and had no paid assistant (he did most of his work at home), he developed the basic ideas of the famous "correspondence principle" in the first two years of this period. A detailed account was published as a *Memoir* of the Danish Academy.

A description of Bohr's ebullience and physical exuberance is given by Nielson:

> When I think of Bohr as he appeared nearly fifty years ago, the speed with which he moved comes to my mind. He would come into the yard, pushing his bicycle, faster than anybody else. He was an incessant worker and seemed always to be in a hurry. Serenity and pipe smoking came much later. He was always friendly and less remote than most Danish professors in those days.[2]

Bohr's greatest influence on world physics began with the dedication, on March 3, 1921, of his famous Institute for Theoretical Physics, which he had proposed as early as 1917. To spend a year or two at this exciting center of physics became the goal of every young physicist. Most of today's top names in physics will be found on the rosters of that institute. Bohr's institute not only attracted the brilliant youngsters but also the well-established physicists of all countries, and it was not unusual to find a few dozen famous men working there at the same time. H. A. Kramers from Holland, O. Klein from Sweden, Dirac from England, Ehren-

---

[2] J. Rud Nielson, "Memories of Niels Bohr," *Physics Today,* 16 (1963), 23.

fest from Holland, Heisenberg from Germany, Brillouin from France, Pauli from Austria, Gamov and Landau from Russia are but a few of the famous names that graced the institute.

After Bohr received the Nobel Prize in 1922, one honor after another was heaped on him, and he was in constant demand as a lecturer. He would prepare his lectures, as he did his papers, with the greatest care, polishing every sentence over and over again, right up to the very moment that he began speaking.

Much of his lecturing took him to foreign countries. In 1933, he came to the United States for the first time, where he lectured at the University of Chicago and at the California Institute of Technology in Pasadena. This was the first of a series of trips to this country; he spent most of his time in the United States (except when he came here during the war and worked at Los Alamos) at the Institute of Advanced Study at Princeton. He thought very highly of many American physicists, particularly Oppenheimer and John C. Slater at MIT, about whom he commented, "There is probably no one in Europe who knows as much about atomic problems as Slater." In his remarks about American physics he clearly indicated his devotion to the idea of the universal quality of the human mind and to the idea that there is no monopoly of knowledge by any one ethnic group or country. He went on to say:

> Who knows where science will flourish most highly a hundred years from now; perhaps in Japan; perhaps in China? We know nothing about such things.

Although Bohr was quick to see positive elements in his colleagues, he was also apt to see the flaws and the irrelevancies. Thus, in spite of considering A. H. Compton an excellent physicist, Bohr felt that his philosophy was too primitive and should have no place in physics. He remarked:

> Compton would like to say that for God there is no uncertainty principle. That is nonsense. In physics we do not talk about God but about what we can know. If we are to speak about God we must do so in an entirely different manner.[3]

In Denmark itself Bohr was vastly admired. The government and the public alike made every effort to demonstrate their esteem. The brewer Carl Jacobsen in 1932 donated a beautiful mansion as a lifetime residence of Denmark's most renowned scientist and scholar. This was a happy occasion for Bohr, for he could now entertain large groups of

---

[3] J. Rud Nielson, *op. cit.,* p. 27.

people and even had room enough to have a number of guests (usually scientists with whom he was collaborating) stay at his house for extended periods.

During this very fruitful period Bohr began to pay greater and greater attention to the underlying philosophical and epistemological aspects of science, and of physics in particular. Thus he became more and more concerned with his principle of complementary or the so-called "Copenhagen interpretation of the quantum theory," and by dint of his great persuasive ability he swung over the great majority of physicists to this point of view. He did this not by publishing any single paper but by constant discussion with the gifted group of physicists assembled at his institute. In the words of Victor F. Weisskopf, who was one of the youngest and most perceptive of that group:

> It was his [Bohr's] greatest strength to assemble around him the most active, the most gifted, the most perceiving physicists of the world. . . .
>
> It was at that time and with those people that the foundations of the quantum concept were created, that the uncertainty relation was first conceived and discussed, that the particle-wave antinomy was for the first time understood. In lively discussions, in groups of two or more, the deepest problems of the structure of matter were brought to light. You can imagine what atmosphere, what life, what intellectual activity reigned in Copenhagen at that time. Here was Bohr's influence at its best. Here it was that he created his style, the "Kopenhagener Geist," the style of a very special character that he imposed on physics. We see him, the greatest among his colleagues, acting, talking, living as an equal in a group of young, optimistic, jocular enthusiastic people, approaching the deepest riddles of nature with a spirit of attack, a spirit of freedom from conventional bonds and a spirit of joy that can hardly be described.
>
> In that great period of physics, Bohr and his disciples touched the nerve of the universe. The intellectual eye of man was opened on the inner workings of Nature that were a secret up to this point. The concept of quantum state was cleared up, its fundamental wholeness, its indivisibility which, however, has that peculiar way of escaping ordinary observation because the very act of such observation would obliterate the conditions of its existence. Bohr, whose penetrating analysis contributed so much to the clarification of these problems, called that remarkable situation "complementary." It defies pictorial description in our accustomed classical terms of physics. . . .[4]

Bohr's concern with presenting his theory of complementarity to the world in as clear and understandable a manner as possible led him to profound problems of philosophy, language, and pedagogy. He always sought

---

[4] Victor F. Weisskopf, "Niels Bohr (A Memorial Tribute)," *Physics Today,* 16 (1963), 59.

better ways of expressing the same idea and he outlined plans for an all-encompassing text that would contain as little formalism as possible and would strongly emphasize the physics. At that time, he said:

> I believe that I have come to a certain stage of completion in my work. I believe that my conclusions have wide application also outside physics [his theory of complementarity]. . . . I should like to write a book that could be used as a text. I would show that it is possible to reach all important results with very little mathematics. In fact, in this manner one would in some respects achieve greater clarity.[5]

He never did write such a book for this was a period of great research activity. He became involved in the famous controversy with Einstein in a series of confrontations and dialogues in which Einstein propounded ingenious quantum-mechanical paradoxes and Bohr, just as ingeniously, resolved them, using Einstein's own relativity theory and principle of invariance to accomplish it. The result of these confrontations was a paper, published by Bohr in honor of Einstein's seventieth birthday, which will remain one of the great classics in the history of physics and philosophy.

This was also the period in which quantum mechanics was being applied to the electromagnetic field. Here Bohr pursued the subject very vigorously in close collaboration with Pauli, Heisenberg, and Dirac who had already made important independent contributions. In particular, in a famous paper published jointly with L. Rosenfeld, Bohr established the basic principles of field quantization and showed that the Heisenberg uncertainty relations apply to the measurement of field quantities just as they do to the measurement of dynamical quantities. It was characteristic of Bohr's concern with presenting the best possible product that one is capable of that, after having worked on this paper with Rosenfeld for more than a year, he was still fearful, on the very eve of its publication, that it might be all wrong and that he could have done a better job.

At this stage of Bohr's career the scientific world was suddenly thrust into the hectic world of nuclear physics with the discovery of the neutron; with his usual vigor Bohr thrust himself into this field. Here he contributed two important concepts: that of the "compound nucleus" and the liquid-drop model of the nucleus. These two concepts made it possible to understand how two nuclei can collide and form a new nucleus with a variety of different particles being emitted.

Then World War II intervened. Bohr's institute, already more than a center of physics, had become a refuge for all those scientists seeking to escape Nazi persecution in the period from 1933 to 1940. When Denmark

---

[5] J. Rud Nielson, *op. cit.*, p. 27.

fell, the institute had to be abandoned, for Bohr refused to collaborate with the Nazis. He barely escaped to Sweden, and from there, via England, to the United States, where he met many of the scientists he had previously helped to slip out of occupied Europe and for whom he had obtained positions in the United States. Bohr's escape from Denmark is itself a very dramatic story. The Danish police had warned him that the Nazis were looking for him, and he managed to cross the Sound of Sweden just ahead of them. He was then flown under the greatest security to London and from there to Los Alamos, where he was known simply as Mr. Nicholas Baker. To mention his true name there was strictly forbidden, for the knowledge that he was there would have revealed what was going on in Los Alamos. Throughout the war, his gold Nobel medal remained in Copenhagen, unknown to the Nazis; it was dissolved in a bottle of nitric acid. After the war, the metal was recovered and recast.

Bohr had already contributed greatly to the exploitation of atomic energy. In January 1939, just before he embarked from Denmark for one of his visits to this country, Frisch and Meitner had told him about the discovery of uranium fission by Hahn and Strassmann. Bohr, as usual, had been impatient to get at the heart of the problem and he could hardly restrain his excitement when John A. Wheeler met him as he walked off the ship. They immediately began a theoretical analysis of the fission process. In a series of brilliant deductions, using his liquid-drop model and his concept of the compound nucleus, Bohr showed conclusively that the isotope U^{235} and not U^{238} undergoes fission. This was the first step in an irreversible process that led to the atomic bomb and to the nuclear chain reaction.

Bohr acknowledged the need for the bomb when he arrived in the United States during the war, but he immediately saw that it would have to be controlled internationally if it were not to lead ultimately to the destruction of the world. He pleaded passionately with both Presidents Roosevelt and Truman to set up plans and political machinery to forestall a nuclear arms race, for he was well aware, early in the game, that the Russians would very quickly develop the bomb. In 1957, after seeing a Russian film on nuclear energy, he commented:

> The Russians got the first nuclear power plant, and they have the largest cyclotron. . . . It was perfectly absurd to believe that the Russians cannot do what others can. . . . There never was any secret about nuclear energy. . . . It is also absurd to expect that the Russians will put up with everything and give up any position of power they may possess. . . .
> The quantum theory does not present any problem to me any more. The all-important problem now is to find a way to prevent nuclear war. . . .[6]

---

[6] J. Rud Nielson, *op. cit.,* p. 29.

Again, when questioned about the horribly destructive hydrogen bomb and Teller's contribution to it, Bohr remarked

> Old physicists who have turned administrators might not think of this solution. However, if you had asked a good class of physics students, two or three of them would have suggested this solution. Anyway the Russians did the very same thing.[7]

Great as Bohr was as a scientist, he was an equally great humanist. A concern for all people and a hatred for injustice were primary ideals even in his early years. He felt that nothing could be achieved in righting the wrongs of society without sacrifice. During the depression, when he first visited this country, he was amazed at the great wealth in the midst of poverty and remarked that in Denmark

> The burdens of the depression are fairly evenly distributed over all layers of the population. . . . Of course one cannot improve conditions for all layers of society without renunciation on the part of some. . . . It is sheer folly to believe that one can achieve anything in this world without renunciation. . . .[8]

He also, very early in his career, saw the need for international cooperation in all human endeavors and was repelled by the type of national jockeying that went on at international conferences. He rejected this kind of interplay in the following words:

> This is the way it goes with international meetings as long as we have independent countries. The aim of most delegates to such meetings seems to be to obtain as many advantages as possible for their own country and to cheat and deceive the others as much as possible. . . . We must be internationalists, and in science we succeed fairly well. . . . All peoples and races are essentially alike; the differences are in their traditions and backgrounds. . . . Every valuable human being must be a radical and a rebel, for what he must aim at is to make things better than they are. . . .[9]

Bohr found great happiness and fulfillment not only in his science but also in his family to whom he was intensely devoted. His personal life was not free of tragedy. In September 1934, the oldest of his five sons (he had no daughters) was drowned in a sailing accident and those who were present had all they could do to restrain Bohr from throwing himself into the sea in a futile attempt to save the boy. His grief was intense and for weeks he was inconsolable. Finally, the pressure of new scientific discoveries and his sense of the continuity of life restored his equilibrium.

---

[7] *Ibid.*, p. 30.

[8] J. Rud Nielson, *op. cit.*, p. 26.

[9] J. Rud Nielson, *op. cit.*, p. 26.

He must have found solace in the writings of the great religious teachers, for he remarked at one point that these teachers had achieved their influence through their power to console those who had suffered great sorrow.

When Niels Bohr died of a heart attack on November 18, 1962, in the midst of active scientific work, his task was almost done; with him a scientific era may have disappeared—the era of the great men who created today's physics. His name is already written under those of Newton and Einstein on the rosters of science.

Let us now look more closely at Bohr's contributions. The year 1913 was a crucial one in the history of atomic theory, and in our understanding of the structure of the atom and of matter; in July of that year one of the greatest of all scientific papers appeared in the *Philosophical Magazine* of London, Edinburgh, and Dublin under the authorship of N. Bohr. The title of this paper, "On the Constitution of Atoms and Molecules," indicated that it might contain some interesting ideas, but hardly heralded the shattering impact its contents were to have on future concepts of atomic structure.

Before this paper on the structure of the hydrogen atom appeared, two important discoveries had been made: one dealing with the properties of radiation and the other with the interaction of atoms with charged particles, that is, with ions. Although at first sight these two developments do not appear to be directly related, they were really the key to Bohr's revolutionary theory of the atom.

We recall that Planck introduced the concept of the quantum of energy and the quantum of action to derive the correct formula for black-body radiation. But except for Einstein's extension of this idea, which led him to introduce the photon and to apply it to the explanation of the photoelectric effect and the specific heats of solids, no one else had applied Planck's quantum concept to anything but the behavior of radiation. The next great step was to be taken by Bohr, who saw quite clearly that Planck's discovery of the quantum of action and Einstein's concept of the photon could be combined with Rutherford's discovery of how α particles are scattered by atomic nuclei to derive a self-consistent planetary (that is, nuclear) atomic model.

Bohr saw that without introducing Planck's ideas into the theory of atomic structure, there was no way to obtain a stable planetary atom. On the other hand, he saw that introducing the Planck constant of action would do two things: lead to a description of stable electronic orbits and demonstrate the kind of discrete line spectrum that is observed.

Let us now see why Rutherford's discovery required a drastic departure from the laws of classical electrodynamics. We saw that to account for the scattering of α particles Rutherford found it necessary to introduce a model of the atom in which the positive charge is concentrated in a nucleus at the center. But, as we noted, the ideas of Rutherford were still somewhat tentative since he only hinted at a planetary model; he dealt only with the nucleus of the atom. In any case, the arrangement of the electrons in precise orbits was not clearly postulated, and the whole question of the stability of an atom constructed according to such a model presented what appeared to be insurmountable difficulties. An electron can be in stable equilibrium with a central positive nucleus only if the electron revolves around the nucleus in a closed orbit (circle or ellipse), for only then is the electrical force of attraction balanced by the centrifugal force acting outwardly on the electron. But, as we have already noted, an electron moving in this way must, according to classical electrodynamical theory, lose energy by radiating, so that it must ultimately spiral into the nucleus.

We see that we can overcome this difficulty if we introduce the kind of discontinuity into atomic processes that Planck introduced in analyzing the emission and absorption of radiation by the walls (actually, the atoms in the walls) of the container housing the radiation. The spiraling of an electron into the nucleus of an atom is clearly a consequence of the continuous change in its motion, as permitted by the classical laws of dynamics. These laws allow an accelerated electron to lose energy continuously by radiation so that there is no way, in terms of classical electrodynamics, for the electron to remain in any one orbit. The slightest change in its state of motion can, according to such a picture, cause it to gain or lose a slight amount of energy, and vice versa.

But if the electron can change its state of motion only discontinuously, that is, in discrete steps, it must then stay in a particular orbit until it emits or absorbs enough energy in one single process to go from one orbit to another. This then leads to discrete orbits, and transitions from one such orbit to another give rise to a discrete spectrum.

Niels Bohr was aware of this when he began his historic work. He was in his early twenties when Rutherford published his paper on the scattering of α particles by heavy nuclei. Bohr was then working in theoretical physics at the Manchester Laboratory under Rutherford and was greatly stimulated by the Rutherford nuclear model and its implications for the quantum theory. Realizing its importance, he set out to see if he could solve the problem of stability by introducing the new quantum concepts. As he states in the paper reprinted here, he recognized that the Rutherford model would "meet with difficulties of a serious nature arising from the apparent instability of the system of electrons: difficulties purposely avoided in atom models previously considered, for example, in the one proposed by Sir J. J. Thomson." And yet he felt sure that the difficulty present in the Rutherford model could be eliminated by introducing a quantity involving the dimension of length.

His reasoning went somewhat as follows: With the Thomson model of an atom one automatically obtains a fundamental length about equal in magnitude to the size of the atom, because this is the diameter of the positive sphere of electricity in which the electrons are supposed to be embedded. The appearance of such a length in the Thomson theory of the atom means that this kind of atom cannot collapse to a dimension less than this and therefore is stable. Bohr notes in the present paper that "such a length does not appear among the quantities characterizing the second [that is, the Rutherford] atom, viz. the charges and masses of the electrons and the positive nucleus; nor can it be determined solely by help of the latter quantities." He means that no quantity having the dimensions of a length can be constructed from the charge and masses and be numerically of the right size for an atom. All such lengths would be much too small.

But here Bohr experiences one of those miraculous insights that so often occur to the creative mind. In looking around for some way to introduce a length of atomic dimensions into the Rutherford model of the atom as naturally as possible, he observed that a new quantity had been introduced into physics seven years previously by Max Planck—Planck's constant, or, as it often is called, "the elementary quantum of action." By the introduction of this quantity, the question of the stable configuration of the electrons in the atoms is essentially changed, as this constant is of such dimensions and of such a magnitude that it, together with the mass and charge of the particles, can determine a length of the order of magnitude required. If Planck's constant is squared and the result divided by the product of the mass of the electron and the square of its charge, the number thus obtained is 10^{-8} cm, which is the size of an atom.

This type of general reasoning used by Bohr to obtain a correct theory is characteristic of all of his work. Einstein, Fermi, Lorentz, and the other outstanding figures of this anthology had the same ability to arrive at an important result without complex mathematical analysis and involved physical arguments. Bohr did not have to analyze all the aspects of the Rutherford model of the atom before discovering what is needed to make it work. His observation that in the Rutherford theory, as it stood, no quantity of the nature of a length and of the right order of magnitude was present, showed him what was wrong and where he would have to look to find the missing length. He was further strengthened in his beliefs by the ease with which the Planck theory of radiation had cleared up many difficulties that had bothered physicists for years; in Bohr's words, the elementary quantum of action had previously demonstrated "the inadequacy of classical electrodynamics in describing the behavior of systems of atomic size." Since the instability of the Rutherford atom was associated with the classical theory of the radiation of electrons moving in closed orbits, why could not the Planck theory straighten things out in this respect as well? Bohr was convinced that it could.

Using elementary algebra, the simple concepts of classical electrostatics, and the Newtonian laws of motion, Bohr derived a simple expression for the frequency of an electron moving in a circular orbit; he noted that according to classical theory, this electron would have to sink into the nucleus because it would lose energy continuously. Then he introduced Planck's constant, imposing the condition that the electron must not radiate continuously but rather in the form of "distinctly separated emissions." The amount of energy radiated during such emissions must be some integral value of Planck's constant multiplied by the frequency of the atom in its orbit. Thus Bohr introduces Planck's constant into the Rutherford model of the atom and at the same time shows that the stability of, and the radiation by, the atom depend in some way upon the integers. The presence of these integers in conjunction with Planck's constant shows the departure of the theory from classical dynamics and electrodynamics.

We briefly note here Bohr's procedure; the details are contained in his famous paper, which we have included in this volume. His procedure is also outlined somewhat more simply in an address on the spectrum of hydrogen delivered in 1913 before the Physical Society in Copenhagen. This address is particularly interesting because it clearly indicates the tentativeness of the quantum theory at the time and the incompleteness of its acceptance. Even Bohr, who was to put the Planck theory to its most important use, stated in this address,

> In formal respects Planck's theory leaves much to be desired; in certain calculations the ordinary electrodynamics is used, while in others assumptions distinctly at variance with it are introduced without any attempt being made to show that it is possible to give a consistent explanation of the procedure used.[10]

Nevertheless, Bohr clearly recognized that "energy quanta" had come to stay and summed up his feelings as follows:

> It is therefore hardly too early to express the opinion that, whatever the final explanation will be, the discovery of "energy quanta" must be considered as one of the most important results arrived at in physics, and must be taken into consideration in investigations of the properties of atoms and particularly in connection with any explanation of the spectral laws in which such phenomena as the emission and absorption of electromagnetic radiation are concerned.[11]

[10] Bohr, "On the Spectrum of Hydrogen," address before Physical Society, Copenhagen, 1913, p. 6.

[11] *Ibid.*, p. 7.

After a brief survey of the laws of radiation and Planck's contribution to these, Bohr proposes to combine these ideas with the results of Rutherford's α-particle scattering experiments and in this way derive a formula for the frequencies of the spectral lines of hydrogen. He chose hydrogen to work with because he asssumed it to be (and correctly so) the simplest atomic structure, having just one electron revolving around a single proton. Moreover, the spectrum of hydrogen had been studied more thoroughly than that of any other atom and the numerical simplicity of Balmer's formula for the spectral lines suggested that a simple algebraic analysis might solve the problem.

Bohr began, then, by picturing an electron as revolving around a proton according to the classical laws of Newtonian mechanics, the centrifugal force on it, resulting from its orbital motion, being balanced by the electrostatic pull of the proton. This leads to the same kind of orbit for the electron around the proton as the planets have around the sun: elliptical orbits, first discovered by Kepler.

But here a difficulty is encountered because a charged particle behaves quite differently from a planet; it would, according to Maxwell's electrodynamics theory, lose energy continuously by radiation, causing the electron's orbit to become smaller and smaller, finally shrinking to the size of the proton. Bohr recognized this and introduced the Planck concept of the quantum to prevent this catastrophe.

Bohr now pictures the electron as being capable of moving in only a discrete set of orbits; while the electron is in any of these orbits, it does not radiate energy, even though classical electrodynamics demands that it must. This use of discrete, nonradiating orbits accomplishes two things: on the one hand, it leads to a set of distinct spectral lines, since a discrete set of frequencies is associated with the discrete orbital motions of the electron; discrete, non-radiating orbits lead to a stable nuclear atom, since one must then have the lowest orbit which is, then, the closest the electron can get to the nucleus. Moreover, discrete orbits can immediately be correlated to a quantum picture of nature, since changes in the atom can only occur in discontinuous steps, the electron changing from one fixed orbit to another; this must therefore involve discrete changes in the energy of the atom or in the action of the electron in the emission or absorption of a quantum.

To account numerically for the actually observed spectral lines, Bohr proceeds as follows: He first notes that in the hydrogen atom the energy of an electron moving around the proton in a Keplerian orbit depends only on the size of the orbit (that is, upon the semimajor axis of the ellipse in which the electron is moving); this is in accordance with the Newtonian laws of motion. We may think of this energy as the negative of the work that would have to be done to tear the electron completely out of this orbit and bring it to a very great distance from the proton, as occurs in ionization. A discrete set of orbits of different sizes thus means a discrete set of energy states for the electron (or for the atom), since the energy of the electron depends on the size of the orbit.

Bohr now introduces a crucial step in his argument. He postulates that the radiation or the absorption of energy occurs only when the atomic system passes from one energy state to another and that each such change in the energy state means the emission or absorption of a quantum of energy $h\nu$, where h is Planck's constant of action and ν is the frequency of the emitted radiation. Since one can assign a definite amount of energy to the electron in any orbit, according to the laws of classical mechanics (just as this can be done for each planet in the solar system), one can calculate all possible energy changes and hence obtain the frequencies of all possible quanta. These should then correspond to the observed spectral lines.

Bohr describes these ideas in a general way in his essay on the spectrum of hydrogen, where he introduces the concept of "stationary states" to describe the discrete orbits:

> During the emission of the radiation the system may be regarded as passing from one state to another; in order to introduce a name for these states, we shall call them "stationary" states, simply indicating thereby that they form some kind of waiting places between which occurs the emission of the energy corresponding to the various spectral lines. As previously mentioned the spectrum of an element consists of a series of lines whose wave lengths may be expressed by the formula (2). By comparing this expression with the relation given above it is seen that—since $\nu = \frac{c}{\lambda}$, where c is the velocity of light—each of the spectral lines may be regarded as being emitted by the transition of a system between two stationary states in which the energy apart from an additive arbitrary constant is given by $chF_r(n_1)$ and $chF_s(n_2)$ respectively. Using this interpretation the combination principle asserts that a series of stationary states exists for the given system, and that it can pass from one to any other of these states with the emission of a monochromatic radiation. We see, therefore, that with a simple extension of our first assumption it is possible to give a formal explanation of the most general law of line spectra.[12]

From this description we note a very important point: each spectral line involves two orbits and hence two different frequencies or two energies, not one as we would have in classical physics.

To complete his derivation of the Balmer formula for the hydrogen spectral lines, Bohr still had to introduce a scheme for picking out among

---

[12] *Ibid.*, p. 11.

all possible orbits the particular discrete set associated with the hydrogen atom. Why should the electron be limited to just these orbits and no others? What magical property do these orbits have that gives them their preferred character? To understand this and to follow Bohr's reasoning we note first that Kepler's third law of planetary motion also applies to the motion of the electron: it can be derived by equating the Coulomb electrostatic pull of the proton on the electron to the centrifugal force on the electron. According to this law, the square of the period of the electron (the period is time in fractions of a second taken to go once around the orbit) is proportional to the cube of the radius of the orbit. This means that the square of the frequency of the electron (frequency being the number of orbital trips made in one second and hence the reciprocal of the period) depends on the cube of the energy, since the energy is related to the size of the orbit. Thus frequency is related to energy.

But from classical physics one can also show that the period of an electron or its frequency and the size of its orbit can be related to its angular momentum. The angular momentum of a particle is a quantity that is obtained by multiplying the radius of the orbit of the particle and its momentum. Since Planck's constant h is in the nature of an angular momentum, Bohr simply assumed that the angular momentum of an electron in an orbit can only equal $\frac{h}{2\pi}$, or $\frac{2h}{2\pi}$, or $\frac{3h}{2\pi}$, etc., since $\frac{h}{2\pi}$ is an indivisible unit of angular momentum. In this way Bohr related the sizes of his discrete orbits to integers and to Planck's constant. From this he then obtained a formula, in terms of Planck's constant and the integer assigned to an orbit, for the energy of the electron.

As Bohr notes in the paper that follows, the theory as he developed it is pretty much of a hybrid, for the dynamic equilibrium of the electron in one of its orbits (Bohr's "stationary states") is treated by means of ordinary classical mechanics and electrostatics, whereas the quantum theory is used to describe what happens when the electron jumps from one stationary state to the other, which is accompanied either by the emission or absorption of a single quantum of *homogeneous* radiation (radiation of a definite frequency).

By using these simple though revolutionary ideas Bohr eliminated the difficulties that plagued all previous theories. In particular, he refers to the work of Nicholson, who had worked extensively on a model of the atom similar to the Bohr model. Nicholson had attempted to obtain the Rydberg-Ritz formula for the hydrogen spectrum, but had failed because, as Bohr points out, "The frequency of lines in a line spectrum is identified with the frequency of vibration of a mechanical system in a distinctly indicated state of equilibrium." And, as Bohr goes on to say, although Nicholson did relate the radiation from his atom to the Planck theory, it could not be a correct picture because such systems are incapable of emitting homogeneous radiation in discrete quantities.

By means of simple algebra and elementary physical concepts, Bohr obtains the correct expression for the frequencies of the spectral lines in the Balmer series in the spectrum of hydrogen. In addition, he shows that his formulas contain the frequencies of the other series in the hydrogen spectra, such as the Paschen and Lyman series. Bohr also shows in this paper that certain series of lines that were thought to be due to hydrogen must, indeed, be due to helium, and he obtains a simple formula for the helium spectrum, which is algebraically similar to the formula for the hydrogen spectrum, differing from it only because the charge on the nucleus of helium is twice the elementary electron charge itself (the charge on the hydrogen nucleus, the proton).

After Bohr obtains the correct formula for the frequencies of the spectral lines, he gives a critical analysis of the assumptions that he made to obtain the formula. He is particularly concerned with the assumptions that different stationary states correspond to the emission of different numbers of energy quanta or photons, and that the frequency of the radiation emitted by an electron that falls from a state of rest at a great distance from the nucleus to a nearer orbit is equal to half the frequency of the motion of the electron in this final stationary state.

He first points out that the assumption of the emission of different numbers of quanta in association with different stationary states is not really necessary for a correct application of the theory; the assumption that one quantum corresponds to each transition of an electron is all that one requires. Here he uses what has since been called the "correspondence principle," for he considers how the electron would behave in passing into an orbit where it moves very slowly. Under these conditions he can compare the results of his theory with the results obtained from the classical electrodynamics, since for very small frequencies the classical picture is correct, and the Planck theory of radiation passes over to the Maxwellian picture.

By using the correspondence principle, Bohr shows that one may correctly assume that only one quantum of energy is emitted, regardless of which orbit the electron moves into. He also uses this principle to validate the assumption that the frequency of the emitted radiation is half the frequency of the motion in the final orbit. One other important point comes out of these considerations. As Bohr points out, and as we have already noted, one can show that the result of the calculation in this paper may be "expressed by the simple condition that the angular momentum of the electron around the nucleus [on the assumption that the orbits are circular] in a stationary state of the system is equal to an entire multiple of a universal value, independent of the charge on the nucleus." This is a statement of a very important principle later generalized by Wilson and Sommerfeld, and contains within it the germs of Heisenberg's principle of indeterminacy.

It is interesting to note in connection with this paper how close Nicholson had come to discovering these results. As Bohr points out: "The possible importance of angular momentum in the discussion of atomic systems in relation to Planck's theory is emphasized by Nicholson." There can be no doubt that Bohr was influenced by and owed a good deal to Nicholson.

Bohr was greatly influenced and encouraged by Rutherford, who thought very highly of him and his work. They spent many hours together in 1912, and, in a letter dated July 24, 1912, Bohr thanked Rutherford for "your suggestions and criticisms [which] have made so many questions so real for me, and I am looking forward so very much to try to work upon them in the following years." While Bohr was preparing his paper, Rutherford advised that Bohr be as brief as possible, consistent with clarity, for as he said: "long papers have a way of frightening readers. It is the custom in England to put things very shortly and tersely in contrast to the Germanic method, where it supposed to be a virtue to be as long winded as possible." On March 6, 1913, Bohr sent what he called "the first chapter" of his paper to Rutherford with the request that the latter communicate it to the *Philosophical Magazine*. Bohr was quite concerned about his use of both classical mechanics and the quantum theory to obtain his results and hoped "that [Rutherford] will find that I have taken a reasonable point of view as to the delicate question of the old mechanics and of the new assumptions introduced by Planck's theory of radiation."

Rutherford recognized the great importance of Bohr's paper and immediately sent it on for publication, but he had many questions about the basic ideas. Thus, in a letter to Bohr on March 20, 1913, he stated, after praising Bohr's ingenious derivation of the hydrogen spectral lines, that "the mixture of Planck's ideas with the old mechanics makes it very difficult to form a physical idea of what is the basis of it all." He then goes on to point out that he considers a "grave difficulty in [Bohr's] hypothesis. . . . How does an electron decide what frequency it is going to vibrate at when it passes from one stationary state to the other? It seems to me that you would have to assume that the electron knows beforehand where it is going to stop."

That it took great courage to publish such a revolutionary theory at that period is clear from a letter that G. Von Hevesy, an outstanding Hungarian chemist working on relativity, wrote to Rutherford in the fall of 1913. He describes his meeting with Einstein at a science congress a few months earlier, shortly after the publication of Bohr's paper, and states that Einstein "told me that he had once had similar ideas but he did not dare to publish them." Einstein considered Bohr's paper to be "of the greatest importance" and "one of the greatest discoveries."

In the last few paragraphs of his paper, Bohr reaches an important conclusion, which was not verified until a number of years later, that indicated that the quantum would have to be extended to processes outside the atom. He notes that in a gaseous mixture of free electrons and electrons bound inside atoms, the bound electrons do not have the same energy that the free electrons have on the average, as determined by the temperature of the gas. Bohr correctly points out that this is so because the bound electrons cannot absorb energy continuously but only in discrete quanta. Hence, collisions between free and bound electrons lead to a new exchange of energy.

Like most of Bohr's important contributions this paper is marked by very little formal mathematics, but by very penetrating physical arguments and bold assumptions of a revolutionary nature. Its important contribution lies in its unification of atomic theory with the Planck theory of radiation.

ooooooo

BOHR

On the Constitution of Atoms and Molecules [13]

INTRODUCTION

IN ORDER TO EXPLAIN THE results of experiments on scattering of α rays by matter Prof. Rutherford has given a theory of the structure of atoms. According to this theory, the atoms consist of a positively charged nucleus surrounded by a system of electrons kept together by attractive forces from the nucleus; the total negative charge of the electrons is equal to the positive charge of the nucleus. Further, the nucleus is assumed to be the seat of the essential part of the mass of the atom, and to have linear dimensions exceedingly small compared with the linear dimensions of the whole atom. The number of electrons in an atom is deduced to be approximately equal to half the atomic weight. Great interest is to be attributed to this atom-model; for, as Rutherford has shown, the assumption of the existence of nuclei, as those in question, seems to

---

[13] Niels Bohr, *Philosophical Magazine*, 26 (1913), 1–19.

be necessary in order to account for the results of the experiments on large angle scattering of the α rays.

In an attempt to explain some of the properties of matter on the basis of this atom-model we meet, however, with difficulties of a serious nature arising from the apparent instability of the system of electrons: difficulties purposely avoided in atom-models previously considered, for instance, in the one proposed by Sir J. J. Thomson. According to the theory of the latter the atom consists of a sphere of uniform positive electrification, inside which the electrons move in circular orbits.

The principal difference between the atom-models proposed by Thomson and Rutherford consists in the circumstance that the forces acting on the electrons in the atom-model of Thomson allow of certain configurations and motions of the electrons for which the system is in a stable equilibrium; such configurations, however, apparently do not exist for the second atom-model. The nature of the difference in question will perhaps be most clearly seen by noticing that among the quantities characterizing the first atom a quantity appears—the radius of the positive sphere—of dimensions of a length and of the same order of magnitude as the linear extension of the atom, while such a length does not appear among the quantities characterizing the second atom, viz. the charges and masses of the electrons and the positive nucleus; nor can it be determined solely by help of the latter quantities.

The way of considering a problem of this kind has, however, undergone essential alterations in recent years owing to the development of the theory of the energy radiation, and the direct affirmation of the new assumptions introduced in this theory, found by experiments on very different phenomena such as specific heats, photoelectric effect, Röntgen-rays, &c. The result of the discussion of these questions seems to be a general acknowledgment of the inadequacy of the classical electrodynamics in describing the behaviour of systems of atomic size. Whatever the alteration in the laws of motion of the electrons may be, it seems necessary to introduce in the laws in question a quantity foreign to the classical electrodynamics, *i. e.* Planck's constant, or as it often is called the elementary quantum of action. By the introduction of this quantity the question of the stable configuration of the electrons in the atoms is essentially changed, as this constant is of such dimensions and magnitude that it, together with the mass and charge of the particles, can determine a length of the order of magnitude required.

This paper is an attempt to show that the application of the above ideas to Rutherford's atom-model affords a basis for a theory of the constitution of atoms. It will further be shown that from this theory we are led to a theory of the constitution of molecules.

In the present first part of the paper the mechanism of the binding of electrons by a positive nucleus is discussed in relation to Planck's theory. It will be shown that it is possible from the point of view taken to account in a simple way for the law of the line spectrum of hydrogen. Further, reasons are given for a principal hypothesis on which the considerations contained in the following parts are based.

I wish here to express my thanks to Prof. Rutherford for his kind and encouraging interest in this work.

BINDING OF ELECTRONS BY POSITIVE NUCLEI

General Considerations

The inadequacy of the classical electrodynamics in accounting for the properties of atoms from an atom-model as Rutherford's, will appear very clearly if we consider a simple system consisting of a positively charged nucleus of very small dimensions and an electron describing closed orbits around it. For simplicity, let us assume that the mass of the electron is negligibly small in comparison with that of the nucleus, and further, that the velocity of the electron is small compared with that of light.

Let us at first assume that there is no energy radiation. In this case the electron will describe stationary elliptical orbits. The frequency of revolution ω and the major-axis of the orbit $2a$ will depend on the amount of energy W which must be transferred to the system in order to remove the electron to an infinitely great distance apart from the nucleus. Denoting the charge of the electron and of the nucleus by $-e$ and E respectively and the mass of the electron by m, we thus get

$$\omega = \frac{\sqrt{2}}{\pi} \frac{W^{3/2}}{eE\sqrt{m}}, \quad 2a = \frac{eE}{W}. \qquad (1)$$

Further, it can easily be shown that the mean value of the kinetic energy of the electron taken for a whole revolution is equal to W. We see that if the value of W is not given, there will be no values of ω and a characteristic for the system in question.

Let us now, however, take the effect of the energy radiation into account, calculated in the ordinary way from the acceleration of the electron. In this case the electron will no longer describe stationary orbits. "W" will continuously increase, and the electron will approach the nucleus describing orbits of smaller and smaller dimensions, and with greater and greater frequency; the electron on the average gaining in kinetic energy at the same time as the whole system loses energy. This process will go on until the dimensions of the orbit are of the same order of magnitude as the dimensions of the electron or those of the nucleus. A simple calculation shows that the energy radiated out during the process considered will be enormously great compared with that radiated out by ordinary molecular processes.

It is obvious that the behaviour of such a system will be very different from that of an atomic system occurring in nature. In the first place, the actual atoms in their permanent state seem to have absolutely fixed dimensions and frequencies. Further, if we consider any molecular process, the result seems always to be that after a certain amount of energy characteristic for the systems in question is radiated out, the systems will again settle down in a stable state of equilibrium, in which the distances apart of the particles are of the same order of magnitude as before the process.

Now the essential point in Planck's theory of radiation is that the energy radiation from an atomic system does not take place in the continuous way assumed in the ordinary electrodynamics, but that it, on the contrary, takes place in distinctly separated emissions, the amount of energy radiated out from an atomic vibrator of frequency ν in a single emission being equal to $\tau h\nu$, where τ is an entire number, and h is a universal constant.

Returning to the simple case of an electron and a positive nucleus considered above, let us assume that the electron at the beginning of the interaction with the nucleus was at a great distance apart from the nucleus, and had no sensible velocity relative to the latter. Let us further assume that the electron after the interaction has taken place has settled down in a stationary orbit around the nucleus. We shall, for reasons referred to later, assume that the orbit in question is circular; this assumption will, however, make no alteration in the calculations for systems containing only a single electron.

Let us now assume that, during the binding of the electron, a homogeneous radiation is emitted of a frequency ν, equal to half the frequency of revolution of the electron in its final orbit; then, from Planck's theory, we might expect that the amount of energy emitted by the process considered is equal to $\tau h\nu$, where h is Planck's constant and τ an entire number. If we assume that the radiation emitted is homogeneous, the second assumption concerning the frequency of the radiation suggests itself, since the frequency of revolution of the electron at the beginning of the emission is 0. . . . The question, however, of the rigorous validity of both assumptions, and also of the application made of Planck's theory, will be more closely discussed in [the section entitled "General Considerations Continued."]

Putting

$$W = \tau h \frac{\omega}{2}, \tag{2}$$

we get by help of the formula (1)

$$W = \frac{2\pi^2 m e^2 E^2}{\tau^2 h^2}, \; \omega = \frac{4\pi^2 m e^2 E^2}{\tau^3 h^3}, \; 2a = \frac{\tau^2 h^2}{2\pi^2 m e E}. \tag{3}$$

If in these expressions we give τ different values, we get a series of values for W, ω, and a corresponding to a series of configurations of the system. According to the above considerations, we are led to assume that these configurations will correspond to states of the system in which there is no radiation of energy; states which consequently will be stationary as long as the system is not disturbed from outside. We see that the value of W is greatest if τ has its smallest value 1. This case will therefore correspond to the most stable state of the system, *i.e.* will correspond to the binding of the electron for the breaking up of which the greatest amount of energy is required.

Putting in the above expressions $\tau = 1$ and $E = e$, and introducing the experimental values

$$e = 4\cdot7 \,.\, 10^{-10}, \frac{e}{m} = 5\cdot31 \,.\, 10^{17}, h = 6\cdot5 \,.\, 10^{-27},$$

we get

$$2a = 1\cdot1 \,.\, 10^{-8} \text{ cm.}, \; \omega = 6\cdot2 \,.\, 10^{15} \frac{1}{\text{sec.}}, \frac{W}{e} = 13 \text{ volt.}$$

We see that these values are of the same order of magnitude as the linear dimensions of the atoms, the optical frequencies, and the ionization-potentials.

The general importance of Planck's theory for the discussion of the behaviour of atomic systems was originally pointed out by Einstein. The considerations of Einstein have been developed and applied on a number of different phenomena, especially by Stark, Nernst, and Sommerfeld. The agreement as to the order of magnitude between values observed for the frequencies and dimensions of the atoms, and values for these quantities calculated by considerations similar to those given above, has been the subject of much discussion. It was first pointed out by Haas, in an attempt to explain the meaning and the value of Planck's constant on the basis of J. J. Thomson's atom-model, by help of the linear dimensions and frequency of an hydrogen atom.

Systems of the kind considered in this paper, in which the forces between the particles vary inversely as the square of the distance, are discussed in relation to Planck's theory by J. W. Nicholson. In a series of papers this author has shown that it seems to be possible to account for lines of hitherto unknown origin in the spectra of the stellar nebulæ and that of the solar corona, by assuming the presence in these bodies of certain hypothetical elements of exactly indicated constitution. The atoms of these elements are supposed to consist simply of a ring of a few electrons surrounding a positive nucleus of negligibly small dimensions. The ratios between the frequencies corresponding to the lines in question are compared with the ratios between the frequencies corresponding to different modes of vibration of the ring of electrons. Nicholson has obtained a relation to Planck's theory showing that the ratios between the wavelength of different sets of lines of the coronal spectrum can be accounted for with great accuracy by assuming that the ratio between the energy of the system and the frequency of rotation of the ring is equal to an entire multiple of Planck's constant. The quantity Nicholson refers to as the energy is equal to twice the quantity which we have denoted above by W In the latest paper cited Nicholson has found it necessary to give the theory a more complicated form, still, however, representing the ratio of energy to frequency by a simple function of whole numbers.

The excellent agreement between the calculated and observed values of the ratios between the wave-lengths in question seems a strong argument in favour of the validity of the foundation of Nicholson's calculations. Serious objections, however, may be raised against the theory. These objections are intimately connected with the problem of the homogeneity of the radiation emitted. In Nicholson's calculations the frequency of lines in a line-spectrum is identified with the frequency of vibration of a mechanical system in a distinctly indicated state of equilibrium. As a relation from Planck's theory is used, we might expect that the radiation is sent out in quanta; but systems like those considered, in which the frequency is a function of the energy, cannot emit a finite amount of a homogeneous radiation; for, as soon as the emission of radiation is started, the energy and also the frequency of the system are altered. Further, according to the calculation of Nicholson, the systems are unstable for some modes of vibration. Apart from such objections—which may be only formal—it must be remarked, that the theory in the form given does not seem to be able to account for the well-known laws of Balmer and Rydberg connecting the frequencies of the lines in the line-spectra of the ordinary elements.

It will now be attempted to show that the difficulties in question disappear if we consider the problems from the point of view taken in this paper. Before proceeding it may be useful to restate briefly the ideas characterizing the calculations [following formulas (2) and (3)]. The principal assumptions used are:

(1) That the dynamical equilibrium of the systems in the stationary states can be discussed by help of the ordinary mechanics, while the passing of the systems between different stationary states cannot be treated on that basis.

(2) That the latter process is followed by the emission of a *homogeneous* radiation, for which the relation between the frequency and the amount of energy emitted is the one given by Planck's theory.

The first assumption seems to present itself; for it is known that the ordinary mechanics cannot have an absolute validity, but will only hold in calculations of certain mean values of the motion of the electrons. On the other hand, in the calculations of the dynamical equilibrium in a stationary state in which there is no relative displacement of the particles, we need not distinguish between the actual motions and their mean values. The second assumption is in obvious contrast to the ordinary ideas of electrodynamics, but appears to be necessary in order to account for experimental facts.

In the calculations [just referred to] we have further made use of the more special assumptions, viz. that the different stationary states correspond to the emission of a different number of Planck's energy-quanta, and that the frequency of the radiation emitted during the passing of the system from a state in which no energy is yet radiated out to one of the stationary states, is equal to half the frequency of revolution of the electron in the latter state. We can, however, also arrive at the expressions (3) for the stationary states by using assumptions of somewhat different form. We shall, therefore, postpone the discussion of the special assumptions, and first show how by the help of the above principal assumptions, and of the expressions (3) for the stationary states, we can account for the line-spectrum of hydrogen.

Emission of Line-Spectra

SPECTRUM OF HYDROGEN General evidence indicates that an atom of hydrogen consists simply of a single electron rotating round a positive nucleus of charge e. The re-formation of a hydrogen atom, when the electron has been removed to great distances away from the nucleus— *e.g.* by the effect of electrical discharge in a vacuum tube—will accordingly correspond to the binding of an electron by a positive nucleus considered [earlier]. If in (3) we put $E = e$, we get for the total amount of energy radiated out by the formation of one of the stationary states,

$$W_\tau = \frac{2\pi^2 m e^4}{h^2 \tau^2}.$$

The amount of energy emitted by the passing of the system from a state corresponding to $\tau = \tau_1$ to one corresponding to $\tau = \tau_2$, is consequently

$$W_{\tau_2} - W_{\tau_1} = \frac{2\pi^2 m e^4}{h^2}\left(\frac{1}{\tau_2^2} - \frac{1}{\tau_1^2}\right).$$

If now we suppose that the radiation in question is homogeneous, and that the amount of energy emitted is equal to $h\nu$, where ν is the frequency of the radiation, we get

$$W_{\tau_2} - W_{\tau_1} = h\nu,$$

and from this

$$\nu = \frac{2\pi^2 m e^4}{h^3}\left(\frac{1}{\tau_2^2} - \frac{1}{\tau_1^2}\right). \tag{4}$$

We see that this expression accounts for the law connecting the lines in the spectrum of hydrogen. If we put $\tau_2 = 2$ and let τ_1 vary, we get the ordinary Balmer series. If we put $\tau_2 = 3$, we get the series in the ultra-red observed by Paschen and previously suspected by Ritz. If we put $\tau_2 = 1$ and $\tau_2 = 4, 5, ..$, we get series respectively in the extreme ultra-violet and the extreme ultra-red, which are not observed, but the existence of which may be expected.

The agreement in question is quantitative as well as qualitative. Putting

$$e - 4\cdot7 . 10^{-10}, \frac{e}{m} = 5\cdot31 . 10^{17}, \text{ and } h = 6\cdot5 . 10^{-27},$$

we get

$$\frac{2\pi^2 m e^4}{h^3} = 3\cdot1 . 10^{15}.$$

The observed value for the factor outside the bracket in the formula (4) is

$$3\cdot290 . 10^{15}.$$

The agreement between the theoretical and observed values is inside the uncertainty due to experimental errors in the constants entering in the expression for the theoretical value. We shall return to consider the possible importance of the agreement in question.

It may be remarked that the fact, that it has not been possible to observe more than 12 lines of the Balmer series in experiments with vacuum tubes, while 33 lines are observed in the spectra of some celestial bodies, is just what we should expect from the above theory. According to the equation (3) the diameter of the orbit of the electron in the different stationary states is proportional to τ^2. For $\tau = 12$ the diameter is equal to $1\cdot6 . 10^{-6}$ cm., or equal to the mean distance between the molecules in a gas at a pressure of about 7 mm. mercury; for $\tau = 33$ the diameter is equal to $1\cdot2 . 10^{-5}$ cm., corresponding to the mean distance of the molecules at a pressure of about $0 \cdot 02$ mm. mercury. According to the theory the necessary condition for the appearance of a great number of lines is therefore a very small density of the gas; for simultaneously to obtain an intensity sufficient for observation the space filled with the gas must be very great. If the theory is right, we may therefore never expect to be able in experiments with vacuum tubes to observe the lines corresponding to high numbers of the Balmer series of the emission spectrum of hydrogen; it might, however, be possible to observe the lines by investigation of the absorption spectrum of this gas [see section entitled "Absorption of Radiation"].

It will be observed that we in the above way do not obtain other series of lines, generally ascribed to hydrogen; for instance, the series first observed by Pickering in the spectrum of the star ζ Puppis, and the set of series recently found by Fowler by experiments with vacuum tubes containing a mixture of hydrogen and helium. We shall, however, see that, by help of the above theory, we can account naturally for these series of lines if we ascribe them to helium.

A neutral atom of the latter element consists, according to Rutherford's theory, of a positive nucleus of charge $2e$ and two electrons. Now considering the binding of a single electron by a helium nucleus, we get, putting $E = 2e$ in the expressions (3), and proceeding in exactly the same way as above,

$$\nu = \frac{8\pi^2 m e^4}{h^3}\left(\frac{1}{\tau_2{}^2} - \frac{1}{\tau_1{}^2}\right) = \frac{2\pi^2 m e^4}{h^3}\left(\frac{1}{\left(\frac{\tau_2}{2}\right)^2} - \frac{1}{\left(\frac{\tau_1}{2}\right)^2}\right).$$

If we in this formula put $\tau_2 = 1$ or $\tau_2 = 2$, we get series of lines in the extreme ultra-violet. If we put $\tau_2 = 3$, and let τ_1 vary, we get a series which includes 2 of the series observed by Fowler, and denoted by him as the first and second principal series of the hydrogen spectrum. If we put $\tau_2 = 4$, we get the series observed by Pickering in the spectrum of ζ Puppis. Every second of the lines in this series is identical with a line in the Balmer series of the hydrogen spectrum; the presence of hydrogen in the star in question may therefore account for the fact that these lines are of a greater intensity than the rest of the lines in the series. The series is also observed in the experiments of Fowler, and denoted in his paper as the Sharp series of the hydrogen spectrum. If we finally in the above formula put $\tau_2 = 5, 6, ..$, we get series, the strong lines of which are to be expected in the ultra-red.

The reason why the spectrum considered is not observed in ordinary helium tubes may be that in such tubes the ionization of helium is not so complete as in the star considered or in the experiments of Fowler, where a strong discharge was sent through a mixture of hydrogen and helium. The condition for the appearance of the spectrum is, according to the above theory, that helium atoms are present in a state in which they have lost both their electrons. Now we must assume that the amount of energy to be used in removing the second electron from a helium atom is much greater than that to be used in removing the first. Further, it is known from experiments on positive rays, that hydrogen atoms can acquire a negative charge; therefore the presence of hydrogen in the experiments of Fowler may effect that more electrons are removed from some of the helium atoms than would be the case if only helium were present.

SPECTRA OF OTHER SUBSTANCES In case of systems containing more electrons we must—in conformity with the result of experiments—expect more complicated laws for the line-spectra than those considered. I shall try to show that the point of view taken above allows, at any rate, a certain understanding of the laws observed.

According to Rydberg's theory—with the generalization given by Ritz —the frequency corresponding to the lines of the spectrum of an element can be expressed by

$$\nu = F_r(\tau_1) - F_s(\tau_2),$$

where τ_1 and τ_2 are entire numbers, and F_1, F_2, F_3, . . . are functions of τ which approximately are equal to

$$\frac{K}{(\tau + a_1)^2}, \frac{K}{(\tau + a_2)^2}, \cdots K$$

is a universal constant, equal to the factor outside the bracket in the formula (4) for the spectrum of hydrogen. The different series appear if we put τ_1 or τ_2 equal to a fixed number and let the other vary.

The circumstance that the frequency can be written as a difference between two functions of entire numbers suggests an origin of the lines in the spectra in question similar to the one we have assumed for hydrogen; i.e. that the lines correspond to a radiation emitted during the passing of the system between two different stationary states. For systems containing more than one electron the detailed discussion may be very complicated, as there will be many different configurations of the electrons which can be taken into consideration as stationary states. This may account for the different sets of series in the line spectra emitted from the substances in question. Here I shall only try to show how, by help of the theory, it can be simply explained that the constant K entering in Rydberg's formula is the same for all substances.

Let us assume that the spectrum in question corresponds to the radiation emitted during the binding of an electron; and let us further assume that the system including the electron considered is neutral. The force on the electron, when at a great distance apart from the nucleus and the electrons previously bound, will be very nearly the same as in the above case of the binding of an electron by a hydrogen nucleus. The energy corresponding to one of the stationary states will therefore for τ great be very nearly equal to that given by the expression (3), if we put $E = e$. For τ great we consequently get

$$\lim \ (\tau^2 \cdot F_1(\tau)) = \lim \ (\tau^2 \cdot F_2(\tau)) = \ . \ . \ . \ . = \frac{2\pi^2 m e^4}{h^3},$$

in conformity with Rydberg's theory.

General Considerations Continued

. . . The possibility of an emission of a radiation of a frequency $[\nu = n\omega]$ may also be interpreted from analogy with the ordinary electrodynamics, as an electron rotating round a nucleus in an elliptical orbit will emit a radiation which according to Fourier's theorem can be resolved into homogeneous components, the frequencies of which are $n\omega$, if ω is the frequency of revolution of the electron.

We are thus led to assume that the interpretation of the equation (2) is not that the different stationary states correspond to an emission of different numbers of energy-quanta, but that the frequency of the energy emitted during the passing of the system from a state in which no energy is yet radiated out to one of the different stationary states, is equal to different multiples of $\frac{\omega}{2}$, where ω is the frequency of revolution of the electron in the state considered. From this assumption we get exactly the same expressions as before for the stationary states, and from these by help of the principal assumptions [given earlier] the same expression for the law of the hydrogen spectrum. Consequently we may regard our preliminary considerations only as a simple form of representing the results of the theory.

Before we leave the discussion of this question, we shall for a moment return to the question of the significance of the agreement between the observed and calculated values of the constant entering in the expressions (4) for the Balmer series of the hydrogen spectrum. From the above consideration it will follow that, taking the starting-point in the form of the law of the hydrogen spectrum and assuming that the different lines correspond to a homogeneous radiation emitted during the passing between different stationary states, we shall arrive at exactly the same expression for the constant in question as that given by (4), if we only assume (1) that the radiation is sent out in quanta $h\nu$, and (2) that the frequency of the radiation emitted during the passing of the system between successive stationary states will coincide with the frequency of revolution of the electron in the region of slow vibrations.

As all the assumptions used in this latter way of representing the theory are of what we may call a qualitative character, we are justified in expecting—if the whole way of considering is a sound one—an absolute agreement between the values calculated and observed for the constant in question, and not only an approximate agreement. The formula (4) may therefore be of value in the discussion of the results of experimental determinations of the constants e, m, and h.

While there obviously can be no question of a mechanical foundation of the calculations given in this paper, it is, however, possible to give a very simple interpretation of the result of the calculation [following formulas (2) and (3)] by help of symbols taken from the ordinary mechanics. Denoting the angular momentum of the electron round the nucleus by M, we have immediately for a circular orbit $\pi M = \dfrac{T}{\omega}$, where ω is the frequency of revolution and T the kinetic energy of the electron; for a circular orbit we further have $T = W$ and from (2), we consequently get

$$M = \tau M_0,$$

where

$$M_0 = \frac{h}{2\pi} = 1 \cdot 04 \times 10^{-27}.$$

If we therefore assume that the orbit of the electron in the stationary states is circular, the result of the calculation can be expressed by the simple condition: that the angular momentum of the electron round the nucleus in a stationary state of the system is equal to an entire multiple of a universal value, independent of the charge on the nucleus. The possible importance of the angular momentum in the discussion of atomic systems in relation to Planck's theory is emphasized by Nicholson.

The great number of different stationary states we do not observe except by investigation of the emission and absorption of radiation. In most of the other physical phenomena, however, we only observe the atoms of the matter in a single distinct state, *i.e.* the state of the atoms at low temperature. From the preceding considerations we are immediately led to the assumption that the "permanent" state is the one among the stationary states during the formation of which the greatest amount of energy is emitted. According to the equation (3), this state is the one which corresponds to $\tau = 1$.

Absorption of Radiation

In order to account for Kirchhoff's law it is necessary to introduce assumptions on the mechanism of absorption of radiation which correspond to those we have used considering the emission. Thus we must assume that a system consisting of a nucleus and an electron rotating round it under certain circumstances can absorb a radiation of a frequency equal to the frequency of the homogeneous radiation emitted during the passing of the system between different stationary states. Let us consider the radiation emitted during the passing of the system between two stationary states A_1 and A_2 corresponding to values for τ equal to τ_1 and τ_2, $\tau_1 > \tau_2$. As the necessary condition for an emission of the radiation in question was the presence of systems in the state A_1, we must assume that the necessary condition for an absorption of the radiation is the presence of systems in the state A_2.

These considerations seem to be in conformity with experiments on absorption in gases. In hydrogen gas at ordinary conditions for instance there is no absorption of a radiation of a frequency corresponding to the line-spectrum of this gas; such an absorption is only observed in hydrogen gas in a luminous state. This is what we should expect according to the above. We have assumed that the radiation in question was emitted during the passing of the systems between stationary states corresponding to $\tau \geqq 2$. The state of the atoms in hydrogen gas at ordinary conditions should, however, correspond to $\tau = 1$; furthermore, hydrogen atoms at ordinary conditions combine into molecules, *i.e.* into systems in which the electrons have frequencies different from those in the atoms. From the circumstance that certain substances in a non-luminous state, as, for instance, sodium vapour, absorb radiation corresponding to lines in the line-spectra of the substances, we may, on the other hand, conclude that the lines in question are emitted during the passing of the system between two states, one of which is the permanent state.

How much the above considerations differ from an interpretation based on the ordinary electrodynamics is perhaps most clearly shown by the fact that we have been forced to assume that a system of electrons will absorb a radiation of a frequency different from the frequency of vibration of the electrons calculated in the ordinary way. It may in this connexion be of interest to mention a generalization of the considerations to which we are led by experiments on the photo-electric effect, and which may be able to throw some light on the problem in question. Let us consider a state of the system in which the electron is free, *i.e.* in which the electron possesses kinetic energy sufficient to remove to infinite distances from the nucleus. If we assume that the motion of the electron is governed by the ordinary mechanics and that there is no (sensible) energy radiation, the total energy of the system—as in the above considered stationary states—will be constant. Further, there will be perfect continuity between the two kinds of states, as the difference between frequency and dimensions of the systems in successive stationary states will diminish without limit if τ increases. In the following considerations we shall for the sake of brevity refer to the two kinds of states in question as "mechanical" states; by this notation only emphasizing the assumption that the motion of the electron in both cases can be accounted for by the ordinary mechanics.

Tracing the analogy between the two kinds of mechanical states, we might now expect the possibility of an absorption of radiation, not only corresponding to the passing of the system between two different stationary states, but also corresponding to the passing between one of the stationary states and a state in which the electron is free; and as above, we might expect that the frequency of this radiation was determined by the equation $E = h\nu$, where E is the difference between the total energy of the system in the two states. As it will be seen, such an absorption of radiation is just what is observed in experiments on ionization by ultraviolet light and by Röntgen rays. Obviously, we get in this way the same expression for the kinetic energy of an electron ejected from an atom by photo-electric effect as that deduced by Einstein, *i.e.* $T = h\nu - W$, where T is the kinetic energy of the electron ejected, and W the total amount of energy emitted during the original binding of the electron. . . .

Experiments on the phenomena of X-rays suggest that not only the emission and absorption of radiation cannot be treated by the help of the ordinary electrodynamics, but not even the result of a collision between two electrons of which the one is bound in an atom. This is perhaps most clearly shown by some very instructive calculations on the energy of β-particles emitted from radioactive substances recently published by Rutherford. These calculations strongly suggest that an electron of great velocity in passing through an atom and colliding with the electrons bound will lose energy in distinct finite quanta. As is immediately seen, this is very different from what we might expect if the result of the collisions was governed by the usual mechanical laws. The failure of the classical mechanics in such a problem might also be expected beforehand from the absence of anything like equipartition of kinetic energy between free electrons and electrons bound in atoms. From the point of view of the "mechanical" states we see, however, that the following assumption—which is in accord with the above analogy—might be able to account for the result of Rutherford's calculation and for the absence of equipartition of kinetic energy: two colliding electrons, bound or free, will, after the collision as well as before, be in mechanical states. Obviously, the introduction of such an assumption would not make any alteration necessary in the classical treatment of a collision between two free particles. But, considering a collision between a free and a bound electron, it would follow that the bound electron by the collision could not acquire a less amount of energy than the difference in energy corresponding to successive stationary states, and consequently that the free electron which collides with it could not lose a less amount.

The preliminary and hypothetical character of the above considerations needs not to be emphasized. The intention, however, has been to show that the sketched generalization of the theory of the stationary states possibly may afford a simple basis of representing a number of experimental facts which cannot be explained by help of the ordinary electrodynamics, and that the assumptions used do not seem to be inconsistent with experiments on phenomena for which a satisfactory explanation has been given by the classical dynamics and the wave theory of light.

46

∘∘∘∘∘∘∘∘∘∘

THE QUANTUM THEORY
IS TESTED

∘∘∘∘∘∘∘∘∘∘∘

James Franck (1882-1964)
Gustav Hertz (b. 1887)

James Franck, one of the outstanding German experimental physicists of the decade prior to World War I, was born in Hamburg on August 26, 1882, and studied at both the universities of Heidelberg and Berlin. Soon after receiving his doctoral degree he went to the Kaiser Wilhelm Institute of Physical Chemistry at Berlin-Dahlem, where he was one of the departmental heads, and began his investigations into atomic structure.

At the Kaiser Wilhelm Institute he collaborated with Gustav Hertz and completed basic experiments on the collisions of electrons with atoms, which demonstrated that an atom can take on energy from collisions only in discrete amounts, in agreement with Bohr's theory. In 1920 Franck was called to the University of Göttingen as full professor of experimental physics. He served there from 1920 until 1935 when he left Germany because of the Hitler racial laws.

While at Göttingen, he established one of the outstanding atomic laboratories in the world, which attracted leading postdoctoral students from all countries. The United States, in particular, owes a great debt of gratitude to Franck for training and inspiring many of the best American experimental physicists.

Although Franck received the Nobel Prize for physics in 1925 for his electron-collision experiments, much of his best work was done in the study of molecular structure, and later in photochemistry, particularly after he came to Johns Hopkins as professor of physics in 1935. In 1938 he was appointed professor of physical chemistry at the University of Chicago and played an important role in the development of atomic energy. He was the leader of a group of scientists on the Manhattan project who felt that the atomic bomb should not have been dropped before warning Japan that we had such a weapon. To this end, he prepared and circulated the famous "Franck Petition," urging President Truman to demonstrate the bomb before authorizing its use. After the war Franck devoted almost all of his research time to the study of photosynthesis. He died in 1964, when still active in his scientific work.

Gustav Hertz was born on July 22, 1887, in Hamburg and studied physics at the universities of Göttingen, Munich, and Berlin, where he served as an assistant in physics from 1913 until the beginning of World War I. After serving in the war and being severely wounded, he came back to Berlin as unpaid lecturer (*Privatdozent*) in 1917 and began the collaboration with Franck that led to the famous Franck-Hertz experiments and the Nobel Prize for physics.

Hertz served as professor of physics at the University of Halle from 1925 to 1928 and then in the same rank at the Technical Institute of Berlin-Charlottenberg. He resigned from this chair in 1934 for political reasons and became director of a research laboratory for the firm of Siemens.

In 1945, he went to the USSR where he is currently continuing his research.

After Niels Bohr had introduced his quantum model of the planetary atom and had used it to derive the correct formula for the Balmer lines of hydrogen, experimental physicists began to devise various ways of probing the atom to see if they could obtain some insight, other than that offered by the spectral lines, into the nature of the discrete orbits and stationary states. Now there are not many ways by which one can try to get a "look at the inside" of an atom; among the accessible methods, only two were available to physicists when Bohr announced his theory. Both involved bombarding the atom with particles: photons, on the one hand, and material particles, such as electrons or atoms, on the other. Since bombarding an atom with photons is essentially the same as studying its spectrum, only collisions between atoms and material particles, such as electrons, seemed to offer a possible new source of information. Consequently James Franck and Gustav Hertz, who were pioneers in this field, turned to electron collisions to study the interior of an atom.

To do this, Franck and Hertz devised a very simple instrument consisting of a long wire surrounded by a wire-mesh cylinder whose axis coincided with that of the wire. Surrounding the wire-mesh cylinder, and very close to it, was an external solid foil cylinder. The apparatus was operated as follows: The atom, to be studied in the form of a gas or vapor under low pressure, were placed in the cylinder surrounding the wire. A current was then sent through the wire until, glowing, it became hot enough to emit electrons. A positive voltage was established between the wire and the mesh so that the electrons were attracted to the mesh. These electrons moved through the vapor to the mesh and passed through it. After passing through the mesh, the electrons reached the surrounding foil, where they were collected. The external foil cylinder G was connected to the ground through a galvanometer so that the number of electrons striking the foil could be measured. Finally, a constant retarding voltage (to decelerate the electrons passing through the mesh) was placed between the mesh cylinder and the outer foil cylinder. This retarding potential could be altered at will so that the number of electrons striking the foil could be controlled.

Suppose now that a certain voltage is placed between the mesh and the glowing, conducting wire. What do we find at the electron-collecting foil cylinder? That depends on a number of things: the accelerating potential between the wire and the mesh; the kind of gas in the cylinder; the retarding potential between the mesh and the external foil. If no gas is present in the cylinder and if the accelerating potential is smaller than the retarding potential, no electrons reach the outer foil and the current in the galvanometer is zero. This means merely that the electrons coming from the wire and passing through the mesh are not moving fast enough to overcome the retarding potential and thus reach the foil. If the accelerating potential is slowly increased until it is exactly equal to the retarding potential, or slightly larger, a current will suddenly be observed in the galvanometer.

We now consider a gas, let us say mercury vapor, present in the cylinder. A gradual increase in the accelerating potential is applied. What effect do the gas atoms have on the electrons? As long as the accelerating potential lies below a certain critical value, which is different for different gases, the situation is exactly the same as though no gas were present. We must keep in mind that the atoms exist only in certain discrete energy states and they can pass from a lower state to a higher (that is, from the ground state to an excited state) only by absorbing a discrete amount of energy, which must be furnished by the colliding electron. Furthermore, only a discrete amount of energy can tear an electron out of any one of the atoms and thus ionize the atom. If now an electron coming from the hot wire collides with a mercury atom, it can give up energy to this atom either by making the atom move faster or by exciting the atom internally. But if the potential that accelerates the electrons as they come from the wire is less than the smallest excitation energy of the mercury atom, the electron, according to the quantum theory, with its discrete energy levels, cannot excite the atom; at most, it can only increase its velocity during a collision. Since a mercury atom is very massive compared to an electron, the colliding electron has little effect on the motion of the atom; the electron bounces off with no loss of energy like a ball bearing bouncing off a massive wall. Such collisions are called "elastic" collisions and have no effect on the stream of electrons coming from the hot wire. In other words, as long as the accelerating potential is below a certain critical value necessary for excitation, the electrons collide with the mercury atoms without loss of energy and the current in the galvanometer of the apparatus is just as though no mercury vapor were present.

Now suppose that the accelerating potential is increased slowly until the electrons acquire just enough energy to excite or to ionize the mercury atoms. Then, according to the quantum theory, these electrons should lose all their energy; their collisions with atoms are "inelastic," *i.e.* they do not "bounce off" the atoms. Franck and Hertz found that this is precisely the case and so demonstrated the existence of discrete energy levels. They discovered that for an electron to excite the mercury atom, it must have no less than 4.9 volts of energy. As soon as the electrons were accelerated to 4.9 volts of energy, the current in the detecting galvanometer fell to zero because the electrons lost all their kinetic energy by inelastic collisions and therefore could not reach the external foil cylinder against the retarding potential. Of course, electrons that were torn out of the mercury atoms could not reach the external cylinder either, because they could not acquire enough kinetic energy from the accelerating potential.

Consider now what happens when the accelerating potential is greater than 4.9 volts. Each electron still suffers an inelastic collision, but it does not lose all of its kinetic energy, only that part represented by falling through 4.9 volts potential difference. In other words, it still has some energy left and can reach the detecting cylinder. Thus, as the accelerating potential is increased steadily beyond 4.9 volts, the current in the galvanometer begins to increase again (after having fallen to zero at 4.9 volts). Now it reaches a greater intensity because added to the initial stream of the electrons from the wire are the electrons torn from the mercury atoms during the collisions. If the accelerating potential is steadily increased from 4.9 volts to twice this value, the current in the galvanometer again suddenly drops to zero because now each electron has just enough energy to excite two atoms in two separate collisions (it loses just 4.9 volts of energy in each collision); when it does so, it loses all its energy. At this higher accelerating potential the electrons acquire enough energy to ionize the atoms closer to the wire than previously. After these initial ionizing collisions near the wire, the electrons

(now with practically no energy) are speeded up again before reaching
the mesh, and suffer ionizing collisions a second time. There is thus a
second maximum in the galvanometer current when the accelerating potential is increased beyond twice the ionization potential.

Franck and Hertz then went on to show that as the accelerating potential is increased, a new maximum appears in the galvanometer current for each integral multiple of the ionization potential. They applied
this technique not only to mercury but to other atoms as well. Moreover,
they demonstrated that electrons moving with the ionization energy
could also excite the mercury resonance line $\lambda = 2536$ angstroms, and
showed that if one multiplies the frequency of this line by Planck's constant h, one obtains exactly the ionization potential of 4.9 volts.

The work of Franck and Hertz was important at this stage of the development of atomic theory because it was not clear from Bohr's theory
of atomic spectra alone whether the quantum theory could be applied to
ordinary mechanical energy of motion, or whether it was limited to the
emission and absorption of radiant energy. These experiments demonstrated that a particle like an electron would transfer its energy in a
collision only in multiples of a fundamental quantum. From this point on
it was clear that the quantum theory would have to be taken into account
in all processes. This is precisely what Bohr had predicted in the last few
paragraphs of his fundamental paper, which we discuss in Chapter 45,
and is also in line with what Einstein had insisted on at the first Solvay
Congress in 1911.

ooooooo

FRANCK and HERTZ

Collisions between Electrons and Mercury Vapor Molecules and the Ionization Potential of Such Molecules [1]

IN A PREVIOUS PAPER WE were able to show
that the ionization potential, that is, the potential through which an electron must fall freely in order to ionize a gas molecule by collision, is a

[1] James Franck and Gustav Hertz, *Verhand. Deut. Physik, Ges.*, 16 (1914), 457–
467—trans. editors.

characteristic quantity for each gas, and we have measured this parameter for He, Ne, Ar, H, O, and N. The method we used is similar to that used by Lenard and by V. Baeyer, and consists of the direct determination of the moment that the colliding electrons induce ionization. It required a great deal of precaution to avoid false results arising from electric double layers and from the initial velocities of the electrons emitted by the glowing wire. Moreover, we had to be especially careful to avoid an apparent ionization limit simulated when the observed ionization lying below a certain velocity of the primary electrons sank below the sensitivity threshold of the apparatus. Such an error, not present in our work, cannot be excluded from the ionization potentials recently published by F. Mayer and may account for the difference between our and F. Mayer's value for the ionization potential of nitrogen. By carefully avoiding this error, we arrived at exactly one volt for this ionization potential. Later attempts to extend this procedure to metallic vapors were unsuccessful because it was impossible to eliminate disturbances arising from heating the apparatus.

To test the relationship between the magnitude of the ionization potential and the other atomic constants, especially radius and proper frequency, which are obtained from quantum theory on the one hand and from atomic models on the other hand, it appeared to us desirable to develop a method whose accuracy exceeds that of the previous method and which can also be applied to metallic vapors. We have succeeded in doing this, as the results of our investigations of collisions between gas molecules and slow electrons show. The new procedure which was first developed only for the case of gases that have no affinity for electrons but which can also probably be applied to other gases is based on the following facts which we discovered in our previous work:

1. In the collision between a gas molecule and an electron whose kinetic energy is smaller than the ionization energy of the molecule, the electron is reflected, in general, but it also suffers a loss of energy which is smaller, the smaller the electron affinity of the gas is. For gases with no electron affinity, this loss is immeasurably small.

2. In a collision between an electron and a gas molecule that results in ionization, the electron loses all its kinetic energy.

3. If the kinetic energy of the electron is equal to or larger than the ionization energy, the probability that the collision will lead to ionization is not small compared to [unity] 1.

The new method of measuring the ionization potential rests on the fact that the ionization energy is the maximum kinetic energy that electrons can have and still be reflected without energy loss after numerous collisions with gas molecules.

Since we wanted to apply this method to measure the ionization potentials of metallic vapors, we first had to convince ourselves that such vapors, insofar as collisions are concerned, really behave like gases without electron affinity, as one may expect from a consideration of their behavior in electrical discharges, and above all, because of the incidence of self-sustaining electrical discharges at large vapor densities and small field intensities. The apparatus used in this investigation and in the final measurement of the ionization potential is shown in [Fig. 46–1].

D is a platinum wire with a thin central section which can be brought to incandescence by a current. N is a fine cylindrical platinum wire mesh with a 4-cm radius surrounding D, and G is a cylindrical platinum foil, which is separated from N by 1 to 2 mm. G was grounded through a galvanometer. Rings of platinum foil were embedded in the glass covering to prevent any current from flowing to the galvanometer from parts of the wire carrying the voltage. Besides glass and platinum, the apparatus contained no fixed parts. All leads were fused into the glass.

Fig. 46–1.

During the measurements the apparatus was enclosed in an electrically heated paraffin bath. The apparatus was connected to a continuously operating pump through a narrow U-tube which was also in the heat bath and which had a mercury-filled section at its lowest point. Since, in addition to this, a drop of mercury was present at the bottom part of the apparatus itself, the pressure of the mercury vapor could not have been essentially lower than that corresponding to the saturation pressure for the given temperature. The precise value of the pressure is of no consequence. Since most of the measurements were made at temperatures between 110° and 115°, the pressure of the mercury vapor was about 1 mm.

The preliminary investigations, which were to show that the mercury vapor behaves like a gas with no electron affinity during collisions between electrons and gas molecules, correspond throughout to those which were carried out earlier on helium. It was found that the electrons are reflected without energy loss from the mercury atoms as long as their velocities correspond to a drop through less than 5 volts. The curves 1 and 2 in [Fig. 46–2] show the energy distribution for two cases, which, just as in the previous investigations, are obtained by graphical differentiation of those curves which give the current measured by the galvanometer as a function of the retarding potential between the wire mesh N and the collecting cylinder.

For curve 1 the accelerating potential between D and N was 4 volts, for curve 2 it was 7.5 volts. We see that throughout, the measurements correspond to those [previously] obtained for helium. The difference in the curve shapes arises from the difference in the geometry of the apparatus that was used. We see from these measurements that the sudden onset of the inelastic collisions in mercury vapor occurs when the electron beam falls through 5 volts; this means that the ionization potential of mercury vapor is 5 volts. To establish this point still more accurately, we then proceeded as follows: For constant retarding voltage between N and G we measured the current flowing through the galvanometer as a function

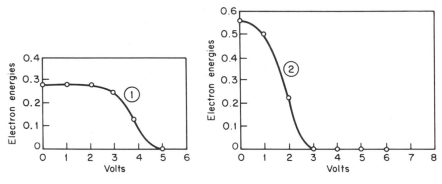

Fig. 46–2.

of the accelerating potential between N and D. The following phenomena are to be expected: As long as the accelerating potential is smaller than the retarding potential, the current is zero. After that it rises until the accelerating potential equals the ionization potential. At that moment the electrons in the neighborhood of the wire mesh suffer inelastic collisions and induce ionization. Since these electrons themselves and those released by ionization have but a very small additional potential to fall through before they reach the mesh, they pass through the mesh with hardly any detectable speed and are thus in no position to move against the retarding potential. The galvanometer current thus falls to zero as soon as the accelerating potential exceeds the ionization potential. If we now increase the accelerating potential still further, the region where the electrons suffer inelastic collisions moves inwardly away from the mesh. The electrons that are present after the inelastic collisions, thus, on their way to the mesh, fall through a potential that is equal to the difference between the accelerating and ionization potentials. As soon as this difference exceeds the retarding potential between N and G, electrons can move against the retarding field and the galvanometer current begins to rise again. Since the total number of electrons is increased by the ionization, this current rises more than it did originally. As soon, however, as the accelerating potential equals twice the ionization potential, the electrons in the neighborhood of the wire mesh suffer inelastic collisions the second time. Since, in these collisions, the electrons lose all their energy and the newly appearing electrons also have no measurable speed, electrons can no longer move against the retarding potential. Hence, as soon as the accelerating potential exceeds twice the ionization potential, the galvanometer current again sinks to zero. Since this same phenomenon recurs whenever the accelerating potential is an integral multiple of the ionization potential, we may expect

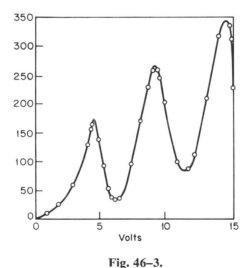

Fig. 46–3.

to obtain a curve which has maxima of increasing size which are spaced at just the ionization potential. The shape of the curves is also actually affected by the fact that there was a potential drop of 1.3 volts between the ends of the glowing wire which is the source of the electrons, and also because for very strong retarding potentials positive ions penetrate into the region between N and G. The first of these effects causes the drop after the potential exceeds an integral multiple of the ionization potential to occur not suddenly but to take place over a 1.3-volt stretch. The second effect causes the maxima to grow more slowly for larger retarding potentials than they ordinarily would. The results of our measurements given in [Fig. 46–3 and Fig. 46–4] show that our expectations were completely fulfilled. The maxima are extraordinarily sharp and therefore allow

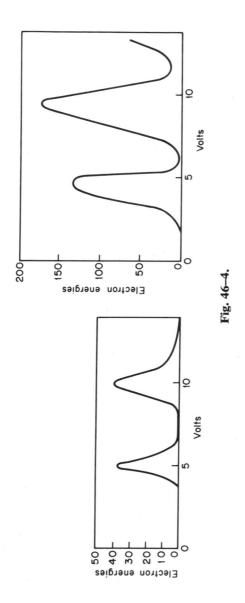

Fig. 46–4.

one to measure the ionization potential very accurately. The values for the spacings between any two successive maxima all lie between 4.8 and 5.0 volts, so that we may take 4.9 volts as the ionization potential of mercury vapor.

To compare this new method of measuring the ionization potential with the old one for an actual example, we have also made measurements on helium. Here the relationships are not nearly so favorable as for mercury, since the latter has a smaller ionization potential than any of the contaminating gases in the container, whereas helium, on the contrary, has the largest ionization potential (20.5 volts). In this case, therefore, all the accompanying gases in the apparatus are ionized at lower

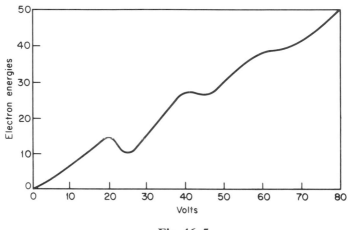

Fig. 46–5.

speeds of the colliding electrons, thus inducing completely inelastic collisions and, as a result, giving rise to a wiping out of the maxima. In spite of this, it is possible from such curves, measured in helium, to determine the ionization potential with considerable accuracy. [Fig. 46–5] shows a curve obtained from measurements in helium which gives a value of 21 volts for the ionization potential in good agreement with the value of 20.5 volts which we found previously. Because of the broad maxima, we must assign a greater inaccuracy to this value than to our previous result, so that the value found for mercury may be considered as the most accurately known ionization potential. This fact has enabled us to prove qualitatively a relationship (first stated in various ways by J. Stark), derived from quantum theory, between the ionization potential and the proper frequency of the electron to be torn out, at least for the case of mercury vapor. Until now all hypotheses which are found in the literature about this agree qualitatively more or less, as required by the order of magnitude relationship among λ, ν, e, m and r expressed by Sommerfeld. Most of the hypotheses state essentially that the frequency of a definite proper vibrational mode of an electron multiplied by the constant h is equal to the energy required for ionization.* For mercury vapor one most readily thinks of the very pronounced proper frequency of the so-called resonance line of mercury λ = 253.6 μμ discovered by Wood. If we calculate the product hν for this frequency, we obtain the energy which an electron would have after falling through a potential drop of 4.84 volts. This is in such good agreement with the value we obtained that we can hardly believe that this is a coincidence.

Since our method of measuring the ionization potential is an indirect one, we must discuss whether the sudden onset of inelastic collisions of the electrons at some critical velocity can be explained in some other way. Indeed, it is possible to interpret the results by assuming that the electron transforms its kinetic energy into optical radiation of wavelength 253.6 μμ as soon as its energy reaches the value hν without at the same time ionization having to take place. This possibility would, naturally, be of quantum theoretic significance and we therefore want to try to detect the appearance of such radiation directly in quartz tubes.

From the following considerations we may conclude with great certainty that ionization as well as optical radiation occurs.

The occurrence of ionization at the collision of 4.9-volt electrons with mercury molecules may be deduced from the following facts:

1. The ionization potential cannot be less than 4.9 volts since then inelastic collisions would have to occur at smaller voltages.

2. The ionization potential can exceed 4.9 volts only by infinitesimal amounts since otherwise in mercury vapor under a pressure of several atmospheres a discharge could set in only at very high field strengths. Since at these pressures the mean free path of the electrons is about 10^{-6} cm, the field strength would have to be so large, that the electrons could in a distance of about 10^{-6} cm pass freely through a potential difference that is equal to the ionization potential minus 4.9 volts. Since, however, ionization in mercury vapor at this pressure occurs for very small voltages, the ionization potential can differ from 4.9 volts only by an extremely small quantity.

3. According to the work of Steubing, mercury vapor is ionized when it is irradiated with light in the spectral region around the line 253.6 μμ. Also Wood concludes from the complete absence of polarization of the

---

* We take this opportunity to point out that the order of the ionization potentials of gases previously investigated, as well as their magnitudes, are obtained if we use the dispersion frequency of the gas as the frequency. For a rigorous proof, however, it is not sufficient to know with certainty the proper frequency from the dispersion.

resonance radiation excited by polarized light that, corresponding to Stark's hypothesis, this resonance radiation—contrary to the sodium resonance radiation—occurs during ionization processes.

SUMMARY

1. We have demonstrated that the electrons in mercury vapor suffer elastic collisions with the molecules up to a certain critical speed.

2. We have described a procedure for measuring this critical speed accurately up to a tenth of a volt. It is equal to the speed acquired by an electron that falls through a potential difference of 4.9 volts.

3. We have shown that the energy of a 4.9-volt electron beam is exactly equal to the quantum of energy associated with the mercury resonance line 253.6 $\mu\mu$.

4. We have discussed why, in the transfer of the energy from the 4.9 volt beam to the mercury molecule, some of the collisions lead to ionization, so that it appears that the ionization potential of mercury is 4.9 volts. Another part of the collisions appears to stimulate the emission of radiation and we surmise that this corresponds to the line 253.6.

47

ooooooooooo

THE DISCOVERY OF
ISOTOPES

ooooooooooo

Frederick Soddy (1877-1956)

One hundred years of chemical atomic theory steadfastly corrobo-rated Dalton's hypothesis that the atoms of the chemical elements were immutable and the atoms of any given element were identical in mass, shape, and size. Actually atomic theory in the first half of the nineteenth century left much to be desired with respect to rigor. Many leading chemists and physicists, among them Davy and Faraday, had grave reser-vations. However, the reorganization of chemistry brought about by Cannizzaro about 1860 (see Chapter 19) went far to promote a wider acceptance of the reality of atoms and, coincidentally, further confirmation was provided by the advances made in kinetic theory by Clausius and Maxwell, and later by Ludwig Boltzmann. Although no serious scientist questioned the immutability of atoms, here and there a voice such as Sir William Crookes's was heard speculating that the atoms of a given element might *not* be identical and that the atomic weight of an element might be the *average* of the weight of several unequally massive atoms having the same chemical properties. The basis for such a belief could easily have been the lingering echo of Prout's hypothesis together with the recognition that some atomic weights, such as chlorine, were by no stretch of the imagination integral.

The first breach produced by experimental evidence in the century-old atomic credo came in 1902 from the researches of Rutherford and Soddy. They showed that the radioelements were characterized by an ephemeral life and that their atoms were transmuted by radioactivity into others of different chemical properties. This discovery led in about a decade to the

779

classification of the decay products into well-ordered radioactive decay series. Thus, thorium atoms of atomic weight 232 (Th^{232}) were found to decay through a long series of transformations to lead of atomic weight 208, while uranium (U^{238}) atoms decayed to lead of atomic weight 206.

As experience with radioactivity increased, there began to emerge more clearly in several minds, and apparently most clearly in Frederick Soddy's, the realization that the radioactive transformations produced atoms of the same chemical species but of different weights. The first awareness of this situation seems to have come to Soddy in 1910 as a result of the chemical nonseparability of radium and mesothorium (Ra^{228}). In his Nobel lecture (1921) he states:

> From this date (1910) I was convinced that this nonseparability of the radioelements was a totally new phenomenon, quite distinct from that of the most closely related pairs, or groups, or elements, hitherto observed in chemistry, and that the relationship was not one of close similarity but of complete chemical identity.[1]

The accuracy of this statement has been confirmed recently by Cranston, one of his early associates, in an article published in the *Proceedings of the Chemical Society* for April 1964. We now recognize such chemically nonseparable atoms as "isotopes." But they did not receive this generic name until 1913, when the term was introduced by Soddy in an article, "Intra-atomic Charge," which appeared in the December 4, 1913, issue of *Nature*. This article was actually more concerned with the establishment of the concept of atomic number. It is therefore reproduced in Chapter 48 with the related paper of van der Broek, who is generally credited with having first introduced the idea of atomic number. The Royal Society obituary article on Soddy notes that the name "isotope" was suggested to him in 1913 by a Dr. Margaret Todd, an Edinburgh M.D., during a conversation that took place in the home of Soddy's father-in-law, Sir George Beilby, in Edinburgh, Scotland.

Soddy himself was an interesting personality. Born in Eastbourne, England, on September 2, 1877, the son of a successful grain merchant, he was brought up in a home of deep Calvinistic tradition. In this strict atmosphere truthfulness was the essential thing and deference to personal feelings was of very secondary consideration. This attitude, impressed on him as a child, persisted throughout his life. His education was begun in the Eastbourne schools and at Eastbourne College, where he first became interested in chemistry. Like the majority of scientists, he was the

---

[1] Muriel Howorth, *The Life Story of Frederick Soddy* (London: New World Publications, 1958), p. 184.

first in his family to show such a bent. From Eastbourne he went on to the University of Aberystwyth, Wales, principally to prepare for Oxford, where he was enrolled at nineteen as a student in Merton College. As an undergraduate he was active in the university Junior Chemical Society. He finished his undergraduate studies after two years, in 1898, with first honors in natural science, and then stayed on at Oxford until the spring of 1900 when, at the age of twenty-three, he applied for a professorship in chemistry at Toronto. The details of this application and its results have already been recounted in the commentary of Chapter 32, preceding the Rutherford and Soddy paper on "The Cause and Nature of Radioactivity." The collaboration with Rutherford was an unlikely partnership between two strong personalities, but it proved to be a happy one because of the complementary abilities of the two men and the contributions each was able to make to the joint effort. Although their work together was finished in the short span of three years, their papers revolutionized the outlook on radioactivity. Alexander Fleck evaluates their accomplishment in the following tribute:

> It is difficult at this distance of time to visualize the immediate effect of these papers on the scientific world of that day. Up to then the ideas of possible explanations of radioactivity rested on a form of continuity of emission of energy analogous in some way to the wave theory of light. Continuity seemed to be the basic idea of the Curies. . . . The effect of the Rutherford and Soddy papers . . . was that of a wave which swept over the scientific world and carried away most if not all of the vague alternatives.[2]

Soddy left McGill in 1903 and worked for a year in London with Sir William Ramsay. In keeping with his love of adventure, this was followed by a lecture tour in western Australia before he took up his duties as lecturer in chemistry at Glasgow University in the fall of 1904. His ten years at Glasgow cover most of the period of his productivity in chemistry, including his discovery of isotopes. Although Soddy had foreseen the existence of the isotope in 1910, he continued to develop his concepts in the following three years. In 1914, he accepted a professorship of chemistry at Aberdeen, but during his stay there he became concerned with investigations relating to England's part in World War I. In 1918, Soddy was appointed Dr. Lee's professor at Oxford and three years later, at the age of forty-four, received the Nobel Prize in chemistry for his work on isotopes.

---

[2] Alexander Fleck, "Memoir on Frederick Soddy," *Biographical Memoirs of Fellows of the Royal Society,* 3 (1957), p. 205.

The war years, with their material destruction and death of valued friends, shifted his interests from chemistry—he became more and more preoccupied with the ills of the world. Economic and financial ideas and the place of money in the social structure of civilization, a theme in which he had shown a pronounced interest as far back as 1906, now assumed a much larger place in his life. Much of his intellectual endeavor after going to Oxford was devoted to an attempt to base a monetary system on energy quantities. The movement gained few disciples and commanded little popular following. In August 1936 his wife, to whom he was deeply devoted, died suddenly. The loss was so crushing that, coupled with the social difficulties connected with his unorthodox economic views and other personal frictions at Oxford, Soddy decided to retire. And so at fifty-nine his resignation from the Dr. Lee's chair was accepted and he severed his formal connection with the academic world. The following year he embarked on a long tour of India and the Far East partly with a view to developing a process for the treatment of monazite sand. On his return he lived briefly at Enstone near Oxford, then moved to Brighton. He continued to write on economic and social questions and on mathematics. He died at Brighton on September 22, 1956, at the age of seventy-nine.

It is evident from this short biography that Soddy was a man of strong opinion and unorthodox views. He had a great sense of adventure, which found outlets in mountain climbing and in travel. His greatest accomplishment was undoubtedly the discovery, in collaboration with Rutherford, of the transmutation of the elements through radioactivity. But his Group Displacement law, cited in the paper below, which is so inextricably bound up with the concept of atomic number and the discovery of isotopes, is also a first-rate scientific achievement. As a mark of his vision, the reader may be even more deeply impressed by the following remarks, which he voiced in an address in Glasgow in 1906 in connection with his researches in radioactivity:

> We cannot regard the existence of this large internal energy as a peculiar property of the element radium . . . yet uranium since it produces radium with evolution of energy must possess all the internal energy of radium and more. . . . But there is no saying . . . how or when a discovery may not be made which will unlock this great store of energy bound up in the structure of the element. We are starting the twentieth century with the prize in full view.[3]

---

[3] Frederick Soddy, The Internal Energy of Elements, address to the March meeting of the Institution of Electrical Engineers, Glasgow Local Section, 13 III, 1906.

The order of presentation of the papers that follow varies from our usual organization in first offering a "dialogue" between Sir Arthur Schuster (who was responsible for bringing Rutherford to Manchester) and Frederick Soddy. Soddy, at a meeting of the Royal Society on February 27, 1913, spoke on the existence of atoms of different atomic weight having the same chemical properties, i.e., identical spectra and non-separability by any known process. Schuster in his letter correctly points out that Soddy must have meant "any known *chemical* process," since atoms of similar chemical behavior but differing mass can be separated by diffusion, centrifuging, or by electric or magnetic methods. Schuster then asks whether an "ionium-thorium" mixture would in fact show only the thorium spectrum; perhaps, he suggests, the spectra of ionium and thorium are identical. Actually we know now that "ionium" is a decay product of uranium; having an atomic number of 90, the same as thorium, it would behave in a fashion chemically identical to this element although its mass is 230 as compared with 232 for thorium. Thus, in modern terminology ionium is an isotope of thorium, Th^{230}. Schuster correctly makes the point that *different* elements cannot have the same spectrum. The confusion here is that ionium and thorium *are* the same element.

In his reply Soddy admits that in speaking of "non-separability" he was thinking only of chemical means. He points out, however, that the periodic law requires that just one element may appear in each place in the periodic table but that radioactive series show that different elements, *not necessarily of the identical atomic mass,* do occupy the same place. He then argues that these "different elements" are chemically identical. The basis for designating substances as "different elements" rested on their different radioactive disintegration rates. Thus thorium (Th^{232}) has a half-life of 1.39×10^{10} years, while ionium (Th^{230}) has a half-life of 8×10^4 years. The basis for putting such substances in the same place in the periodic table was their chemical inseparability and identical spectra. The latter point, however, Soddy admitted, was based on only one case, ionium and thorium. He goes on to point out that Th-X and radium would be a crucial test of identical spectra. In this connection, we know now that Th-X is Ra^{224}.

In presenting the evidence for isotopes we next present a report entitled "Chemistry at the British Association Meeting" which is a résumé of the British Association meeting held at Birmingham in September 1913. It gives not only a succinct account of Soddy's views described in his letter of March 15, but also shows the development of his ideas and adds a further significant idea—the Group Displacement law—which pins down the nature of the chemical change occurring when an α-particle or a β-particle is emitted. The report concludes with a list of experiments by Alexander Fleck, a collaborator of Soddy, noting a number of radioactive substances that are chemically identical. In order for the modern reader to appreciate the results more fully, the isotopic designation of the radio-active substances appears in brackets under these substances. We mention once again that the word "isotope" does not appear anywhere in these papers, apparently being coined sometime between September and the middle of November 1913.

Nothing has been mentioned in these comments regarding any search for isotopic species in the stable elements. Although the idea of isotopes had first occurred in connection with the radioactive elements, J. J. Thomson's researches with positive rays disclosed that neon consisted of two isotopic species. Thus the actual *recognition* of isotopes for both radioactive and stable atoms appears to have taken place almost simultaneously.

ºººººººº

SCHUSTER

The Radio-Elements and the Periodic Law [4]

AT A MEETING OF THE Royal Society on February 27th, Mr. F. Soddy made a verbal communication which was published under the above title in the *Chemical News* of the following day. The importance of the conclusions which are drawn justifies an examination of the evidence on which they rest. I do not approach the question unsympathetically, and I am quite willing to take some risks, but, when asked to accept a theory, I like to draw a distinction between a guess, a reasonable generalisation, and a well-established conclusion. If Mr. Soddy only wishes to put forward a theory which is not inconsistent with the facts so far as they are known at present, I have nothing to say, but if he claims anything approaching to experimental proof, some critical comment may be forgiven.

Mr. Soddy believes in the existence of a number of bodies which differ in molecular weight but "are non-separable by any known process"; these are also supposed to have identical spectra. Among "known processes" I count gravitation, diffusion, and mechanical processes, such as separation

---

[4] Arthur Schuster, *Nature* (Letters to the Editor), 91 (1913), 30–31.

by centrifugal forces, among which diffusion, perhaps, is the only available one. Is there any reason to suppose that molecules which, ex hypothesi, differ in mass, cannot be separated by diffusion? Some of the bodies concerned are gaseous, others no doubt are volatisable, and though diffusion may not act very effectively, owing to the close approximation of the densities, the presumption is that the molecules, having different masses, travel with different speeds, and that it is therefore incorrect to call two gases with different densities "non-separable by any known process."

Electrical and magnetic forces are also agents which can be applied to distinguish between molecules having different masses. Such forces should be considered before any sweeping assertions are made.

It is possible that Mr. Soddy wishes his statement to be limited to the ordinary chemical processes, and as he is trying to prove a negative, it is perhaps unfair to be too critical, but one cannot help remembering the time when neodym and praesodym were "non-separable," and reflecting how many substances might not be separated at the present moment if their optical properties had not given us a clue. No doubt radio-active tests are severe, and the chemical properties of the bodies in question are probably more nearly equal than those of the older chemistry, but there is a vast interval between "very similar" and "identical."

Incidentally, we may reflect that these bodies which are believed to be "non-separable" actually separate themselves of their own free accord in the natural course of their subsequent history, but this may only prove the perversity of nature.

According to Mr. Soddy's theory, the non-separable bodies have identical spectra. This is the vital issue, which, if made good by experiment, will help us to overlook many weaknesses in the argument. The evidence here rests entirely on one experimental fact. It was shown by Russell and Rossi, and also by Exner and Haschek, that a mixture of ionium and thorium does not show in the electric arc lines which can be assigned to ionium, the spectrum of the mixture being identical with that of pure thorium. Assuming that ionium is the only intermediate product between thorium-II. and radium, the life of ionium is 100,000 years, and the ionium-thorium preparation of Russell and Rossi must have contained about 16 per cent. of ionium. But these authors also point out that if the length of life is reduced to 12,000 years, the preparation would only contain 2 per cent., and the absence of ionium lines would be accounted for. At present the radio-active evidence seems in favour of the longer period, and the absence of ionium lines wants explaining; nevertheless, it seems to me to be going ahead too quickly to make a sweeping assertion that not only is the spectrum of ionium identical with that of thorium, but that the same holds in all similar cases, for the accumulated evidence of the spectra of known bodies has all been in the direction of indicating that optical properties of absorption and radiation discriminate in the most decisive manner between bodies which are otherwise similar in chemical properties.

Granting now for the sake of argument that the bodies in question have spectra which cannot be distinguished from each other, it remains to examine the alternative that the bodies are actually identical. It is said that they have different molecular weights, because one has been formed from the other by an expulsion of one α and two β particles. This argument is not necessarily conclusive, as a mass equal to that expelled may have been picked up again in the process. It may be urged that the subsequent history of these bodies shows that they are essentially different. Though a strong argument, this is not quite the last word, because, granting for a moment the temporary identity of two systems, the particular instability which determines their future may depend on their past.

Taking all arguments into consideration, we are left with an interesting theory consistent with our present knowledge but supported by very little real evidence. It may be presumptuous for one who can only claim to be an amateur in modern physics to express an opinion, but having in a previous generation taken part in establishing the fact that the same element can have different spectra according to its molecular constitution, one cannot, without good cause, accept the belief that different elements can have the same spectrum. Mr. Soddy's case would be much strengthened if he could adduce positive instead of merely negative evidence, and this might be supplied if the bodies grouped together with thallium lines could be shown to give the thallium spectrum, assuming thallium not to be present in the raw material.

००००००००

SODDY

The Radio-Elements and the Periodic Law [5]

I AM GRATEFUL TO PROF. Schuster for the opportunity he has afforded by his letter (NATURE, March 13) for the discussion of the wide generalisations that have been made with regard to the position of the radio-elements in the periodic table, consequent on the recent experimental work of A. Fleck and of the theoretical suggestions of A. S.

---

[5] Soddy, *Nature* (Letters to the Editor), 91 (1913), 57–58.

Russell and K. Fajans. The whole question is one in which it is important that there should not be any doubt as to the real nature of the evidence adduced. Prof. Schuster's criticism of my views on the subject could scarcely be more sympathetic or helpful, and can only result in a maturer outlook on this important question.

Granting for the sake of argument the possibility of the existence of groups of elements not necessarily of identical atomic mass, with identical chemical properties and spectra, the only known direct manner in which the existence of the members of these groups could be separately recognised is radio-active evidence, in which one member is formed from another, not directly, but through the intermediary of other elements, possessing, necessarily as now appears, completely different chemical properties. Hence it is natural that at first direct evidence should be confined practically to the subject of radio-activity, and much depends upon whether that evidence is considered real evidence approaching experimental proof, or whether it is regarded as merely negative in character.

In the first place, I admit when I wrote the expression, "non-separable by any known process," I had in mind chemical processes. It is unusual and illustrative of the peculiarities of the problem that the relatively rough and partial means of physical analysis, to which Prof. Schuster refers, may be expected ultimately to succeed where the most refined and delicate methods of chemical analysis may be expected to fail. But so it is, and I agree with Prof. Schuster that it should ultimately be possible partially to separate by purely physical methods certain members of these chemically identical groups by virtue of the slight differences in their molecular masses. In fact, a year ago I commenced an experiment to try to effect a partial separation of the two uraniums by diffusion in solution. This case is an exceptionally favourable one as an alteration in the relative concentration of the two uraniums by only a few per cent. should be detectable without any uncertainty by radio-active methods.

Although the term "non-separable" I think connotes present inability, without implying, necessarily, anything as regards what may be possible in the future, I do, however, think that there are good grounds for believing that the *chemical* non-separability of elements occupying the same place in the periodic table is due to the general character of chemical methods rather than the state of refinement and delicacy attained at any particular time. The chemical analysis of matter has given us the periodic law, and there is no case known of two or more ordinary elements with claims to the same place in the periodic table. In this connection the case of the rare-earth group of elements is necessarily excluded, as these elements certainly do not obey the law without modification. In all other parts of the table the rule is that there is only one element for each place, and each place signifies a separate chemical type differentiated in a regular manner from its neighbours. But now the radio-active series have shown that different elements, not necessarily of identical atomic mass, do occupy the same place, and that when this occurs these elements possess identical chemical nature. It is therefore an inference supported by the known facts of chemical analysis that the single place in the periodic classification represents the limits of the analysis of matter by chemical methods, rather than the ultimate analysis into homogeneous types, such as is usually implied in the conventional view of elements.

Prof. Schuster admits that the chemical properties of these non-separable groups of radio-elements are probably more nearly equal than those of the longer-known elements, but claims that there is a vast interval between "very similar" and "identical." I do not like the term "very similar." It is ambiguous, and may mean nothing more than that the experimental examination has been neither skilled nor exhaustive enough to disclose the differences, if any exist. Unless this is the case, I feel that the proper term to use is "identical." Otherwise the word "identical" ought to be expunged from scientific language altogether. Unless there is some reason to foresee a qualification being required by the further progress of knowledge, a definite statement ought to be preferred in science to an ambiguous one, which on account of its vagueness must necessarily remain true for all time. Scientific statements can only express present knowledge, including in this term reasonable inferences from the whole field of such knowledge.

The term "chemically identical" has not been applied until after an examination, not, of course, in every case, but in every possible case, and in sufficient numbers of cases to reveal the general law, as skilled and exhaustive as the present art of chemical analysis allows, and, what is equally of importance, by the use of methods for detecting changes in relative concentration as delicate as any that exist. The example quoted of praseodymium and neodymium ought to be more closely examined. These elements proved to be separable as soon as optical methods of revealing their separate existence became known. In the case of the radio-elements the separate radio-active nature of each individual of the group is exactly known, the proportion of each in any mixture can be quantitatively evaluated. Yet they are non-separable. That some mixture to-day may still be classed as a homogeneous element because no means exist for the separate identification of its components does not affect the fact that some mixtures of elements capable of separate identification are chemically non-separable.

Difficulties of chemical analysis are often not connected with the methods of separation at all, but with the means of determining whether or not a separation has been effected, which, in the case of the difficult rare-earth group are relatively crude and sometimes misleading.

The suggestion, that in the disintegration process a mass equal to that of the α particle previously lost may be picked up, is not a probable one, but even if it is admitted, and it is supposed that parent and product have the same mass, it does not affect the view that they are two absolutely distinct types of matter, disintegrating at different speeds and in certain cases with expulsion of different kinds of rays. The attempt to meet this by supposing that the particular instability which determines their future may depend on their past is equivalent to admitting the essential difference between the two types. Besides it can be stated definitely that for any one kind of instability, or for any one radio-active change, the past exercises absolutely no influence upon the events of the future. The period of average life of an atom depends neither upon how long it has already been in existence nor upon any other known condition. It is independent of concentration or the environment in which the atom disintegrates. These features of radio-active change are against the view that anything of the nature of atomic synthesis is going on concurrently with the disintegration, or that disintegration is conditioned by the drain of energy from the atom by radiation, as is so often affirmed.

The mass of evidence that has been accumulated that different elements have identical chemical nature is not accurately described as purely negative in character. The statement that A is non-separable from B is negative in form only. It contains explicitly an infinite number of definite positive statements that A is separable from C or D, or any other of the hundred or more known elements, or any conceivable mixture of them, by chemical methods, which are exactly indicated by the statement. It is not necessary that A and B should in every case coexist, though in certain cases—the two uraniums is a good example—they have never been obtained apart. Mesothorium-II. ordinarily occurs free from actinium, and the putting in of the latter substance is a voluntary experimental device to show that once mixed these two elements are chemically non-separable. The complete chemical nature of either, or of any other of the radio-elements, could be described in detail *ab initio,* but the negative form is brief and complete.

I do not think there are weaknesses in this part of the argument. It has been a slowly growing theoretical development, and I do claim for it something approaching experimental proof.

As regards the view that chemically identical groups of elements have the same spectrum, this admittedly I put forward on a single case, that of ionium and thorium. It rests entirely on the validity and generality of the α and β ray change rules, but, if these are true, ionium must be the direct product of uranium-II.; its period cannot be less than 100,000 years, and its proportion in the preparations spectroscopically examined less than 16 per cent. and 10 per cent. respectively. Any other view requires the assumption that one or more α ray and twice as many β ray changes remain to be discovered in the series, and it can be stated with some certainty that no such changes remain unknown.

Frankly, I do not expect Prof. Schuster or anyone else to accept a view of this kind, put forward on a single thread of evidence. The value of the view is merely that it suggests definite new lines of work, difficult and costly, but still experimentally feasible.

Prof. Schuster points out that the members of the thallium group, for example, ought to give the thallium spectrum in absence of thallium in the material. The latter condition is easy to ensure. But the case is not a very favourable one on the radio-active side, as thorium-D, the best example of the group to select, has a period of average life of only 4·5 minutes. The case, however, might be within the resources of some radium institute.

Since Prof. Schuster made this suggestion, I have gone into the experimental feasibility of getting evidence of this kind, and have decided to concentrate on the case of thorium-X, the spectrum of which should be identical with that of radium. It is a particularly crucial case. The spectrum reaction of radium is excessively delicate, and the amount of this element can be easily evaluated in quantities thousands of times less than can be spectroscopically detected. The chemical work is complicated, but really exceptionally favourable and elegant.

Mesothorium-I. is non-separable from radium, and radiothorium from ionium, the parent of radium, so that if radiothorium is grown from ionium-free mesothorium it can be purified from radium to any extent and left to produce thorium-X. Naturally, however, the work will require some years, but it should be within the resources of the individual investigator. At the same time, it will be possible to try during the course of the work a large number of similar cases, if a sufficient supply of the primary material, mesothorium-I. can be obtained. This inference as to the spectra is purely a personal view, and is to be taken merely as a suggestion until further evidence is forthcoming. But I would not have made it if I thought it inconsistent with any known evidence.

Chemistry at the British Association Meeting [6]

THE DISCUSSION ON RADIO-ACTIVE ELEMENTS and the periodic law attracted a very large audience. Unfortunately the

---

[6] Report, *Nature*, 92 (1913), 331–332.

counterattractions of Sir J. J. Thomson's new gas limited it to an hour and a half, but Mr. Soddy, who opened it, was properly very brief. His main conclusion, based on the existence of chemically identical and non-separable groups of elements may be summarised as follows:

The chemical analysis of matter is not an ultimate one. It has appeared ultimate hitherto, on account of the impossibility of distinguishing between elements which are chemically identical and non-separable unless these are in the process of change the one into the other. But in that part of the periodic table in which the evolution of the elements is still proceeding, each place is seen to be occupied not by one element, but on the average, for the places occupied at all, by no fewer than four, the atomic weights of which vary over as much as eight units. It is impossible to believe that the same may not be true for the rest of the table, and that each known element may be a group of non-separable elements occupying the same place, the atomic weight not being a real constant, but a mean value, of much less fundamental interest than has been hitherto supposed. Although these advances show that matter is even more complex than chemical analysis alone has been able to reveal, they indicate at the same time that the problem of atomic constitution may be more simple than has been supposed from the lack of simple numerical relations between the atomic weights.

The general law is that in an α-ray change, when a helium atom carrying two atomic charges of positive electricity is expelled, the element changes its place in the periodic table in the direction of diminishing mass and diminishing group number by two places. In a β-ray change, when a single atomic charge of negative electricity is expelled from the atom as a β particle, and also in the two changes for which the expulsion of rays has not yet been detected, the element changes its position in the table in the opposite direction by one place.

The discussion was continued by Mr. A. Fleck, who has determined experimentally what element each of the short-lived radio-elements most resembled, and whether it was separable from the ordinary element by fractional methods.

The results of the work show that:

1. Uranium-X [Th^{234}] and radio-actinium [Th^{227}] are chemically identical with thorium.

2. Mesothorium-2 [Ac^{228}] is chemically identical with actinium.

3. Radium-A [Po^{218}] is chemically identical with polonium.

4. Radium-C [Bi^{214}], thorium-C [Bi^{212}], actinium-C [Bi^{211}], and radium-E [Bi^{210}] are chemically identical with bismuth.

5. Radium-B [Pb^{214}], thorium-B [Pb^{212}], and actinium-B [Pb^{211}] are chemically identical with lead.

6. Thorium-D [Pb^{208}] and actinium-D [Pb^{207}] are chemically identical with thallium.

In the cases in which the inseparable elements are common elements these latter have all atomic weights above 200, and occupy one or other of the last twelve places of the periodic table.

48

○○○○○○○○○○

THE POSITIVE RAYS

○○○○○○○○○○○

J. J. Thomson (1856-1940)

The discovery of the electron, in a great measure owed to the brilliant analysis of Sir. J. J. Thomson, was quickly followed by the discovery of the proton. This stemmed directly from the work by Goldstein on what he called "canal rays." Thomson, in his Bakerian lecture of 1913, "Rays of Positive Electricity," which falls at the end of this commentary, describes Goldstein's observations and deductions, saying that

> Goldstein [in 1886] observed that when the cathode in a vacuum tube was pierced with holes, the electrical discharge did not stop at the cathode; behind the cathode beams of light could be seen streaming through the holes. . . . He ascribed these pencils of light to rays passing through the holes into the gas behind the cathode; and from their association with the channels through the cathode he called them *Kanalstrahlen*.

That the particles in these rays are positively charged is shown by their motion toward the cathode; this was proved experimentally by W. Wien, who deflected them in strong magnetic fields. Wien also demonstrated, from the ratio of their charge to their mass, that these positively charged particles are more than a thousand times more massive than electrons are.

The step from the recognition that canal rays consist of positively charged massive particles to the discovery of the proton was not so easy as it might appear, for, as Thomson notes, "The composition of these positive rays is much more complex than that of cathode rays [that is, the electrons], for, whereas the particles in the cathode rays are all of the same kind, there are in the positive rays many different kinds of particles."

The problem that arose, then, was to develop an experimental method

793

to separate out the various particle components (that is, to obtain a mass spectrum) in the canal rays. In his Bakerian lecture, Sir J. J. Thomson described a simple device, involving electric and magnetic fields, that is the forerunner of the modern mass spectrometer. Thomson points out in his address that a stream of charged particles moving in a straight line can be deviated by applying at right angles to this stream parallel electric and magnetic fields. The simultaneous action of the electric and the magnetic fields causes the beam to be deflected from its original direction. The electric field deflects the beam in one direction say left or right, the magnetic field deflects it up or down.

A simple algebraic analysis shows that both the magnetic deflection and the electric deflection of a particle in the beam depend on the ratio of the electric charge to the mass of the particle and on the speed of the particle. If, then, the electric and magnetic fields are kept at constant strength, no two particles will strike the receiving surface at the same point unless they have the same initial speed and the same ratio of charge to mass. In this way, a spectrum of the canal rays is obtained on the surface and each point in the spectrum represents a particular value of the speed and of the ratio of charge to mass.

In his analysis of this procedure, Thomson points out that all the particles which have a given value of the ratio of charge to mass strike the surface along a parabola so that each kind of particle has its own parabola. Thus, if the canal rays are allowed to strike a photographic plate, one can see at a glance, by counting the number of parabolas recorded on the plate, how many kinds of particles are in the beam.

The parabola corresponding to hydrogen ions (protons) is the one that is deflected most, and since the ratio of charge to mass is known this ratio can easily be read off for all other kinds of particles using the positions of their parabolas relative to the position of the hydrogen parabola.

Using this type of analysis, Thomson discovered that the particles in the beam of canal rays could be divided into ionized (he called them "electrified") atoms and ionized molecules. Since his experimental arrangement permitted him to determine what multiple of the unit charge was on any ion, he could determine the mass of this ion as compared to the mass of a proton from the position of the ion's parabola relative to the parabola of the proton.

From the positions of the parabolas on the photographic plate, Thomson was thus able to catalogue the atomic and molecular weights of the various elements and compounds in the tube.

ⱺⱺⱺⱺⱺⱺⱺ

T H O M S O N

Rays of Positive Electricity [1]

I N 1 8 8 6 , G O L D S T E I N O B S E R V E D T H A T when the cathode in a vacuum tube was pierced with holes, the electrical discharge did not stop at the cathode; behind the cathode, beams of light could be seen streaming through the holes in the way represented in [Fig. 48–1]. He

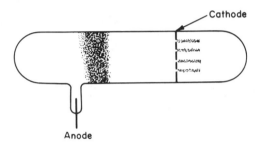

Fig. 48–1.

ascribed these pencils of light to rays passing through the holes into the gas behind the cathode; and from their association with the channels through the cathode he called these rays *Kanalstrahlen*. The colour of the light behind the cathode depends upon the gas in the tube: with air the light is yellowish, with hydrogen rose colour, with neon the gorgeous neon red, the effects with this gas being exceedingly striking. The rays produce phosphorescence when they strike against the walls of the tube; they also affect a photographic plate. Goldstein could not detect any deflection when a permanent magnet was held near the rays. In 1898, however, W. Wien, by the use of very powerful magnetic fields, deflected these rays and showed that some of them were positively charged; by measuring the electric and magnetic deflections he proved that the masses of the particles in these rays were comparable with the masses of atoms of hydrogen, and

[1] Sir J. J. Thomson, *Proceedings of the Royal Society* (London), Series A, 89 (1913), 1–20.

thus were more than a thousand times the mass of a particle in the cathode ray. The composition of these positive rays is much more complex than that of the cathode rays, for whereas the particles in the cathode rays are all of the same kind, there are in the positive rays many different kinds of particles. We can, however, by the following method sort these particles out, determine what kind of particles are present, and the velocities with which they are moving. Suppose that a pencil of these rays is moving parallel to the axis of x, striking a plane at right angles to their path at the point O; if before they reach the plane they are acted on by an electric force parallel to the axis of y, the spot where a particle strikes the plane will be deflected parallel to y through a distance y given by the equation

$$y = \frac{e}{mv^2} A,$$

where e, m, v, are respectively the charge, mass, and velocity of the particle, and A a constant depending upon the strength of the electric field and the length of path of the particle, but quite independent of e, m, or v.

If the particle is acted upon by a magnetic force parallel to the axis of y, it will be deflected parallel to the axis of z, and the deflection in this direction of the spot where the particle strikes the plane will be given by the equation

$$z = \frac{e}{mv} B,$$

where B is a quantity depending on the magnetic field and length of path of the particle, but independent of e, m, v. If the particle is acted on simultaneously by the electric and magnetic forces, the spot where it strikes the plane will, if the undeflected position be taken as origin, have for coordinates

$$x = 0, \qquad y = \frac{e}{mv^2} A, \qquad z = \frac{e}{mv} B. \qquad (1)$$

Thus no two particles will strike the plane in the same place, unless they have the same value of v and also the same value of e/m; we see, too, that if we know the value of y and z, we can, from equation (1), calculate the values of v and e/m, and thus find the velocities and character of the particles composing the positive rays.

From equation (1) we see that

$$z^2 = \frac{e}{m} y \frac{B^2}{A}, \qquad z = yv \frac{B}{A}. \qquad (2)$$

Thus all the particles which have a given value of e/m strike the plane on a parabola, which can be photographed by allowing the particles to fall on a photographic plate. Each type of particle in the positive rays will produce a separate parabola, so that an inspection of the plate shows at a glance how many kinds of particles there are in the rays; the measurement of the parabolas, and the use of equation (2), enables us to find the values of m/e corresponding to them, and thus to make a complete analysis of the gases in the positive rays. To compare the values of m/e corresponding to the different parabolas, we need only measure the values of z on these parabolas corresponding to a constant value of y. We see from equation (2) that the values of e/m are proportional to the squares of the values of z. Thus, if we know the value of e/m for one parabola, we can with very little labour deduce the values of e/m for all the others. As the parabola corresponding to the hydrogen atom is found on practically all the plates, and as this can be at once recognised, since it is always the most deflected parabola, it is a very easy matter to find the values of m/e for the other particles. Photographs made by the positive rays after they have suffered electric and magnetic deflections are reproduced in [Fig. 48–2]. The apparatus I have used for photographing the rays is shown in [Fig. 48–3].

A is a large bulb of from 1 to 2 litres capacity in which the discharge passes, C the cathode placed in the neck of the bulb. . . .

The form of cathode which I have found to give the best pencil of rays is shown in Fig. 48–3. The front of the cathode is an aluminium cap, carefully worked so as to be symmetrical about an axis: this cap fits on to a cylinder made of soft iron with a hole bored along the axis; the object of making the cathode of iron is to screen the rays from magnetic force while they are passing through the hole. A case fitting tightly into this hole contains a long narrow tube which is the channel through which the rays pass into the tube behind the cathode. This tube is the critical part of the apparatus, and failure to obtain a good pencil of rays is generally due to some defect here. As the length of this tube is very long in proportion to its diameter—the length of most of the tubes I have used is about 6 cm. and the diameter from $0 \cdot 1$ to $0 \cdot 5$ mm.—it requires considerable care to get it straight enough to allow an uninterrupted passage to the rays. . . . It is useless to attempt to experiment with positive rays unless this tube is exceedingly straight. The rays themselves exert a sand blast kind of action on the tube and disintegrate the metal; after prolonged use the metallic dust may accumulate to such an extent that the tube gets silted up, and obstructs the passage of the rays. The cathode is fixed into the glass vessel by a little wax; the joint is made tight so that the only channel of communication from one side of the cathode to the other is through the tube in the cathode. The wax joint is surrounded by a water jacket J to prevent the wax being heated by the discharge. The arrangements used to produce

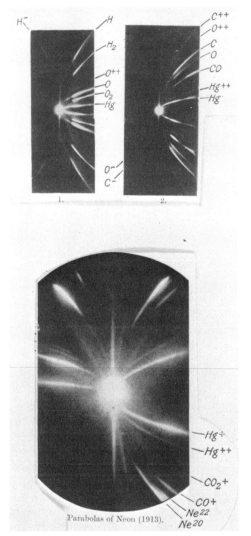

Fig. 48–2. Positive ray parabolas.

the electric and magnetic fields to deflect the rays are shown at L and M.
An ebonite tube is turned so as to have the shape shown in [Fig. 48–3],
L and M are two pieces of soft iron with carefully worked plane faces,
placed so as to be parallel to each other, these are connected with a battery of storage cells and furnish the electric field. P and Q are the poles of
an electromagnet separated from L and M by the thin walls of the ebonite
box: when the electromagnet is in action there is a strong magnetic field
between L and M; the lines of magnetic force and electric force are by

this arrangement parallel to each other and the electric and magnetic fields are as nearly as possible coterminous. . . . Plates of soft iron are placed between the electromagnet and the discharge tube to prevent the discharge from being affected by the magnetic field.

The pressure in the tube behind the cathode must be kept very low, this is done by means of a tube containing charcoal cooled by liquid air. The pressure on the other side of the cathode is much higher. . . .

The parabolas are determined by the values of *e/m,* thus an atom with a single charge would produce the same parabola as a diatomic molecule with a double charge. We can, however, by the following method distinguish between parabolas due to particles with a single charge and those due to particles with more than one charge.

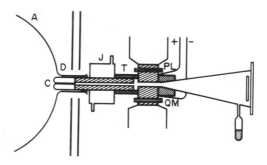

Fig. 48–3.

The parabolas are not complete parabolas, but arcs starting at a finite distance from the vertical, this distance is by equation (1) inversely proportional to the maximum kinetic energy possessed by the particle. This maximum kinetic energy is that due to the charge on the particle falling from the potential of the anode to that of the cathode in the discharge tube. Consider now the particles which have two charges: these acquire in the discharge tube twice as much kinetic energy as the particles with a single charge. Some of these doubly charged particles will lose one of their charges while passing through the long narrow tube in the cathode, and will emerge as particles with a single charge; they will, however, possess twice as much kinetic energy as those which have had one charge all the time. Thus the stream of singly charged particles emerging from the tube will consist of two sets, one having twice as much kinetic energy as the other; the particles having twice the kinetic energy will strike the plate nearer to the vertical than the others, and will thus prolong beyond the normal length the arc of the parabola corresponding to the singly charged particle. . . .

If the atom acquired more than two charges the prolongation of the atomic line would be still longer. If, for example, it could acquire eight charges it would be prolonged until its extremity was only one-eighth of the normal distance from the vertical. . . .

Using this method to distinguish between singly and multiply charged systems we find that the particles which produce the parabolas on the photographic plates may be divided into the following classes:

1. Positively electrified atoms with one charge.
2. Positively electrified molecules with one charge.
3. Positively electrified atoms with multiple charges.
4. Negatively electrified atoms.
5. Negatively electrified molecules.

The production of a charged molecule involves nothing more than the detachment of a corpuscle from the molecule, that of a charged atom requires the dissociation of the molecule as well as the electrification of the atom. . . .

The rarity of the doubly charged molecule seems to indicate that the shock which produces the double charge is sufficiently intense to dissociate the molecule into its atoms. The uniformity of the intensity of the parabolas corresponding to the multiply charged atoms shows that they acquire this charge at one operation and not by repeated ionisation on their way to the cathode.

The occurrence of the multiple charge does not seem to be connected with the valency or other chemical property of the atom. . . . Elements as different in their chemical properties as carbon, nitrogen, oxygen, chlorine, helium, neon, a new gas whose atomic weight is 22, argon, krypton, mercury, all give multiply charged atoms. The fact that these multiple charges so frequently occur on atoms of the inert gases proves, I think, that they are not produced by any process of chemical combination.

All the results point to the conclusion that the occurrence and magnitude of the multiple charge is connected with the mass of the atom rather than with its valency or chemical properties. We find, for example, that the atom of mercury, the heaviest atom I have tested, can have as many as 8 charges, crypton can have as many as 5, argon 3, neon 2, and so on. There is evidence that when these multiple charges occur the process of ionisation is generally such that the atom starts either with one charge or with the maximum number, that in the ionisation of mercury vapour, for example, the mercury atom begins either with 1 charge or with 8, and that the particles which produce the parabola corresponding to 5 charges, for example, started with 8 and lost 3 of them on its way through the tube in the cathode. . . .

THE USE OF POSITIVE RAYS AS A METHOD OF CHEMICAL ANALYSIS

Since each parabola on the photograph indicates the presence in the discharge tube of particles having a known value of $m/e,$ and as by the methods described above we can determine what multiple e is of the unit charge, we can, by measuring the parabolas, determine the masses of all the particles in the tube, and thus identify the contents of the tube as far as this can be done by a knowledge of the atomic and molecular weights of all its constituents. The photograph of the positive rays thus gives a catalogue of the atomic and molecular weights of the elements and compounds in the tube. This method has several advantages in comparison with that of spectrum analysis, especially for the detection of new substances; for, with this method, when we find a new line we know at once the atomic or molecular weight of the particle which produced it. Spectrum analysis would be much easier and more efficient if from the wavelength of a line in the spectrum we could deduce the atomic weight of the element which produced it, and this virtually is what we can do with the positive-ray method.

Again, in a mixture the presence of one gas is apt to swamp the spectrum of another, necessitating, in many cases, considerable purification of the gas before it can be analysed by the spectroscope. This is not the case to anything like the same extent with the positive rays; with these the presence of other gases is a matter of comparatively little importance.

With regard to the sensitiveness of the positive ray method, I have made, as yet, no attempt to design tubes which would give the maximum sensitiveness, but with the tubes actually in use there is no difficulty in detecting the helium contained in a cubic centimetre of air, even though it is mixed with other gases, and I have not the slightest doubt a very much greater degree of sensitiveness could be obtained without much difficulty.

I will illustrate the use of the method by some applications. The first of these is to the detection of rare gases in the atmosphere. Sir James Dewar kindly supplied me with some gases obtained from the residues of liquid air; the first sample had been treated so as to contain the heavier constituents. The positive-ray photograph gave the lines of xenon, krypton, argon, and a faint line due to neon; there were no lines on the photograph unaccounted for, and so we may conclude that there are no heavy unknown gases in the atmosphere occurring in quantities comparable with that of xenon. The second sample from Sir James Dewar contained the lighter gases; the photograph *shows that, in addition to helium and neon, there is another gas with an atomic weight about 22. This gas has been* *found in every specimen of neon which has been examined,** including a very carefully purified sample prepared by Mr. E. W. Watson and a specimen very kindly supplied by M. Claud, of Paris. . . . The substance giving the line 22 also occurs with a double charge, giving a line for which $m/e = 11$. There can, therefore, I think, be little doubt that what has been called neon is not a simple gas but a mixture of two gases, one of which has an atomic weight about 20 and the other about 22. The parabola due to the heavier gas is always much fainter than that due to the lighter, so that probably the heavier gas forms only a small percentage of the mixture.

---

* Editors' italics.

49

ooooooooooo

TRANSMUTATION OF AN ELEMENT

ooooooooooo

Ernest Rutherford (1871-1937)

Although Rutherford's paper on the nuclear atom may be considered as the high point of his scientific career, he was still to do a great deal of research work of the very highest order. The period immediately after Bohr's fundamental paper appeared was one of great scientific activity, and new discoveries were being announced in all the great European laboratories. Rutherford was busy giving lectures, attending conferences, and corresponding with scientists all over the world, and, wherever he went, he advocated seeking all possible ways of obtaining very high voltages. "I think it is a matter of pressing importance, at the present time," he said, "to devise electrical machines of the highest possible voltages." With the nuclear atom an established fact, Rutherford reasoned that one could probe the positively charged nucleus (the neutron had not yet been discovered) only with very high energy ions, and very high voltages would be needed to produce these. Although very energetic α particles were available from radioactive nuclei, only very weak beams (that is, very few α particles per second) could be obtained for any one experiment because of the scarcity of radioactive elements.

In 1914, the British Crown recognized Rutherford's great scientific achievements by knighting him, which pleased but also somewhat embarrassed him for, as he wrote to Hevesy, "it is, of course, very satisfactory to have one's work recognized by the powers that be, but the form of recognition is also a little embarrassing for a relatively youthful and impecunious Professor like myself. However, I trust it will not interfere with my future activities." This honor in no way affected Rutherford's attitude toward his work, his colleagues or his students. He went about his laboratory, as always, concerning himself with the details of everyone's project and announcing himself by his loud laugh long before he arrived to discuss the details of an experiment. He took great pride in the successes achieved by his co-workers and was very happy that "the laboratory had [not even] one piece of bad work to its discredit."

During this period, Rutherford was in constant correspondence with scientists over the entire world. He was particularly interested in the work of Hahn and Lise Meitner, who were studying the nature of gamma rays. Hahn and Meitner argued that these were electromagnetic waves emitted by the radioactive nucleus when it readjusts itself to a new equilibrium position after emitting an α particle or β particle. This point of view proved to be true and was supported by Rutherford who was busily trying to measure the wave lengths of gamma rays. After Rutherford returned from the United States, where he had given the first William E. Hale lecture to the National Academy of Sciences on "The Structure of the Atom and the Evolution of the Elements," he returned to Manchester to continue with his gamma-ray experiments.

By this time Moseley, whom Rutherford had nurtured at Manchester and who had subsequently gone to Oxford, was obtaining his phenomenal results on the X-ray spectra of the elements. He kept Rutherford constantly informed on the progress of his work, even though Rutherford no longer had any direct contact with it. This emphasizes one of the special qualities that Rutherford had—the knack of imparting to everyone who worked with him the feeling that he was a kind of "father-confessor" for all scientific problems—always available for consultation and advice. Everyone working in the Manchester laboratory in those years recalls that it was a very happy family with Rutherford as "father." Geiger summed it up in these words: "Nothing was so refreshing or so inspiring as to spend an hour . . . alone with Rutherford. . . . I would be loth to part with the memory . . . spent in fellowship with a mastermind."

With the advent of World War I, the character of the Manchester laboratory began to change and the "family" of research students was quickly broken up, with many of the younger men going into the war industries. Interestingly enough, during those early war years Rutherford was in fairly constant communication by mail with the scientists of the Central Powers. Soon Rutherford himself was involved in war research work and diverted part of his laboratory to finding ways of detecting submarines. He also was active as a member of the Board of Inventions and Research. During the last year of the war, he spent a good deal of time in Washington as a member of a British Mission to the U.S.A.

In spite of all these war activities, Rutherford still managed to do fundamental experiments in physics and to begin his famous experiments on the artificial disintegration of nitrogen by alpha-particle bombardment, which we discuss below. He completed these experiments by 1919 and published his epoch-making results in four papers—one of which we have included below—in the *Philosophical Magazine,* Volume 37. This research was the last scientific work that Rutherford did at Manchester, for he accepted the post of Cavendish Professor at Cambridge, when J. J. Thomson resigned to devote his full time to directing the College as Master of Trinity. When Rutherford came to Cambridge in 1919, he found that he had also been appointed Director of the Cavendish Laboratory and a Fellow of Trinity College.

In 1920 Rutherford gave the Bakerian lecture to the Royal Society for the second time, presenting a complete theory of radioactivity. During the presentation he proposed two new ideas that were very prophetic, but about twelve years before their time. He suggested first the possibility of a mass 2 isotope of hydrogen, which was subsequently discovered by Urey, and second the existence of a neutral particle of unit mass. This particle, the neutron, was later discovered by Chadwick. The same year, at a meeting of the British Association, Rutherford suggested that the nucleus of the hydrogen atom be called the "proton," and this name was quickly adopted by the scientific community.

This was a period of great lecture activity for Rutherford; he was in demand everywhere and had to refuse most of these invitations. At the same time, he was receiving honors from all over the world: an honorary degree from Copenhagen; foreign member of the Royal Academy of Science at Amsterdam; Professor of Natural Philosophy at the Royal Institution, the Order of Merit, etc. In spite of all this, Rutherford went right along with his scientific work as though the scientist part of him acted quite independently of his more mundane part. He continued—with Chadwick as collaborator—to bombard nuclei of all kinds with α particles and was trying, even then, to induce artificial radioactivity by this bombardment. They succeeded in disintegrating many kinds of nuclei. At the same time, he tried to find, without success, the neutron whose existence he had already postulated. In 1925 he was elected President of the Royal Society and held this office for five years. He was so elated by this that his exuberance was communicated to everyone around him and acted as a stimulant to his students. In 1931 he was created a Baron and became Baron Rutherford of Nelson. He immediately sent a cable to his mother, who had visited him the year before: "Now Lord Rutherford, more your honor than mine, Ernest." But these happy events were also mixed with tragedy. In 1930 his daughter and only child, Eileen, who had married the mathematical physicist R. H. Fowler, died soon after giving birth to her fourth child.

The years from 1930 until his death, from a strangulated hernia on October 19, 1937—he was then 66 years old—were very exciting and productive ones both for himself and his Cavendish Laboratory, for scientific discoveries of the greatest importance were being made all over the world. In 1932 Chadwick had discovered the neutron; shortly after that Cockroft and Walton had induced artificial radioactive decay with proton bombardment, and in 1933 Anderson had discovered the positron. These events were soon followed by Fermi's probing of nuclei with slow neutrons, and the world was suddenly thrust into the nuclear age. Although Rutherford had done as much as, if not more than, any one single man to usher in this age, he did not live to see either its destructive or constructive qualities although he certainly had a fairly good idea of the new discoveries that were to come.

He was a simple man in the sense that Einstein was simple, for they both saw the universe as a very orderly place whose secrets could be discovered by a direct and uncomplicated approach. In a tribute to Rutherford in 1932 Bohr described Rutherford as follows: "If a single word could be used to describe so vigorous and many-sided a personality, it would certainly be 'simplicity': Indeed, all aspects of his life are characterised by a simplicity of a similar kind to that which he has claimed of nature, which he is able to discover, where others before were not able to discover, where others before were not able to see it." He was certainly the greatest experimental physicist of his day; his achievements were so important that most of the developments in physics today stem from the work that he did.

Perhaps the greatest tribute to him as a person was that given by a man who knew him for thirty years: "Rutherford never made an enemy and never lost a friend."

After his basic analysis of the experiments on the scattering of α particles by heavy nuclei, which finally led to the nuclear model of the atom and to Bohr's theory of atomic spectra, Rutherford began a series of experiments in 1915 on the scattering of α particles by light atoms. These experiments, designed to obtain more detailed information about the nuclear atom, resulted in the first artificially induced nuclear transformation of an element. The description of this remarkable phenomenon, which occurred in 1919, is contained in the fourth of a series of papers that appeared in the *Philosophical Magazine*, and is reproduced here.

Rutherford begins the discussion of his particle collision experiments by noting that radium, in the form of a thin coating on the metal, produces scintillations on a zinc-sulfide screen. But in this case the screen is so far away that these scintillations cannot be due to the α particles emitted by the radium, since such particles are absorbed in relatively short distances by the gas between the radium source and the screen. He then points out that these scintillation-producing particles have all the properties of fast protons. Still, he does not know whether they were knocked out of the radium C atoms by the α particles or whether they are hydrogen atoms that were attached to the metal surface and then kicked out by the α particles. A hydrogen ion—the atom without its electron—is, of course, a proton.

Since protons knocked out of radium C would represent an entirely new physical phenomenon, Rutherford decided to study these "natural" scintillations in more detail. To do this he decided to vary the amount of gas between his scintillation screen and the radium C source of α particles and also to use various thicknesses of absorbing foils. In this way he could determine the energy (the range) of the scintillation-producing particles and thus get some idea of their character. He began by first evacuating his apparatus as completely as possible and then putting in various quantities of dry oxygen and dry carbon dioxide. In both cases he found, as was expected, that the number of scintillations decreased with increasing concentrations of the two gases. This simply verified that the proton-like particles were more effectively absorbed (that is, were robbed of their kinetic energies) if more gas atoms were introduced. More gas atoms meant more collisions and more collisions meant a greater slowing down of the particle.

Rutherford then repeated the experiment using dry air instead of pure oxygen or carbon dioxide, and obtained a "surprising effect." He found that the introduction of dry air did not diminish the number of scintillations but rather increased this number. The word "surprising" was something of an understatement, for Rutherford was certainly aware of the full significance of these results. He had already shown that oxygen alone decreased the scintillation count so that the increase could only be due to the nitrogen in the dry air. This could only mean that the α particles, in passing through the gas, had collided with nitrogen atoms and had knocked protons out of these atoms.

To check this point Rutherford considered all other possible sources of protons (he refers to them as H atoms—for hydrogen—in this paper) that could have given rise to the observed scintillations, and he demonstrated conclusively that they could have come only from the nuclei of the nitrogen atoms. He still did not know whether these particles were protons or atomic nuclei of mass Z, but in either case he knew that this meant that "the nitrogen atom [nucleus] was disintegrated under the intense forces developed in a close collision with a swift α particle, and that the hydrogen atom which is liberated formed a constituent part of the nitrogen nucleus."

He points out that this conclusion is in agreement with the observed range of the nitrogen atoms after they have been hit by α particles. Since they are less massive than oxygen atoms, nitrogen atoms should travel

19 per cent farther than oxygen atoms suffering similar collisions. But this is not the case; the nitrogen atoms move about as far in air as the oxygen atoms. As Rutherford points out this is exactly what one could expect if the collision energy is divided between the ejected proton and the residual nucleus.

The importance of Rutherford's results for the future of atomic physics was of a twofold nature. First, he demonstrated experimentally that nuclei of atoms contain individual protons. This had already been surmised, but no one had proved it empirically. Second, his experiment showed that nuclei could be disrupted and changed into other nuclei; this was the first example of the artificial transmutation of chemical elements.

Although Rutherford had no idea of the nature of nuclear forces, he set up a simple model (which is close to our modern concept) of the nitrogen nucleus to account for the observations. He suggested that the 14 particles inside the nitrogen nucleus arrange themselves into three α particles and two other particles, one of which is a proton. These two particles are pictured as moving in the outer regions of the nucleus and are therefore easily knocked out by an α particle collision. Since Rutherford knew nothing about neutrons in 1919, he spoke of these two outer particles as "either two hydrogen nuclei or one of mass 2." We now know that one of these particles is a proton and the other is a neutron.

ᴏᴏᴏᴏᴏᴏᴏ

RUTHERFORD

Collision of α Particles with Light Atoms IV. An Anomalous Effect in Nitrogen [1]

IT HAS BEEN SHOWN IN paper I. that a metal source, coated with a deposit of radium C, always gives rise to a number of scintillations on a zinc sulphide screen far beyond the range of the α particles. The swift atoms causing these scintillations carry a positive charge and are deflected by a magnetic field, and have about the same range and energy as the swift H atoms produced by the passage of α particles through hydrogen. These "natural" scintillations are believed to be

---

[1] Sir Ernest Rutherford, *Philosophical Magazine*, 37 (1919), 578–587.

due mainly to swift H atoms from the radioactive source, but it is difficult to decide whether they are expelled from the radioactive source itself or are due to the action of α particles on occluded hydrogen.

COUNTING SCINTILLATIONS

As the systematic counting of H scintillations under varied conditions is a rather difficult and trying task, it may be of some value to mention the general arrangements found most suitable and convenient in practice. Using the excellent zinc sulphide screens, specially prepared by Mr. Glew, the scintillation due to a high-speed H atom appears as a fine brilliant star or point of light, very similar in appearance and intensity to that produced by an alpha particle about 3 mm. from the end of its range. Near the end of the range of the H atom, the scintillation becomes very feeble, and can only be observed on a dark background. Consequently, in a heterogeneous beam of H atoms, the actual number counted per minute is to some extent dependent on the luminosity of the background seen in the microscope. It is important to adjust and keep the luminosity of the screen to the right amount throughout the whole interval of an experiment. This is most simply done by means of a small "pea"-lamp fixed in a metal tube in which the current is varied. While weak scintillations are readily counted on a dark background, it is difficult under such conditions to keep the eye focussed on the microscope image and the eye rapidly becomes fatigued and counting becomes erratic. The microscope employed had a magnification of about 40 and covered a field of 2 mm. diameter. This in practice was found to be a very convenient magnification. In later experiments, special zinc sulphide screens were prepared in which the smaller crystals were sifted through a fine gauze on to a glass plate covered with a thin layer of adhesive material. These fine crystals completely covered the plate several crystals deep. With such a screen, the H scintillations appeared larger and more diffuse, probably due to the scattering of the light in passing through the thick layer of crystals, and were more easily counted, while weak scintillations could be counted on a brighter background than with the ordinary screen. At the same time, the layer of crystals was so uniform, that each incident H atom produced a scintillation.

In these experiments, two workers are required, one to remove the source of radiation and to make experimental adjustments, and the other to do the counting. Before beginning to count, the observer rests his eyes for half an hour in a dark room and should not expose his eyes to any but a weak light during the whole time of counting. The experiments were made in a large darkened room with a small dark chamber attached to which the observer retired when it was necessary to turn on the light

for experimental adjustments. It was found convenient in practice to count
for 1 minute and then rest for an equal interval, the times and data being
recorded by the assistant. As a rule, the eye becomes fatigued after an
hour's counting and the results become erratic and unreliable. It is not
desirable to count for more than 1 hour per day, and preferably only a
few times per week.

Under good conditions, counting experiments are quite reliable from
day to day. Those obtained by my assistant Mr. W. Kay and myself were
always in excellent accord under the most varied conditions. It was usually
arranged that the number of scintillations to be counted varied between
15 and 40 per minute.

EXPERIMENTAL ARRANGEMENT

For experiments with hydrogen and other gases, the active disk D
[Fig. 49–1] was mounted at a convenient height parallel to the screen on a

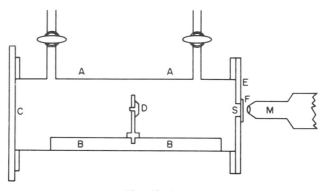

Fig. 49–1.

metal bar B which slid into a rectangular brass box A, 18 cm. long, 6 cm.
deep, and 2 cm. wide, with metal flanges at both ends fitting between
the rectangular poles of a large electromagnet. One end was closed by a
ground glass plate C, and the other by a waxed brass plate E, in the centre
of which was cut a rectangular opening 1 cm. long and 3 mm. wide.
This opening was covered by a thin plate of metals of silver, aluminum or
iron, whose stopping power for α particles lay between 4 and 6 cm. of air.
The zinc sulphide screen F was fixed opposite the opening and distant 1
or 2 mm. from the metal covering. By means of two stopcocks, the vessel was filled with the gas to be examined either by exhaustion or displacement. It is a great advantage to have the zinc sulphide screen outside
the apparatus, in order to avoid contamination due to volatilized active

matter, and for the easy introduction of absorbing material between the end plate and the screen.

In practice, the source was introduced into the brass vessel at a convenient distance from the screen, and the air exhausted. The α rays after traversing the end plate fell on the screen, and the marked luminosity due to them was a guide in fixing the microscope M in the centre of the opening. The diameter of the field of view (2 mm.) was less than the width of the opening (3 mm.).

Since the number of H atoms observed under ordinary conditions is less than one in a hundred thousand of the number of α particles, H atoms, projected in the direction of the α particles, can only be detected when the α rays are stopped by the absorbing screens. It was not found possible to bring an intense source closer than 3 cm. from the screen on account of the luminosity excited in it by the γ rays and swift β rays, which prevented counting of weak scintillations. A strong magnetic field was necessary to bend away the β rays which caused a very marked luminosity on the screen. A field of 6000 gauss was generally employed for this purpose.

The apparatus employed to study these "natural" scintillations is the same as that described in paper I. The intense source of radium C was placed inside a metal box about 3 cm. from the end, and an opening in the end of the box was covered with a silver plate of stopping power equal to about 6 cm. of air. The zinc sulphide screen was mounted outside, about 1 mm. distant from the silver plate, to admit of the introduction of absorbing foils between them. The whole apparatus was placed in a strong magnetic field to deflect the β rays. The variation in the number of these "natural" scintillations with absorption in terms of cms. of air is shown in [Fig. 49–2], curve A. In this case, the air in the box was exhausted and absorbing foils of aluminum were used. When dried oxygen or carbon dioxide was admitted into the vessel, the number of scintillations diminished to about the amount to be expected from the stopping power of the column of gas.

A surprising effect was noticed, however, when dried air was introduced. Instead of diminishing, the number of scintillations was increased, and for an absorption corresponding to about 19 cm. of air the number was about twice that observed when the air was exhausted. It was clear from this experiment that the α particles in their passage through air gave rise to long-range scintillations which appeared to the eye to be about equal in brightness to H scintillations. A systematic series of observations was undertaken to account for the origin of these scintillations. In the first place we have seen that the passage of α particles through nitrogen and oxygen gives rise to numerous bright scintillations which have a range of about 9 cm. in air. These scintillations have about the range to be expected if they are due to swift N or O atoms, carrying unit charge, produced by collision with α particles. All experiments have consequently been made with an absorption greater than 9 cm. of air, so that these atoms are completely stopped before reaching the zinc sulphide screen.

It was found that these long-range scintillations could not be due to the presence of water vapour in the air; for the number was only slightly reduced by thoroughly drying the air. This is to be expected, since on the average the number of the additional scintillations due to air was equivalent to the number of H atoms produced by the mixture of hydrogen at

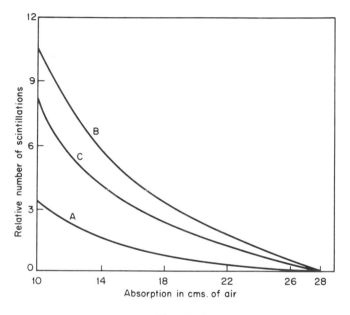

Fig. 49–2.

6 cm. pressure with oxygen. Since on the average the vapour pressure of water in air was not more than 1 cm., the effects of complete drying would not reduce the number by more than one sixth. Even when oxygen and carbon dioxide saturated with water vapour at 20° C. were introduced in place of dry air, the number of scintillations was much less than with dry air.

It is well known that the amount of hydrogen or gases containing hydrogen is normally very small in atmospheric air. No difference was observed whether the air was taken directly from the room or from outside the laboratory or was stored for some days over water.

There was the possibility that the effect in air might be due to liberation of H atoms from the dust nuclei in the air. No appreciable difference, however, was observed when the dried air was filtered through long plugs of cotton-wool, or by storage over water for some days to remove dust nuclei.

Since the anomalous effect was observed in air, but not in oxygen, or carbon dioxide, it must be due either to nitrogen or to one of the other gases present in atmospheric air. The latter possibility was excluded by comparing the effects produced in air and in chemically prepared nitrogen. The nitrogen was obtained by the well-known method of adding ammonium chloride to sodium nitrite, and stored over water. It was carefully dried before admission to the apparatus. With pure nitrogen, the number of long-range scintillations under similar conditions was greater than in air. As a result of careful experiments, the ratio was found to be 1·25, the value to be expected if the scintillations are due to nitrogen.

The results so far obtained show that the long-range scintillations obtained from air must be ascribed to nitrogen, but it is important, in addition, to show that they are due to collision of α particles with atoms of nitrogen through the volume of the gas. In the first place, it was found that the number of the scintillations varied with the pressure of the air in the way to be expected if they resulted from collision of α particles along the column of gas. In addition, when an absorbing screen of gold or aluminium was placed close to the source, the range of the scintillations was found to be reduced by the amount to be expected if the range of the expelled atom was proportional to the range of the colliding α particles. These results show that the scintillations arise from the volume of the gas and are not due to some surface effect in the radioactive source.

In [Fig 49–2] curve A the results of a typical experiment are given showing the variation in the number of natural scintillations with the amount of absorbing matter in their path measured in terms of centimetres of air for α particles. In these experiments carbon dioxide was introduced at a pressure calculated to give the same absorption of the α rays as ordinary air. In curve B the corresponding curve is given when air at N.T.P. is introduced in place of carbon dioxide. The difference curve C shows the corresponding variation of the number of scintillations arising from the nitrogen in the air. It was generally observed that the ratio of the nitrogen effect to the natural effect was somewhat greater for 19 cm. than for 12 cm. absorption.

In order to estimate the magnitude of the effect, the space between the source and screen was filled with carbon dioxide at diminished pressure and a known pressure of hydrogen was added. The pressure of the carbon dioxide and of hydrogen were adjusted so that the total absorption of α particles in the mixed gas should be equal to that of the air. In this way it was found that the curve of absorption of H atoms produced under these conditions was somewhat steeper than curve C of [Fig. 49–2]. As a consequence, the amount of hydrogen mixed with carbon dioxide required to produce a number of scintillations equal to that of air, increased with the increase of absorption. For example, the effect in air was equal to about 4 cm. of hydrogen at 12 cm. absorption, and about 8 cm. at 19 cm. absorption. For a mean value of the absorption, the effect was equal to about 6 cm. of hydrogen. This increased absorption of H atoms under similar conditions indicated either that (1) the swift atoms from air had a somewhat greater range than the H atoms, or (2) that the atoms from air were projected more in the line of flight of the α particles.

While the maximum range of the scintillations from air using radium C as a source of α rays appeared to be about the same, viz. 28 cm., as for H atoms produced from hydrogen, it was difficult to fix the end of the range with certainty on account of the smallness of the number and the weakness of the scintillations. Some special experiments were made to test whether, under favourable conditions, any scintillations due to nitrogen could be observed beyond 28 cm. of air absorption. For this purpose a strong source (about 60 mg. Ra activity) was brought within 2·5 cm. of the zinc sulphide screen, the space between containing dry air. On still further reducing the distance, the screen became too bright to detect very feeble scintillations. No certain evidence of scintillations was found beyond a range of 28 cm. It would therefore appear that (2) above is the more probable explanation.

In a previous paper (III.) we have seen that the number of swift atoms of nitrogen or oxygen produced per unit path by collision with α particles is about the same as the corresponding number of H atoms in hydrogen. Since the number of long-range scintillations in air is equivalent to that produced under similar conditions in a column of hydrogen at 6 cm. pressure, we may consequently conclude that only one long-range atom is produced for every 12 close collisions giving rise to a swift nitrogen atom of maximum range 9 cm.

It is of interest to give data showing the number of long-range scintillations produced in nitrogen at atmospheric pressure under definite conditions. For a column of nitrogen 3·3 cm. long, and for a total absorption of 19 cm. of air from the source, the number due to nitrogen per milligram of activity is ·6 per minute on a screen of 3·14 sq. mm. area.

Both as regards range and brightness of scintillations, the long-range atoms from nitrogen closely resemble H atoms, and in all probability are hydrogen atoms. In order, however, to settle this important point definitely, it is necessary to determine the deflexion of these atoms in a magnetic field. Some preliminary experiments have been made by a method similar to that employed in measuring the velocity of the H atom. The main difficulty is to obtain a sufficiently large deflexion of the stream of atoms and yet have a sufficient number of scintillations per minute for counting. The α rays from a strong source passed through dry air between two parallel horizontal plates 3 cm. long and 1·6 mm. apart, and the number of scintillations on the screen placed near the end of the plates was observed for different strengths of the magnetic field. Under these conditions, when the scintillations arise from the whole length of the column of air between the plates, the strongest magnetic field available reduced the number of scintillations by only 30 per cent. When the air was replaced by a mixture of carbon dioxide and hydrogen of the same stopping power for α rays, about an equal reduction was noted. As far as the experiment goes, this is an indication that the scintillations are due to H atoms; but the actual number of scintillations and the amount of reduction was too small to place much reliance on the result. In order to settle this question definitely, it will probably prove necessary to employ a solid nitrogen compound, free from hydrogen, as a source, and to use much stronger sources of α rays. In such experiments, it will be of importance to discriminate between the deflexions due to H atoms and possible atoms of atomic weight 2. From the calculations given in paper III., it is seen that a collision of an α particle with a free atom of mass 2 should give rise to an atom of range about 32 cm. in air, and of initial energy about ·89 of that of the H atom produced under similar conditions. The deflexion of the pencil of these rays in a magnetic field should be about ·6 of that shown by a corresponding pencil of H atoms.

DISCUSSION OF RESULTS

From the results so far obtained it is difficult to avoid the conclusion that the long-range atoms arising from collision of α particles with nitrogen are not nitrogen atoms but probably atoms of hydrogen, or atoms of mass 2. If this be the case, we must conclude that the nitrogen atom is disintegrated under the intense forces developed in a close collision with a swift α particle, and that the hydrogen atom which is liberated formed a constituent part of the nitrogen nucleus. We have drawn attention in paper III. to the rather surprising observation that the range of the nitrogen atoms in air is about the same as the oxygen atoms, although we should expect a difference of about 19 per cent. If in collisions which give rise to swift nitrogen atoms, the hydrogen is at the same time disrupted, such a difference might be accounted for, for the energy is then shared between two systems.

It is of interest to note, that while the majority of the light atoms, as is well known, have atomic weights represented by $4n$ or $4n+3$ where n is a whole number, nitrogen is the only atom which is expressed by $4n+2$. We should anticipate from radioactive data that the nitrogen nucleus consists of three helium nuclei each of atomic mass 4 and either

two hydrogen nuclei or one of mass 2. If the H nuclei were outriders of
the main system of mass 12, the number of close collisions with the bound
H nuclei would be less than if the latter were free, for the α particle in a
collision comes under the combined field of the H nucleus and of the central mass. Under such conditions, it is to be expected that the α particle
would only occasionally approach close enough to the H nucleus to give
it the maximum velocity, although in many cases it may give it sufficient
energy to break its bond with the central mass. Such a point of view would
explain why the number of swift H atoms from nitrogen is less than the
corresponding number in free hydrogen and less also than the number of
swift nitrogen atoms. The general results indicate that the H nuclei, which
are released, are distant about twice the diameter of the electron ($7 \times$
10^{-13} cm.) from the centre of the main atom. Without a knowledge
of the laws of force at such small distances, it is difficult to estimate the
energy required to free the H nucleus or to calculate the maximum velocity
that can be given to the escaping H atom. It is not to be expected, *a priori,*
that the velocity or range of the H atom released from the nitrogen atom
should be identical with that due to a collision in free hydrogen.

Taking into account the great energy of motion of the α particle expelled from radium C, the close collision of such an α particle with a light
atom seems to be the most likely agency to promote the disruption of the
latter; for the forces on the nuclei arising from such collisions appear to
be greater than can be produced by any other agency at present available.
Considering the enormous intensity of the forces brought into play, it is
not so much a matter of surprise that the nitrogen atom should suffer disintegration as that the α particle itself escapes disruption into its constituents. The results as a whole suggest that, if α particles—or similar
projectiles—of still greater energy were available for experiment, we might
expect to break down the nucleus structure of many of the lighter atoms.

I desire to express my thanks to Mr. William Kay for his invaluable
assistance in counting scintillations.

50

ooooooooooo

THE DIVERSITY OF ATOMS

ooooooooooo

Francis William Aston (1877-1945)

Soddy's discovery of isotopes through research in the radiochemical elements about the year 1910, and their demonstration in the next three years, must have suggested to more than one investigator that such atoms should be sought in the stable elements. However, the way such a search might be started was by no means clear, and it remained for J. J. Thomson with his positive ray apparatus to open the doors for such investigations in 1912. As we have already seen, Thomson analyzed a sample of very pure neon, and his apparatus showed that atoms of mass 20 and 22 were present in the gas. The possibility that the atoms of mass 22 found in the positive rays might be NeH_2 prompted Thomson to put F. W. Aston, his assistant, to work on the diffusion separation of the gas. After most laborious efforts, Aston achieved what appeared to be a significant separation of fractions of differing mass, but the advent of World War I prevented further research on the problem.

During the war Aston was assigned to the Royal Aircraft Establishment at Farnborough and toward the latter part of the war conceived the idea of extending the isotope study by developing a mass spectrograph as an improvement of Thomson's parabola method. The spectrograph that he designed was built at Cambridge in 1919 following his return to the laboratory and the details are presented in his paper which follows, together with photographs of the mass spectra obtained with its use. Neon was the first element examined and its isotopy was immediately revealed; atomic masses of 20 and 22 (on the scale $0 = 16$) were clearly present, the precision of the mass numbers being estimated at one-tenth per cent.

This spectrograph was used to analyze some fifty elements in the following six years, revealing the almost universal existence of isotopes.

817

Exceptions appeared in the elements of odd atomic number, the great majority of these having no isotopes; i.e., atoms of one mass only were present. Aston assumed that the most important result of the research was the discovery that the measured mass of all the atoms, except hydrogen, was integral on the basis $0 = 16$. This was called the whole number rule. But a second and subsequently a third mass spectrograph of increasing precision showed that this was not substantiated by more precise measurements. Aston's research thus showed that Prout's hypothesis, made more than a hundred years previously and intermittently revived, was untenable. The addition of masses, equal to that of hydrogen, did not give the masses of the succeeding elements in the periodic table. It was also clear that the elements were *not* built up, as the whole number rule suggested, of mass units equal to one-sixteenth of the oxygen atom.

On the other hand, to Prout's credit, the existence of the nuclear atom made it appear that all the elements were made up of protons and electrons, the elemental building material of hydrogen atoms. But even from this point of view it was evident that the masses of the elements were not arrived at by the simple addition of the masses of the protons and electrons of which they were apparently composed. The elemental masses as measured by the spectrograph showed a "mass defect" as compared to the sum of the masses of their free constituent particles. This defect in mass was explained, on the basis of Einstein's mass-energy equation $E = mc^2$, as representing the energy that was radiated away in the formation of the nucleus. It was therefore the "binding energy" of the particles in the nucleus, and the greater the mass defect the more stable the nucleus. The further clarification of this point of view had to await the advent of experimental nuclear physics in the 1930's and the discovery of the neutron. These subjects will be presented in later chapters.

It is convenient at this point to summarize the nomenclature brought into physics by these advances in the measurement of atomic masses. The *atomic number* was defined as the number of (integral) elementary nuclear positive charges; the *mass number* was taken as the nearest whole number to the mass of the isotope considered (later it was taken to be the number of protons and neutrons in the nucleus). The *mass* of the isotope was its mass on the scale $0 = 16$, although this subsequently had to be changed owing to the discovery that oxygen itself had isotopes. The reference atom was then changed to a comparison of masses on the basis that the most prevalent isotope of oxygen was of mass 16. In order to convey an idea of the stability of nuclei, Aston later introduced a quantity called the "packing fraction," defined as the ratio of the mass defect to the mass number. Further use of these quantities will appear in later papers. Before closing this commentary it must be pointed out that the importance of determining the isotopic constitution of the elements and the individual isotopic masses drew many able investigators to this field and resulted in the invention of several different mass spectrometers. For details regarding the outstanding investigators and their instruments the reader should consult the indexes of the various physical journals.

Until he came to Cambridge, Aston had a rather varied career. The son of a metal merchant, he was born in a suburb of Birmingham, England, and as a youth displayed a strong bent for experimenting with mechanical devices and with chemicals. He graduated from secondary school with highest honors in mathematics and science and entered Mason College, later the University of Birmingham, in 1893. His chemistry teachers at Birmingham were Tilden and Frankland and in physics he studied under J. H. Poynting. With Frankland he worked on problems in organic chemistry, publishing his first paper in 1901. By no means was all of his work done in university laboratories, for in 1896 he fitted up a loft at his home as a private laboratory and workshop and here he carried on private research for many years. In 1900 he entered the employ of a brewing company and continued in industrial work until 1905 when he returned to university work on a scholarship. In 1908, on the death of his father, he took a year off to make a trip around the world. On his return he continued working on glass discharge tubes and on vacuum apparatus to exhaust them, including an automatic Toepler-type pump of his own construction. His outstanding skill in this field led in 1910 to his association with J. J. Thomson at Cambridge as a research assistant. He was soon engaged with Thomson on the development of the latter's positive-ray apparatus and on the diffusion separation of neon in 1913.

After service in World War I, he returned to Cambridge to work independently on his mass spectrograph. He was made a fellow of Trinity College, Cambridge, in 1919 and maintained his residence in the college for the remainder of his life. By 1922 his isotope work was deemed to be so outstanding that he was awarded the Nobel Prize in chemistry. As time went on, other able investigators entered this field, but Aston continued his investigations, increasing the precision of his work.

In his mature years Aston was a quiet, reserved man; above average height, he had an erect carriage. He was a strong individualist and maintained from his youth the conservative views characteristic of a middle-class upbringing in the late Victorian period. He was fond of travel and sports, and his interest in and knowledge of music was so extensive that he served for many years as the music critic of the *Cambridge Review*. In finance, he was also unusually able, so that toward the end of his life he had amassed considerable means. His biographer for the Royal Society summed up his life, perhaps most aptly, with the phrase: "Aston's life was a chain of uninterrupted success."

ooooooo

ASTON

Positive Rays and Isotopes [1]

IN THE ATOMIC THEORY PUT forward by John Dalton
in 1801 the second postulate was: "Atoms of the same element are
similar to one another and equal in weight." For more than a century this
was regarded by chemists and physicists alike as an article of scientific
faith. The only item among the immense quantities of knowledge acquired
during that productive period which offered the faintest suggestion against
its validity was the inexplicable mixture of order and disorder among the
elementary atomic weights. The general state of opinion at the end of
last century may be gathered from the two following quotations from Sir
William Ramsay's address to the British Association at Toronto in
1897:—

"There have been almost innumerable attempts to reduce the differences
between atomic weights to regularity by contriving some formula which
will express the numbers which represent the atomic weights with all their
irregularities. Needless to say, such attempts have in no case been successful. Apparent success is always attained at the expense of accuracy,
and the numbers reproduced are not those accepted as the true atomic
weights. Such attempts, in my opinion, are futile. Still, the human mind
does not rest contented in merely chronicling such an irregularity; it
strives to understand why such an irregularity should exist. . . . The
idea . . . has been advanced by Prof. Schutzenburger, and later by Mr
Crookes, that what we term the atomic weight of an element is a mean;
that when we say the atomic weight of oxygen is 16, we merely state that
the average atomic weight is 16; and it is not inconceivable that a certain
number of molecules have a weight somewhat higher than 32, while a
certain number have a lower weight."

This idea was placed on an altogether different footing some ten years
later by the work of Sir Ernest Rutherford and his colleagues on radioactive transformations. The results of these led inevitably to the conclusion

---

[1] Francis W. Aston, *Nature,* 105 (1920), 617–619.

that there must exist elements which have chemical properties identical for all practical purposes, but the atoms of which have different weights. This conclusion has been recently confirmed in a most convincing manner by the production in quantity of specimens of lead from radio-active and other sources, which, though perfectly pure and chemically indistinguishable, give atomic weights differing by amounts quite outside the possible experimental error. Elements differing in mass but chemically identical and therefore occupying the same position in the periodic table have been called "isotopes" by Prof. Soddy.

At about the same period as the theory of isotopes was being developed by the radio chemists at the heavy end of the periodic table an extremely interesting discovery was made by Sir J. J. Thomson, which carried the attack into the region of the lighter and non-radio-active elements. This was that, when positive rays from gases containing the element neon were analysed by electric and magnetic fields, results were obtained which indicated atomic weights roughly 20 and 22 respectively, the accepted atomic weight being 20·2. This naturally led to the expectation that neon might be a mixture of isotopes, but the weight 22 might possibly be due to other causes, and the method of analysis did not give sufficient accuracy to distinguish between 20·0 and 20·2 with certainty. Attempts were made to effect partial separation first by fractionation over charcoal cooled in liquid air, the results of which were absolutely negative, and then by diffusion, which in 1913 gave positive results, an apparent change in density of 0·7 per cent. between the lightest and heaviest fractions being attained after many thousands of operations. When the war interrupted the research, it might be said that several independent lines of reasoning pointed to the idea that neon was a mixture of isotopes, but that none of them could be said to carry the conviction necessary in such an important development.

By the time work was started again the isotope theory had been generally accepted so far as the radio-active elements were concerned, and a good deal of theoretical speculation had been made as to its applicability to the elements generally. As separation by diffusion is at the best extremely slow and laborious, attention was again turned to positive rays in the hope of increasing the accuracy of measurements to the required degree. This was done by means of the arrangement illustrated in [Fig. 50–1]. Positive rays are sorted into an extremely thin ribbon by means of parallel slits S_1S_2, and are then spread into an electric spectrum by means of the charged plates P_1P_2. A portion of this spectrum deflected through an angle θ is selected by the diaphragm D and passed between the circular poles of a powerful electromagnet O the field of which is such as to bend the rays back again through an angle ϕ more than twice as great as θ. The result of this is that rays having a constant mass (or more correctly constant m/e) will converge to a focus F, and that if a photographic plate is

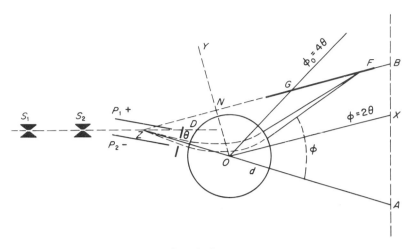

Fig. 50–1.

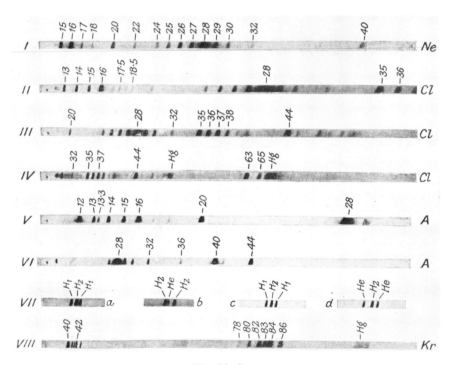

Fig. 50–2.

placed at *GF* as indicated, a *spectrum dependent on mass alone* will be obtained. On account of its analogy to optical apparatus, the instrument has been called a positive-ray spectrograph and the spectrum produced a mass-spectrum.

[Fig. 50–2] shows a number of typical mass-spectra obtained by this means. The number above the lines indicates the masses they correspond to on the scale $O = 16$. It will be noticed that the displacement to the right with increasing mass is roughly linear. The measurements of mass made are not absolute, but relative to lines the mass of which is known. Such lines, due to hydrogen, carbon, oxygen, and their compounds, are generally present as impurities or purposely added, for pure gases are not suitable for the smooth working of the discharge tube. The two principal groups of these reference lines are the C_1 group due to C (12), CH (13), CH_2 (14), CH_3 (15), CH_4 or O (16), and the C_2 group 24–30 containing the very strong line 28, C_2H_4 or CO. In spectrum i. the presence of neon is indicated by the lines 20 and 22 situated between these groups. Comparative measurements show that these lines are $20 \cdot 00$, $22 \cdot 00$ with an accuracy of one-tenth per cent., which removes the last doubt as to the isotopic nature of neon.

The next element investigated was chlorine; this is characterised by four strong lines 35, 36, 37, 38, and fainter ones at 39, 40; there is no trace of a line at $35 \cdot 46$, the accepted atomic weight. From reasoning which cannot be given here in detail it seems certain that chlorine is a complex element, and consists of isotopes of atomic weights 35 and 37, with possibly another at 39. The lines at 36, 38 are due to the corresponding HCl's.

Particles with two, three, or more electronic charges will appear as though having half, a third, etc., their real mass. The corresponding lines are called lines of the second, third, or higher order. In spectrum ii. the lines of doubly charged chlorine atoms appear at $17 \cdot 5$ and $18 \cdot 5$. Analyses of argon indicate that this element consists almost entirely of atoms of weight 40, but a faint component 36 is also visible. Spectra v. and vi. are taken with this gas present; the former shows the interesting third order line at $13\frac{1}{2}$. Krypton and xenon give surprisingly complex results; the former is found to consist of no fewer than six isotopes, the latter of five (spectra viii. and ix.). Mercury is certainly a complex element probably composed of five or six isotopes, two of which have atomic weights 202 and 204; its multiply charged atoms give the imperfectly resolved groups, which are indicated in several of the spectra reproduced in [Fig. 50–2].

By far the most important result obtained from this work is the generalisation that, with the exception of hydrogen, all the atomic weights of all elements so far measured are exactly whole numbers on the scale $O = 16$ to the accuracy of experiment (1 in 1000). By means of a special method, some results of which are given in spectrum vii., hydrogen is found to be 1·008, which agrees with the value accepted by chemists. This exception from the whole number rule is not unexpected, as on the Rutherford "nucleus" theory the hydrogen atom is the only one not containing any negative electricity in its nucleus.

The results which have so far been obtained with eighteen elements make it highly probable that the higher the atomic weight of an element, the more complex it is likely to be, and that there are more complex elements than simple. It must be noticed that, though the whole number rule asserts that a pure element must have a whole number atomic weight, there is no reason to suppose that all elements having atomic weights closely approximating to integers are therefore pure.

The very large number of different molecules possible when mixed elements combine to form compounds would appear to make their theoretical chemistry almost hopelessly complicated, but if, as seems likely, the separation of isotopes on any reasonable scale is to all intents impossible, their practical chemistry will not be affected, while the whole number rule introduces a very desirable simplification into the theoretical aspects of mass.

X-RAYS AND THEIR CONTRIBUTION TO THE RIDDLE OF MATTER

oooooooooo

51

○○○○○○○○○○

INTERFERENCE PHENOMENA

○○○○○○○○○○

Max von Laue (1879-1960)

Walter Friedrich (b. 1883)

Paul Knipping (1883-1935)

Max von Laue, like Max Born, is one of the few remaining great physicists whose lives have spanned the period from the inception of the quantum and relativity theories up to the present time; and, like Max Born, he has contributed extensively to the development of modern physics.

He was born on October 9, 1879, in the small village Pfaffendorf b. Koblenz (Rhein) and spent his childhood and early manhood there. After completing his gymnasium studies, he entered the University of Strassburg to study mathematics and physics and then went on to Göttingen, Munich, and finally Berlin, where he obtained his Ph.D. in theoretical physics in 1903.

Immediately after obtaining his doctorate, he began one of the most productive research careers in the history of modern physics. Although his contributions to physics are to be found in all branches of the subject, he devoted most of his creative efforts to physical optics, thermodynamics, and relativity theory. He was one of the first to recognize the great importance of Einstein's work, and his book on the theory of relativity is still one of the best on this subject.

His great interest in physical optics led him to the general problem of the interference of light, and, when X-rays were discovered, he quite

827

naturally turned his attention to the interference of X-rays, and he immediately became involved in controversy as to the nature of these rays. It was clear to him that, if X-rays were, indeed, electromagnetic waves, they would have to be of much shorter wavelength than that of visible light, since X-rays could not be refracted or diffracted the way visible light is.

He therefore reasoned that if one could obtain a diffraction grating with the lines spaced much closer together than in an ordinary optical grating, one should observe X-ray diffraction. This led him to the idea of using the atoms forming the lattice structure of a crystal as a diffraction grating. After working out of the theory for this type of diffraction, Laue had Friedrich and Knipping perform the experiment—with results that completely supported the theory. Laue received the Nobel Prize in physics for this work in 1914.

Aside from his work on the diffraction of X-rays, von Laue has made important contributions to the field of physical optics, crystallography, electromagnetic theory, relativity theory, superconductivity, solid state theory, and atomic theory. His more than one-hundred-and-thirty original papers have appeared in the most important physical journals in the world. In addition to his research papers, he has written numerous articles on the historical aspects of physics, with special emphasis on the roles of individual physicists in the development of physics.

While he was doing his trail blazing work on the theory of X-ray diffraction, he was assistant professor of theoretical physics at the University of Munich. He left Munich in 1914 to take the chair of theoretical physics at the University of Frankfurt, where he remained until 1919, when he was invited to become professor of theoretical physics at the University of Berlin. At the same time, he was director of the Kaiser Wilhelm Institute of Physics in Berlin, where he remained until 1943. He then went on to the Max Planck Institute of Physics in Göttingen and, in 1957, became director of the Kaiser Wilhelm Institute for Physics, Chemistry and Electrochemistry. In 1953, he became director of the Fritz Haber Institute of the Max Planck Society of Berlin-Dahlem.

Besides the Nobel Prize, von Laue has been awarded the 1932 Max Planck Medal and the 1950 Gold Medal of the Indian Association for the Cultivation of Science.

After X-rays had been discovered by Roentgen in 1895, a considerable controversy arose as to their nature. That they were not deflected in an electric or magnetic field was no clear proof that they were not particles, for they might very well have been neutral particles of some sort and thus unresponsive to electromagnetic forces. It was never evident that they were electromagnetic waves, since it was very difficult to observe their wave properties; as we now know, their wavelengths are very short. Nevertheless by 1911 more and more evidence had been accumulated in favor of the electromagnetic-wave thesis. Thus the experiments of C. G. Barkla in 1911 demonstrated that X-rays are scattered from small particles in suspension (droplets of water in a cloud, or dust particles) the way light is scattered in a dusty medium. Moreover, Barkla also showed that X-rays can excite atoms in a body to emit fluorescence radiation.

Both of these phenomena convinced Max von Laue that X-rays are electromagnetic waves, but of such short wavelength that their wave character would be very difficult to establish by the usual interference and diffraction experiments. That the X-ray waves are electromagnetic in character was clear to Laue because they can set atoms, which consist of electrical charges, vibrating. Here then was a challenge to Laue to devise some method of demonstrating the interference of X-ray waves.

To appreciate the difficulty of the problem, we must understand that observable interference between waves can occur only if the dimensions of the particles, apertures, or other sources of the interference are not very much larger than the wavelength of the waves themselves. Thus, light waves can be made to interfere and give observable interference patterns by having them pass through two small holes that are very close together. In the same way, light reflected from a surface of very many closely spaced parallel lines—the diffraction grating—gives an interference or a diffraction pattern. Anyone can easily see such a pattern by allowing light to glance off a long-playing record, since the surface grooves are close together. Since the wavelength of ordinary white light is about one fifty-thousandth of an inch, one must have a few thousand lines per inch on a diffraction grating to obtain good results. But such a diffraction grating is much too coarse for X-rays, which have wavelengths 100 to 1000 times smaller than ordinary light.

Laue, therefore, introduced a very ingenious idea: to use the regular array of the atoms in the lattice structure of a crystal as the grating. This idea goes back to Bravais, who suggested in 1850 that a crystal is a regular lattice structure with the atoms occupying the lattice points of the crystal. The difference, however, between a crystal lattice structure and an ordinary surface grating is that the former is a space lattice, and hence three-dimensional, whereas the latter is a two-dimensional pattern. But aside from the difference in complexity, the problem of the interference of waves scattered from these two types of gratings is the same. Moreover, since the distance between two neighboring atoms in a crystal is about one-hundred-millionth of a centimeter, the geometrical situation is desirable for X-rays, which have wavelengths of the same order of magnitude.

The theoretical analysis of the interference of X-rays scattered from a crystal, as given by Laue, is in essence quite simple and straightforward. Since the atoms in a crystal are arranged symmetrically, one can picture the crystal as consisting of elementary patterns or cells that are repeated over and over again like the pattern in wallpaper or floor coverings. Such a fundamental cell is defined by three vectors (in Laue's paper the vectors A_1, A_2, A_3) starting from a point of reference. The position of any atom in the crystal, relative to this reference point, can be calculated by doubling, tripling, quadrupling, and so on, these vectors (that is, laying off these vectors one after the other) until we arrive at the atom in question. This is like reaching any corner in a city in which the streets are laid out in a regular pattern. We can always get to any corner by following one street after another. This is the content of equation (1) of Laue's paper.

Suppose now that an atom in a crystal is set vibrating by incident X-rays. This atom, then, sends out waves of its own in various directions. What does a wave of this sort look like, at a great distance from the atom? There is first the amplitude of vibration of the wave. This is what Laue calls ψ in equation (2). But this amplitude must be diminished by the factor r [shown in the denominator of equation (2)] because the wave gets weaker and weaker as we go farther and farther away from the source, that is, the atom. The reason for this is that the wave spreads out like the surface of a spherical balloon that is being blown up. Finally, a factor must be included to show that the amplitude of the wave at a given point oscillates with a definite frequency, or, put differently, that if we move a distance λ (the wavelength) along the wave (assuming for the moment that the wave is fixed in space), the amplitude changes from a maximum to a minimum and back again to a maximum. This is the exponential factor e^{-ikr} where i is the square root of -1 and k is proportional to the reciprocal of the wavelength.

If we put these three factors together, we get Laue's equation (2), which gives the wave emitted by a single atom. To find the total effect, at a point, of all the atoms that are oscillating and emitting waves together, we must sum all these contributions taking into account that each atom is at a different distance from this point. However, before doing this Laue took one more thing into account: at any point there is present not only the electromagnetic field of the waves coming from the excited atoms, but also the field of the waves that excite the atoms. In other words, while waves emitted by the crystal are moving away from the crystal, there are at the same time waves moving toward the crystal; both of these contribute to the electromagnetic field intensity. The field conditions at a point are thus the result of outgoing spherical waves and an incoming plane wave which Laue represents at the point r by the exponential factor $e^{-ik(x\alpha_0 + y\beta_0 + z\gamma_0)}$ where $(\alpha_0, \beta_0, \gamma_0)$ give the direction of propagation of the incoming wave and x, y, z are the coordinates of the point. This factor must therefore also be included, and then the sum of this expression must be taken over all atoms in the crystal. This is the content of expression (3) in Max von Laue's work. Here the Greek letter Σ stands for sum.

To evaluate this sum Laue makes a few simplifying assumptions: essentially that the distance between any two atoms in the crystal is small compared to the distance of any atom from the distant point r, and obtains the expression (6), which is the crucial result of the paper. It gives the field intensity at a particular point and shows (because of the sine functions in the denominator, which vary periodically from 0 to 1) that in a particular plane perpendicular to the direction of the incident ray and at the distance r from the crystal the intensity varies from point to point. A photographic plate, made to coincide with this plane would therefore show a pattern of dark spots if X-rays are, indeed, waves.

This pattern is called an X-ray diffraction pattern; from its geometry one can not only calculate the wavelength of the X-rays but also find out a great deal about the structure of the crystal.

The second part of this paper is devoted to the experimental verification of Laue's analysis for which he won the Nobel Prize in 1914. Laue suggested to W. Friedrich and P. Knipping that they try to obtain a diffraction pattern by actually scattering X-rays from specific crystals. Following this suggestion, Friedrich and Knipping carried out the experiment described in the second half of the paper we have reproduced here.

The experimental arrangement was extremely simple. The rays from an X-ray tube were limited to a thin bundle by a series of small diaphragms arranged along a line, and the crystal that was to be investigated was set up on a rotatable table. The orientations of the crystal with respect to the X-rays were carefully measured with a telescope and photographic plates were placed around the crystal to intercept the scattered X-rays.

Just as Laue had predicted, Friedrich and Knipping found regular diffraction patterns on the photographic plates, indicating, first, that X-rays have wave properties and showing, second, that crystals do have a regular lattice structure.

Laue's theory, and the work of Friedrich and Knipping in verifying it, opened up vast new areas of research both on the structure of matter and on the properties of short-wavelength electromagnetic waves. A direct outgrowth was the trail-blazing work of Sir William Henry Bragg and his son in the use of X-ray diffraction patterns in the analysis of crystal structure.

ᴏᴏᴏᴏᴏᴏᴏ

F R I E D R I C H,   K N I P P I N G,   and   L A U E

Interference Phenomena for X-Rays [1]

T H E O R E T I C A L   P A R T   (M.   L A U E)

Introduction

Barkla in recent years has shown that X-rays suffer a scattering in passing through matter quite similar to the scattering of light in a cloudy medium, but that, in addition to this, these rays stimulate the atoms of the matter to emit a spectrally homogeneous characteristic radiation (fluorescence radiation) that is exclusively characteristic of the body.

On the other hand, Bravais in 1850 introduced into crystallography the theory that the atoms in a crystal are arranged in a space lattice. If the X-rays are truly electromagnetic waves, one would surmise that the space lattice structure, as a result of the excitation of the atoms by free or forced vibrations, would give rise to interference effects; interference phenomena similar in nature to those obtained in optics with a grating. The constants of this space lattice can be derived easily from the molecular weight of the crystal, its density, the number of molecules per gram mole, and the crystallographics data. We always find that they are of the order of 10^{-8} cm, while the wavelengths of the X-rays are of the order of 10^{-9} cm, as measured in diffraction experiments by Walter and Pohl and in accordance with the work of Sommerfeld and Koch. It is, of course, to be expected that the situation here will be considerably more complex than for a one- or two-dimensional grating because of the threefold periodicity of a space lattice.

The Messrs Friedrich and Knipping at my suggestion have demonstrated experimentally the correctness of my conjecture.

The Theory and Its Qualitative Comparison with Observations

We wish to formulate the above ideas mathematically. Let the rectangular coordinates of the mid-point of any atom be x,y,z relative to the origin of the coordinate system taken at the mid-point of one particular

---

[1] W. Friedrich, P. Knipping, and M. von Laue, trans. Editors, *Sitzungsberichte d. Bayer. (Akademie der Wissenschaften,* 1912), 303–322.

atom. Let the space lattice of the crystal be of the most general kind: of the triclinic type, where the length of the sides of an elementary parallelepiped may be arbitrary and the angles they make with each other are arbitrary. By special choice of these lengths and angles we can always obtain other kinds of space lattices. If the lengths and directions of the three edges of a parallelepiped are given by the vectors A_1, A_2, A_3, the mid-point of any atom is given by

$$x = MA_{1x} + NA_{2x} + PA_{3x}$$
$$y = MA_{1y} + NA_{2y} + PA_{3y} \qquad (1)$$
$$z = MA_{1z} + NA_{2z} + PA_{3z}$$

where *m, n, p* are negative or positive integers that specify the atom.

We assume that a single atom vibrates in a pure sinusoidal way (simple harmonic motion). This does not apply rigorously here any more than it does in optics. But just as in optics, we can here also represent inhomogeneous radiation spectrally as a sum of pure harmonic (sinusoidal) vibrations by means of a Fourier analysis. A wave diverging from an atom can then be represented at a great distance as

$$\psi \frac{e^{-ikr}}{r} \qquad (2)$$

where r is the distance from the atom, ψ is a function of the direction from the atom and $k = \dfrac{2\pi}{\lambda}$, where λ is the wavelength of the X-rays that subsequently interfere. If the atom, as is usually the case in optics, is small compared to λ, ψ is a constant. Here, however, we must contend with the possibility, and experiments seem to support this conjecture, that because the dimensions of the atom are comparable to the wavelength, variations with directions occur. If we now take into account that the waves are propagated with the speed of light we see that we must include the factor $e^{-ik(x\alpha_0 + y\beta_0 + z\gamma_0)}$ where α_0, β_0, and γ_0 are the direction cosines of the incident primary X-radiation. Regardless of the detailed features of the incident radiation and how the individual atoms vibrate, we obtain by superposition of all elementary waves

$$\sum \psi \frac{e^{-ik(r + x\alpha_0 + y\beta_0 + z\gamma_0)}}{r}. \qquad (3)$$

We calculate this sum only for points whose distances are very large compared to the dimensions of the irradiated section of the crystal and we further introduce the approximation, usual in lattice theory, that the denominator in (3), the distance r of the point from the scattering atom, may be replaced by R, its distance from the origin of coordinates, and we assign to ψ the value corresponding to the direction (α, β, γ) of R. However, for r in the exponent we introduce the approximate value

$$r = R - (r\alpha + r\beta + r\gamma).$$

If we take into account (1) the sum (3) becomes

$$\psi(\alpha, \beta, \gamma) \frac{e^{-ikR}}{R} \sum e^{ik[x(\alpha - \alpha_0) + y(\beta - \beta_0) + z(\gamma - \gamma_0)]}$$

$$= \psi(\alpha, \beta, \gamma) e^{\frac{-ikr}{R}} \sum_{M, N, P} e^{i(MA + NB + PC)} \tag{4}$$

Where

$$A = k[A_{1x}(\alpha - \alpha_0) + A_{1y}(\beta - \beta_0) + A_{1z}(\gamma - \gamma_0)] \text{ etc.} \tag{5}$$

Let the irradiated part of the crystal be bounded by planes which are parallel to the surfaces of the elementary parallelepiped. Then the summation over M extends from some integer $-M$ to $+M$, over N from $-N$ to $+N$, and over P from $-P$ to $+P$. The positions of the intensity maxima are independent of this assumption. The intensity of the vibration (4) is then given by

$$\frac{|\psi(\alpha, \beta, \gamma)|^2}{R^2} \frac{\sin^2 MA}{\sin^2 \frac{1}{2}A} \frac{\sin^2 NB}{\sin^2 \frac{1}{2}B} \frac{\sin^2 PC}{\sin^2 \frac{1}{2}C} \tag{6}$$

Each of these sine quotients has a maximum value when its denominator vanishes. The conditions for these maxima are

$$A = 2\pi h_1$$

that is

$$A_{1x}\alpha + A_{1y}\beta + A_{1z}\gamma = h_1\lambda + A_{1x}\alpha_0 + A_{1y}\beta_0 + A_{1z}\gamma_0, \text{ etc.} \tag{7}$$

[Here Laue considers certain of the geometrical properties of the scattered beam and obtains the interference conditions—Editors.]

We consider these relations [that is, (7)] more closely for irradiation of a regular crystal in one of the directions A_1, A_2, A_3.

In this case the three edges have the same length A and are mutually perpendicular so that we may take these as our coordinate axes.

Equations (7) then become

$$\alpha = h_1 \frac{\lambda}{A}, \beta = h_2 \frac{\lambda}{A}, 1 - \gamma = h_3 \frac{\lambda}{A} \tag{8}$$

On a plate perpendicular to the incident ray the curves $\alpha = $ constant and $\beta = $ constant are hyperbolas whose mid-point coincides with the point of intersection of the primary ray. If only the first two conditions of (8) are fulfilled, we see the well-known cross-grating spectrum in which the intensity is a maximum at every point of intersection of two hyperbolas. But the circles $\gamma = $ constant whose centers also coincide with the point of intersection of the primary ray pick out only those of the crossed-grating spectra which lie sufficiently close to one of these circles; that is, we observe these circles on this plate not as complete circumferences but only as distinct points. The circles

$$1 - \gamma = h_3 \frac{\lambda}{A} \tag{9}$$

which arise because of the periodicity of the crystal in the direction of the radiation have their counterparts in optics in the rings, observed since Newton, in diffraction phenomena from dust particles scattered on a strongly reflecting glass surface.

General Conclusions

We consider now, without any reference to the formulas, to what extent our investigations establish the wave nature of the X-radiation.

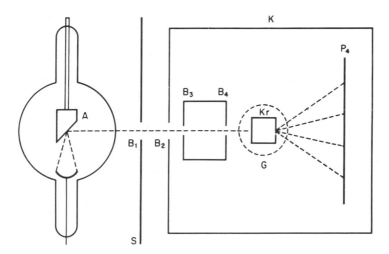

Fig. 51–1. Schematic arrangement of Friedrich and Knipping apparatus.

That the radiation emanating from the crystal has wave characteristics is demonstrated by the sharpness of the intensity maxima, which can be easily understood as interference phenomena but can hardly be explained in terms of corpuscles. . . . But we might still doubt the wave character of the primary rays. Suppose, however, that the atoms in the crystal were excited by corpuscular radiation. . . . Only such rows of atoms could be made to oscillate coherently as were struck by the same corpuscle, that is, rows of atoms parallel to the z-axis. Atoms separated along the x and y directions by a given amount would have to be excited by different corpuscles; a definite phase difference between their vibrations could not occur. . . . The broken appearance of the circles could not be understood.

EXPERIMENTAL PART (W. FRIEDRICH AND P. KNIPPING)

To test the previous part of this paper experimentally the following experimental arrangement . . . was used. Of the X-rays emanating from the anti-cathode A of an X-ray tube a small 1-mm bundle was selected by means of apertures (B_1 to B_4). This bundle passed through the crystal (Kr) set up on a goniometer (G). Photographic plates in various directions and at various distances were set up around the crystal to register the intensity distribution of the secondary radiation from the crystal. To protect the apparatus against unwanted background radiation, a large lead screen (S) and A lead container (K) were used.

. . . The diaphragms B_1 to B_3 were used to screen out radiation scattered from the walls, while the diaphragm B_4 was used to limit the X-ray bundle striking the crystal. This diaphragm had an aperture of 0.75 mm and was bored in a 10-mm thick lead shield which could be so adjusted that the axis of the aperture coincided exactly with the axis of the telescope [used for observing the angular adjustment of the crystal] and the ray bundle respectively.

Preliminary Experiment with Provisional Apparatus

. . . Since we initially thought that we were dealing with fluorescent radiation we had to use a crystal which contained, as one of its components, a metal of considerable atomic weight in order to obtain for the experiment secondary radiation of suitable character which was of maximum possible intensity and at the same time homogeneous. According to Barkla metals of atomic weight between 50 and 100 are to be considered first. Since we did not have at hand a good crystal which contained such metals, we used for the preliminary experiment a passably well-grown copper sulfate crystal. This was placed rather arbitrarily in the apparatus and the X-rays were incident approximately perpendicular to the surface. Two photographic plates were placed about 40 mm from this crystal—at positions P_2 (not shown) and P_4. . . . The plate at P_4 showed, in addition to the intersection point of the primary ray, a series of obviously ordered spots.

To convince ourselves that these spots were caused by the crystal structure of the copper sulfate, copper sulfate crystals were pulverized and placed in a small paper sack and the previous experiment was repeated under similar conditions. The large ordered spots on plate P_4 were no longer present.

. . . Since the experiments described above proved that the previous analysis could be verified experimentally, we decided to have the better apparatus (described above) constructed, at the same time carrying out additional observations on zinc-blende, rock salt, and lead sulfide. These gave results quite similar to those obtained with copper sulfide.

Experiments with Crystal Precisely Oriented to the Primary Rays

With our definitive apparatus we repeated the previous experiments. The orientation of the copper crystal was as close to the previous setting as possible.

On plates P_3 and P_4 [not shown] we obtained figures similar to the previous one, but because of the smaller diaphragm apertures the ordered spots were smaller. It is to be noted that the sizes of the images on different plates are related to each other in the same way as the distances of these plates from the crystal are related. This shows that the radiation is propagated entirely from the crystal. Further we see that the sizes of the various spots are the same on different plates regardless of their distances from the crystal. This indicates that the radiation causing a single spot leaves the crystal as a parallel beam.

It is to be expected that the images from crystals having a regular structure will be more obvious and easier to understand than in the case of the triclinic copper sulfate crystal because we may assume that crystals with regular structures have the greatest possible simplicity.

. . . The results of this experiment show that the spots are arranged completely symmetrically with respect to the point of intersection. We can delineate two pairs of mutually perpendicular symmetry planes in the photographic image. If we choose any one of spots in the figure which does not lie in a plane of symmetry, we can bring this spot into coincidence with seven other related spots by reflections and rotations through 90°. If a spot lies in a plane of symmetry, we can bring it into coincidence with corresponding spots.

This fact, that there is a complete fourfold multiplicity on the plate is one of the most beautiful proofs of the space-lattice structure of the crystal and it proves also that no other property but that of the space lattice enters into account here.

We must still show that only one precise orientation of the crystal is necessary to obtain identical images in repeating an experiment.

[In this paper, we have deleted material that is not completely germane. A discussion of symmetry properties and various arrangements of the crystal is omitted. It was shown that if the crystal orientation is changed the photographic pattern changes. Special results with diamond and rock salt are discussed—Editors.]

. . . Along with these investigations into the relationship of the lattice structure of the crystal to the spots, we have tried to determine the character of the radiation causing the spots. That we are, indeed, dealing here with secondary X-rays makes it probable that the radiation passes through considerable thicknesses of metal, for example through the plate holder made of sheet steel.

[Here the authors discuss the measurement of the hardness of the secondary rays—Editors.]

. . . A comparison of the hardness of the rays corresponding to different rings of spots leads one to surmise that these are of different penetrating powers. This, to be sure, is not surprising if we are dealing with proper radiation of the crystal [radiation characteristics of the crystal]; for, since the crystal consists of zinc and sulfur atoms, both the zinc and sulfur atoms can emit radiations that are of different hardness. . . .

52

ooooooooooo

BRAGG'S LAW

ooooooooooo

William Henry Bragg (1862-1942)
William Lawrence Bragg (b. 1890)

Laue's suggestion that a crystal should act as a diffraction grating for X-rays and thus supply proof that they are electromagnetic waves of very short wavelength was, as we have seen, amply verified in 1912 by the experiment of Friedrich and Knipping. In this experiment a very thin pencil of X-rays was incident perpendicularly on the face of a thin zinc-sulfide crystal. Placed a few centimeters behind the crystal was a photographic plate with its surface also perpendicular to the direction of the X-ray beam. The pattern of spots formed on the photographic plate after exposing the crystal to X-rays was accounted for by Laue on the assumption that the X-rays were composed of a small number of short wavelengths whose diffraction by the atoms of the crystal resulted in the pattern.

This analysis was immediately examined by W. L. Bragg, then a young research student with Sir J. J. Thomson at Cambridge. Bragg proceeded to show that the Laue pattern could be analyzed in a much simpler way, that it was unnecessary to make the restricting assumption of the presence of only a few wavelengths in the X-ray beam. Bragg adopted the view that the incident X-rays consisted of a continuous spectrum extending over a wide range of wavelengths. To simplify Laue's treatment he supposed that the atoms of the exposed crystal act as diffraction centers and radiate secondary waves. When a wave pulse falls on a plane it is reflected; if it falls on a number of atoms situated in a plane, they act as centers of disturbance, so that the secondary waves from the atoms build

839

up a wave front exactly as if the pulse had been reflected from the plane according to the manner of Huygens' construction for reflection. The intensity of the reflected wave depends, of course, on the number of atoms present in the crystal plane, the intensity being greater as the density of atoms in the plane is increased

It must be remembered, however, that in a crystal the atoms are arranged regularly in space, so that if a plane is passed through one set of atoms, say the set of atoms composing a crystal face, then a parallel plane may be passed through the next set of atoms lying underneath the surface layer. The secondary waves from the atoms in the lower plane, when reflected in the same way, may or may not be in phase with the reflected waves from the top layer. Whether or not they are depends upon the perpendicular distance "d" between the atom planes, the wavelength λ of the incoming X-rays, and finally the angle of incidence θ between the ray and the surface of the plane. The relationship between these variables is easily derived from geometric considerations and, as shown by Bragg (and repeated in most books on elementary modern physics), is given by $n\lambda = 2d \sin \theta$, an equation that is now known as Bragg's law. Here n represents what is called the "order of the spectrum," a term that has the same meaning as for optical gratings where several sets of complete spectra of the source may be produced by increasing angles of incidence to the grating.

At the time Bragg proposed the above relation, the generation of X-rays was believed to take place in the sudden deceleration of electrons within the X-ray tube as they struck the anticathode, usually a heavy metal. Classical electromagnetic theory required that such decelerations must produce radiation, so it was assumed that an electromagnetic pulse was radiated when each electron was stopped by collision with the "target" of the tube. It was shown by G. J. Stoney in 1898 that such a stream of pulses could be analyzed into wave trains, giving the appearance of a continuous spectrum. On the other hand, C. G. Barkla had shown that when X-rays strike a second substance, this substance can emit a "characteristic" radiation or radiations as well as scatter the original X-rays. All this knowledge was very fragmentary and the nature of the spectra of X-ray sources remained to be explored. Added to this was the whole field of crystal structure of which only the rudiments were known. This brief résumé gives approximately the background for the following paper by W. L. Bragg and his father W. H. Bragg, then professor of physics at the University of Leeds.

In order to investigate the spectrum of an X-ray source, a spectrometer, similar in many respects to an optical spectrometer, was devised by the elder Bragg. To get approximately parallel rays the investigators used a "collimator" consisting of a lead block pierced by a hole whose size could be regulated by a slit. The X-ray beam, so limited, emerged as a thin ribbon of radiation directed at the analyzing crystal placed upon a rotatable table whose vertical axis was at the center of the instrument. The reflecting face of the crystal was arranged so that it contained the axis of the table. The X-ray beam reflected from the crystal face was then intercepted by an ionization chamber, the current in the chamber being proportional to the intensity of the reflected X-rays. Relative intensities were thus determined by the ratios of the ion-chamber currents.

The X-rays in this experiment were produced by a tube containing a platinum anticathode. From considerations outlined above it might be expected that a continuous spectrum would be present, and on the basis of Barkla's results perhaps a "characteristic" radiation as well. Using rock salt as the reflecting crystal, and slowly varying the angle of incidence θ, the intensity of the reflected radiation was found to follow the curve shown in Fig. 52–4, I. Here there are three peaks or three monochromatic radiations, C_1, B_1, and A_1, which are repeated as a second-order spectrum, and also probably as a third order at the largest angles shown. The general appearance of these lines was found to be the same if a different cleavage face of the crystal was used, as in II, or if other crystals were used, such as zinc blende. Thus it was discovered that the X-ray emission spectrum of the anticathode was composed of a continuous spectrum *on which were superimposed definite monochromatic "lines."* W. H. Bragg later showed that these lines, which became known as the K emission lines, were indeed characteristic of the target emitting the rays. H. G. J. Moseley soon demonstrated that characteristic K lines are generated for all chemical elements used as the anticathode in an X-ray tube, and that the frequency of these lines increases as the atomic weight of the anticathode increases, *with some exceptions.* These exceptions were very important, for they shed a new light on the periodic table of the elements, as we shall discover in the article on Moseley and his measurement of the high-frequency spectrum of the elements.

In order to find the actual wavelength of the X-ray lines by the use of the formula $n\lambda = 2d \sin \theta$, Bragg had to know the value of d appropriate to the orientation of the crystal being used. In order to specify the orientation (and therefore the reflecting surface presented to the X-rays), Bragg makes use in the paper of what are called "Miller indices." Without going into detail, the atom planes appropriate to the Miller indices 100, 110, and 111 for a cubic crystal, such as rock salt, are shown in Fig. 52–1 below. Reference is made in the paper to each of these indices. The problem in this investigation was to make the selection for d that corresponded to the actual physical situation in the experiment. The Braggs discuss this and make a calculation for the wavelength of the B line, using the group 4 NaCl as "the smallest complete unit of the crystal pattern."

(This corresponds to a simple cube with Na and Cl atoms at successive corners as one goes around the cube.) The value found was 1.78Å, which is too large; a more acceptable value is about 1.10Å.

The importance of this research was twofold: It showed (1) that the X-ray emission spectrum of an element is characteristic of that element, and (2) that X-rays can be used as a powerful and precise means

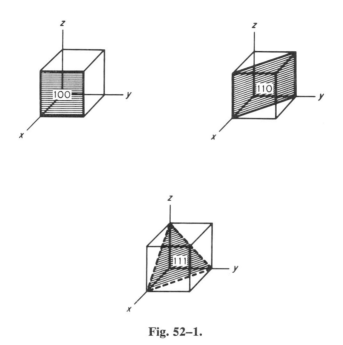

Fig. 52–1.

of crystal analysis. Both of these discoveries opened up large fields of investigation; although X-ray emission spectra were fully mapped out in the course of a few decades, X-rays continue to be widely used as an analytical tool in the problems of the structure of matter.

The discoverers of these innovations present interesting personal histories, although at the time of this writing much more biographical material is available for W. H. Bragg than for his son, W. L. Bragg, who is currently director of the Royal Institution in London, as his father was before him.

William Henry Bragg, the son of a retired officer of the merchant navy, was born on a farm near Carlisle in the north of England on July 2, 1862. At seven, he was sent away to school, and in 1875, at the age of thirteen, to King William College on the Isle of Man. Here he stood high in his studies, especially in mathematics, but, as he himself often said, his life was far from happy. He was a quiet boy, not socially minded, and did not mix well. The religious atmosphere of the school depressed him and the Bible readings, emphasizing punishments for the sins of this life, caused him "acute fear and misery."

In 1881, at the age of nineteen, he entered Trinity College, Cambridge, still a shy and lonely young man, with a liking for boating and tennis, but with a main outlet in study. He entered Cambridge on a small scholarship and earned a larger one for the following years. He took his B.A. in 1884, placing as third wrangler in the mathematical tripos, Part I. This success was entirely unexpected; writing about it many years later he said, "I was lifted into a new world. I had new confidence, I was extraordinarily happy. I can still feel the joy of it." As an added fillip to the achievement he states that the great philosopher-to-be Alfred North Whitehead, who had taken the examinations the year before and again with Bragg's class, came to him and shook his hand saying "May a Fourth Wrangler congratulate a Third?" Bragg continued at Cambridge for another year, then quite by chance heard that Horace Lamb had resigned his professorship in mathematics and physics at the University of Adelaide in Australia. Bragg applied for the position; after being interviewed by J. J. Thomson and Lamb, who had come to England, he was soon awarded the appointment. He had studied only a minimum of physics, but the electors, guided by Thomson's and Lamb's recommendations, attached little importance to this. At any rate he read the subject on his passage out to the island continent. In his new environment he felt completely at home. His shyness vanished; he liked teaching, and through perseverance he became an interesting and polished speaker. In 1889 he married Gwendoline Todd, the daughter of the Postmaster General and government astronomer of South Australia.

Until 1904, Bragg had done nothing that could be called research. But in that year he was called upon to give the presidential address to the Australian Association for the Advancement of Science at Dunedin and chose for his discourse a review of radioactivity. He became so interested in the subject that he began experiments to measure the range of α particles and the ionization they produced along their paths. Thus at the age of forty-one he was just beginning research in a new country with little support, far from the centers of active research and the stimulation that comes from associating with able workers in a difficult and rapidly moving field. Any assessment of his probable success as a contributing scientist would have been bleak indeed. It is surprising, therefore, that as a consequence of his work in the ensuing few years, Rutherford proposed him for fellowship in the Royal Society—an honor accorded him in 1907. In 1908 he accepted the chair of physics at the University of Leeds and thus returned to the European main stream of physics. At Leeds he resumed his early interest in X-rays and investigated the ionizing effect of X-rays arising from the secondary electrons released by the rays. In 1912, when Friedrich, Knipping, and Laue announced their discovery of the diffraction of X-rays, Bragg was ready to apply these results to wider research. His discovery of the X-ray line spectrum of the elements and the application of the rays to crystal analysis is given in the appended paper.

The 1915 Nobel Prize was awarded to the Braggs for their contributions to crystal analysis. The elder Bragg was then fifty-three and W. L., his son, was a mere twenty-five. Both father and son were active in scientific work at that time, supporting England's participation in World War I. The elder Bragg was appointed Quain professor at University College, London, in 1915, an appointment which he held until 1923, when he was made head of the Royal Institution following Sir James Dewar. He remained in that post until his death on March 12, 1942.

Among his later honors were a knighthood in 1920, the Copley medal of the Royal Society in 1930, the Order of Merit in 1931, and the presidency of the Royal Society in 1935 at the age of seventy-three. Among his many accomplishments, not the least were his highly successful Christmas lectures at the Royal Institution. Intended for a juvenile audience, they include "The World of Sound," "Concerning the Nature of Things," "Old Trades and New Knowledge," and the "Universe of Light." All of these lectures were published and are masterpieces of sprightly scientific prose. Bragg will always be remembered by those who were fortunate enough to be his auditors for, combined with a quiet, warm dignity, he spoke with a deceptive ease and naturalness. He was a profound and sincere man full of enthusiasm for science and for new ideas. Considering his late start in physics, his achievements are a great tribute to his energy and profound ability.

William Lawrence Bragg, his son, was born at Adelaide, Australia, on March 31, 1890. He was educated at the University of Adelaide, graduating with first honors in mathematics in 1908. The following year he entered Trinity College, Cambridge, finishing in 1912 with first honors in the natural science tripos. In November of that year he published his first paper in the *Proceedings of the Cambridge Philosophical Society,* simplifying Laue's analysis of X-ray diffraction. This is the paper commented upon at the beginning of this article. It was this paper and the one written jointly with his father that formed the basis for the Nobel Prize in physics in 1915. The joint studies of father and son from 1912–1915 on crystal analysis were published in their book, *X-Rays and Crystal Structure,* which appeared in 1915. In 1919, after war service, young Bragg was appointed Langworthy professor of physics at the University of Manchester. He was then only twenty-nine years old. He remained at Manchester until 1937, when he accepted a post as director of the National Physical Laboratory. In 1938 he was called to Cambridge to be Cavendish professor of physics, succeeding Lord Rutherford who died in that year. He continued as Cavendish professor until 1953, when he became Fullerian professor of chemistry and scientific director of the Royal Institution of Great Britain, a post he currently occupies.

୦୦୦୦୦୦୦

W. H. and W. L. BRAGG

The Reflection of X-Rays by Crystals [1]

IN A DISCUSSION OF THE Laue photographs it has been shown that they may conveniently be interpreted as due to the reflection of X-rays in such planes within the crystal as are rich in atoms. This leads at once to the attempt to use cleavage planes as mirrors, and it has been found that mica gives a reflected pencil from its cleavage plane strong enough to make a visible impression on a photographic plate in a few minutes' exposure. It has also been observed that the reflected pencil can be detected by the ionisation method.

For the purpose of examining more closely the reflection of X-rays in this manner we have used an apparatus resembling a spectrometer in form, an ionisation chamber taking the place of the telescope. The collimator is replaced by a lead block pierced by a hole which can be stopped down to slits of various widths. The revolving table in the centre carries the crystal. The ionisation chamber is tubular, 15 cm. long and 5 cm. in diameter. It can be rotated about the axis of the instrument, to which its own axis is perpendicular. It is filled with sulphur dioxide in order to increase the ionisation current: both air and methyl iodide have also been used occasionally to make sure that no special characteristics of the gas in the chamber affect the interpretation of the results. The ionisation current is measured directly. A balance method has not been

---

[1] William Henry Bragg and William Lawrence Bragg, *Proceedings of the Royal Society* (London), Series A, 88 (1913), 428–438.

used as we have not found it possible to deflect a suitable portion of the
primary rays into a balance chamber.

[A section describing some details of the apparatus is omitted—Editors.]

Let us suppose that a crystal is placed on the revolving table so that
the cleavage face passes through the axis of the instrument. Let the incident pencil fall on the face and make an angle θ with it [in Fig. 52–5,
OPR] and let the crystal be kept fixed while the ionisation chamber is revolved step by step through a series of angles including the double of θ
[as measured from OP extended in Fig. 52–4], the ionisation current being
measured at each step. The results of such a set of measurements are
shown in [Fig. 52–2]. In this case the crystal is rock-salt; and it has been
placed so that the incident pencil makes an angle of $8\cdot3°$—as given by
the apparatus—with the incident beam. The points marked in the figure

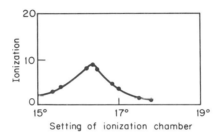

Fig. 52–2. Regular reflection from cleavage face of rock-salt glancing
angle 8.3°.

show the result of setting the ionisation chamber at various angles and
measuring the current in each case. The maximum effect is not quite at
$16\cdot6°$, but at a point somewhat less than $16\cdot4°$. The defect from the
double angle is due in part to want of symmetry and accuracy of the apparatus; but not much of it is caused in this way. It is rather due to the
difficulty of setting the crystal face exactly; sometimes this is much accentuated by "steps" on the face of the crystal. The error can be eliminated by swinging over the ionisation chamber to the other side [of RP
extended] and taking corresponding observations, in a manner analogous
to the method of finding the angle of a prism on the spectrometer. . . .

When the actual relation between the angles of the crystal mirror and
the ionisation chamber has been determined, the mirror and chamber may
be swept together through an extended range, keeping the relation between the angles such that the chamber always shows the maximum current for each setting of the crystal. It is convenient to use the wide slits
for a preliminary examination of this kind. When the effect is small
the wide slits can alone be used. But in a number of cases it is possible to

use the narrow slits in order to make a closer survey, and where this is done much more information can be obtained.

The curve in [Fig. 52–3] shows the results of a sweeping movement of this kind, the crystal being iron pyrites. Curves for rock-salt are drawn in

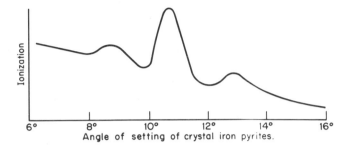

Fig. 52–3. Reflection from face (100) of iron pyrites, at varying angles of incidence. Abscissa—Angle of incidence of rays on crystal face; Ordinate—Strength of reflected beam, arbitrary scale.

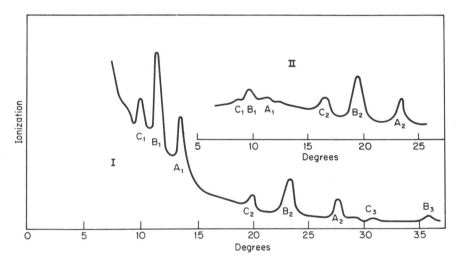

Fig. 52–4. Reflection (I) from face (100) and (II) from face (III) of rock-salt. The curves show the variation of strength of reflected beam with angle of incidence.

[Fig. 52–4], I and II. It will be observed that there are peculiar and considerable variations in the intensity of the reflection at different angles. The three peaks marked A, B, and C are common to the curves of all crystals so far investigated, *e.g.* zinc blende, potassium ferrocyanide, potassium bichromate, quartz, calcite, and sodium ammonium tartrate. They are readily distinguishable by their invariable form, relative magnitudes, and spacings. Moreover, the absorption coefficients of the rays reflected at these separate angles do not vary with the nature of the crystal or the state of the bulb. It happens that the actual angles of reflection of the three sets of rays are nearly the same for several crystals.

The use of the narrow slits permits a closer examination of these effects; but, of course, it takes much longer time to make, and more space to exhibit. . . .

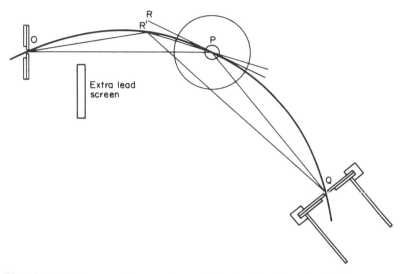

Fig. 52–5. Diagram of apparatus—O, bulb slit; P, axis of instrument; PR, PR', two positions of crystal face; Q, slit of ionisation chamber.

When these homogeneous beams are isolated by the use of narrow slits, it is possible to determine their absorption coefficients in various substances. In the end, there is no doubt, this will be done with great accuracy; for the present, our results must only be looked on as provisional. They are, perhaps, right to 5 per cent.; for many purposes this is quite sufficient. In the case of rock-salt we find the mass absorption coefficients in aluminium of A, B, and C to be $25 \cdot 5$, $18 \cdot 8$, and $10 \cdot 6$ respectively, the last being the most doubtful and probably too low. The absorption coefficient of the B-rays in Ag is 74, and Cu 140, in Ni 138; these values are approximate. We have made no exhaustive determination of the coefficients in the case of various crystals, but in a number of cases, all those tried, we have found them to be the same. There can be little doubt the three peaks are, in all cases, due to the same three sets of homogeneous rays, rays which do not change with the state of the bulb, but may well do so with the nature of the anticathode. It will be observed that the absorption coefficient of the least penetrating set is very nearly that found by Chapman for the characteristic radiation of platinum.

The angles at which the special reflections of these rays take place are not the same for all crystals, nor for all faces of the same crystal, as [Table 52–1] shows. The angles can be determined with great accuracy; even with our rough apparatus they are probably within 1 per cent. of the truth.

TABLE 52–1

	A.	B.	C.
Rock-salt, cube face {100}	27·3	23·1	19·9
" face {111}	48·5	40·2	34·0
Potassium ferrocyanide	27·2	23·1	19·8
Calcite, cleavage plane {100}	25·4	21·6	—
Iron pyrites, cube face {100}	28·5	24·2	20·8
Zinc blende, cleavage plane {110}	40·0	33·0	27·5
	(approx.)		(approx.)
Potassium bichromate	22·4	19·8	—

The readings for zinc blende and calcite are not corrected for errors of setting.

The difference in the case of the two faces of rock-salt suggested an attempt to find a repetition of the characteristic three peaks at multiples or sub-multiples of those at which they were first observed. For the sines of 11·55 and 20·1 (half the angles of the chamber settings of the B peak in the two cases) are 0·200 and 0·344 respectively. These are very nearly in the ratio $1 : \sqrt{3}$. If the effects are true diffraction effects such a relation might be expected. The {111} planes are further apart than the {100} planes in the ratio $2 : \sqrt{3}$; the sines of angles of special reflection should be in the inverse ratio, viz., $\sqrt{3} : 2$. True, the sines of the angles have been increased in the ratio $1 : \sqrt{3}$, instead of diminished in the ratio $2 : \sqrt{3}$, but it is not at all unlikely that a spectrum in one case is being compared with a spectrum of higher or lower order in the other. We, therefore, made a search for other spectra and found them at once. In the case of rock-salt we found traces of a third. The full rock-salt curves are shown in [Fig. 52–4] for the two kinds of face. The peaks first found are marked A_1, B_1, C_1, and their repetitions A_2, B_2, C_2; there is a trace of B_3 also. The corrected angular positions of B_1, B_2, B_3 are 23·1°, 47·3°, and 73·3°. The sines of the halves of these angles are 0·200, 0·401, and 0·597, and are very nearly in the proportion $1 : 2 : 3$. The absorption coefficient of the rays at B_2 is the same as that of the rays at B_1.

In the case of the rock-salt section {111} a spectrum occurs at half the angles first found. This is shown in [Fig. 52–4], II. It is not at all strongly marked, and the question at once arises as to why the second spectrum should be so much stronger than the first in this case and so much weaker in the case of the face {100}. A large amount of the general falling away of intensity at small angles, so obvious in Curve II as compared with Curve I, is undoubtedly due to the fact that the {111} face used was not extended enough to catch the whole pencil of rays from the bulb slit at so glancing an angle.

There can be little doubt as to the interpretation of these results. The three peaks A, B, and C represent three sets of homogeneous rays. Rays of a definite quality are reflected from a crystal when, and only when, the crystal is set at the right angle. This is really an alternative way of stating the original deduction of Laue. The three sets of rays are not manufactured in the crystal, because all their properties are independent of the nature of the crystal. An absorbing screen may be interposed with the same effect before or after the rays have struck the crystal. This was found by Moseley and Darwin,* and we have verified it in the case of aluminium.

Since the reflection angle of each set of rays is so sharply defined, the waves must occur in trains of great length. A succession of irregularly spaced pulses could not give the observed effect. In the application of electromagnetic theory to monochromatic light on the one hand, and to homogeneous X-rays on the other, there is no difference to be considered beyond that of wave-length.

These results do not really affect the use of the corpuscular theory of X-rays. The theory represents the facts of the transfer of energy from electron to X-ray and *vice versa,* and all the phenomena in which this transfer is the principal event. It can predict discoveries and interpret them. It is useful in its own field. The problem remains to discover how two hypotheses so different in appearance can be so closely linked together.

It is of great interest to attempt to find the exact wave-length of the rays to which these peaks correspond. On considering Curve I, Fig. 52–3, it seems evident that the peaks $A_1 B_1 C_1, A_2 B_2 C_2$ are analogous to spectra of the first and second orders, because of the absence of intervening sets of peaks. The value of n in the equation

$$n\lambda = 2d \sin \theta$$

seems clear. The difficulty of assigning a definite wave-length to the rays arises when we attempt to determine the value of $d,$ the distance of plane from plane.

---

* We learn that Messrs. Moseley and Darwin have lately been making experiments similar to some of those recorded here. Their results, which have not been published, agree with ours.

There is strong evidence for supposing that the atoms of a cubic crystal like rock-salt, containing two elements of equal valency, are arranged parallel to the planes {100} in planes containing equal numbers of sodium and chlorine atoms. The atoms in any one plane are arranged in alternate rows of each element, diagonal to the cube axes, successive planes having these rows opposite ways. The question arises as to whether the value of *d* is to be taken as that between two successive planes, or two planes identical in all respects. The value of *d* in the one case is twice that in the other.

The centres of the atoms of sodium and chlorine, regarded for the time being as identical, arc arranged in a point system, having as unit of its pattern a cube with a point at each corner and one at the centre of each cube face. The dimensions of this elementary cube can be found in the following way:—

If the side of the cube is of length *a,* the volume associated with each point in the point system will be $\frac{1}{4}a^3$.

The mass of a hydrogen atom being $1 \cdot 64 \times 10^{-24}$ grm. and the density of rock-salt $2 \cdot 17$, we have

$$\frac{1}{\frac{1}{4}a^3} \frac{1}{2}(35 \cdot 5 + 23) \times 1 \cdot 64 \times 10^{-24} = 2 \cdot 17.$$

This gives

$$a = 4 \cdot 45 \times 10^{-8}.$$

The distance between planes passing through atoms identical in all respects is this distance *a*. The wave-length, as calculated in this way, is

$$\lambda = 2a \sin \theta = 1 \cdot 78 \times 10^{-8}$$

for the peak B.

But half-way between these planes which are identical in all respects are situated planes containing the same number of sodium and chlorine atoms, though the arrangement is not in all respects the same. Possibly this tends to make the odd spectra due to the first lot of planes disappear, and, if this is the case, we must halve the first estimate of the wave-length, and put

$$\lambda = 0 \cdot 89 \times 10^{-8}.$$

The difference between these two values corresponds to taking as a unit of the point system—

(1) The group 4NaCl, the smallest complete unit of the crystal pattern.

(2) The individual atom of either nature, associated with only one-eighth of the volume of the complete unit.

We have also examined the reflection from the (110) face of the rock-salt, and have found the peaks situated at such angles as indicate that the ratio of the distance between these parallel planes to the distance between planes parallel to the face (100) is as $1 : \sqrt{2}$. Combined with the position of the peaks reflected from the (111) face, this indicates that the point system which the diffracting centres form has as element of its pattern that suggested above, a cube with a point at each corner and one at the centre of each face. Of the three elementary cubic space lattices, this is the only one in which the distance between the (111) planes is greater than that between any other of the planes of the system.

The wave-length as calculated from the reflection on the (110) face of zinc blende agrees within the errors of experiment with that calculated above.

The wave-lengths to be associated with the spots in the photographs taken by Laue of the diffraction of X-rays by crystals are much smaller than these values. They belong to the region in which we have found reflection to take place at all angles, a region in which the peaks do not obviously occur. This agrees with the distribution of intensity amongst the spots.

The experimental method can be applied to the analysis of the radiation from any source of X-rays. It may, however, be able to deal only with intense radiations. The three sets of rays issuing from the bulb we have been using have angles of reflection whose sines are $0 \cdot 236$, $0 \cdot 200$, $0 \cdot 173$. The reciprocals of these are $4 \cdot 24$, 5, and $5 \cdot 78$. The frequencies, and therefore, according to Planck, the corresponding quantum energies, are in arithmetical progression. In this there is some hint of analogy with Rutherford's recent work on the energies of the various types of β-ray from RaC.

Prof. Barkla has lately communicated to the Physical Society an account of certain experiments in which a diffuse pencil of X-rays, when reflected on the cleavage plane of a crystal, acted on a photographic plate, producing a series of bands. The effect which we have been describing is clearly identical in part with that which Prof. Barkla has described. It is impossible, of course, to criticise a communication of which we have seen an abstract only. But it seems probable that the ionisation method can follow the details of the effect more closely than the photographic method has so far been able to do: and that in this way it is possible to distinguish between those bands which represent distinct sets of rays, and those which are repetitions of one and the same set.

53

ooooooooooo

ATOMIC NUMBER

ooooooooooo

Antonius van der Broek (1870-1926)

Many ideas in physics have come into focus as the result of simultaneous or nearly simultaneous developments in different branches of the subject. The development of the concept of atomic number seems to have been a phenomenon of this kind. In this instance the simultaneous developments were the Rutherford α-particle scattering theory and the X-ray scattering measurements of C. G. Barkla. Each investigation led the author to conclude that the number of electrons per atom is equal to half the atomic weight of the atom, with the restriction in Barkla's case that the generalization was made for the light elements only. Thus the X-ray scattering data for carbon (substituted in J. J. Thomson's scattering theory) gave the number of electrons in this atom as six, just half the atomic weight of twelve.

The development of Rutherford's nuclear atom model again raised the question of the possible number of elements. It should be remembered that in 1911, the year of Rutherford's proposal and Barkla's measurements, only highly conjectural answers could be given. Nevertheless, an attempt to cast some light on this problem was made by the Dutch physicist van der Broek, who suggested in a short note to *Nature,* reprinted at the end of this commentary, that because the atomic weight of uranium (the heaviest element then known) was about 240, the proposals of Rutherford and Barkla indicated a total of 120 elements in the periodic table. By using a "cubic" construction of Mendeleev's for the periodic system of the elements, van der Broek found a mean difference between consecutive atomic weights equal to 2. Thus an atomic weight of 240 for uranium gave 120 possible elements. He therefore suggested that *if* Mendeleev's cubic model should prove correct, then each element could be characterized by the number of possible permanent charges of *both* signs. Applied to uranium, one might conclude that the metal would have 120 "permanent" positive charges and 120 "permanent" negative charges. The location of these charges was not specified.

Two years later, in a second letter to *Nature* (also reprinted in this chapter), van der Broek again returned to the idea of an atomic numbering scheme, stating that his earlier suggestion had been that "to each possible intra-atomic charge corresponds a possible element." But in the meantime research had shown that for uranium, the last element in the table, the number of [nuclear?] charges was "not . . . even approximately . . . half the atomic weight," if the experimental results were reasonably accurate. Rutherford's nuclear atom theory, however, showed that for a constant incidence of α particles on a scattering foil, and at a constant angle of scattering, the quantity (N/ntZ^2) should be constant. Here N is the number of α particles scattered at a fixed angle θ, n is the number atoms per cm^3 of the foil, t is its thickness, and Z is the number of positive charges in the nucleus. Stated another way, the number of scattered α particles per atom of scatterer divided by the square of the nuclear charge should be constant. In his article that follows, van der Broek makes this observation and notes that because the nuclear charge was unknown for the elements used in the foils, Geiger and Marsden, in order to test the constancy of the ratio, used as a proportional number the atomic weight, A. He then gives two sets of data from Geiger and Marsden's paper showing that N/ntA^2 is not constant but shows a significant decrease as the atomic weight A increases for the elements copper, silver, tin, platinum, and gold. On the other hand, if A is replaced by M, the number of the place each element occupies in the periodic table, a constant number (within small limits) does result. Essentially, this evidence constitutes the basis for the idea of atomic number and for attributing its "discovery" to van der Broek. It should be emphasized that the preponderant evidence for the validity of the atomic number idea comes from the very powerful support given to it by Moseley's research, which will be presented in Chapter 54.

Before closing this commentary a word of explanation should be given regarding the final sentence in van der Broek's note in *Nature*, 92 (1913). The only atomic particles known at that time were electrons and protons. In accounting for atomic weights, the electrons can be neglected to a first approximation as their mass is of the order of 1/2000th of the proton. For example, if we try to reconcile the mass of an atom of copper with its atomic number, then some uncertainty ensues. The atomic number of copper is 29; on a naïve basis let us assume that these 29 positive charges are produced by 29 protons. Because the atomic weight of copper is 63.57 there is a large mass deficit. It was therefore assumed that additional positive charges in the form of protons or α particles were present in the nucleus to supply the requisite mass but that the charge on these additional particles was annulled by the negative charge that was carried by electrons which were also assumed to be present in the nucleus.

From these few remarks it will be evident that of necessity only the crudest guesses about nuclear structure could be made at that time. This was a problem that became much clearer after nuclear masses became amenable to precise measurement, isotopes were recognized, and the neutron was discovered. As a point in favor of assuming the presence of electrons in the nucleus, the emission of β rays by radioactive nuclei is cited by Soddy in the article that follows Van der Broek's. Present evidence indicates that nuclei are composed of neutrons and protons. By rather elementary arguments involving the wave nature of particles, it can be shown that electrons cannot be localized in a space of the dimensions of the nucleus. Such a requirement could be fulfilled only if the electrons were to move at speeds considerably in excess of that of light, a condition forbidden by the theory of relativity.

Because the idea of intra-atomic charge is so closely related to atomic number and to isotopes, a final article by Soddy is appended to the notes by van der Broek. It should be pointed out that *it is in this article that the term isotope is first used in scientific literature.*

Antonius van der Broek [1] was born in Zoeterwoude in the Netherlands on May 5, 1870, and lived most of his life in Deventer and Noordwijk. He was trained for the law but he was also an amateur scientist who published a number of papers, of which only the few dealing with the idea of atomic number are notable. With respect to his first statement of the atomic number idea, published in 1911 in the *Physikalische Zeitschrift,* it is reported that Rutherford expressed considerable annoyance that a layman should publish "a lot of guesses for fun without sufficient foundation."

Van der Broek appears to have been something of an eccentric. His philosophy of life made him a vegetarian and his attire was marked, in a more conforming era, by the peculiarity of wearing sandals. Although he was deeply interested in science he did not cultivate scientific acquaintances or engage in the activities of organized science. It appears on the contrary that he shunned the company of professional scientists. He died in Bilthoven at the age of fifty-six on October 26, 1926.

---

[1] The authors are indebted for information on the life of van der Broek to M.E. 't Hart, Director of the Royal Netherlands Academy of Sciences and Letters.

ooooooo

VAN DER BROEK

The Number of Possible Elements and Mendeléev's "Cubic" Periodic System [2]

ACCORDING TO RUTHERFORD'S THEORY OF "single scattering" ("On the Scattering of α and β Particles by Matter and the Structure of the Atom"), and to Barkla's "Note on the Energy of Scattered X-Radiation," the numbers of electrons per atom is half the atomic weight; thus, for U, about 120. Now a reconstruction of Mendeléeff's "cubic" periodic system, as suggested in his famous paper "Die Beziehungen zwischen den Eigenschaften der Elemente und ihren Atomgewichten," gives a constant mean difference between consecutive atomic weights = 2, and thus, from H to U, 120 as the number of possible elements. Hence if this cubic periodic system should prove correct, then the number of possible elements is equal to the number of possible permanent charges of each sign per atom, or to each possible permanent charge (of both signs) per atom belongs a possible element.

Intra-Atomic Charge [3]

IN A PREVIOUS LETTER TO Nature the hypothesis was proposed that the atomic weight being equal to about twice the intra-atomic charge, "to each possible intra-atomic charge corresponds a possible element," or that "if all elements be arranged in order of increasing atomic weights, the number of each element in that series must be equal to its intra-atomic charge."

Charges being known only very roughly (probably correct to 20 per cent.), and the number of the last element Ur in the series not being equal even approximately to half its atomic weight, either the number of ele-

---

[2] A. van der Broek, *Nature,* 87 (1911), 78.
[3] A. van der Broek, *Nature,* 92 (1913), 372 f.

ments in Mendeléeff's system is not correct (that was supposed to be the case in the first letter), or the intra-atomic charge for the elements at the end of the series is much smaller than that deduced from experiment (about 100 for Au).

Now, according to Rutherford, the ratio of the scattering of α particles per atom divided by the square of the charge must be constant. Geiger and Marsden, putting the nuclear charge proportional to the atomic weight, found values, however, showing, not constancy, but systematic deviation from (mean values) $3 \cdot 825$ for Cu to $3 \cdot 25$ for Au. If now in these values the number M of the place each element occupies in Mendeléeff's series is taken instead of A, the atomic weight, we get a real constant $(18 \cdot 7 \pm 0 \cdot 3)$; hence the hypothesis proposed holds good for Mendeléeff's series, but the nuclear charge is not equal to half the atomic weight. Should thus the mass of the atom consist for by far the greatest part of α particles, then the nucleus too must contain electrons to compensate this extra charge.

TABLE 53-1 *Table of the Ratio of the Scattering per Atom Divided by A^2 Compared with That Divided by M^2*

	I.	II.	Mean	Mean $\times 5 \cdot 4$	Mean $A^2 \times M^2$	M
Cu	$3 \cdot 7$	$3 \cdot 95$	$3 \cdot 825$	$20 \cdot 6$	$18 \cdot 5$	29
Ag	$3 \cdot 6$	$3 \cdot 4$	$3 \cdot 5$	$18 \cdot 9$	$18 \cdot 4$	47
Sn	$3 \cdot 3$	$3 \cdot 4$	$3 \cdot 35$	$18 \cdot 1$	$19 \cdot 0$	50
Pt	$3 \cdot 2$	$3 \cdot 4$	$3 \cdot 3$	$17 \cdot 8$	$18 \cdot 6$	82
Au	$3 \cdot 4$	$3 \cdot 1$	$3 \cdot 25$	$17 \cdot 5$	$18 \cdot 4$	83
Mean $3 \cdot 44$	$3 \cdot 45$	$3 \cdot 445$	$18 \cdot 6$	$18 \cdot 6$	

ଡଡଡଡଡଡଡ

SODDY

Intra-Atomic Charge [4]

THAT THE INTRA-ATOMIC CHARGE OF an element is determined by its place in the periodic table rather than by its atomic weight, as concluded by A. van der Broek, is strongly supported by the

[4] Frederick Soddy, *Nature*, 92 (1913), 399–400.

recent generalisation as to the radio-elements and the periodic law. The successive expulsion of one α and two β particles in three radio-active changes in any order brings the intra-atomic charge of the element back to its initial value, and the element back to its original place in the table, though its atomic mass is reduced by four units. We have recently obtained something like a direct proof of van der Broek's view that the intra-atomic charge of the nucleus of an atom is not a purely positive charge, as on Rutherford's tentative theory, but is the difference between a positive and a smaller negative charge.[5]

Fajans, in his paper on the periodic law generalisation, directed attention to the fact that the changes of chemical nature consequent upon the expulsion of α and β particles are precisely of the same kind as in ordinary electrochemical changes of valency. He drew from this the conclusion that radio-active changes must occur in the same region of atomic structure as ordinary chemical changes, rather than with a distinct inner region of structure, or "nucleus," as hitherto supposed. In my paper on the same generalisation, published immediately after that of Fajans, I laid stress on the absolute identity of chemical properties of different elements occupying the same place in the periodic table.

A simple deduction from this view supplied me with a means of testing the correctness of Fajans's conclusion that radio-changes and chemical changes are concerned with the same region of atomic structure. On my view his conclusion would involve nothing else than that, for example, uranium in its tetravalent uranous compounds must be chemically identical with and non-separable from thorium compounds. For uranium X, formed from uranium I by expulsion of an α particle, is chemically identical with thorium, as also is ionium formed in the same way from uranium II. Uranium X loses two β particles and passes back into uranium II, chemically identical with uranium. Uranous salts also lose two electrons and pass into the more common hexavalent uranyl compounds. If these electrons come from the same region of the atom uranous salts should be chemically non-separable from thorium salts. But they are not.

There is a strong resemblance in chemical character between uranous and thorium salts, and I asked Mr. Fleck to examine whether they could be separated by chemical methods when mixed, the uranium being kept unchanged throughout in the uranous or tetravalent condition. Mr. Fleck will publish the experiments separately, and I am indebted to him for the result that the two classes of compounds can readily be separated by fractionation methods.

This, I think, amounts to a proof that the electrons expelled as β rays

---

[5] Soddy assumed that electrons had to be present in the nucleus in order to account for the β rays expelled in radioactive atoms—Editors.

come from a nucleus not capable of supplying electrons to or withdrawing them from the ring, though this ring is capable of gaining or losing electrons from the exterior during ordinary electrochemical changes of valency.

I regard van der Broek's view, that the number representing the net positive charge of the nucleus is the number of the place which the element occupies in the periodic table when all the possible places from hydrogen to uranium are arranged in sequence, as practically proved so far as the relative value of the charge for the members of the end of the sequence, from thallium to uranium, is concerned. We are left uncertain as to the absolute value of the charge, because of the doubt regarding the exact number of rare-earth elements that exist. If we assume that all of these are known, the value for the positive charge of the nucleus of the uranium atom is about 90. Whereas if we make the more doubtful assumption that the periodic table runs regularly, as regards numbers of places, through the rare-earth group, and that between barium and radium, for example, two complete long periods exist, the number is 96. In either case it is appreciably less than 120, the number were the charge equal to one-half the atomic weight, as it would be if the nucleus were made out of α particles only. Six nuclear electrons are known to exist in the uranium atom, which expels in its changes six β rays. Were the nucleus made up of α particles there must be thirty or twenty-four respectively nuclear electrons, compared with ninety-six or 102 respectively in the ring. If, as has been suggested, hydrogen is a second component of atomic structure, there must be more than this. But there can be no doubt that there must be some, and that the central charge of the atom on Rutherford's theory cannot be a pure positive charge, but must contain electrons, as van der Broek concludes.

So far as I personally am concerned, this has resulted in a great clarification of my ideas, and it may be helpful to others, though no doubt there is little originality in it. The same algebraic sum of the positive and negative charges in the nucleus, when the arithmetical sum is different, gives what I call "isotopes" or "isotopic elements," because they occupy the same place in the periodic table. They are chemically identical, and save only as regards the relatively few physical properties which depend upon atomic mass directly, physically identical also. Unit changes of this nuclear charge, so reckoned algebraically, give the successive places in the periodic table. For any one "place," or any one nuclear charge, more than one number of electrons in the outer-ring system may exist, and in such a case the element exhibits variable valency. But such changes of number, or of valency, concern only the ring and its external environment. There is no in- and out-going of electrons between ring and nucleus.